W9-BLC-126

PHYSICS

This book is in the

ADDISON-WESLEY SERIES IN PHYSICS

PHYSICS

WAYNE E. HAZEN
University of Michigan

ROBERT W. PIDD
General Atomic, San Diego, California

ADDISON-WESLEY PUBLISHING COMPANY, INC.

READING, MASSACHUSETTS

Printed in the United States of America

Library of Congress Catalog Card No. 62-14061

Second Printing—December 1965

ADDISON-WESLEY PUBLISHING COMPANY, INC.
READING, MASSACHUSETTS • Palo Alto • London
NEW YORK • DALLAS • ATLANTA • BARRINGTON, ILLINOIS

Preface

The motivation for this text came from the organization of a "Unified Science" curriculum for selected students in the College of Engineering at the University of Michigan. This curriculum has become a part of the Honors Program in the College of Literature, Science, and the Arts. The Unified Science Program consists of a special freshman-sophomore program in mathematics, physics, and chemistry. It is designed for the serious student who plans to major in any of the sciences, including pre-medicine. These courses are designed to stress the basic ideas of each subject, with the degree of rigor possible for the serious student.

Since the physics course begins in the entering semester for most students, calculus is not used for the first few weeks, by which time differentiation has been introduced in the mathematics courses. No serious compromise results, since this time is well occupied with constant velocity kinematics (including velocity transformations), inertial mass, conservation of momentum, and force.

The subject matter of the first semester of physics in the University of Michigan program has been confined primarily to particle mechanics, finishing with topics in special relativity. It has been found that the students gain renewed interest and enthusiasm during the study of relativity. Two semesters of chemistry follow the first semester of physics. Since the chemistry course includes the subjects of heat, thermodynamics, and kinetic theory, we do not include these topics in our general physics course. Thus, our second semester of physics (which most students take in their fourth semester of school) begins with electricity. However, since the present text includes the topics of heat, thermodynamics, and kinetic theory, it is suitable for traditional curricula. As with most general physics texts, the material can be covered, in a manner of speaking, in two semesters, but three semesters are to be preferred.

In this text, an attempt has been made to emphasize the origin and meaning of "formulas." To this end, an unusually large proportion of problems is designed to force consideration of the derivation and meaning of equations. If it is felt that there is a corresponding paucity of simple substitution problems in some chapters, these can easily be obtained from other texts. Most of the specialized equations, for example, the equations for height and range of projectiles, have been left for the problem sections; this, in the hope that the students will be less inclined to try to memorize all of the equations or will be less diverted from the main course of the argument.

An attempt has been made to treat each topic with reasonable rigor. It will be obvious to the thoughtful teacher who bothers to read the book that there are many lapses. For example, we have fallen into the usual trap of basing our discussion of work and energy on the idea of "work by *a* force," without foreseeing the difficulties that eventually stem from failure to recognize that interaction forces occur in pairs.

British engineering units have not been introduced since engineers will be amply trained in their use in later courses. The "applied physics" topic of geometrical optics has been included because this subject is not usually included in later courses.

Advice by those of our colleagues who have taught recitation sections in the program has proved invaluable.

September, 1964

W. A. H.
R. W. P.

Contents

7. DYNAMICS (INSTANTANEOUS QUANTITIES)

8. PERIODIC MOTION

9. IMPULSE, WORK, AND ENERGY

10. GRAVITATION, ANGULAR MOMENTUM, AND SATELLITES

11. CENTER OF MASS; NONINERTIAL REFERENCE FRAMES

12. SUMMARY IN DEDUCTIVE FORM

13. SPECIAL RELATIVITY

14. RIGID BODIES

15. TEMPERATURE, THE GAS LAWS, AND HEAT

16. THE FIRST LAW OF THERMODYNAMICS

17. THE SECOND LAW OF THERMODYNAMICS

18. KINETIC THEORY OF HEAT

30. ATOMIC PHYSICS: THE STRUCTURE OF THE ATOM (QUANTUM MECHANICS)

31. WAVE MECHANICS

32. THE NUCLEUS

APPENDIX

1

Introduction to Mechanics

1–1 INTRODUCTION

Physics is a science which deals with the behavior of the inanimate world. This world is classified by contemporary physicists into two categories: matter and electromagnetic radiation. Mechanics is the branch of physics concerned specifically with material systems, their interaction, motion, and configuration. Historically, an understanding of mechanical systems antedated the discovery of the laws governing electromagnetic systems. Therefore most of the fundamental definitions of physical terms are expressed in the language of mechanics. Mechanics is usually regarded as the foundation upon which the other branches of physics are built.

The first part of this text is restricted to the classical mechanics of particles. The term "classical" means, of course, "distinct from modern," but it also imposes two well-defined restrictions. The first is that classical mechanics applies to systems which are considerably larger than the dimensions of atoms or molecules of matter (about 10^{-8} cm). The term "particle" is an abstraction, by which we mean a material object of "negligible" size. One accomplishes the extension of the mechanics of particles to the mechanics of finite bodies quite literally by regarding the finite body as a system of connected particles. Thus particle mechanics lies at the base of all mechanics.

The second restriction is that the laws of classical mechanics apply only to material bodies whose relative velocities are small compared with the velocity of light. These sweeping restrictions serve both to define our introductory topic and to suggest the advanced developments of the subject in the realms of atomic mechanics, mechanics of rigid and fluid systems, and relativistic mechanics.

In these general remarks, we should also say a word about the restriction to inanimate systems. Certainly, living systems are made up of the kind of matter which physics describes. To this extent, mechanics is useful to the life sciences. In fact, the emergence of the modern discipline of biophysics promises the elimination of the barrier between the study of living and nonliving systems.

1–2 DEFINITIONS

The foundations of physics rest on a set of strict definitions of all terms employed. The selection of particular definitions is based on subsequent demonstration of their usefulness. In the case of some of the simpler quantities, a subjective notion of the concept to be defined can be given. This descriptive notion can be useful, but a person is in difficulty if he tries to describe all derived quantities in everyday language; it is really necessary to use a mathematical formulation of the definitions of derived quantities.

But the definition of physical quantities is not completed with a mathematical definition. We are starting with classical physics, which deals only with quantities that are measurable. Therefore, rules for measurement must be included at least implicitly in a definition. We will see that the rules of measurement for the basic quantities (mass, length, and time) include (1) the adoption of an arbitrary *standard* and (2) a system of *comparison* with the standard. The system of comparison can be indirect, but in classical physics it is uncomplicated, in principle. It will be seen later (in the discussion of relativity, for example) that the system of comparison may involve unsuspected subtleties. In such cases, we must use a carefully analyzed *operational* definition that includes the exact procedure of measurement.

1-3 EXPERIMENT AND THEORY

The laws of physics are meant to describe the results of quantitative observation of natural processes. Quite often a body of experimental facts is developed to an advanced stage before the theory connecting all these facts is recognized and formulated. Equally often, a correct theory which has been argued from particulars will break the bounds of acquired information and will predict the results of untried experiments. However, the test of the theory is that it must never conflict with the facts of observation. A physical theory consists of a set of postulates and definitions from which the results of experiment can be predicted with arbitrary precision. This statement in itself suggests the provisional and vulnerable nature of theory: while a hundred facts may support a theory, one fact can break it. There are, nevertheless, theories which are supported by millions of data in which there is no conflict whatever. Such theories are exemplified by those covering the fields of classical mechanics, thermodynamics, and classical electricity and magnetism.

A topic in science, such as classical mechanics, is essentially closed to any basic revision when all conflict and inconsistency are removed. It should be remembered, however, that during their development, the theories that now are well-established were controversial. For the few hundred years that the laws of mechanics have been known, they have been subject to criticism and revision. In fact, we have no reason to consider any law of physical science as beyond question. However, we are quite confident that no good experimental evidence will be found to contradict classical laws within the realm of low velocities and macroscopic sizes.

1-4 ERROR

Physics is referred to as one of the exact sciences. The term "exact" is meaningful only if its limitations are known. An exact science is based on measurements, and measurements are of limited precision. Moreover, a theory, however precisely stated, is known to be correct only to the precision with which it has been tested. Thus, the term "exact" refers to a recognition of the limits of precision, and not to absolute precision. There is no notion of absolute precision in physics.

A body of experimental data is usually a set of numbers. These numbers have the usual mathematical properties and conform to operations such as multiplication and addition. They may be used in equations. However, if these numbers represent physical data, the strict mathematical operations must be qualified. For example, the number 4 may be uniquely defined in mathematics. In physics the number must be qualified by the accuracy to which the number is known. The statement "4 meters long" implies a crude measurement of a length which, if repeated, may give values as low as 3.5 m or as high as 4.5 m. The correct expression for the length, if this is the case, is 4.0 ± 0.5 m. If the accuracy is greater than this, it will be apparent from the number of quoted figures, which are called significant figures. For example, 4.125 is a number having 4 significant figures; the implication is that the fifth figure is unknown or uncertain. If, for example, the fifth figure is known to be zero, the number is written 4.1250, and then the sixth figure is uncertain. However carefully a datum is measured, there is no such thing as absolute precision. The measuring instrument or the way it is used may be responsible for the lack of precision. In other cases the physical system will limit precision quite independently of the fineness of the measuring instrument employed. Any figures that lie beyond the limits of precision are outside the realm of physics.

Errors or uncertainties are propagated in mathematical operations. Suppose that the lengths of

1

Introduction to Mechanics

1-1 INTRODUCTION

Physics is a science which deals with the behavior of the inanimate world. This world is classified by contemporary physicists into two categories: matter and electromagnetic radiation. Mechanics is the branch of physics concerned specifically with material systems, their interaction, motion, and configuration. Historically, an understanding of mechanical systems antedated the discovery of the laws governing electromagnetic systems. Therefore most of the fundamental definitions of physical terms are expressed in the language of mechanics. Mechanics is usually regarded as the foundation upon which the other branches of physics are built.

The first part of this text is restricted to the classical mechanics of particles. The term "classical" means, of course, "distinct from modern," but it also imposes two well-defined restrictions. The first is that classical mechanics applies to systems which are considerably larger than the dimensions of atoms or molecules of matter (about 10^{-8} cm). The term "particle" is an abstraction, by which we mean a material object of "negligible" size. One accomplishes the extension of the mechanics of particles to the mechanics of finite bodies quite literally by regarding the finite body as a system of connected particles. Thus particle mechanics lies at the base of all mechanics.

The second restriction is that the laws of classical mechanics apply only to material bodies whose relative velocities are small compared with the velocity of light. These sweeping restrictions serve both to define our introductory topic and to suggest the advanced developments of the subject in the realms of atomic mechanics, mechanics of rigid and fluid systems, and relativistic mechanics.

In these general remarks, we should also say a word about the restriction to inanimate systems. Certainly, living systems are made up of the kind of matter which physics describes. To this extent, mechanics is useful to the life sciences. In fact, the emergence of the modern discipline of biophysics promises the elimination of the barrier between the study of living and nonliving systems.

1-2 DEFINITIONS

The foundations of physics rest on a set of strict definitions of all terms employed. The selection of particular definitions is based on subsequent demonstration of their usefulness. In the case of some of the simpler quantities, a subjective notion of the concept to be defined can be given. This descriptive notion can be useful, but a person is in difficulty if he tries to describe all derived quantities in everyday language; it is really necessary to use a mathematical formulation of the definitions of derived quantities.

But the definition of physical quantities is not completed with a mathematical definition. We are starting with classical physics, which deals only with quantities that are measurable. Therefore, rules for measurement must be included at least implicitly in a definition. We will see that the rules of measurement for the basic quantities (mass, length, and time) include (1) the adoption of an arbitrary *standard* and (2) a system of *comparison* with the standard. The system of comparison can be indirect, but in classical physics it is uncomplicated, in principle. It will be seen the sides of a rectangle are measured as 4.56 and 7.68, and the mathematical operation is to find the area. By multiplying the lengths 4.56 and 7.68 to find the area, we obtain as a formal product 35.0208. But a result written in such a manner implies that the area is known more accurately (six significant figures) than either of the sides (three significant figures). The study of the propagation of errors is deferred to a laboratory course. It suffices for present purposes to simply state a rule that the number of significant figures in the result is no greater than the number of significant figures in the least accurate number involved in the calculation. Follow this rule in *all* numerical problem work. In the application of it to the problem above, the area is correctly written 35.0, and the numbers 208 are actually undetermined. They are meaningless and should not be written.

Our intent will be to give the numerical data for problems to a reasonable and consistent number of significant figures. However, there will be occasional oversights. For example, if we state that an object travels 54 m in 3 sec, assume that we really mean to write 3.0 sec.

1–5 SCALE

There is an important distinction between size and precision. The figure 0.0000123 m is no more precise, in terms of percent, than the number 123×10^4 m. In both numbers the zeros are included to place the decimal point and are not significant figures. The accuracy of the two numbers is the same: three significant figures. The position of the decimal point is arbitrary and depends on a *scale factor*. A millimeter (mm) is 0.001 m. A kilometer (km) is 1000 m. The distance 251 mm may be translated to read 0.000251 km. Both figures represent the same length, the same measurement, and the same precision. The position of the decimal point depends on the scale chosen. The distance from here to the sun may be a very "large" number, 93,000,000 miles, or a very "small" number, 0.00048 parsec, depending on the scale.

The terms "large" and "small" have no absolute meaning in physics. Magnitudes are comparative. A meaningful statement of magnitudes is this: The radius of the earth's orbit about the sun is large *compared with* the diameter of the earth.

1–6 UNITS

If the number 10 represents the measurement of a length in meters, it is written 10 m. The unit so denoted follows the number as a multiplicative factor in all operations which apply to the unit as well as to the number. If an object travels 3 m in 10 sec, the ratio 3 m/10 sec measures the speed. The result of the division is 0.3 m/sec. As another example, 10 m multiplied by 3 m is $10 \text{ m} \times 3 \text{ m} = 30 \text{ m}^2$.

1–7 BASIC DEFINITIONS IN MECHANICS

Length, mass, and *time* are the principal concepts upon which mechanics is built in the schemes that are most frequently used. Other physical quantities appear as combinations of these three. It is possible to use other groups of quantities as basic measures. For example, in the most frequently used British engineering units, *length, force,* and *time* are the principal notions.

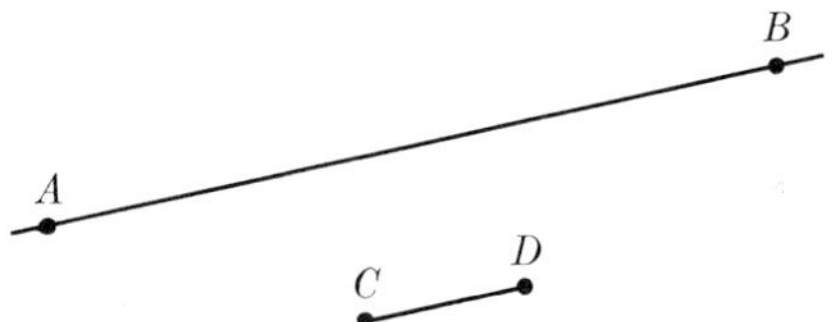

Fig. 1–1. A length AB that is to be measured in terms of a standard length CD.

Length. Length is the measure of spatial intervals. The measurement of length is performed, as is any physical measurement, by the technique of comparison. The idea of comparing the spatial separation of the points A and B with the separation of the points C and D (Fig. 1–1) is the following: $\overline{CD}$ can be "fitted" several times into the interval $\overline{AB}$. The procedure is this: lay $\overline{CD}$ beside $\overline{AB}$, starting with C coincident on A. Then, marking the position D, slide C to that position, and mark D again, and so on. The result of the measurement (Fig. 1–2) is a number, a ratio, expressing the number of times, including fractions, that the length $\overline{CD}$ can be fitted along $\overline{AB}$.

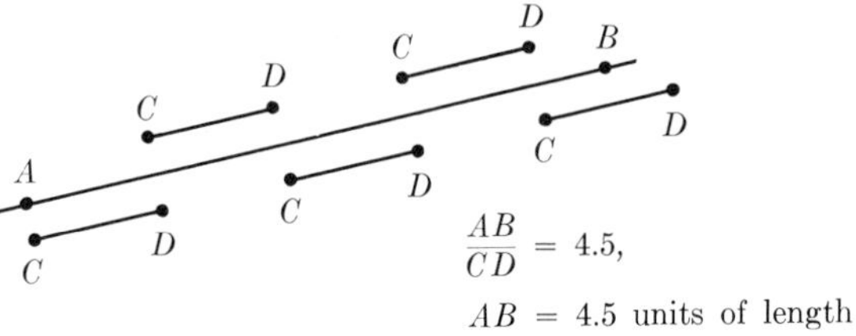

FIG. 1–2. The process of measurement of length AB in terms of the standard CD.

If this procedure is to be followed, a standard length $\overline{CD}$ must be adopted. For local comparisons, any object may be used—a stick, an eraser, a hand. But for worldwide comparison, for the ready communication of results by different observers, a universal standard must be chosen. There are several such standards, the important ones being specified by legislation. The point to note is that the choice of a standard is a completely arbitrary act and has no "natural" significance in itself. The standard we adopt here is the meter, defined in 1889 as the distance marked by two scratches on a platinum-iridium bar housed at Sèvres, near Paris. In 1960, the standard meter was redefined as 1,650,763.73 wavelengths of the orange-red line in the spectrum of isotope 86 of krypton. The simplest instrument used for measuring length is a ruler. If there is relative motion between object and ruler, observations must be made simultaneously at C and at D (see Relativity).

It is important to note that the standard of comparison and the standard operations may, and often must, be extended to equivalent or secondary procedures. The distances between planets are not measured by the operation described above, nor is the radius of an atom so measured. The standard thermometer defined in thermodynamics would melt at many interesting temperatures.

The meter is associated with a set of convenient multiples and submultiples:

$$
\begin{aligned}
1 \text{ kilometer} &= 1000 \text{ meters} = 10^3 \text{ meters},\\
1 \text{ centimeter} &= 0.01 \text{ meter} = 10^{-2} \text{ meter},\\
1 \text{ millimeter} &= 0.001 \text{ meter} = 10^{-3} \text{ meter},\\
1 \text{ micron} &= 0.000001 \text{ meter} = 10^{-6} \text{ meter}.
\end{aligned}
$$

The prefixes kilo, centi, milli, and micro are also used for other physical dimensions.

Time. Occurrences or happenings of physical processes, that is, *events*, have ordered sequences. Event A occurs before B, and C after B, and so on. Moreover, the events have intervals between them, as well as order. For example, some repetitive process may have been performed four times between events A and B, but only twice between B and C. Time intervals are measured by comparison with a standard interval associated with some repetitive physical process.

A periodic system is one which repeats its geometrical motion identically. In a definition of time, it cannot be proved that the motion chosen as the standard is repeated identically in time. Since there is no other standard with which a comparison could be made, the proof or assumption would have no sense. Some examples of periodic systems are the rotation of the earth about its axis, the motion of the earth in its orbit around the sun, the motion of a pendulum, the vibration of a weight suspended by a spring, and the frequency of radiation emitted or absorbed by atoms or molecules. The standard system chosen from these is the average time for the revolution of the earth about the sun. The standard unit is a fraction of the year, $1/365 \cdot 24 \cdot 60 \cdot 60$, called the second. In 1960, it was decided to choose the solar year 1900 as the standard.* An instrument for the measurement of time is a clock.

* Within a few years, the standard will undoubtedly be changed to a frequency associated with radiation emitted from an atom or molecule.

Any secondary repetitive system, such as a pendulum, may be calibrated against the established standard. The period or time for one complete swing of the pendulum may for convenience be adjusted until it equals 1 sec. Then the time interval between events A and B is found by *counting* the number of swings of the pendulum, including fractions, which are executed in the interval AB. The result is a number, the ratio of the size of the interval AB to the size of the standard interval of time.

Mass. The third basic quantity that we use in mechanics is inertial mass. Since relatively complex ideas are involved, their development will be taken up later. The standard for mass is a cylinder, and it, too, is kept at Sèvres, near Paris. Its mass is one kilogram by definition.

1–8 CONVERSION OF UNITS

Identities and equations are the two ways used to convert units systematically. Consider length as an example. The conversions have been expressed as *identities* in the preceding section. (Note that the symbol "≡" is commonly used to designate identities which include definitions, e.g., "equality by definition.") From the table of identities, 1 km ≡ 1000 m. Since this is an identity, 1 km can be replaced by 1000 m wherever it occurs; conversely, 1 m = $\frac{1}{1000}$ km, and 1 m can be replaced by $\frac{1}{1000}$ km wherever it occurs. Note that the units are carried along with the numerical values of the quantities at all times.

An alternative way of using *identities* is possible. Since 1 km ≡ 1000 m, simple division of both sides by 1 km gives 1 ≡ 1000 m/km. Note that the units have been carried along with the quantities as usual. The number one on the left side is dimensionless (it is a pure number). Consequently, we can introduce this "one," and therefore its equivalent, 1000 m/km, into any part of an equation as a multiplicative factor. For example, we calculated speed in an earlier section by implicitly using the equation (really a definition), speed $s = d/t$, where d is distance and t is time. By substitution of numerical values for d and t, we obtained $s = 3$ m/10 sec. But suppose that we wish to have the result in kilometers per second. Using the present method, we would introduce the factor 1000 m/km into the right side of the denominator (why not the numerator?). The result would be

$$s = \frac{3\text{ m}}{10\text{ sec} \times 1000\text{ m/km}} = 3 \times 10^{-4}\text{ km/sec.}$$

Note the cancellation of meters as units from the equation.

If an *equation* is used for conversion of units, the example chosen above becomes $l(\text{m}) = 1000 \times L(\text{km})$, where l and L are ordinary algebraic quantities. This latter method is ordinarily used when the conversion is made in an equation expressed in symbols. It is used principally in subjects such as electricity and magnetism.

1–9 SUMMARY

The definitions give a prescription for measuring length and time quantitatively in terms of standards that are chosen by international agreement. The standard unit of time can obviously be reproduced, in principle, by an isolated observer without access to a bureau of standards. The standard unit of length could not be so reproduced before 1960. However, the standard meter has now been defined in units of the wavelength of a spectrum line emitted by krypton-86 and therefore can be reproduced in any laboratory. Hence, the standard unit of length can also be reproduced, in effect, by an isolated observer.

The definitions of length and time are abstract ideas which have gradually been incorporated into man's thinking. They are a distillate of man's practical experience in dealing with these quantities.

The units of length and time which we have established are, respectively, the meter and the second. The system of units used in this text is called the meter-kilogram-second system or, abbreviated, the mks system. The definition of the kilogram of mass is deferred to Chapter 4. All other quantities in mechanics are defined and measured in terms of length, mass, and time in this system. For convenience, it is customary to give special names to particular combinations of the basic units, as we shall see in succeeding chapters.

Problems

1. Set up an example of how you would measure the width of a river you could not cross. Tell what quantities must be measured and how the answer is found. How would you prove that the measurement you made corresponds to the operational definition of length given in this chapter?

2. How would you measure
(a) the distance between the moon and the earth?
(b) the size of the moon?
(c) the radius of the earth?

3. List some repetitive disturbances in nature which may have led man to the idea and convenience of time measurement.

4. How would you measure the length of the year in units of days? (The answer is roughly $365\frac{1}{4}$.)

5. Can length be measured along a curved line? What is a straight line? How would you measure the circumference of a circle with sufficient accuracy to obtain a value of π to, say, four significant figures?

6. In making a measurement such as that shown in Fig. 1–2, the observer is usually at leisure to align the ends C and D, one after the other, since CD is usually at rest relative to AB during each process of alignment. What additional precaution is necessary when CD is in continuous motion relative to AB? Can a single observer make the measurement in this latter case?

7. The solar day is defined as the average period of time that has elapsed between successive crossings of an earth meridian (north-south plane through the zenith) by the sun. The sidereal day is defined as the average period of time that has elapsed between successive crossings of an earth meridian by a star. What is the difference between the two days in seconds?

8. Describe a method for measuring an area directly in terms of a unit area. How would the unit area be established?

9. The dimensions of a board are measured to be: length, 2.125 m; width, 10.1 cm; thickness, 5.2 cm.
(a) Find the volume of the board. How large is the uncertainty?
(b) Find the total surface area. How large is its uncertainty?

10. An airplane requires 2.5 h to travel between two cities that are 1505 miles apart.
(a) Find the average speed in miles per hour.
(b) Convert the speed to meters per second (0.30 m = 1 ft).

2

Descriptive Mathematics in Physics

2–1 INTRODUCTION

In this chapter, we present a summary of some simple mathematical definitions and operations which may already be familiar to the reader. The topics chosen for review have useful physical as well as mathematical applications.

Any subject is purely descriptive and qualitative without quantitative data. Furthermore, the usefulness of quantitative data is restricted until they can be incorporated into a mathematical framework. The reader may, as an exercise, wish to investigate some of the major areas of human thought, such as psychology, biology, social science, and anthropology, to find out whether they are purely descriptive, or exact, or at some stage of a combination of both.

The reader is expected to be familiar with many topics which do not appear in this chapter, e.g., algebra, including the solution of quadratic and simultaneous equations, and trigonometry, including the use of trigonometric identities.

2–2 COORDINATE SYSTEMS

In Section 1–7, we discussed the idea of spatial separation or distance between points A and B. The question now raised is how can the position of B relative to A be specified? Obviously, a direction is also involved. But an additional question is now implied: direction relative to what? It is customary to utilize a *coordinate system* in order to specify positions of points. In the above discussion, a so-called spherical polar coordinate system was implied when we spoke of distance and direction for the specification of position. However, since the reader is more familiar with the cartesian coordinate system, and perhaps the cylindrical polar coordinate system, the discussion that follows will be confined to these systems. In addition, the discussion will largely be limited to two-dimensional systems.

The *cartesian system* consists of three mutually perpendicular lines (called axes) that intersect at a common point. A so-called right-handed system of cartesian coordinates in three dimensions is shown in Fig. 2–1. The units of length marked off on the axes establish a lattice of lines throughout space. Then the location of P relative to the origin O can be stated without ambiguity. In Fig. 2–1, one can reach point P from O by moving 3 units along the X-axis ($x = 3$), 4 units parallel to the Y-axis ($y = 4$), and 4 units parallel to the Z-axis ($z = 4$). The order of the above three steps is of no consequence.

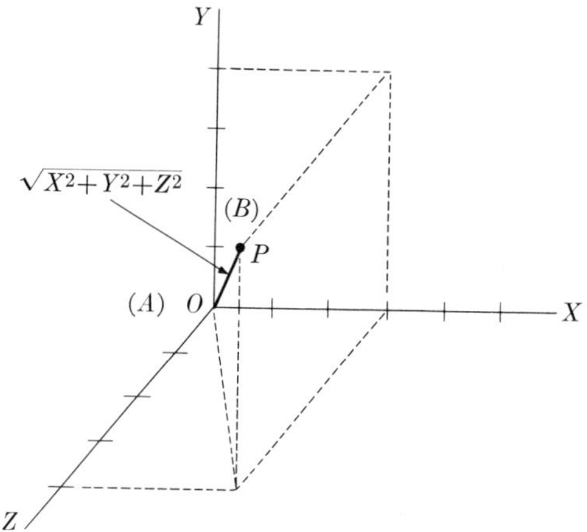

FIG. 2–1. The position of a point P relative to a cartesian coordinate system.

Let us now return to the original question of the specification of the position of B relative to A. The origin of the cartesian coordinate system can be placed at A, and B will then occupy position P. The cartesian coordinates (x, y, z) of point P specify the position of B relative to A.

If we wish to return to the ideas of distance and direction of B relative to A, we see by the Pythagorean theorem that the distance is

$$OP = \sqrt{x^2 + y^2 + z^2}. \qquad (2\text{–}1)$$

The direction is specified implicitly by the values of x, y, and z.

A *polar coordinate* system explicitly involves the specification of angles. Therefore, we will first review the measurement of angles.

An *angle* measures the opening between two intersecting lines. In trigonometry, the unit of angular measure is usually the degree. In physics, most equations are constructed in such a way that angles *must* be measured in *radians*. The radian measurement of angular opening is made by constructing an arc subtended by the sides of the angle and centered on their point of intersection. Let the length of the arc be s and the radius of the arc be r (Fig. 2–2).

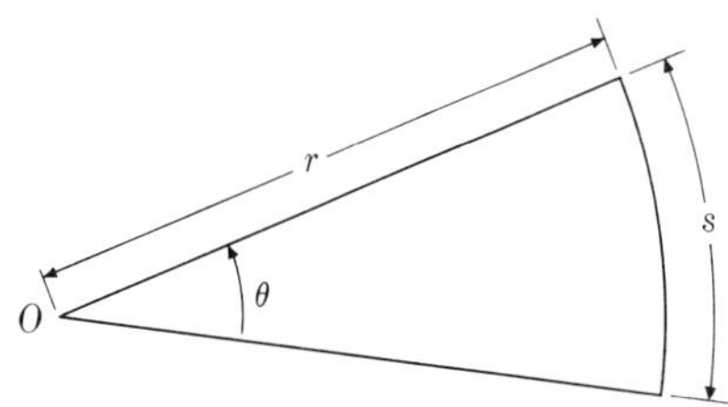

FIG. 2–2. The geometrical relationships among arc, radius, and angle.

Then the angle θ is defined as

$$\theta = \frac{s}{r} \text{ radians.} \qquad (2\text{–}2)$$

The ratio of s to r is dimensionless, since the units cancel. This dimensionless unit is called the radian (abbreviated rad). The unit one radian

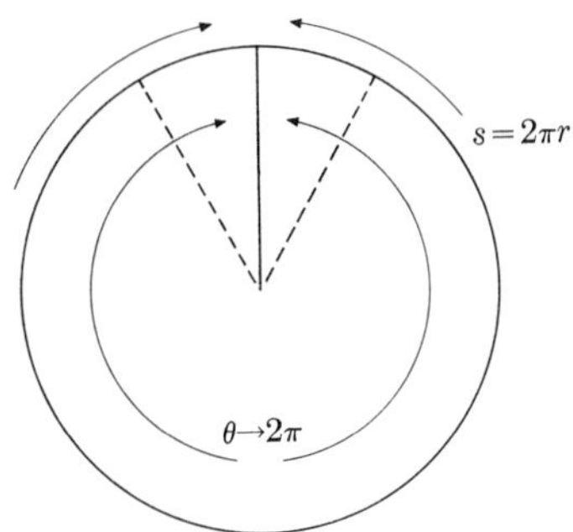

FIG. 2–3. The case of a full circle, for which the angle goes to 2π radians.

(1 rad) is the angle whose arc length equals the radius. For example, if $s = r$, then

$$\theta = \frac{s}{r} = \frac{r}{r} = 1 \text{ rad.}$$

The number of radians in a complete circle, where the lines open until they meet again (Fig. 2–3), is found by letting $s = 2\pi r$.

Then Eq. (2–2) gives

$$\theta = \frac{s}{r} = \frac{2\pi r}{r} = 2\pi \text{ rad.}$$

A degree is $\frac{1}{360}$ of the opening in a complete circle. Since there are 360 degrees, or 2π radians, in a circle, then 360 deg $\equiv 2\pi$ rad. Hence

$$1 \equiv \frac{360 \text{ deg}}{2\pi \text{ rad}} = \frac{360 \text{ deg}}{6.28 \text{ rad}} = 57 \frac{\text{deg}}{\text{rad}}$$

is the conversion factor between the two systems of angular measure (see Section 1–8). Radian measure is used most in mathematical operations.

We return now to the question of *polar coordinates*. The position of a point P relative to O on a plane may be specified by a distance r and an angle θ (Fig. 2–4), where r is the distance from O to P and θ is the angle between the line OP and a reference line such as OX. It is customary to consider θ as positive when it is measured in the counterclockwise direction as shown.

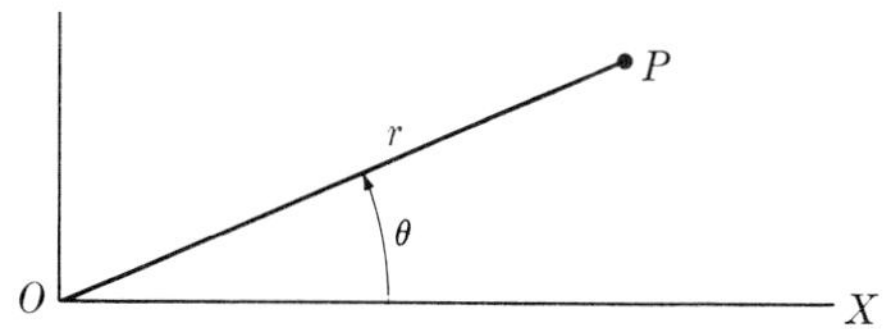

Fig. 2–4. The position of a point P specified in polar coordinates.

If the problem involves three-dimensional space, a third quantity is required in order to specify the position of P. In cylindrical polar coordinates the third quantity is the height of P above the plane of the paper in Fig. 2–4.

2–3 TRIGONOMETRY

The sides of a right triangle are related by the following definitions (the symbol ≡ denotes "equality by definition"):

$$\sin \alpha \equiv \frac{A}{C} \equiv \cos \beta,$$

$$\cos \alpha \equiv \frac{B}{C} \equiv \sin \beta,$$

$$\tan \alpha \equiv \frac{A}{B} \equiv \cot \beta,$$

where the meaning of the symbols is given in Fig. 2–5. The functions $\sin \alpha$, $\cos \alpha$, etc., are tabulated so that, given the angles and one side, the other sides may be found. For right triangles, as above, $\alpha + \beta = 90°$.

Much of the analysis in mathematics and physics involves either small angles or angles

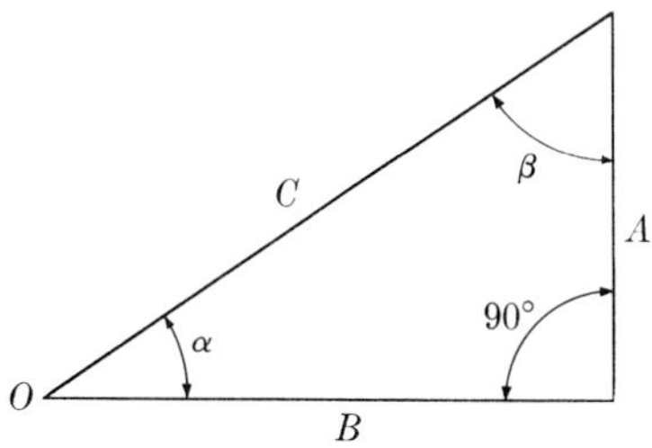

Fig. 2–5. A right triangle.

that go to zero as a limit. Therefore limiting values of the trigonometric functions are of importance in physics and mathematics.

Example 1. If α is small compared with 1 rad, then $\sin \alpha \cong \alpha$. (The symbol $\cong$ denotes approximate equality.)

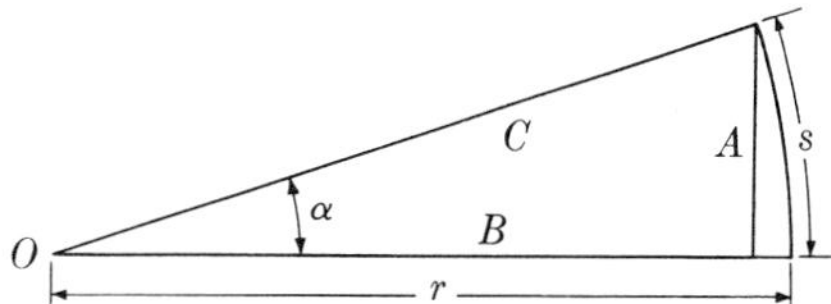

Fig. 2–6. A right triangle with the geometrical diagram for the definition of the angle α in terms of the arc s and the radius r included.

Proof: When α approaches zero, the chord A approaches the arc s (Fig. 2–6). In mathematical nomenclature we write

$$A \to s \qquad \text{as } \alpha \to 0,$$

where the symbol $\to$ means "approaches." Then, in the limiting case, $\sin \alpha \equiv A/r \to s/r \equiv \alpha$, or $\sin \alpha \to \alpha$. For example,

$$\begin{aligned} \sin\ (1 \text{ rad}) &= 0.8415, \\ \sin\ (0.1 \text{ rad}) &= 0.0998, \\ \sin\ (0.01 \text{ rad}) &= 0.0100. \end{aligned}$$

In more formal notation, we write

$$\lim_{\alpha \to 0} \sin \alpha = \alpha, \tag{2–3}$$

where the left-hand expression is read "limit of $\sin \alpha$ as α goes to zero."

Example 2. If α is small (compared with 1 rad) then $\tan \alpha \cong \alpha$.

Proof: As before, when $\alpha \to 0$, the chord A approaches s, but in addition $B \to r$. Therefore,

$$\tan \alpha \equiv \frac{A}{B} \to \frac{s}{r} \equiv \alpha, \qquad \text{or} \qquad \tan \alpha \to \alpha. \tag{2–4}$$

Example 3. From the above, it also follows that $\sin \alpha \cong \tan \alpha$, for small α.

Oblique triangles will also occur in future analysis. The student should review the laws of sines and cosines for any plane triangle. In addition, identities involving sums or products of trigonometric functions, functions of sums of angles, etc., will occasionally be needed.

2–4 RELATIONSHIPS BETWEEN COORDINATE SYSTEMS

The specification of the position P relative to the coordinate axes may be quoted in cartesian form, (x, y), or polar form, (r, θ). From Fig. 2–7 it can be seen that the equations

$$x = r \cos \theta \qquad \text{and} \qquad y = r \sin \theta \tag{2–5}$$

express the cartesian coordinates in terms of the polar coordinates. The equations

$$r = \sqrt{x^2 + y^2}$$

and

$$\theta = \arctan \frac{y}{x} \qquad \text{or} \qquad \theta = \tan^{-1} \frac{y}{x} \tag{2–6}$$

express the polar coordinates in terms of the cartesian coordinates.

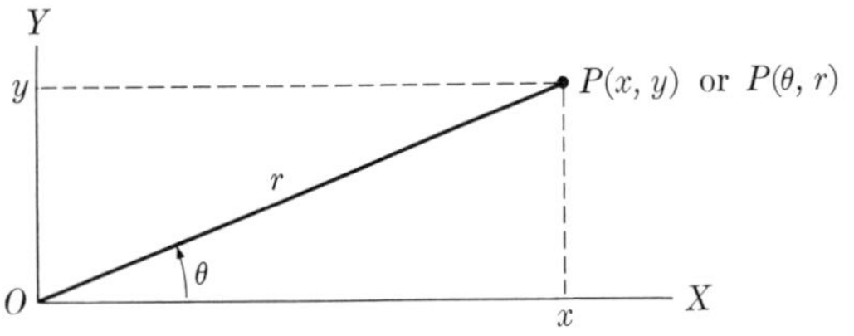

Fig. 2–7. The geometrical relationship between cartesian and polar coordinates.

2–5 VECTORS

Physical quantities which are specified by magnitude alone are called *scalar* quantities. Typical examples of scalar quantities are temperature, volume, and time. Another class of quantities occurs in physics for which magnitude is only a partial specification, and direction, or orientation, must also be given. Such quantities are called *vector* quantities. Examples of vector quantities which will later be discussed in detail are velocity, displacement, and some kinds of forces. A force is a directed agent that causes change in motion. Velocity may be directed north, east, etc. Displacement denotes directed change in position.

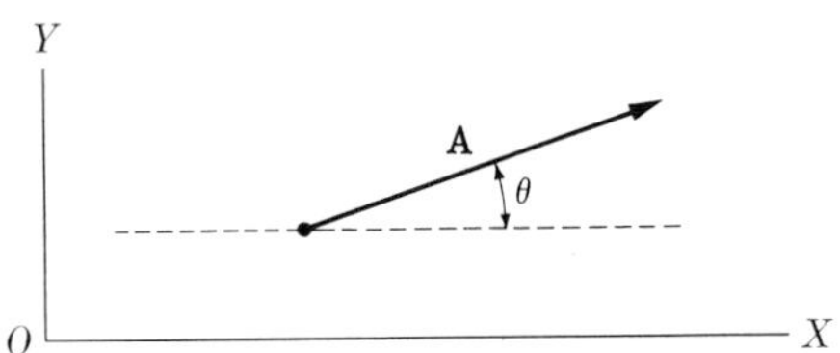

Fig. 2–8. Specification of a vector **A**.

A physical quantity that is a vector may be represented geometrically by a line, as in Fig. 2–8. The length of the line **A** measures the magnitude of the physical quantity, and θ measures the orientation relative to the coordinate system. In cases where ambiguity arises, the technical term "sense" is used to designate which of the two possible directions a particular vector has along a given line.

The vector **A** is a geometrical representation of a physical quantity. The length in meters, as drawn, is intended to measure, say, the magnitude of a force or a velocity. Thus a scale factor is required. For example, the scale conversion may be 2 cm of length = 4 newtons of force, which should be read "2 cm represents 4 newtons."

In book print, the symbol for a vector is a boldface letter (**A**); otherwise, it is shown as a letter with a half-arrow drawn above ($\vec{A}$). These symbols denote a vector quantity (velocity, force, etc.) which has magnitude and direction. In many operations, it is convenient to have a means of representing the magnitude of the vector. For this purpose we use vertical bars. Thus, the magnitude of the vector **A** is $|\mathbf{A}|$. Such deliberate notation will be used only when the discussion might otherwise be obscure. Generally, a more informal representation of magnitude will be used; we will write $|\mathbf{A}|$ as an italic letter A, for instance.

Vector mathematics is a complete subject within itself. In this text we will use vector addition and subtraction in particular, and vector algebra in general. In this section, no physical significance will be attached to the vectors. One comment will, however, be made at this time and repeated later for the sake of emphasis. As in the case of scalars, the addition or subtraction of vector quantities that have different basic units has no significance, i.e. the process is nonsensical.

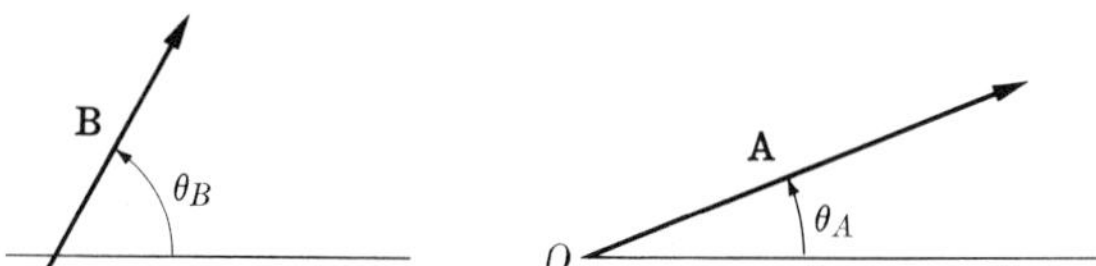

FIG. 2–9. Specification of vectors **A** and **B**.

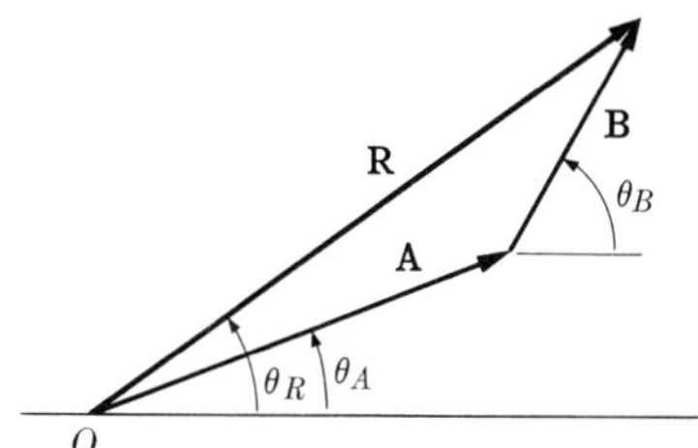

FIG. 2–10. The sum of **A** and **B**.

Addition of vectors is defined as follows: The sum of the two vectors **A** and **B** (Fig. 2–9) is obtained by placing the tail of **B** upon the head of **A**, while preserving the length and orientation of both **A** and **B** (Fig. 2–10). Then the vector **R**, which is drawn from the tail of **A** to the head of **B** so as to close the triangle, is the sum of **A** and **B**. The vector **R** is often called the "resultant" of **A** and **B**. The process is symbolized by

$$\mathbf{R} \equiv \mathbf{A} + \mathbf{B}. \tag{2–7}$$

The vectors **R**, **A**, and **B** form a triangle, and if the angles (orientations) and magnitudes of **A** and **B** are known, the ordinary trigonometric laws can be used to find the orientation and magnitude of **R**. Or, graphically, **A** and **B** can be drawn to scale, and the length and orientation of **R** can be measured with a ruler and a protractor. The above is called the triangle or polygon method of vector addition (or subtraction).

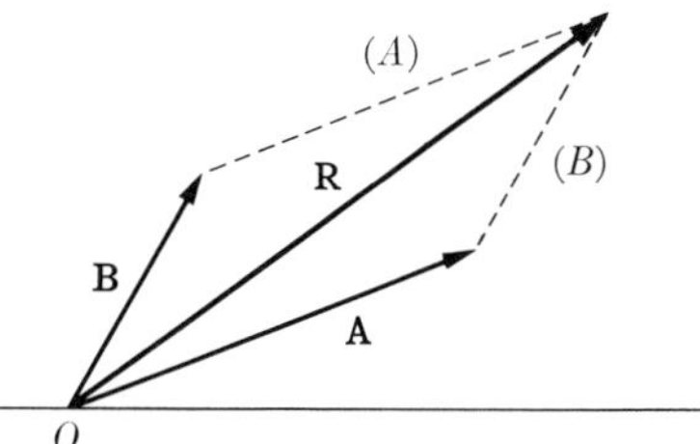

FIG. 2–11. The sum **R** of **A** and **B** by the parallelogram method.

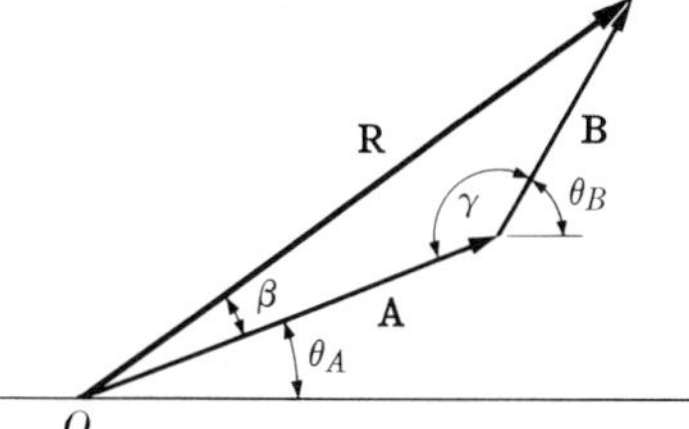

FIG. 2–12. The sum **R** of **A** and **B** by the triangle (polygon) method.

We note that the order of addition is of no consequence: that is, $\mathbf{A} + \mathbf{B} = \mathbf{B} + \mathbf{A}$ (see Fig. 2–11). Furthermore, it can be seen from geometry that the tails of **A** and **B** can be placed at a common origin, and **R** is then the diagonal (starting from the tails of **A** and **B**) of a parallelogram whose sides are **A** and **B** (see Fig. 2–11). This is commonly called the *parallelogram method* of vector addition. In all these manipulations, the absolute positions of the vectors have been unimportant. We have moved them about at will, preserving only their magnitudes and directions.

As an example of the analytical method of vector addition, suppose that the given quantities are **A**, θ_A, **B**, and θ_B (Fig. 2–12). The angle within the triangle of Fig. 2–12 would then be $\gamma = \theta_A + 180° - \theta_B$, and the law of cosines could be used to find **R**, namely, $R^2 = A^2 + B^2 - 2AB \cos \gamma$. The direction of **R** can be found, using the law of sines: $\sin \beta/B = \sin \gamma/R$. Then the direction of **R** can be given as $(\theta_A + \beta)$ above the x-axis.

2–6 COMPONENTS OF VECTORS

The above process of vector addition (or composition) can be reversed. The reverse process is called resolution of a vector into components. Unlike the composition procedure, which leads to a unique result, the resolution procedure can lead to an infinity of results, unless further conditions are specified. Ordinarily, one of these conditions is that the vector be resolved into only two components; the other condition is the specification of the two directions along which the components are to lie. In practice the two directions are usually at right angles.

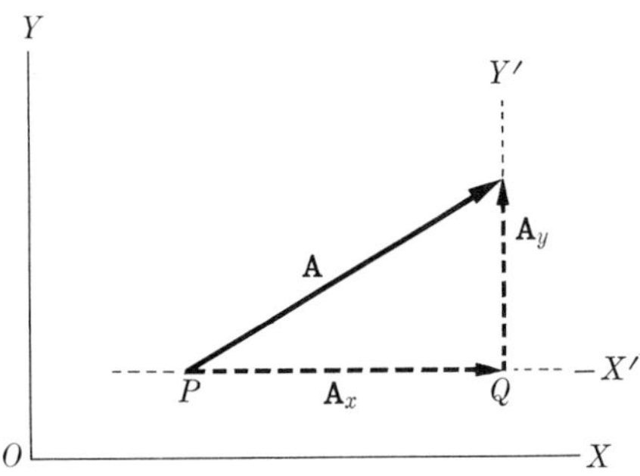

FIG. 2–13. A vector **A** resolved into cartesian components $\mathbf{A}_x$ and $\mathbf{A}_y$.

Either of the two methods (triangle or parallelogram) can be used for the resolution of a vector into components. The triangle method is illustrated in Fig. 2–13. A line PX' is drawn parallel to the OX-axis and passing through the tail of the vector. A second line QY' is drawn through the head of the vector and parallel to OY. The intersection of these two lines (at Q) defines one

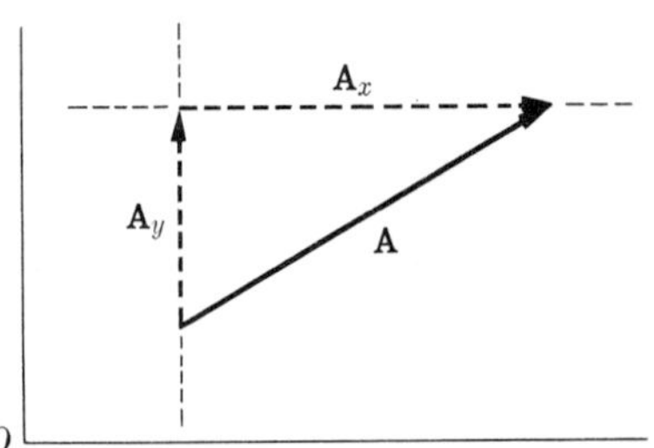

FIG. 2–14. An alternative resolution of **A** into cartesian components.

end of each component vector; the head or tail of **A** defines the other end of each component. The vectors $\mathbf{A}_x$ and $\mathbf{A}_y$ in Fig. 2–13 are the components of **A** along OX and OY, respectively, or simply the x- and y-components of **A**. Just as in vector addition, we can form another triangle (Fig. 2–14) or a parallelogram (Fig. 2–15). The equation for all cases is $\mathbf{A} = \mathbf{A}_x + \mathbf{A}_y$.

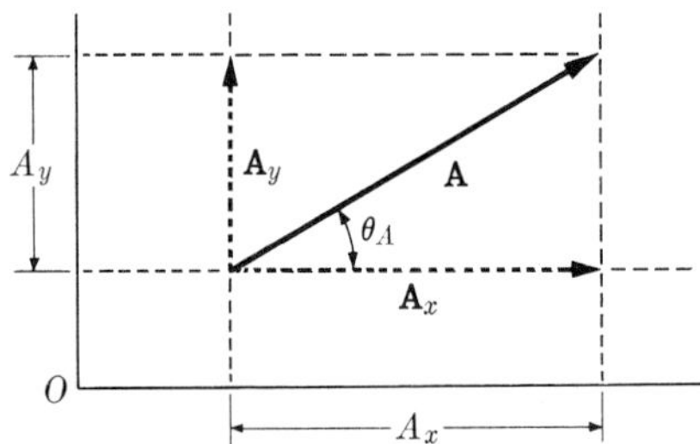

FIG. 2–15. Another form of resolution of **A** into cartesian components.

Another point is illustrated in Fig. 2–15, i.e., the lengths of $\mathbf{A}_x$ and $\mathbf{A}_y$ can be considered as scalars, A_x and A_y, since the directions of $\mathbf{A}_x$ and $\mathbf{A}_y$ are specified by the choice of axes. (How are the senses of $\mathbf{A}_x$ and $\mathbf{A}_y$ specified if only A_x and A_y are stated?)

Since the axes were chosen to be mutually perpendicular, the components are also projections on the axes. This is true *only* for perpendicular axes. In this case, we have

$$A_x = A \cos \theta_A, \qquad A_y = A \sin \theta_A. \tag{2–8}$$

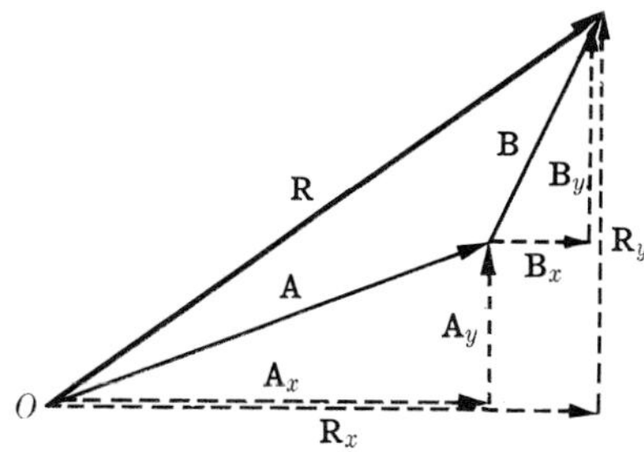

Fig. 2–16. The sum **R** of **A** and **B** demonstrated in cartesian components.

Returning to the problem of addition, we see by inspection of Fig. 2–16 that the components of **R** are the scalar sums of the components of **A** and **B**. Therefore the addition of **A** and **B** can be performed by the component method in the following way.

1. Choose cartesian axes OX and OY.
2. Resolve **A** and **B** into cartesian components.
3. Add together the magnitudes of the x-components of **A** and **B** and the y-components of **A** and **B** according to the laws of scalar addition (including $+$ and $-$ signs).
4. Then these summed components are the components of **R**, that is,

$$R_x = A_x + B_x, \qquad R_y = A_y + B_y. \tag{2–9}$$

5. The magnitude of **R** is

$$|\mathbf{R}| = (R_x^2 + R_y^2)^{1/2}. \tag{2–10}$$

6. The orientation of **R** is given by θ, where

$$\tan\theta = \frac{R_y}{R_x} = \frac{A_y + B_y}{A_x + B_x}. \tag{2–11}$$

By resolution into components, we reduce the geometric problem of vector addition to a problem involving only the trigonometry of right triangles and the algebra of scalar quantities.

The diagram in Fig. 2–16 is based on the triangle method. In practice, you may prefer to picture the process by placing the tails of all vectors at the origin of coordinates. This method is illustrated (for a problem with a new choice of A and B) in Fig. 2–17, which shows the components of the vectors, **A**, **B**, and **R**.

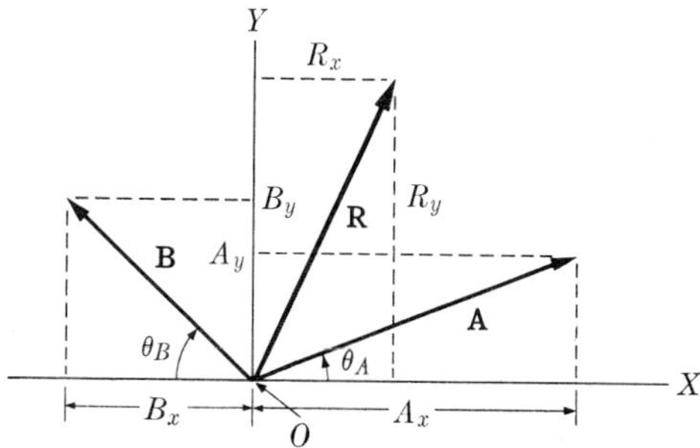

Fig. 2–17. The sum **R** of **A** and **B** shown in cartesian components.

Equations (2–8), (2–9), (2–10), and (2–11) are then used to find the resultant:

$$R_x = A\cos\theta_A + B\cos\theta_B, \qquad R_y = A\sin\theta_A + B\sin\theta_B. \tag{2–12}$$

It is sometimes convenient to choose coordinates so that at least one vector lies along a coordinate axis. The problem of Fig. 2–17 would appear graphically as in Fig. 2–18 if cartesian coordinates OX' and OY' are chosen with OX' parallel to vector **A**.

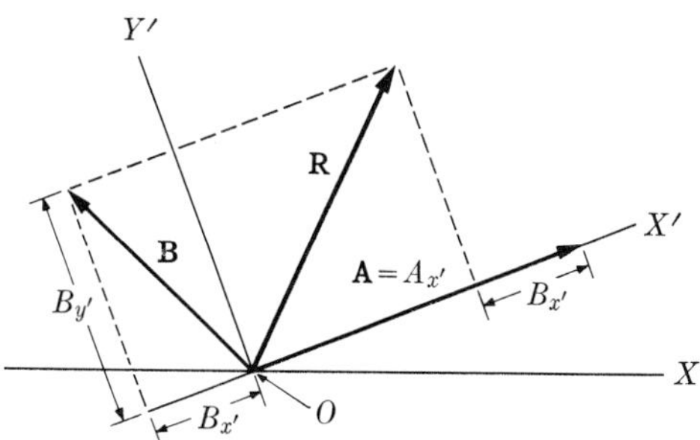

Fig. 2–18. The sum **R** of **A** and **B** with a choice of axes different from those in Fig. 2–17.

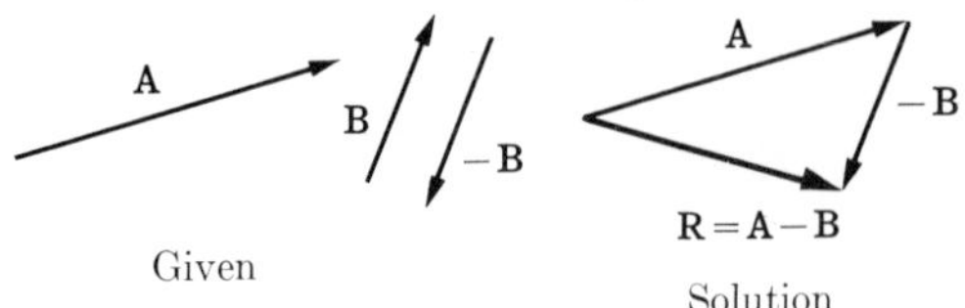

FIG. 2-19. The difference **R** of **A** and **B**.

2-7 VECTOR SUBTRACTION

The *difference* **R** between **A** and **B** is, by definition, the sum of **A** and (−**B**), where (−**B**) is defined to be the original vector **B** rotated by 180°, or π radians. The mathematical statement is

$$\mathbf{R} = \mathbf{A} - \mathbf{B} = \mathbf{A} + (-\mathbf{B}). \qquad (2\text{–}13)$$

Vector subtraction now proceeds in the same manner as vector addition; any of the methods in Section 2-6 can be used. As an illustration of the polygon method, **B** is subtracted from **A** in Fig. 2-19. The vector **R**, constructed so that $\mathbf{R} = \mathbf{A} + (-\mathbf{B})$, is defined as the vector difference, as stated above.

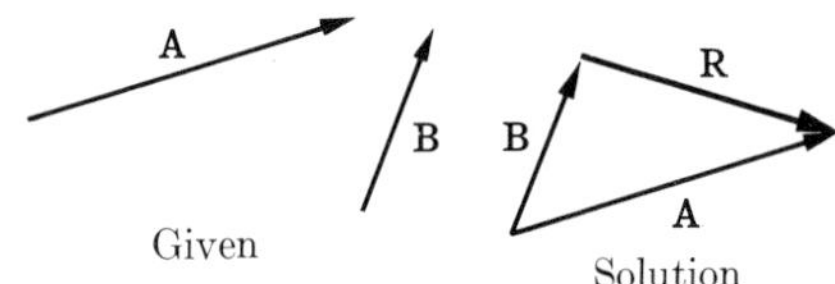

FIG. 2-20. The difference **R** of **A** and **B**.

An equivalent procedure for the construction of **A** − **B** can be formulated by transposing the −**B** in Eq. (2-13), thus obtaining $\mathbf{R} + \mathbf{B} = \mathbf{A}$. The construction in Fig. 2-20 illustrates one method of utilizing this formulation: the tails of the given vectors **A** and **B** are placed together, and **R** is then a vector drawn from the head of **B** to the head of **A**. Thus, $\mathbf{R} + \mathbf{B} = \mathbf{A}$, as required.

The magnitude and direction of **R** can be found by solving the triangles or by the method of components.

2-8 ADDITION (OR SUBTRACTION) OF MORE THAN TWO VECTORS

The addition or subtraction of a system of more than two vectors is a simple extension of the rules given above for two vectors. In the *polygon* method the process is continued, as shown in Fig. 2-21, for the case of $\mathbf{R} = \mathbf{A} + \mathbf{B} - \mathbf{C}$.

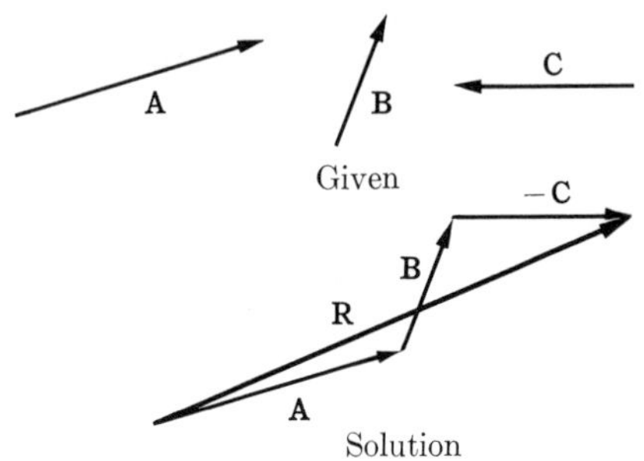

FIG. 2-21. The polygon method of geometrical display of $\mathbf{A} + \mathbf{B} - \mathbf{C}$.

In the *parallelogram* method, we make use of the idea expressed in the following equation:

$$\mathbf{R} = (\mathbf{A} + \mathbf{B}) - \mathbf{C}; \qquad (2\text{–}14)$$

that is, two vectors can first be added, and their resultant can subsequently be added to the next vector, etc.

In the *component* method, the extension of Eqs. (2-8) through (2-12) to the case of more than two vectors should be obvious.

2-9 SUMMARY

The two coordinate systems, cartesian and polar, that we shall most frequently use in this text are reviewed. The subtleties of choice of coordinate system when the motion of objects is involved are left until later.

A great many physical quantities can be classified as either scalar or vector. The rules for finding the sums, differences, products, and quotients of scalar quantities are known to the reader whether the scalars are numbers or algebraic expressions. The rules for finding sums and differences of vector quantities have been introduced here. It may be remarked that there are also rules for finding "products" of vector quantities. These rules will be introduced in the text. One should not be misled into believing that scalars and vectors are the only kinds of physical quantities. There are still different rules for mathematical operations for such categories as tensors, spinors, and pseudoscalars, to mention a few.

The process of vector addition is expressed by

$$\mathbf{R} = \mathbf{A} + \mathbf{B},$$

where $\mathbf{R}$ is the vector sum of $\mathbf{A}$ and $\mathbf{B}$. This process can be carried out directly in terms of the vectors themselves, as symbolized in the above equation, or it can be performed in terms of scalar operations by resolving the vectors $\mathbf{A}$ and $\mathbf{B}$ into components. A vector $\mathbf{A}$ is said to be resolved into components $\mathbf{A}_x$ and $\mathbf{A}_y$ if

$$\mathbf{A} = \mathbf{A}_x + \mathbf{A}_y.$$

The components can have any direction in general, but one of the most useful choices is directions that are mutually perpendicular, i.e., cartesian components.

The process of addition of vectors $\mathbf{A}$ and $\mathbf{B}$ by the method of components is shown by

$$\mathbf{R}_x = \mathbf{A}_x + \mathbf{B}_x, \qquad \mathbf{R}_y = \mathbf{A}_y + \mathbf{B}_y,$$

where all the quantities are scalars. If the above are cartesian components, the magnitude of the sum is given by

$$|\mathbf{R}| = (R_x^2 + R_y^2)^{1/2}$$

and the direction by

$$\tan\theta = \frac{R_y}{R_x},$$

where θ is the angle with the x-axis.

Vector subtraction is defined by

$$\mathbf{R} = \mathbf{A} - \mathbf{B} = \mathbf{A} + (-\mathbf{B}),$$

where $-\mathbf{B}$ is vector $\mathbf{B}$ reversed in direction. The process then becomes the same as that of addition, and the same methods can therefore be used.

The extension to more than two vectors is obvious.

Problems

In *all* the problems involving vector quantities, make a moderately accurate free-hand vector diagram showing the relationships among the vectors. The diagram is most helpful if it is made *before* you do the analytical solution. Make the diagram large enough so that it can be easily understood and easily labeled.

1. What coordinate system would you choose to specify the position of objects in a rectangular room? Why?

2. What coordinate system would you choose in order to describe the paths of the planets? Why?

3. The distance between Detroit and San Francisco is about 4000 km and the radius of the earth is about 6400 km. Find the "angle" between Detroit and San Francisco, in radians, as seen from the center of the earth. What is the angle in degrees?

4. Prove that

$$\lim_{\alpha\to 0} \cos\alpha = 1.$$

5. There is a sense associated with time, i.e., we distinguish between the past and the future. Is time a vector?

6. Can you find unambiguously the component of a vector in a given direction?

7. Given a vector, can you resolve it into two components?

8. Three vectors can be added to obtain a resultant. Can the process be reversed, i.e., can a vector be resolved into *three* components lying along specified directions in a plane?

9. Under what conditions can the resultant of two vectors be zero? Do the same restrictions apply if the resultant of three vectors is zero?

10. In the theory of atomic structure, vector quantities are used that have integral values and that can have only integral sums. Find all possible sums for two such vectors whose magnitudes are 2 and 3.

11. Vector **A** is 3 units long and is directed 30° above the x-axis toward the right. Vector **B** is 4 units long and is directed 60° above the x-axis toward the left. By the triangle or parallelogram method and by the component method, find the sum and difference of **A** and **B**, remembering that each answer requires two quantities.

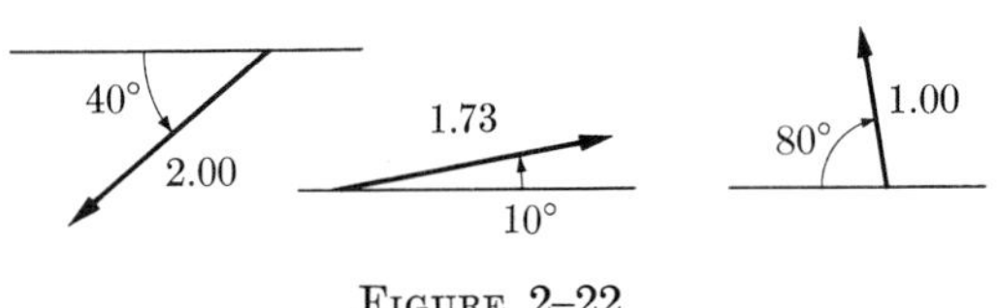

FIGURE 2–22

12. Prove that the sum of the three vectors in Fig. 2–22 is zero. Also, find the sum if any of the three vectors is reversed in direction.

13. The angle between vector **A** of length 3 units and vector **B** of length 5 units is 60°. Find the difference **B** — **A** by the triangle, the parallelogram, and the component methods.

14. Given two vectors of equal magnitude (v), find an expression for their vector difference in terms of the magnitude (v) and the angle between the two vectors (θ).

15. Given two vectors **A** and **B** that make an angle θ with each other, prove, by using the method of components taken along perpendicular axes, that the resultant has the magnitude,

$$R = \sqrt{A^2 + B^2 + 2AB \cos \theta}.$$

Why is the $+$ sign used with the $2AB \cos \theta$ term?

16. Can you specify uniquely the position of a point in a plane by choosing any pair among the quantities x, y, θ, and r?

17. The sum of two vectors is 6 units, and it is directed 135° relative to $+OX$. If one vector is also 6 units long and is directed along the $+OX$-axis, find the other vector.

18. Repeat Problem 17 for the case in which the *difference* of the two vectors is 6 units at 135° relative to OX. Is there only one solution to this problem as it is stated?

19. The sum of two vectors is **S**, and their difference is **D**. Make a diagram, using the parallelogram method, to show that **S** — **D** is twice one of the original vectors.

20. Make diagrams showing the addition of the three vectors of Fig. 2–22 by the parallelogram method.

3

Kinematics of Point Masses

3–1 INTRODUCTION

Since equations of kinematics describe the motion of material objects, kinematics is a topic in descriptive mathematics. The attributes of motion which are important to mechanics are displacement, velocity, and acceleration. Each of these terms is used in common parlance in essentially the sense in which we will use them. In this chapter we define these terms analytically and find that the definitions give the relationships among them. Kinematics itself is introductory to the study of the physics of motion (dynamics), which is introduced in Chapter 4.

The analysis in this section will be confined to motion of translation and will neglect any effect of rotation. The motion of a finite object can then be described by the motion of a representative point in the object. For this reason, we speak of the motions of a "point mass." The word "particle" will also be used, even though it has a different connotation in atomic physics.

The positions a particle occupies as it moves about in space may be referred to a system of coordinate axes. The locus of these coordinate points is a line called the trajectory of a particle. In the simplest motion, "rectilinear motion," a particle moves along a straight line. The trajectory, then, is this line, and a complete description of the motion is contained in a quotation of the coordinate points which the particle occupies and the time corresponding to each coordinate given in chronological order. For example, the character of the motion can be contained in a table of experimental data such as Table 3–1. In a simple situation such as the one portrayed in Table 3–1, an algebraic equation can be written relating x to t:

$$x = 10t^2. \tag{3–1}$$

TABLE 3–1

Space coordinate, x, m	Time coordinate, t, sec
$x_0 = 0$	$0 = t_0$
10	1
40	2
90	3

This is called the equation of motion. Note that we have made the reasonable assumption that the motion has the same form at intermediate times.

If the motion of a particle is confined to a plane in space, rather than to a line, two coordinates (for example, x, y) and the time t are used to describe the motion. While the extension to three-dimensional motion is clear, its added complexity is not treated in this text. There are, in fact, natural reasons in particle mechanics for a predominant importance of rectilinear motion and of planar motion.

In the first part of this book, our discussion will be restricted to motion of translation. We sometimes specify this restriction by speaking of the mechanics of point particles or point masses, indicating that finite objects are replaced by imaginary objects of negligible dimensions but with the inertial and gravitational mass of the object. (Mass will be treated in detail in later chapters.) Alternatively, let us say, without proof at this time, that the mechanics of translation can be treated independently of rotation.

3–2 THE POSITION VECTOR AND DISPLACEMENT

The space and time coordinates in planar motion can be x, y, and t. A plot of a possible path

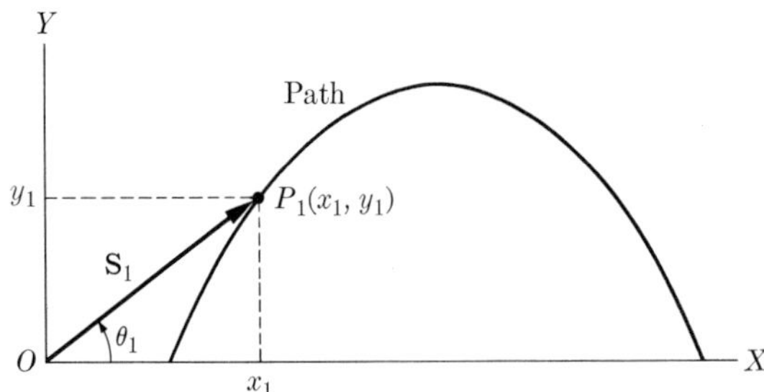

Fig. 3–1. A point P_1 on the path of a particle specified by a coordinate system and the position vector $\mathbf{S}_1$ in the chosen coordinate system.

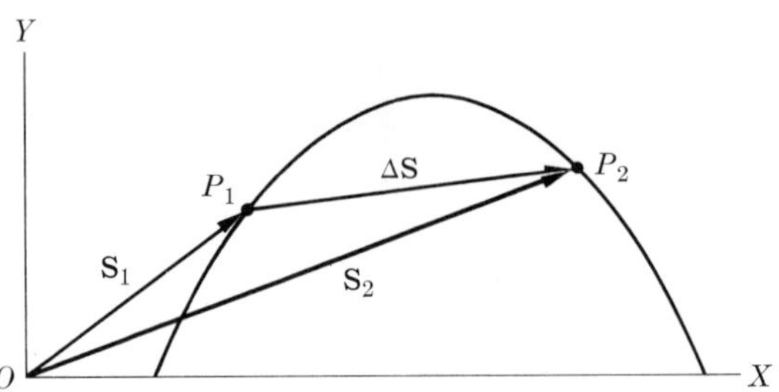

Fig. 3–2. Specification of two points on the path of a particle by two position vectors $\mathbf{S}_1$ and $\mathbf{S}_2$, and the description of the displacement by $\Delta\mathbf{S}$.

of motion or trajectory is shown in Fig. 3–1. The time cannot be shown graphically in such a plot. The particular example in Fig. 3–1 might be the parabolic path of a baseball in the absence of effects due to the air.

Let the position of the particle at some point on the path be denoted by (x_1, y_1). This location can also be described by the use of polar coordinates, namely, the length of a radius vector drawn from the origin of the coordinate system to the point and the orientation θ_1 of the vector relative to an axis. Such a vector is called the *position vector* of the particle at that point. In Fig. 3–2, the vector $\mathbf{S}_1$ is the position vector for the particle at P. The magnitude of the position vector $|\mathbf{S}_1|$ is the polar radius. The direction of $\mathbf{S}_1$ is θ_1, the polar angle. In summary, the position vector of a particle is a vector drawn from the origin of the reference system to the particle itself. Note that $\mathbf{S}$ depends on the choice of reference system as well as on the position of P.

We shall now assume that position vectors are true vectors, i.e., we shall assume that the rules of Chapter 2 can be used. Strictly, we are justified in this only because experiments with measured positions validate the above assumption.

Let the particle move to Point 2 on the trajectory (Fig. 3–2). Then the new position vector is $\mathbf{S}_2$. In this case, the position vector changes in length and direction. The *displacement* in the interval of motion from Point 1 to Point 2 is defined as the vector difference between $\mathbf{S}_2$ and $\mathbf{S}_1$, which we shall call $\Delta\mathbf{S}$ (to be read "delta S"). Therefore, we have

$$\Delta\mathbf{S} \equiv \mathbf{S}_2 - \mathbf{S}_1 \equiv \text{displacement}. \tag{3–2}$$

As discussed in Section 2–7, the above equation denoting vector subtraction can be transformed by transposing the negative term, giving

$$\mathbf{S}_2 = \mathbf{S}_1 + \Delta\mathbf{S}, \tag{3–3}$$

which leads to the useful physical picture that displacement is the quantity that we add to $\mathbf{S}_1$ in order to obtain $\mathbf{S}_2$. The construction of $\Delta\mathbf{S}$ is shown in Fig. 3–2. Given the original location of the particle, the displacement $\Delta\mathbf{S}$ determines the new location.

The position vector $\mathbf{S}$ can be described in terms of cartesian components x and y. Similarly, the displacement $\Delta\mathbf{S}$ can be described in terms of cartesian components Δx and Δy. The reader can easily show that $\Delta x = x_2 - x_1$ and $\Delta y = y_2 - y_1$.

3–3 COMPOSITION OF DISPLACEMENTS (MOVING OBSERVERS)

The trajectory of a particle depends on the observer, that is, the reference system. For example, when a person riding on a truck tosses a stone straight up, the stone rises and falls vertically according to the observation of the person on the truck. (We have assumed that the motion of the truck is uniform and that the air resistance on the stone is negligible.) But to an observer on the ground, the trajectory of the stone is not along a vertical line, since the stone also advances horizontally (and actually follows a parabolic path according to the latter observer).

We now consider quantitatively the effect of the choice of observer, that is, of reference coordinate system, on the description of the path of an object. The description of the path is made in terms of the position of the object at various times. Therefore, we will analyze the effect of choice of coordinate system on the description of position and displacement.

Consider first the case of a point P that is *stationary* relative to the coordinate system $O'X'Y'$. The position vector $\mathbf{S}'$ is then the same for all times, and the displacement relative to this coordinate system is zero for any elapsed time. But now consider a second observer, that is, coordinate system, whose origin is not coincident with $O'X'Y'$. This second system is labeled OXY. The position of O' relative to O is specified by a position vector $\mathbf{D}$ as in Fig. 3–3. From this figure we see that the relationship of position vectors $\mathbf{S}'$ and $\mathbf{S}$ for the two coordinate systems is $\mathbf{S} = \mathbf{S}' + \mathbf{D}$.

If observer O' is in motion relative to O, the vectors $\mathbf{D}$ and $\mathbf{S}$ will change with time. If we use subscripts 1 and 2 to indicate positions at two

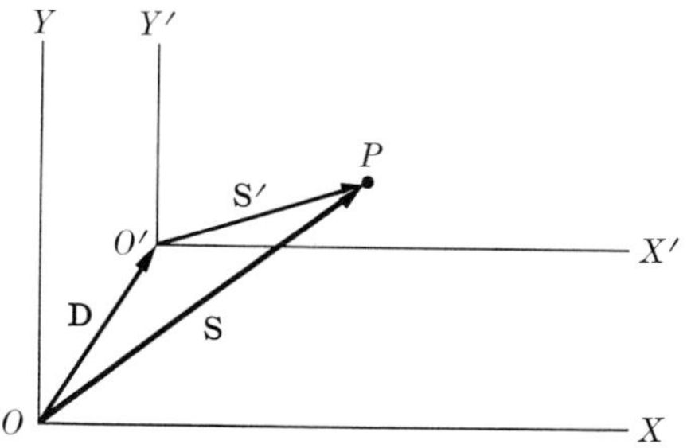

Fig. 3–3. The position of point P specified by reference to either of two sets of axes.

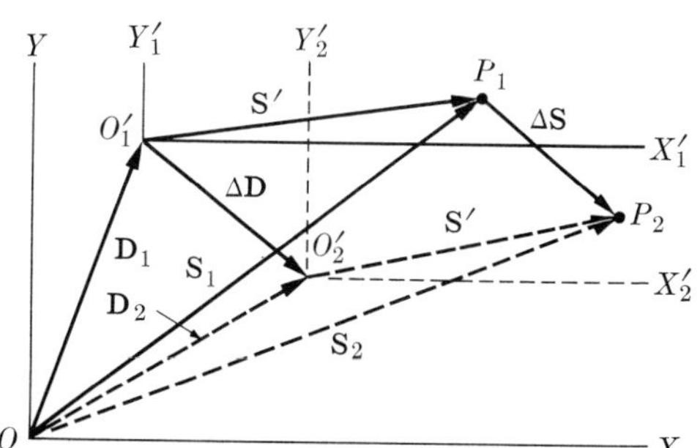

Fig. 3–4. The point P is stationary relative to the primed axes, but the primed axes are in motion relative to the unprimed axes. The displacements of the primed axes and of the point P from Instant 1 to Instant 2 are shown.

different instants of time, the position vectors are related by

$$\mathbf{S}_1 = \mathbf{S}' + \mathbf{D}_1, \qquad \mathbf{S}_2 = \mathbf{S}' + \mathbf{D}_2. \tag{3–4}$$

Although there is no displacement of P as seen by O' (P was assumed to be fixed relative to O'), there is a displacement as seen by O. The latter displacement is defined by $\Delta\mathbf{S} = \mathbf{S}_2 - \mathbf{S}_1$, as usual (Fig. 3–4). The relationship among the displacements, found by subtracting Eqs. (3–4), is

$$\Delta\mathbf{S} = \Delta\mathbf{D}.$$

Therefore, O' observes no displacement of P, while O observes a displacement of P that is the same as the displacement of O' relative to O.

Our real interest, however, lies in the more general case in which the point is moving in the $O'X'Y'$-system. Equations (3–4) then become

$$\mathbf{S}_1 = \mathbf{S}'_1 + \mathbf{D}_1, \qquad \mathbf{S}_2 = \mathbf{S}'_2 + \mathbf{D}_2, \tag{3–5}$$

and the relationship among displacements,

$$\Delta\mathbf{S} = \Delta\mathbf{S}' + \Delta D, \tag{3–6}$$

follows by subtraction of Eqs. (3–5). The diagram is left as an exercise for the reader.

Another type of notation is frequently used for Eq. (3–6), namely,

$$\Delta \mathbf{S}_{AO} = \Delta \mathbf{S}_{AO'} + \Delta \mathbf{S}_{O'O}, \qquad (3\text{–}7)$$

which is read "the displacement of A relative to O equals," etc.

We note in passing that neither coordinate system is to be preferred to the other for the observation of displacements or of the trajectory. However, it will be seen later that when forces and *changes* in velocity are considered, there are important differences among some types of coordinate systems.

3–4 AVERAGE VELOCITY

Velocity involves time as well as position. Consider again that part of the trajectory of a particle between Points P_1 and P_2, as in Fig. 3–2. Let t_1 and t_2 represent the instants of time when the particle is at P_1 and then at P_2, respectively, and let Δt be defined by

$$\Delta t \equiv t_2 - t_1. \qquad (3\text{–}8)$$

Then the average velocity $\bar{\mathbf{v}}$ between P_1 and P_2 is defined by

$$\bar{\mathbf{v}} \equiv \frac{\mathbf{S}_2 - \mathbf{S}_1}{t_2 - t_1} = \frac{\Delta \mathbf{S}}{\Delta t}, \qquad (3\text{–}9)$$

where $\mathbf{S}_2$, $\mathbf{S}_1$, and $\Delta\mathbf{S}$ have their usual meanings. The direction $\bar{\mathbf{v}}$ is the direction $\Delta\mathbf{S}$, since they are the only vectors in the equation. Note that a coordinate system is implicitly involved. The displacement $\Delta\mathbf{S}$ depends on the particular system, and therefore $\mathbf{v}$ is relative to the chosen system. Since $\Delta\mathbf{S}$ can be specified by cartesian components Δx and Δy, the average velocity can be written in terms of cartesian components $\bar{v}_x = \Delta x/\Delta t$ and $\bar{v}_y = \Delta y/\Delta t$.

The word "speed" may sometimes be used for the magnitude of the velocity. It is also sometimes used for speed along the trajectory, $\Delta l/\Delta t$, where Δl is the actual path length. We shall try to avoid ambiguity when using the word speed in this text.

Points 1 and 2 could have been chosen anywhere along the trajectory. Hence, Eq. (3–9) applies to any part (or all) of the motion.

In classical mechanics, the discussion is restricted to cases in which there are no complications in the measurement of $\Delta\mathbf{S}$ or Δt. We simply assume that all observers agree on length of meter sticks, clock rates, and clock synchronization.

The chief use of the concept of average velocity is pedagogical.

3–5 UNIFORM VELOCITY (RECTILINEAR MOTION)

Consider the special case in which $\bar{\mathbf{v}}$ is constant. The fact that the direction of the velocity is constant requires that the trajectory be a straight line (the motion is rectilinear). The fact that the magnitude is constant determines that equal distances are covered in equal times. This motion is called "uniform rectilinear motion." Such motion occurs quite frequently, at least to a good degree of approximation. As examples, we think of the motion of boats and airplanes during the major part of their journeys, of some cars on straight highways, of bullets early in their flight, of falling raindrops, and of electrons during most of their flight in cathode-ray tubes.

It is convenient to rewrite Eq. (3–9) in the form

$$\mathbf{S}_2 = \mathbf{S}_1 + \bar{\mathbf{v}}(t_2 - t_1). \qquad (3\text{–}10)$$

If the origin of coordinates and time are chosen so that $\mathbf{S}_1 = 0$ when $t_1 = 0$, then Eq. (3–10) becomes

$$\mathbf{S} = \bar{\mathbf{v}}t, \qquad (3\text{–}11)$$

where the subscripts are no longer necessary. Often the scalar form

$$S = vt \qquad (3\text{–}12)$$

can be used without ambiguity.

According to our equations, we determine velocity by measuring a length (displacement) and a time interval. However, there exist instruments (speedometers) that measure velocity "directly" by means of velocity-dependent forces or other velocity-dependent quantities.

3–6 RELATIVE VELOCITIES (MOVING REFERENCE FRAMES)

The observed velocity of a particle depends on the choice of coordinate system, if we consider coordinate systems that are in relative motion. In order to compare velocities as measured from two different coordinate systems, we return to Section 3–3, and to Eq. (3–7) in particular. If Eq. (3–7) is divided through by Δt, the time required by the particle to move from Point 1 to Point 2, and if the definitions of average velocities are used, we have

$$\bar{\mathbf{v}}_{AO} = \bar{\mathbf{v}}_{AO'} + \bar{\mathbf{v}}_{O'O}, \tag{3–13}$$

which is read "average velocity of (A) relative to O," etc.

In the special case of uniform velocities, we can omit the bars:

$$\mathbf{v}_{AO} = \mathbf{v}_{AO'} + \mathbf{v}_{O'O}, \tag{3–14}$$

where each velocity is constant in magnitude and direction.

In many cases, we may not consciously think in terms of coordinate systems. Therefore, we might simply write

$$\mathbf{v}_{ac} = \mathbf{v}_{ab} + \mathbf{v}_{bc}, \tag{3–15}$$

where a, b, and c refer to "objects," for example, airplane, air, and ground. Remember that each $\mathbf{v}$ involves a reference or coordinate system, specified by the second subscript.

If it is desired to interchange the observed object with the reference object, we have

$$\Delta\mathbf{S}_{ab} = -\Delta\mathbf{S}_{ba},$$

and, hence,

$$\mathbf{v}_{ab} = -\mathbf{v}_{ba}. \tag{3–16}$$

Although we advocate relying on basic principles rather than on memory, we must admit that memory aids are convenient and useful. Several possibilities will now be suggested. A method that is almost an appeal to basic principles is simply to think of the motion of a relative to c, as the resultant of a's motion relative to b and b's motion relative to c. For example, as a man walks in a train, his motion relative to the ground is the sum of his motion relative to the train and the train's motion relative to the ground, that is,

$$\mathbf{v}_{MG} = \mathbf{v}_{MT} + \mathbf{v}_{TG},$$

where M, G, and T stand for man, ground, and train, respectively.

Another method, which is a mechanical aid, is to note that the "adjacent" subscripts are the same in all the relative velocity equations *as we have written them.* For example, in Eq. (3–15) the b's are adjacent, etc. This does *not* mean that these equations can be written only in this way; velocities are proper vectors and can be added in any order. For example, Eq. (3–15) can equally well be written $\mathbf{v}_{ac} = \mathbf{v}_{bc} + \mathbf{v}_{ab}$, or in other ways.

Finally, a very simple mechanical aid is to label heads and tails of the vectors of motion, the head with the object in question and the tail with the reference object. A vector diagram can then be drawn immediately by assembling the vectors so that similar labels coincide.

Example 1. Let a boat be propelled in water with a velocity $\mathbf{v}_{bw}$. The first index, b, in the notation refers to the object in motion, which is the boat. The second index, w, refers to the medium or system which is used as the reference frame. In this case the reference system is the water, and the direction and rate of travel are found by reference to floats that are carried along by the water if the water is in motion. Let the velocity of the body of water relative to the earth be $\mathbf{v}_{we}$, where the same system of notation is used. Then the velocity of the boat relative to the earth, $\mathbf{v}_{be}$, is found by the vector addition of $\mathbf{v}_{bw}$ and $\mathbf{v}_{we}$, that is,

$$\mathbf{v}_{be} = \mathbf{v}_{bw} + \mathbf{v}_{we}.$$

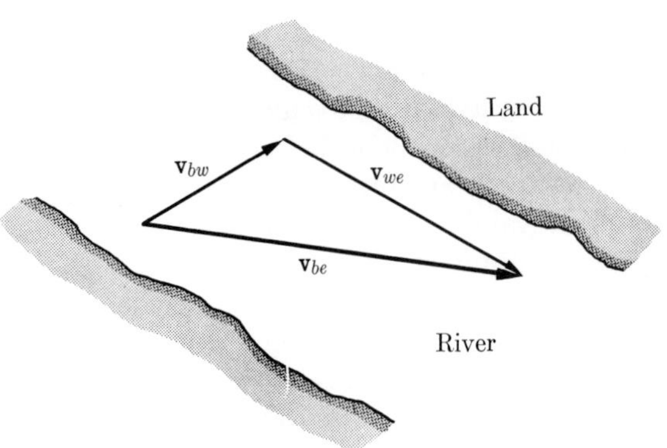

Fig. 3–5. The relative velocities of the boat-water-earth system. The subscripts b, w, and e refer to the boat, water, and earth, respectively.

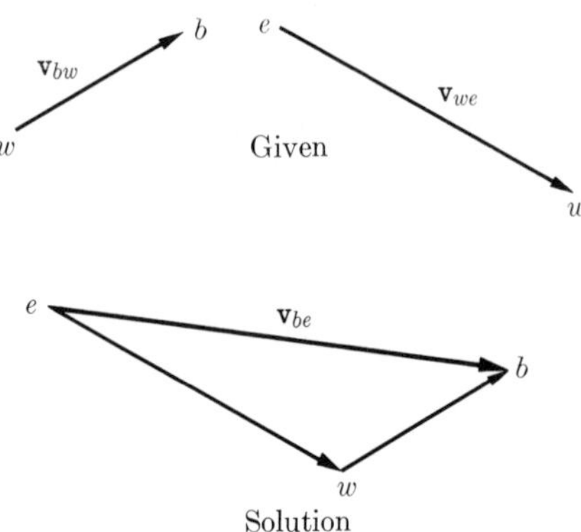

Fig. 3–6. Illustration of the method of labeling the heads and tails of relative motion vectors as an aid in construction of the relative velocity vector diagram.

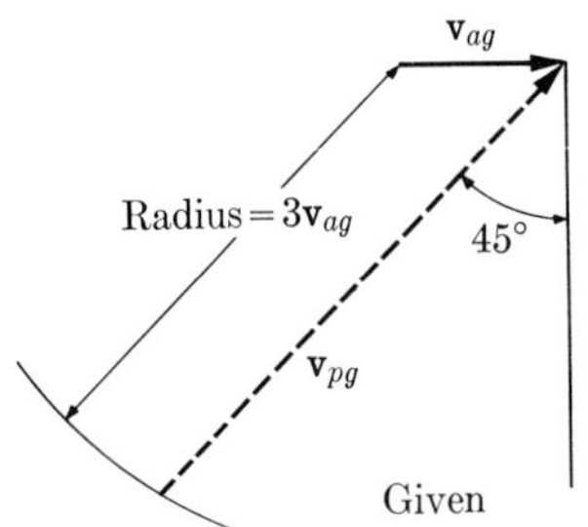

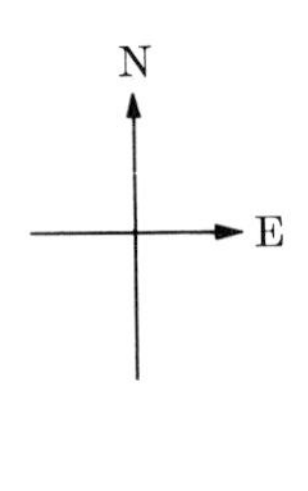

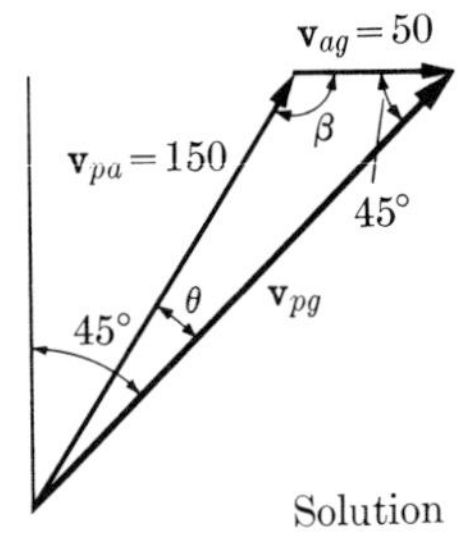

Fig. 3–7. Geometrical construction of a relative velocity diagram when one vector $\mathbf{v}_{ag}$ is given, but only the direction of the second vector $\mathbf{v}_{pg}$ and the magnitude of the third vector $\mathbf{v}_{pa}$ are given.

The vector diagram is given in polygon form in Fig. 3–5. A diagram using the method of labeling heads and tails of vectors is shown in Fig. 3–6.

Example 2. A wind blows from west to east at a speed of 50 km/hr. An airplane is capable of a speed of 150 km/hr relative to the air, and the pilot wishes to go to a city that is due northeast. In what direction should the airplane be pointed, and what will be the ground speed of the airplane?

Solution: Let us denote the velocity of the plane relative to air by $\mathbf{v}_{pa}$, the velocity of the plane relative to ground by $\mathbf{v}_{pg}$, and the velocity of the air relative to ground by $\mathbf{v}_{ag}$. Then the statement of the problem is interpreted as follows:

(1) $\mathbf{v}_{ag} = 50$ km/hr, east;

(2) $\mathbf{v}_{pg}$ = unknown magnitude directed northeast (because the displacement is to be northeast relative to the earth);

(3) $\mathbf{v}_{pa} = 150$ km/hr, direction unknown.

Using the theory of velocity addition, we write

(4) $\mathbf{v}_{pg} = \mathbf{v}_{pa} + \mathbf{v}_{ag}$.

If we draw a vector diagram first, we start with $\mathbf{v}_{ag}$ since it is completely known. The *direction of* $\mathbf{v}_{pg}$ is known and can be indicated by a line (Fig. 3–7). Finally, we know the length of $\mathbf{v}_{pa}(= 3v_{ag})$ and where its head should lie; therefore we draw an arc of radius 3 times the length of $\mathbf{v}_{ag}$. The intersection of the arc and the line of $\mathbf{v}_{pg}$ must then be the point common to the tails of $\mathbf{v}_{pg}$ and $\mathbf{v}_{pa}$.

The numerical results can be found trigonometrically. From the law of sines,

$$\frac{\sin\theta}{50} = \frac{\sin 45^\circ}{150}, \qquad \text{or} \qquad \sin\theta = 0.24,$$

and

$$\theta = 14^\circ.$$

Angle β is therefore 121°. From the law of cosines,

$$v_{pg}^2 = 50^2 + 150^2 - 2 \times 50 \times 150 \cos 121^\circ,$$

or $\mathbf{v}_{pg} = 180$ km/hr in a direction 45° east of north, and $\mathbf{v}_{pa}$ is 31° east of north.

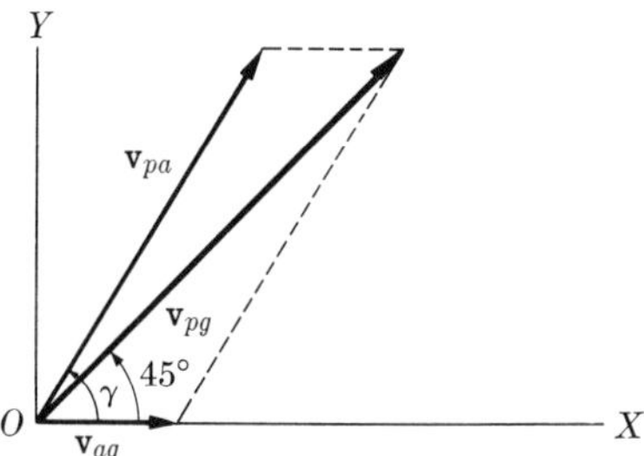

FIG. 3–8. A vector diagram for the airplane problem drawn in a manner suited to the cartesian component method of analysis.

There are many other methods of analysis, all of which, however, will be based on vector addition or subtraction of velocities. As a review, we might indicate a component method. Choose a cartesian coordinate system OXY as shown in Fig. 3–8. For the sake of variety, the parallelogram method of addition is shown. The vector equation $\mathbf{v}_{pg} = \mathbf{v}_{pa} + \mathbf{v}_{ag}$ is now replaced by two scalar equations, one for the X-component and one for the Y-component:

$$v_{pg} \cos 45^\circ = v_{pa} \cos\gamma + v_{ag}, \qquad (3\text{–}17)$$

$$v_{pg} \sin 45^\circ = v_{pa} \sin\gamma + 0. \qquad (3\text{–}18)$$

Since v_{pa} and v_{ag} are given, there are only two unknowns, γ and v_{pg}, which can be found. (Note that we must use ingenuity, since trigonometric functions are involved. In this case, Eq. (3–17) can be solved for cos γ, and Eq. (3–18) can be solved for sin γ. When the equations are then squared and added, the γ-dependence drops out and v_{pg} alone remains as an unknown in the resulting equation.)

If more than three objects are involved, the extension of the arguments is obvious. For example, the displacement becomes

$$\Delta\mathbf{S}_{ad} = \Delta\mathbf{S}_{ab} + \Delta\mathbf{S}_{bc} + \Delta\mathbf{S}_{cd}, \qquad (3\text{–}19)$$

with a corresponding result for velocities.

3–7 CHANGE IN VELOCITY

It is common knowledge that the velocity of objects can change. We consider here the special case in which a particle moving with constant velocity $\mathbf{v}_1$ changes to a new constant velocity $\mathbf{v}_2$ during a time interval Δt (all measured with respect to a single coordinate system). The *change in velocity*, $\Delta\mathbf{v}$, is defined by

$$\Delta\mathbf{v} = \mathbf{v}_2 - \mathbf{v}_1. \qquad (3\text{–}20)$$

The change in velocity $\Delta\mathbf{v}$ can be written in terms of cartesian components, Δv_x and Δv_y. The reader can easily show that $\Delta v_y = v_{2y} - v_{1y}$ and $\Delta v_x = v_{2x} - v_{1x}$. Just as in the case of displacement, Eq. (3–20) can be rewritten

$$\mathbf{v}_2 = \mathbf{v}_1 + \Delta\mathbf{v} \qquad (3\text{–}21)$$

to express the physical idea that the new velocity is the previous velocity plus the change in velocity.

In the special case of *rectilinear motion*, in which all the vectors lie along the same line, scalar equations can be used in place of Eqs. (3–20) and (3–21). The sense of the vectors is then specified by plus and minus signs.

Example 3. A car travels northward at a uniform velocity of 20 km/hr. It turns and travels eastward at 10 km/hr. What is the change in velocity?

Solution: Figure 3–9 shows the graphical construction that satisfies Eq. (3–21). From geometry and trigonometry, $\Delta\mathbf{v} = \sqrt{500}$ km/hr directed $26\frac{1}{2}°$ east of south.

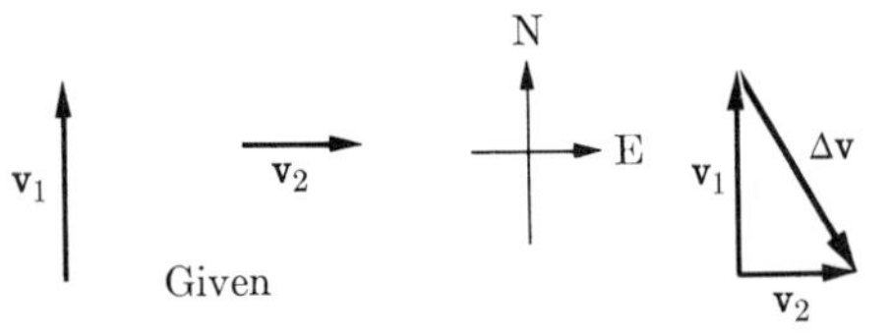

Fig. 3–9. Vector diagram for the change in velocity of a car that turns a corner. Its velocity changes from $\mathbf{v}_1$ to $\mathbf{v}_2$.

Example 4. A particle moves in a circle of radius r at uniform speed v. Find the change in velocity when the position vector of the particle changes direction by amount $\Delta\theta$.

Solution: The relationship among the various vectors is shown in Fig. 3–10. *Note that there are two different vector quantities on one diagram,* position vectors and velocity vectors. Their directions are directly related, but their magnitudes are not simply related. From geometry and trigonometry, $\Delta v = 2v \sin (\Delta\theta/2)$, where v is the magnitude of the velocity.

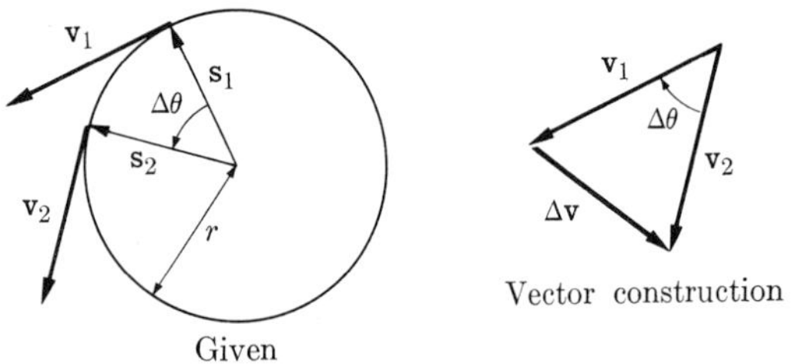

Fig. 3–10. The change in velocity $\Delta\mathbf{v}$ from velocity $\mathbf{v}_1$ to velocity $\mathbf{v}_2$ of a point that moves with uniform speed on a circle.

3–8 SUMMARY

The position of a point relative to a given coordinate system can be specified by the position vector $\mathbf{S}$ drawn from the origin of coordinates to the point in question.

The displacement of a point moving relative to a given coordinate system is defined by

$$\Delta\mathbf{S} \equiv \mathbf{S}_2 - \mathbf{S}_1,$$

where $\mathbf{S}_1$ and $\mathbf{S}_2$ are the position vectors at two different times, that is, at two different positions on the path of motion.

If a second coordinate system O' is in motion relative to the first system O, the displacements of a moving point in the two coordinate systems are related by

$$\Delta\mathbf{S} = \Delta\mathbf{S}' + \Delta\mathbf{D},$$

where $\Delta\mathbf{D}$ is the displacement of the O' system relative to the O system.

Average velocity is defined by

$$\bar{\mathbf{v}} \equiv \frac{\Delta\mathbf{S}}{\Delta t},$$

where $\Delta\mathbf{S}$ is the displacement during the time interval Δt.

If the velocity is constant in direction, the motion is rectilinear and the equation of motion can be written

$$\mathbf{S}_2 = \mathbf{S}_1 + \bar{\mathbf{v}}(t_2 - t_1).$$

The velocities of a point specified in two different coordinate systems that are in relative motion are related by

$$\mathbf{v}_{ab} = \mathbf{v}_{ac} + \mathbf{v}_{cb},$$

where $\mathbf{v}_{ab}$ signifies the velocity of a relative to b, etc.

If the velocity of a point changes, the change in velocity is defined by

$$\Delta\mathbf{v} \equiv \mathbf{v}_2 - \mathbf{v}_1.$$

The change in velocity is independent of the coordinate system for systems that move with constant relative velocities.

All of the above vector operations can be done in terms of components.

Problems

1. Draw the position vector at two different times for a particle moving in a circle. Where is the origin of coordinates conveniently chosen?

2. Draw the position vector relative to an observer on the ground at two different times for an airplane that flies horizontally directly overhead.

3. A particle moves from P_1 to P_2 as seen by an observer in the OXY system. Prove that the displacement is the same for observers in either the OXY or the $O'X'Y'$ system, provided that the systems have no relative motion (Fig. 3–11).

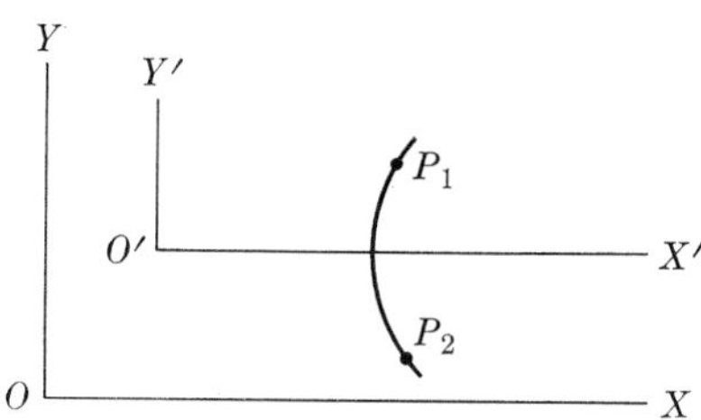

FIGURE 3–11

4. Draw a diagram similar to that in Fig. 3–4 from the viewpoint of observer O', that is, keeping $O'X'Y'$ fixed in position.

5. Draw vector diagrams (large scale) illustrating Eqs. (3–5) and (3–6) and their interrelationships.

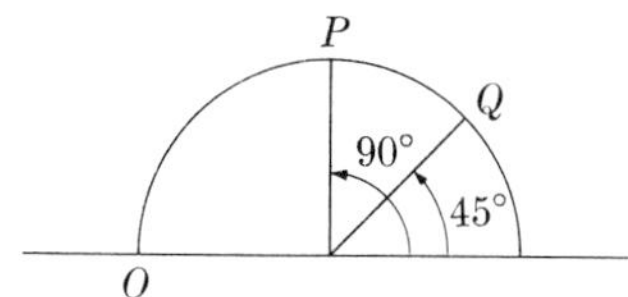

FIGURE 3–12

6. A particle travels at constant speed on a circle of 2-m radius. The time required for the particle to to travel a full circle is 8 sec. Choose the origin shown in Fig. 3–12 as O (not at the center of the circle).

(a) Find the magnitude and direction of the position vector when the particle is at P.

(b) Find the magnitude and direction of the position vector when the particle is at Q.

(c) What is the displacement for the interval bounded by P and Q? Give the magnitude of the displacement in meters and the direction of the displacement vector.

(d) What is the average velocity (magnitude in meters per second, and direction) in the interval PQ?

7. One car travels 100 m straight north from an intersection while another car travels 50 m east from the same intersection. What is the displacement of the second car relative to the first? of the first relative to the second? How would your answers be changed if the second car had started from a point 100 m east of the intersection?

8. If the time interval for the motion in Problem 7 was 2 sec, what was the average velocity of each car? By using velocity vectors, find the average velocity of the second car relative to the first. Check your result by using the relative displacement of Problem 7.

9. Repeat the solution of Problem 7 by the component method.

10. An airplane is supposed to travel from A in a direction due north to B and then return to A. The distance between A and B is L. The air speed of the plane is $\mathbf{v}_{pa}$ and the wind velocity is $\mathbf{v}_{ag}$.

(a) Show that the time for the round trip in still air, $\mathbf{v}_{ag} = 0$, is

$$t_a = \frac{2L}{v_{pa}}.$$

(b) Show that the time for the round trip when the wind is directed due east (or west) is

$$t_b = \frac{t_a}{\sqrt{1 - (v_{ag}^2/v_{pa}^2)}}.$$

(c) Show that the time for the round trip when the wind is directed due north (or south) is

$$t_c = \frac{t_a}{1 - (v_{ag}^2/v_{pa}^2)}.$$

(d) What is the feasibility of trips (b) or (c) when $v_{ag} = v_{pa}$? For a given v_{ag}, which time is greater, t_b or t_c?

11. A river flowing 3 km/hr is one-half mile wide. Two men who row at 5 km/hr in still water start from a dock on one shore at the same time. One man rows to a point directly across the river and back. The other rows directly downstream one-half mile and back. How much time is required for each? Which trip takes longer? What is the solution when the velocity of the river is 5 km/hr?

12. Rain is falling directly downward toward the earth at 40 km/hr. An observer traveling in a car at 60 km/hr looks at the rain through his side window. What is the velocity of the raindrops (magnitude and direction) relative to this observer? Show in your diagram the directions and senses of all three velocity vectors.

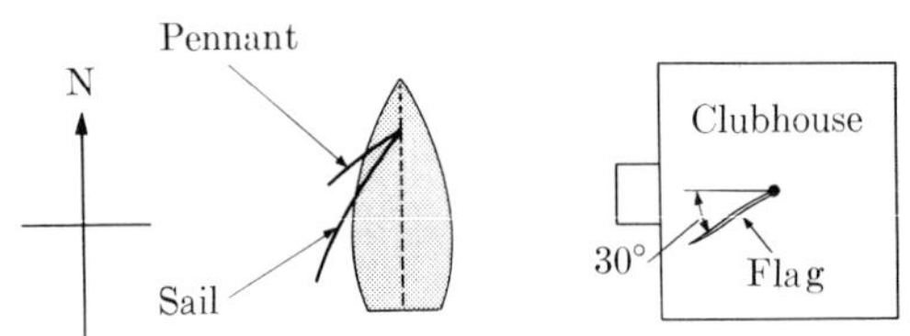

FIGURE 3–13

13. The pennant on the masthead of a sailboat streams back at an angle of 45°, as shown in Fig. 3–13, but the flag on the clubhouse extends out at 30° south of west.

(a) If the speed of the boat is 10 km/hr, find the true wind velocity.

(b) Find the apparent wind velocity for an observer on the boat.

14. A baseball comes toward a batter nearly horizontally with a speed of 20 m/sec. The batter hits the ball, and it leaves his bat with a speed of 25 m/sec. What is the change in velocity of the ball

(a) if he hits a "line drive," i.e., if the ball leaves his bat horizontally?

(b) if he hits a fly ball that leaves his bat at 45° above the horizontal?

15. The "aberration" of starlight is an apparent angular displacement of stars due to the *velocity* of the earth in its orbit (not to be confused with parallax of near stars due to the *displacement* of the earth along its orbit). Find the direction of arrival of light from a star at a time when the star is directly away from the sun, as shown in Fig. 3–14. A year is 3.2×10^7 sec, the velocity of light is 3×10^8 m/sec, and the radius of earth's orbit is 1.5×10^{11} m.

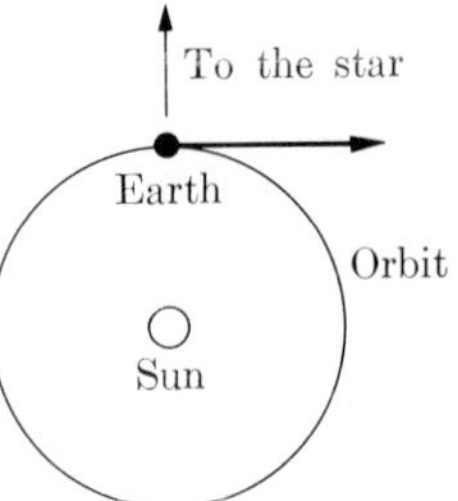

FIGURE 3–14

16. The velocity of sound in still air is 300 m/sec, that is, the velocity relative to air is 300 m/sec. A jet pilot flying horizontally at 200 m/sec is directly above a dynamite factory when he hears an explosion. From the direction of the arrival of the sound, the pilot judges the direction of the explosion to be 30° forward of vertical.

(a) Was it the dynamite factory that exploded?

(b) What was the "true direction" of the site of the explosion, that is, in what direction will the pilot see the dust cloud if he looks immediately upon hearing the explosion?

17. Remembering that vectors have magnitude and direction, (a) state what a given displacement and the corresponding average velocity have in common. (b) Must the reference frame be the same for both? (c) In a diagram that displays positions, displacements, and average velocities of a point, is it necessary that displacement and corresponding average velocity vectors have common origins? Should their lengths be equal?

18. A boy throws a snowball at a passing truck at the instant the truck is just opposite him at a distance of 15 m. (a) If the horizontal speed of the snowball is twice that of the truck, in what horizontal direction must the snowball be thrown in order to hit the truck? (b) A rider on the back of the truck throws a return snowball at the boy after the truck has traveled 15 m from the point directly opposite the boy. In what horizontal direction must this snowball be thrown in order to hit the boy, given that the speed of the snowball (relative to the thrower) is twice that of the truck?

19. An object moves from Point 1 to Point 2. (a) Show that $\Delta S_x = x_2 - x_1$ and $\Delta S_y = y_2 - y_1$. (b) Show that $\Delta v_x = v_{2x} - v_{1x}$ and $\Delta v_y = v_{2y} - v_{1y}$.

4

Interaction of Particles (Mass, Momentum, and Force)

4–1 INTRODUCTION

In previous chapters, we developed quantitative methods for describing certain types of motion. We found that the derived quantity, velocity, together with the basic quantities of length and time, sufficed for the description of the simplest types of motion.

The concept of *change in velocity* was then introduced (Section 3–7) as a useful tool to describe more complicated motion. We now turn to the question of what factors affect the motion of an object, that is, we now go a step beyond the mere description of *how* a particle moves and ask *why* does it move in the observed manner. In particular, we ask, "How can the motion be predicted or understood quantitatively?" Two new quantities will be useful in order for us to answer the above questions within the framework of so-called Newtonian mechanics. These quantities are *inertial mass* and *interaction force*, which we shall call simply *mass* and *force* when no ambiguity is likely to result.

The mass of an object is an intrinsic property of that object, a property that is independent of its motion and of its environment (in classical mechanics). Mass is the intrinsic property that determines the change in velocity of the object for a given effect of the environment on the object. On the other hand, interaction forces are the tools for describing the effects of the environment on the motion of the object. We shall be quite unspecific about the nature of forces in this chapter, discussing only their effects. The usefulness of the ideas developed in this chapter will not become apparent until specific forces and force laws are taken up in the chapters that follow.

The concepts of mass and force cannot be completely separated, since we shall find that one of the two is defined in terms of the other (force in terms of mass in the mks and cgs units, and mass in terms of force in English engineering units).

4–2 MASS

In the absolute systems of units, mass is selected as the third fundamental mechanical quantity (after length and time), and force becomes a derived quantity.

The concept of inertial mass is more or less well understood qualitatively in everyday experience. Nearly everyone realizes that a truck with a 200-horsepower engine picks up speed more slowly than a passenger car with the same engine and attributes this fact to the greater inertia of the truck. The quantitative measurement, however, requires considerably more care in formulation.

As in the case of length and time, we require a standard unit and a means of comparison with that standard. The method of comparison is, in principle, to measure the mutual effects on the motions of the standard and of the object of unknown mass when the two are permitted to interact.

In principle, the two objects are to be far enough away from other objects so that there will be no other factors affecting the motion of the two. In practice, we shall see that the effects of other objects can be "balanced out" well enough to make their effects negligible.

The ideal choice of frame of reference for determining the motion is a complex question. For the moment, we shall assume that the laboratory is a suitable frame of reference. Its suitability (or usefulness) is confirmed by the simplicity of the results about to be described. A reference frame that gives the results to be described is called an inertial reference frame.

It is found experimentally that when two objects interact, the velocities of the objects change in a systematic and simple way. In particular, it is found that the changes in velocities of any two interacting bodies can be described in a systematic way if we assign an inertial mass, m, to each body according to the equation

$$m_A \, \Delta v_A = -m_B \, \Delta v_B, \tag{4–1}$$

where the subscripts A and B refer to bodies A and B, respectively. The utility of this definition lies in the fact that the inertial mass, when so defined, is an intrinsic property of a body; it is independent of the nature of the interaction, i.e., of the nature of the force; it is independent of the mass of other bodies; and it is independent of the shape, size, or state of the body, etc. The mass, so defined, is directly proportional to the size (volume) of any particular substance. The usefulness of the above concept and definition of mass will be evident in the rest of the study of mechanics. The present discussion is confined to classical mechanics.

The *standard unit of mass* is the mass of a metal cylinder, kept at Sèvres, France, and it is called the kilogram. The mass of any other object can, in principle, be measured in terms of a standard by measuring the respective changes in velocity that occur during an interaction between the standard and the other object and by applying Eq. (4–1).

The result is a definition of mass, m_x, in terms of a standard mass, m_s, given by

$$m_x \equiv -m_s \frac{\Delta v_s}{\Delta v_x} \cdot \tag{4–2}$$

It is to be emphasized that our definition of mass is on exactly the same footing as our earlier definitions of length and time, namely, the concept has been discussed, and a prescription has been given for measuring mass in terms of the arbitrarily chosen standard.

We have now introduced the three basic units of the meter-kilogram-second (mks) system of units. Length and time were defined in Chapter 2 and mass in the present chapter. No additional mechanical quantities can have independent arbitrary standards of units in the mks system. All other mechanical quantities are defined in terms of length, time, and mass, directly or indirectly.

In the other commonly used metric system of units, the cgs system, the fundamental units are the centimeter ($\frac{1}{100}$ of a meter), the gram ($\frac{1}{1000}$ of a kilogram), and the second.

Suppose that we now consider actual experimental possibilities for making comparative mass measurements. It was stated earlier that the interaction of two bodies was being utilized. It will be seen later that it is impossible to have interactions that are completely restricted to those between two bodies. Therefore, the best that can be done is to make the interactions due to the other bodies negligibly small or irrelevant. The effect of the earth can be made small by arranging for motion and interaction in a horizontal plane. The effect of the earth will still be felt indirectly because of friction (if we use carts on a track) or because of changes in height (if we use pendulum-type supports or free flight). But these secondary effects can be made small.

Example 1. Two carts are arranged to roll on a straight horizontal track. At least one cart is set in motion so that a collision occurs. As a result of the collision (interaction), the velocities of both carts change. Let the velocities be v_A and v_B before the collision and v'_A and v'_B after the collision, as indicated in Fig. 4–1. Then Eq. (4–1) becomes

$$m_A(v'_A - v_A) = -m_B(v'_B - v_B). \tag{4–3}$$

The convention that has been used is to choose a posi-

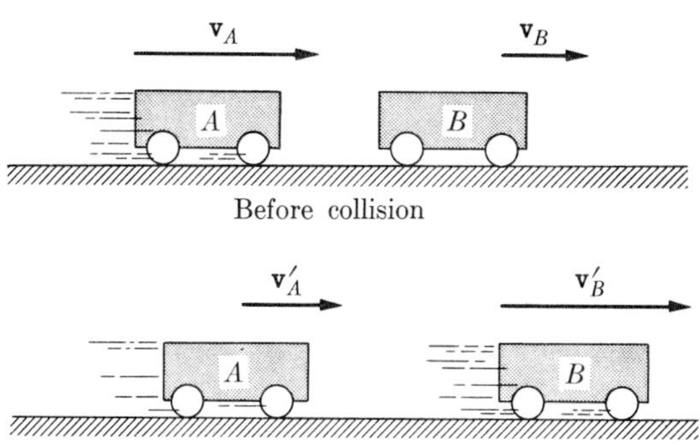

FIG. 4–1. The convention of specification of velocities before and after a linear collision.

tive direction, in this case to the right. Then we assign positive *magnitudes* to vectors directed to the right, negative to the left, when numerical values are substituted.

(a) Suppose that B is initially at rest and A is moving to the right at speed 0.5 m/sec. After the collision B moves 0.3 m/sec, and A rebounds (moves to the left) at 0.1 m/sec.

Then we have

$$m_A(-0.1 - 0.5) = -m_B(0.3) \quad \text{and} \quad m_A = 0.5\, m_B;$$

that is, B has twice the mass of A.

(b) Suppose that a piece of putty is fixed to B at the point of contact with A so that the carts will become attached and move together after the collision. It is now found that the common velocity of A and B is 0.167 m/sec after the collision. From Eq. (4–3), we have, as before,

$$m_A(0.167 - 0.5) = -m_B\, 0.167 \quad \text{or} \quad m_A = 0.5\, m_B.$$

(c) A spring is fastened to the front of A such that the spring (not A itself) touches B during the collision. It is found that A rebounds with a speed of 0.17 m/sec to the left, while B moves to the right at 0.33 m/sec after the collision. From Eq. (4–3), we again find that $m_A = 0.5\, m_B$.

(d) Magnets are fixed on A and B so as to produce a repulsion force acting at a distance without actual contact between the carts. (We thoughtfully choose to put a magnet on B that is twice the size of the magnet on A. Why?) The results for velocities after the collision are the same as in (c), that is, once again $m_A = 0.5\, m_B$.

Example 2.

(a) The carts of Example 1(d) are at rest and are held close together by a string against the force of repulsion exerted by the magnets. The string is broken by burning it with a match (in order to prevent the effect of a third body that might occur if a knife or scissors were used). The velocity of A is now 0.4 m/sec to the left, and that of B is 0.2 m/sec to the right. From Eq. (4–3), we have $m_A(-0.4 - 0) = -m_B(0.2 - 0)$, or $m_A = 0.5\, m_B$ as before.

(b) A compressed spring replaces the magnets of (a). By measuring velocities after the string is burned, we again find that $m_A = 0.5\, m_B$.

(c) A small charge of powder is used to blow the carts apart. The resulting velocities still give $m_A = 0.5\, m_B$.

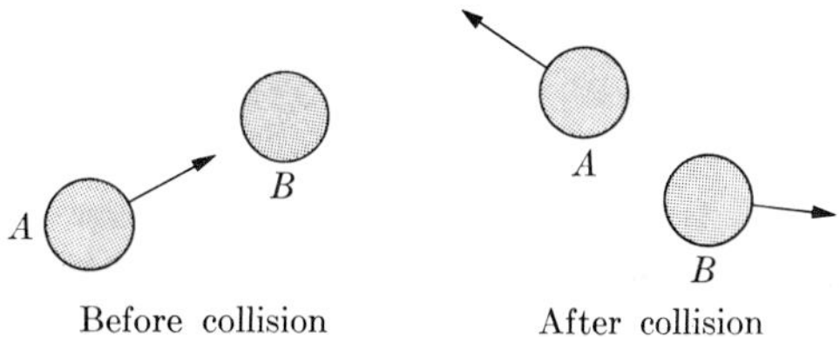

FIG. 4–2. Velocities of two objects before and after a collision in two dimensions.

Example 3. A two-dimensional collision is observed when A and B are replaced with low-friction, air-cushioned disks (devices that provide low-friction support for motion in *two* dimensions). As seen from above, the collision might occur as in Fig. 4–2.

A vector construction is used to find $\Delta\mathbf{v}_A \equiv \mathbf{v}'_A - \mathbf{v}_A$ (Fig. 4–3).

We find that $\Delta\mathbf{v}_A = -2\Delta\mathbf{v}_B$, and therefore, from Eq. (4–1), we have $m_A = 0.5\, v_B$ as before.

When other carts (C, D, etc.) are tried in various combinations with each other and with A and B, it is found that the ratios of masses are internally

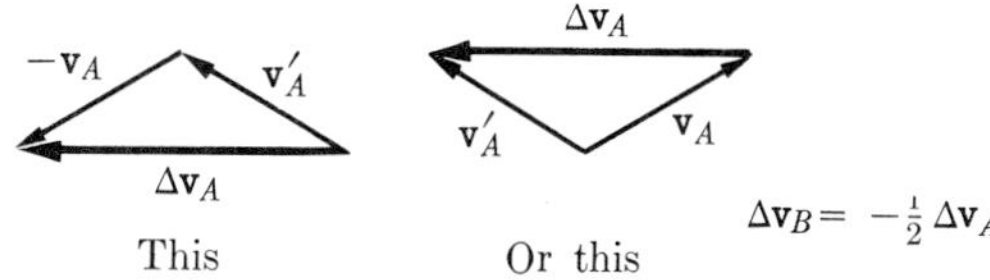

FIG. 4–3. Two methods for finding the change in momentum of A in Example 3.

consistent. *If the carts are combined, it is found that the masses are additive.*

A standard or known mass can be used for one of the interacting masses. Then the second mass can be determined in terms of the standard. For example, if m_B in the above examples is a standard mass of one kilogram, the interaction "measures" m_A as 0.5 kg.

Conclusion: From the definition of Eq. (4–1) or (4–2) and the results of experiments, it is found that an intrinsic property, inertial mass, that is *independent of the nature or magnitude of the force of interaction* between the two bodies can be assigned to each body.

The *mass density* (ρ) of a substance is defined by

$$\rho = m/V, \tag{4–4}$$

where V is the volume. Unlike the mass itself, density is dependent on the physical state of the object, that is, its phase, its temperature, etc., and also on the external pressure. The units of density are kg/m^3 or gm/cm^3 in the absolute metric systems.

If we study the interaction of the earth and moon, or of the earth and sun, etc., the simplicity of Eq. (4–1) would *not* result when the laboratory (observatory) is used as the reference frame. It is necessary to choose the sun as the reference frame in order to have the result of Eq. (4–1). Thus the sun is a better approximation to an inertial reference frame than a laboratory frame on the earth. However, the laboratory is sufficiently nearly an inertial frame for many purposes.

4–3 MOMENTUM

Consider the motion of an object of mass m. The expression $m\,\Delta\mathbf{v}$ or $m\mathbf{v}' - m\mathbf{v}$ that has occurred frequently in the above discussions is called "change in momentum," or, basically, $m\mathbf{v}$ is called *momentum*. The letter $\mathbf{p}$ is commonly used to denote momentum. The definition is expressed by

$$\mathbf{p} \equiv m\mathbf{v}, \tag{4–5}$$

where it is noted that momentum is a vector quantity.

The change in momentum of a particle can then be defined as

$$\Delta\mathbf{p} \equiv \mathbf{p}' - \mathbf{p}, \tag{4–6}$$

which leads to

$$\Delta\mathbf{p} = m\mathbf{v}' - m\mathbf{v} = m\,\Delta\mathbf{v} = \Delta(m\mathbf{v}), \tag{4–7}$$

where the delta notation has been used in the usual way.

There is an implied generalization in Eq. (4–7) contained in the notation $\Delta(m\mathbf{v})$, namely, that the mass m and/or the velocity $\mathbf{v}$ may change. This generalization will be utilized in the development of relativistic mechanics.

4–4 CONSERVATION OF MOMENTUM

Now from the point of view of momentum consider the interaction of two objects. The equation for definition of mass (Eq. 4–1), when rewritten in terms of momentum (Section 4–3), becomes

$$\Delta\mathbf{p}_A = -\Delta\mathbf{p}_B, \tag{4–8}$$

where the subscripts refer to objects A and B, respectively.

By simple transposition, we can rewrite Eq. (4–8) as

$$\Delta\mathbf{p}_A + \Delta\mathbf{p}_B = 0. \tag{4–9}$$

Then if we represent the change in momentum of the system by

$$\Delta\mathbf{p}_s \equiv \Delta\mathbf{p}_A + \Delta\mathbf{p}_B, \tag{4–10}$$

we see that

$$\Delta\mathbf{p}_s = 0. \tag{4–11}$$

Equations (4–8) through (4–10) are possible ways of stating the *law of conservation of momentum* for two objects. Each of the three equations is a statement that there is no change in the total momentum of an isolated system of two bodies, that is, the total momentum is constant.

Alternatively, we can transpose terms in Eq. (4–3) and write

$$m_A\mathbf{v}_A + m_B\mathbf{v}_B = m_A\mathbf{v}'_A + m_B\mathbf{v}'_B \qquad (4\text{–}12)$$

or

$$\mathbf{p}_A + \mathbf{p}_B = \mathbf{p}'_A + \mathbf{p}'_B. \qquad (4\text{–}13)$$

Equations (4–12) and (4–13) are additional ways of stating the law of conservation of momentum for two objects. Each of the two equations states that the total initial momentum of an isolated system of two bodies equals the total final momentum after interaction of the two bodies. These equations can also be written in component form, as can all vector equations. Thus, Eq. (4–13) can be written

$$\begin{aligned}(p_A)_x + (p_B)_x &= (p'_A)_x + (p'_B)_x,\\ (p_A)_y + (p_B)_y &= (p'_A)_y + (p'_B)_y.\end{aligned} \qquad (4\text{–}14)$$

As in Section 4–2, it is assumed that there is no effect exerted by other bodies on A and B during the interaction of A and B. In practice, the effect of C can be balanced by the effect of D, as in the case of carts on a track. Or the effects of other objects may simply be negligible because their forces are comparatively small, as in the case of an explosion of an artillery shell in midair, where the gravitational force is very small compared with the explosive force.

Examples 1, 2, and 3 illustrate the law of conservation of momentum. You will note from the examples that momentum is conserved regardless of the nature of the interaction force.

The law of conservation of momentum applies to systems of *any number* of interacting bodies so long as no unbalanced outside forces act on the system. This follows from the fact that the *changes* in momentum occur in equal and opposite pairs for interactions between any two bodies in the system. Hence, no net momentum changes can occur due to interactions between bodies *within* the system. The conservation equations for two bodies are merely extended to include the additional objects of the selected system. For example, Eq. (4–13) becomes

$$\mathbf{p}_A + \mathbf{p}_B + \mathbf{p}_C = \mathbf{p}'_A + \mathbf{p}'_B + \mathbf{p}'_C, \qquad (4\text{–}15)$$

or, more compactly expressed,

$$\sum\mathbf{p} = \sum\mathbf{p}' \qquad (4\text{–}16)$$

where $\sum$ is a symbol for summation.

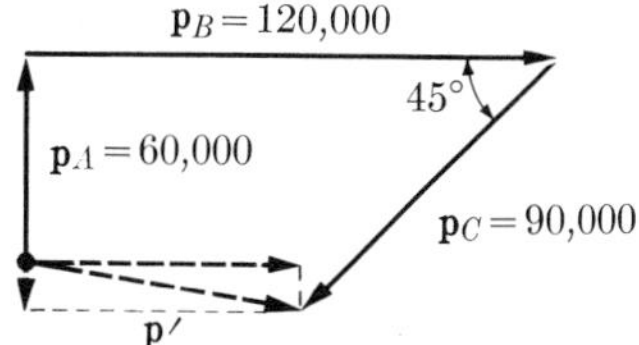

FIG. 4–4. The total momentum in a three-body, completely inelastic collision (Example 4).

Example 4. In a three-way collision, car A of mass 1200 kg going north at 50 m/sec hits car B of mass 1500 kg going east at 80 m/sec. The two cars interlock and almost immediately are struck by a truck of mass 3000 kg going southwest at 30 m/sec. If all three are interlocked, what is the velocity of the "system" immediately after collision, i.e., before friction forces with the road affect the velocity appreciably?

Since each car has the same velocity after the collision, we can write Eq. (4–15) simply as $\mathbf{p}_A + \mathbf{p}_B + \mathbf{p}_C = \mathbf{p}'$. From Fig. 4–4 and a bit of geometrical analysis, we see that $\mathbf{p}'$ has an eastward component of 57,000 and a southward component of 3000 kg-m/sec. To find the components of the final velocity, we divide the components of $\mathbf{p}'$ by the total mass of 5700 kg, obtaining 10 m/sec eastward and 3.6/5.7 m/sec southward.

4–5 AVERAGE FORCE

The time interval during which the change of velocity occurs when objects interact did not appear explicitly in the discussion of preceding sections. We now introduce this time interval Δt during which the change in velocities, $\Delta\mathbf{v}_A$

or $\Delta\mathbf{v}_B$, occurs. The *force of interaction*, averaged over the time interval Δt, is then *defined* by

$$\overline{\mathbf{F}} \equiv m\,\frac{\Delta\mathbf{v}}{\Delta t}. \tag{4–17}$$

Expressed in terms of the fundamental units of the mks system, m is in kilograms (Section 4–2), $\Delta\mathbf{v}$ is in meters per second, and Δt is in seconds. Therefore the *units of force* are the meter-kilogram per second squared. For the sake of brevity, this combination is customarily called the *newton*, in honor of Sir Isaac Newton. The abbreviation for newton will be n. (In the cgs system, the unit of force is called the *dyne*.)

The quantity $\Delta\mathbf{v}/\Delta t$ is defined as average acceleration $\bar{\mathbf{a}}$. The detailed discussion of acceleration will be left until a later chapter.

The introduction of the definition of force (Eq. 4–17) is not particularly fruitful in itself; it appears to be only a conveniently compact way of describing the effect of an interaction. The tremendous importance and usefulness of the idea of force will only become evident when we find that "laws" of force of interaction between objects can be discovered, that is, the ways in which the forces depend on properties of the interacting bodies such as charge, gravitational mass, etc., and on the relative positions of the interacting bodies.

One convenience of the force concept will be utilized at once. If object A interacts simultaneously with more than one other object, it is found experimentally that the result is the same as if a single force equal to the vector sum of the forces of the individual interactions had acted on A.

4–6 NEWTON'S SECOND LAW

Equation (4–17), which is a definition of average force, is a *specialized* statement of Newton's second law. Using the concept of momentum defined and developed in Section 4–3, we can make an alternative formulation, that is, $\overline{\mathbf{F}} \equiv m\,\Delta\mathbf{v}/\Delta t$ and (Eq. 4–17) can be written

$$\overline{\mathbf{F}} = \frac{\Delta\mathbf{p}}{\Delta t}. \tag{4–18}$$

In words, the average force on a particle equals the mass times the change in velocity divided by the time interval, *or* the average force equals the change in momentum divided by the time interval in which the change occurred.

As stated in the preceding section, if more than one object exerts an interaction force on object A, it is found experimentally that the resulting change in momentum of A is correctly predicted by Eq. (4–18), where $\mathbf{F}$ is the *sum*, or *resultant*, of all the forces exerted *on* A. The formal statement is that the principle of superposition applies to forces, that is, each force is unaffected by the presence of the others. By employing the usual notation for sums, we generalize Eq. (4–18) one step and have

$$\sum\overline{\mathbf{F}} = m\,\frac{\Delta\mathbf{v}}{\Delta t}. \tag{4–19}$$

In the special case of constant forces, which is a good approximation in many instances, the bar that denotes average can be omitted. Furthermore, we anticipate later chapters and state without proof at this time that we can let the time interval Δt become vanishingly small. Instantaneous force (denoted by $\mathbf{F}_i$) is then defined as the limiting value of $\overline{\mathbf{F}}$ as Δt goes to zero.

Therefore, it will be found that an expression of the form of Eq. (4–19) is universally applicable when interaction forces alone occur. The expression $\sum\mathbf{F}$ is the *resultant* of all forces exerted on m by other objects. ("Unbalanced force" is a term sometimes used in place of resultant force.)

If two or more masses are connected in such a way that $\Delta\mathbf{v}/\Delta t$ is the same for all the masses, it is obvious from the definition of force that

$$\sum\overline{\mathbf{F}} = \left(\sum m\right)\frac{\Delta\mathbf{v}}{\Delta t}, \tag{4–20}$$

where $\sum\overline{\mathbf{F}}$ is the sum of the *outside* forces acting on the system whose mass is expressed by $\sum m$. Masses connected by inextensible strings or rods, or masses that are directly coupled, constitute such systems.

Newton's second law will probably be the most frequently used idea in this text.

Any of the vector quantities under discussion can be resolved into components. Hence, vector equations such as (4–20) can be written in component form. In cartesian component form (two dimensions), Eq. (4–18) becomes

$$\sum\overline{F}_x = (\sum m)\,\frac{\Delta v_x}{\Delta t}, \qquad \sum\overline{F}_y = (\sum m)\,\frac{\Delta v_y}{\Delta t}. \tag{4–21}$$

Example 5. Suppose that the time duration of the collision in Example 1(a) was 0.02 sec and m_A was 0.5 kg. Find the average force of interaction between A and B.

From Eq. (4–17), we have $\overline{F}_A = m_A\,\Delta v_A/\Delta t = 0.5\,(-0.1 - 0.5)/0.02$, or $\overline{F}_A = -15$ n. The minus sign indicates that the force *on* A (exerted *by* B) is to the left, as expected. The force $\overline{F}_B$ can be stated immediately as $\overline{F}_B = +15$ n, from Newton's third law (Section 4–8). These are *average* forces acting during the time interval Δt.

4–7 NEWTON'S FIRST LAW

Consider the special case of an object moving at uniform (constant) velocity. The change in velocity is then zero, and the right sides of Eqs. (4–17) through (4–21) are in each case zero. When the left sides of these equations are considered, it is seen that either there are no interaction forces at all acting *on* the body or the (vector) sum of all the interaction forces acting *on* the body is zero.

The formal statement of Newton's first law is usually the reverse of the above explanation. The law states that if no external forces act on a body or if the sum of the external forces is zero, the body remains at rest or in a state of uniform rectilinear motion. As noted above, the first law is a special case of the second law (Section 4–6).

One physical situation covered by the statement of Newton's first law occurs frequently in nature: most objects are at rest. The other situation, motion with constant velocity, occurs occasionally: raindrops fall at constant velocity, winds and rivers frequently have constant velocity, etc.

The state of motion required by the conditions of the first law is called *equilibrium,* specified as "static" equilibrium if the body remains at rest and "dynamic" equilibrium if it is moving at constant velocity. Ordinarily, the above adjectives will *not* be used in this text; equilibrium will specify constant velocity, including the special case of zero velocity.

4–8 NEWTON'S THIRD LAW

In Section 4–2 it was found (Eq. 4–1) that $m_A\,\Delta\mathbf{v}_A = -m_B\,\Delta\mathbf{v}_B$ for all the great variety of interactions discussed therein. When both sides of this equation are divided by Δt, there results

$$\frac{m_A\,\Delta\mathbf{v}_A}{\Delta t} = -\frac{m_B\,\Delta\mathbf{v}_B}{\Delta t}. \tag{4–22}$$

Using Eq. (4–17), we then obtain

$$\overline{\mathbf{F}}_A = -\overline{\mathbf{F}}_B, \tag{4–23}$$

which is a result of the definitions *and* of experimental observation. The change in velocity of A was produced by B, and conversely. Therefore, $\overline{\mathbf{F}}_A$ is the force exerted *by B on A*, and $\overline{\mathbf{F}}_B$ is the force exerted *by A on B*.

The usual statement of Eq. (4–23) is called "Newton's third law":

When two bodies, A and B, interact, the force exerted by A on B is equal and opposite to the force exerted by B on A. You are reminded that this law results from the definition of force and the generalization from experimental results of the sort discussed in Section 4–2.

The terms "action" and "reaction" are frequently applied to the members of a pair of forces of interaction. It should be noted that there is no preference in the choice of which force to call the action force. The third law is not necessarily valid in the case of nonmechanical forces, for example, electromagnetic forces.

4–9 GRAVITATIONAL UNITS

In the second general system of units, the *gravitational* system, the choices of fundamental quantities are length, time, and force. In the English-speaking world, this system is widely used by engineers. The foot, second, and pound-force are the standard units. Inertial mass then becomes a derived quantity, defined by Newton's second law. The situation is a bit confusing because an *absolute* system is also used in which the standard units of length, time, and mass are the foot, second, and pound-mass.

If the data for a problem are given in British units, we suggest that you convert to the metric system before doing the analysis. Useful conversion identities are

$$\begin{aligned} 1\text{ kg} &= 2.2\text{ lb} \qquad \text{or} \qquad 1\text{ lb} = 0.454\text{ kg},\\ 1\text{ ft} &= 0.30\text{ m}, \\ 1\text{ in} &= 2.54\text{ cm}. \end{aligned} \tag{4–24}$$

4–10 SUMMARY

Inertial mass is defined in terms of the changes in velocities $\mathbf{v}_A$ and $\mathbf{v}_B$ of two interacting objects A and B; thus

$$m_A\,\Delta\mathbf{v}_A = -m_B\,\Delta\mathbf{v}_B,$$

where m_A and m_B are the inertial masses of the objects. The basic unit of mass in the mks system is the kilogram, which is the mass of a cylinder stored in the archives at Sèvres, France.

When a two-body interaction has the above simple form, the reference frame is an inertial frame.

The meter, kilogram, and second are the basic units in mechanics in the mks system of units. All others are based on these three.

Momentum is defined by

$$\mathbf{p} \equiv m\mathbf{v}.$$

Conservation of momentum is a generalization of the results of experimental observation. It is, in fact, the generalization upon which the above definition of mass is based. However, the generalization is valid for any number of interacting objects, provided that there are no outside forces on the system. A possible expression for conservation of momentum among objects A, B, C, etc., is

$$\mathbf{p}_A + \mathbf{p}_B + \mathbf{p}_C + \cdots = \text{constant}.$$

It is the *force* exerted by one object on another that causes the change in momentum of an object in a two-body interaction. The average force during the interval Δt is defined by

$$\overline{\mathbf{F}} \equiv m\,\frac{\Delta\mathbf{v}}{\Delta t}.$$

If more than one force acts on an object of mass m, it is found that the effects usually add vectorially; thus

$$\Sigma\overline{\mathbf{F}} = m\,\frac{\Delta\mathbf{v}}{\Delta t}.$$

This is a statement of Newton's second law.

Newton's first law states that in the absence of any unbalanced external force, an object remains at rest or in a state of motion with constant velocity.

Another result of observation and the above definition of force is the third law of Newton, that the force by A on B is equal and opposite to the force by B on A.

Problems

1. Is the statement, "Mass is a measure of the quantity of matter," equivalent to the definition of mass in Eq. (4–1)?

2. What is your mass in kg?

3. In order to determine the masses of carts A and B in Fig. 4–1, two sets of measurements were made in which the carts, starting from rest, were pushed apart. With the carts unloaded, A acquired a speed of 0.50 m/sec, while B acquired a speed of 0.30 m/sec. With a standard 1-kg mass added to A, the speeds became 0.40 m/sec and 0.45 m/sec for A and B, respectively; they again start from rest. Find the masses of the carts.

4. Is a clock necessary for the measurement of mass by the method discussed in Section 4–2? Explain in detail.

5. What would result if the negative sign were omitted in the defining equation for mass (Eq. 4–1)?

6. Why is momentum a vector quantity?

7. Cart A has a mass of 1.5 kg. While traveling 0.20 m/sec, it runs into a fixed bumper at the end of its track. What is its change in momentum (a) if it sticks to the bumper? (b) if it rebounds with a speed of 0.10 m/sec? Discuss the question of conservation of momentum in the above experiment.

8. A truck of mass 5000 kg is traveling north at a constant speed of 30 m/sec. It turns onto a road, north 74° east while maintaining constant speed.
(a) What is the change in momentum of the truck?
(b) How is momentum conserved?

9. A "baby flattop" aircraft carrier of mass 10,000 metric tons is coasting without power at a velocity of 2 km/hr due south when a bomber of mass 50 metric tons, traveling north at a speed of 200 km/hr, attempts an emergency landing on it. The bomber skids the length of the flight deck and leaves the flight deck at a speed of 50 km/hr. What is the speed of the carrier after the bomber leaves its flight deck? (Neglect the resistance of the water on the ship.) Is it necessary to convert the speeds to meters per second in this problem?

10. A satellite is moving "horizontally" at a velocity of 8 km/sec relative to the earth. It is desired that the 50-kg pay load be dropped straight down toward the earth by ejecting it horizontally from the rocket.
(a) What must be the velocity of the pay load relative to the earth immediately after ejection?
(b) What will be the velocity of the satellite after ejection if the total mass was 450 kg, including the pay load?

11. An empty railroad car of mass 10^5 kg coasts at 0.5 m/sec beneath a stationary coal hopper.
(a) If 2×10^5 kg of coal are dumped into the car, what is its velocity when loaded?
(b) What will be its velocity if the coal is now dumped by opening the hoppers in the bottom of the car and the coal falls straight down relative to the car?
(c) Suppose that, all at one time, the coal is thrown backward off the car in such a way that the coal is at rest relative to the earth as it leaves the car. What is the velocity of the empty car?
(d) Under what conditions would the result be the same as in (c) if the coal is thrown at an angle relative to the motion of the car?

12. In Problem 14, Chapter 3, let the mass of the ball be 0.40 kg and the mass of the bat 6.0 kg. Find the velocity of the bat immediately after collisions in parts (a) and (b) if the initial velocity of the bat was horizontal and 5 m/sec.

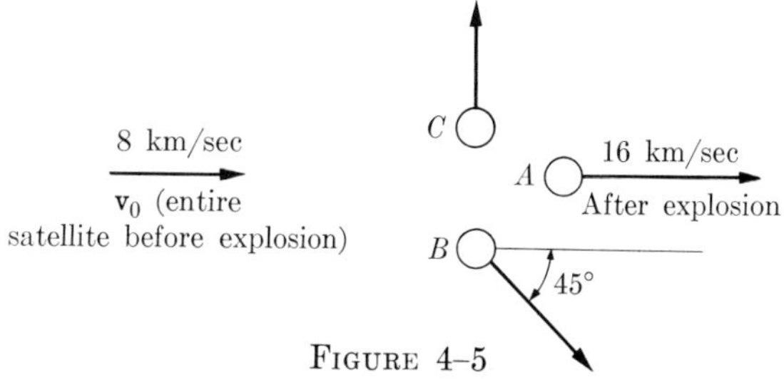

FIGURE 4–5

13. Suppose that the satellite of Problem 10 malfunctions and blows up into three equal masses moving in a horizontal plane in directions seen from the earth as shown in Fig. 4–5. If $v_A = 2v_0$, find v_B and v_C
(a) by the component method, and
(b) by the vector method.

14. (Review problem) Find the velocities v_B and v_C as seen from fragment *A* in Problem 13.

15. In earlier chapters, it was seen that displacement and velocity depend on the coordinate system if one system is moving relative to the other. Now consider *change in velocity*, e. g., the change in velocity of a car when it turns a corner at constant speed, as seen from the earth and as seen from an airplane flying overhead at constant velocity.

(a) Do the problem analytically by writing one equation for the relative velocities before the car turns the corner and another after it turns the corner. Subtract one equation from the other, and prove that $\Delta \mathbf{v}$ is independent of coordinate systems moving at uniform relative velocity.

(b) Make a vector diagram demonstrating a graphic proof of the above.

16. From the results of Problem 15(a), what can you say about the effect of moving coordinate systems (a) on the conservation of momentum? (b) on Newton's laws? Explain.

17. If the "push" in Problem 3 lasted 0.2 sec, find the average force on *A* and on *B*.

18. If the collisions in Problem 7 lasted 0.015 sec, find the average force in both cases.

19. If the truck in Problem 8 made the turn in 3 sec, what was the average (vector) force on the truck?

20. If the blowup in Problem 13 lasted 0.02 sec, what were the average forces on each of the three parts? What was the vector sum of the three forces?

21. (a) Give an operational definition in words of one newton of force.

(b) Repeat part (a) for the dyne.

(c) What is the dyne in terms of units of length, mass, and time?

22. Can you think of any forces that are not additive? Consider the case of the force between two atoms in a molecule of hydrogen gas (Fig. 4–6). In (a) there is a force on *A* by *B*; in (b) there is force on *A* by *C*; but is there a force on *A* by both *B* and *C* in (c)? What is the experimental evidence?

What is the situation in the case of oxygen where an O_3 molecule does exist? Is O_3 abundant? Does an O_4 molecule exist?

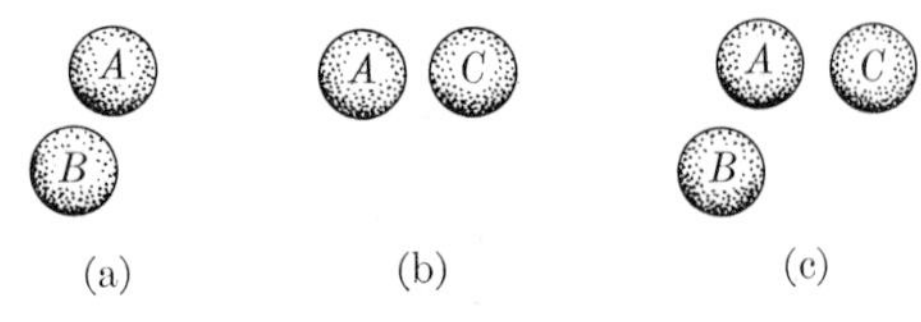

FIGURE 4–6

23. The expression "average force" has been used frequently in this chapter. You should have asked, "Average with respect to what? time? distance? or what?" Can you answer the question?

24. Assume that constant forces **A** and **B** act on a body of mass 2 kg for a time of 3 sec (Fig. 4–7).

(a) If the body was initially at rest, find its final velocity.

(b) If the body had an initial velocity of 4 m/sec in a direction opposite to **A**, what is its final velocity?

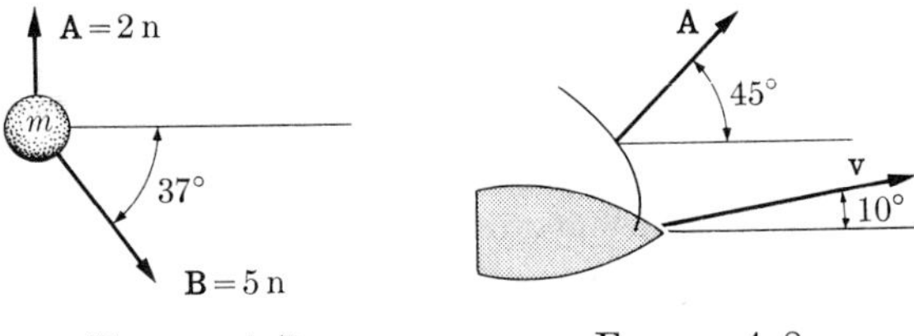

FIGURE 4–7 FIGURE 4–8

25. A sailboat moves at constant velocity under the influence of horizontal forces by the wind (**A**) and by the water (Fig. 4–8). The latter is not shown.

(a) Find the horizontal force exerted by the water.

(b) Find the components of the force exerted by the water, perpendicular and parallel to the direction of motion.

26. Give two examples of Newton's third law in the situation of Problem 25, stating clearly what bodies are involved in each case.

27. Length, time, and force are the fundamental units in the gravitational system of units. Using the British system as an example (foot, second, and pound), give the unit of *mass* as expressed in terms of the fundamental units? What is the unit of *momentum?*

28. Would it be possible to choose other combinations as fundamental units, such as length, mass, and force? Describe how to find the unit of time in this case. What would be the experimental arrangement for calibrating a clock?

29. Consider the earth-moon system and ignore the motion of this system around the sun. The moon rotates about the "earth" in a circle of radius 400,000 km in 28 days.

(a) What is the change in momentum of the moon in 14 days (let m be the mass of the moon)?

(b) What must be the change in momentum of the earth in 14 days?

(c) Is the earth stationary in the earth-moon system?

(d) The mass of the earth is 80 times that of the moon. What is the change in *velocity* of the earth in 14 days?

(e) What is the consequent radius of the circular path of the earth in the earth-moon system? Compare this radius with the radius of the earth, which is about 6400 km.

5

Forces; Equilibrium

5-1 INTRODUCTION

If force were nothing but the quantity defined by Newton's second law, the introduction of the concept of force would not be particularly useful. However, as we study the interactions of objects and use the above definition of force, we discover *laws of force,* that is, systematic dependence of the forces on relative positions, properties, etc., of the interacting objects. This field of physics is by no means closed at the present time; a large proportion of today's research effort is devoted to studies of the interactions of elementary, subatomic particles. In this chapter, some of the force laws will be introduced. For the sake of simplicity, much of the discussion will be confined to the special case of equilibrium.

In the previous chapters, the formal relationships between forces and motion were defined. Brief references were made to a few types of actual forces. In this chapter, these and other types of forces will be treated in more detail. Application will be made to the special case of equilibrium, the case covered by Newton's first law.

From a subjective viewpoint, the idea of physical force is known from the experience of human exertion, the exercise of pushing or pulling with our arms. A push or a pull can set an object in motion, deflect it from its course of motion, or slow it down, all of these effects involving a change of velocity. Or the push or pull can simply "balance" other forces and thus maintain an object at rest or in motion at constant velocity.

Conversely, everyone has experienced pushes or pulls exerted *on him by* outside agents. Everyone is frequently conscious of the push of the floor on his feet (but usually unconscious of the pull of the earth on his entire body). When an elevator, airplane, or automobile changes velocity rapidly, the passenger is conscious of the push or pull (exerted on some part of his body) that changes his velocity. These wholly qualitative ideas were expressed on a quantitative basis in the previous chapter. It was also shown in the previous chapter that the pushes or pulls do not necessarily produce changes in velocity if more than one force acts on the object.

Most of the material of the previous chapters has been based on a set of definitions and mathematical manipulations. However, at least two of the important ideas were "laws of nature" which can be derived only by induction and generalization from experimental observation. These were the ideas of inertial mass and of superposition of many kinds of forces. We shall now turn to additional examples of laws that are generalizations from experimental observations. These laws will be of two kinds. One kind is exemplified by Newton's law of universal gravitation. Although it is always recognized that a law of this sort might have to be modified to fit some startling new experimental discovery in the future, we have a feeling that such a law will always be found to hold within the realm of classical physics. The constant of proportionality in such a law is another kind of question, since it cannot be known any more accurately than the definition of the standards for the system of units and the accuracy of measurements in verifying the law. But we have the feeling that the dependence on mass and on distance given by Newton will never be contradicted by experiments restricted to the scale of space, time, and velocities that we now deal with.

The second kind of law is exemplified by Hooke's law of elasticity or the laws of sliding friction. Such laws are considered to be approximations in all respects, that is, not only in the constants of proportionality but also in the functional dependence on the variables in question. In principle, "correct" laws for the functional relationships in this second category can be derived from the basic laws of forces on the atomic scale, thus raising the second type of law to the same status as the first type.

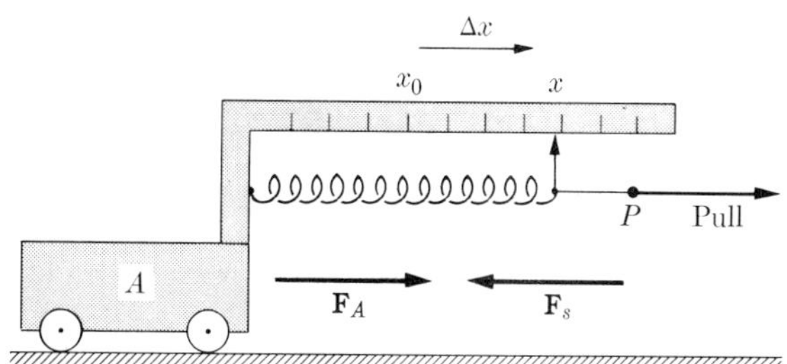

FIG. 5–2. The direct measurement of an external force acting on an object A.

5–2 FORCES DUE TO ELASTICITY (CALIBRATION OF A SPRING)

The exertion that we call push or pull can have physical effects other than to cause change in velocity, and in this point lies an idea for an instrument to measure force directly. A pull exerted at the free end of a spring attached to a wall will result in an elongation of the spring (Fig. 5–1). When transient effects are eliminated, the free end of the spring will come to rest at x. Many flexible objects can be reproducibly distorted—changed in size or shape—through the exertion of a push or a pull. It remains to be seen experimentally whether such stationary effects can be usefully related to the basic definition of force given in Chapter 4. Let us contrive an experiment to discover such a connection.

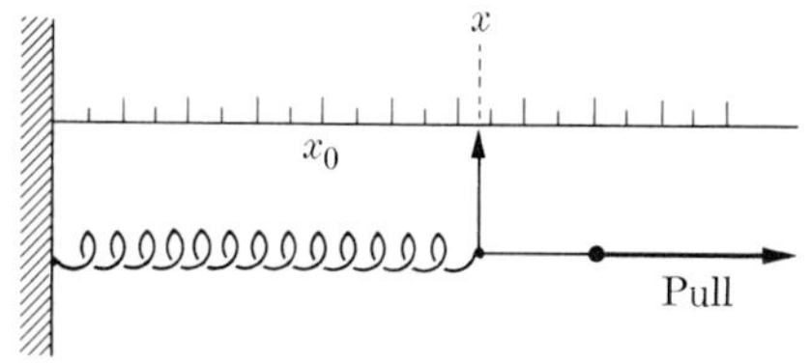

FIG. 5–1. The extension of a spring from length x_0 to length x due to an external pull.

The end of the spring that was fixed to the wall is now attached to a "free material object," approximated by a cart A, as in Fig. 5–2. It has already been discovered that a gentle pull results in a slight elongation of the spring, and a stronger pull results in a greater elongation. We take the elongation to be some kind of measure of the magnitude of the pull. It need not be a linear measure; we require only that a definite amount of elongation correspond to a definite amount of pull, i.e., we require reproducibility. Then an exertion is made such that the pointer measuring elongation stays at a fixed point on the scale. It is discovered at once that the *change* in velocity of the material object is, for a given time interval, always the same for a given elongation. This result alone is sufficient to establish that there is a useful connection between this elongation measure and the quantity $m\,\Delta\mathbf{v}/\Delta t$ that we have defined as force.*

Next, different settings on the scale can be established by different pulls, and the corresponding velocity changes per time interval can be measured. For each spring setting, we calculate the force from the measured quantities m, $\Delta\mathbf{v}$, and Δt, using the definition of force ($\overline{\mathbf{F}} = m\,\Delta\mathbf{v}/\Delta t$). For this particular spring system, we find that the force is linearly proportional to the elongation $x - x_0$, where x_0 is the unstretched length (see Fig. 5–3). Therefore, we can write the quantitative relationship

$$F_A = k(x - x_0), \qquad (5\text{–}1)$$

where k is a property of the particular spring.

* Imagine the experimental result to be quite different: a pull that gives a fixed point on the elongation scale results in a continuously increasing or decreasing value of $m\,\Delta v/\Delta t$! Then the procedure of establishing a relationship between elongation and force as we have defined it would be effectively blocked.

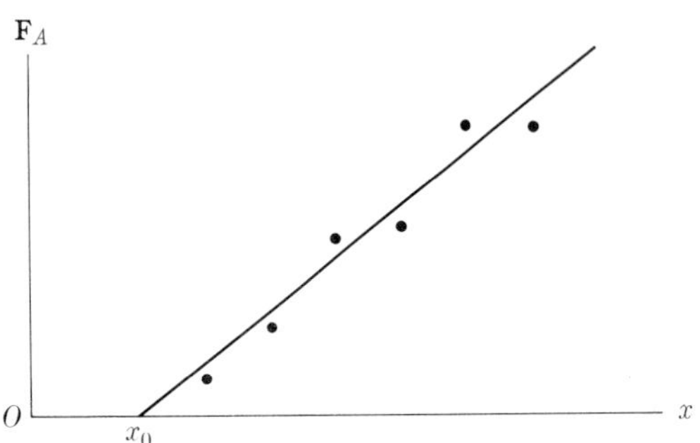

FIG. 5-3. The force $\mathbf{F}_A$ exerted by a spring as a function of its length x.

Often it is the force exerted *by* the "free" end (P in Fig. 5-2) of the spring that we wish to consider. This force would be written

$$F_s = -k(x - x_0), \tag{5-2}$$

where the minus appears because F_s is directed oppositely to the spring elongation $x - x_0$.

If the spring is used to transmit a push to the cart instead of a pull, the results are the same. Therefore Eq. (5-1) and (5-2) apply equally to a stretched and to a compressed spring.

Thus with a suitable choice of standards and units, we can conceive of the spring as a force-measuring device. In fact, this spring would be a linear force-measuring device, although the linearity is an accident of the system chosen and not essential to the logic. There are a few subtleties that are left for the problems.

In painstaking fashion, we have analyzed a particular physical system to arrive at this conclusion: force can be reproducibly related to the geometric condition of the spring. Thus, we have devised a convenient and practical *instrument* for measuring force directly, an instrument called a "spring scales" or a "spring balance." It can be calibrated in newtons by using $\mathbf{F} = m\,\Delta\mathbf{v}/\Delta t$. The important advantage of this instrument is that it can be used for static as well as dynamic measurements of force. From Newton's third law, it can be stated that the force F_x (the force to be measured), which is exerted *on* the spring at point P, is equal and opposite to the force F_s exerted *by* the spring at point P (see Fig. 5-4). This equality holds whether or not the velocity of point P is changing, as long as P has negligible inertial mass.

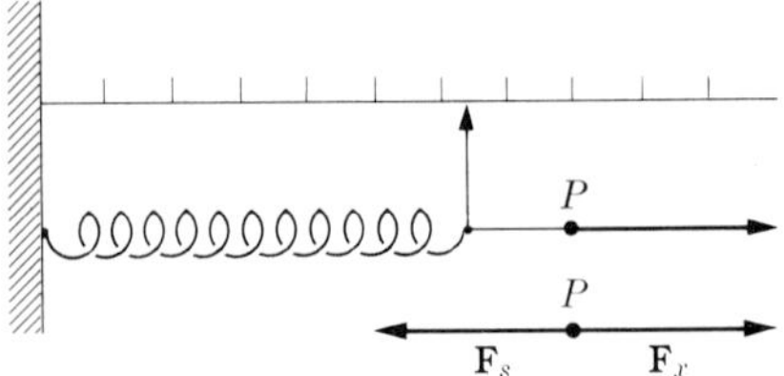

FIG. 5-4. Diagram of the forces acting on point P.

Besides finding a convenient instrument, we have determined a *force law* (Eq. 5-2) that will be used later on in systems involving springs. The problem of deriving the force law for springs from the basic forces among the atoms that constitute a spring is a current research field in solid state physics. In this text, we must be satisfied with the macroscopic law for springs found experimentally above. Note that the spring has *not* been introduced as a standard of force, but only as an instrument.

5-3 GRAVITATIONAL FORCE AT THE EARTH'S SURFACE (WEIGHT)

It is common experience that the earth exerts a downward pull on objects. In most circumstances we are not directly conscious of this pull on our bodies, i.e., we do not feel the pull directly; we feel only the results when we jump or fall, or when our feet become tired. However, we are conscious of the pull of the earth on other objects whenever we lift or hold one of them. We then speak of the pull by the earth as the *weight* of the object.

By using the spring balance, we can study the pull of the earth experimentally. It is, of course, immediately discovered that the pull is vertical. In order to measure the magnitude of the pull on object A, we hang it on a spring balance (Fig. 5-5). We then read the magnitude of the gravitationa

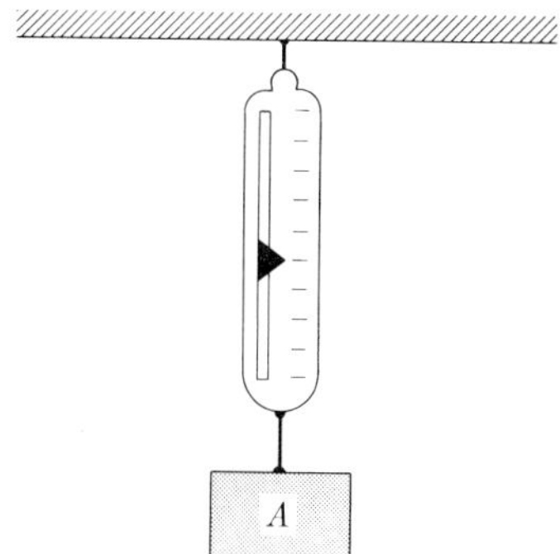

FIG. 5–5. A spring used to measure the pull of the earth on A, that is, its weight.

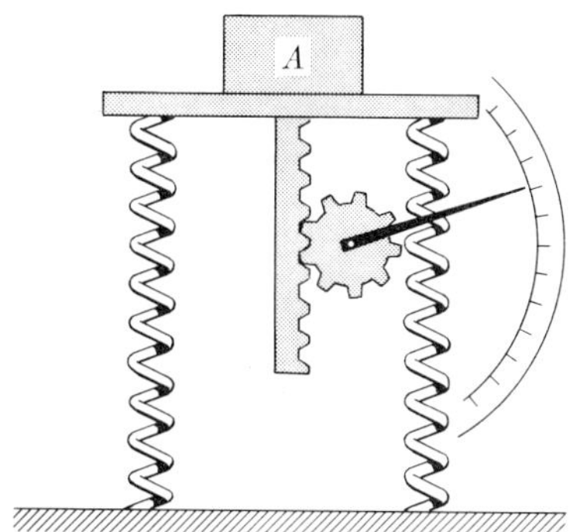

FIG. 5–6. Schematic diagram of spring platform scales. The pointer deflection is proportional to the deflection of the springs.

force (the *weight* of the object) directly from the scale. The weight of an object is always to be measured in force units (newtons in mks units or dynes in cgs units).

When the weight of objects is studied in detail, a remarkable regularity becomes apparent: the weight is directly proportional to the inertial mass. Using the customary notation, we have

$$W = mg \text{ (newtons)}, \qquad (5\text{–}3)$$

where W is the weight and m is the inertial mass of the object. The proportionality constant g must have the dimensions of l/t^2. The constant g is *not* a universal constant; its value depends on the location of the laboratory, i.e., its altitude and latitude and the local distribution of masses such as mountains, ore deposits, etc. However, g varies only a few tenths of a percent with changes of a few thousand meters in latitude, longitude, or altitude. For most purposes, therefore, we shall simply use

$$g = 9.8 \text{ m/sec}^2 \quad (= 980 \text{ cm/sec}^2) \qquad (5\text{–}4)$$

for laboratories on the earth's surface.

The remarkable result above indicates that mass has two aspects, inertial and gravitational. Within the precision of present-day experiments (1 part in 10^{11}) inertial mass is directly proportional to gravitational mass. For convenience the proportionality constant is chosen as one.

The spring scales could have been inverted. This arrangement (Fig. 5–6) is utilized in the spring-type platform scales such as the kitchen scales and bathroom scales. As shown in the figure, a "rack and pinion" are used to drive a pointer or circular indicator.

The *apparent weight* of an object is usually defined as the reading that a spring balance would show if a given object were placed on it. Examples will be considered in later chapters in which the apparent weight differs from the actual weight.

A very common application of the results summarized by Eq. (5–3) is the process of weighing in order to determine mass. This procedure is so universal that metric spring balances usually have the graduations labeled in kilograms or grams. Strictly speaking, these scales are then accurate

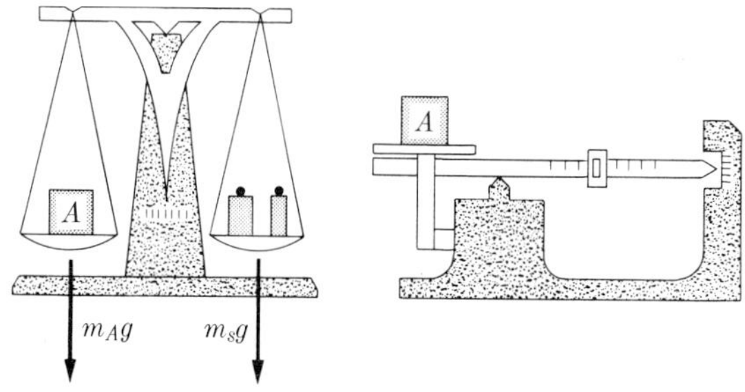

FIG. 5–7. Schematic diagrams of balances that compare the forces of the earth on masses.

only where the value of g is the same as it was at the place where the scales were calibrated (usually 9.80 m/sec^2).

The second type of scales simply compares the pull of the earth on a standard mass with the pull of the earth on the unknown mass. The equal-arm analytical balance used in chemistry laboratories is of this type, as are the unequal-arm balances, which are the most widely used scales (Fig. 5-7).

5-4 GRAVITATIONAL FORCE BETWEEN POINT MASSES

We will now consider another special case of gravitational attraction, leaving the more general discussion until later. However, one of the points of the general discussion will be anticipated at this time: for the purpose of analyzing gravitational effects external to the object, the distributed mass of spherically symmetric objects can be replaced by the same total mass concentrated at a point at the center.

In 1798, Sir Henry Cavendish performed an experiment that served to measure the gravitational attraction between two masses within the laboratory. The method was, in principle, the same as that discussed in Section 5-3, that is, a spring was calibrated to measure force and then used to determine the unknown or postulated properties of the force under investigation. In this case, a very sensitive device capable of supporting an appreciable weight was needed. The device is a torsion balance in which a wire or fiber supports weight by vertical pull but measures force by the twisting effect (Fig. 5-8). The wire hangs vertically and supports a bar on whose ends equal masses m are attached. Fixed masses m are placed so that a twisting effect is produced by the forces F of gravitational attraction between m and m'. The magnitude of the forces can be measured by the angular twist of the wire.

The results of Cavendish's experiment directly confirmed the hypothesis of Sir Isaac Newton that the gravitational force F_G is given by

$$F_G = Gmm'/r^2, \qquad (5\text{-}5)$$

where r is the distance between the centers of m and m', and G is a constant. The value of G found from the measurements is

$$\begin{aligned} G &= 6.673 \times 10^{-11}\ \text{n-m}^2/\text{kg}^2 \\ &= 6.673 \times 10^{-8}\ \text{dyne-cm}^2/\text{gm}^2. \qquad (5\text{-}6) \end{aligned}$$

This dependence on distance also applies to the attraction exerted on objects by the earth, if we assume that Eq. (5-5) is universally applicable. This prediction is supported by experiments that will be described later.

Note that the equality of inertial and gravitational mass has been assumed in the notation in this section.

Gravitational force is an example of action at a distance that is evident on the macroscopic scale. One should note, however, that a real object can be named as the origin of gravitational force, just as in all cases of interaction forces. Later, we will develop the idea that action at a distance takes place through the agency of a field.

The vector nature of F_G is not explicit in the right-hand side of Eq. (5-5). The vector equation would be written

$$\mathbf{F}_G = Gmm'\mathbf{r}/r^3, \qquad (5\text{-}7)$$

where $\mathbf{r}$ is a position vector extending from the center of m to the center of m', if the force $\mathbf{F}_G$ is the force on m.

Since the gravitational attraction on a mass m at the surface of the earth is called its weight W,

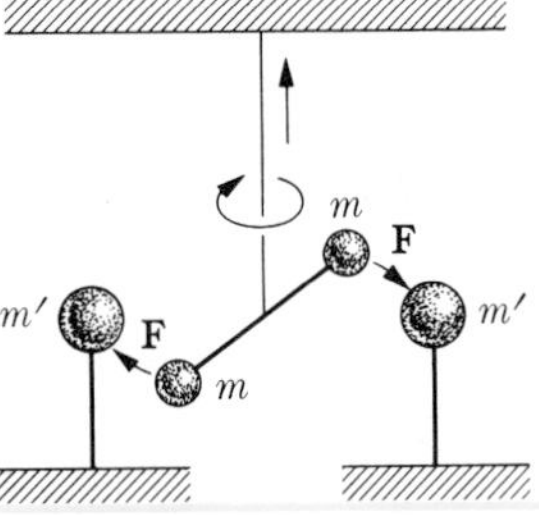

Fig. 5-8. Schematic diagram of a method for measuring the gravitational force between two masses, m and m', in the laboratory.

we have $F_G = W$ at the surface of the earth. By using this idea, it is possible to calculate the mass of the earth (see Problems).

5–5 ELECTRIC FORCE

Another type of universal force is discovered when electrically charged objects are investigated. An additional physical quantity, the *electric charge*, must be defined in order to make the analysis of the experiments with electric forces quantitative. The definition of electric charge is effectively incorporated in the force law that describes the experimental results. It is called *Coulomb's law* and can be written

$$F = K\frac{qq'}{r^2}, \tag{5–8}$$

or, in vector form,

$$\mathbf{F} = Kqq'\mathbf{r}/r^3,$$

where K is a constant, q and q' are the magnitudes of the interacting charges, and r is their separation. In the mks system, q and q' are in coulombs and K is 8.987×10^9 n-m^2/coul^2. In the cgs system, the constant K is set equal to one, and Eq. (5–8) is used to define the unit charge, stat coulomb. (Actually the coulomb per second, or electric current, is the basic unit in the mks system; hence K cannot arbitrarily be made unity.)

The electric force is a vector directed along a line joining the charges. In contrast with the gravitational case, there are two kinds of electric charge, plus and minus. It is found that unlike charges attract and like charges repel. This directional information is contained implicitly in Eq. (5–8), since q and q' can have plus or minus signs.

If the charges are in motion, there is a magnetic force in addition to the electric force. The magnetic force is a function of the velocities of the charges as well as the magnitude of the charges. The vector equation contains three vectors in addition to the force, namely, two velocities and the relative position vector between the charges. Since vector multiplication results, this equation will be left until later.

Electric and magnetic (or, simply, electromagnetic) forces act through the intermediary of a field. The physical reality of this field is a matter of everyday experimental experience in the detection of individual entities of the field; these are called photons. On the other hand the "reality" of the gravitational field has not yet been demonstrated directly by the detection of gravitons.

5–6 CONTACT FORCES

Gravitational and electromagnetic forces do not require contact between the interacting bodies even in the macroscopic sense. We now turn to the class of forces that result specifically from actual contact (in the macroscopic sense) of the interacting bodies. It has been found convenient to resolve the contact force into two components: parallel and perpendicular to the surface of contact of the bodies (Fig. 5–9). The perpendicular component is called the *normal force*, and the parallel component is called the *friction force*. In Fig. 5–9, the force on A exerted *by* B is shown as $\mathbf{F}_A$. The normal force $\mathbf{N}$ and the friction force $\mathbf{F}_R$ are the perpendicular components of $\mathbf{F}_A$ as shown.

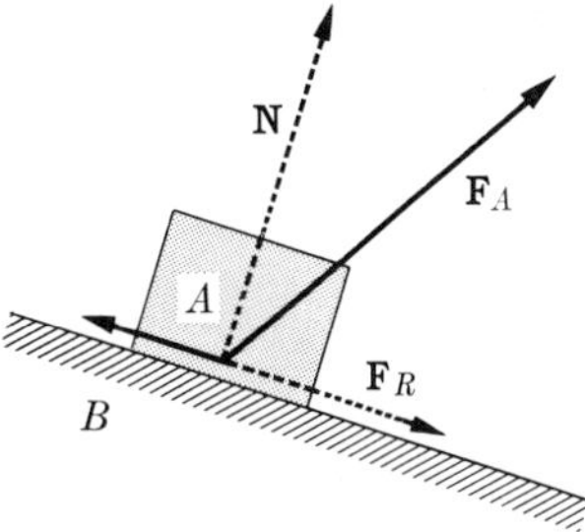

FIG. 5–9. Resolution of the force $\mathbf{F}_A$ exerted on A by the inclined plane B into its friction component $\mathbf{F}_R$ and the normal component $\mathbf{N}$. Other forces acting on A are not shown.

There is a double utility in resolving the contact force into components: $\mathbf{F}_R$ is along the line of possible relative motion between the objects, and $\mathbf{F}_R$ will be found to depend on the normal component $\mathbf{N}$ of the contact force.

A brief comment on the mechanism of contact forces may be of interest. The normal force between solids can be described macroscopically as due to elastic deformation in the region of contact. A finite deformation occurs when the objects come in contact. The deformation gives rise to an elastic force of the sort examined for the simple springs (Section 5–2). For example, when a book is placed on the table, both the book and the table are compressed in the region of contact. The mechanism of the parallel or friction component is more difficult to describe in other macroscopic terms. Microscopically, it is usually ascribed to temporary local "pressure welding" between projections on the surfaces. Static friction force (no slipping) is essentially an elastic type of force deriving from the lateral deformation of the welded projections that occurs when a lateral external force (T) is applied to the object. The sum of the elastic forces increases if T is increased, until the point where some of the local "welds" begin to break. Object A then begins to slide, new projections come into contact and weld momentarily, etc. The sum of all of the elastic restoring forces at a given instant is the kinetic friction force. Discussion of the mechanisms of contact forces when fluids are involved is better left until the kinetic theory of matter is considered.

5–7 FRICTION

Laymen use this term in essentially the sense that it is used in physics. Next to gravitational pull, friction is probably the most frequently experienced force in every day life. However, our most striking experiences with friction result from such sudden changes from static to sliding friction as occur when we slip unexpectedly, either on foot or in a car.

Friction forces can be divided into several categories: (a) static friction between solids which are not in relative motion, (b) sliding or rolling friction between solid objects (either dry or lubricated), (c) fluid friction between a fluid and a solid moving relative to the fluid, and (d) fluid friction between parts of the fluid.

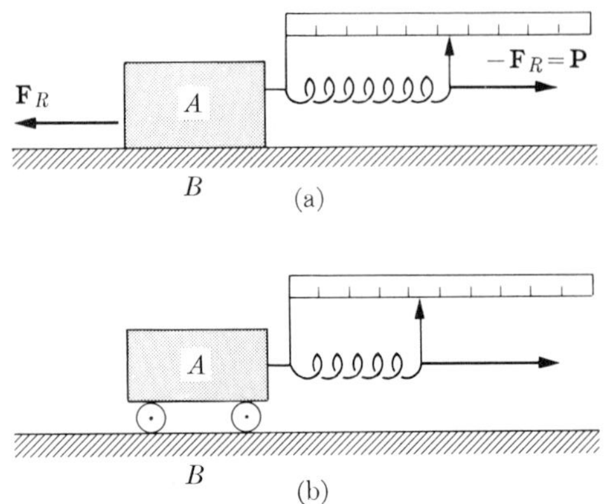

Fig. 5–10. A method of measuring the friction force $\mathbf{F}_R$ in terms of the pull by a calibrated spring.

Experimental studies of static friction can be made by methods such as those shown in Fig. 5–10, where force $\mathbf{P}$ is an external pull whose magnitude is measured by the spring. The other horizontal force on A is the friction force $\mathbf{F}_R$. Part (a) illustrates a measurement of sliding friction, and part (b) illustrates a measurement of rolling friction. Static friction is measured by $\mathbf{P}$ when there is no relative motion of A to B, and sliding or rolling friction is measured when there is relative motion at constant velocity.

The only horizontal forces on A in the arrangements of Fig. 5–10 are the pull of the spring and the force of friction. The only vertical forces *on* A are the gravitational pull of the earth and the normal force exerted *by* B [via the rollers in (b)]. The diagram for the forces on A is shown in Fig. 5–11. According to Newton's first law,

$$\sum \mathbf{F} = 0, \quad \text{or} \quad \sum F_x = 0 \quad \text{and} \quad \sum F_y = 0,$$

if the object remains at rest or in motion at constant velocity.

Consequently, $P + F_R = 0$, and $P = -F_R$ is a direct measure of the friction force if the horizontal velocity is constant or if A remains at rest.

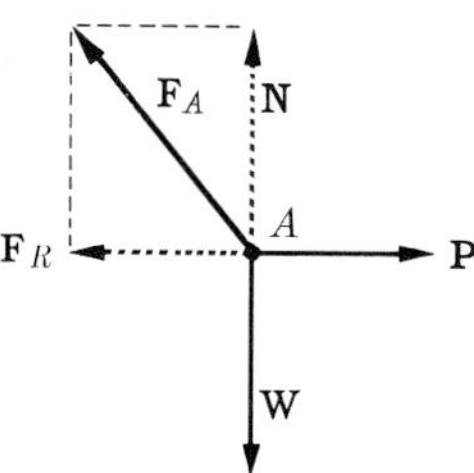

FIG. 5–11. Force diagram of the forces acting on the object A in Fig. 5–10(a).

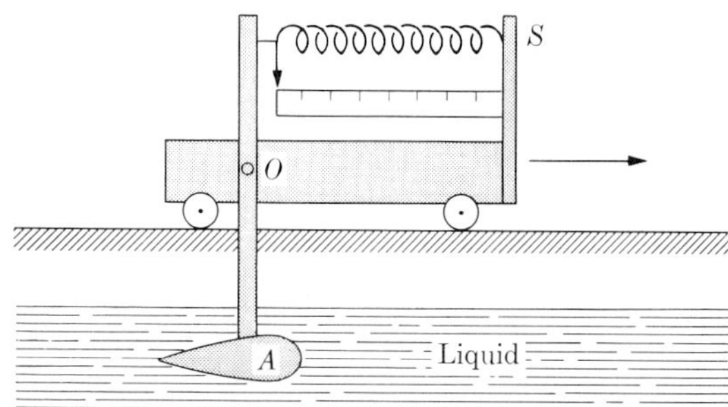

FIG. 5–12. Schematic diagram of a method for measuring the friction force on an object A that is moving relative to a fluid. The compression of the spring is a measure of the friction force.

The results of measurements of static friction show that F_R can have any value from zero to a maximum that (a) depends on the nature of the surfaces, (b) depends directly on the normal force, and (c) is independent of the area of contact. Quantitatively,

$$F_R \text{ (maximum static)} \equiv \mu_0 N, \qquad (5\text{–}9)$$

where μ_0 is called the coefficient of static friction. Equation (5–9) is the definition of μ_0. In this particular example, $N = -W = -m_A g$. Does $N = -W$ in the example of Fig. 5–9?

The results for sliding friction are that F_R depends on the material and N but is approximately independent of area and velocity. Quantitatively,

$$F_R \text{ (sliding)} \equiv \mu N, \qquad (5\text{–}10)$$

where μ is called the coefficient of sliding friction. This is the definition of μ.

Fluid friction can be measured by a method similar to that in Fig. 5–10 if the object A is boatlike in character and floats on the liquid. If, on the other hand, the friction of the totally immersed object is to be studied, an arrangement such as that in Fig. 5–12 might be used. The friction force exerted by the liquid on A is transmitted to the spring, S, via a rod pivoted at O. The spring balance then reads the friction force. In wind-tunnel testing for air friction, the object is stationary in the laboratory, and the fluid flows past the object.

The results of measurements show that fluid friction depends on the nature of the fluid and on the size, shape, orientation, and velocity of the object. At very low velocities, fluid friction on a sphere is

$$F_R = 6\pi\eta r v, \qquad (5\text{–}11)$$

where η is the coefficient of viscosity (a constant that is characteristic of the fluid), r is the radius of the sphere, and v is the velocity of the sphere in the fluid. As the velocity increases, the dependence of fluid friction on velocity rapidly changes to approximately a v^2-dependence.

The direction of any friction force is always opposite to the direction of motion, i.e., in the sense $-\mathbf{v}$.

5–8 TENSION AND THRUST (STRINGS AND RODS)

In many situations, objects indirectly exert contact forces by means of interconnecting strings (or ropes) or rods. The masses of strings and rods are to be assumed negligible compared with the objects that they join unless otherwise specified. In addition, a string is assumed to be frictionless, perfectly flexible, and completely inextensible. It can exert only a pull, or *tension* force, but never a push or *thrust*. Rods are assumed to be perfectly rigid and inextensible. They can exert forces of thrust or tension.

Whenever the mass of strings or rods can be neglected, their only effect is to transmit forces from one object to another.

The meaning of tension in a string is sometimes unclear to students. It is simply the force exerted by one segment of the string on a neighboring segment and is the same as the force exerted by the end of the string on the object to which it is fastened.

5–9 SYSTEMS

It has already been made clear that at least two objects are required in order to have forces of interaction. If one of two interacting objects has much greater mass than the other, we customarily neglect the effect of the interaction on the motion of the heavier mass (or choose it as our reference frame of coordinates). For example, when a stone is dropped, the force of interaction between the stone and the earth results in changes in velocity of each. However, $\Delta \mathbf{v}$ of the earth is negligible and therefore the earth is chosen as the reference frame.

In circumstances in which the masses are comparable, the effect of the interaction on the motion of all the comparable masses must be considered. Any number of these masses may be selected as the *system* under consideration, and the laws of motion will apply to the system. External forces acting *on* the chosen system and the mass of the chosen system will then determine the changes from its initial motion. We have already expressed Newton's second law in a form suitable for application to systems (Eq. 4–18). Forces *internal* to the system will cancel out in pairs according to Newton's third law. We presented earlier the conservation of the total momentum of a system with no unbalanced outside forces acting on it.

In some of our most frequently occurring exercises, the objects in a system will interact directly by contact forces; in others, strings, pulleys, and rods are used as connecting links. When the masses of these connecting links are negligible, their only effect is to transmit contact forces from one object to another, with or without a change in direction.

The pulleys that appear in the problems will usually be assumed to have negligible mass and negligible friction. They will therefore change only the direction of the force exerted by the string or rope that passes over them.

5–10 STATICS OF POINT MASSES

Various types of forces have been examined in some detail, and the ideas presented will now make it possible to apply Newton's laws to a greater variety of physical problems than in Chapter 4. Our attention, however, will be confined to problems in which the first and third laws apply.

Systems of which all parts satisfy the first law are called static systems. The positions of the parts of the system are usually fixed relative to one another. Such a system is said to be in equilibrium. As seen earlier, the condition for equilibrium is

$$\sum \mathbf{F} = 0, \tag{5–12}$$

or, in cartesian components,

$$\sum F_x = 0, \qquad \sum F_y = 0, \qquad \sum F_z = 0, \tag{5–13}$$

where the F's represent forces exerted *on* the object or system in question *by* outside objects.

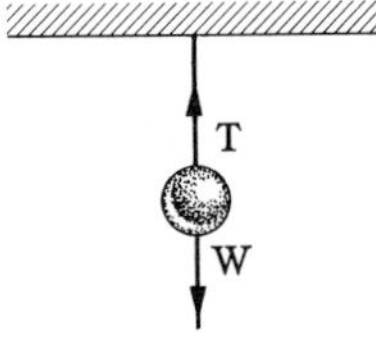

FIG. 5–13. The forces acting on an object that hangs from a string.

Example 1. The process of weighing is usually a problem of statics.

In Fig. 5–13, a material object is shown suspended by a string in the earth's gravitational field. The object remains motionless. There are two outside forces applied on the object—the downward pull of gravity **W** and the upward pull of the string **T** (equal to the tension in the string). The system is static. The condition for equilibrium (Eq. 5–12) yields $\mathbf{T} + \mathbf{W} = 0$.

Since the forces **T** and **W** are colinear, we may represent them by their magnitudes T and W. The directions of the forces are then given by a plus or minus sign indicating that the force is upward or downward. If we call the upward direction positive, then $\mathbf{T} + \mathbf{W} = 0$ becomes $T + W = 0$ or simply $T = -W$. The tension and weight are equal in magnitude, but opposite in direction, as indicated by the signs. (The question of sign convention is partly a matter of personal preference. In the present example we can say instead that the symbols T and W represent special values of forces, and therefore we should immediately assign plus and minus to these special values. From this point of view, we would write $T - W = 0$ or $T = W$.)

The weight can be measured by observing the tension in the string. This is done by inserting a spring balance into the string. (The spring will not read "true" weight if the velocity of the system is changing.)

Example 2. An object is supported by a string which is in turn supported by two strings attached to the ceiling, as shown in Fig. 5–14. The weight of the object is W. Find the tensions T_1, T_2, and T_3 in the three strings.

Solution: Choose a nontrivial point in the system. A trivial point would be Q. The point Q is acted upon by two forces, T_2 in one direction along the string and T_2 in the other direction. Since the tension is known to be unchanging along the string, the application of the static condition to the point Q (the sum of all the forces on Q is zero) gives us no additional information.

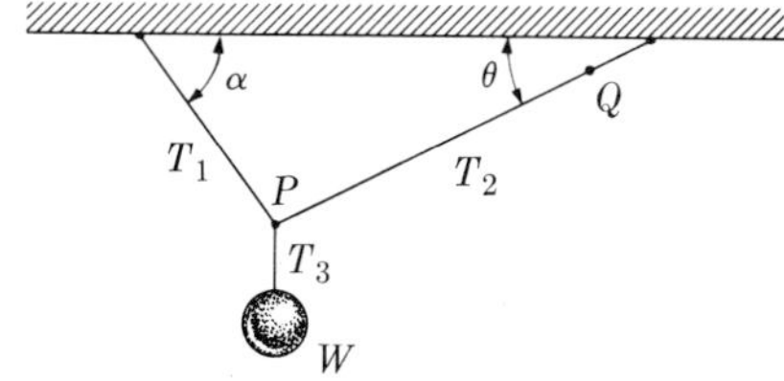

FIG. 5–14. An object W supported indirectly by two strings.

The point P is not trivial. All the forces of interest, T_1, T_2, and T_3, act upon this point. The application of the static condition at P gives us a relationship among the forces of interest: $\mathbf{T}_1 + \mathbf{T}_2 + \mathbf{T}_3 = 0$, where $|\mathbf{T}_3| = W$.

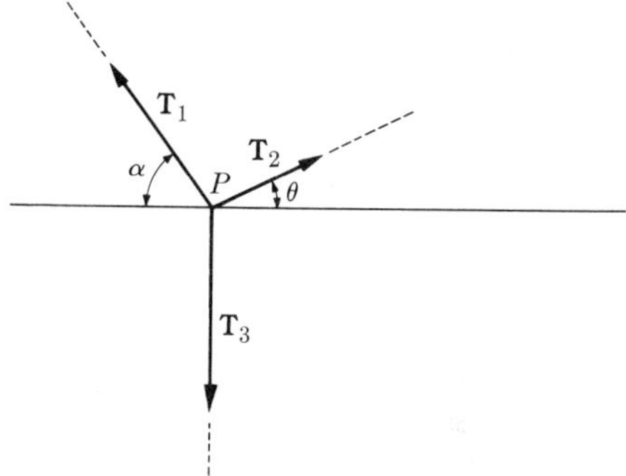

FIG. 5–15. Force diagram for the point P of Fig. 5–14.

Figure 5–14 is called the "space diagram" of the system. It shows the position and orientation of the elements of the system. In Fig. 5–15 we show a "force diagram." Forces in strings act along the strings. Thus the force angles are obtained directly from the space diagram but the *force magnitudes are not.* (Occasionally, triangles in the space diagram are similar to triangles in the force diagram, and this information can be used for the solution.) The diagram showing the directions of the forces *on* P is given in Fig. 5–15. (The forces are shown acting outward on P.) In this example, it seems obvious that the forces on P are in fact outward. But in more complex problems involving rods, the sense may not be obvious from inspection. In such cases, we assume a sense for each force, and if the solution gives a negative sign for any force, we know that it is directed oppositely to the assumed sense.

The remainder of the solution is simply vector mathematics.

(a) Vector polygon method: by sliding the vectors of Fig. 5–15, either of the triangles of Fig. 5–16 can be obtained. They both satisfy the equation

$$\mathbf{T}_1 + \mathbf{T}_2 + \mathbf{T}_3 = 0.$$

If W $(= T_3)$, θ, and α are the given quantities, then by using the law of sines, we have

$$T_1 = T_3 \frac{\sin(90 - \theta)}{\sin(\theta + \alpha)} \quad \text{and} \quad T_2 = T_3 \frac{\sin(90 - \alpha)}{\sin(\theta + \alpha)}$$

as direct trigonometric solutions for T_1 and T_2 in terms of the given quantities.

(b) Parallelogram method: here the vectors must be added two at a time. In this case we know that the sum of two of the vectors must be equal and opposite to the third vector, since

$$(\mathbf{T}_1 + \mathbf{T}_2) = -\mathbf{T}_3 \quad \text{or} \quad (\mathbf{T}_1 + \mathbf{T}_3) = -\mathbf{T}_2,$$

or

$$(\mathbf{T}_2 + \mathbf{T}_3) = -\mathbf{T}_1.$$

The parallelograms for each case are illustrated in Fig. 5–17. The trigonometric solutions using the law of sines would proceed as before.

(c) Component method: any of the figures above could be used as the diagram for the component method, but Fig. 5–15 is probably simplest. The reasonable choice of axes is horizontal and vertical (Fig. 5–18). The solution then is

$$\sum F_x = T_2 \cos\theta - T_1 \cos\alpha = 0,$$
$$\sum F_y = T_2 \sin\theta + T_1 \sin\alpha - T_3 = 0,$$

which are two equations in two unknowns, T_1 and T_2.

Example 3. A block A slides at constant velocity down a plane inclined at an angle θ with the horizontal. Find the coefficient of sliding friction.

Solution: The space and force diagrams are first drawn as in Fig. 5–19. The force diagram shows the external forces *on* A, namely, $\mathbf{F}_P$, the force exerted by the plane and $\mathbf{W}$, the force exerted by the earth. Newton's first law gives $\mathbf{F}_P + \mathbf{W} = 0$, which does *not* solve the problem. It is necessary to consider the normal and frictional components of $\mathbf{F}_P$ as in Section 5–7. Figure 5–20(a) illustrates the resolution into cartesian components, parallel and perpendicular to the plane.

In Fig. 5–20(a) we make use of the information that $\mathbf{F}_P = -\mathbf{W}$ and write

$$N = -W\cos\theta,$$
$$F_R = -W\sin\theta,$$

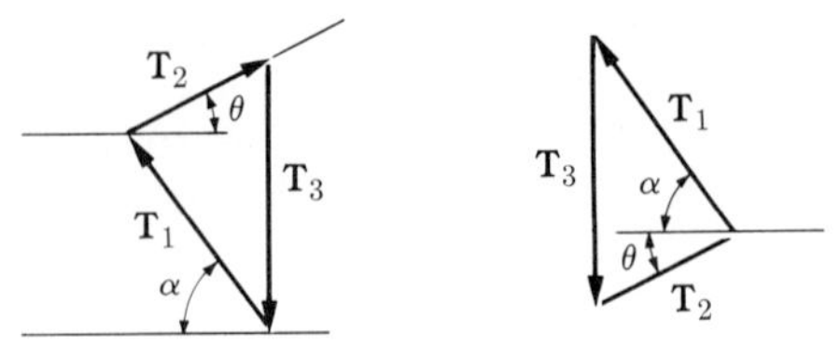

Fig. 5–16. Vector summation of the forces shown in Fig. 5–15.

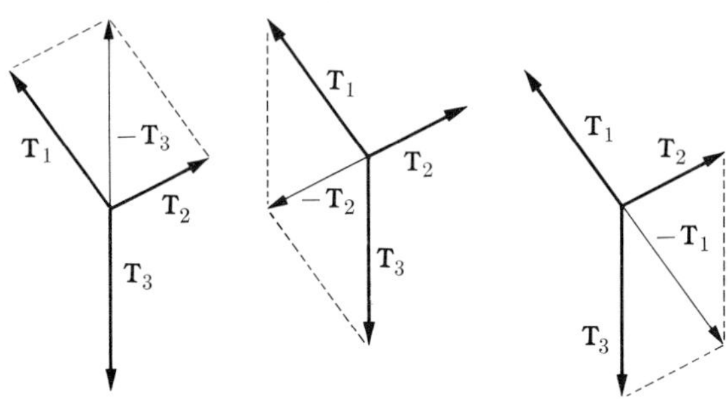

Fig. 5–17. Vector summation of the forces shown in Fig. 5–15.

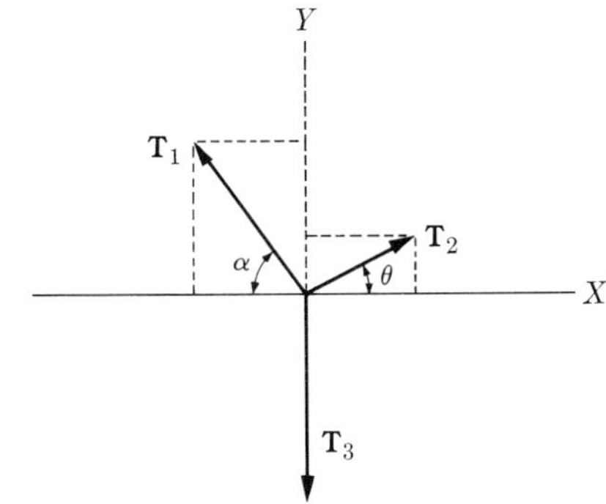

Fig. 5–18. Vector summation of the forces shown in Fig. 5–15.

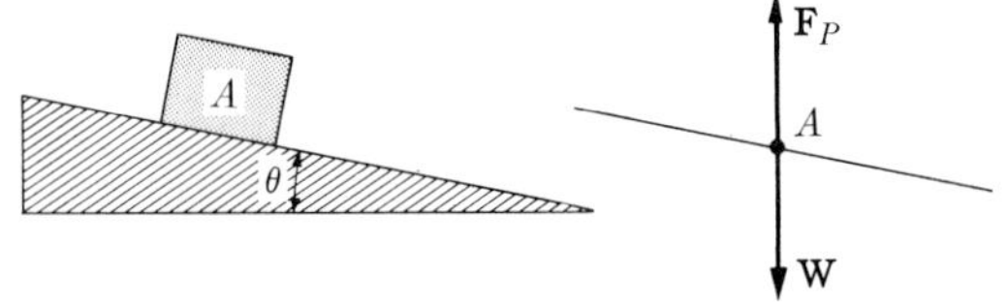

Fig. 5–19. A block A on an inclined plane and the force diagram for A when it moves at constant velocity.

from which we can find μ by its definition:

$$\mu \equiv F_R/N = \sin\theta/\cos\theta = \tan\theta.$$

An alternative approach is shown in Fig. 5–20(b) where *both* **W** and $\mathbf{F}_P$ are resolved into components. *This latter method is generally more useful* when additional forces are involved.

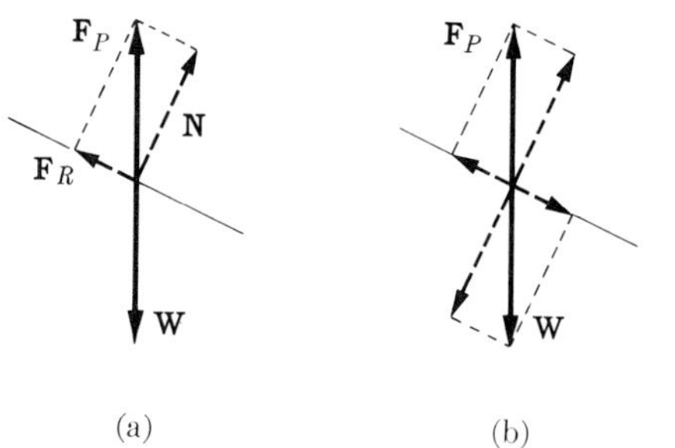

Fig. 5–20. Resolution of the forces of Fig. 5–19 into cartesian components parallel and perpendicular to the plane.

Example 4. A sled of mass m is pulled at constant velocity along a horizontal surface by a force **P** in the rope. What is the angle of the rope if the coefficient of sliding function is μ?

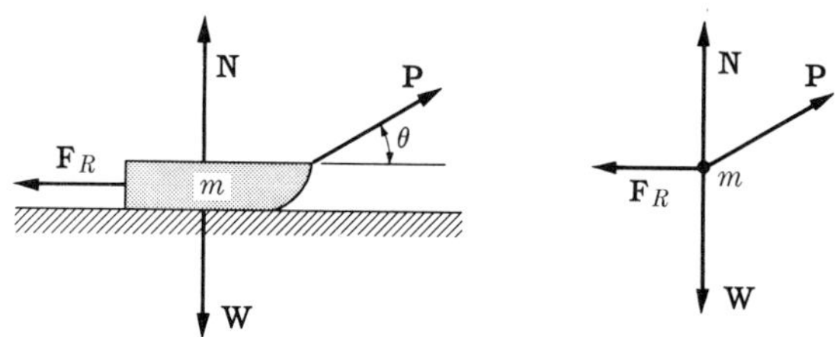

Fig. 5–21. The forces on a sled.

Solution: Diagrams are drawn first (Fig. 5–21), where **N** and $\mathbf{F}_R$ are the components of the force exerted *by* the ground *on* the sled. Using the method of horizontal and vertical components, we have

$$\sum F_x = P\cos\theta - F_R = 0,$$
$$\sum F_y = N + P\sin\theta - W = 0.$$

In addition, we have $F_R = \mu N$, and $W = mg$. The unknowns W, F_R, and N can be eliminated, leaving an equation for θ in terms of the given quantities P, m, and μ:

$$\cos\theta = \frac{\mu mg}{P} - \mu\sin\theta.$$

Squaring both sides and noting that $\cos^2\theta = 1 - \sin^2\theta$, we have

$$1 - \sin^2\theta = \left(\frac{\mu mg}{P} - \mu\sin\theta\right)^2,$$

a quadratic equation in $\sin\theta$ that can be solved by the quadratic formula.

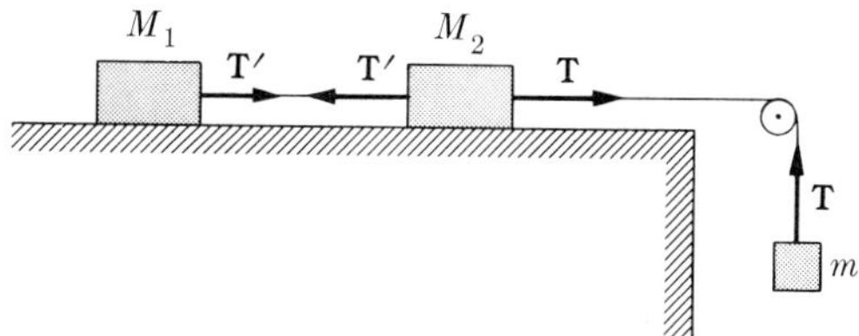

Fig. 5–22. A system of blocks interconnected by massless, stretchless strings.

Example 5. Blocks of mass M_1 and M_2 are pulled at constant velocity by a falling mass as shown in Fig. 5–22. The coefficient of sliding friction is μ. Find the tensions in the strings and the magnitude of the falling mass.

Solution: Let m be the mass of the falling object, and let T and T' be the tensions in the strings as shown in Fig. 5–22. Since M_1 and M_2 move in the same direction with the same motion, we can consider them together as a system. The forces on the M_1 M_2 system and the forces on m are shown in Fig. 5–23.

Newton's first law, when applied to the vertical forces, gives

$$T - mg = 0 \tag{5–14}$$

and

$$N - (M_1 + M_2)g = 0. \tag{5–15}$$

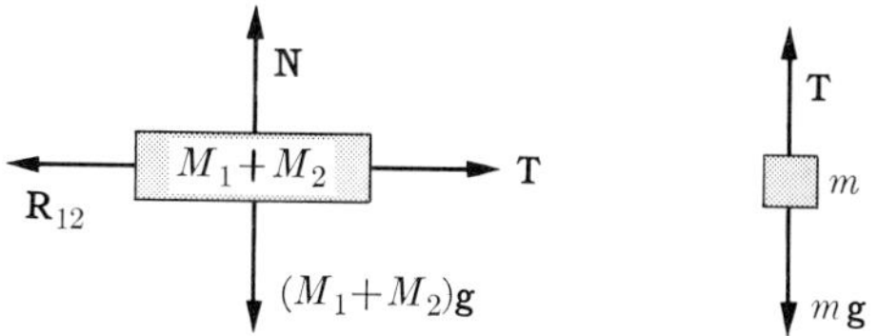

Fig. 5–23. Forces acting on the system M_1M_2 and on m.

For the horizontal forces, we have

$$T - R_{12} = 0. \tag{5–16}$$

But the definition of coefficient of friction leads to

$$R_{12} = \mu N = \mu(M_1 + M_2)g,$$

which, combined with Eq. (5–16), gives the solution for the tension T:

$$T = \mu(M_1 + M_2)g.$$

This last relation, combined with Eq. (5–14), gives the mass of the falling object:

$$m = T/g = \mu(M_1 + M_2).$$

In order to find T', it is necessary to consider component parts of the $M_1\ M_2$ system separately. For example, if M_1 is considered by itself, we find that

$$T' = \mu M_1 g.$$

5–11 SUMMARY

It is found experimentally that the force exerted by many simple springs can be described by

$$F = -k(x - x_0)$$

to a high degree of approximation. In the above, $x - x_0$ is the linear displacement of the end of the spring from its normal length and k is a constant. A spring can be used as a convenient device for measuring forces. It is found that the gravitational force **W** on a mass m is

$$\mathbf{W} = mg,$$

where g is a constant independent of m but dependent on the location at which the measurement is made. Near the surface of the earth, g is 9.8 m/sec^2.

Newton's law of universal gravitational attraction,

$$F = G\,\frac{mm'}{r^2},$$

which was deduced from observation of motion within the solar system, was experimentally verified on the laboratory scale by Cavendish.

Electric and magnetic forces are the other kinds of forces that are easily measured in macroscopic-scale experiments. They also follow an inverse square law.

Contact forces (forces resulting from atomic-scale electric and magnetic forces) can be classified in terms of normal forces, tensions, and friction forces. It is found experimentally that the friction force between solids is given by

$$F = \mu N,$$

where N is the normal force and μ is in many cases approximately independent of area of contact and velocity. Friction forces due to fluid motion are velocity dependent.

Newton's laws can be applied to systems of objects as well as to individual objects. In the special case of static systems or objects, Newton's second law reduces to the condition for equilibrium

$$\sum \mathbf{F} = 0.$$

Examples of the analysis of static systems are given.

Problems

In the following problems, use $g = 10\ \text{m/sec}^2$ or $1000\ \text{cm/sec}^2$ unless otherwise specified. Make space and force diagrams for each problem. Be careful to include *all* the external forces acting on the object in question, and *only* the forces acting *on* that object, when you are considering the motion of that particular body.

1. Show that the change in velocity of a mass m that is pulled for a time Δt by a spring that is stretched to a length x is $\Delta v = -(k/m)(x - x_0)\,\Delta t$, where k is the spring constant and x_0 is its normal length.

2. Define the spring constant of a spring. What are its units in the mks and cgs systems?

3. A stretched rubber band exerts a restoring force that is a function of the amount it is stretched but is also a slowly varying function of time. Discuss the possibility of a rubber band as the basis of a force-measuring instrument.

4. Two identical springs with spring constant K and unstretched length l_0 are joined together as in Fig. 5–24. (a) Find the vertical restoring force on P as a function of displacement y. (b) What is the form of the force law when $y \gg l_0$? (Use the binomial expansion.) (c) What is the force law when $y \ll l_0$?

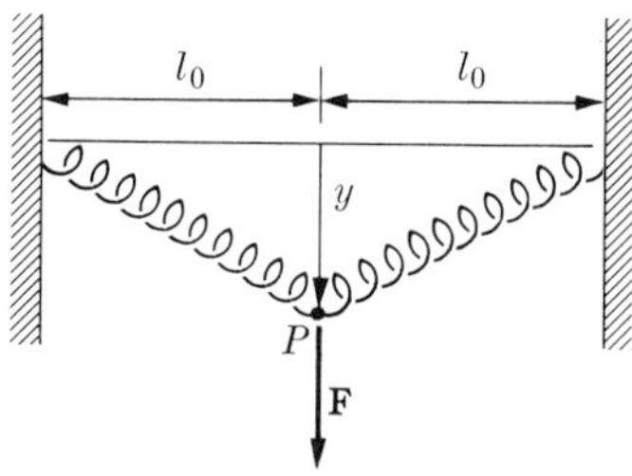

FIGURE 5–24

5. A force $\mathbf{F}_1$ extends a spring from x_0 to x_1. A force $\mathbf{F}_2$ extends the spring from x_0 to x_2. Show that $\Delta F = K\,\Delta x$ or that, in terms of the force exerted *by* the spring, $\Delta F = -K\,\Delta x$.

6. Is the statement, "Mass is a measure of the quantity of matter," more nearly applicable to inertial mass or to gravitational mass?

7. A spring of length 10 cm is stretched to a length of 30 cm when a 3-kg mass is hung on it. What is the value of the spring constant?

8. Show that the units of g in Eq. (5–3) are m/sec^2.

9. At the surface of the moon the spring of Problem 7 is stretched to 14 cm when the 3-kg mass is hung on it. (a) Find the value of g at the moon's surface. (b) What is the weight of the 3-kg mass at the moon?

10. Derive an expression for g at the surface of any spherical object in terms of the radius and mass of the object.

11. Is the inertial mass as defined by Eq. (4–2) the same on the moon as on the earth? Explain.

12. Show that the gravitational force between two spheres of mass density ρ and radius r that just touch each other is $\frac{4}{9}\pi^2 G\rho^2 r^4$.

13. (a) Find the mass of the earth from the law of universal gravitation and the observed gravitational force at the earth's surface. (b) Using the result of (a), find the weight of a second earth when it is placed as close as possible to the earth. (c) Is the mass found in (a) gravitational or inertial mass?

14. (a) Why not set $G = 1$ in the law of universal gravitation (Eq. 5–5)? Comment on the convenience of the size of the force unit that would result if G were set equal to 1 and Eq. (5–5) were therefore used to define the unit of force.
(b) Could an arbitrary choice of units then be made for each of the quantities, length, mass, and time? Explain.

15. Find the resultant gravitational force on one of three equal masses m placed at the corners of an equilateral triangle of side l.

16. The masses of the electron and proton are 9×10^{-31} and 1.6×10^{-27} kg, respectively, and their charges are minus and plus 1.6×10^{-19} coul, respectively. Find the ratio of gravitational to electrical attraction between the electron and proton.

17. Would you say that contact forces are basically electrical or gravitational in character? Give reasons.

18. What is the microscopic origin of the contact force between a stationary balloon and the air?

19. How large is the coefficient of static friction between solids and fluids? Does your answer agree with Eq. (5–11)?

20. A pile of papers has a mass of 0.5 kg and a coefficient of sliding friction of 0.1.

(a) What force is required to slide the entire pile of papers at constant velocity?

(b) What force is required to pull out a sheet of paper from the center of the pile at constant velocity, presuming the upper half of the pile is held in place above the lower half? Is the force constant?

(c) Repeat part (b) for a single sheet at fractional depth f in the pile.

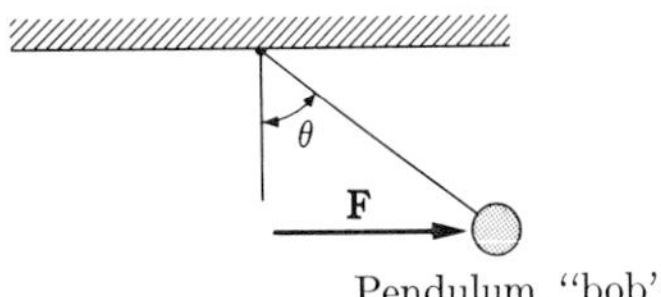

FIGURE 5–25

21. A simple pendulum is made by suspending a material particle, called the pendulum "bob," at one end of a weightless string (Fig. 5–25). The weight of the bob is W. The upper end of the string is fixed in space as shown. A horizontal force **F** is applied to the bob, and the pendulum is deflected from the vertical direction by an angle θ. Express the force **F** in terms of the resulting angle of deflection θ and the weight of the bob W. In terms of W, what is the magnitude F when $\theta = 30°, 60°, 90°$?

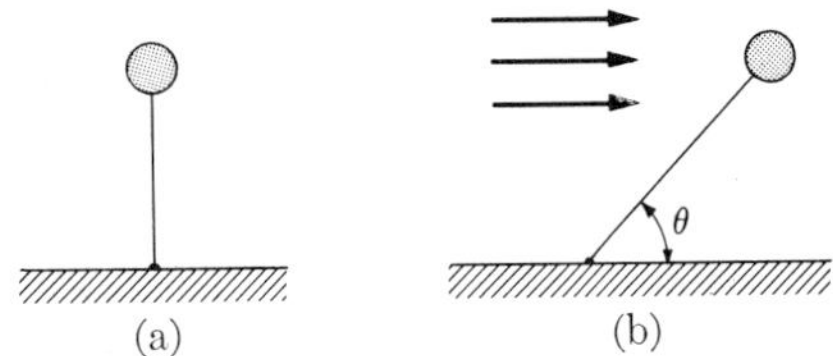

FIGURE 5–26

22. A captive balloon of mass 10 kg is buoyed upward by the atmosphere with a force of 500 n (Fig. 5–26).

(a) What is the tension in the cable?

(b) A strong wind arises and pushes on the balloon with a horizontal force of 50 n. (The wind does not affect the buoyant force.) What is the tension **T** in the rope, and what is the angle θ between rope and ground when the wind is blowing?

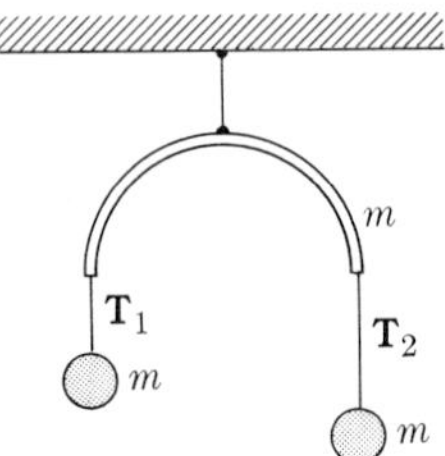

FIGURE 5–27

23. A string passes through a massless, frictionless tube and supports equal masses on each end (Fig. 5–27).

(a) Find the tensions T_1 and T_2 and the tension in the string supporting the tube, giving reasons for each step of your solution.

(b) How would your results be affected if the masses m were in motion? What would be the nature of their motion?

(c) What are the tensions if the mass of the tube is also m?

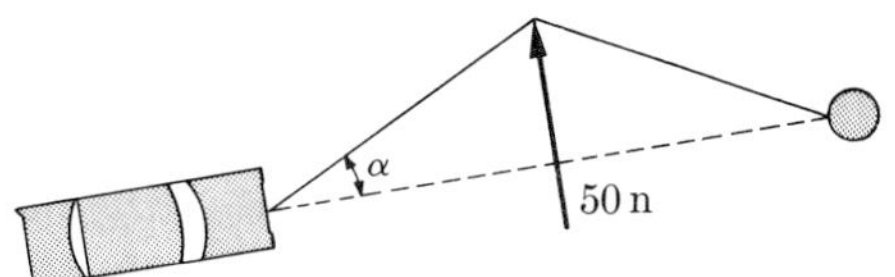

FIGURE 5–28

24. A force of 500 n is required to pull a car out of a ditch. The circumstances are that a man can exert a force of 50 n, that he has a rope, and that there is a tree nearby. He ties the rope taut between the car and tree, and when he pushes horizontally at the middle of the rope, as shown in Fig. 5–28, the rope stretches elastically due to the tension and deflects through an angle α.

(a) How large is α when a tension of 500 n is developed?

(b) Will this be sufficient to pull the car out?

(c) How large is the "spring constant" of the rope if the car and tree are 15 m apart?

25. An object of mass m rests on a spring balance in an elevator. What is the apparent weight of the object

(a) when the elevator ascends with a constant velocity v?

(b) when it descends with the same velocity?

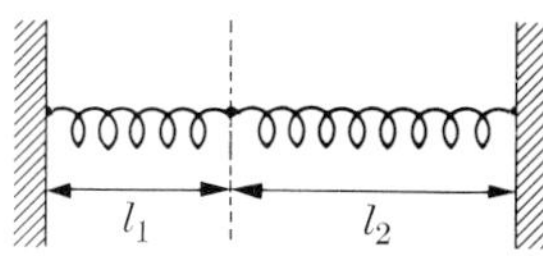

FIGURE 5–29

26. Spring one and spring two, which have natural lengths 2 m and 3 m, respectively, are connected together and stretched so that the free ends are connected to walls 6 m apart (Fig. 5–29). The spring constants are $K_1 = 10$ n/m and $K_2 = 20$ n/m. What are the stretched lengths, l_1 and l_2, of the springs?

27. Two springs have separate force laws $F_1 = K_1x_1$ and $F_2 = K_2x_2$. They are connected together as shown in Fig. 5–30. Show that the force law for the free end of the system is $F = Kx$, where $K = (K_1K_2)/(K_1 + K_2)$. The x's represent *increases* in lengths in all cases.

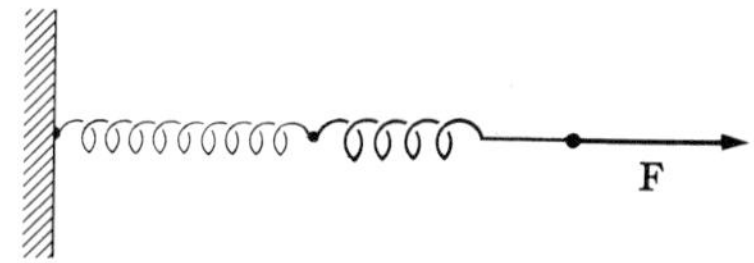

FIGURE 5–30

28. A mine employee who was an amateur scientist suggested that the gravitational constant G could be found by measuring the angle between two adjacent wires which are hung in the vertical shaft of a deep mine and which support lead balls at the bottom ends.

(a) Find the expected angle (or difference in wire spacing, top and bottom) for lead spheres of radius r (nearly touching each other) on wires of length 1000 m. Does the experiment seem feasible for reasonable values of r? The density of lead is 11 gm/cm^3.

(b) Would the wires be parallel in the absence of attraction between the spheres?

29. A mass m is pushed at constant velocity by a horizontal force up a plane that is inclined at an angle θ (Fig. 5–31). The coefficient of sliding friction is μ.

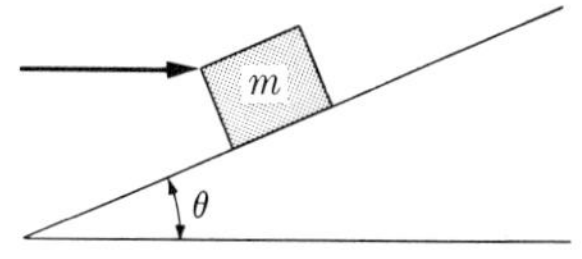

FIGURE 5–31

(a) Find the force F.

(b) Find F if the mass has a constant velocity *down* the plane.

(c) Is F always positive in case (b)?

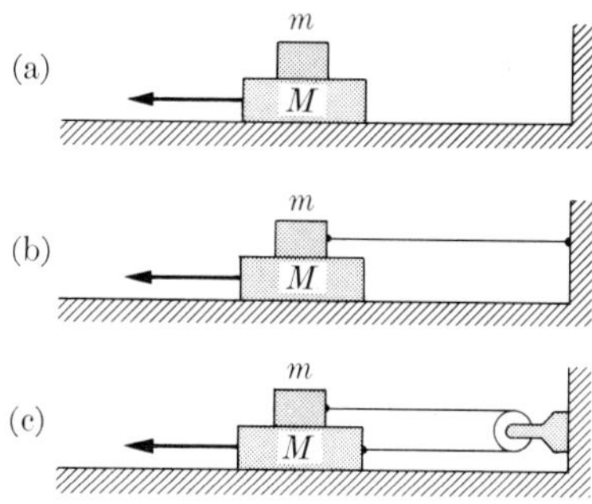

FIGURE 5–32

30. In Fig. 5–32, the mass m is 5 kg, the mass M is 10 kg, and the coefficient of sliding friction is 0.2. Find the force F required to move M at constant velocity in each case.

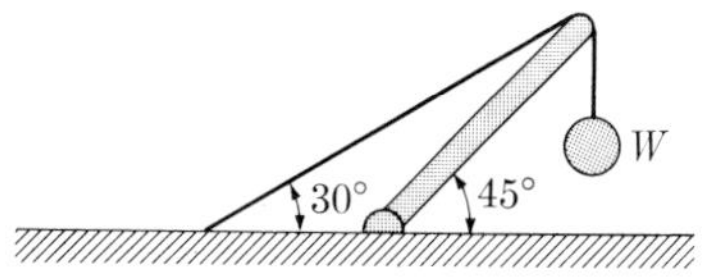

FIGURE 5–33

31. A weight of 120 n is suspended by a derrick as shown in Fig. 5–33. The strut is freely pivoted.

(a) Find the tensions in the ropes and the force on the strut if the weight of the strut is negligible.

(b) Find the force exerted by the entire derrick system (rope plus strut) on the ground.

32. A flexible rope of mass m is hung between two hooks at the same height as shown in Fig. 5–34. At its ends the rope makes an angle θ with the wall.

FIGURE 5–34

(a) Find the force on the ends of the rope.
(b) Find the tension in the rope at its lowest point.
(c) Is the tension in the rope uniform?
[*Hint:* Consider the entire rope or half the rope as the system.]

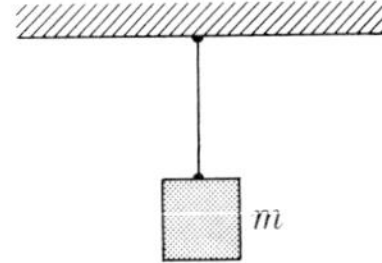

FIGURE 5–35

33. A block of mass m is hanging at rest on a string (Fig. 5–35).
(a) Draw a vector diagram of the forces acting *on* m.
(b) What is the reaction to each force in part (a), and on what object does it act?
(c) Which of the above forces are equal according to Newton's first law? third law?
(d) If the string is cut, does the first law still apply? the third law? Explain.

34. A horse is pulling a cart at constant speed. Neglecting air resistance, make a force diagram and label each force with the agent that exerts the force
(a) for the horse and cart as a system,
(b) for the cart alone
(c) for the horse alone.

35. Suppose that the cable of the balloon in Fig. 5–26(a) breaks. The balloon rises at increasing velocity but reaches an essentially constant velocity (terminal velocity) of 5 m/sec after a few seconds. Find the value of the constant K, assuming that the air resistance law for the balloon is Kv^2.

36. What are the units of the coefficient of viscosity in Eq. (5–11)?

37. Small raindrops experience air resistance that follows the law of Eq. (5–11). The coefficient of viscosity of air is about 2×10^{-4} cgs units. Find the size of raindrops (fog) that fall at a constant speed of 0.5 cm/sec.

38. In a lecture demonstration, a cart of mass 1 kg is pulled on a horizontal track by a spring that is elongated 12 cm. The cart starts at rest and has a velocity of 750 cm/sec after 2.1 sec. The cart is then hung vertically (at rest) on the same spring, and the elongation is now 32 cm. Find the value of g.

39. Why must the proportionality constant g in Eq. (5–3) have the dimensions of length/(time)^2?

6

Kinematics (Instantaneous Velocity and Acceleration)

6–1 INTRODUCTION

In Chapter 3 the description of motion was carried to the point of including the vector quantities, position, displacement, *average* velocity, and change in velocity. In Chapters 4 and 5 the forces of interaction between objects were treated in detail, and their effect on motion was considered as far as *total change* in velocity is concerned. The special case of no change in velocity (statics) was studied in detail.

A more general description of motion will now be given. The central ideas will be *instantaneous* values of variables of the motion and their interrelationships. The concept of instantaneous value of the position vector (or of its scalar components in a component treatment) is implicit in the description of any motion, i.e., the position is specified by means of equations that give the coordinates as functions of the time. Velocity was introduced as a measure of change in instantaneous position, with average velocity defined as $\bar{\mathbf{v}} = \Delta\mathbf{S}/\Delta t$ (Eq. 3–9).

In this chapter, the discussion of velocity will be continued and the concept of acceleration will be introduced. The methods will be applied to various types of observed motion.

6–2 VELOCITY

The average velocity can be expressed in cartesian components by simply resolving $\Delta\mathbf{S}$ into its cartesian components Δx, Δy, and Δz. In the two-dimensional case (see Fig. 6–1), the result is

$$v_x = \Delta x/\Delta t, \quad (6\text{–}1)$$

$$v_y = \Delta y/\Delta t. \quad (6\text{–}2)$$

Average velocity is defined for definite and finite intervals of motion. The change in average velocity along a course of motion can be mapped out along the trajectory by setting up a whole series of intervals and ascribing to each interval a "local" value of average velocity. If the intervals are made ever so numerous and ever so fine, one has a practical knowledge of the velocity for every point in the motion. However, the definition of a "point velocity" must remain analytically ambiguous if the size of the intervals is left unspecified. In fact, the size can be specified for unlimited precision by insisting that each interval be of zero size. We shall now demonstrate how the value of velocity at a point can be defined.

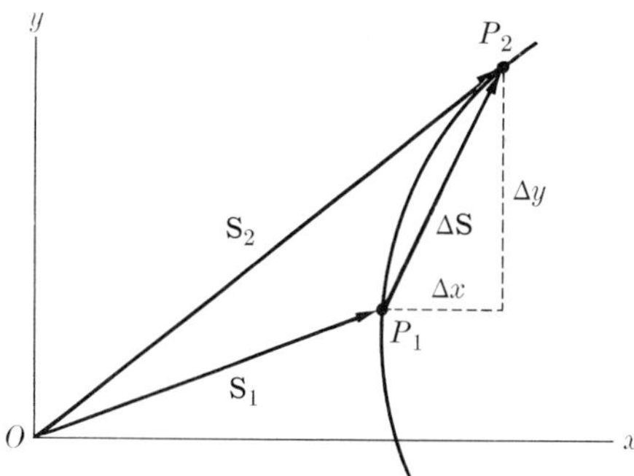

Fig. 6–1. Resolution of the displacement $\Delta\mathbf{S}$ into cartesian components.

Let an interval of motion be bounded by points P_1 and P_2 as in Fig. 6–1. The average velocity for this interval is, by definition, $\bar{\mathbf{v}} = \Delta\mathbf{S}/\Delta t$ as usual. As P_2 is chosen closer and closer to P_1, the interval becomes progressively more local to point 1. The average velocity of a particle for an interval bounded on one side by point 1 approaches, as the interval is made indefinitely small, the "point velocity" of the particle at P_1. However, since time is considered to be the independent variable, we usually translate the above into terms of time. We do this by simply noting that P_2 approaches P_1 as t_2 approaches t_1 (where t_2 and t_1 are the instants of time corresponding to points P_2 and P_1, respectively). The term *instantaneous velocity* is then used to specify the velocity at the instant of time t_1 obtained by finding the average velocity as t_2 approaches t_1.

The quantitative expression of the definition of instantaneous velocity (expressed in the notation for limits introduced earlier) is

$$\mathbf{v} \equiv \lim_{t_2 \to t_1} \frac{\Delta \mathbf{S}}{t_2 - t_1}, \tag{6–3}$$

or simply

$$\mathbf{v} \equiv \lim_{\Delta t \to 0} \frac{\Delta \mathbf{S}}{\Delta t}, \tag{6–4}$$

which is read; "the limit of $\Delta\mathbf{S}/\Delta t$ as Δt goes to zero." The vector equation can be written in component form as

$$v_x \equiv \lim_{\Delta t \to 0} \frac{\Delta x}{\Delta t}, \qquad v_y = \lim_{\Delta t \to 0} \frac{\Delta y}{\Delta t}, \qquad v_z = \lim_{\Delta t \to 0} \frac{\Delta z}{\Delta t}. \tag{6–5}$$

The analytical procedure specified in the definitions Eq. (6–5) for instantaneous velocity can be displayed in a graph of the component in question versus time. In Fig. 6–2, a graph of x versus t is chosen as an example. Remember that Δt and Δx are simply abbreviated notations for $t_2 - t_1$ and $x_2 - x_1$, where x_1 and x_2 are the x-coordinates of the motion at times t_1 and t_2, respectively.

If a line is drawn between the points $P_1(x_1, t_1)$ and $P_2(x_2, t_2)$ on the curve in Fig. 6–2, we see that the *slope* of this line is $\Delta x/\Delta t$, that is,

$$\bar{v}_x = \Delta x/\Delta t = \tan \bar{\phi}, \tag{6–6}$$

where $\bar{\phi}$ is the slope angle as shown in Fig. 6–2.

In the limit as $\Delta t \to 0$, point P_2 approaches P_1 and the line P_1P_2 approaches the tangent T to the curve at point P_1. Thus, a cartesian component of instantaneous velocity v_x equals the slope of the tangent to a curve of coordinate versus time at the instant of time in question. In Fig. 6–2 this slope is $L/\Delta t$. Thus, graphically,

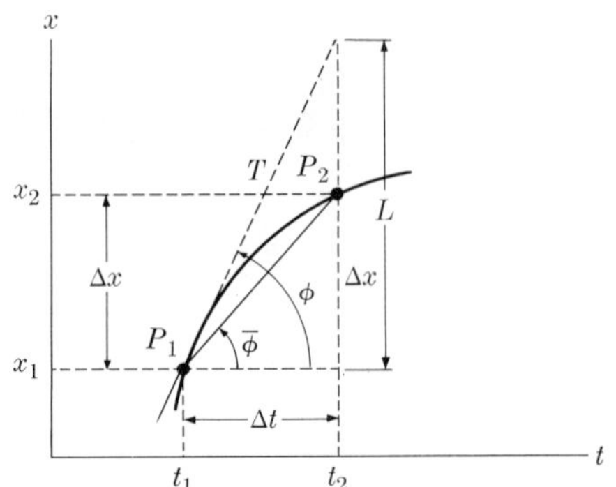

Fig. 6–2. The cartesian component of motion x versus time. Note that the graph is *not* the path of the particle in space. The slope of the curve, $L/\Delta t$, at point P_1 is the instantaneous velocity at time t_1.

$$v_x = \tan \phi = \frac{L}{\Delta t}. \tag{6–7}$$

Similar equations will result for the y- and the z-components.

Finally, there is the question of the mathematical method for determining instantaneous velocity. The prescription for finding scalar velocity components is given in Eq. (6–5) and in the above discussions. For an arbitrary dependence of coordinate on time, it is necessary to actually find the slope of the curve by graphical methods or to use numerical methods, first to find $x_2 - x_1$ for a chosen $t_2 - t_1$ and then to see what the asymptotic numerical value of $(x_2 - x_1)/(t_2 - t_1)$ becomes as $t_2 - t_1$ is made smaller and smaller.

However, there are many classroom problems in which we assume that a coordinate has a relatively simple time-dependence during a certain period of time. Also, there are many real-life motions that can be very well approximated by such simple functions during parts of the motion. Since the process for finding instantaneous velocity is identical with the process for finding the relation between many other pairs of quantities, this process, which is called differentiation, has become a standard part of mathematics of the calculus. The standard abbreviated notation for our example is dx/dt; thus

$$\frac{dx}{dt} \equiv \lim_{\Delta t \to 0} \frac{\Delta x}{\Delta t} \tag{6–8}$$

where dx/dt is called the derivative of x with respect to t. Therefore, for two-dimensional cartesian coordinates the instantaneous velocity components are written [from the definitions given by Eqs. (6–5) and (6–8)]:

$$v_x = \frac{dx}{dt}, \tag{6–9}$$

$$v_y = \frac{dy}{dt}. \tag{6–10}$$

The resultant instantaneous velocity is then found from its rectangular components by the usual methods of right-triangle geometry and trigonometry.

The topic of differentiation is taught properly in a mathematics course. We shall simply give a crude derivation here for the case of a power law (or a polynomial with power law terms). Consider $x = bt^n$, where x is a coordinate, b is a constant, t is the time, and n is any number.

Following the prescription, we find $x_2 = bt_2^n$ and $x_1 = bt_1^n$ and take the difference:

$$x_2 - x_1 = bt_2^n - bt_1^n.$$

Remembering that we are going to let $t_2 \to t_1$, we now write t_2 in the form $t_1 + \Delta t$, so that the procedure will be one of letting $\Delta t \to 0$. Then we have

$$\frac{\Delta x}{\Delta t} = \frac{b(t_1 + \Delta t)^n - bt_1^n}{\Delta t}, \tag{6–11}$$

which, by expansion of the binomial, becomes

$$\frac{\Delta x}{\Delta t} = \frac{b\{t_1^n + nt_1^{n-1}\,\Delta t + n(n-1)t_1^{n-2}(\Delta t)^2 + \cdots\} - bt_1^n}{\Delta t}. \tag{6–12}$$

By cancellation and division, we obtain

$$\frac{\Delta x}{\Delta t} = b\{nt_1^{n-1} + n(n-1)t^{n-2}\,\Delta t + \cdots\}, \tag{6–13}$$

where the unwritten terms contain higher-order terms in Δt, that is, Δt to powers greater than one.

Finally, we are ready to let $\Delta t \to 0$. We then find from Eq. (6–13) that

$$\lim_{\Delta t \to 0} \frac{\Delta x}{\Delta t} = nbt^{n-1}, \tag{6–14}$$

when $x = bt^n$. In notation of the calculus, if $x = bt^n$, then

$$\frac{dx}{dt} = nbt^{n-1}, \tag{6–15}$$

where dx/dt is called the derivative of x with respect to t. The subscript has been dropped because t_1 could have been chosen anywhere during the time that $x = bt^n$. The exponent n was not restricted to integral values in our derivation. If $n = 0$, then x is constant, and we see that the derivative of a constant is zero. The derivatives of negative powers are larger negative powers.

The same formula holds for any quantity that is a power law function of another quantity. In calculus courses, y and x probably will be the symbols used.

The above results, and others that you can obtain for yourself, are some of the mathematical tools to be used in this book. For x a function of t as shown, the derivatives are

$$\begin{aligned} x &= \text{constant:} \quad dx/dt = 0, \\ x &= bt^n: \quad dx/dt = nbt^{n-1}, \\ x &= f_1(t) + f_2(t) + \cdots: \\ &\quad dx/dt = df_1(t)/dt + df_2(t)/dt + \cdots, \end{aligned} \tag{6–16}$$

where the standard notation $f(t)$, meaning "function of t," has been used. We shall also use $x(t)$,

$v(t)$, etc., on occasion to indicate that the quantity in question is to be expressed as a function of time.

Therefore, returning to physics, we have derived a method for finding the instantaneous velocity component corresponding to a coordinate that can be represented by a power of t, for example,

$$x = bt^n, \qquad v_x = \frac{dx}{dt} = nbt^{n-1}, \tag{6–17}$$

or a sum of such terms if x is represented by a sum of powers of t.

In vector notation, we need only one equation,

$$\mathbf{v} = \frac{d\mathbf{S}}{dt}, \tag{6–18}$$

where $\mathbf{S}$ is the position vector as usual. For actual calculation, the component method is usually most convenient.

Example 1. Given $x(t) = bt^4 - c/t^3$, where b and c are constants, find the velocity as a function of time.

Solution:

$$v_x(t) = \frac{dx}{dt} = 4bt^3 + \frac{3c}{t^4}.$$

6–3 ACCELERATION

Changes in velocity have been discussed in earlier chapters with reference to the effects of interactions between bodies. However, the treatment was restricted to changes from one *constant* velocity to another *constant* velocity. Now that instantaneous velocity has been defined, a more general treatment of velocity change can be made.

The definition of instantaneous velocity (given in Section 6–2) establishes an analytical means of describing the rate of travel of an object, whether the rate is constant or variable. The motion of a material object falling freely in the earth's gravitational field is a common example of motion with varying velocity. A stone can be observed to travel ever faster as the distance or time of fall becomes greater. Galileo suggested that the change in the rate of fall might be systematic and that a new quantity should be defined to describe such variations. Since the net change in velocity in any instance should depend on how long the variation is allowed to develop, he proposed that the variation should be measured per unit of time. The introduction of such a quantity, called acceleration, marked the beginning of mechanical analysis as it is known today. The average acceleration for an interval of motion is defined as the change in velocity in the interval of motion divided by the corresponding change in time, that is,

$$\bar{\mathbf{a}} \equiv \frac{\mathbf{v}_2 - \mathbf{v}_1}{t_2 - t_1} \frac{\text{m/sec}}{\text{sec}} \tag{6–19}$$

or

$$\bar{\mathbf{a}} \equiv \frac{\Delta\mathbf{v}}{\Delta t} \frac{\text{m}}{\text{sec}^2}. \tag{6–20}$$

This defining vector equation contains two features: The direction of acceleration is in the direction of the change in velocity. The magnitude of acceleration, which has no special name, is the magnitude of the change in velocity divided by Δt, that is,

$$|\bar{\mathbf{a}}| = \frac{|\Delta\mathbf{v}|}{\Delta t} \frac{\text{m}}{\text{sec}^2}. \tag{6–21}$$

Note that the acceleration is not related to velocity, but rather to change in velocity. If a rectilinear velocity changes from 0 to 10 m/sec in 1 sec, the acceleration is the same as if the velocity changed from 100 m/sec to 110 m/sec in 1 sec. If a rectilinear velocity is decreasing, the acceleration vector is opposite in direction to the velocity vector (Fig. 6–3).

In the two-dimensional case, the vector equations above can be used, or the velocities can be

FIG. 6–3. Change in velocity $\Delta\mathbf{v}$.

resolved into cartesian components. We would then obtain a set of equations of the form

$$\bar{a}_x = \frac{\Delta v_x}{\Delta t}. \tag{6–22}$$

The description of the change in velocity per unit of time for freely falling bodies turns out to be simple indeed. The change is constant for all portions of the motion. We shall shortly return to a study of this simple motion. The study of more complex motion requires a definition of instantaneous acceleration.

6–4 INSTANTANEOUS ACCELERATION

We use the same limiting process as that used in the definition of instantaneous velocity. The average acceleration in the interval bounded by points 1 and 2 is given by Eq. (6–21). This value of average acceleration pertains only to this interval. The value will generally be different as the size and position of the interval are changed. The instantaneous acceleration at point 1 in the motion is defined to be the value which the ratio $\Delta \mathbf{v}/\Delta t$ approaches as the interval is made infinitely small (with 1 as the beginning of the interval), that is,

$$\mathbf{a} \equiv \lim_{t_2 \to t_1} \frac{\mathbf{v}_2 - \mathbf{v}_1}{t_2 - t_1} \quad \text{or} \quad \mathbf{a} \equiv \lim_{\Delta t \to 0} \frac{\Delta \mathbf{v}}{\Delta t}. \tag{6–23}$$

Using the same calculus notation as before, we have

$$\mathbf{a} \equiv \frac{d\mathbf{v}}{dt}. \tag{6–24}$$

Unless otherwise specified, the term acceleration is used to denote instantaneous value of acceleration.

The vector equation can be expressed in cartesian components:

$$a_x = \frac{dv_x}{dt}, \qquad a_y = \frac{dv_y}{dt}. \tag{6–25}$$

When the velocity components are powers of t, or polynomials in powers of t, the differentiation to obtain the acceleration follows the rules developed in Section 6–2, that is, Eq. (6–16).

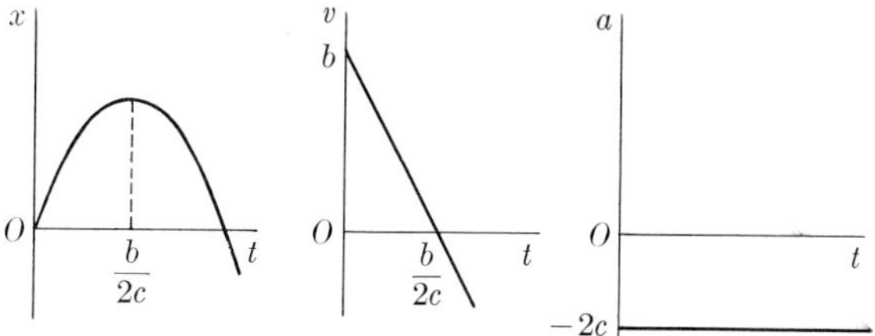

FIG. 6–4. Graphs of the coordinate x, of the velocity v, and of the acceleration a as functions of time.

Example 2. The position of a particle moving along a straight line is measured as a function of time. The results of measurement are summarized by the equation $x(t) = bt - ct^2$, where b and c are constants. What are the velocity of the particle and the acceleration of the particle as functions of time? By definition of v, we have $v = dx/dt = b - 2ct$. Also, by definition of a, we have $a = dv/dt = -2c$. The acceleration is constant and negative. The position and velocity are variable and are positive or negative depending on the time. The graphs of x, v, and a for the above example are given in Fig. 6–4.

6–5 INTEGRATION APPLIED TO KINEMATICS

The analytical method of computing velocity and acceleration from a known displacement formula is differentiation. The derivative of position with respect to time is velocity. The derivative of velocity with respect to time is acceleration. It is apparent that we could compute still higher rates of change, such as the rate of change of acceleration. In point of fact, the rate of change called acceleration is a natural stopping point in the fabrication of derivatives in kinematics: acceleration is a derivative of peculiar significance in the physics of motion. It will be shown in Chapter 7 that the analysis of a mechanical problem often leads to a knowledge of acceleration of a mechanical system. In Chapter 5, we introduced this idea in the course of defining average force in terms of change in velocity. Then the subsequent kinematic problem requires that, given the acceleration, we find the velocity and position of the system. This inversion of the differentiation process is of special significance in physics.

Consider kinematics as an example. Let the x-component of the acceleration of a particle be known as a function of time, that is, suppose that $a_x(t)$ is given. The problem then is to find $v_x(t)$ and to find $x(t)$.

The procedure of reversing the differentiation sequence is called *integration*. The rules for integration presented here are given the name *antidifferentiation*. For the purposes of our present analysis, the rules as stated are sufficient. Nevertheless, a special symbolism is attached to the integration process, and the student is asked to memorize and use the symbolism. The intention and utility of the symbols will become evident in both a mathematics course and in later parts of this text.

We recall the symbols used for the differentiation process, e.g., the symbols used to describe the kinematic relationships and definitions. For example, given the x-component of position expressed as a function of time, $x(t)$, the velocity is written

$$v_x(t) = \frac{dx(t)}{dt}, \tag{6–9'}$$

and the acceleration is written

$$a_x(t) = \frac{dv_x(t)}{dt}. \tag{6–25'}$$

For the antidifferentiation process the following notation is used. Given the acceleration as a function of time, $a_x(t)$, the velocity function is written

$$v_x(t) = \int a_x(t)\,dt. \tag{6–26}$$

The symbol $\int$ is the integral sign. Under the integral sign are two factors whose meanings we shall now establish.

We are to find a function $f(t)$ such that

$$\frac{df(t)}{dt} = a_x(t). \tag{6–27}$$

Under the integral sign are first the required result of differentiation, $a(t)$, and second the symbol dt indicating that we are operating with respect to the time variable. This is the meaning of the symbols $a(t)$ and dt as they are used here. After the function $f(t)$ is found, we assert that the velocity is this function plus an arbitrary constant:

$$v_x(t) = f(t) + c. \tag{6–28}$$

Following the same sequence of operations, we find the position by a second integration:

$$x(t) = \int v_x(t)\,dt. \tag{6–29}$$

We are required here to find a function $g(t)$ such that

$$\frac{dg(t)}{dt} = v_x(t); \tag{6–30}$$

then the position is the function $g(t)$ plus another constant d:

$$x(t) = g(t) + d. \tag{6–31}$$

In summary, given $a(t)$, we have for the integration process in kinematics the notation (for any cartesian component)

$$v(t) = \int a(t)\,dt = f(t) + c, \tag{6–32}$$

$$x(t) = \int v(t)\,dt = g(t) + d, \tag{6–33}$$

where the rules for finding $f(t)$ and $g(t)$ have been given.

More is to be learned about the nature and interpretation of the integration process. However, a basic distinction between differentiation and integration, as presented here, will remain a permanent one: the rules for finding a derivative can be explicitly stated as the simple, deductive algebraic steps contained in the limit process illustrated in Section 6–3. The rules for finding a derivative can always be obtained, however tedious the operation may be, if the derivative exists in the first place. This is not so with integration. In integration we must recall the result of a particular process of differentiation which suits the case. There is no explicit deductive rule, such as the delta process, which can be used to find the answer.

Since we have learned to differentiate powers of t (or polynomials in powers of t), it is this case that we can now integrate.

Given

$$a(t) = bt^n, \tag{6–34}$$

we seek $f(t)$ such that Eq. (6–27) is satisfied. We know that a power law is a possible solution. If we try

$$f(t) = Bt^{m+1}, \tag{6–35}$$

we have

$$\frac{df(t)}{dt} = (m + 1)Bt^m, \tag{6–36}$$

which satisfies Eq. (6–27), if $(m + 1)Bt^m = bt^n$, that is, $m = n$ or $m + 1 = n + 1$, and $B = b/(n + 1)$. Therefore we have

$$f(t) = \frac{b}{n+1}\, t^{n+1}, \tag{6–37}$$

and a solution to the problem is

$$v(t) = \frac{b}{n+1}\, t^{n+1} + c. \tag{6–38}$$

Hence, in the formal notation of Eq. (6–32), the equation

$$\int bt^n\, dt = \frac{b}{n+1}\, t^{n+1} + c \tag{6–39}$$

is a formula for integration of a power law. The demonstration that this is the only solution is left for a calculus course. The above is called an indefinite integral because of the appearance of the arbitrary constant c, which is fixed only by the conditions of a particular problem.

Equation (6–39) holds for all values of n *except* $n = -1$. This might be expected since there is no way of getting a power (-1) by differentiation of powers of t. This gap will be filled now without proof. The derivative for $b \ln t$ is

$$\frac{d(b \ln t)}{dt} = bt^{-1}, \tag{6–40}$$

where ln stands for the natural logarithm, i.e., to the base e. The corresponding antiderivative formula is then

$$\int bt^{-1}\, dt = b \ln t + c. \tag{6–41}$$

The constants c and d in Eqs. (6–28) and (6–31) are, in many cases, determined from knowledge of particular values of $\mathbf{v}$ and x at some particular time, but not necessarily the values of v and x at $t = 0$.

It can be demonstrated that we can integrate a polynomial in powers of t term by term, using Eq. (6–39) for each term. Of course, only one constant, c, need be appended to the series of terms.

The above procedure can be applied to the problem of finding the position, given the velocity, if the velocity can be expressed in powers of t.

For two-dimensional motion, each cartesian component can be treated as above, since we have seen that differentiation can proceed independently for each cartesian component.

6–6 MOTION IN ONE DIMENSION (RECTILINEAR MOTION)

If any one aspect of the motion (position, velocity, or acceleration) can be expressed as an explicit function of time, the other two aspects can be obtained, in principle, by differentiation or integration as described in the preceding sections. In particular, the actual formulas have been derived for the case of polynomials in powers of t.

If we are starting with experimental observation, it is usually the position as a function of

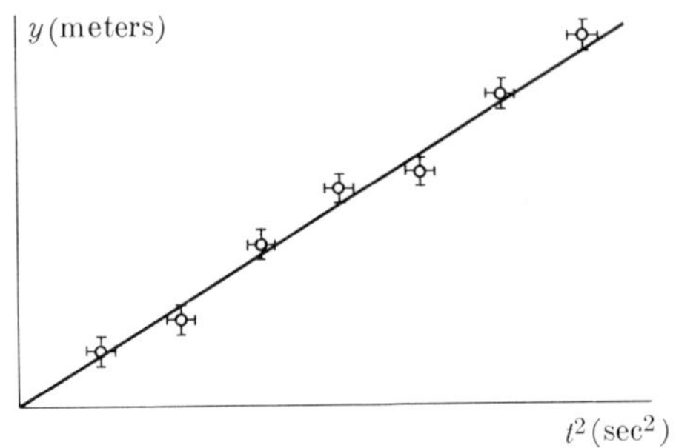

FIG. 6–5. The results of an experimental observation on the vertical distance of fall, y, as a function of the square of the time of fall, t^2. The data are well represented by a straight line as shown.

time that is known. The velocity and acceleration are then deduced. Consider, as an example, the fall in air of a dense object starting from rest. Letting y be the distance and t the time, we find that a graph of y versus t^2 is a straight line, within the accuracy of the measurements (Fig. 6–5). The equation of the graph is found to be

$$y = 4.9t^2 \text{ (m)}, \tag{6–42}$$

where y is in meters and t is in seconds. Then

$$v_y \equiv \frac{dy}{dt} = 2 \times 4.9t = 9.8t \text{ (m/sec)}, \tag{6–43}$$

and

$$a_y \equiv \frac{dv_y}{dt} = 9.8 \text{ (m/sec}^2\text{)}. \tag{6–44}$$

The same result is obtained near the earth's surface for all dense objects at distances of fall up to many meters. The significance of this result is left until later, but, since this universal value of a_y for free fall is numerically and dimensionally equal to g of Eq. (5–4), we use the symbol g from now on.

A generalization of the equations of motion of a dense object moving freely in a vertical direction can now be formulated from our generalization that $a_y = g = 9.8$ m/sec^2.

By integrating once, we obtain the velocity

$$v_y = \int a_y\,dt = \int g\,dt = gt + c, \tag{6–45}$$

and if it is the velocity v_{0y} at $t = 0$ that is known, then

$$v_y = v_{0y} + gt. \tag{6–46}$$

By integrating again, we find the position,

$$y = \int v_y\,dt = \int (v_{0y} + gt)\,dt = v_{0y}t + \tfrac{1}{2}gt^2 + c', \tag{6–47}$$

and again c' can be expressed in terms of y_0, the value of y at $t = 0$, if this information is known. Then

$$y = y_0 + v_{0y}t + \tfrac{1}{2}gt^2. \tag{6–48}$$

In all the above, the downward direction has implicitly been chosen as positive, if g is considered to be $+9.8$ m/sec. If the upward direction is chosen as positive, it is customary to write the terms containing g with a negative sign, although this is a matter of taste. It is only when the numerical value of g is used that there can be no valid difference of opinion on the proper sign of the term containing g, once a convention of positive direction has been chosen.

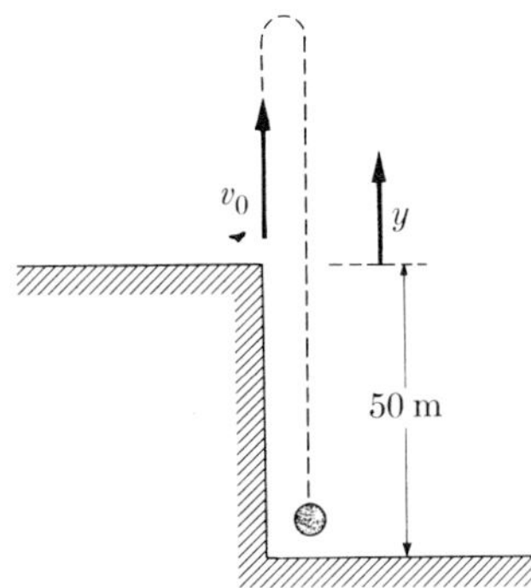

FIG. 6–6. Motion of the ball of Example 3.

Example 3. From the top of a building 50 m high, a ball is projected upward with an initial velocity of 10 m/sec. It is projected from a position just beyond the edge of the building so that it misses the building on the way down to the ground.

Questions:

1. What is the maximum height attained by the ball?
2. At what time does it reach its maximum height?
3. When does the ball again reach its starting position?
4. When does the ball strike the earth?
5. What is the total distance traveled in flight?
6. With what velocity does the ball strike the ground?

Solution: Let the starting position $y_0 = 0$ and the starting time $t_0 = 0$. The equations of motion are Eqs. (6–46) and (6–48). We choose the upward direction to be positive so that $v_0 = +10$ m/sec and $g = -9.8$ m/sec^2. Then using this convention, we have specifically

$$v = 10 - 9.8t, \qquad y = 10t - 4.9t^2.$$

When the maximum height is attained, the velocity is at the point of reversal. It is instantaneously zero, and therefore

$$v = 0 = 10 - 9.8t.$$

Then

$$t = \frac{10}{9.8} = 1.02 \text{ sec}$$

at the maximum altitude. The displacement at this time (the maximum height) is

$$y = 10 \times 1.02 - 4.9(1.02)^2 = 10.2 - 5.1 = 5.1 \text{ m}.$$

When the ball returns to the origin, the displacement is again zero, that is,

$$y = 0 = 10t - 4.9t^2 \qquad \text{or} \qquad t(4.9t - 10) = 0.$$

The roots of this equation are the starting time,

$$t = 0,$$

and

$$t = \frac{10}{4.9} = 2.04 \text{ sec},$$

which is exactly twice the time to reach the maximum altitude.

The ball travels upward 5.1 m, downward 5.1 m, and then 50 m to the ground. The *total distance* traveled is

$$d = 5.1 + 5.1 + 50 = 60.2 \text{ m}.$$

But when the ball strikes the ground, the *position* is -50 m. Using the *position* equation, we have

$$-50 = 10t - 4.9t^2.$$

The quadratic equation gives $t = 4.3$ sec (and $t = -2.3$ sec), where the root, $t = -2.3$ sec, represents an extension of the motion in reverse time from the origin. At the ground the velocity is

$$v = 10 - 9.8t = 10 - 9.8 \times 4.3 = -32 \text{ m/sec}.$$

Any rectilinear motion with *constant* acceleration is described by Eqs. (6–46) and 6–48) with g replaced by the acceleration in question.

The equations would be

$$\begin{aligned} a &= \text{constant}, \\ v &= v_0 + at, \\ x &= x_0 + v_0t + \tfrac{1}{2}at^2. \end{aligned} \qquad (6\text{–}49)$$

Rectilinear motion with *nonuniform* acceleration can be analyzed at this stage of the course, if the acceleration can be expressed as a polynomial in powers of t. We simply follow the rules for antidifferentiation in order to evaluate the terms in the formal relationships of Eqs. (6–32) and (6–33).

Example 4. The acceleration of a certain object in rectilinear motion is well represented by $a = a_0[1 - (w^2t^2/2)]$, where a_0 and w are constants. If $v = 0$ at $t = 0$, find the equations of motion.

Solution:

$$\begin{aligned} v &= \int a\,dt = \int a_0\left[1 - \frac{w^2t^2}{2}\right]dt \\ &= \int a_0\,dt - \int a_0\frac{w^2t^2}{2}\,dt = a_0\left(t - \frac{w^2t^3}{6}\right) + c \\ &= a_0\left(t - \frac{w^2}{6}t^3\right), \end{aligned}$$

where $c = 0$ because $v = 0$ at $t = 0$. The position is

found by a second antidifferentiation:

$$x = \int v\,dt = \int a_0 t\,dt - \int a_0 \frac{w^2}{6} t^3\,dt$$

$$= \frac{a_0}{2} t^2 - a_0 \frac{w^2}{24} t^4 + c'$$

$$= x_0 + \frac{a_0}{2} t^2 - a_0 \frac{w^2}{24} t^4,$$

where $x = x_0$ at $t = 0$.

6–7 TWO-DIMENSIONAL MOTION (CARTESIAN COMPONENTS)

It has already been shown that the aspects of motion expressed in cartesian components are the same (for each component) as for the one-dimensional case considered above. Therefore, the equations of motion in the preceding section can be applied to each cartesian component. If some aspect of a component of motion can be expressed as polynomials in powers of t, the other aspects of that component can be derived by means of the derivative and integral formulas above.

In the special case of two-dimensional free motion for short distances near the earth, it is convenient to choose the horizontal and vertical as cartesian coordinates because the acceleration then has only a vertical component, g. If the origin is chosen so that $x = x_0$ and $y = y_0$ at $t = 0$, the initial position and velocity can be displayed as shown in Fig. 6–7. The initial velocity $\mathbf{v}_0$ can be resolved into components as shown.

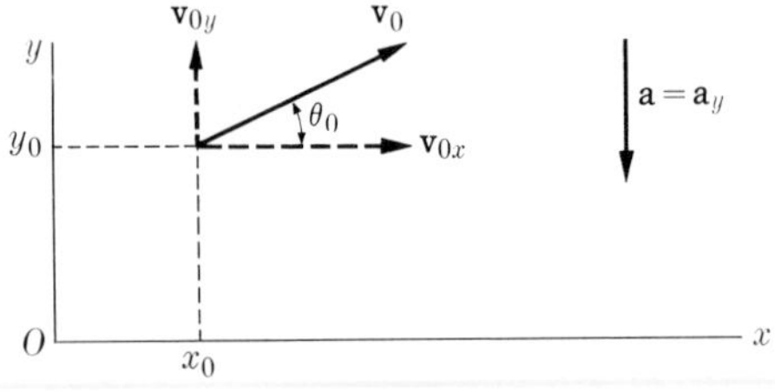

FIG. 6–7. The specification of initial velocity and of the acceleration of an object by cartesian coordinates parallel and perpendicular to the surface of the earth.

The equations of motion are then found *either* by integration:

$$a_x = 0.$$

$$v_x = \int a_x\,dt = 0 + c = v_{0x},$$

$$x = \int v_x\,dt = v_{0x}t + c' = x_0 + v_{0x}t,$$

and

$$a_y = -g,$$

$$v_y = \int a_y\,dt = -gt + c = v_{0y} - gt,$$

$$y = \int v_y\,dt = v_{0y}t - \tfrac{1}{2}gt^2 + c'$$

$$= y_0 + v_{0y}t - \tfrac{1}{2}gt^2,$$

or by direct substitution in Eq. (6–49):

$$a_x = 0, \qquad a_y = -g,$$
$$v_x = v_{0x}, \qquad v_y = v_{0y} - gt,$$
$$x = x_0 + v_{0x}t, \qquad y = y_0 + v_{0y}t - \tfrac{1}{2}gt^2. \tag{6–50}$$

In either case, $v_{0x} = v_0 \cos\theta_0$ and $v_{0y} = v_0 \sin\theta_0$.

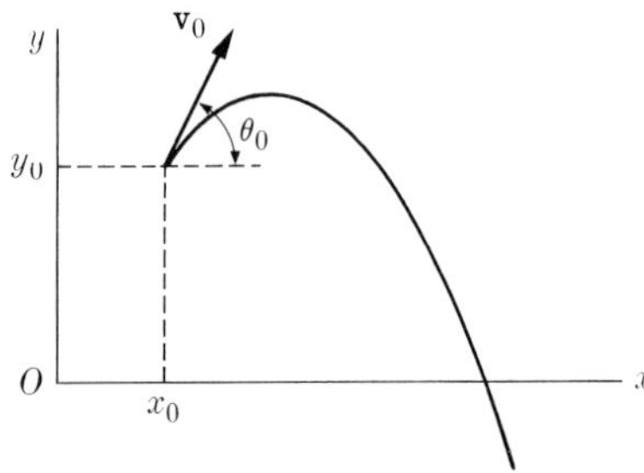

FIG. 6–8. The trajectory of an object projected at a velocity v_0 that is not large enough to make the displacement comparable to the dimensions of the earth.

The *shape* of the trajectory can be found by eliminating t between the equations for x and for y. The trajectory is found to be parabolic (Fig. 6–8).

It should be noted that Eq. (6–50) holds for positive *or* negative values of velocities and positions. The values of x and y are the position coordinates measured from the origin of coordinates.

Example 5. A ball is projected with an initial horizontal velocity of 10 m/sec from the edge of a cliff 50 m high.

Questions:

1. What is the time of flight?
2. What is the position at which the ball strikes the earth?
3. What is the velocity as a function of time?
4. What is the direction of motion at any time?
5. What is the geometric form of the trajectory?

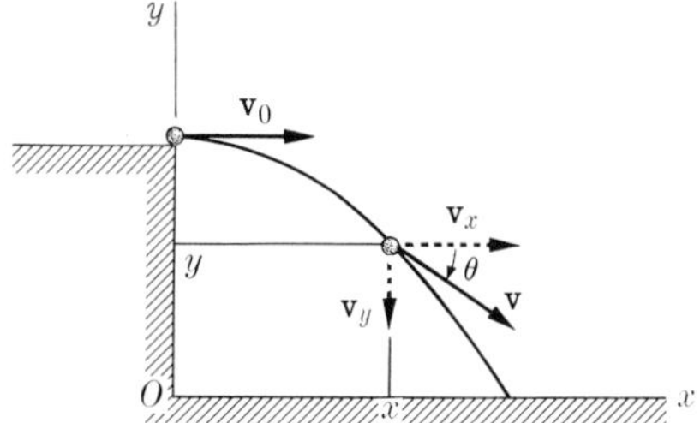

FIG. 6–9. The special case of initial velocity that is horizontal.

Analysis: If coordinates are chosen as in Fig. 6–9, the equations of motion are:

$$v_x = 10, \qquad v_y = -9.8t,$$
$$x = 10t, \qquad y = 50 - 4.9t^2.$$

Solution: The questions can now be answered as follows:

1. Time of flight is the time when $y = 0$. Therefore $t_m = \sqrt{50/4.9} = 3.2$ sec.

2. The horizontal position at the above time is

$$x_m = 10 \times 3.2 = 32 \text{ m}.$$

3. The magnitude of the velocity is

$$v = \sqrt{10^2 + 9.8^2t^2} = \sqrt{100 + 96t^2},$$

and the direction is given by

$$\tan\theta = -\frac{9.8t}{10} \quad \text{or} \quad \theta = \tan^{-1}(-0.98t).$$

4. The direction of motion is given by the direction of the velocity.

5. The form of the trajectory is found by eliminating t between the equations for x and y: $x = 10t$ and $y = 50 - 4.9t^2$. The result is

$$y = 50 - 0.049x^2,$$

which is the equation of a parabola.

Two-dimensional motion can be described in *vector notation.* The position vector **S** has been used frequently. Then in vector notation the velocity is

$$\mathbf{v} = \frac{d\mathbf{S}}{dt}, \tag{6–51}$$

and acceleration becomes

$$\mathbf{a} = \frac{d\mathbf{v}}{dt}. \tag{6–52}$$

Conversely, if the acceleration **a** is given, the process of antidifferentiation can be written

$$\mathbf{v} = \int \mathbf{a}\, dt,$$
$$\mathbf{S} = \int \mathbf{v}\, dt. \tag{6–53}$$

In the *special* case of *constant acceleration,* we then have

$$\mathbf{v} = \mathbf{a}t + \mathbf{c} \quad \text{and} \quad \mathbf{S} = \tfrac{1}{2}\mathbf{a}t^2 + \mathbf{c}t + \mathbf{c}', \tag{6–54}$$

which become

$$\mathbf{v} = \mathbf{v}_0 + \mathbf{a}t \quad \text{and} \quad \mathbf{S} = \mathbf{S}_0 + \mathbf{v}_0 t + \tfrac{1}{2}\mathbf{a}t^2, \tag{6–55}$$

if the initial values of position and velocity ($\mathbf{S}_0$ and $\mathbf{v}_0$) are given.

6–8 TWO-DIMENSIONAL MOTION (POLAR COORDINATES)

The position of a particle can be specified in cartesian components by stating x, y, and z as functions of time. In the special case of two-dimensional motion, two components will suffice, for example, x and y, if the OXY-plane is chosen in the plane of the motion.

The position of a particle moving in a plane can also be specified by the polar coordinates r and θ. Its motion can be specified by giving these coordinates as functions of time. Velocity and acceleration can be defined in the same way that cartesian coordinates are, but the formulation of the expressions in terms of components is relatively more complex. Therefore we begin with a special case, that of *uniform circular motion.*

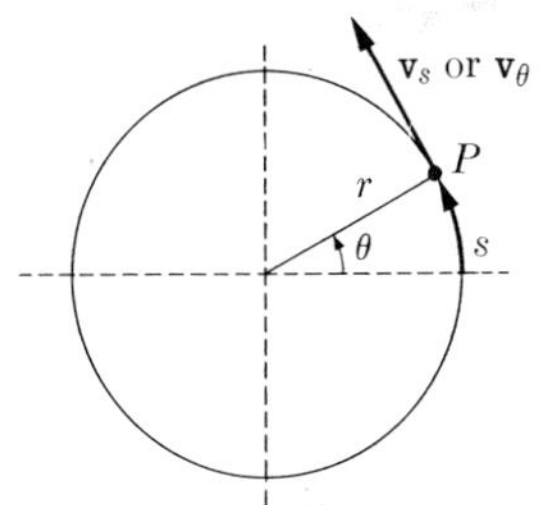

Fig. 6–10. The polar coordinates and polar specification of velocity at a point P in circular motion.

The polar coordinates of a particle P in uniform circular motion (Fig. 6–10) can be found as follows: Since the path is a circle, the origin of the coordinates is chosen at the center, and we then have

$$r = r_0 = \text{constant}. \tag{6–56}$$

Since the motion is uniform, the speed v_s along the path is uniform

$$v_s \equiv \frac{ds}{dt} = \text{constant}, \tag{6–57}$$

where s is the length measured along the arc (Fig. 6–10). But since the arc length $s = r\theta$ and since $r =$ constant,

$$v_s = r\,\frac{d\theta}{dt} = \text{constant}. \tag{6–58}$$

The factor $d\theta/dt$ is usually abbreviated by ω (Greek omega),

$$\omega \equiv \frac{d\theta}{dt}, \tag{6–59}$$

and is called the angular velocity. It is constant for uniform circular motion, since v_s and r are constants. It is possible to reverse the argument by defining uniform circular motion as circular motion at uniform *angular* velocity. Finally, we note that $v_s = v_\theta$, where v_θ is the velocity component perpendicular to r at point P. Then Eq. (6–58) can be rewritten

$$v_\theta = r\omega. \tag{6–60}$$

The remaining important properties of the polar components of uniform circular motion will now be obtained from definitions and the methods of the calculus. Since ω is constant, we have for the angular coordinate

$$\theta = \int \omega\, dt = \omega t + \theta_0$$

and

$$\alpha \equiv \frac{d\omega}{dt} = 0, \tag{6–61}$$

where α (Greek alpha) is the angular acceleration. We note in passing that ω and α are vectors, but their vector properties can be ignored for the moment.

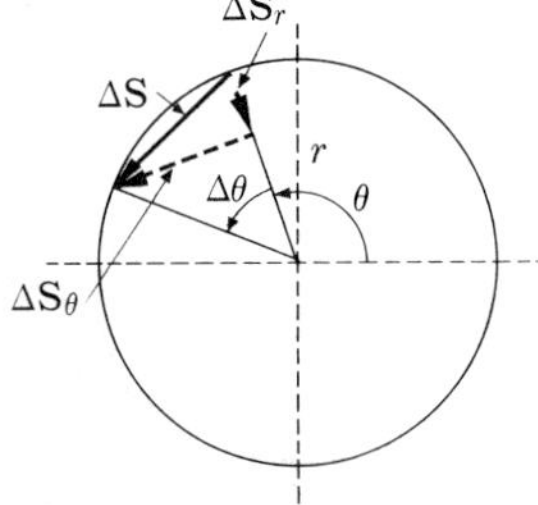

Fig. 6–11. Polar components of a displacement $\Delta\mathbf{S}$ in the case of circular motion.

For the radial component we must utilize the vector properties immediately. Thus, r is the radial component of the position vector $\mathbf{S}$, and Δr is the radial component of the displacement (Fig. 6–11):

$$r = S_r$$

and

$$\Delta r = \Delta S_r. \tag{6–62}$$

The radial component of velocity then becomes

$$v_r \equiv \lim_{\Delta t \to 0} \frac{\Delta S_r}{\Delta t}. \qquad (6\text{–}63)$$

From similar triangles (Fig. 6–11), we see that

$$\frac{\Delta S_r}{\Delta S} = \frac{(\Delta S/2)}{r}.$$

But since

$$\Delta S \simeq r\,\Delta\theta = r(\omega\,\Delta t),$$

Eq. (6–63) becomes

$$v_r = \lim_{\Delta t \to 0} \frac{r^2\omega^2(\Delta t)^2}{2r\,\Delta t} = 0. \qquad (6\text{–}64)$$

Consequently, the velocity components can be written

$$v_r = 0, \qquad v_\theta = r\omega. \qquad (6\text{–}65)$$

We turn now to the acceleration. The reader might conclude from Eq. (6–65) that the acceleration is zero, since both velocity components appear to be constant. However, the direction of the velocity is *not* constant, and we must therefore return to the definition of acceleration

$$\mathbf{a} \equiv \frac{d\mathbf{v}}{dt} \equiv \lim_{\Delta t \to 0} \frac{\Delta \mathbf{v}}{\Delta t}. \qquad (6\text{–}66)$$

The motion of the particle traveling at uniform speed along a circular path is described by a velocity vector whose magnitude is constant but whose direction is continually rotating in space. The acceleration of the particle is connected with this velocity rotation. A definite and calculable change in velocity is entailed when the particle advances from point 1 to point 2 on the circle (Fig. 6–12). The change in velocity is found by the rule for the subtraction of two vectors:

$$\Delta \mathbf{v} = \mathbf{v}_2 - \mathbf{v}_1. \qquad (6\text{–}67)$$

The geometrical construction of this difference is shown in the isosceles triangle of Fig. 6–13, which can be solved if the constants of the motion are given. The average acceleration is then the ratio,

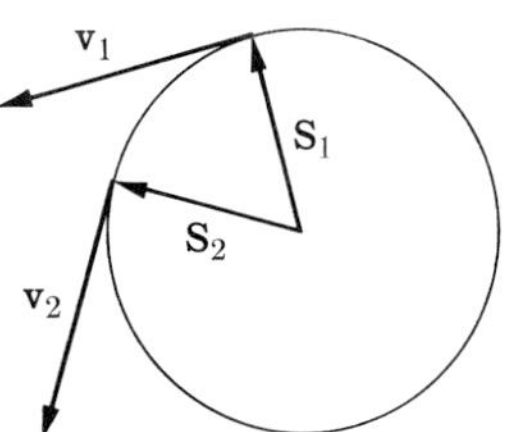

FIG. 6–12. The positions and velocities at points 1 and 2 in the case of uniform circular motion.

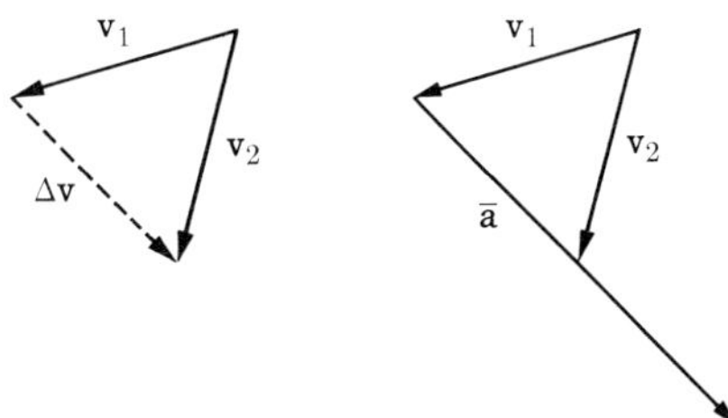

FIG. 6–13. The change in velocity (left) and the acceleration (right) between points 1 and 2 in the case of uniform circular motion.

$$\bar{\mathbf{a}} = \frac{\Delta \mathbf{v}}{\Delta t}, \qquad (6\text{–}68)$$

where Δt is the time interval for the motion from 1 to 2. The direction of the average acceleration $\bar{\mathbf{a}}$ is the direction of $\Delta\mathbf{v}$, but the length of $\bar{\mathbf{a}}$ is not necessarily the same as the length of $\Delta\mathbf{v}$ (Fig. 6–13). Why not?

By looking at a diagram containing both position and velocity vectors and also their changes (Fig. 6–14), we see that the isosceles triangles $S_1S_2\,\Delta S$ and $v_1v_2\,\Delta v$ are similar because the equal arms are mutually perpendicular.

From the similar triangles,

$$\frac{\Delta v}{v} = \frac{\Delta S}{r}.$$

When we divide each side of the equation by the time interval Δt required for displacement ΔS, we have

$$\frac{\Delta v}{v\,\Delta t} = \frac{\Delta S}{\Delta t \cdot r}. \qquad (6\text{–}69)$$

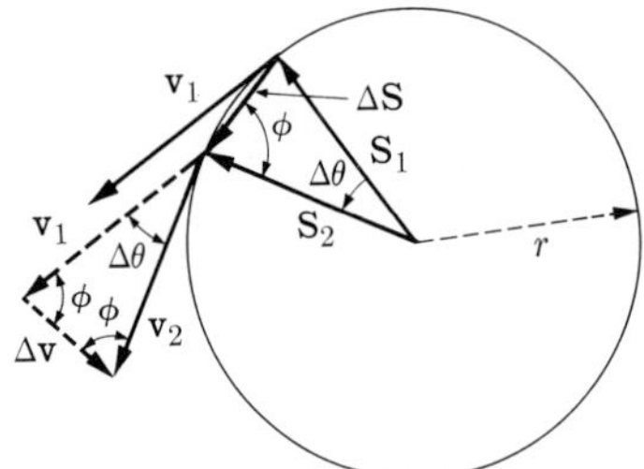

Fig. 6-14. The geometric relationships among the position, displacement, velocity, and change in velocity vectors in the case of uniform circular motion.

Solving for $\Delta v/\Delta t$, we have an expression for the average acceleration of the particle, $\bar{a}$:

$$\bar{a} \equiv \frac{\Delta v}{\Delta t} = \frac{v}{r}\frac{\Delta S}{\Delta t}, \tag{6-70}$$

or

$$\bar{a} = \frac{v}{r}\,\bar{v}. \tag{6-71}$$

Note that the symbol v stands for the magnitude of the instantaneous velocity, a constant. Also, r is a constant of the motion. Now the instantaneous acceleration is found by letting the time interval Δt become infinitesimally small. This limiting process has two consequences:

1. *Direction of* $\bar{\mathbf{a}}$: As $\Delta t \to 0$, the angle $\Delta\theta \to 0$, and the isosceles angles ϕ in both the space and the velocity triangle approach 90°, that is

$$\phi \to 90^\circ, \quad \text{as } \Delta\theta \to 0.$$

Then $\Delta\mathbf{v}$ becomes perpendicular to $\mathbf{v}$ in this limit Referring to the original diagram, we see that $\Delta\mathbf{v}$ and therefore $\bar{\mathbf{a}}$ approach a direction inward along the radius of motion. In the limit as $\Delta t \to 0$, we denote the instantaneous acceleration as a_r to show that it is in the radial direction (Fig. 6-15).

2. *Magnitude of* $\bar{\mathbf{a}}$: From the definition (Eq. 6-66)

$$\mathbf{a} = \lim_{\Delta t \to 0} \frac{\Delta\mathbf{v}}{\Delta t}$$

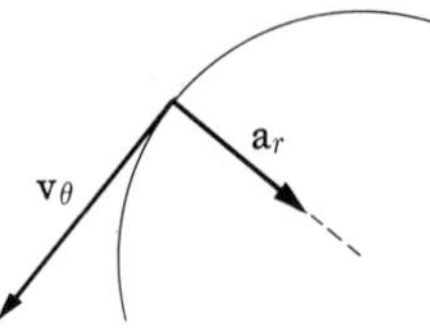

Fig. 6-15. The relative directions of the velocity and acceleration vectors in the case of uniform circular motion.

and Eq. (6-69), we have

$$a_r = \lim_{\Delta t \to 0}\left(\frac{v}{r}\frac{\Delta S}{\Delta t}\right) \quad \text{or} \quad a_r = \frac{v}{r}\left(\lim_{\Delta t \to 0}\frac{\Delta S}{\Delta t}\right),$$

which yields

$$a_r = \frac{v^2}{r}. \tag{6-72}$$

It is seen that the acceleration is purely radial, and therefore $a_\theta = 0$. "Centripetal acceleration" is a common name for a_r.

The equations of motion for a particle moving at constant speed on a circular path are

$$\begin{aligned} r &= \text{constant}, \\ \theta &= \omega t, \\ v_r &= 0, \\ v_\theta &= \text{constant} = \omega r, \\ a_r &= \frac{v_\theta^2}{r}\ (=\omega^2 r = \omega v_\theta), \\ a_\theta &= 0. \end{aligned} \tag{6-73}$$

Before closing this development, we propose to introduce some new kinematic quantities—*cycles per second, frequency, and period of motion*—which are appropriate to the description of circular motion.

A particle traveling with *uniform* speed on a circle will execute complete excursions around the circle in equal times. The time for the execution of a complete circle of motion is called the "period" of the motion. The execution of a full circle of motion is called a "complete cycle." The symbol for period is τ (Greek tau), where

$$\tau = \text{time for the execution of one cycle.}$$

Also, the number of cycles of motion can be counted for some definite length of time t. This count of cycles, n (including fractions), divided by the time during which the count is made, is called the "frequency" of the motion:

$$f = \frac{n}{t} \frac{\text{cycles}}{\text{sec}}. \tag{6–74}$$

We assert that when $n = 1$, then $t = \tau$, by definition. Then we have the following relationship between f and τ:

$$f = \frac{1}{\tau}$$

or

$$\tau = \frac{1}{f}. \tag{6–75}$$

The period of motion and the frequency of motion are inverse definitions. In summary, because of the repetitive nature of circular motion, we can assign to the motion the attributes of frequency f and period τ.

Returning now to the equation of motion $\theta = \omega t$ (Eq. 6–73), we substitute the value of $\theta = 2\pi$ corresponding to the time for one revolution τ, and obtain $2\pi = \omega\tau$. In consequence,

$$\omega = \frac{2\pi}{\tau} = 2\pi f, \tag{6–76}$$

and the equations of motion (6–73) can be written in alternative forms, such as

$$\begin{aligned} \theta &= \omega t = 2\pi f t = \frac{2\pi t}{\tau}, \\ v_\theta &= \omega r = 2\pi f r, \\ a_r &= \frac{v_0^2}{r} = \omega^2 r = (2\pi f)^2 r. \end{aligned} \tag{6–77}$$

In the case of *nonuniform circular motion,* the equations for the r-components remain unchanged, since r is still constant:

$$\begin{aligned} r &= r_0 = \text{constant}, \\ v_r &= 0, \\ a_r &= \omega^2 r. \end{aligned} \tag{6–78}$$

Of course, a_r now varies in magnitude as well as in direction, since ω is no longer a constant.

The angular coordinate θ will no longer be a linear function of time. The angular coordinate, the angular velocity, and the angular acceleration are related (by definitions) in terms of differentiation or integration:

$$\begin{aligned} \omega &\equiv \frac{d\theta}{dt}, \\ \alpha &\equiv \frac{d\omega}{dt}, \\ \omega &= \int \alpha\, dt, \\ \theta &= \int \omega\, dt. \end{aligned} \tag{6–79}$$

The θ-component of linear velocity v_θ is

$$v_\theta \equiv \left(\frac{dS}{dt}\right)_\theta. \tag{6–80}$$

Since dS is the same as the element of arc ds (for circular motion),

$$v_\theta = \frac{ds}{dt} = \frac{d(r\theta)}{dt} = r\frac{d\theta}{dt} = r\omega, \tag{6–81}$$

as in the case of uniform circular motion. The difference is that ω, and hence v_θ, are not constant.

6–9 NONCIRCULAR MOTION

The path could be described as a succession of approximately circular arcs, centered on a succession of points, with a succession of radii. Such a description entails an accelerated coordinate system, and therefore it is not generally useful. A noncircular path described from an ordinary co-

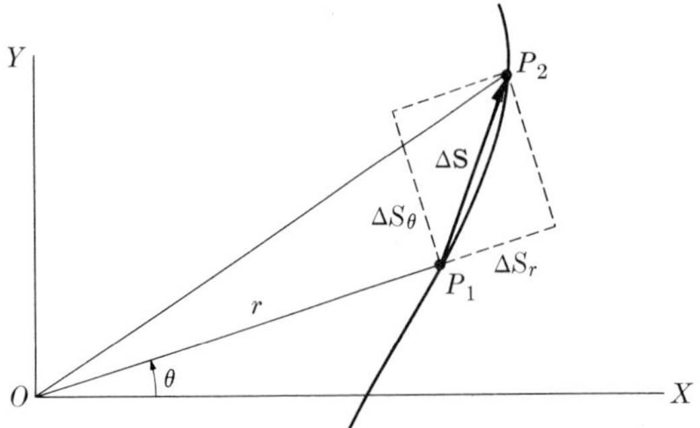

Fig. 6–16. The polar components of a displacement $\Delta \mathbf{S}$.

ordinate system is shown in Fig. 6–16, where a displacement $\Delta \mathbf{S}$ is resolved into its θ- and r-components. The reader is reminded that ΔS_θ is not in general tangent to the path, it is perpendicular to r, and hence it is tangent to a circle. We shall now determine the velocity components. Unlike the case of circular motion (see Fig. 6–11 and the associated analysis), $\Delta S_r/\Delta t$ does not vanish as Δt goes to zero.

Figure 6–17 shows the changes Δs and Δr in arc and in radius, in addition to the components of the displacement. For small values of Δs, the angle $\Delta\theta$ becomes small, and the distinction between the elements of displacement and the corresponding elements of radius and arc becomes even smaller; consequently,

$$\Delta S_r \to \Delta r, \qquad \Delta S_\theta \to \Delta s. \tag{6–82}$$

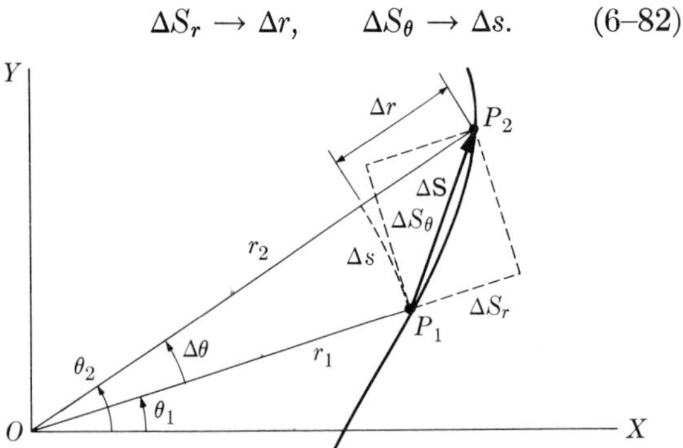

Fig. 6–17. The polar components (ΔS_r and ΔS_θ) of displacement ($\Delta \mathbf{S}$) and the changes (Δs and Δr) in coordinates during motion from P_1 to P_2.

But, from the definition of angle in radian measure, $\Delta s = r_1\,\Delta\theta$ and

$$\Delta S_\theta \to r\,\Delta\theta, \tag{6–83}$$

where the subscript for r has been dropped because $r_1\,\Delta\theta$ and $r_2\,\Delta\theta$ are indistinguishable when $\Delta \mathbf{S}$ is small. (The difference is a small quantity of the second order.)

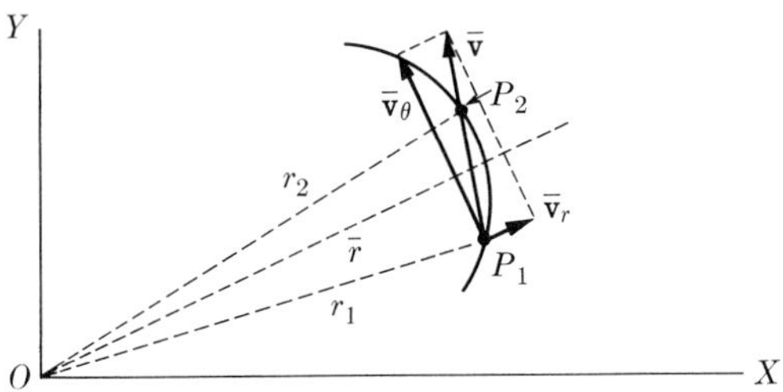

Fig. 6–18. The polar components ($\bar{v}_r$ and $\bar{v}_\theta$) of the average velocity in the circular motion between P_1 and P_2.

Finally, the polar components of average velocity become

$$\bar{v}_r \equiv \frac{\Delta S_r}{\Delta t} = \frac{\Delta r}{\Delta t}, \qquad \bar{v}_\theta \equiv \frac{\Delta S_\theta}{\Delta t} = \frac{\bar{r}\,\Delta\theta}{\Delta t}, \tag{6–84}$$

where v_r is called the r-component and v_θ the θ-component. It is again emphasized that the θ-component is tangent to a circle (*not* to the path); v itself is tangent to the path in the limit of small ΔS (Fig. 6–18). Three things in the figure may require explanation. The graph itself is a space diagram. The velocity vectors are inserted onto the space diagram, and therefore the scales have different units. This difference has been emphasized by drawing $\bar{v}$ longer than ΔS. Second $\bar{v}$ is the average velocity, and therefore its components have been drawn parallel and perpendicular to the *average* position vector (strictly the time-averaged position vector). Third, the specification of the direction of $\bar{v}_\theta$ from $\bar{r}\Delta\theta/\Delta t$ in Eq. (6–84) is not clear. This question will be deferred until Section 6–10.

The instantaneous velocities will be written

$$v_r = \frac{dr}{dt}, \qquad v_\theta = r\,\frac{d\theta}{dt} = r\omega. \qquad (6\text{–}85)$$

The polar components of acceleration are given by

$$a_r = \left(\frac{d\mathbf{v}}{dt}\right)_r, \qquad a_\theta = \left(\frac{d\mathbf{v}}{dt}\right)_\theta, \qquad (6\text{–}86)$$

where the right-hand sides are the scalar components indicated by the subscripts. The special case of uniform circular motion was treated earlier. In this case the change in velocity was found to be purely radial, and consequently a_θ was zero.

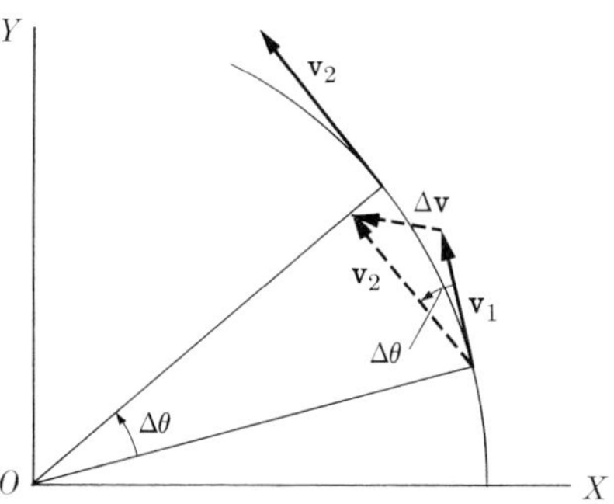

FIG. 6–19. The change in velocity $\Delta\mathbf{v}$ of an object in circular motion.

In the next more general case, *circular motion at varying speed*, we return to the definition of a_θ and write

$$a_\theta = \lim_{\Delta t \to 0} \left(\frac{\Delta\mathbf{v}}{\Delta t}\right)_\theta. \qquad (6\text{–}87)$$

The geometry of the construction of $\Delta\mathbf{v}$ is shown in Fig. 6–19. Since v_1 and v_2 are perpendicular to r_1 and r_2, respectively, the angle between v_1 and v_2 is also $\Delta\theta$. Then from the law of cosines we have

$$\Delta v^2 = v_1^2 + v_2^2 - 2v_1v_2 \cos \Delta\theta, \qquad (6\text{–}88)$$

which, for small angles, becomes

$$\Delta v^2 = v_1^2 + v_2^2 - 2v_1v_2\left(1 - \frac{(\Delta\theta)^2}{2}\right). \qquad (6\text{–}89)$$

Equation (6–89) is easily rearranged to the form

$$\Delta v^2 = (v_2 - v_1)^2 + v_1v_2(\Delta\theta)^2. \qquad (6\text{–}90)$$

In all the above equations, the velocity symbols represent the magnitudes of the velocities in question. Consequently, for this case of circular motion, we can replace v_2 and v_1 by the θ-components, which permits us to write

$$v_2 - v_1 = \Delta v_\theta$$

and

$$v_1v_2 = v_\theta(v_\theta + \Delta v_\theta) = v_\theta^2 + v_\theta\,\Delta v_\theta. \qquad (6\text{–}91)$$

However, the last term in Eq. (6–91) will result in a small quantity of higher order than the other terms and therefore can be dropped. Substituting the expressions of Eq. (6–91) into Eq. (6–90) and dividing through by $(\Delta t)^2$, we have

$$\frac{(\Delta v)^2}{(\Delta t)^2} = \frac{(\Delta v_\theta)^2}{(\Delta t)^2} + v_\theta^2\,\frac{(\Delta\theta)^2}{(\Delta t)^2}$$

or

$$a^2 = a_\theta^2 + v_\theta^2\,\omega^2 \qquad (6\text{–}92)$$

for the acceleration in the case of nonuniform circular motion. From the form of Eq. (6–92), we see that a_θ and $v_\theta\,\omega$ are perpendicular components of the acceleration. The direction of a_θ is determined by Δv_θ and is therefore perpendicular to r (Fig. 6–20). By differentiation of v_θ in Eq. (6–85),

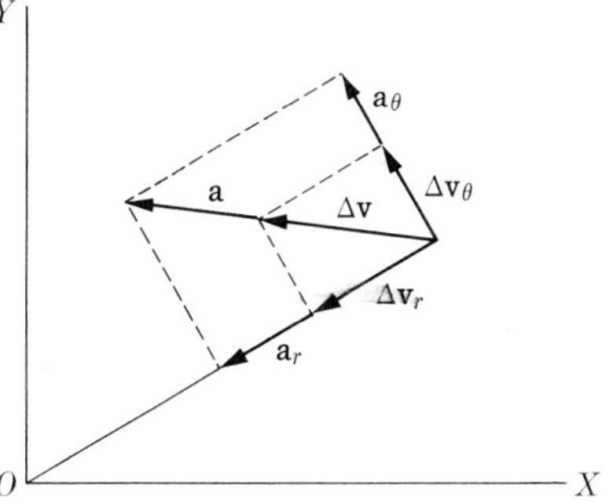

FIG. 6–20. The polar components of the change in velocity and of the acceleration in the case of circular motion.

keeping r constant, we have

$$a_\theta = r\frac{d\omega}{dt} = r\alpha. \qquad (6\text{–}93)$$

The other component, $v_\theta\omega$, is radial as expected. It is the term that we have previously written in the additional forms

$$a_r = v_\theta\omega = \frac{v^2}{r} = \omega^2 r. \qquad (6\text{–}94)$$

Detailed analysis of the acceleration in polar coordinates for motion that is not circular will not be given here. However, the vector relationships among the quantities is the same as in Fig. 6–20; that is, the change in velocity $\Delta\mathbf{v}$ determines the direction of the acceleration $\mathbf{a}(= \Delta\mathbf{v}/\Delta t)$. The acceleration can then be resolved into its polar components a_θ and a_r.

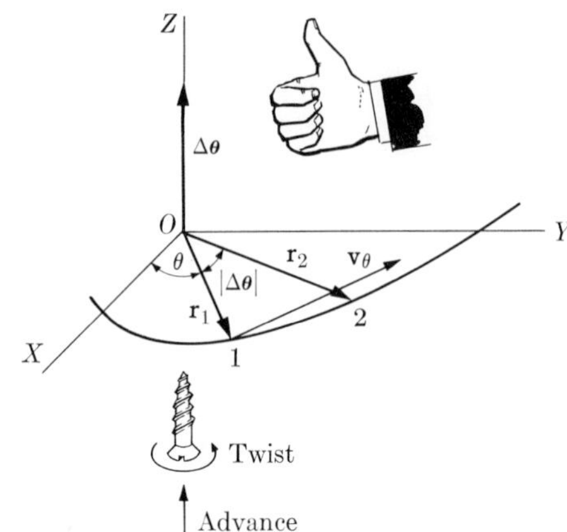

FIG. 6–21. The right-hand rule for finding the direction of the infinitesimal angular displacement vector $\Delta\boldsymbol{\theta}$ when an object moves from point 1 to 2.

6–10 THE VECTOR PRODUCT

The simplest vector equation is of the type $\mathbf{a} = d\mathbf{v}/dt$, in which only two vector quantities appear. Both the vectors, therefore, must be in the same direction. (The magnitudes of the vectors can be different.) The second type of vector equation that we have used can have more than two vectors, but it requires only the addition (or subtraction) of vectors. For example, we have $\Delta\mathbf{v} = \mathbf{v}_2 - \mathbf{v}_1$. In this equation the direction of $\Delta\mathbf{v}$ depends on both $\mathbf{v}_1$ and $\mathbf{v}_2$.

We now come to a third type of vector relationship, as exemplified by the equation $v_\theta = r\,d\boldsymbol{\theta}/dt$ (Eq. 6–85). The direction of v_θ is perpendicular to r (Fig. 6–20). This paradoxical situation can be resolved by (a) defining $d\boldsymbol{\theta}$ as a vector and (b) defining a process of *vector multiplication*. It is therefore necessary to define vector multiplication (and to specify a direction for $d\boldsymbol{\theta}$). Strictly speaking, $d\boldsymbol{\theta}$ obeys the rules of vector addition only if it is infinitesimal; we therefore assume $d\boldsymbol{\theta}$ to be infinitesimal. The direction of $d\boldsymbol{\theta}$ is the direction of an axis perpendicular to the plane of the radii $\mathbf{r}_1$ and $\mathbf{r}_2$, which are the arms of the angle $d\boldsymbol{\theta}$. The sense is that of the direction of advance of a right-handed screw when the screw is twisted from $\mathbf{r}_1$ to $\mathbf{r}_2$ (Fig. 6–21). In the present example, $\mathbf{r}_1$ and $\mathbf{r}_2$ lie in the XY-plane, and $d\boldsymbol{\theta}$ will be parallel to the OZ-axis. (This is a special case.) Another rule for determining the sense of the $d\boldsymbol{\theta}$ vector is to curl the fingers of the right hand in the plane and direction of rotation of $\mathbf{r}_1$ into $\mathbf{r}_2$. The thumb then points in the direction of $d\boldsymbol{\theta}$ as in Fig. 6–21.

Thus we now have two vectors, $\mathbf{r}$ and $d\boldsymbol{\theta}$, whose product gives the direction of $\mathbf{v}_\theta$. When written in vector form, the ordering of terms in Eq. (6–85) is conventionally reversed, and a cross is used for the multiplication sign; thus

$$\mathbf{v}_\theta = \frac{d\boldsymbol{\theta}}{dt} \times \mathbf{r}. \qquad (6\text{–}95)$$

This is called a *vector* or *cross product.* The direction of the product vector $\mathbf{v}_\theta$ is given by a rule similar to the one above: the product vector is in the direction of advance of a right-handed screw that is twisted from the direction of the first vector into the direction of the second vector (through the angle $\angle$ 180°). Also, the right-hand rule can

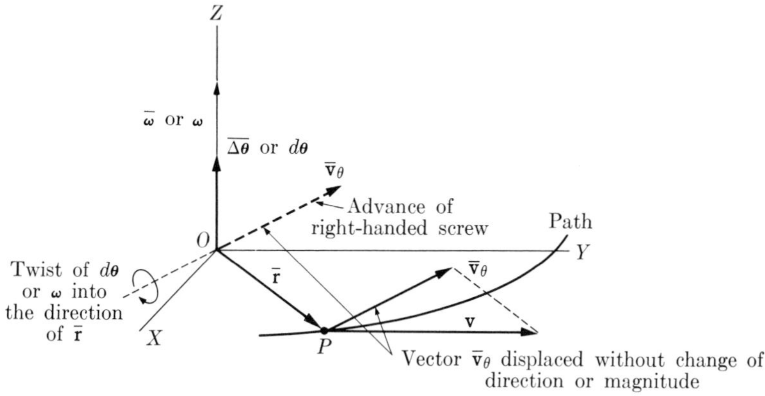

FIG. 6–22. Geometric relationship among the vectors of Eq. (6–96).

be used (Fig. 6–22). The instantaneous values of the quantities in Eq. (6–95) are of course related in the same way, namely,

$$\mathbf{v}_\theta = \frac{d\boldsymbol{\theta}}{dt} \times \mathbf{r} = \boldsymbol{\omega} \times \mathbf{r}. \tag{6–96}$$

In general terms, the vector product is written

$$\mathbf{A} = \mathbf{B} \times \mathbf{C}, \tag{6–97}$$

where the direction of **A** is given by the above rules and its magnitude by

$$|\mathbf{A}| = |\mathbf{B}|\,|\mathbf{C}| \sin \beta, \tag{6–98}$$

with β the angle between **B** and **C** (Fig. 6–23). Note that **A** is perpendicular to the plane of **B** and **C**.

The radial acceleration in uniform circular motion is also a vector. The simplest vectorial expression comes from the form $a_r = v_\theta \omega$ of Eq. (6–94). It can be seen from Fig. 6–24 that

$$\mathbf{a}_r = \boldsymbol{\omega} \times \mathbf{v}_\theta, \tag{6–99}$$

where the dashed-line vectors $\mathbf{v}_\theta$ and $\mathbf{a}_r$ have been

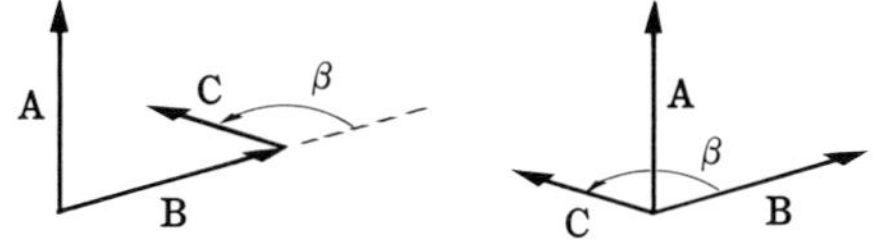

FIG. 6–23. Geometric relationship among the vectors involved in the cross product of Eq. (6–97).

slid from point P to the origin in order to make the vector product clearer. Note that this diagram displays *four* different physical quantities; therefore the scales for the four vectors in Fig. 6–24 are all different.

Equation (6–99) could also be expressed in the vector form

$$\mathbf{a}_r = \boldsymbol{\omega} \times (\boldsymbol{\omega} \times \mathbf{r}), \tag{6–100}$$

which is a so-called triple vector product.

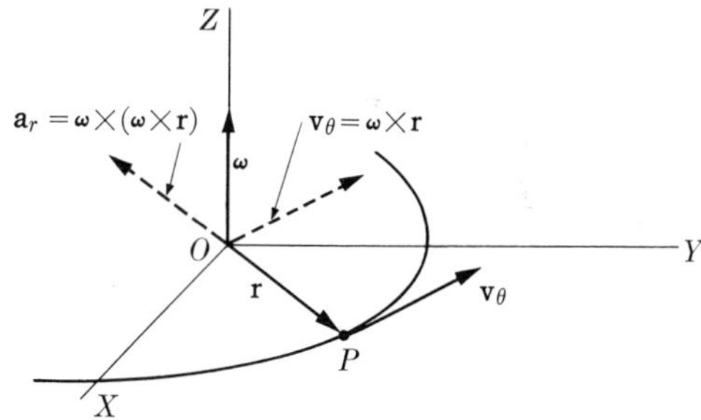

FIG. 6–24. Geometric relationship among the vectors of Eqs. (6–96) and (6–100).

6–11 SUMMARY

The instantaneous velocity is defined by

$$\mathbf{v} \equiv \lim_{\Delta t \to 0} \frac{\Delta \mathbf{S}}{\Delta t},$$

which in the notation of the calculus is the process of differentiation,

$$\mathbf{v} = \frac{d\mathbf{S}}{dt}.$$

The cartesian components are

$$v_x = \frac{dx}{dt}, \qquad v_y = \frac{dy}{dt}.$$

The graphical representation of a velocity component as the slope of a curve of the coordinate versus time is presented.

The formulas for differentiation of polynomials in powers of the independent variable (in this case the time) are given.

The acceleration is defined, in a manner similar to that of velocity, by

$$\mathbf{a} = \frac{d\mathbf{v}}{dt}, \qquad a_x = \frac{dv_x}{dt}, \qquad a_y = \frac{dv_y}{dt},$$

with a similar graphical interpretation as the slope of a curve of a velocity component versus time.

The opposite process of finding the position coordinates from the velocity components or finding the velocity components from the acceleration components is called antidifferentiation. Formulas are given for the case of polynomials in powers of time.

In the case of one-dimensional motion, one coordinate, and thus one velocity component, and one acceleration component suffice if the coordinate is chosen along the direction of motion. If the acceleration is constant in direction, it is usually convenient to analyze two-dimensional motion in cartesian components, with one axis chosen parallel to the acceleration.

Uniform circular motion is most easily described in polar coordinates, with the origin at the center of the circle. The velocity can be described by a single component v_θ that is perpendicular to the position vector $\mathbf{r}$. This velocity component is related to the angular velocity ω, where

$$\omega \equiv \frac{d\theta}{dt},$$

by the equation

$$v_\theta = \omega r.$$

Since ω is constant in uniform circular motion, the angular acceleration α, defined by

$$\alpha \equiv \frac{d\omega}{dt},$$

is zero. The coordinate angle θ is found (from integration of ω) to be

$$\theta = \theta_0 + \omega t.$$

The radial coordinate r is constant, and consequently the radial component of velocity is zero:

$$v_r = 0.$$

The acceleration is purely radial with

$$a_r = \omega^2 r.$$

(The θ-component of the acceleration a_θ is therefore zero.)

In *nonuniform circular motion*, we have

$$r = \text{constant} \qquad \theta = \int \omega\, dt \qquad v_\theta = \omega r$$

$$v_r = 0 \qquad \omega = \int \alpha\, dt \qquad a_\theta = \alpha r$$

$$a_r = \omega^2 r \qquad \text{or}$$

$$\alpha = \frac{d\omega}{dt}$$

$$\omega = \frac{d\theta}{dt}$$

In general for two-dimensional motion described in polar coordinates, we have the general relationships

$$v_r = \frac{dr}{dt}, \qquad v_\theta = \omega r,$$

$$a_r = \left(\frac{d\mathbf{v}}{dt}\right)_r, \qquad a_\theta = \left(\frac{d\mathbf{v}}{dt}\right)_\theta.$$

However, the case (central force) that we shall pursue in later chapters is the one in which a_θ is zero and in which a_r is known as a function of r rather than of t. Consequently, a different general approach will be developed at that time.

The formal vectorial relationships among the quantities in some of the above equations are given by the vector (cross) products

$$\mathbf{v}_\theta = \boldsymbol{\omega} \times \mathbf{r},$$
$$\mathbf{a}_r = \boldsymbol{\omega} \times \mathbf{v}_\theta.$$

In the case of periodic motion, e.g., in a circular path, it is convenient to use the concepts of period τ and frequency f, where τ is the time per cycle and f is the number of cycles per unit time. We have

$$\tau = \frac{1}{f}.$$

In the special case of uniform circular motion, we also have

$$\omega = \frac{2\pi}{\tau} = 2\pi f,$$

and, therefore,

$$\theta = \theta_0 + 2\pi f t,$$
$$v_\theta = 2\pi f r,$$
$$a_r = (2\pi f)^2 r.$$

Problems

In the following problems, let $g = 10$ m/sec, unless otherwise specified, and let 1 yr $= 3.1 \times 10^7$ sec.

1. Give an example of motion where average velocity and instantaneous velocity are the same. For your example, write the equation for position as a function of time and prove that $\bar{v} = v$ by using the definitions.

2. In an experiment a boy is pursuaded to run, walk, and finally crawl as fast and as long as he can. In the first 50-sec period he runs 400 m, and in each succeeding 50-sec period he covers half as much distance as in the period before.

(a) Using the definition, find his average speed for the first 250, 200, 150, 100, and 50 seconds.

(b) Make a graph of the results of part (a).

(c) Extrapolate to $t = 0$ to find his instantaneous velocity just after starting.

3. Make a smooth curve of distance versus time for Problem 2.

(a) Find the instantaneous velocity at 50-sec intervals from slopes of the curve, and plot v versus t, drawing a smooth curve to represent the points. Does the initial value agree with Problem 2(c)? What is the value of v as $t \to \infty$?

(b) Repeat the above for instantaneous acceleration.

4. Show by a direct application of the "Δ" process that if

$$x(t) = ct \qquad (c = \text{constant}),$$

then

$$v = c.$$

5. Show by a direct application of the "Δ" process that if

$$x(t) = \frac{c}{t} \qquad \text{where } c = \text{constant},$$

then

$$v(t) = -\frac{c}{t^2}.$$

Check your answer by applying the general rule for differentiation of powers.

6. The position of a particle in rectilinear motion is

$$x = 10 + 20t^2 - 30t^4.$$

(a) What is the velocity as a function of time?
(b) What is the acceleration as a function of time?
(c) What is the initial position of the particle?
(d) What is the initial velocity of the particle?
(e) What is the initial acceleration of the particle?
(f) At what times is the velocity zero?

7. A particle in rectilinear motion has an acceleration given by

$$a(t) = 3t^2.$$

At $t = 0$, the displacement is $+10$ m and the velocity is -20 m/sec. Show by integration that the equation for $v(t)$ is

$$v = v_0 + t^3$$

and that the equation for displacement is

$$x = x_0 + v_0 t + \frac{t^4}{4}.$$

8. A particle is started toward the right at a velocity of 10 m/sec. The acceleration is 1 m/sec^2 toward the left. At what three times is the magnitude of the distance from the origin equal to 1 m?

9. Using the following equations for displacement and velocity in rectilinear motion under *constant acceleration,*

$$x = v_0 t + \tfrac{1}{2}at^2,$$

$$v = v_0 + at,$$

prove that the time-independent relationship

$$v^2 = v_0^2 + 2ax$$

holds for this type of motion.

10. Show that the velocity of fall for a ball dropped from rest in the gravitational field is

$$v = \sqrt{2gy},$$

where g is the constant acceleration due to gravity and y is the displacement from the point of release.

11. A ball is thrown directly upward so that it reaches a height of 10 m. At what initial velocity is it thrown?

12. A stone is thrown into the air from ground level at any initial velocity in any direction.

(a) Prove that the time of going up equals the time of going down, and that each is one-half the time of flight.

(b) Prove that the velocity of striking the earth is equal in magnitude to the initial velocity.

13. A kicked football remains in the air 4 sec. How high did it rise?

14. A block of wood is shot along a table top which is 1 m above floor level. After the block leaves the edge of the table, it strikes the floor at a horizontal distance of 5 m from the table edge. What was the velocity of the block as it left the table edge?

15. The exercise in this chapter illustrating two-dimensional motion is to be generalized. Let a particle leave the earth's surface with initial velocity v_0, elevated at an angle θ above the horizontal direction (Fig. 6–25). The acceleration is constant and is equal to g downward. (The acceleration in the x-direction is zero.) Using the equations of motion which are appropriate for this system, prove that the following are true.

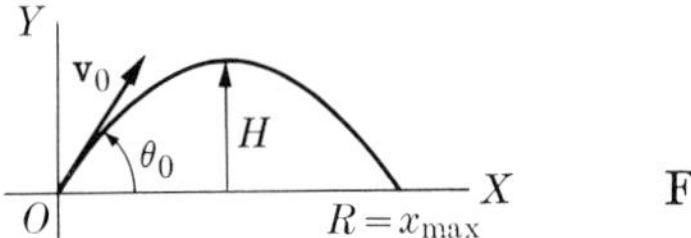

FIGURE 6–25

(a) The time of flight of the projectile is

$$t_R = \frac{2v_0 \sin \theta_0}{g}.$$

(b) The maximum altitude attained by the projectile is

$$H = \frac{v_0^2 \sin^2 \theta_0}{2g}.$$

(c) The range of the projectile is

$$R = \frac{2v_0^2 \sin \theta_0 \cos \theta_0}{g}.$$

Prepare three separate graphs, assuming a constant magnitude for v_0 in which, (a) t, the time of flight, is the ordinate, and θ_0 is the abscissa; (b) H is the ordinate, and θ_0 the abscissa; (c) R is the ordinate, and θ the abscissa. It will be sufficient to let θ assume 30° steps from $\theta_0 = 0°$ to $\theta_0 = 90°$.

16. A ski jumper leaves the jump horizontally, as shown in Fig. 6–26. Where will he strike the 30° slope if his take-off velocity is 40 m/sec?

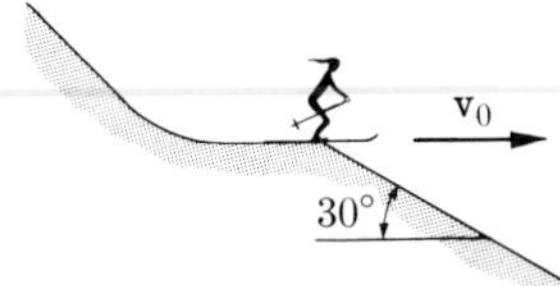

FIGURE 6–26

17. Give examples of instances when (a) velocity is zero during accelerated motion, (b) acceleration and velocity are opposite in direction, (c) displacement from the origin and velocity are opposite in direction.

18. An object starting from rest has cartesian components of acceleration $a_x = 10t$ and $a_y = 5t^2$ in m/sec^2.

(a) What are the units of the "5" and of the "10" in the above equations?

(b) Find the position and velocity after 5 sec.

(c) Find the equation of the path.

(d) Find the polar coordinates as functions of time.

19. In Problem 18, find the radial component and θ-component of the velocity when $t = 2$ sec.

20. A native hunter with a blowgun fires directly at a monkey hanging from a tree limb (Fig. 6–27). The monkey drops at the instant he sees the dart leave the gun. Use the vector form (Eq. 6–55) of equations to prove that the monkey should have held fast to the limb.

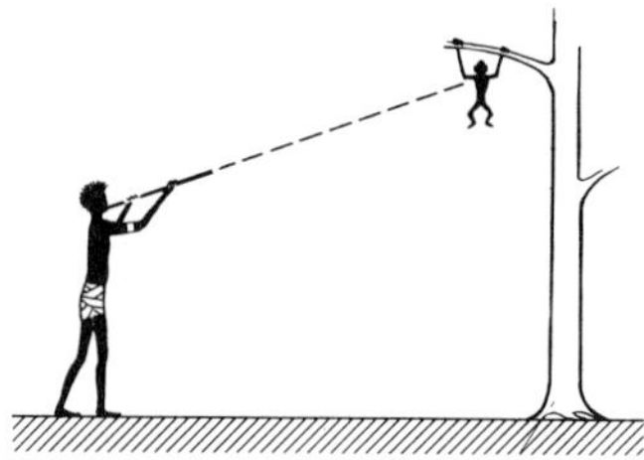

FIGURE 6–27

21. A projectile of mass 12 kg is fired upward at an angle of 53° with a velocity of 1000 m/sec. At the highest point in its path it explodes into fragments of mass 4 kg and 8 kg.

(a) If the 4-kg mass is brought instantaneously to rest by the explosion, where will the 8-kg mass strike the ground, assuming that the ground is level?

(b) Derive the equations for the velocity of the 8-kg mass relative to the 4-kg mass after the explosion.

22. In Problem 15(c), the range R of a projectile was found.

(a) Use a trigonometric identity involving 2θ or $\theta/2$ to express R in terms of $\sin 2\theta_0$.

(b) Prove that the maximum range occurs at $\theta_0 = \pi/4$.

23. Expressed in cartesian coordinates, A has a velocity

$$v_{Ax} = 2, \qquad v_{Ay} = t,$$

while B has a velocity

$$v_{Bx} = 2t, \qquad v_{By} = \tfrac{1}{2}t^2.$$

Find the velocity of A relative to B as a function of time.

24. A particular elevator design requires that there be no accelerations or decelerations greater than $g/2$ in its motion. What is the minimum time (starting and stopping at rest) to get between floors separated by 20 m? Is the time dependent on whether the elevator is ascending or descending?

25. A rocket reaches a height of 150 km with a vertical speed of 2 km/sec when its fuel is exhausted. How long will it continue to rise? What will be its maximum height? Assume that g is 10 m/sec^2.

26. Derive the equations for the cartesian coordinates, x and y, as functions of time for a particle in uniform circular motion.

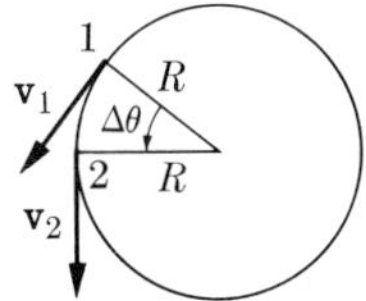

FIGURE 6–28

27. A particle travels at constant speed v on a circle of radius R (Fig. 6–28). The particle moves from position 1 to position 2 on the circle. The angular opening between 1 and 2 is $\Delta\theta$.

(a) Show that the time is $\Delta t = R\,\Delta\theta/v$.

(b) Show that the average acceleration is

$$\bar{a} = \left(\sqrt{2}\,\frac{\sqrt{1 - \cos\Delta\theta}}{\Delta\theta}\right)\frac{v^2}{R}.$$

(c) Compute the factor in parentheses for $\Delta\theta = 90°$, 30°, 10°, 1°. Explain your results.

28. A projectile is fired with speed v_0 at an angle θ_0.

(a) What is its velocity at the top of its trajectory? its acceleration?

(b) Since the acceleration is perpendicular to the velocity at the top of the trajectory, the path is "instantaneously circular." Find the radius of the circle.

29. A pilot is to be tested at an acceleration of 10 g by being whirled in a horizontal circle of radius 5 m.
(a) What is the required angular velocity?
(b) What is the pilot's speed?

30. The earth's radius is 6400 km, and its distance from the sun is 15×10^7 km. Find the acceleration (at a point on the equator) due to the earth's rotation, and compare this acceleration with the acceleration due to the motion around the sun. Compare both with g.

31. A satellite in a circular orbit near the earth has an acceleration of about g. What is its period of revolution about the earth?

32. Derive an expression for the radial acceleration at the earth's surface due to the earth's rotation as a function of radius R, latitude λ, and period τ. What is the direction of the acceleration?

33. What are the direction and magnitude of the vector angular velocity of the earth?

7

Dynamics (Instantaneous Quantities)

7-1 INTRODUCTION

In the previous chapter the methods of treating instantaneous velocity and acceleration were presented. We are now in a position to consider the conservation of momentum and Newton's laws with more generality than we did in earlier chapters. Furthermore, we will be able to analyze situations in which the forces are known. The problem is to predict the future motion in terms of the initial conditions of motion.

7-2 CONSERVATION OF MOMENTUM WHILE VELOCITY IS CHANGING

Previously, we considered the total change of momentum from one state of constant velocity to another state of constant velocity. This limitation was dictated only by the fact that instantaneous velocity had not yet been defined. The definition of mass, which led to the conservation of momentum principle in two-body interactions, is expressed in terms of change in velocity. The change in velocity can just as well be from one instantaneous velocity to another. Direct experimental verification of the conservation principle is more difficult in this case, and for this reason the simpler case of constant velocities before and after interaction was considered first.

In terms of instantaneous velocities, the observed effect of interaction of bodies A and B (which we used to define mass) can be written

$$m_A \, \Delta\mathbf{v}_A = -m_B \, \Delta\mathbf{v}_B, \qquad (7\text{-}1)$$

where $\Delta\mathbf{v}_A$ and $\Delta\mathbf{v}_B$ are the changes in *instantaneous* velocities during any common time interval Δt of the interaction. When Eq. (7-1) is written out completely and the terms are transposed, the result is

$$m_A\mathbf{v}_{A0} + m_B\mathbf{v}_{B0} = m_A\mathbf{v}_A + m_B\mathbf{v}_B, \qquad (7\text{-}2)$$

where $\mathbf{v}_A$ and $\mathbf{v}_B$ are instantaneous velocities at any time t and $\mathbf{v}_{A0}$ and $\mathbf{v}_{B0}$ are *the velocities at some reference time* t_0.

Example 1. A man standing on a cart (whose wheels are frictionless) starts walking on the cart. If the masses of man and cart are 60 and 120 kg, respectively, what is the relationship between their velocities? Assume that the cart had initial velocity v_0.

Solution: Eq. (7-2) gives $(m_c + m_M)\, v_0 = m_c v_c + m_M v_M$, where the subscripts refer to cart (c) and man (M). The relationship between instantaneous velocities is therefore $v_M = 3v_0 - 2v_c$. These velocities are relative to the ground.

Instantaneous momentum is defined as

$$\mathbf{p} \equiv m\mathbf{v}, \qquad (7\text{-}3)$$

where $\mathbf{v}$ is the instantaneous velocity. (In the case of variable mass, m is the instantaneous mass.) The conservation of momentum can then be stated in terms of the instantaneous momenta $\mathbf{p}_A$ and $\mathbf{p}_B$, of A and B:

$$\mathbf{p}_A + \mathbf{p}_B = \text{constant}, \qquad (7\text{-}4)$$

where the form of the statement has been altered slightly for the sake of variety.

The extension to three or more interacting bodies that was made in Chapter 4 can also be made for instantaneous momentum:

$$\sum \mathbf{p} = \text{constant}, \qquad (7\text{-}5)$$

where the summation is over all objects within a system that experiences no resultant external force.

As usual, all the vector equations of this section can be written in component form.

7-3 INSTANTANEOUS FORCE

Average force was defined in Chapter 4 by

$$\overline{\mathbf{F}} \equiv m \frac{\Delta \mathbf{v}}{\Delta t}.$$

In the formal process of taking the limit as $\Delta t \to 0$, the average acceleration $\Delta \mathbf{v}/\Delta t$ becomes the instantaneous acceleration. The corresponding limiting value of $\overline{\mathbf{F}}$ is defined as the instantaneous force $\mathbf{F}$, that is,

$$\mathbf{F} \equiv m \frac{d\mathbf{v}}{dt} = m\mathbf{a}. \qquad (7\text{-}6)$$

If expressed in terms of momentum, the average force is

$$\overline{\mathbf{F}} = \frac{\Delta \mathbf{p}}{\Delta t},$$

which becomes

$$\mathbf{F} = \frac{d(m\mathbf{v})}{dt} = \frac{d\mathbf{p}}{dt}, \qquad (7\text{-}7)$$

where $\mathbf{p}$ is the instantaneous momentum.

The principle of superposition is as valid for instantaneous forces as for average forces; hence

$$\sum \mathbf{F} = m\mathbf{a} \quad \text{or} \quad \frac{d\mathbf{p}}{dt}, \qquad (7\text{-}8)$$

when there is more than one interaction force on mass m. Similarly, if two or more masses are chosen as a system, Eq. (7-8) can be written

$$\sum \mathbf{F} = (\sum m)\mathbf{a}, \qquad (7\text{-}9)$$

or Eq. (7-7) can be written

$$\sum \mathbf{F} = \sum \frac{d\mathbf{p}}{dt}. \qquad (7\text{-}10)$$

The above are statements of Newton's second law expressed in the general terminology of instantaneous values. The third law also applies to instantaneous forces: Eq. (7-1) can be divided through by Δt, and the limit can be taken as $\Delta t \to 0$, giving

$$m_A\mathbf{a}_A = -m_B\mathbf{a}_B \qquad (7\text{-}11)$$

or

$$\mathbf{F}_A = -\mathbf{F}_B. \qquad (7\text{-}12)$$

The interaction force of B on A is equal and opposite to the interaction force of A on B *at any instant.*

7-4 NEWTON'S LAWS OF MOTION

In kinematics, the motion of a particle is treated as a description problem. No question is asked about why the motion is of a particular form. In dynamics we ask about the physical determinants of the motion of material objects. The determinants are force and mass, which were defined in Chapter 4.

Let us review the statements of the laws of motion.

1. A material object in a state of rest or of uniform rectilinear motion remains in the state of rest or of uniform rectilinear motion unless acted upon by a resultant external force.

2. The time rate of change of momentum of a material object is equal to the sum of the external forces applied to the object, that is, $\sum \mathbf{F} = d\mathbf{p}/dt$, where $\sum \mathbf{F}$ is the sum of the external forces and $\mathbf{p}$ is the particle momentum, which is defined as the product of mass and particle velocity: $\mathbf{p} \equiv m\mathbf{v}$ [Eq. (7-3)].

3. To every action there is an equal and opposite reaction.

These three laws contain an elaborate structure of physical ideas and definitions. A brief discussion of the laws follows. Deductively, we say that the *first law* describes a special case contained in the second law. According to the second law, if the sum of external forces is zero, the time rate of change of momentum is zero, and the momentum is therefore a constant vector quantity. Since in classical mechanics mass is a constant attribute of matter, then a constant value of momentum corresponds to a constant velocity.

It is preferable, however, to start with the first law as an aid to understanding the concepts. The first law ascribes to matter the intrinsic property of a "natural" kind of motion. When matter is isolated from outside influence, either "directly" by having *no* outside forces or indirectly by arranging for $\sum \mathbf{F} = 0$, its natural motion is uniform rectilinear motion. This is the first property ascribed to matter by Newton's laws.

While the first law is certainly found to be applicable to physical systems as we observe and describe them when $\sum \mathbf{F} = 0$, the idea of a body on which *no* external forces act tends to strain the imagination. Thinking ahead to the description of the gravitational force law, we find that a body near the surface of the earth or indeed at any place in the universe is subjected to an external gravitational force. The idea of a material object floating in uniform rectilinear motion in empty space must remain at best an imaginary or limiting concept.

We must also ask, "rest or uniform rectilinear motion relative to what?" Position and velocity, as kinematic quantities, are meaningless unless a reference system is given. Position and velocity are "relative" quantities. The answer is that a whole family of references exists, within which the Newtonian laws are valid. One such reference system is attached to the fixed stars of the universe. All other reference systems which are in *uniform rectilinear* motion relative to the star system are also valid, as we shall see in Section 7–7.

Only external forces affect the motion of a material system. A mechanical system, a set of material objects, may contain internal forces. These can cause internal strain or internal motion. But the motion of the system as a whole is unaffected by the internal forces, since they cancel vectorially in pairs.

Prior to Newtonian science, there was a notion that force is required to sustain motion. Aristotle asserted that the *natural state of objects is to be at rest*, and he was certainly correct so far as the real world of ponderable objects on earth is concerned. There is always friction of some kind, and therefore a (second) force is required to "overcome" friction. The important point is *not* to forget the friction force in the discussion. When a *single* external force is applied to an object, the velocity is *changed*, not sustained. Galileo introduced the idealization of an object experiencing no impediments (i.e., friction) to motion in a horizontal plane. (Galileo implicitly used the idea of $\sum F_y = 0$ to narrow the discussion to horizontal motion, thus straining our imagination in only one dimension.) Newton introduced the complete abstraction or idealization, i.e., a situation with *no* forces acting. The effect of forces on motion can then be clearly understood, *after* the question of motion with no forces has been settled.

The *second law* states the effect of single or resultant forces on an object or system. The complete phrase, "sum of all external interaction forces," is usually to be understood when we use Newton's second law. The question of *noninteraction* forces will be left until later.

The *third law*, as we have seen, follows from the definition of mass, which is based on experimental observation.

7–5 SINGLE FORCES

Except in problems composed for academic exercises, we know of no example in which only *one* force acts on an object (to say nothing of an example in which *no* force acts on an object). However, there are a few situations in which one force is so much greater than all the other forces that it is a good approximation to neglect all but the one force.

One of the examples is that of free fall (motion of dense objects in the atmosphere at velocities small enough so that air resistance is negligible); another is motion of satellites near enough to the earth so that the gravitational forces by the moon and sun have nearly the same effect on the satellites as on the earth. In the former case, dense objects were specified in order that the buoyant force of the air be negligible. In the latter case, the effects of the moon and sun are negligible when the center of the earth is chosen as the origin of coordinates.

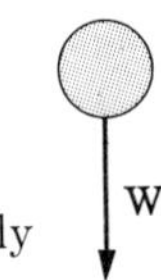

FIG. 7–1. Force on a freely falling object.

In Section 6–7 we discussed free-fall motion over small enough distances so that the direction and magnitude of the gravitational pull by the earth can be considered constant. This motion can now be "understood" in terms of Newton's laws as follows: When the forces by the air are negligible, there is only one force, **W**, which is the pull by the earth (Fig. 7–1) on a free body. This force is directed toward the center of the earth and its magnitude is given by Newton's law of gravitation [Eq. (5–5)]. For displacements of a few kilometers in height and/or horizontal distance, the value of **W** is constant to within less than one percent according to the law of gravitation. Since this is the only force, Newton's second law, $\sum \mathbf{F} = m\mathbf{a}$, gives $\mathbf{W} = m\mathbf{a}$. When **W** can be considered constant, the acceleration will be constant. As mentioned earlier, it is customary to use the symbol **g** to denote this particular acceleration.

For satellite motion in the vicinity of the earth, the only force is the pull by the earth (after the rockets are burned out). The force diagram is given by Fig. 7–1, but **W** is not constant. Consequently, Newton's second law indicates that the acceleration is not constant. The motion is fairly complex. One special case, circular motion at constant speed, is relatively simple to analyze completely. Only certain features of other types of satellite motion will be analyzed in this text.

7–6 APPLICATION OF NEWTON'S LAWS

The most difficult part of the analysis at this stage of your knowledge will probably be that of setting up the problem. The mathematics of the solutions of problems in this course is relatively simple once the problems have been formulated in equation form. An attempt will now be made to anticipate some of the most frequently occurring difficulties by outlining the ideas that must be considered.

(a) *Reference frame.* This question will be discussed in more detail later. For the present, a few guiding comments will be made. For observations within the laboratory, we choose a reference frame that is stationary relative to the laboratory. For most motion on a larger scale outside the laboratory, but at or near the surface of the earth, we still choose a reference frame fixed relative to the earth. But for satellite motion or long-distance projectile motion (or any "free-fall" motion in which the curvature of the path is nearly as small as the curvature of the earth), a reference frame is chosen with origin at the earth's center but with its direction fixed relative to the stars. For motion on the scale of the solar system, the sun should be chosen as the origin with the direction of the frame fixed relative to the stars.

The above systems are satisfactory approximations to so-called inertial systems for each particular class of problem.

(b) *Choice of object or system.* The choice of an object or system whose motion is to be analyzed in order to solve a particular problem is sometimes obvious. In other cases, the choice may require skill in order that the desired unknowns can be evaluated. But no matter what the choice, it is absolutely necessary that you realize that you have made a choice of object or system (even though it be an unconscious choice) before you start to use Newton's laws in the analysis.

(c) *Forces.* The pertinent forces are those exerted by real objects *on* the chosen object or system. Only forces by real objects, i.e., interaction forces, appear in Newton's laws when the type of reference frames specified in (a) are used, and only those acting *on* the object or system in question can affect the motion of that system as a whole. These forces will always be exerted by objects external to the selected object or system, since internal forces cancel out in action-reaction pairs. (An object cannot exert a force on itself, however, and so-called inertial forces do *not* play a role when the choice of reference frames is made as above.)

The systematic way to analyze the forces on the chosen object is to draw a diagram showing *only* the forces that act on the selected object. Then ask two questions: have *all* of the forces exerted by other objects on the selected object been included, and have *only* forces exerted by real, external objects been included? This force diagram should be carefully drawn so that the analysis involved in finding the resultant force (or whatever relationship among the forces is required) can be clearly visualized.

(d) *Forces and motion.* The relationship between forces and motion is given by Newton's second law. Usually, either the motion must be known so that the resultant force can be obtained from the acceleration, or all the forces must be known so that the acceleration can be predicted; thus the order of the steps in the analysis cannot be prescribed.

Example 2. Let two masses, $m_1 = 2$ kg and $m_2 = 3$ kg, be connected by a string. A force $\mathbf{F}_1 = 10$ n is applied to m_2, as shown in Fig. 7–2. What is the acceleration of the masses? What is the tension in the string connecting the objects?

Solution: First consider an enumeration of all forces and draw a diagram such as that in Fig. 7–2.

1. The applied force is $\mathbf{F}_1$. The reaction to $\mathbf{F}_1$ is $-\mathbf{F}_1$, but it does *not* act on m_2. (It acts on the object exerting $\mathbf{F}_1$.)

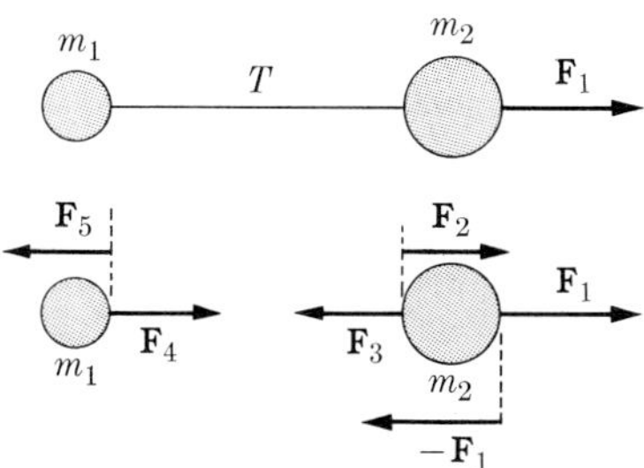

FIG. 7–2. Force on the system m_1m_2 (top) and the forces on components of the system m_1m_2 (bottom).

2. The force applied by m_2 *on* the string is $\mathbf{F}_2$. The force exerted by the string *on* m_2 is $\mathbf{F}_3$. Thus $\mathbf{F}_2$ and $\mathbf{F}_3$ constitute an action-reaction pair.

3. The force exerted by the string on m_1 is $\mathbf{F}_4$. The force exerted by m_1 on the string is $\mathbf{F}_5$.

4. The tension is $T = |\mathbf{F}_5| = |\mathbf{F}_4| = |\mathbf{F}_3| = |\mathbf{F}_2|$. Why?

First consider the *two* masses to be the system under consideration (Fig. 7–3).

FIG. 7–3. The system m_1m_2 of Example 2.

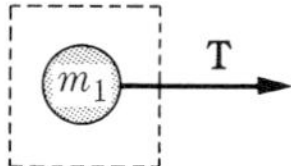

FIG. 7–4. Mass m_1 of Example 2.

The mass of the system is $m = m_1 + m_2$. Since the only outside force is F_1, we have $\sum F = F_1$. Then $\sum F = ma$ becomes $F_1 = (m_1 + m_2)a$ for this system. Therefore, $a = F_1/(m_1 + m_2)$, which means that a is now known in terms of given quantities. But so long as this choice of system is retained, T cannot be found, for it occurs as an internal force. Choose m_1 to be the new system, as in Fig. 7–4. Then T becomes an outside force acting upon the system. The mass is $m = m_1$, and the force is $\sum F = T$. Therefore $\sum F = ma$ for this system becomes $T = m_1a$. Substituting the known value a, we have $T = F_1m_1/(m_1 + m_2)$ or $T = 4$ n. Finally, for a check on the mathematics, select m_2 as the system (Fig. 7–5). We have $\sum F = F_1 - T$. Then for this third system $\sum F = ma$ becomes $F_1 - T = m_2 a$, where all the values are known. Substituting these values, we have 10 n − 4 n = 3 kg · 2 m/sec² or 6 n = 6 n, a satisfactory check.

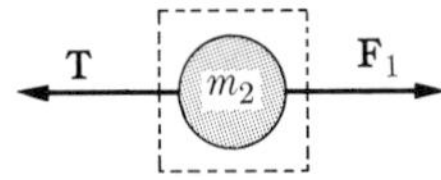

FIG. 7–5. Mass m_2 of Example 2.

Example 3. A mass m_1 on an inclined plane is connected to a freely hanging mass m_2 by means of a massless, frictionless pulley and string, as shown in Fig. 7–6. The coefficient of friction is μ. (a) If m_1 is given an initial velocity v_0, *up* the plane, how long will it continue to rise? (b) What is the tension in the string?

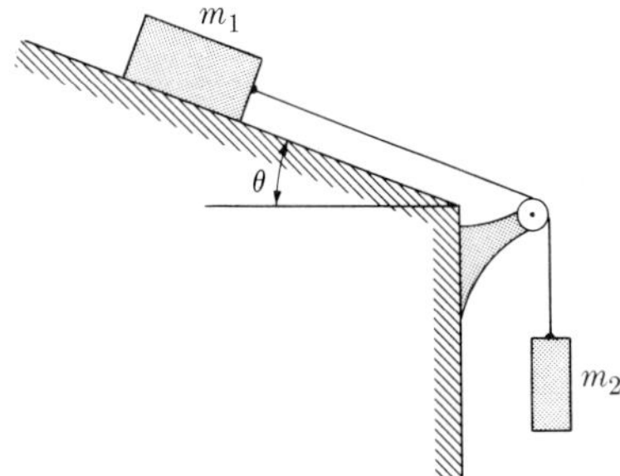

FIG. 7–6. The system of Example 3.

Solution: Since the string and pulley are massless and frictionless, the tension in the string is uniform and the forces T by the string on m_1 and m_2 are equal in magnitude (Fig. 7–7). If we assume the string to be inextensible, the accelerations of m_1 and m_2 are also equal in magnitude. The forces *on* m_1 are shown in the left half of Fig. 7–7, and the forces *on* m_2 are shown in the right half. Since m_1 can only move parallel to the plane, the resultant force on m_1 must be parallel to the plane. In the case of m_1, it is therefore convenient to consider components of forces parallel ($F_{\parallel}$) and perpendicular ($F_{\perp}$) to the plane. We thus have (for m_1)

$$F_{\perp} = N - m_1 g \cos\theta$$

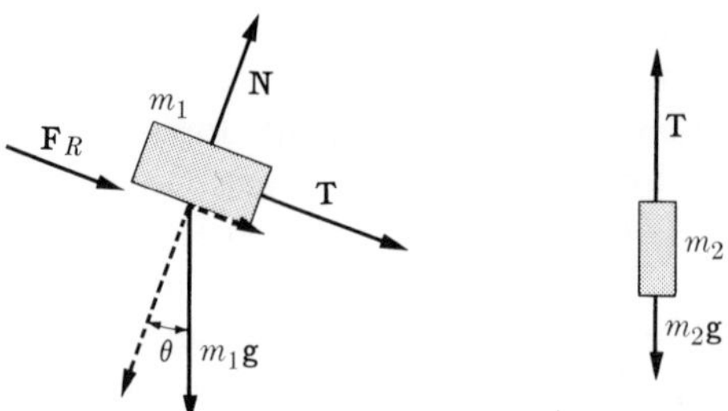

FIG. 7–7. Forces on the components of the system of Example 3.

and

$$F_{\parallel} = T + m_1 g \sin\theta + F_R = m_1 a$$

as expressions of Newton's second law. The friction force can be written

$$F_R = \mu N,$$

where, from the equation for perpendicular components,

$$N = m_1 g \cos\theta.$$

Thus the equation for parallel components becomes

$$T + m_1 g \sin\theta + \mu m_1 g \cos\theta = m_1 a,$$

which has two unknowns, T and a.

We now consider m_2. The obvious choice of coordinates is vertical and horizontal. The second law gives

$$m_2 g - T = m_2 a.$$

Since the two preceding equations have the same two unknowns, T and a, they can be solved for these unknowns, thus answering part (b).

Part (a) can be solved by using the acceleration from the above. Since the forces are constant, the acceleration is constant. Therefore, $v = v_0 + at$, and when $v = 0$ (at the highest point of the motion), we have $t = v_0/a$, with a as determined from the forces.

Example 4. Let a man stand on a spring scales in an elevator (Fig. 7–8). His "apparent weight" W_a is defined as the reading of the scales. His static weight W_s is by definition the reading of the scales when the elevator remains at rest or in uniform motion, that is, $W_s = mg$ by the first law. Now let the system be accelerated upward with acceleration a. The scales

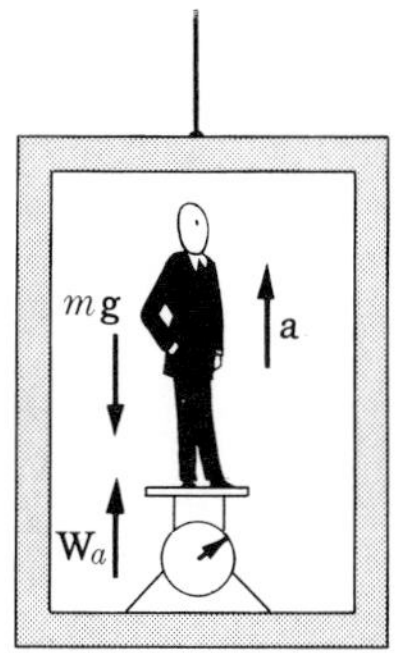

FIG. 7–8. The system of Example 4.

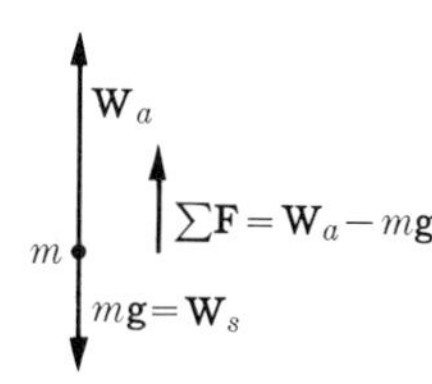

FIG. 7–9. Forces on the man in Example 4.

exert the only upward force on the man, and this force is the scale reading W_a. The downward force on the man is $W_s = mg$. Then, choosing the man to be the mechanical system, we obtain the force diagram of Fig. 7–9. If we choose the upward direction as positive, then $\sum F = ma$ gives $W_a - mg = ma$ or $W_a = W_s + ma$. The apparent weight is greater than the "true" or static weight.

If the acceleration is downward, then $\sum F = ma$ gives $W_a - mg = -ma$ or $W_a = W_s - ma$.

These effects are felt by the elevator passenger as an increase or decrease in the normal upward push on his feet. Note that nothing was said about which way the elevator was *moving* in the above analysis. It could have been moving either way in either case, or it could have been instantaneously at rest!

Example 5. An object of mass m and velocity $v_0 = v_x$ experiences a force $F = F_y = bt^2$. Find the motion of m.

Solution: Since $F_x = 0$, Newton's laws give $a_x = 0$, and, by integration, we have $v_x =$ constant and $x = x_0 + v_x t$.

Since $F_y = bt^2$, the second law gives $a_y = bt^2/m$. By integration, we have $v_y = (b/3m)t^3$ (since $v_{y0} = 0$) and $y = (b/12m)t^4 + y_0$.

7–7 MOVING COORDINATE SYSTEMS

In Chapter 3 it was shown that transformations, from one reference frame (set of coordinate axes) to another frame at rest relative to the first, result in transformations of the position vector; but displacements and therefore all other kinematical quantities remain invariant. It was also shown that transformations from one frame to another which is in relative motion at constant velocity result in changes in the position vector and *also* in the displacement and average velocity vectors. We shall now extend the analysis to less restricted cases.

By dividing Eq. (3–7) ($\Delta \mathbf{S}_{AO} = \Delta \mathbf{S}_{AO'} + \Delta \mathbf{S}_{O'O}$) by Δt and applying the limit process to the result, we can conclude immediately that the instantaneous velocity transformation is the same as the average or uniform velocity transformation:

$$\mathbf{v}_{AO} = \mathbf{v}_{AO'} + \mathbf{v}_{O'O}, \qquad (7\text{–}13)$$

where the $\mathbf{v}$'s can be instantaneous values. This result could also have been obtained directly by differentiating the equation for the position transformation, $\mathbf{S}_{aO} = \mathbf{S}_{aO'} + \mathbf{S}_{O'O}$, with respect to time.

We can now go one step farther by taking derivatives of the terms in Eq. (7–13) with respect to t. The result is

$$\mathbf{a}_{AO} = \mathbf{a}_{AO'} + \mathbf{a}_{O'O}, \qquad (7\text{–}14)$$

from which we see that acceleration remains unchanged only if the reference frames are *unaccelerated* relative to one another; that is, only if $\mathbf{a}_{O'O} = 0$, do we have

$$\mathbf{a}_{AO} = \mathbf{a}_{AO'}. \qquad (7\text{–}15)$$

We find that Newton's laws are invariant under a *constant* velocity transformation by simply multiplying Eq. (7–15) by mass:

$$m\mathbf{a}_{AO} = m\mathbf{a}_{AO'},$$

or

$$\sum \mathbf{F}_O = \sum \mathbf{F}_{O'}. \qquad (7\text{–}16)$$

In Section 7–4 it was stated that Newton's laws hold in a reference frame that is fixed relative to the distant stars. We can now add, "or any reference frame moving at constant velocity relative to the distant stars." Two points of principle arise: (a) the distant stars are not fixed, and (b) the earth is accelerating at least in its revolution about the sun. The answer to both questions is one of neglect of small quantities: (a) the distant stars appear fixed in ordinary observations, and (b) the accelerations of the earth in its orbit and of a point on the earth due to its rotation are small (and can be taken into account if necessary).

Another point should be mentioned at this time. The frames of reference in which Newton's laws are valid, as we have stated them, are called *inertial frames.* In the discussion thus far, all forces have been interaction forces, i.e., there has always been a physical object that exerts each force. Therefore, we call a frame of reference an "inertial frame" if Newton's laws hold when only forces of interaction are included. We recommend that you choose an inertial frame when doing your analysis. Methods of analysis in *non*inertial or accelerated frames will be discussed later.

7–8 TWO- AND THREE-DIMENSIONAL MOTION

If the acceleration or forces are simple when expressed in cartesian coordinates, analysis is most conveniently carried out in these coordinates. Newton's second law is then written in the component form

$$\sum F_x = \frac{dp_x}{dt} = ma_x,$$

$$\sum F_y = \frac{dp_y}{dt} = ma_y, \qquad (7\text{–}17)$$

where the force and acceleration components are the instantaneous values.

Cartesian components are useful, for example, when forces are fixed in direction or when an object is constrained to move along a straight path.

In *circular motion,* the symmetry of the motion immediately suggests polar coordinates. In Chapter 6 it was shown that the acceleration in the case of uniform circular motion has constant magnitude but is variable in direction (always directed oppositely to the radius vector). The various expressions for the magnitude of the acceleration in uniform circular motion were

$$a_r = \frac{v_\theta^2}{r} = \omega^2 r = (2\pi f)^2 r = \omega v_\theta, \quad \text{etc.} \qquad (7\text{–}18)$$

If Newton's second law is applied, the resultant force on an object of mass m is

$$(\sum F)_r = ma_r, \qquad (7\text{–}19)$$

where a_r is given by knowledge of the motion [Eq. (7–18)]. The resultant force is directed inward along the radius vector that defines the position of m, since a_r is so directed.

Conversely, if the resultant force on a body is constant in magnitude around a circular path and always directed toward the center, the object can move in that circular path when given the appropriate initial velocity. This is a special case of the central force problem, which will be treated more generally later.

Two precautions should be emphasized. An inertial frame has been used in the above formulation of circular motion. Consequently, $\sum \mathbf{F}$ represents the vector sum of *interaction* forces, forces exerted by objects that can always be identified. If a rotating frame of reference is chosen, it is a *non*inertial frame because it is accelerated. *Non*-interaction forces will then occur. You are advised *not* to use a noninertial frame until you have mastered the method of inertial frames.

The term *centripetal force* is frequently used in circular motion. This is simply a special name for $(\sum F)_r$ in circular motion and is *not* a mysterious *additional* force that appears in circular motion. The phraseology, "centripetal force *is* ma_r," is a misleading way of stating that "centripetal force *equals* ma_r."

One of the times that *three-dimensional* aspects of motion occur is in circular motion. However, the acceleration must be zero in the direction perpendicular to the circle; hence the problem reduces to one of statics in that direction.

Example 6. A mass m whirls in a horizontal circle of radius r on the end of a string of length l, as shown in Fig. 7–10. Find the frequency of rotation.

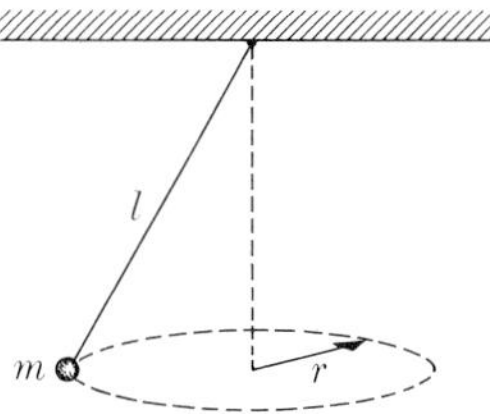

FIG. 7–10. The system of Example 6.

Solution: First draw a force diagram for m (Fig. 7–11). The only interaction forces on m are the pull of the earth, $\mathbf{W} = mg$, and the pull of the string, $\mathbf{T}$. The vector sum of $\mathbf{W}$ and $\mathbf{T}$ must be in the direction of acceleration a_r, that is, toward the center of the circle, as shown.

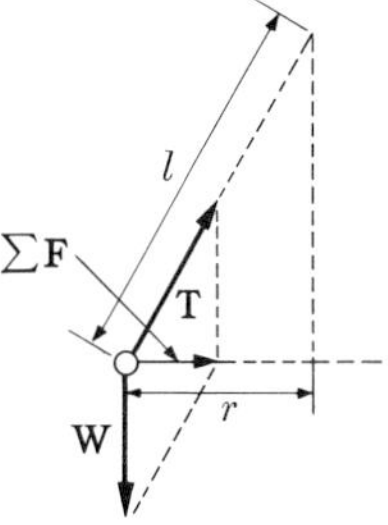

FIG. 7–11. Forces on the mass m of Example 6.

From similar triangles, $(\sum F)/W = r/\sqrt{l^2 - r^2}$, or $\sum F = mgr/\sqrt{l^2 - r^2}$ in terms of the given quantities. In terms of the desired quantity f, the acceleration is $a_r = (2\pi f)^2 r$. Finally, using the second law,

$$\sum F = ma_r,$$

we have

$$\frac{mgr}{\sqrt{l^2 - r^2}} = m(2\pi f)^2 r \quad \text{or} \quad f = \frac{\sqrt{g}}{2\pi \sqrt[4]{l^2 - r^2}}.$$

Example 7. Find the mass of the earth from the observed motion of the moon and the constant of universal gravitation G.

Solution: If the earth is used as the origin of an approximately inertial frame with the direction of the axes fixed relative to the stars, Newton's second law, $\sum F = ma_r$, becomes $Gmm^1/r^2 = m(2\pi)^2 r/T^2$, where m is the mass of the moon and T is its period of revolution (Fig. 7–12). The mass of the earth is then $m^1 = (2\pi)^2 r^3/GT^2$ in terms of observable quantities.

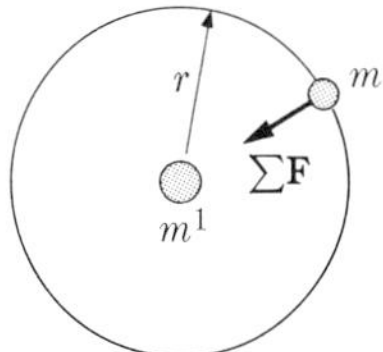

FIG. 7–12. The earth m' and moon m system of Example 7.

Example 8. In Chapter 6 we considered the observed weight of an object to be the same everywhere on the surface of the earth. While this is approximately true, there are two principal causes for an actual variation in the observed weight of an object. One derives from the fact that the earth is not a sphere, but rather an oblate spheroid. This effect of variation in the earth's radius will be treated in Chapter 10. Here we treat a second cause of variation, a particle at any point on the earth except at the geographic poles is in a state of circular motion.

If a man stands on a spring scales at the earth's equator, the reading of the scales is affected by the fact that the system (the man) is being carried along in circular motion by the spin of the earth. The man experiences a centripetal acceleration which must be sustained by a resultant force. Two outside forces act on the man: an upward force by the scales, F_S, and a downward force due to the gravitational pull by the earth W_E. The symbol W_E denotes the static weight of the man, the weight which would be observed if he were at the same distance from the center of the earth but at a pole of the earth. The statics law does not apply; that is, F_S does not equal W_E. Rather, since the man is accelerated radially inward, the inward force is greater than the outward force, that is, $W_E > F_S$. We will define the actual reading of the scales (F_S) to be the "apparent weight" of the man; then $\sum F = ma$ becomes $W_E - F_S = m\omega^2 R$, where ω is the angular velocity of the earth and R is the radius of the earth. The reading of the scales, or the man's apparent weight, is $F_S = W_E - m\omega^2 R$, which is less than the stationary weight by an amount $m\omega^2 R$. Of greatest interest is the ratio of the weights. For example,

$$\frac{F_S}{W_E} = 1 - \frac{m\omega^2 R}{W_E} = 1 - \frac{m\omega^2 R}{mg} = 1 - \frac{\omega^2 R}{g}.$$

Since $R = 6.4 \times 10^6$ m and $\omega = 7.3 \times 10^{-5}$ rad/sec, we find that $F_S/W_E = 1 - 0.0034 = 99.68\%$. The pull by the earth differs from the weight measured with the scales by about 0.3%. (Should g, in principle, be the value measured at the equator? Is this latter question of quantitative consequence in the present problem?)

A force called *centrifugal force* is commonly associated with circular motion. The popular use of this expression is foreign to the description of the motion in an *inertial* frame, and the use of the term can be entirely misleading. Actually, the confusion is partly resolved by an inspection of Newton's third law as it applies to this motion. Centripetal force must be a member of an action-reaction pair. If a stone is whirled on a string, the string must pull inward on the stone. This inward force is the external force applied to the circulating object. This is the force which, according to our rules of forces, must appear in Newton's laws. The string in turn must pull outward on the central point of support. This might be called the centrifugal force when it is applied to an object that is considered stationary. Thus the centrifugal force does not enter into the dynamics of the stone problem. It must never be thought that the stone itself experiences an outward interaction force equal and opposite to the inward force. If so, it would move in a straight line.

Still considering the circular motion of a stone on a string, let the string be cut at some point in the motion. Then the centripetal force vanishes at this instant, and there is no unbalanced inward force acting on the stone. The stone enters into free flight, tangent to the circle at the point of cutting, with an initial velocity equal to the instantaneous velocity at the point of cutting.

In summary, so long as the inward force is applied, the direction of the velocity vector of the stone is changing ever inward, tangent to the circle. When the force is released, the inward acceleration ceases and free flight ensues. This motion is illustrated by mud "flung" tangentially from a spinning wheel or by sparks "flying off" a grinding wheel.

Another possible use of the term centrifugal force occurs with *systems* of objects in circular motion. Consider a simple case of water in a bucket that is whirled in a vertical circle at arm's length. The bucket experiences an outward force exerted *by* the water, a force that might be called a centrifugal force. The question of whether this force is equal and opposite to the inward force on the bucket by the hand of the demonstrator is left for the reader to consider.

A third possible use of the term centrifugal force occurs in the discussion of *noninteraction* forces arising when rotating (*non*inertial) frames of reference are used. This discussion is left for a later chapter.

Now briefly consider *circular motion not at constant speed.* Polar coordinates are chosen for simplicity. The forces, or the resultant force, on the object are therefore to be resolved into components F_r and F_θ. The acceleration components can then be related to the force components by the second law, as usual. The result is

$$(\Sigma \mathbf{F})_\theta \quad \text{or} \quad \Sigma F_\theta = ma_\theta,$$

$$(\Sigma \mathbf{F})_r \quad \text{or} \quad \Sigma F_r = ma_r = \frac{mv_\theta^2}{r}. \tag{7–20}$$

As an illustration, consider the motion of an object constrained to move in a vertical circle at the end of a string (Fig. 7–13). At any point where $v_\theta \neq 0$, there must be a radial acceleration

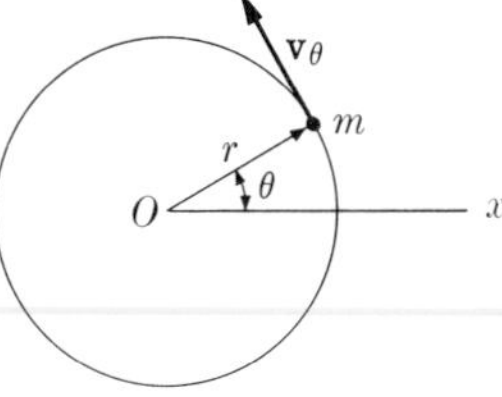

FIG. 7–13. Circular motion of a mass m.

component a_r, and hence the resultant acceleration cannot be tangent to the path. The force diagram is shown in Fig. 7–14, from which we obtain $\sum F_\theta = -mg \cos \theta$ and $\sum F_r = -T - mg \sin \theta$. The second law then gives $a_\theta = -g \cos \theta$ and $a_r = -(T/m) - g \sin \theta$, which are shown in Fig. 7–15. Since neither T nor v_θ are known, there is not enough information thus far to solve the problem completely. If v_θ or T is given for a particular θ, the forces and accelerations can be found. In Chapter 9 conservation of energy will be used to carry the solution farther.

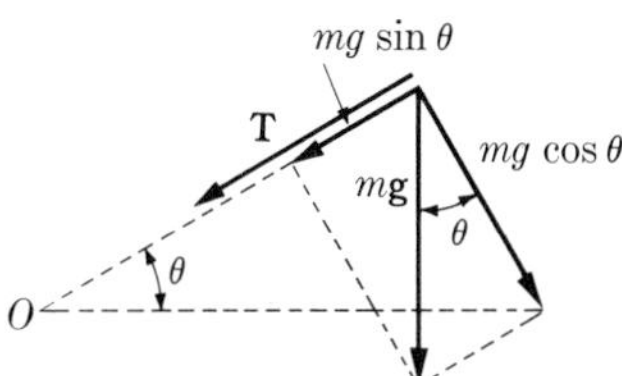

Fig. 7–14. Forces on a mass m that moves in a circle in a vertical plane.

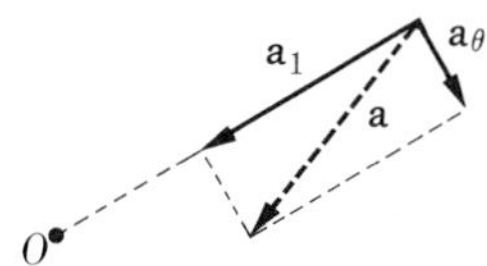

Fig. 7–15. Acceleration of the mass m due to the forces shown in Fig. 7–14.

7–9 THE THIRD LAW IN CIRCULAR MOTION

Thus far it has been tacitly assumed that the interaction forces that cause circular motion of an object are exerted by objects so massive that their motion is unaffected by the interaction. This condition, of course, is not universally true. Consider the case of Fig. 7–16 where masses m_A and m_B are connected by a string and are free to move without friction in a horizontal plane. Suppose that m_A is in circular motion at constant speed v_A.

Can m_B be stationary in the steady state? The answer is "no." Since m_A is accelerated, the string must exert a force *on* m_A. This force is effectively exerted by B (the string is merely a link). By the third law the force (F_B) by A *on* B is equal and opposite to the force (F_A) *by* B *on* A. Consequently, B experiences a force that is constant in magnitude and rotating uniformly in direction, and therefore B experiences an acceleration with the same properties. Hence B cannot remain at rest in the steady state; the only possible steady-state motion is circular motion at constant speed.

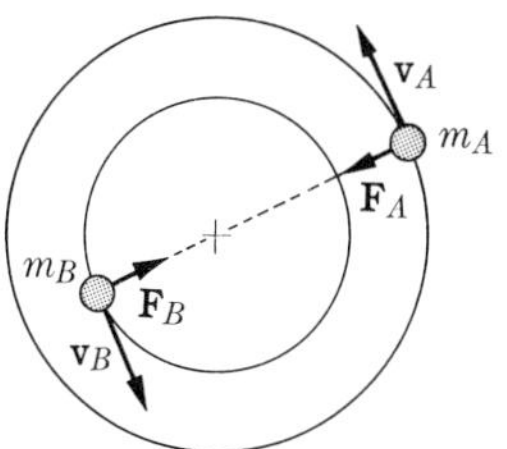

Fig. 7–16. An isolated system of two masses m_A and m_B that have a force of interaction **F**.

The radii r_A and r_B of the circles can be found as follows: Since the forces on A and on B are equal and opposite, i.e., since

$$F_A = -F_B,$$

we have

$$m_A \omega_A^2 r_A = -m_B \omega_B^2 r_B, \tag{7–21}$$

where the ω's must be equal since F_A and F_B must rotate at the same angular velocity. The minus sign indicates that the r's are oppositely directed. Since the minus sign can be dropped when we consider magnitudes, we have

$$m_A r_A = m_B r_B. \tag{7–22}$$

Since $r_A + r_B$ is the separation of A and B, there are two equations in two unknowns.

In Example 6, the radius of the circle described by the earth on the other end of the string is negligibly small. (The case of Example 7 is the subject of Problem 46.)

7–10 FORCES BY STREAMS OF MATERIAL

The average force on a single particle A due to collision with another object B is given by

$$\overline{\mathbf{F}}_A = m_A \frac{\Delta \mathbf{v}}{\Delta t}, \qquad (4\text{–}17)$$

where the force is averaged over the time Δt and $\Delta \mathbf{v}$ is the change in velocity experienced by the colliding mass m. If a stream of particles, each of mass m_0, strikes the object at the rate dn/dt per second, the total mass m striking during Δt is

$$m = m_0 \frac{dn}{dt} \Delta t. \qquad (7\text{–}23)$$

The average force is then

$$\overline{\mathbf{F}}_B = -m_0 \frac{dn}{dt} \Delta \mathbf{v}, \qquad (7\text{–}24)$$

where the minus sign indicates force *on* B due to change in momentum of A. As m_0 is made smaller and smaller, the flow of particles becomes essentially continuous so that $m_0(dn/dt) = dm/dt$ and

$$\mathbf{F} = -\frac{dm}{dt} \Delta \mathbf{v}, \qquad (7\text{–}25)$$

where the force is now the instantaneous force. In terms of density ρ and volume V, we have $dm/dt = \rho\, dV/dt$, assuming that ρ is constant. But since $V = As$, where A is the cross-sectional area of the stream and s its length, we have $m_0 dn/dt = \rho dV/dt = \rho A\, ds/dt = \rho A v$, if A is assumed constant. Therefore

$$\mathbf{F} = -\rho A v\, \Delta \mathbf{v} \qquad (7\text{–}26)$$

for the force exerted on an object by a continuous stream of material of density ρ impinging on that object. Note that the $\Delta \mathbf{v}$ appearing in these equations is simply the total change in velocity of any portion of the impinging material from its state before the interaction to its state after the interaction. The velocity v is the velocity of the fluid relative to the object which the fluid strikes.

Example 9. A water wheel intercepts a stream of water which comes off, on the average, at half its incident speed at an angle of 45°, as shown in Fig. 7–17. Find the force exerted in the horizontal direction on a vane of the wheel while the vane is stationary.

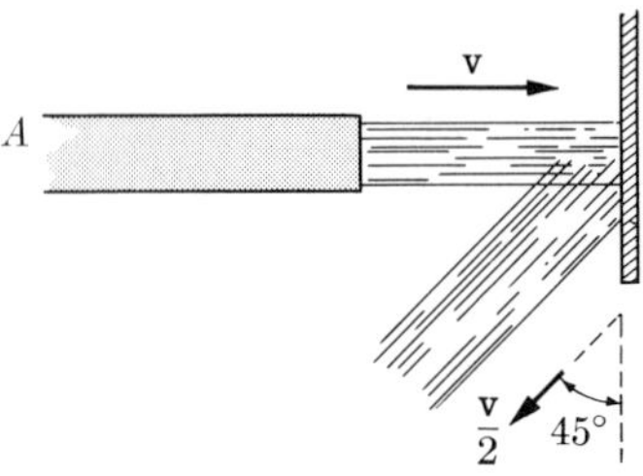

FIG. 7–17. A column of moving water with velocity $\mathbf{v}$ strikes a water wheel and is ejected with velocity $\mathbf{v}/2$ (Example 9).

Solution: The change in velocity Δv_x in the horizontal direction is $v_{fx} - v_{0x} = -(v \cos 45°/2) - v$ or $v_x = -v(1 + \sqrt{2}/4)$. Therefore the force on the vane due to the water is $F_x = \rho A v^2(1 + \sqrt{2}/4)$.

In the case of a stream of material ejected from a body (rocket propulsion), the equations of this section are equally valid. However, the velocity of the ejected material *relative to the rocket*, $\mathbf{v}_{FR}$, is usually one of the known quantities, and this quantity is the $\Delta \mathbf{v}$ of the ejected material as observed from the rocket, since the material is initially at rest in the rocket. The various relative velocities of ejected material (F), rocket (R), and earth (E) are shown in Fig. 7–18. (The analysis of the relationships among the velocities is left for the problems.) In many cases the ejected material is simply the burned fuel.

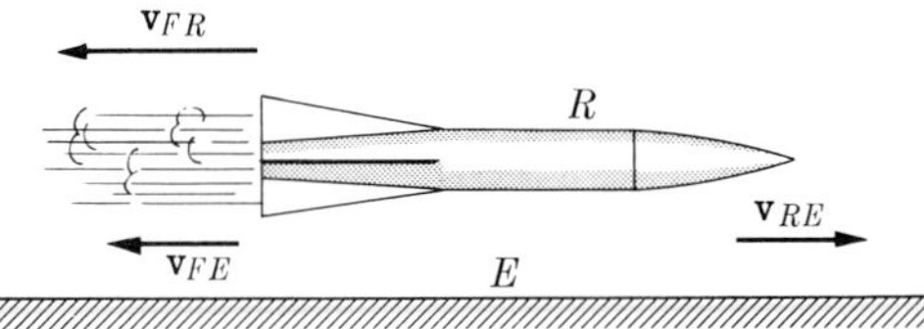

FIG. 7–18. The relative velocities of the components involved in rocket propulsion.

As already noted Δv_F, the change in velocity of ejected material (fuel), is v_{FR} (the ejection velocity of the fuel relative to the rocket). Therefore, the force exerted on the rocket by the discharging fuel is [from Eq. (7–25)]

$$\mathbf{F}_R = -\frac{dm}{dt}\mathbf{v}_{FR}, \qquad (7\text{–}27)$$

where dm/dt is the mass rate of discharge of fuel.

By Newton's second law, the acceleration of the rocket is

$$\mathbf{a}_R = -\left(\frac{dm}{dt}\right)\frac{\mathbf{v}_{FR}}{m}, \qquad (7\text{–}28)$$

in which all three factors on the right may be functions of the time, and at least one, m, must be a function of time.

In jet propulsion in the atmosphere, air that is usually at rest relative to the earth is taken in by the engine and discharged along with the fuel gases. Equation (7–27) would then apply to the fuel component of the discharged material, but $\Delta\mathbf{v}$ for the air component would be the discharge velocity of the air mass relative to the earth. Why?

7–11 SUMMARY

The instantaneous momentum of a system of objects, $\sum m\mathbf{v}$, remains constant in the absence of an outside resultant force, regardless of the nature of the internal forces.

The instantaneous force on an object is defined by

$$\mathbf{F} = m\frac{d\mathbf{v}}{dt},$$

where $\mathbf{F}$ is the only force acting on the mass m. In the case of forces that add vectorially, Newton's second law becomes

$$\sum\mathbf{F} = m\, d\mathbf{v}/dt,$$

or, more generally,

$$\sum\mathbf{F} = \sum d\mathbf{p}/dt,$$

where the instantaneous values of all quantities are used. The third law also applies to instantaneous values of the forces, that is,

$$\mathbf{F}_A = -\mathbf{F}_B.$$

Newton's laws and their application to simple problems are discussed.

A coordinate system in which Newton's laws hold in the above form and in which the forces are all forces of interaction is an *inertial system*. It is shown that any coordinate system moving at uniform velocity relative to a known inertial system is itself an inertial system. It is further shown that a system that is accelerating relative to a known inertial system cannot be an inertial system.

Newton's laws are conveniently used in component form in many cases of motion in two or three dimensions. Examples are given, particularly for circular motion.

The dynamics of motion, when one component of a system is a fluid that changes velocity, are treated. Rocket motion is treated as one of the examples.

Problems

Review Section 7–6 before working these problems. Let $g = 10$ m/sec^2, unless otherwise specified. Note that the angles of a "3, 4, 5" right triangle are 37° and 53°.

1. Two objects A and B move without friction in a horizontal line. They interact and the momentum of A is $p_A = p_0 - bt$, where p_0 and b are constants, and t is the time. Find the momentum of B as a function of time (a) if B started from rest, and (b) if the initial momentum of B was $-p_0$.

FIGURE 7–19

2. Two objects of mass 3 kg and 5 kg are connected by a stretched light spring (Fig. 7–19). The system is on a horizontal frictionless surface. They are released and drawn together by the spring. At an instant when the acceleration of the 5-kg body is 10 m/sec^2, what is the acceleration of the 3-kg body? Which of Newton's laws have you used in this problem? How did you use them?

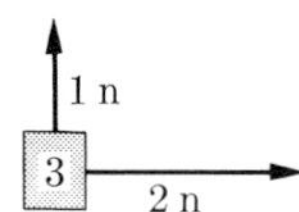

FIGURE 7–20

3. A body of mass 3 kg is subjected to only two forces, as shown in Fig. 7–20. What is the acceleration? What are the direction and magnitude of the velocity as a function of time, starting from rest?

4. A body is traveling on a frictionless horizontal surface with an initial velocity of 10 m/sec toward the right. It suddenly comes to a region where the coefficient of friction is 0.5. Where and when will the mass come to rest?

5. A single force of 50 n acts on a 4-kg mass which is in contact with a 2-kg mass, as shown in Fig. 7–21.

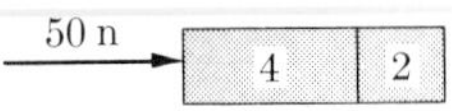

FIGURE 7–21

(a) What is the "force of contact" between the two masses if they are on a frictionless surface (i.e., what force is exerted by m_1 on m_2? by m_2 on m_1)?

(b) Repeat part (a) for the case of the blocks on a horizontal surface with a coefficient of sliding friction of 0.1. What happens when $\mu = \frac{5}{6}$?

(c) Repeat part (a) for the case of the surface in (b) sloping down to the left at an angle of 37° with the 50-n force parallel to the slope. Solve for both directions of motion.

(d) Was the direction of motion of consequence in (a) or in (b)?

6. Given that the acceleration of any material particle in the earth's gravitational field is 9.8 m/sec^2, what is the gravitational force, in newtons, on a 1-kilogram mass?

7. An object of mass 20 kg is traveling toward the right at 10 m/sec on a frictionless horizontal surface. At $t = 0$ a constant lateral force of 5 n is applied. Where is the body 10 sec later?

8. The resultant force on an object of mass m is $F = F_0 - kt$, where F_0 and k are constant and t is the time. Find the acceleration. By integration find the velocity and position equations.

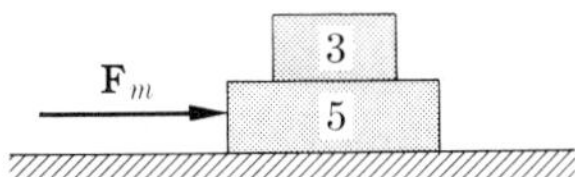

FIGURE 7–22

9. One block of mass 3 kg is placed on top of another of mass 5 kg. Assume that there is no friction between the 5-kg block and the table. The coefficients of static and sliding friction are 0.2 and 0.1, respectively. What is the maximum, $\mathbf{F}_m$, of the force $\mathbf{F}$ if the blocks move together (see Fig. 7–22)? What will be the acceleration when the maximum force is applied? What is the acceleration of the 3-kg block when $\mathbf{F}$ is greater than $\mathbf{F}_m$?

10. A 10-kg wedge is supported between a vertical wall and a 5-kg block, as shown in Fig. 7–23. All surfaces have identical friction properties, except the wall, which is frictionless.

(a) Find the coefficient of friction if the wedge falls at constant velocity.

(b) Can the velocity be constant if the floor is also frictionless? Explain.

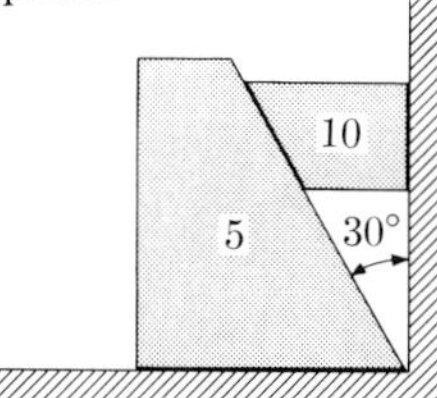

FIGURE 7–23

11. What are the tensions T_1 and T_2 in Fig. 7–24? Why are they not equal?

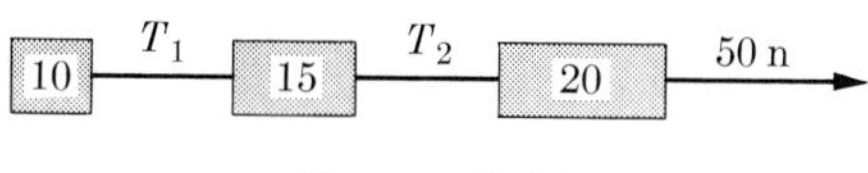

FIGURE 7–24

12. Objects of mass m_1 and m_2 are attached to the ends of a string which is hung over a pulley (Fig. 7–25).

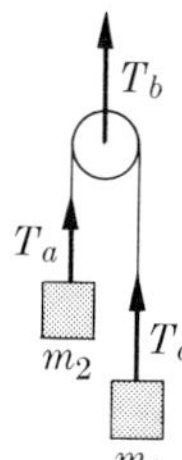

FIGURE 7–25

(a) Prove that the acceleration of the system is

$$a = \frac{m_2 - m_1}{m_2 + m_1} g.$$

(b) Prove that the tension in the string attached to the objects is

$$T_a = 2g \frac{m_1 m_2}{m_1 + m_2}.$$

(c) Prove that the tension in the support of the pulley is

$$T_b = 4g \frac{m_1 m_2}{m_1 + m_2}.$$

What is T_a when $m_1 = m_2$? What is T_a when $m_1 = 0$? when $m_2 = 0$? What is T_b when $m_1 = m_2$? What is T_b when either m_1 or m_2 is zero?

13. In *each* of the following:

(a) Draw vectors showing the external forces acting on the "italicized" object.

(b) Label each vector with the name of the body that exerts the force.

(c) In a second drawing, make a vector diagram that includes the resultant (labeled $\sum \mathbf{F}$):

(i) A *feather* falling at uniform velocity; (ii) A *football* while in contact with the kicker's boot; (iii) a *football* at the highest point in its path; (iv) a *mass* hanging by a string from the ceiling of a truck, while the truck is descending a uniform slope of angle θ with constant acceleration a; (v) after the truck in part (iv) plunges over a cliff and falls with acceleration $0.9g$.

14. An object of 1-kg mass is supported in a man's hand in the earth's gravitational field.

(a) What is the force exerted by the man on the object, if the acceleration is 4 m/sec^2 upward? 4 m/sec^2 downward?

(b) What is the acceleration if $T = 4$ n? if $T = 8$ n?

(c) What is the direction of the motion in each of the above cases?

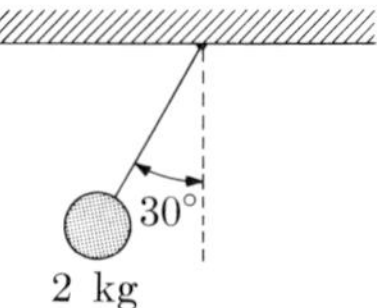

FIGURE 7–26

15. A 2-kg stone is suspended by a string which is attached to the ceiling of a railroad car that is on a horizontal track.

(a) What is the acceleration of the car if the steady deflection of the string from vertical is $\theta = 30°$ (Fig. 7–26)? What is the tension in the string when $\theta = 30°$?

(b) What are the angle of deflection and the tension in the string when the acceleration of the car is 5 m/sec^2?

(c) Which way is the railroad car traveling? Explain.

16. A 10-kg object is suspended on a spring balance in an elevator. What is the acceleration of the elevator if the apparent weight of the object is 50 n? 150 n?

17. A man of static weight W_S stands on scales in an elevator. The scales read $W_S/3$. What is the

acceleration? Is it upward or downward? Is the elevator moving upward or downward?

18. A 5-kg mass is observed to move in a path such that $x = 6t$, $y = 5 - 2t^3$, and $z = 2t + 4t^2$. Find the resultant force on the mass. (x is in meters, t in seconds, etc.)

19. An object of mass m is observed to have an acceleration a. Can you tell how many forces act on m? What information can you give about the forces? Explain.

20. An airplane is climbing at an angle β above the horizontal. Curtains in the aisle are observed to hang back at an angle γ from their normal position (Fig. 7–27). What is the acceleration of the plane when: (a) $\gamma = \beta$? (b) $\gamma > \beta$?

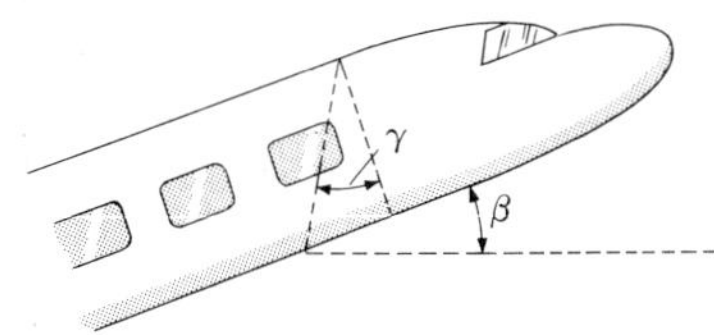

FIGURE 7–27

21. We have assumed that the forces at the two ends of a string are equal and opposite. Thus, $\sum \mathbf{F} = 0$. How can this be true when the acceleration $\neq 0$?

22. A 1-kg mass rests on a 10-kg mass which in turn rests on a horizontal surface, as shown in Fig. 7–28. The force F varies with the time t measured in seconds such that $F = 0.2t$ n. If the coefficient of static friction is 0.2 and the coefficient of sliding friction is 0.15 between all surfaces, find the motion of each block as a function of time.

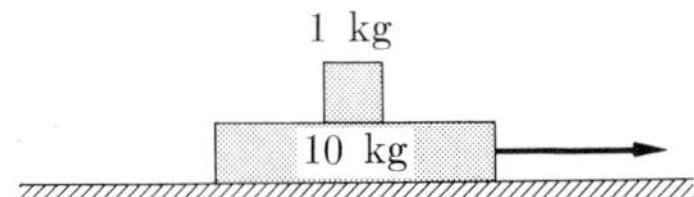

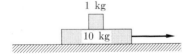

FIGURE 7–28

23. A mass of 2 kg is hung on a spring that follows Hooke's law with a constant of 200 n/m.

(a) What is the acceleration of the mass the instant after it is hung on the spring and released?

(b) Find the elongation of the spring when the acceleration of the mass is zero.

(c) What is the acceleration as a function of the elongation of the spring?

(d) Can you find the velocity from the result of (c)?

(e) Repeat the above problem for the case in which the spring force follows the law $F = -kx^3$.

FIGURE 7–29

24. A 60-kg painter standing on a 30-kg platform pulls on a rope, as shown in Fig. 7–29. The pulley is frictionless.

(a) What is the motion, if the painter pulls on the rope with a force of 50 n?

(b) What are the forces on the painter in (a)?

25. Objects A and B are connected by a light string that passes over a pulley P (Fig. 7–30). The mass and friction of P are negligible. The masses of A and B are 3 kg and 1 kg, respectively.

(a) If the upward force $\mathbf{F}$ on the pulley increases with time t as $5t^2$ n, find the accelerations of A and B as functions of t.

(b) Find the acceleration after B reaches the pulley.

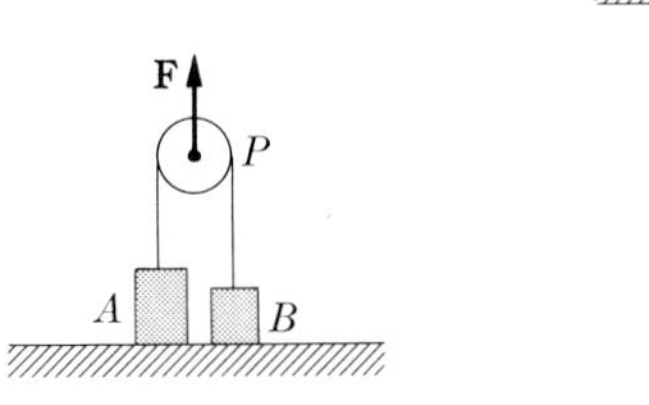

FIGURE 7–30

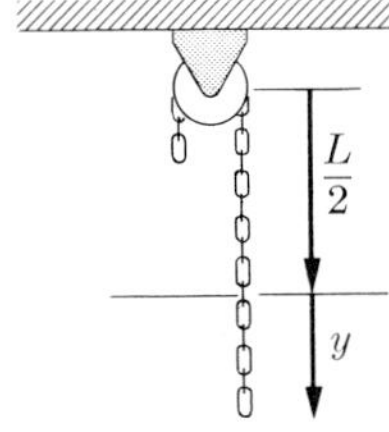

FIGURE 7–31

26. A chain of length L and mass M is hung over an ideal pulley of small diameter, as shown in Fig. 7–31. The chain is released from rest with $y = y_0$.

(a) Find the acceleration as a function of y.

(b) What is the initial value of the acceleration?

(c) The maximum value?

(d) Can you integrate the expression found in (a) in order to obtain the velocity?

27. A certain airplane has a mass of 10^5 kg and a top speed of 1800 km/hr in level flight.

(a) Assuming that the maximum thrust by the engine is 10^6 n and that the force of air resistance is kv^2, find the value of k. What are its units?

(b) Using the value of k from (a), find the terminal velocity of the plane when it is pointed straight down, assuming the same engine thrust as in (a).

28. The above plane is used to obtain a "freely falling" laboratory ($a = g$) for short periods of time. Suppose that the plane turns straight down when flying as slowly as possible and reaches the straight-down direction when $v = 600$ km/hr.

(a) How long can the plane be a "freely falling" laboratory in such a dive?

(b) How far will it travel?

(c) Derive the equation for the required engine thrust during the downward flight (i) as a function of velocity, and (ii) as a function of time.

29. Show that the plane of Problem 27 can take off vertically (using $g = 9.8$ m/sec^2).

30. The "freely falling" laboratory of Problem 28 can be realized by having the plane turn straight up while flying at top speed. If its speed is 1200 km/hr when it reaches the vertical upward direction, (a) find the maximum time for its "free-fall" flight straight up. (b) Find the required engine thrust as a function of velocity and as a function of time.

FIGURE 7–32

31. In actual fact, an airplane's "free-fall" flight is made by following an upward arc, as shown in Fig. 7–32. The forces on the plane may be separated into gravitational force, engine thrust (along the plane's axis), air drag (opposite to the direction of motion), and airlift (perpendicular to the plane's axis).

(a) What is the condition on the horizontal component of velocity throughout the "free-fall" arc?

(b) Make force diagrams showing that the plane cannot be pointed along the flight path while (i) climbing or (ii) descending.

32. A boat is traveling at speed v_0 when its motor stops.

(a) If the water resistance is kv^2, show that $dv/dt = -kv^2/m$.

(b) By inverting the derivative in (a), we have $dt/dv = -m/(kv^2)$. Show by antidifferentiation that $t = (m/kv) + c$, and find c from the initial conditions.

(c) Solve (b) explicitly for $v(t)$, and integrate to find $x(t)$. [*Hint:* See Eq. (6–4), and let $t - c = t'$.]

(d) How far does the boat travel?

33. A mass m is supported by a string, as shown in Fig. 7–33.

(a) What are the forces acting on m?

(b) What is the "reaction" force to each force on m?

(c) In each of the following, which forces are equal and *why:* (i) when m continues at rest, (ii) when m is moving at constant velocity, (iii) when m is moving upward at diminishing velocity, (iv) if the string is released while m is traveling upward, (v) when m is at rest at the highest point in its path after the string was released in (iv)?

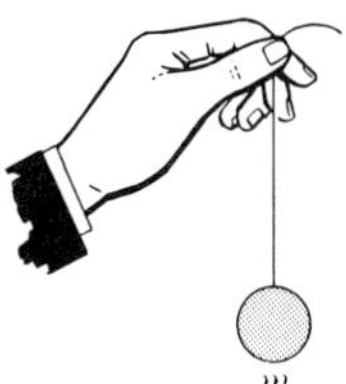

FIGURE 7–33

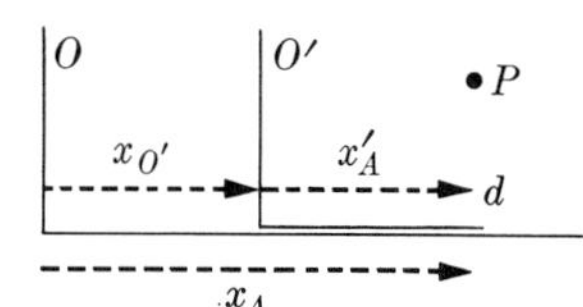

FIGURE 7–34

34. In the text we derived the equation for relative velocities ($v_{AO} = v_{AO'} + v_{O'O}$) by considering displacements measured in frames O and O' moving at uniform relative velocity. Derive the relative velocity equation in the special case of x-components by starting with $x_A = x'_A + x_{O'}$ (Fig. 7–34) and differentiating.

35. (a) What frame of reference is used in the analysis of Example 8?

(b) Is it assumed to be an inertial frame? Why?

(c) Can the earth be an inertial frame for this example?

(d) If the analysis were extended to include the motion of the earth in its orbit, what reference frame would be chosen? Which of the frames would then be assumed to be inertial?

36. What would be the length of the day, in hours, if the earth were rotating so fast that a man standing at the equator would have no apparent weight? Under the above conditions, would a stone fall when the man drops it? Explain.

37. A stone is whirled in a horizontal circle at the end of a string 2 m long. The mass of the stone is 0.1 kg. It is known from static tests that the string will break under a tension of 2 n. What is the maximum frequency of the motion, in cycles per second, which can be sustained by this system? What is the angle of the string?

38. A particle is on the equator of the earth. Find the linear velocity of the particle numerically in meters per second, the angular velocity in radians per second, and the radial acceleration in meters per second squared.

39. Must the speed of a particle change if its acceleration is not zero? Explain.

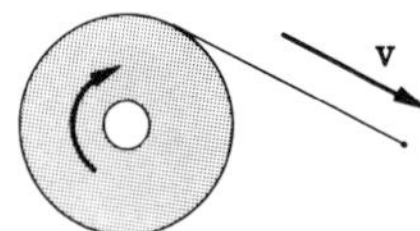

FIGURE 7–35

40. A string is wrapped around a wheel which is mounted on an axle (Fig. 7–35). The radius of the wheel is 0.30 m. The string is pulled at a rate of 5 m/sec.

(a) What is the angular velocity of the wheel?

(b) What is the frequency of rotation in cycles per second?

(c) What is the acceleration of a point on the rim of the wheel?

41. (a) Draw vectors showing the external forces acting on the "italicized" object.

(b) Label *each* force vector with the name of the object that exerts the force.

(c) In a second diagram show the addition of the vectors to obtain a resultant **F**.

(i) A truck *driver* while the truck passes over the crest of a hill of radius R at constant speed v; (ii) the truck *driver* while the truck rounds an unbanked curve of radius R at speed v; (iii) a *mass* on a string (that is, a pendulum) at the highest point in its arc; (iv) the above *mass* moving through the lowest point in its arc.

42. A mass m at the end of a spring (Fig. 7–36) rotates in a circle at constant angular velocity ω on a horizontal frictionless surface. The unstretched length of the spring is l_0, and the spring constant is k.

(a) Find the radius of the circle.

(b) What is the minimum possible value of k that will permit the motion?

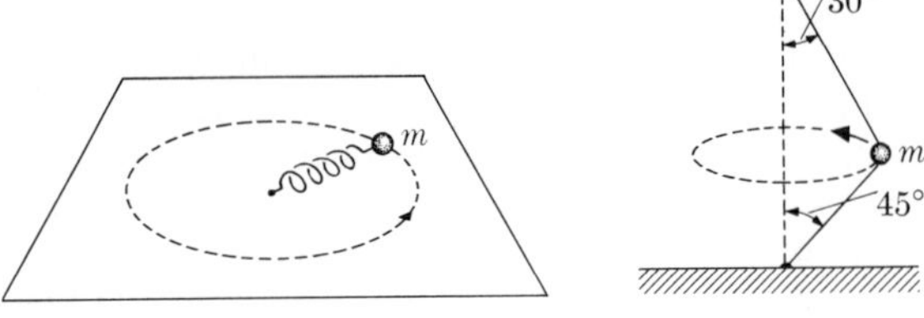

FIGURE 7–36 FIGURE 7–37

43. A mass of 0.5 kg is rotating in a horizontal circle of radius 50 cm at a frequency of $4/\pi$. Two strings are used for support, as shown in Fig. 7–37. Find the tensions in the strings.

44. A car rounds a curve of radius r at speed v.

(a) Show that the maximum speed on a flat road is $\sqrt{\mu r g}$, where μ is the coefficient of static friction.

(b) Show that the friction force is zero if the road is banked at an angle θ, given by $\tan \theta = v^2/rg$.

(c) Find the maximum speed at which a car will not slip on a road banked at angle θ with coefficient of static friction μ.

45. As a lecture demonstration, a physics professor whirls a pail containing 2 kg of water in a vertical circle of radius 1.2 m. Assume uniform angular velocity.

(a) What is the longest possible period of revolution (*assuming uniform angular velocity*) that is possible if the water remains in the pail?

(b) What is the force exerted by the pail on the water at the bottom of the circle?

(c) At shoulder height?

(d) If the pail weighs 10 n, find each of the forces acting on the pail at the bottom of the circle.

46. (a) Due to the rotation of the earth, what is the acceleration of an object at rest on the earth at 60° latitude? (The radius of the earth is 6400 km.)

(b) What is the direction of the resultant force on the object?

(c) If the object hangs from a string, what is the direction of the string?

47. The mass of the earth is about 80 times the mass of the moon, and the distance between the earth and the moon is about 400,000 km. Find the radius of the circle in which the earth moves due to the effect of the moon.

48. Two masses, m_1 and m_2, are connected by a string and move in circular paths of radii r_1 and r_2 on a horizontal frictionless surface, as shown in Fig. 7–38.

(a) Prove that the linear momentum of the system is zero.

(b) In one-half revolution the momentum of m_1 changes by $2m_1\mathbf{v}_1$. Is momentum conserved? Explain.

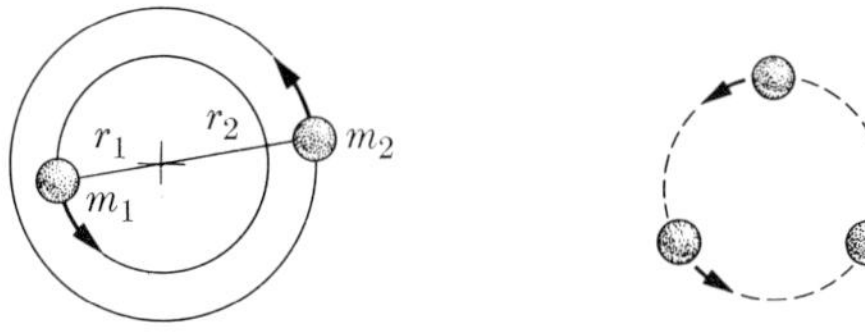

FIGURE 7–38

FIGURE 7–39

49. Three equal masses are isolated in space and move in the same circular path (Fig. 7–39) at equal intervals under the influence of their mutual gravitational attractions. Derive an equation relating the period, radius of the orbit, and mass of the objects.

50. Find the period of a satellite that circles the earth just above the atmosphere at 6500 km from the earth's center. (Assume that the gravitational force is the same as at the earth's surface.)

51. At what height must a satellite be placed in an equatorial circular orbit in order to remain continuously above the same point of the equator? Would it be reasonable to assume that the force of gravity is the same as at the earth's surface?

52. Find the period of a particle of mass m in a circular orbit in a region where the particle experiences an inverse cube-central force.

53. Show that the change in velocity of the rocket fuel when observed from the earth is in fact $\mathbf{v}_{FR}$ in the notation of Fig. 7–18.

54. The exhaust velocity of the fuel in a certain rocket at takeoff is 1000 m/sec. Show that the mass of the rocket plus fuel must diminish at least at the rate of 1%/sec in order for the rocket to take off vertically.

55. A certain jet-powered speedboat takes in water from the lake and ejects a stream of water of radius 10 cm at a velocity of 30 m/sec relative to the boat.

(a) What is the initial acceleration of the boat if its mass is 500 kg?

(b) What is the thrust on the boat when the boat is traveling 15 m/sec?

(c) What is the top speed of the boat if friction is completely neglected?

56. A small rocket fired from a balloon near the top of the atmosphere has a total mass of 400 kg, of which 200 kg is fuel.

(a) If the fuel burns at the rate of $4t$ kg/sec, where t is in seconds, when will the fuel be exhausted? [*Hint:* Find $m(t)$ from the knowledge that $dm/dt = -4t$.]

(b) Using the results of (a) and assuming that the fuel gases are exhausted at 1000 m/sec, what is the acceleration of the above rocket as a function of time?

(c) Make a graph of acceleration versus time.

57. (a) Show that a power law for rate of fuel burning in a rocket, that is, $dm/dt = bt^n$, cannot give a uniform acceleration for any value of the exponent n. (It is only an exponential function that can give uniform acceleration.)

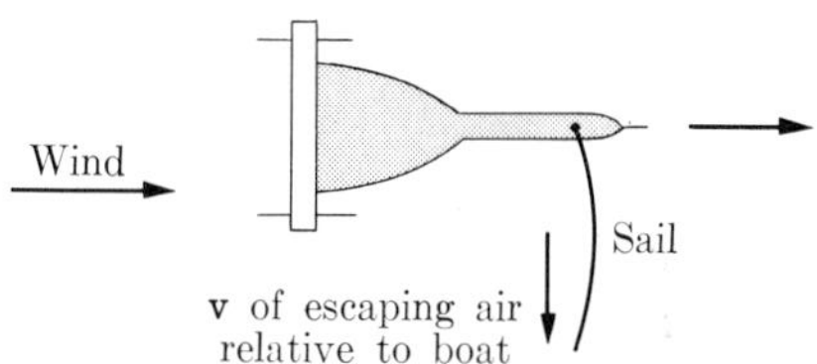

FIGURE 7–40

58. An iceboat of mass 200 kg and sail area $A = 10\ \text{m}^2$ is directed straight downwind with its sail at right angles to the wind and its motion (Fig. 7–40). The coefficient of friction μ of the runners on ice is 0.01. The density of air is about 1.3 kg/m^3. Assume that the air that is stopped by the sail flows off parallel to the sail relative to the boat, as shown. The wind is 12 m/sec, or about 30 mph.

(a) Find the force on the sail while the iceboat is at rest, and the initial acceleration when the boat starts from rest, assuming that the static friction μ is also 0.01.

(b) Show that the maximum speed of the boat relative to the earth, v_{be}, in terms of wind velocity v_{we} is

$v_{be} = v_{we} - \sqrt{\mu mg/\rho A}$. How great is this velocity in our example?

(c) What is the maximum possible speed no matter how large the sail or how small the friction?

59. The iceboat of Problem 58 now turns so that the wind (relative to the earth) comes directly from the side (Fig. 7–41). If the sail is at 30° and the iceboat is at rest:

(a) Find the force on the sail, assuming air escapes along the sail with no drag.

(b) Find the force components in the direction in which the iceboat is pointed, assuming that the runners penetrate the ice sufficiently to prevent sideward motion.

(c) Show that the maximum possible speed of the boat when the wind is from the side (neglecting friction completely) is $v_{be} = v_{we}/\tan\theta$, where θ is the angle of the sail with respect to the boat's motion.

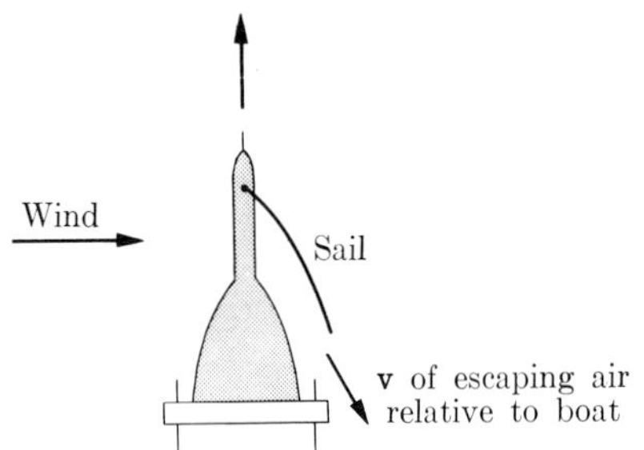

FIGURE 7–41

60. Generalize the conditions of Problem 59 to the case where the iceboat is in motion at velocity v_{be} with the sail at an angle γ with respect to the motion (Fig. 7–42).

(a) Show that the wind force component in the direction of motion is $F_w = \rho A(v_{be}^2 + v_{we}^2)\sin^2(\beta - \gamma)\sin\gamma$, where $\beta - \gamma$ is the angle between the apparent wind $\mathbf{v}_{wb}$ and the sail, that is, $\tan\beta = v_{we}/v_{be}$.

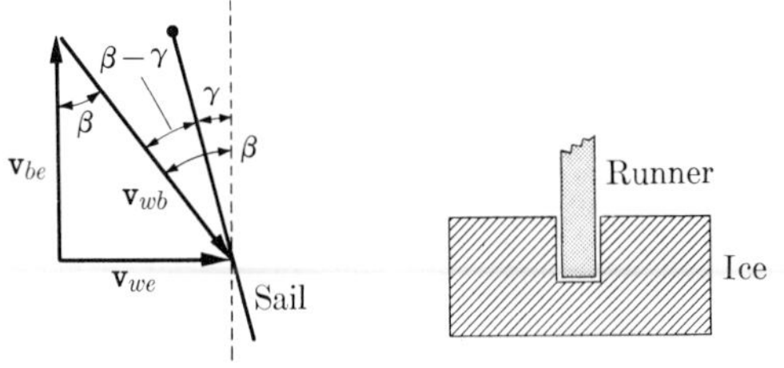

FIGURE 7–42 FIGURE 7–43

(b) When the speed of the boat is high compared with the wind velocity, the angles β and γ are small. Show that $F_w \simeq \rho A v_{be}^2(\beta - \gamma)^2\gamma$ and that the friction force $F_R \simeq \mu mg + \mu A v_{be}^2(\beta - \gamma)^2$.

(c) Find an expression for the "maximum velocity" and show that it is truly maximum when $\gamma = (\beta + 2\mu)/3$.

(d) Using the results of (c), find the maximum speed of the iceboat under these conditions. (Actually, the wind drag along the sail and the lift due to reduced pressure behind the sail are not negligible.)

61. A current experiment to test the equivalence of inertial and gravitational mass is designed to compare the motions of two objects of different material in their orbital motion around the sun. In principle, objects A and B are balanced as shown (Fig. 7–44). Both move in circular orbits of radius R around the sun and, as far as that motion is concerned, Newton's second law gives

$$m'g_s = mv^2/R.$$

(a) Which mass in the equation is gravitational and which is inertial?

(b) Explain qualitatively what will happen to the balance if

$$m'_A/m_A \neq m'_B/m_B.$$

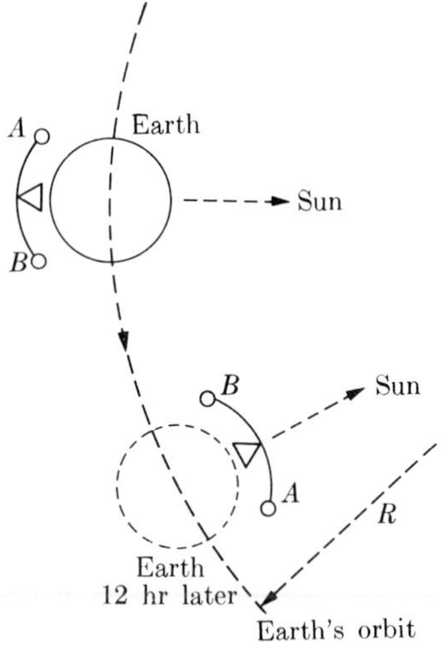

FIGURE 7–44

8

Periodic Motion

8–1 INTRODUCTION

In Section 6–8, we considered an example of periodic motion, namely, uniform circular motion. The concepts of frequency, period, and angular velocity were introduced as possible ways of quantitatively characterizing the periodicity. This chapter will contain a few remarks about periodic motion in general and a detailed discussion of the special case of simple harmonic motion. The composition of general periodic motion in terms of simple harmonic components will be considered briefly. Finally, simple examples of forced harmonic motion will be analyzed.

8–2 PERIODIC MOTION KINEMATICS IN GENERAL

Any object's motion that repeats itself regularly in time is called periodic. The time between two adjacent repetitions is called the period and its reciprocal is called the frequency, for which we use the symbols τ and f, respectively. As usual, in nature there are probably no examples of truly periodic motion, but there are many examples of motion that is periodic to within a high degree of accuracy. Examples are the motions of the planets and their *satellites*, moving parts in machines and clocks, particles in wave motion, and atoms vibrating and rotating according to the semiclassical models of molecular structure.

The motion can be described by giving the position coordinates, components of velocity, etc., as functions of time or by specifying the position vector, velocity vector, etc., as functions of time. Choosing the cartesian component of position as a representative example, we might have a dependence on time as shown in Fig. 8–1. We see that the coordinate y_0 repeats periodically every interval of time, τ, and so does the slope of the curve and its rate of change of slope, i.e., the velocity and acceleration. In compact mathematical terminology, we write $y = f(t) = f(t + n\tau)$, where n is an integer. When the function of t repeats, the time derivatives repeat. The motion of the object is then periodic in its y-coordinate. The other coordinates may or may not be periodic.

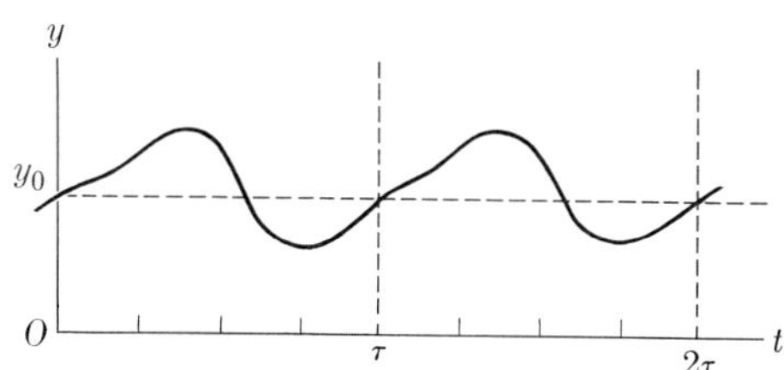

Fig. 8–1. The coordinate y of an object as a function of time t. The motion is seen to be periodic, repeating in each interval of time τ.

The dependence of y on time displayed in Fig. 8–1 might occur in nature as the vertical position of a cork floating on water that is disturbed by wave motion.

The particular dependence of y on t in this case cannot be represented by any of the functions that you have studied: power laws *are not* repetitive; trigonometric functions *are* repetitive but none has the form of Fig. 8–1. We will return at the end of this chapter to the problem of analytical representation of curves such as those in Fig. 8–1.

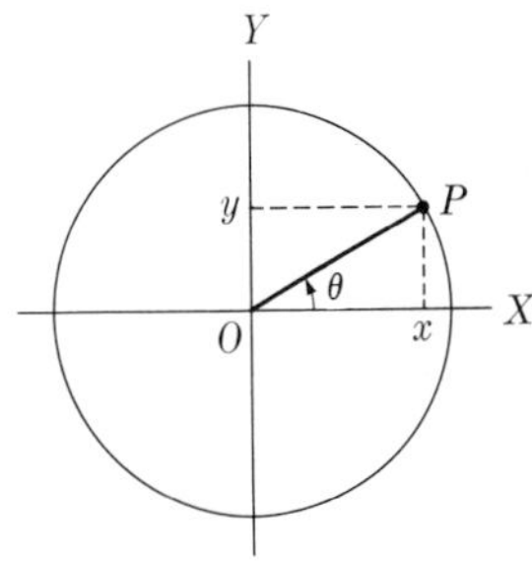

FIG. 8-2. Cartesian components of the position of a point P that is constrained to move in a circular path.

8-3 CIRCULAR MOTION; DERIVATIVES OF THE SINE AND COSINE

We first consider *uniform* circular motion. In polar coordinates the motion is described by

$$\begin{aligned} r &= \text{constant}, \\ \theta &= \omega t = 2\pi f t = 2\pi t/\tau. \end{aligned} \tag{8-1}$$

Neither r nor θ is periodic in a strict sense. The position, velocity, and acceleration vectors do, however, repeat periodically. The periodic nature can be given explicitly when the motion is described in cartesian components x and y (Fig. 8-2). (The circular motion need not be uniform in order to be periodic; that is, θ could be any periodic function of t with a period simply related to the period of revolution.) Figure 8-3 shows the position, velocity, and acceleration of point P that moves in uniform circular motion. The directions of v_θ and a_r have been derived earlier. We see from the figure that

$$\begin{aligned} x &= r\cos\theta, \\ v_x &= -v_\theta \sin\theta, \\ a_x &= -a_r \cos\theta. \end{aligned} \tag{8-2}$$

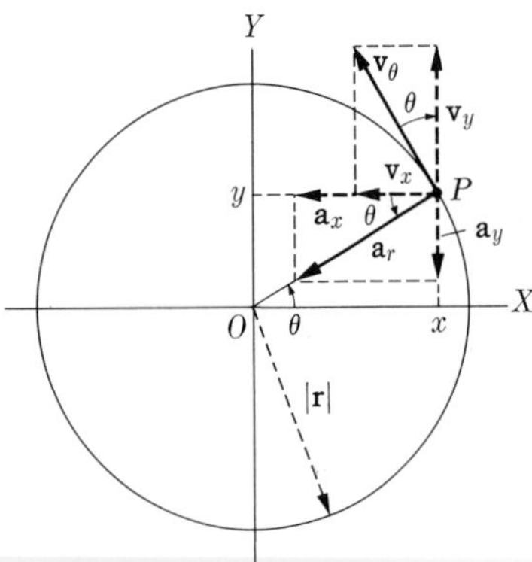

FIG. 8-3. Cartesian components of the position, velocity, and acceleration of a point P that moves in a circular path at constant speed.

Since $\theta = \omega t$ for uniform circular motion and also $v_\theta = \omega r$ and $a_r = \omega^2 r$ (for any circular motion), Eq. (8-2) may be written

$$\begin{aligned} x &= r\cos(\omega t), \\ v_x &= -r\omega \sin(\omega t), \\ a_x &= -r\omega^2 \cos(\omega t). \end{aligned} \tag{8-3}$$

Similarly, for the y-components we have

$$\begin{aligned} y &= r\sin(\omega t), \\ v_y &= r\omega \cos(\omega t), \\ a_y &= -r\omega^2 \sin(\omega t). \end{aligned} \tag{8-4}$$

Now, recalling that $v_x \equiv dx/dt$ and $v_y \equiv dy/dt$, we obtain from Eq. (8-3)

$$\frac{d}{dt}(\cos\omega t) = -\omega \sin(\omega t) \tag{8-5}$$

and from Eq. (8-4)

$$\frac{d}{dt}(\sin\omega t) = \omega \cos(\omega t). \tag{8-6}$$

Returning now to the component equations (8-3) and (8-4), we see that x and y are periodic in t and have the same period ($\tau = 2\pi/\omega$) as the circular motion. This particular periodic motion of x and y is called *simple harmonic motion*. Graphs of y, v_y, and a_y (Eq. 8-4) are given in Fig. 8-4.

Finally, the differentiation formulas of Eqs. (8-5) and (8-6) can be generalized by returning to a consideration of *nonuniform* circular motion.

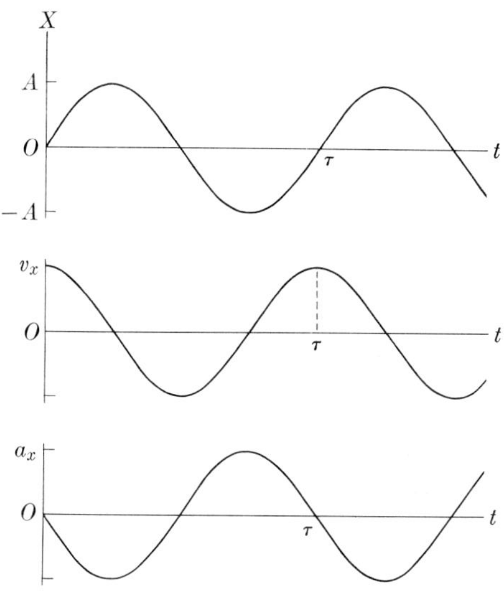

FIG. 8–4. Graphs of the position, velocity, and acceleration of a point that moves with simple harmonic motion. The amplitude is A, the period is τ, and the initial phase angle is 0.

The first two equations of (8–2) can be written

$$x = r \cos \theta,$$
$$v_x = -r(d\theta/dt) \sin \theta, \qquad (8\text{–}7)$$

since $v_\theta = \omega r$ and $\omega \equiv d\theta/dt$. Similarly, for the y-components,

$$y = r \sin \theta,$$
$$v_y = r(d\theta/dt) \cos \theta. \qquad (8\text{–}8)$$

Since $v_x = dx/dt$ and $v_y = dy/dt$, Eqs. (8–7) and (8–8) lead to

$$\frac{d(\cos \theta)}{dt} = -(\sin \theta)\,\frac{d\theta}{dt},$$
$$\frac{d(\sin \theta)}{dt} = (\cos \theta)\,\frac{d\theta}{dt}. \qquad (8\text{–}9)$$

8–4 KINEMATICS OF SIMPLE HARMONIC MOTION

A point is said to have simple harmonic motion if, in general, its position as a function of time is given by

$$x = A_0 + A \sin (Bt + C), \qquad (8\text{–}10)$$

where A_0, A, B, and C are constants. The constant A_0 is usually made zero by the appropriate shift of the x-axis. The constant A then is equal in magnitude to the maximum or minimum value of x. It is called the *amplitude*. The angle $\theta = (Bt + C)$ is called the *phase* angle.

The value of $\sin (Bt + C)$, and hence of x, repeats each time $Bt + C$ increases by 2π, that is, when $Bt_2 + C - (Bt_1 + C) = 2\pi$ or $B(t_2 - t_1) = 2\pi$. But the repetition time $t_2 - t_1$ is the period τ, by definition. Therefore, $\tau = 2\pi/B$ or

$$B = 2\pi/\tau = 2\pi f = \omega. \qquad (8\text{–}11)$$

The constant C is called the initial phase angle and is conveniently denoted by θ_0. The equation for simple harmonic motion is then written

$$x = A \sin (2\pi f t + \theta_0), \qquad (8\text{–}12)$$

where x represents any coordinate (linear or angular), and $2\pi f$ can be written in alternative forms ω or $2\pi/\tau$, if convenient.

The value of θ_0 is determined by any set of known values of the variables, for example, the initial conditions. In many cases, we are free to choose as we wish. If it is convenient to choose $x = 0$ at $t = 0$, we have $0 = \sin \theta_0$, which can lead to $\theta_0 = 0$ and therefore,

$$x = A \sin (2\pi f t). \qquad (8\text{–}13)$$

(Note that the initial velocity was assumed to be positive when the value $\theta_0 = 0$ was chosen in preference to $\theta = \pi$.) If it is convenient to choose $x = A$ at $t = 0$, we have $1 = \sin \theta_0$, which can lead to $\theta = \pi/2$ and, therefore [since $\sin (\theta + \pi/2) = \cos \theta$],

$$x = A \cos (2\pi f t). \qquad (8\text{–}14)$$

The velocity and acceleration can be obtained from their definitions by the process of differentiation. For velocity, we have $v_x = dx/dt = d(A \sin \theta)/dt$, where $\theta = 2\pi ft + \theta_0$. Applying the rules of differentiation, we write

$$\begin{aligned} v_x &= d(A \sin \theta)/dt = A\, d(\sin \theta)/dt \\ &= A \cos \theta \frac{d\theta}{dt} \\ &= A \cos \theta\, d(2\pi ft + \theta_0)/dt \\ &= A(\cos \theta) 2\pi f. \end{aligned}$$

Therefore

$$v_x = 2\pi f A \cos (2\pi ft + \theta_0), \tag{8–15}$$

and similarly

$$a_x = -(2\pi f)^2 A \sin (2\pi ft + \theta_0). \tag{8–16}$$

Equations (8–12), (8–15), and (8–16) can be written

$$x = x_m \sin (2\pi ft + \theta_0), \tag{8–17}$$

$$v_x = v_{xm} \cos (2\pi ft + \theta_0), \tag{8–18}$$

$$a_x = -a_{xm} \sin (2\pi ft + \theta_0), \tag{8–19}$$

where x_m, etc. represent the maximum values of displacement, velocity, etc.

Further derivatives can be taken, but we have already seen in our studies of dynamics that the acceleration is determined by the forces. Hence the acceleration is the natural stopping place.

In most cases, we are free to choose the zero of time however we wish, i.e., the initial conditions are partly a matter of choice. When a choice has been made, the value of θ_0 is fixed by the choice. For example, the motion of a pendulum at small amplitude is approximately simple harmonic, as we shall see later. A reasonable choice of coordinate x to describe the motion is the horizontal displacement from the center (equilibrium) position. If we set the pendulum into motion by pulling it to one side by an amount x_m and then releasing it from rest, a natural choice of zero time is the moment of release. If the above choice is made, we have $x = x_m$ at $t = 0$ for the initial conditions. Equation (8–17) then leads to $x = x_m \sin (0 + \theta_0)$ or $\sin \theta_0 = 1$. Consequently, $\theta_0 = \pi/2$, but since $\sin (2\pi ft - \pi/2) = \cos 2\pi ft$, we have $x = x_m \cos 2\pi ft$ for the above *particular choice of initial conditions.* We can make an equally reasonable choice of initial conditions by starting the timer when the pendulum passes through the midpoint of its motion. With this choice, we have $x = 0$ at $t = 0$; the result is that $\theta_0 = 0$ and $x = x_m \sin 2\pi ft$ for this particular choice of initial conditions. Any other choices are, of course, equally possible, and each leads to a particular value of θ_0.

From Eqs. (8–12) and (8–16), we see that

$$a_x = -(2\pi f)^2 x, \tag{8–20}$$

where $(2\pi f)^2$ is a constant for a particular case. Equation (8–20) *can be used as a statement of the condition that simple harmonic motion will result* if a system is set in motion. It has the advantage of not containing the time *explicitly* and of being in a form suited to a discussion of dynamics such as that in the next section. The question of time-independent relationship, including velocity, is left to the problems.

The velocity and acceleration could alternatively have been found from our observation in Section 8–3 that a cartesian component of uniform circular motion is simple harmonic motion. Hence the velocity and acceleration can also be obtained as cartesian components of the velocity and acceleration of a point in uniform circular motion. Since we used this idea to obtain the formulas for differentiation in the first place, it is not surprising that we have this result. The derivative method is given because it is the general approach to kinematics.

Graphs of position, velocity, and acceleration for simple harmonic motion, as described in Eqs. (8–12), (8–15), and (8–16), are shown in Fig. 8–5.

When it is possible or reasonable to choose the initial conditions so that $x = 0$ when $t = 0$, the

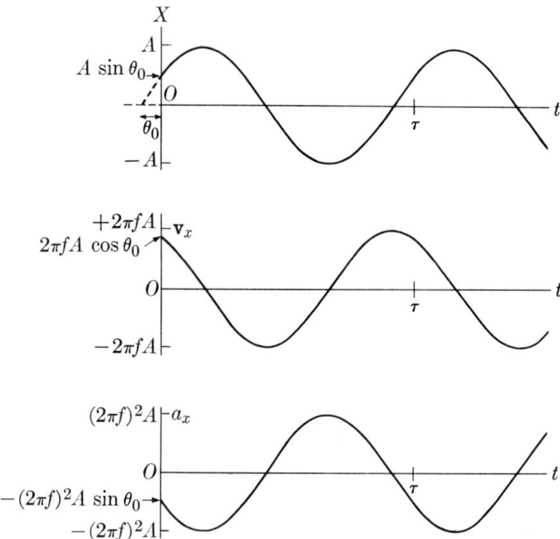

FIG. 8–5. The same graphs as in Fig. 8–4 but with initial phase angle θ_0.

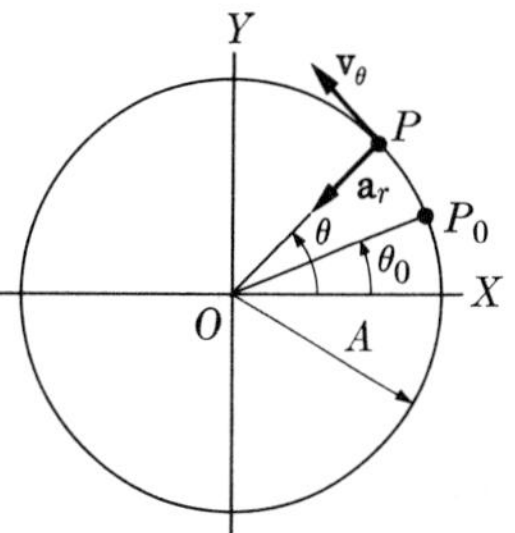

FIG. 8–6. The reference-circle method for portraying simple harmonic motion. The projection of the motion of point P onto a diameter of the circle moves with simple harmonic motion if P moves at constant speed along the circle.

graphs of Fig. 8–5 are shifted and take on the simpler appearance of Fig. 8–4.

The case of graphs when $x = A$ at $t = 0$ is left for the reader.

A graphical method of displaying many features of simple harmonic motion is the *reference circle* representation. This is simply the method that we used in finding the derivatives of trigonometric functions, namely, the projection on a diameter of the uniform motion of a point in a circular path. The radius of the reference circle is the amplitude A of the simple harmonic motion. The period of revolution is the period of the simple harmonic motion, and the angular position at $t = 0$ is the initial phase angle θ_0. In Fig. 8–6, point P moves around the circle with period τ, starting with P_0 at $t = 0$. The projections of P, of its velocity v_θ, and of its acceleration a_r onto any diameter describe simple harmonic motion. If we choose the diameter along the OX-axis, Eqs. (8–12), (8–15), and (8–16) describe the motion. The amplitudes of the velocity and of the acceleration of the simple harmonic motion are simply v_θ and a_r of the circular motion of point P. The projection onto OY can be used to depict simple harmonic motion with y as the coordinate.

There are not many everyday examples in which we can predict simple harmonic motion from kinematical considerations alone. For example, in reciprocating engines, the piston approximates simple harmonic motion if the connecting rod is long. There are, however, many cases in which an observation of position versus time shows that the motion is essentially simple harmonic. Examples are found in mass-spring combinations of many sorts, in pendulums, etc.

Example 1. A point executes simple harmonic motion of amplitude 10 cm at a frequency of 2 cycles/sec. Find the shortest time of travel from 8 cm to 5 cm displacement, and the velocity when the displacement is 8 cm.

Solution. (a) Choosing the approach of Eq. (8–13), etc., let $x = 0$ at $t = 0$. Then $x = 10 \sin (4\pi t)$, and the time at $x = 8$ is found from the equation $8 = 10 \sin (4\pi t)$ or $\sin (4\pi t) = 0.8$ or $(4\pi t) = \sin^{-1} 0.8 = 53°$. But degrees are not a suitable unit if we wish to have t in seconds. (Why not?) Therefore, $4\pi t = 53 \times 2\pi/360°$ or $t = 53/720 = 0.0735$ sec. Similarly, at $x = 5$, we have $(4\pi t) = \sin^{-1} 0.5$ and $t = 0.0415$ sec. The time to go from $x = 5$ to $x = 8$ is therefore 0.032 sec.

(b) The reference circle could have been used. In this case, we might have altered the appearance of the analysis, but the content would have been essentially the same.

For the velocity, $v_x = dx/dt = 40\pi \cos(4\pi t)$. When $x = 8$ cm, we have seen that $\sin(4\pi t) = 0.8$; therefore $\cos(4\pi t) = 0.6$ and $v_x = 24\,\pi$ cm/sec.

8–5 DYNAMICS OF A FREE SIMPLE-HARMONIC OSCILLATOR

By definition, simple harmonic motion is characterized by sinusoidal time-dependence of the coordinate in question. It was shown in Section 8–4 that the acceleration is then proportional to the displacement and oppositely directed [Eq. (8–20)].

If Newton's second law is now used in order to introduce forces into the discussion, we have

$$\sum F_x = ma_x = -(2\pi f)^2 mx. \qquad (8\text{–}21)$$

Equation (8–21) indicates that simple harmonic motion will result whenever a system is subject to a resultant force that is proportional to the displacement and oppositely directed. Such a force is called a *linear restoring force* and is a special case of restoring forces in general. The expression for a linear restoring force is usually written simply

$$F_x = -kx, \qquad (8\text{–}22)$$

where k is the restoring force constant. In terms of this constant, it is seen [from Eqs. (8–21) and (8–22)] that

$$f = \frac{1}{2\pi}\sqrt{k/m} \qquad (8\text{–}23)$$

or

$$\tau = 2\pi\sqrt{m/k}, \qquad (8\text{–}24)$$

where f and τ are the frequency and period of the simple harmonic motion that can result due to a linear restoring force. The constant $\omega = 2\pi f$ could also be used to specify the periodicity of the motion.

The mechanical system that executes simple harmonic motion due to a linear restoring force within the system is called a *linear* or *harmonic oscillator*.

There are many examples of space-dependent forces that can be represented by a linear restoring force as the first approximation. Two cases have been considered in earlier sections: first, the spring, which was found to exert a linear force $F = -k(x - x_0)$, within its elastic limits; second, uniform circular motion, in which a cartesian component of the resultant force can be shown to be a linear restoring force.

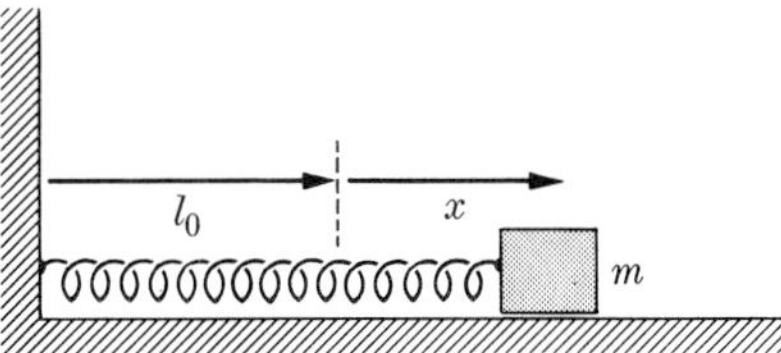

Fig. 8–7. A spring-mass system in which the mass is constrained to move along a horizontal line.

The case of a *spring* is simplest (a) if motion on a frictionless horizontal surface is considered, and (b) if the origin of coordinates is chosen so that x_0 in the force law is zero. These conditions are illustrated in Fig. 8–7, where a mass m on a frictionless surface is fixed to a spring of normal length l_0. Then the resultant force on m becomes $\sum F = -kx$, which means that $a = -(k/m)x$, the condition for simple harmonic motion. The frequency [Eq. (8–23)] is therefore $f = (1/2\pi)\sqrt{k/m}$. If we choose $x = A$ at $t = 0$, the equations of motion are $x = A\cos(\sqrt{k/m}\,t)$, etc.

If the *spring* is hung *vertically* as in Fig. 8–8, the resultant force on m is

$$\sum F = -ky' - mg, \qquad (8\text{–}25)$$

where y' is the displacement measured from the position of the end of the unloaded spring (measured positively in the upward direction). The ky'-term is negative because the force exerted *by* the spring is downward in Fig. 8–8. Since Eq. (8–25) can be rewritten

$$\sum F = -k\left(y' + \frac{mg}{k}\right), \qquad (8\text{–}26)$$

we can simply choose $y = y' + mg/k$ and have

$$\sum F = -ky, \tag{8–27}$$

which gives simple harmonic motion. The above change of variable corresponds to measuring y from an origin that is mg/k units below our original choice. Physically, this origin is the rest position of m when it is in equilibrium, since at equilibrium we have

$$\sum F = ky_0' - mg = 0,$$

or

$$y_0' = mg/k,$$

where y_0' is the distance of the equilibrium point below the position of the unloaded spring (Fig. 8–8).

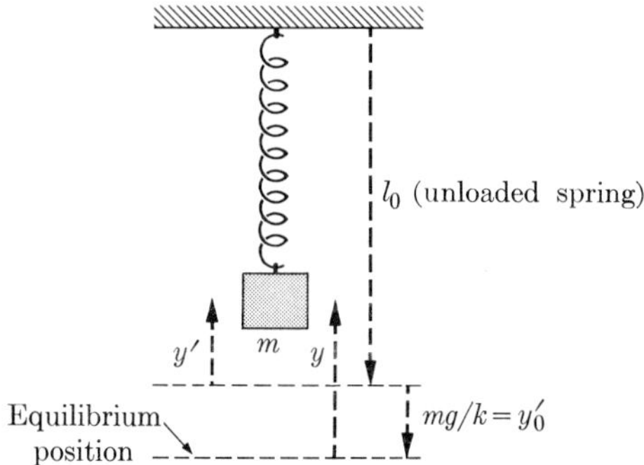

FIG. 8–8. A spring-mass system in which the mass can move along a vertical path.

The above procedure is the systematic nonintuitive approach. We might instead have noted that Eq. (8–25), together with the equilibrium condition $ky_0' = mg$, immediately gives $F = -k(y' + y_0')$, and therefore $F = -ky$, where y is measured from the rest equilibrium position. The effect of any *constant* force that is external to the spring-mass system and that acts along the direction of the spring axis is simply to shift the center point of the motion (in case of a linear restoring force). We have shown that the center point of the motion is the rest equilibrium position.

Examples of linear and nonlinear spring combinations are included in the problems.

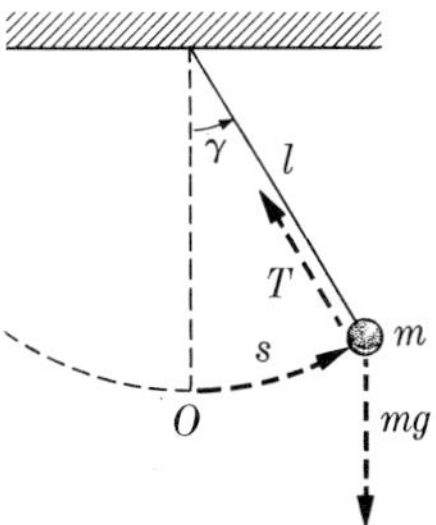

FIG. 8–9. The forces on a simple pendulum.

8–6 LINEAR FORCE APPROXIMATIONS

(A) SIMPLE PENDULUM

The designation "simple" usually means that a mass (m) is hung from a rigid support by means of a string or rod whose length l is large compared with the dimensions of the mass but whose mass is negligible compared with the mass m (Fig. 8–9). Then the motion is that of a mass point acted upon by the gravitational force mg and the tension of the string T.

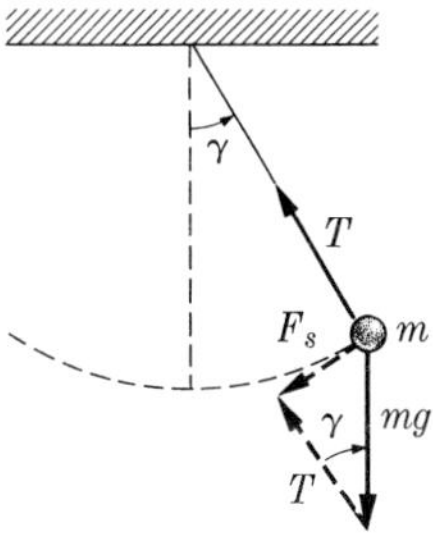

FIG. 8–10. The resultant force F_s on the mass m of a simple pendulum.

The angular coordinate γ is the reasonable choice of variable, since the motion is along the arc of a circle. An equivalent coordinate is the displacement s, measured along the arc (since $s = l\gamma$, where l = constant). The s-component of the resultant force is simply the s-component of mg (Fig. 8–10), or

$$F_s = -mg \sin \gamma. \tag{8–28}$$

The acceleration component is then

$$a_s = -g \sin \gamma, \tag{8–29}$$

which gives periodic motion because the acceleration is dependent only on the coordinate and is opposite to the displacement. But the motion is *not* simple harmonic since the restoring force is not linear. In intermediate physics courses you will learn to find the period,

$$\tau = 2\pi\sqrt{\frac{l}{g}}\left(1 + \tfrac{1}{4}\sin^2\frac{\gamma_m}{2} + \cdots\right), \qquad (8\text{–}30)$$

where γ_m is the angular amplitude.

Returning now to Eq. (8–28), we find that if the angle γ is small, we have $\sin\gamma \simeq \gamma$. Therefore, if γ is never large, i.e., if the amplitude γ_m is small, then

$$F_s \simeq -mg\gamma = -(mg/l)s, \qquad (8\text{–}31)$$

which is a linear restoring force. The acceleration is then

$$a_s = -(g/l)s, \qquad (8\text{–}32)$$

and the period [comparing with Eq. (8–20)] is

$$\tau = \frac{1}{f} = 2\pi\sqrt{l/g}. \qquad (8\text{–}33)$$

The question of the accuracy of Eq. (8–33) can be answered easily only by looking at Eq. (8–30). We find that the accuracy is better than 1% for an amplitude up to 23°.

(B) MOLECULAR VIBRATIONS

The force between two atoms in a molecule must be attractive down to certain distances of separation but repulsive for smaller distances. The force must also go toward zero at large distances and become very large at a distance of an atomic diameter. Figure 8–11 displays the force qualitatively. The equilibrium separation is d_0 and the minimum separation is d_m.

If the separation d_0 is chosen as the reference, there is a restoring force that is approximately proportional to the displacement for small displacements. The straight line tangent to the force curve at d_0 illustrates this linear approximation.

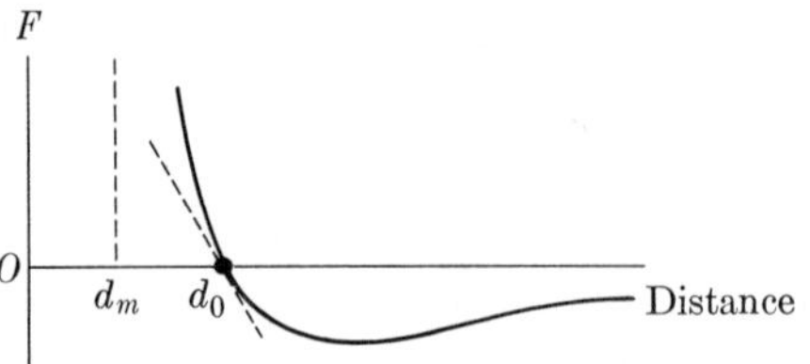

Fig. 8–11. The force F on one atom of a diatomic molecule as a function of the separation of the atoms. The force can be approximated by a force that varies linearly with displacement from the equilibrium separation d_0 if the displacements are small (dashed straight line at point d_0).

Insofar as classical mechanics can describe molecular vibrations at all, the above approximation agrees with observation.

8–7 ANALYSIS OF COMPLEX PERIODIC MOTION

The term "complex," as it is used here, simply means *not* simple harmonic. In some cases complex periodic motion may actually appear to be *less* complex than simple harmonic motion.

Since the relationships among the quantities of motion are particularly straightforward in the case of simple harmonic motion, it is very convenient to describe other periodic motions by a superposition of simple harmonic motions of different frequencies, initial phases, and amplitudes. In many cases, it is convenient to choose sine and cosine terms with zero initial phase angles ($\theta_0 = 0$), with frequencies that are integral multiples of a "fundamental" frequency f, and amplitudes that depend on the particular complex motion. The terms are called harmonics: the term with frequency f is called the first harmonic; the term with frequency $2f$, the second harmonic, etc.

Example 2. Consider a ball that rolls back and forth between two walls separated by distance $2D$ (Fig. 8–12).

If the collisions are assumed to be perfectly elastic, the position of the ball as a function of time will be

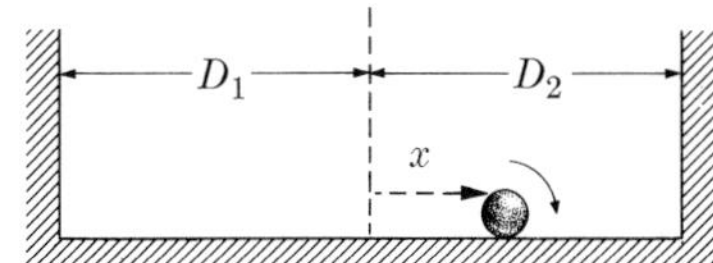

FIG. 8–12. A ball rolling back and forth between two walls with which it makes perfectly elastic collisions.

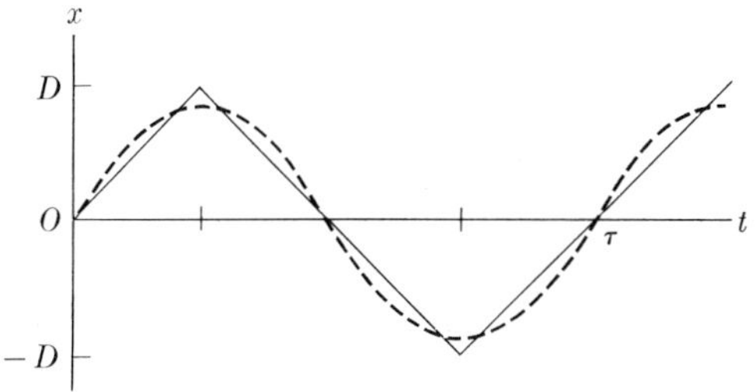

FIG. 8–13. Graph of position x versus time t for the ball of Fig. 8–12. The motion is periodic. The graph can be roughly approximated by a sine curve, as shown by the dashed line.

as shown in Fig. 8–13. The period is the time for a complete round trip to both walls. We have chosen $x = 0$ with velocity to the right at $t = 0$. It is obvious that the first approximation to Fig. 8–13 is a sine curve with period τ, as shown by the dashed line. The higher harmonics have frequencies and amplitudes that are obtained by so-called "Fourier analysis," which you may learn in mathematics courses. The complete ensemble of terms is written

$$x = \frac{8D}{\pi^2}\left(\sin 2\pi\, ft - \tfrac{1}{9}\sin 6\pi\, ft + \tfrac{1}{25}\sin 10\pi\, ft - \cdots\right) \tag{8–34}$$

and is called a "Fourier series." The first harmonic (first term) is too low at the peaks and too high elsewhere (Fig. 8–13). The second harmonic (second term) adds to the peaks and subtracts from the sides, giving a better approximation to the triangular curve, and so on.

It is left as a problem to find the Fourier series for velocity and acceleration. The purpose of the Fourier method is to permit the description of complex periodic motions in terms of sines and cosines, which are easily manipulated during integration and differentiation.

8–8 HARMONIC OSCILLATOR UNDER EXTERNAL FORCES

The effect of a uniform force has already been seen to be a simple displacement of the center position for a harmonic oscillator. We now consider another special case, one in which a simple harmonic external force is applied to the oscillator. For example, suppose that the support for a spring-mass system is not stationary but moves up and down with simple harmonic motion y_s (Fig. 8–14). The effect on the system is that the length of the spring and, hence, the force on m depend not only on the displacement of m but also on the position of the upper end of the spring.

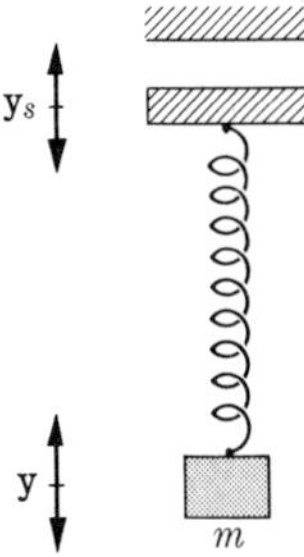

FIG. 8–14. A mass-spring system in which the spring support is forcibly moved with simple harmonic motion.

If we let y_s and y represent the displacements (upward positive) of the top and bottom ends, respectively (Fig. 8–14), then applying Newton's second law to m, we have

$$F_y = -k(y - y_s) = ma_y, \tag{8–35}$$

where k is the spring constant. Since $y_s = Y \sin \omega t$, where Y is the amplitude and ω is $2\pi f$ for the motion of the support, Eq. (8–35) can be written

$$-ky + kY\sin(\omega t) = m\frac{d^2y}{dt^2}. \tag{8–36}$$

The acceleration has been written as a derivative in order to have an equation containing only y, t, and a derivative of y. This is called a *differential equation*.

One technique for solving differential equations is the "educated guess." In the present case, we guess that the solution will be of the form

$$y = A \sin (\omega t), \qquad (8\text{–}37)$$

since we know that the second derivative is again the sine function. If the trial solution Eq. (8–37) is substituted in Eq. (8–36), we obtain

$$-kA \sin \omega t + kY \sin \omega t = -m\omega^2 A \sin \omega t, \qquad (8\text{–}38)$$

from which we have

$$A = Y \frac{k/m}{(k/m) - \omega^2}. \qquad (8\text{–}39)$$

The natural frequency of the oscillator ω_0 is $\sqrt{k/m}$; therefore Eq. (8–39) can be written

$$A = Y \frac{\omega_0^2}{\omega_0^2 - \omega^2}. \qquad (8\text{–}40)$$

Thus the mass is in simple harmonic motion, having the frequency of the external driving force and an amplitude that is a function of the driving frequency. A graph of amplitude versus ω is given in Fig. 8–15. At the natural frequency ω_0, *resonance* results and the amplitude goes to infinity (a) in the absence of friction, and (b) if the spring force remains linear for large displacements. Another feature of interest is that the amplitude approaches Y at low frequencies and zero at high frequencies. Finally, the motion of m is in phase with the driving force when $\omega < \omega_0$, but 180° out of phase when $\omega > \omega_0$, a feature that is indicated by "negative" amplitude for $\omega > \omega_0$ in Fig. 8–15, and Eq. (8–40).

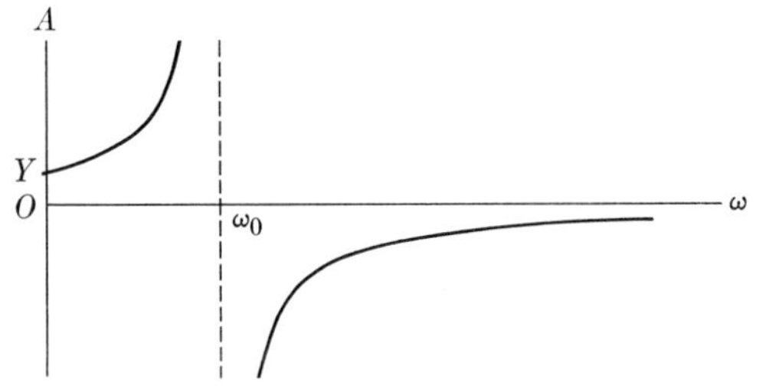

FIG. 8–15. The amplitude of motion of the mass m of Fig. 8–14 as a function of the frequency of the forced motion of the upper end of the spring. The frequency is expressed in terms of $\omega = 2\pi f$. The natural frequency of the spring-mass system is $\omega_0 = 2\pi f_0$.

8–9 NONHARMONIC DRIVING FORCES

It has already been stated in Section 8–7 that nonharmonic periodic functions can usually be expressed in Fourier series. An external driving force can also be so expressed. The problem of the response of an harmonic oscillator to the force can then be solved by the method found in Section 8–8.

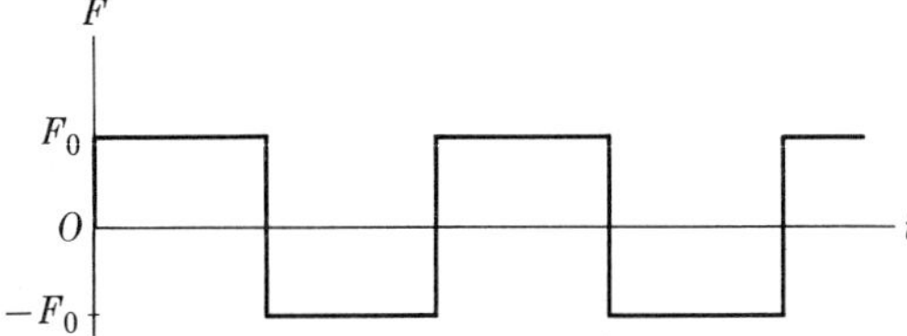

FIG. 8–16. Graph of the time dependence of a square-wave driving force.

Example 3. Consider a "square-wave" driving force, i.e., a force which is constant in magnitude but reverses direction periodically (Fig. 8–16), applied to the mass in a spring-mass system. The square wave can be written in terms of sines in a Fourier series as follows:

$$F_e = F_0 \frac{4}{\pi} (\sin \omega t + \tfrac{1}{3} \sin 3\omega t + \tfrac{1}{5} \sin 5\omega t + \cdots). \qquad (8\text{–}41)$$

Solution: Newton's second law,

$$\sum F = m\, d^2x/dt^2,$$

then gives

$$F_e - kx = m\, d^2x/dt^2. \qquad (8\text{–}42)$$

The guess for a solution is

$$x = A \sin \omega t + B \sin 3\omega t + C \sin 5\omega t + \cdots. \qquad (8\text{–}43)$$

Substituting this guess in Eq. (8–42), we have

$$\begin{aligned}\frac{4}{\pi} F_0(\sin \omega t + \tfrac{1}{3} \sin 3\omega t + \tfrac{1}{5} \sin 5\omega t + \cdots)\\ - k(A \sin \omega t + B \sin 3\omega t + C \sin 5\omega t + \cdots)\\ + m(Aw^2 \sin \omega t + B9\omega^2 \sin 3\omega t\\ + C25\omega^2 \sin 5\omega t + \cdots) = 0. \qquad (8\text{–}44)\end{aligned}$$

The expression (8–44) can be zero for all values of t only if the coefficient of each different type of sine term is zero: therefore

$$\begin{aligned}\frac{4}{\pi} F_0 - kA + m\omega^2 A &= 0,\\ \frac{4}{\pi} F_0 - kB + 9m\omega^2 B &= 0, \qquad \text{etc.}\end{aligned} \qquad (8\text{–}45)$$

Noting that k/m is ω_0^2 of the free oscillations of the spring-mass combination and rearranging terms, we have

$$\begin{aligned}A &= \frac{4}{\pi}\frac{F_0}{m}\Big/(\omega_0^2 - \omega^2),\\ B &= \frac{4}{3\pi}\frac{F_0}{m}\Big/\{\omega_0^2 - (3\omega)^2\}, \qquad (8\text{–}46)\\ C &= \frac{4}{5\pi}\frac{F_0}{m}\Big/\{\omega_0^2 - (5\omega)^2\}.\end{aligned}$$

Or if the external force is applied by a square-wave displacement (with amplitude X) of the supported end of the spring as in Section 8–8, we obtain

$$\begin{aligned}A &= \frac{4}{\pi} X \frac{\omega_0^2}{\omega_0^2 - \omega^2},\\ B &= \frac{4}{3\pi} X \frac{\omega_0^2}{\omega_0^2 - (3\omega)^2}, \qquad \text{etc.}\end{aligned} \qquad (8\text{–}47)$$

The motion of the mass at the end of the spring is therefore given by Eq. (8–43) with the coefficients of Eqs. (8–46) or (8–47). It is seen that there are resonances when the external force has frequencies $f = f_0, f_0/3, f_0/5$, etc., but the resonances are weaker the lower the frequency of the external force. Further, it is seen that the first term in Eq. (8–43) dominates for all $\omega > \omega_0$ and for $\omega < \omega_0$ but not too close to $\omega_0/3$. Finally, as ω is lowered farther, the second, third, etc., terms dominate as $\omega \simeq \omega_0/3$, $\omega \simeq \omega_0/5$, etc.

The effect of nearly any periodic driving force on an harmonic oscillator can be analyzed in the above manner. We have limited our treatment to the so-called "steady-state" solution (the periodic motion with constant amplitude that occurs a long time after the periodic driving force started) and to the case of negligible damping (i.e., negligible friction forces). The friction force must be finite, even though small, so that the steady motion will be approached in a finite time. In addition, we have considered nonharmonic oscillators and nonharmonic driving forces separately, but we have not treated the combination of the two.

8–10 SUMMARY

Periodic motion is a motion that repeats itself regularly as time passes. Uniform circular motion is treated first since it is a simple type of periodic motion. *Simple harmonic motion* is introduced by a description of uniform circular motion in cartesian coordinates. In addition, the derivatives and antiderivatives of trigonometric functions are obtained from the kinematical relations among the cartesian components of uniform circular motion. The results are

$$\begin{aligned}x &= r \cos \omega t,\\ v_x &= -\omega r \sin \omega t,\\ a_x &= -\omega^2 r \cos \omega t,\end{aligned}$$

for the equations of simple harmonic motion in the x-direction.

If the initial conditions are generalized, we write

$$\begin{aligned}x &= r \sin(\omega t + \theta_0),\\ v_x &= \omega r \cos(\omega t + \theta_0),\\ a_x &= -\omega^2 r \sin(\omega t + \theta_0).\end{aligned}$$

If the maximum values x_m, v_m, and a_m are introduced, we have

$$x = x_m \sin(\omega t + \theta_0),$$
$$v_x = v_m \cos(\omega t + \theta_0),$$
$$a_x = -a_m \sin(\omega t + \theta_0).$$

When time is eliminated, we have relations such as

$$a_x = -\omega^2 x.$$

Newton's second law can be used to introduce forces into the discussion, resulting in the following dynamics equations for simple harmonic motion:

$$\sum F_x = -m\omega^2 x = -kx,$$

$$f = \frac{1}{2\pi}\sqrt{k/m}.$$

It is seen that a linear restoring force characterizes simple harmonic motion. Examples of springs and the simple pendulum are treated.

Examples are given of the description of periodic motion that is not simple harmonic in terms of series of harmonic sine or cosine terms.

Finally, the case of a system with a linear restoring force which is driven by an externally applied periodic force is discussed. If the driving force is simple harmonic with angular frequency ω, the amplitude of motion of the oscillator is

$$A = Y \frac{\omega_0^2}{\omega_0^2 - \omega^2},$$

where ω_0 is the natural angular frequency of the oscillator and Y depends on the amplitude of the driving force. If the driving force is not simple harmonic, it can be described by a series of simple harmonic terms. The resulting motion of the driven system can then be analyzed in terms of a series of simple harmonic terms. The example of a square-wave driving force is treated.

Problems

1. Carry out the steps by which Eq. (8–5) was derived from Eq. (8–3).

2. Under what special conditions could $a_x \equiv dv_x/dt$ and Eq. (8–3) be used to derive Eq. (8–6)?

3. Suppose that in the circular motion of an object ω is not constant but is, for example, equal to kt. Which of the Eqs. (8–3) are invalidated and why?

4. What are the constants in Eq. (8–12) if the amplitude is 5 cm, the frequency is 180 rpm, and $x = -2.5$ cm at $t = 0$? What if v_0 is negative?

5. Show that $v_x^2 + (2\pi f)^2 x^2 = (2\pi f)^2 A^2$ for simple harmonic motion. [*Hint:* Make use of $\sin^2\theta + \cos^2\theta = 1$.]

6. Show that $a_x^2 + (2\pi f)^2 v_x^2 = (2\pi f)^4 A^2$ for simple harmonic motion. (See Problem 5.)

7. Equation (8–12) is one way of giving the position in simple harmonic motion. Another general form is $x = D\sin(2\pi ft) + E\cos(2\pi ft)$. Find D and E in terms of the constants in Eq. (8–12).

8. Show that the period in simple harmonic motion can be expressed as $T = 2\pi\sqrt{-x/a_x}$.

9. A point P in rectilinear motion is observed to move so that $x = 14\cos(0.1\,t + 0.5)$, where all quantities are in the mks system.

(a) What are the frequency, period, and amplitude of the motion?

(b) What are the initial conditions?

(c) What are the maximum velocity and acceleration?

(d) What are the position, velocity, and acceleration at $t = 5$?

(e) Make rough graphs of position, velocity, and acceleration versus time.

(f) Draw the reference circle for the motion.

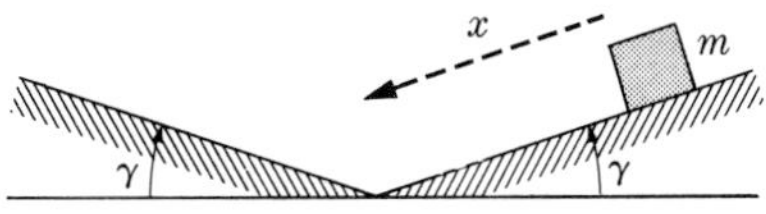

FIGURE 8–17

10. A mass m slides back and forth between two frictionless inclined planes, as shown in Fig. 8–17.

(a) Find the period of the motion.

(b) Is the period independent of amplitude?

11. A certain automobile has a mass of 1000 kg. When 4 passengers of total mass 200 kg get into the car, the car is lowered 5 cm. What is the natural frequency of the loaded car, neglecting the effect of the shock absorbers?

12. A mass rests on a platform which is caused to execute simple harmonic motion in the vertical direction with a period of 2 sec. At what amplitude A_m of the motion will the mass leave the board? In what part of the motion does it leave the board if $A > A_m$?

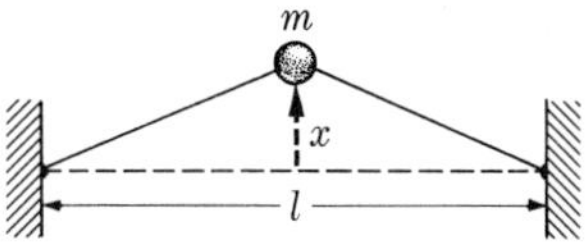

FIGURE 8–18

13. A mass m is held by two equal wires that are stretched between walls, as shown in Fig. 8–18. The tension T in the wires is so large that the change in tension for small lateral displacements, as shown, is negligible. Gravitational effects are likewise negligible. Prove that the motion of m is simple harmonic for small lateral displacements, and find the period. What limits the approximations?

14. A mass m rests on a horizontal frictionless surface. It is connected between two springs (each with force constant k), as shown in Fig. 8–19. The springs are attached to pins separated by $2l_0$, where l_0 is the length of the unstretched springs.

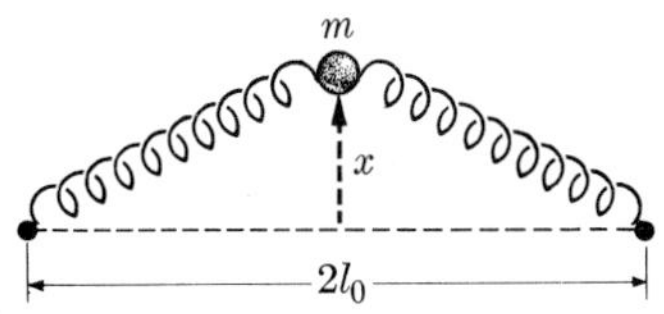

FIGURE 8–19

(a) Find the restoring force for the lateral displacement x.

(b) Will the motion be simple harmonic for small displacements?

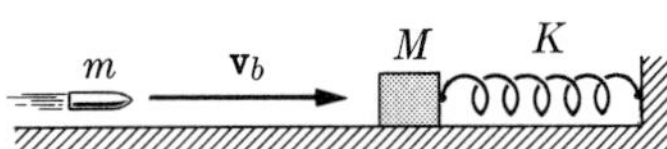

FIGURE 8–20

15. At $t = 0$, a bullet of mass m strikes and embeds itself in a mass M which rests on a frictionless table and is fixed to a spring of constant K (Fig. 8–20). If the velocity of the bullet was v_b before it struck the block, find the equations of motion of the block and bullet after the collision.

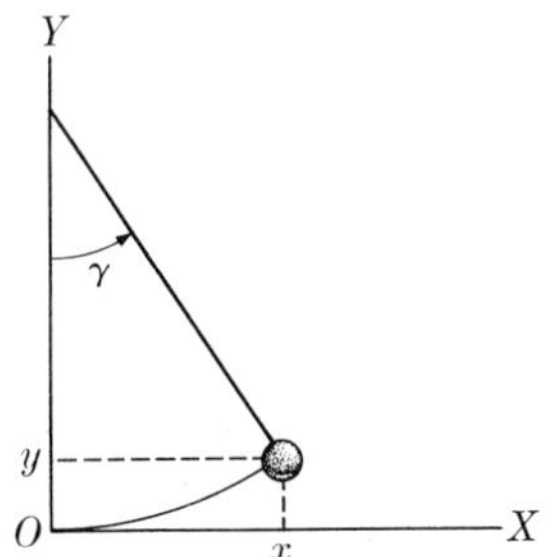

FIGURE 8–21

16. Resolve the motion of a simple pendulum into cartesian components, as shown in Fig. 8–21. Prove that the x-component of motion is simple harmonic for small amplitudes. Is y simple harmonic?

17. In going from Eq. (8–31) to Eq. (8–32), mass was canceled from both sides of an equation.

(a) Were these masses basically the same physical quantities?

(b) Write Eq. (8–33) without cancellation of the masses.

(c) What experiment would you perform to establish the equality of these masses for various materials?

18. Make a graph for restoring force as a function of the displacement s, measured along the arc for a simple pendulum (Fig. 8–9), for values of s between $-(\pi/2)\,l$ and $+(\pi/2)l$. Indicate the linear restoring force approximation on the graph.

19. Derive an equation for the ratio of the periods of a pendulum at two different distances R_1 and R_2 from the center of the earth (near a pole where effects of rotation are negligible). What would be the percent change in period per meter of altitude? Let R of earth equal 6400 km.

20. Assume a restoring force on m, $F = -kx^2$. Show by direct differentiation that $x = A \sin \omega t$ leads to a contradiction of Newton's second law, and hence that the motion cannot be simple harmonic.

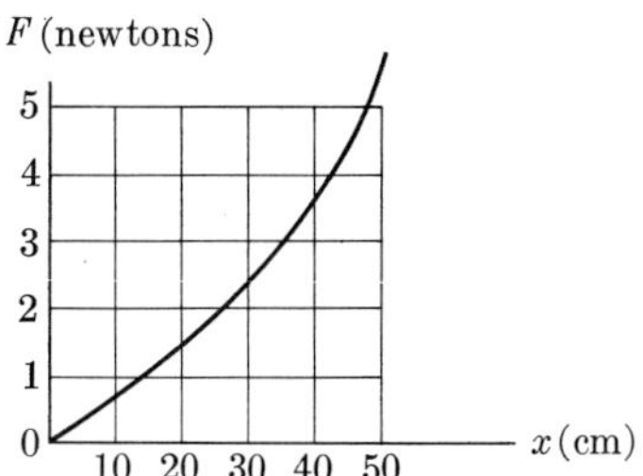

FIGURE 8–22

21. The force law for a certain rubber band is shown in Fig. 8–22, where F is the force that stretches the end a distance x from the unstretched position. Find the period for small amplitude oscillations about the equilibrium rest position (a) when a mass of 50 gm is hung on the band, and (b) when a mass of 400 gm is hung on the band.

22. (a) Write the equation for the angle γ of a simple pendulum at small amplitude γ_0 as a function of time (Fig. 8–9). (b) Draw the reference circle for the above motion.

23. The sawtooth graph of position versus time in Fig. 8–13 is represented by the Fourier series of Eq. (8–34).

(a) Draw the graph of velocity versus time from simple inspection of Fig. 8–13. Does your graph agree with the direct prediction from the motion itself in Fig. 8–12?

(b) Repeat (a) for the acceleration.

(c) Find the Fourier series for velocity by differentiating Eq. (8–34), and sketch the first two terms on the graph of (a). Does the series show promise of representing the velocity graph?

(d) Repeat (c) for the acceleration.

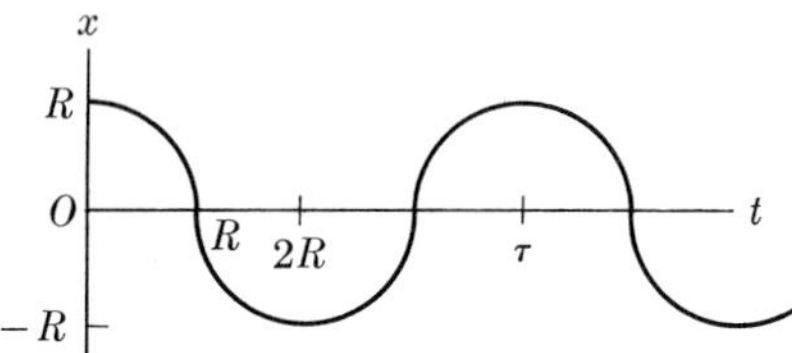

FIGURE 8–23

24. A certain periodic motion in the x-direction has a time graph that consists of sections of circles of radius R, as shown in Fig. 8–23.

(a) How is the magnitude of the period related to the amplitude? Do they have the same units?

(b) What would be the form of the first term in the Fourier series for this curve? Would its amplitude be equal to R? Sketch the approximate shape of the first term.

25. The automobile of Problem 11 goes over a washboard road that is sinusoidal in profile with a horizontal distance between peaks of 1 m.

(a) What is the critical speed of the automobile for which resonance will occur?

(b) If the peak-to-valley height in the washboard is 10 cm, what will be the amplitude of vibration of the car at twice the critical speed? at half the critical speed? (Which is preferable?) Neglect damping.

(c) If the washboard profile is more nearly sawtooth than sinusoidal, what other speeds [besides the speed in (a)] would be uncomfortable for the driver?

26. A conical pendulum consists of a simple pendulum that is set in motion in a three-dimensional path, as shown in Fig. 8–24. The path of m is approximately an ellipse lying nearly in a horizontal plane.

(a) Indicate the result of resolution of the motion into cartesian components x and y in the horizontal plane by writing simple harmonic motion equations

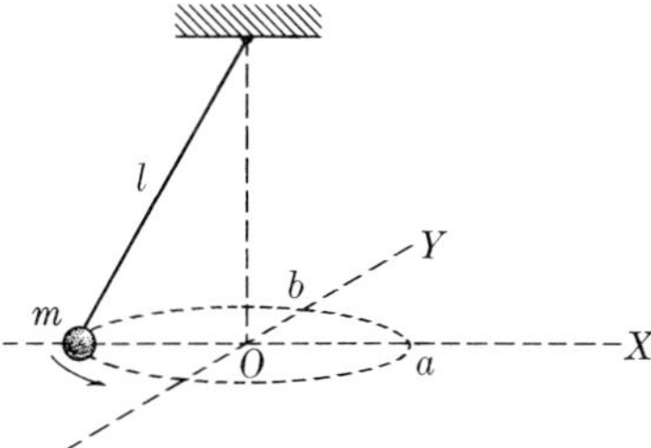

FIGURE 8–24

for x and for y with the appropriate amplitudes, frequencies, and initial phases for small amplitudes.

(b) What do you think will happen if the motion is such that the ellipse is very eccentric and the x-amplitude is quite large?

27. Find the resultant force on m (Fig. 8–17) as a function of γ [$= \arctan\,(dy/dx')$], where x' is measured along the horizontal. How should the slope of the surface vary with x' if the motion is to be simple harmonic in the coordinate x'?

28. Show that the resultant force on a cart that is on a straight, frictionless track tangent to the earth's surface is $F = -Gmm'x/(R^2 + x^2)^{3/2}$, where R is the earth's radius. Show that the restoring force is linear for small displacements and find the period.

29. A mass of 50 gm rests on a horizontal, frictionless surface. The mass is fixed between two rubber bands that follow the force law of Fig. 8–22. Find the period of small longitudinal oscillations if the bands are initially stretched (a) by 40 cm (80 cm for both) and (b) by 10 cm.

9

Impulse, Work, and Energy

9–1 INTRODUCTION

In earlier chapters, we discussed one of the general conservation principles, conservation of momentum. It was found that momentum is always conserved in a system when no resultant external force acts on the system. For more generality, we will now consider changes in momentum caused by external forces. It will be found that the *time integral* of the external force determines the change in momentum. The integral of force with respect to *distance* (line integral) will then be introduced. It will lead to the idea of another conservation principle, the conservation of energy.

9–2 IMPULSE AND MOMENTUM

In Chapter 4 the change in momentum caused by a force was found by rewriting Newton's second law in the form

$$\overline{F}\,\Delta t = m\Delta v \quad \text{or} \quad \Delta p, \tag{9–1}$$

where $\overline{F}$ was the average force. We can let Δt approach zero and replace $\overline{F}$ by the *instantaneous* force F. Then it is necessary to form a sum in order to find the effect of F during a finite time interval. Thus, we write

$$\sum_{t_0}^{t_f} \overline{F}\,\Delta t = \sum_{p_0}^{p_f} \Delta p, \tag{9–2}$$

where the summations are over adjacent time intervals extending from t_0 to t_f and p_0 to p_f, respectively. The sum on the right is obviously just $p_f - p_0$, but the sum on the left requires further investigation. It is the sum of the products $\overline{F}\Delta t$. Each product is approximately the area under the F versus t curve in the time interval Δt at that point (Fig. 9–1). The sum corresponding to the time division made in Fig. 9–1 is

$$\overline{F}_1\,\Delta t_1 + \cdots + \overline{F}_4\,\Delta t_4, \tag{9–3}$$

which is the sum of rectangular areas. The sum is approximately the area under the F versus t curve. As the Δt's are made smaller and correspondingly more numerous, the sum approaches exactly the area under the F versus t curve as the Δt's $\to 0$. The operation is called a *definite integral* and is symbolized and defined by

$$\int_{t_0}^{t_f} F\,dt \equiv \lim_{\Delta t\to 0} \sum_{t_0}^{t_f} F\,\Delta t. \tag{9–4}$$

It will be shown in a mathematics course that the definite integral can be evaluated by use of antiderivatives or indefinite integrals (in fact, areas under curves have already been discussed in terms of antiderivatives).

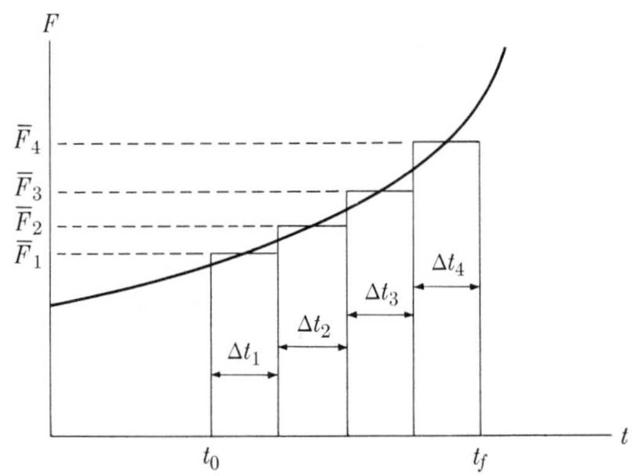

FIG. 9–1. Graphical representation of a sum of rectangular areas that approximates the area under a curve of F versus t.

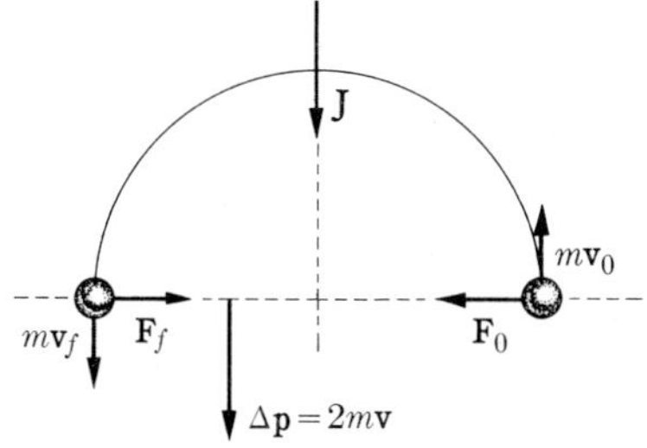

FIG. 9–2. A mass m in uniform circular motion. A half-revolution is depicted. The momenta, forces, change in momentum, and impulse are shown for motion through a half-revolution.

The physical term for the expression in Eq. (9–4) is *impulse* (J), and we see that the change in *momentum* of a system is equal to the impulse by the external force (or resultant external force, in general); that is,

$$\mathbf{J} \equiv \int_{t_0}^{t_f} \mathbf{F}\, dt = \mathbf{p}_f - \mathbf{p}_0. \qquad (9\text{–}5)$$

The impulse $\mathbf{J}$ is a vector quantity since $\mathbf{F}$ is a vector, but the direction of $\mathbf{F}$ may vary with time. Hence the direction of $\mathbf{J}$ is a weighted time-average of the direction of $\mathbf{F}$. For example, consider the motion of the moon during half a revolution around the earth. The change in momentum is $2mv$ and is directed as shown in Fig. (9–2). Therefore $J = 2mv$ and is in the direction of Δp. The force, however, is directed toward the earth and changes direction continuously. Since F is constant in magnitude, we can understand, from a symmetry argument, why the time-integrated value is in the direction of Δp.

As usual with vector quantities, actual calculations are frequently more easily done in cartesian components. Equation (9–5) can be written in cartesian components in the usual manner.

The method of impulses is chiefly useful when the force is of short duration, as in collisions. Then the force starts and ends nearly at zero (Fig. 9–3). The total impulse is the total area under the curve of F versus t and equals the total change in momentum of the object on which the impulse acts.

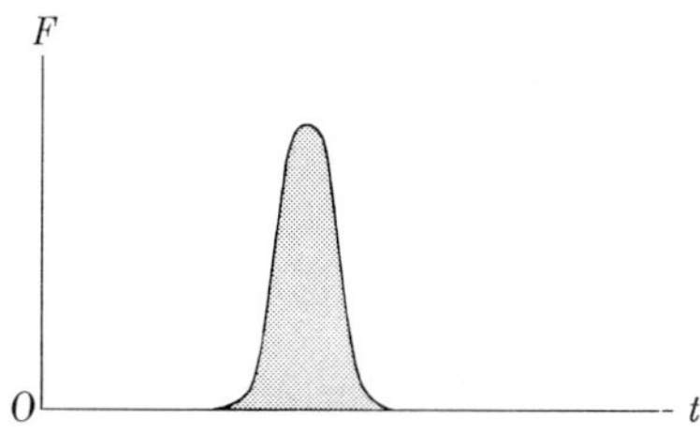

FIG. 9–3. Graph of F versus time t for an impulsive type of force. The area under the curve is the magnitude of the impulse J.

Impulses between two interacting bodies must be equal and opposite, since the momentum changes are equal and opposite. When one of the bodies is much more massive than the other, the effect of the impulse on the larger body may not be evident, since its change in velocity will be small.

The method of impulses is of greatest use in treating collisions of such short duration that one of the objects does not move appreciably during the collision. A traditional example is the parlor trick of snatching a napkin from under a glass of water or the lecture demonstration of snatching a sheet of paper from under a piece of chalk. In either case, the force varies with time roughly as shown in the graph of Fig. 9–4. Since the magnitudes F (static) and F (sliding), are not time-dependent, the impulse on the glass or chalk, and hence the change in momentum, can be made as small as desired by decreasing the time of inter-

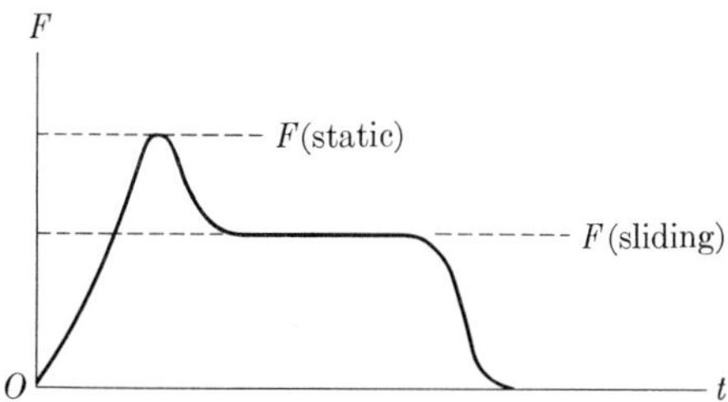

FIG. 9–4. Graph of force F versus time t for the impulsive friction force of Example 1.

action. The curve of Fig. 9-4 is simply compressed horizontally. If the change in momentum is sufficiently small, the glass will not be given sufficient velocity to cause it to continue sliding to the edge of the table.

Example 1. Find the final momentum of an object initially at rest, if the resultant force is $10t^2$ n up to 2 sec and zero thereafter. Use the impulse method.

Solution: The impulse equals the change in momentum, $\int_0^\infty F\,dt = p$. The impulse can be evaluated by integrating $F = 10t^2$ in the interval $t = 0$ to $t = 2$:

$$\int_0^\infty F\,dt = \int_0^2 10t^2\,dt = \left(\tfrac{10}{3}t^3\right)_{t_0=0}^{t_f=2}$$

$$= \tfrac{80}{3}\text{ n sec or kg m/sec.}$$

Therefore $p = \frac{80}{3}$ kg m/sec. (Note that the impulse from $t = 2$ to $t = \infty$ is zero because $F = 0$.)

9-3 WORK

Another force integral, work, is taken along the path followed by the object in question. The discussion of work will be used as an introduction to the concept of conservation of energy. The integral in question is called a "line" integral. We shall see that it cannot always be evaluated in the same way as the integrals that have been considered in the previous sections.

The definition of the work W done by a force F on an object that moves from a point (1) to a point (2) is

$$W \equiv \int_1^2 |\mathbf{F}| \cos\theta |d\mathbf{s}| \qquad (9\text{-}6)$$

or, in the more compact vector notation (see below)

$$W \equiv \int_1^2 \mathbf{F}\cdot d\mathbf{s}, \qquad (9\text{-}7)$$

where θ is the angle between the force at a given point of the path and the tangent to the path at the point in question (Fig. 9-5), and $d\mathbf{s}$ is an element of displacement along the path followed by the object. As $d\mathbf{s}$ becomes vanishingly small, its direction becomes the same as the direction of the tangent to the path.

The above type of integral is a line integral, since it is taken along the path followed by the object. In general, the value of the integral depends on the choice of path between the two points. For example, in Fig. 9-5, the work may depend on whether the object follows the solid-line path or the dashed-line path. However there are certain types of forces, known as conservative forces, for which the work depends only on the initial and final positions of the object and not at all on the path.

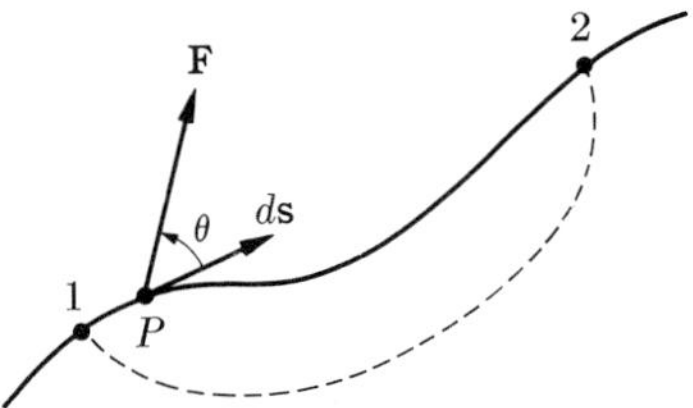

FIG. 9-5. An object at point P in a path of motion from 1 to 2. A force $\mathbf{F}$ acts at angle θ to the infinitesimal displacement $d\mathbf{s}$ along the path. An alternative path is shown by the dashed line.

The units of work are newton-meter in the mks system, which is the *joule*. The cgs unit, dyne-centimeter, is the *erg*.

Work is a scalar quantity, although it is defined in terms of two vectors, $\mathbf{F}$ and $d\mathbf{s}$. The two vectors occur as a product that is termed a *dot* or *scalar product*. The definition of the mathematical operation of taking the scalar product of two vectors is

$$\mathbf{F}\cdot d\mathbf{s} = |\mathbf{F}|\,|d\mathbf{s}| \cos\theta,$$

where θ is the angle between the two vectors.

It is necessary to use an inertial reference frame when only interaction forces are to be considered. Before generalizing any further, we shall consider some simple examples of work.

9–4 RECTILINEAR MOTION WITH CONSTANT FORCE (DIRECTION AND MAGNITUDE)

Consider the work by a force F (a force by an external agent) acting on a mass m that is free to move along a straight-line path, as in Fig. 9–6. If the Ox-axis is chosen in the direction of the rectilinear path followed by m, as in Fig. 9–6, the path element ds can be written dx, and $F \cos \theta$ becomes F_x. If the object moves directly from (1) to (2), as in Fig. 9–6, the work done by the constant force F is simply

$$W = \int_{x_1}^{x_2} F_x\, dx = F_x \int_{x_1}^{x_2} dx = F_x(x_2 - x_1). \tag{9–8}$$

In this *special case*, we see that the work is simply the projection of the force on the line of motion times the distance traveled.

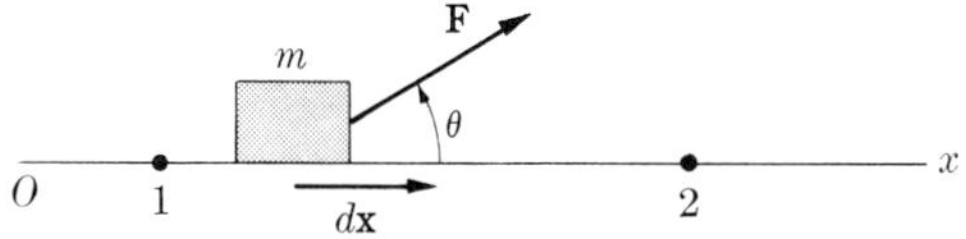

Fig. 9–6. A mass m in rectilinear motion along the x-axis. An external force **F** acts at angle θ, which may be a function of x.

If the force is at right angles to the path of motion, no work is done. For example, the vertical force required to support an object while the object is carried in a horizontal plane does no work, according to our definition of work in physics.

If the path followed by the object involves a reversal of direction (Fig. 9–7), the integral must be taken along the entire path, since the integral is a line integral. For example, if the object first goes beyond x_2 to x_P and then reverses its motion and returns to x_2, the work integral must be evaluated in two parts, one part for the motion to the right and the other for the motion to the left. Therefore

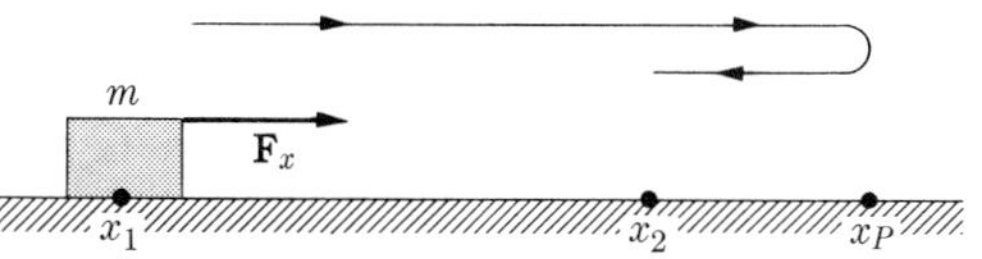

Fig. 9–7. A mass m in rectilinear motion moves from x_1 to x_P and then retraces a portion of its path, ending at x_2.

$$W = \int_{x_1}^{x_P} F_x\, dx + \int_{x_P}^{x_2} F_x\, dx$$

$$= F_x(x_P - x_1) + F_x(x_2 - x_P), \tag{9–9}$$

or simply

$$W = F_x(x_2 - x_1), \tag{9–10}$$

which is the same as for motion along the direct path from x_1 to x_2. The physical reason for the above result is that the work done by force F (that is, the external agent exerting the force F) *on m* during the motion from x_2 to x_P is equal to the work done *by m* on the external agent during the motion from x_P to x_2. Thus in this special case there is a cancellation of the work done *by* the external agent in any parts of that path that are retraced. The conclusion is that for the case of rectilinear motion the work done by a constant force is independent of the path between two points.

It is necessary, in principle, to be careful with the signs of the terms. For example, we might choose the positive x-axis to the right, as usual. Then, $ds = dx$ for motion to the right and $ds = -dx$ for motion to the left. But, since the angle θ is measured from the direction of ds, the $\cos \theta$ factor reverses sign when we change the direction of ds (in this case where the direction of the force is constant). Consequently, there is *no* change in sign of the integrand with change in the sense of the motion, in this case. (If the force changes direction with change in direction of the motion, the situation is different, as we shall see in a moment.)

9–5 RECTILINEAR MOTION WITH UNIFORM FRICTION FORCE

A friction force is always directed oppositely to the motion. Consequently, the sign of the friction force depends on the direction of motion. For example, in moving directly from a point (1) to a point (2), as in Fig. 9–8, the component of the friction force F_R in the direction of motion is negative, and the work is

$$W = \int_{x_1}^{x_2} -F_R\,dx = -\,F_R(x_2 - x_1), \quad (9\text{–}11)$$

where the negative sign in the result indicates that work is done *on* the external agent *by* the mass m. When the motion is reversed, the sign of F_R reverses. For example, if m moves from (1) to a point P and then returns to (2), as in Fig. 9–9, the work done *by* the friction force is

$$W = \int_{x_1}^{x_P} -F_R\,dx + \int_{x_P}^{x_2} F_R\,dx$$
$$= -F_R(x_P - x_1 + x_P - x_2). \quad (9\text{–}12)$$

This result depends on the path. In fact, we could have found the work by taking F_R out of the integral, since it remains constant. The result is

$$W = -F_R \int_1^2 ds = -F_R L, \quad (9\text{–}13)$$

where L is the total path length traversed by m in going from (1) to (2).

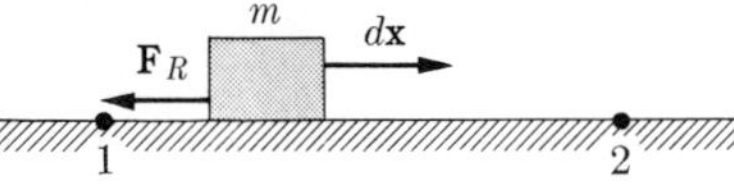

FIG. 9–8. A mass m that experiences a friction force $\mathbf{F}_R$ while in rectilinear motion.

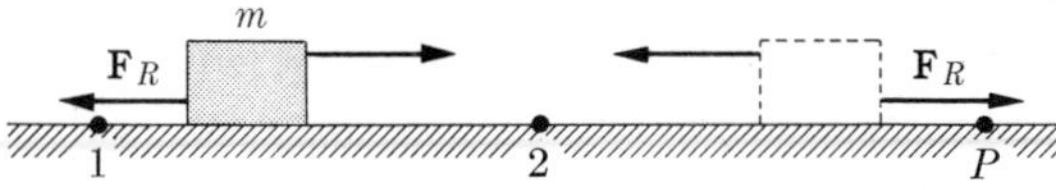

FIG. 9–9. A mass m that retraces a portion of its path while experiencing a friction force $\mathbf{F}_R$.

9–6 RECTILINEAR MOTION WITH A POSITION-DEPENDENT FORCE

If a force depends only on position and the motion is rectilinear, the work can be calculated if we take into account the fact that the force is variable. As in the previous examples, the integral must be divided into parts if the object retraces portions of its path. If the force is *not* dependent on the direction of motion (i. e., if it is not a friction force), the contribution to the work integral when the path is traversed in one sense is equal in magnitude and opposite in sign to the contribution when the same portion of the path is traversed in the opposite sense. Expressed formally, the integral for retraced portions of the path is

$$\int_{x_1}^{x_1} F\,dx = \int_{x_1}^{x_2} F\,dx + \int_{x_2}^{x_1} F\,dx$$
$$= \int_{x_1}^{x_2} F\,dx - \int_{x_1}^{x_2} F\,dx = 0. \quad (9\text{–}13')$$

There remains only the portion of the integral corresponding to the motion directly from the initial to the final position. Therefore, the work done by a position-dependent force during rectilinear motion is independent of the path taken between two points.

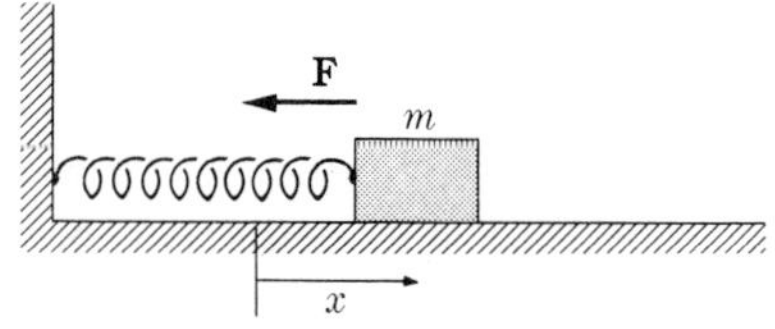

FIG. 9–10. A mass m that experiences a force by a spring.

Example 2. Calculate the work done on a mass m by a spring that is connected to m. The spring follows Hooke's law, and the motion is rectilinear.

Solution: Choose as coordinate the displacement x of the end of the spring from its unstretched position (Fig. 9–10). The force exerted by the spring is then $F = -kx$. The work by the spring when m moves from x_1 to x_2 is given by

$$W = \int_{x_1}^{x_2} -kx\,dx = -k\left(\frac{x_2^2}{2} - \frac{x_1^2}{2}\right). \qquad (9\text{–}14)$$

This result is independent of path, according to our general conclusion in the first part of this section. The case in which x is not chosen to be zero for the unstretched spring is left for the problems.

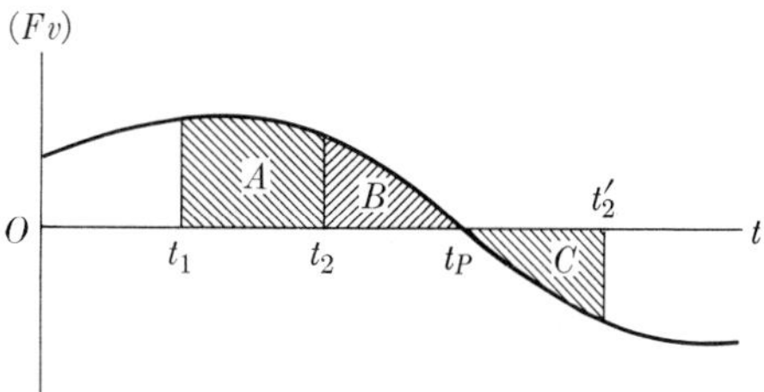

FIG. 9–11. A graph of Fv versus time. The net area under the curve is equal to the work. For example, the work from t_1 to $t_{2'}$ is $A + B - C$.

9–7 WORK EXPRESSED AS AN ORDINARY INTEGRAL: POWER

The definition of work (Eq. 9–7) can be expressed in terms of the parameter time in the following way: If we multiply and divide by dt in Eq. (9–7), the result is

$$W = \int_1^2 \mathbf{F}\cdot\frac{d\mathbf{s}}{dt}\,dt = \int_1^2 \mathbf{F}\cdot\mathbf{v}\,dt, \qquad (9\text{–}15)$$

where $\mathbf{F}$ and $\mathbf{v}$ are to be expressed as functions of t in order for us to evaluate the integral. With time as the variable, there are no complications even when the motion is reversed. Therefore the integral of Eq. (9–15) is an ordinary integral and can be represented graphically by the area under a curve of $\mathbf{F}\cdot\mathbf{v}$ versus t.

As an illustration of the graphical representation of the integral for work in the form of Eq. (9–15), we consider the example of Fig. 9–7 and Eqs. (9–9) and (9–10). The times t_1, t_2, t_P, and t_2' represent the instants of passage through points x_1, x_2, x_P, and x_2, respectively. The graphical representation for a particular type of motion would appear as in Fig. 9–11. The area under the curve between two abscissae represents the value of the integral between those two times (abscissae). From the results of Section 9–4, we know that the areas B and C are equal and therefore cancel, leaving area A as the net result for the work.

The formulation of work in Eq. (9–15) is convenient in the case of friction forces that are velocity dependent.

The physical quantity *power* P is defined by

$$P \equiv \frac{dW}{dt}. \qquad (9\text{–}16)$$

From Eq. (9–15) we see that power can also be expressed as

$$P = \mathbf{F}\cdot\mathbf{v}. \qquad (9\text{–}17)$$

The work can then be expressed as

$$W = \int_1^2 P\,dt. \qquad (9\text{–}18)$$

9–8 WORK AND ENERGY

When work is done on an object or system, it is found that there is always an increase in some form of the quantity that we shall call energy. Conversely, if work is delivered *by* an object or system, a decrease in some form of energy of the system is always found. The above statements are called the law of energy conservation. In mechanics, we shall be chiefly concerned with so-called mechanical forms of energy, with the exception of the energy transformed into heat energy by friction forces. The transformations among heat energy, chemical energy, and mechanical energy are the subject of thermodynamics. The transformations between electrical and mechanical energy are considered in the study of electricity. Special cases involving transformations among particular forms of mechanical energy will be developed first.

In the preceding sections, two different kinds of results were found for the mechanical work done by forces. In one case the work was independent of path. A force that does this kind of work is a *conservative force.* We have seen that a force that depends only on position does work that is independent of path for rectilinear motion. Therefore such a force is conservative in rectilinear motion. In the other case, the work depended on the path. The example was friction forces, which are called dissipative forces, or more generally, *nonconservative* forces.

9–9 POTENTIAL ENERGY IN RECTILINEAR MOTION

We will now extend the discussion of *conservative* forces. It was shown in Section 9–6 that in one-dimensional motion, the work by a force that depends only on position is independent of the path. Such a force was called a *conservative* force. Because, in this case, the work in a displacement between two points depends only on the position of the points, it is convenient to define a quantity called *potential energy* such that the *change* in potential energy between two points is equal to the work done by the conservative force in a displacement between the two points. Since work *by* the force increases some other form of energy, the potential energy associated with the force must decrease when the force does work. Thus the change in potential energy ΔV is the negative of the work done by the force:

$$\Delta V_{21} \equiv V_2 - V_1 \equiv -\int_{x_1}^{x_2} F_x\, dx, \qquad (9\text{–}19)$$

where F_x is the conservative force in question.

The integral can be evaluated along a path going directly from (1) to (2), since the result is independent of the path.

Furthermore, it is possible, and in many cases convenient, to define *the* potential energy V at a point by *arbitrarily* assigning zero potential energy to a particular point and then defining *the* potential energy at any other point as the difference in potential energy between the point in question and the point chosen for zero potential energy. It should be emphasized that there is no natural law that indicates that one particular point must be chosen as the zero of potential energy.

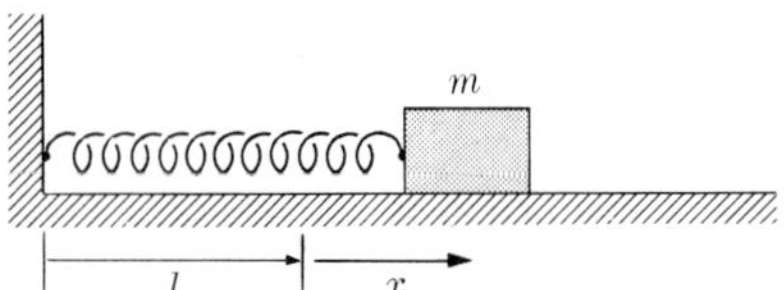

FIG. 9–12. A mass m fixed to a spring of normal length l.

Example 3. A mass m resting on a horizontal surface is fixed to the free end of a horizontal spring of normal length l, as in Fig. 9–12. (a) Show that the spring force is conservative, and (b) find an expression for the potential energy.

Solution: Choose a coordinate system as shown in Fig. 9–12. If we assume that the spring obeys Hooke's law, the force by the spring on m can be written in the form $F = -kx$, for the above choice of coordinate x. (a) The force is conservative for one-dimensional motion, since it depends only on position. (b) Choosing the potential energy to be zero at $x = 0$, we can find the potential energy at any point x_1 from

$$V(x_1) = \Delta V(\text{from } x = 0 \text{ to } x = x_1)$$
$$= -\int_{x=0}^{x_1} F\, dx = -\int_0^{x_1} -kx\, dx = \tfrac{1}{2}kx_1^2.$$

The result is shown graphically in Fig. 9–13. For motion from x_1 to x_2, we have a calculation similar

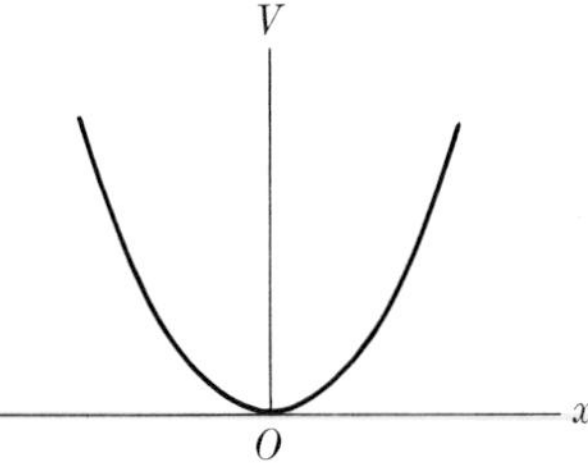

FIG. 9–13. Potential energy V as a function of the change in length x of a spring.

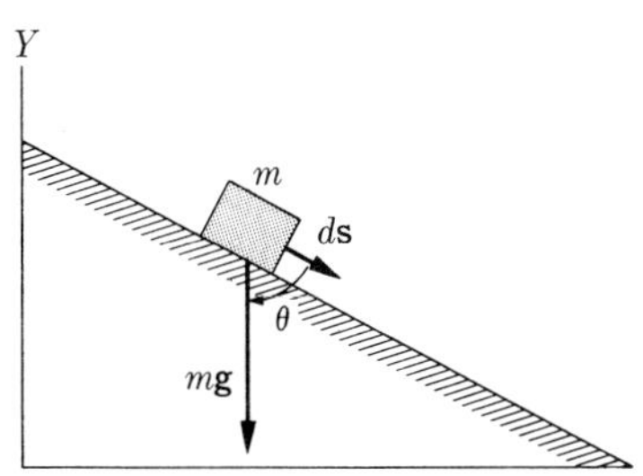

FIG. 9–14. A mass m on an inclined plane.

to the above, with the result

$$\Delta V = \tfrac{1}{2}kx_2^2 - \tfrac{1}{2}kx_1^2. \qquad (9\text{–}20)$$

Near the surface of the earth, the gravitational force is constant. Therefore, in rectilinear motion near the earth, the gravitational force is a conservative force. Consequently, the work done by gravity in rectilinear motion can be described by a change in potential energy (with the appropriate negative sign):

$$\Delta V = -\int \mathbf{F} \cdot d\mathbf{s} = -\int_{s_1}^{s_2} mg \cos\theta \, ds. \qquad (9\text{–}21)$$

From Fig. 9–14, we see that $\cos\theta\, ds$ is simply $-dy$, where y is a vertically upward cartesian coordinate. Therefore Eq. (9–21) becomes

$$\Delta V = mg(y_2 - y_1). \qquad (9\text{–}22)$$

Actually, Eq. (9–22) is not restricted to rectilinear motion, since it will be shown in a later section that a constant force is a conservative force for any path of motion.

9–10 WORK BY FRICTION: HEAT ENERGY

The work done by a friction force is not only a function of the end points of the path of motion, but it is also a function of the path itself or even of the velocity and other quantities. Therefore friction is a nonconservative force, and the concept of potential energy cannot be used.

In general, friction and other dissipative forces diminish the mechanical energy of the object or system in question. The decrease Q is equal to the work by the friction or other dissipative forces.

The products of the work by friction forces are varied. In the case of sliding friction, the principal product is heat energy, which will be studied in detail later. In the case of fluid friction, an additional product is increased kinetic energy (Section 9–11) of portions of the fluid.

9–11 KINETIC ENERGY IN RECTILINEAR MOTION

Thus far we have considered the work done by individual forces. We now consider the work done by the resultant of all the external forces acting on an object. The principle of superposition of ordinary forces permits us to replace the sum of the work integrals of the individual forces by the single expression for the work by the resultant of the forces. We shall find that a new concept arises, that of *kinetic energy*. The concept arises as follows: For rectilinear motion, the resultant force can lie only along the line of motion. Choosing the x-axis in the direction of motion and using Newton's second law, we have

$$\sum F = \sum F_x = ma_x. \qquad (9\text{–}23)$$

Remembering that

$$a_x \equiv \frac{dv_x}{dt},$$

we can write the work by the resultant force in the form

$$W = \int_{x_1}^{x_2} \sum F_x \, dx = \int_{x_1}^{x_2} m \frac{dv_x}{dt} \, dx. \qquad (9\text{–}24)$$

If the dt in the denominator is now associated with the dx factor in place of the dv_x factor, Eq. (9–24) becomes

$$W = \int m \, dv_x \frac{dx}{dt}.$$

But dx/dt is only the velocity, and therefore

$$W = \int_{v_1}^{v_2} mv_x \, dv_x.$$

Since m is a constant in classical mechanics, we have

$$W = m \left.\frac{v^2}{2}\right]_{v_1}^{v_2}$$

or

$$W = \tfrac{1}{2}mv_2^2 - \tfrac{1}{2}mv_1^2 \tag{9–25}$$

for the work by the *resultant force.*

It is convenient to give the terms of the form $\frac{1}{2}mv^2$ the special designation *kinetic energy,* represented by T:

$$T \equiv \tfrac{1}{2}mv^2. \tag{9–26}$$

We then state that the work by the resultant force on an object equals the change in kinetic energy of the object:

$$W = T_2 - T_1$$

or

$$W = \Delta T. \tag{9–27}$$

Example 4. An object of mass m is pulled along a horizontal surface by a force P at an angle of 30°. If the coefficient of friction is μ and the initial velocity is v_0, find the velocity after the object has moved a horizontal distance l. Use the energy method.

Solution: Choose cartesian coordinates in the horizontal and vertical direction. Since there is no y-component of motion (assuming that $P < mg \sin 30°$), the work is $W = \int_0^l \sum F_x\, dx = \frac{1}{2}mv_l^2 - \frac{1}{2}mv_0^2$, where $\sum F_x = P \cos 30° - \mu(mg - P \sin 30°)$. The integral is easily evaluated, since the integrand, $\sum F_x$, is constant. We have $\sum F_x \int_0^l dx = \sum F_x x|_0^l = \sum F_x l$, which leads us to the solution for v at l, namely

$$\sum F_x l = \tfrac{1}{2}mv_l^2 - \tfrac{1}{2}mv_0^2 \text{ or } v_l = \sqrt{(2\sum F_x l/m) + v_0{}^2},$$

where

$$\sum F_x = P \cos 30° - \mu mg + \mu P \sin 30°.$$

The above example, and in fact most one-dimensional problems, could be solved almost as easily by using Newton's laws directly. The value of the work-energy method will become more evident when we consider two-dimensional motion.

9–12 CONSERVATION OF ENERGY

We have seen that the work by the resultant force equals the change in the quantity $\frac{1}{2}mv^2$, which we defined as kinetic energy T. But the work by the resultant force can be written as the sum of the work contributions W_A, etc., by the individual forces F_A, etc. We therefore have

$$W_A + W_B + \cdots = T_2 - T_1. \tag{9–28}$$

We have also seen that some forces can be classified as conservative, meaning that the work by these forces depends only on the end points of the motion. Therefore the work by conservative forces can be specified by $V_1 - V_2$, where the potential energy V depends only on the end points. The other forces are dissipative. The work done by them depends on the path, velocity, etc. Since the work by such forces is negative, it is reasonable to represent it by a negative quantity $-Q$. Thus the work by the individual forces can be separated into two parts, and Eq. (9–28) can be written

$$V_1 - V_2 - Q = T_2 - T_1, \tag{9–29}$$

where $V_1 - V_2$ is the change in potential energy, Q is the energy dissipated by friction or other forces that transform mechanical energy into other forms, and $T_2 - T_1$ is the change in kinetic energy. We can rearrange terms in Eq. (9–29) and write

$$V_1 + T_1 = V_2 + T_2 + Q, \tag{9–30}$$

which states that the initial mechanical energy $V_1 + T_1$ equals the mechanical energy at a later time plus the loss in mechanical energy to other forms.

Strictly speaking, we should consider Q to be partly made up of a change in potential energy for cases in which the dissipated energy can, in fact, be partly returned to the mechanical form. For example, when a motor drives an electric generator that in turn charges a storage battery, some of the dissipated mechanical energy is stored as chemical potential energy in the battery. A portion of this chemical energy can be returned to the form of mechanical energy by means of an electric motor. However, until the subject of thermodynamics is treated, we shall usually let Q include all nonmechanical forms of macroscopic energy.

From the discussion in the preceding paragraph, we see that, for a force to be conservative, a general condition is that the work is reversible in the sense that work done on the agent that exerts the force can be regained as work done by the agent.

Example 5. A block of mass m rests on a horizontal table. (a) One end of a compressed spring is placed against the mass and then released. The mass slides 90 cm before coming to rest. (b) When the mass is hung from the same spring in a vertical position, the spring is stretched 20 cm. Find the coefficient of friction.

Solution: Choose the spring plus mass as a system, and let the amount of compression of the spring in (a) be Δx. If we choose the potential energy of the undistorted spring to be zero, the potential energy of the compressed spring will be $\frac{1}{2}k(\Delta x)^2$. The initial kinetic energy is zero. After the mass has been released and has come to rest, the potential energy and the kinetic energy of the system are zero, but energy Q has been dissipated by the work done by friction. The friction force $F_R = \mu N = \mu mg$. From conservation of energy as expressed in Eq. (9–30), we have

$$V_1 + 0 = 0 + 0 + Q = \int F_R\, ds,$$

$$\tfrac{1}{2}k\,(\Delta x)^2 = \mu mg\, 0.90.$$

But from part (b), we have

$$mg = k\, 0.2.$$

Solving the two equations for μ, we finally obtain

$$\mu = \frac{1}{0.45}\,(\Delta x)^2.$$

In the above, it was assumed that the spring obeys Hooke's law.

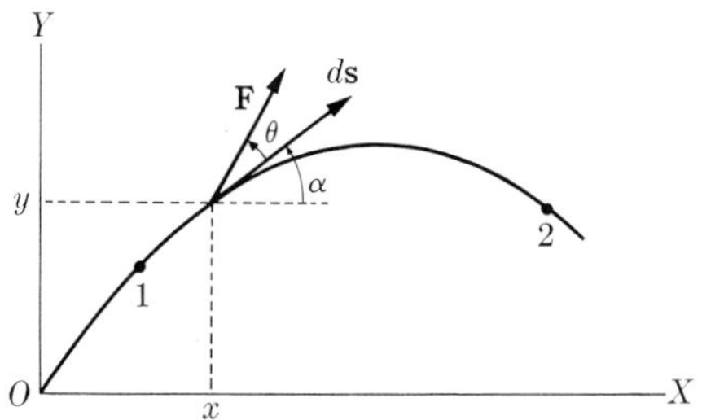

FIG. 9–15. A force **F** acting on an object as it moves along a path in the xy-plane.

9–13 TWO-DIMENSIONAL MOTION

Thus far we have been considering the special case of rectilinear motion because of its relative simplicity. We now return to the more general discussion introduced in Section 9–3. In that section, work was defined in terms of an integral, particularly a line integral. A more complete definition of the line integral is now in order.

When work is defined in the incremental form ΔW, we have

$$\Delta W = F \Delta s \cos\theta, \tag{9–31}$$

where $\overline{F}$ is the average force in the displacement Δs. The differential form would then be

$$dW = F ds \cos\theta, \tag{9–32}$$

where dW is the limiting value of ΔW as Δs becomes very small. The average force then becomes the force F at a point.

In Fig. 9–15 the trajectory of an object is plotted and the force F is shown at a point (x, y) of the trajectory. The work done by F as the object moves along its trajectory from 1 to 2 is the integral of $F \cos\theta$ (the component of F in the direction of motion) taken along the trajectory, a so-called *line integral*. The line integral is not the same as the integrals previously considered. In our present example, the path between 1 and 2 is to be divided into chords (Fig. 9–16). The values of F and θ are obtained for each chord. The line integral of $F \cos\theta$ is then defined as the limit of the sums of the products $F \cos\theta\, \Delta s$ as

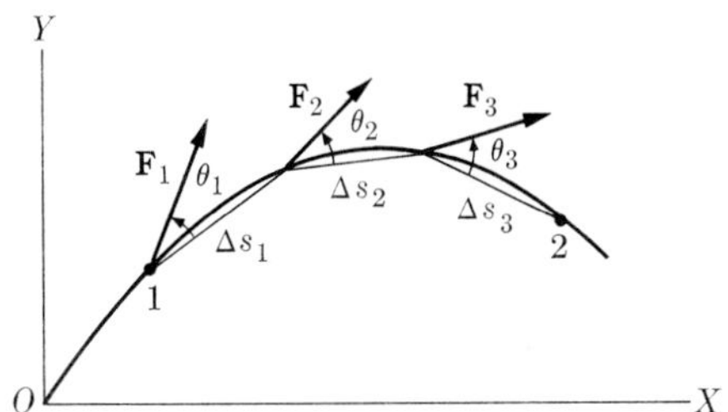

FIG. 9–16. The force **F** acting on an object shown at three points on its path of motion from 1 to 2.

the number of chords goes to infinity. Since the lengths of the chords approach zero and their directions approach tangents to the path as their number goes to infinity, in the limit the symbol ds replaces Δs and the integral sign replaces the summation sign. In formal notation, we write

$$W = \lim_{\Delta s \to 0} \sum_{1}^{2} F \cos \theta \, \Delta s = \int_{1}^{2} F \cos \theta \, ds, \tag{9–33}$$

which is to be contrasted with an ordinary integral, such as Eq. (9–4). The line integral in the form of Eq. (9–33) *cannot* be interpreted as the area under the curve of $F \cos \theta$ versus s except in special cases.

In two-dimensional motion, it is convenient to use cartesian components on occasion. Work can be expressed in cartesian components by noting that

$$F_x \, dx + F_y \, dy = F \cos \theta \, ds. \tag{9–31}$$

We can prove Eq. (9–34) by resolving F and ds into their components (Fig. 9–15)

$$\begin{aligned} F_x &= F \cos (\theta + \alpha), \\ F_y &= F \sin (\theta + \alpha), \\ dx &= ds \cos \alpha, \\ dy &= ds \sin \alpha, \end{aligned} \tag{9–35}$$

substituting into Eq. (9–34), and using the trigonometric expansions for the functions of the sum of angles.

Therefore, work can be expressed in the form

$$W = \int_{1}^{2} (F_x \, dx + F_y \, dy), \tag{9–36}$$

for two dimensions. A third term, in z, occurs for three dimensions.

In some cases the dependence of work on the path in two dimensions is readily ascertained from Eq. (9–36). Examples are left for the problems.

In principle, the line integral can be related to ordinary integrals by expressing all variables in terms of a parameter, such as time, as follows:

$$\begin{aligned} W &= \int_{t_1}^{t_2} \left(F_x \frac{dx}{dt} \, dt + F_y \frac{dy}{dt} \, dt \right) \\ &= \int_{t_1}^{t_2} \left(F_x \frac{dx}{dt} + F_y \frac{dy}{dt} \right) dt, \end{aligned} \tag{9–37}$$

where F_x, etc., are to be expressed as functions of time. Equation (9–37) then becomes an ordinary integral. We have already stated that the integrand, in this form, is the quantity called power. When written explicitly in terms of velocity, we have

$$W = \int_{t_1}^{t_2} (F_x v_x + F_y v_y) \, dt. \tag{9–38}$$

The integrals of Eqs. (9–37) and (9–38) can be evaluated in the usual way, i.e., the integrand is first expressed as a function of t, the antiderivative is found, and the result is the difference between the terms obtained by substitution of t_2 and t_1. However, the above method is useful only in special cases, since it requires detailed knowledge of the velocity of the object. Much of the power and simplicity of the work-energy method are lost in the above formulation.

When two or more forces act on the object in question, each force can be resolved into components. The work by each force can then be calculated and the results added to obtain the total work. However, from the superposition principle, we see that the result is the same as the work done by the resultant of the forces in question; thus, for two forces F_A and F_B, we have

$$W = W_A + W_B$$
$$= \int_1^2 (F_{Ax}\,dx + F_{Bx}\,dx + F_{Ay}\,dy + F_{By}\,dy)$$

or

$$W = \int_1^2 [(\textstyle\sum F_x)\,dx + (\sum F_y)\,dy]. \qquad (9\text{–}39)$$

From the above, we can use Eq. (9–34) to write

$$W = W_A + W_B = \int_1^2 (\textstyle\sum F) \cos\theta\, ds, \qquad (9\text{–}40)$$

which shows more explicitly that the total work by the forces on an object is the work by the resultant of the forces.

In the case of dissipative forces, such as friction, the work integral is path-dependent. In the case of certain other forces, the work is independent of path, as we have seen in the discussion of rectilinear motion. The condition for path independence in two-dimensional motion is that the expression in Eq. (9–34) be an exact differential, that is,

$$F_x\,dx + F_y\,dy = -dV. \qquad (9\text{–}41)$$

When this condition holds, we have

$$W = \int_1^2 (F_x\,dx + F_y\,dy)$$
$$= -\int_1^2 dV = V_1 - V_2, \qquad (9\text{–}42)$$

where the minus sign was introduced in Eq. (9–41) so that V represents the quantity that has earlier been defined as *potential energy*. Forces that meet the condition of Eq. (9–41) are called conservative forces. We see from Eq. (9–42) that the work by conservative forces depends only on the end points of the motion in the two-dimensional case, just as in the case of rectilinear motion. The general mathematical test for the validity of Eq. (9–41) is that

$$\partial F_x/\partial y = \partial F_y/\partial x, \qquad (9\text{–}43)$$

where the notation $\partial(\ )/\partial(\ )$ means that the other independent variables are held constant while the differentiation is being performed with respect to the variable in question. Special cases of conservative forces in two-dimensional motion will be considered in later sections.

9–14 KINETIC ENERGY IN TWO-DIMENSIONAL MOTION

When a mass m is acted upon by more than one force while moving along some path, we can calculate the work done by the resultant of all external forces in component form by using Eq. (9–39) which is repeated below for convenience:

$$W = \int_1^2 [(\textstyle\sum F_x)\,dx + (\sum F_y)\,dy]. \qquad (9\text{–}39)$$

If $\sum F$ represents the sum of *all* the external forces on the object, Newton's second law permits the substitutions $\sum F_x = ma_x$ and $\sum F_y = ma_y$ in the integrand. In order to reduce the integral to one variable, the acceleration components can be written dv_x/dt and dv_y/dt. The first term in the integrand becomes

$$m\,\frac{dv_x}{dt}\,dx = m\,\frac{dx}{dt}\,dv_x = mv_x\,dv_x = \tfrac{1}{2}m\,d(v_x)^2. \qquad (9\text{–}44)$$

Since similar results are obtained for the y-term, the integral becomes

$$W = \int_1^2 \tfrac{1}{2}m[d(v_x)^2 + d(v_y)^2]. \qquad (9\text{–}45)$$

A remarkable simplification occurs when it is remembered that $v_x^2 + v_y^2 = v^2$, and therefore

$d(v_x)^2 + d(v_y)^2 = d(v^2)$, namely,

$$W = \int_1^2 \tfrac{1}{2}m\, d(v^2) = \tfrac{1}{2}mv_2^2 - \tfrac{1}{2}mv_1^2. \qquad (9\text{–}46)$$

The argument can be extended to three dimensions, with the same final result as above. The work by the resultant force can be calculated by doing the line integral of the resultant force or separately for individual forces and then adding. The appropriate choice will depend on the particular problem. *The important point is that we must finish by including the work by all external forces.*

Because of the general nature of the result expressed in Eq. (9–46), the terms on the right are called *kinetic energy,* just as in the case of rectilinear motion. We shall use the symbol T, for kinetic energy, i.e., we shall write

$$T \equiv mv^2/2, \qquad (9\text{–}47)$$

where v represents the magnitude of the velocity. The statement of Eq. (9–24) can then be abbreviated

$$W_{12} = T_2 - T_1 \equiv \Delta T. \qquad (9\text{–}48)$$

In words, the work done *by* the resultant force *on* an object equals the *gain* in the object's kinetic energy. If instead, work is done *by* the object, this work equals the object's *loss* of kinetic energy. If correctly and consistently used, the signs will take care of the above distinction. For example, when the work is calculated by Eq. (9–39), work is done *on* the object by $\sum F_x$ when $\sum F_x$ and dx have the same sign (i.e., are in the same direction), but work is done *by* the object when $\sum F_x$ and dx have opposite signs. The situation is the same for the y-components.

9–15 FORCES OF CONSTRAINT

One type of force that can be ignored in calculating the work is force of constraint. This term is applied when an object is constrained to move over a particular surface or along a particular path. We have had many examples of a special case of the former, namely, constraint to motion in a horizontal plane. An inclined plane constrains the motion to a sloping surface, a string fixed at one end can constrain the motion to a spherical surface, etc. In the above cases we have assumed that the forces are such that the object does not leave the surface. Constraint to a particular path is commonly achieved with a track or channel of some kind. In the case of a rollercoaster the wheels may be such that the track can "hold" the object either up or down. If the object has a hole in it, its path can be constrained by requiring it to slide on a wire or rod.

In all cases of constraints, the force of constraint is defined as the normal component of force exerted by the constraining agent (the tangential component is called friction, as usual). Since the force of constraint is perpendicular to the motion at all points of the path, this force can never do work directly on the constrained object. (A friction force *resulting* from the constraining force will, of course, do work on the constrained object.) In addition, a constraining force can change the direction of motion.

9–16 TWO-DIMENSIONAL MOTION NEAR THE EARTH

If the path of motion is sufficiently localized, the gravitational constant g, and hence the weight of an object, can be considered constant in magnitude and in direction. Consider an object that follows a path of any form, such as in Fig. 9–17. The object follows this path because of forces of constraint. Consider the work done by the constant gravitational force mg. From the definition of work by a force, the work by mg is given by

$$W = \int_1^2 F \cos\theta\, ds = mg \int_1^2 \cos\theta\, ds. \qquad (9\text{–}49)$$

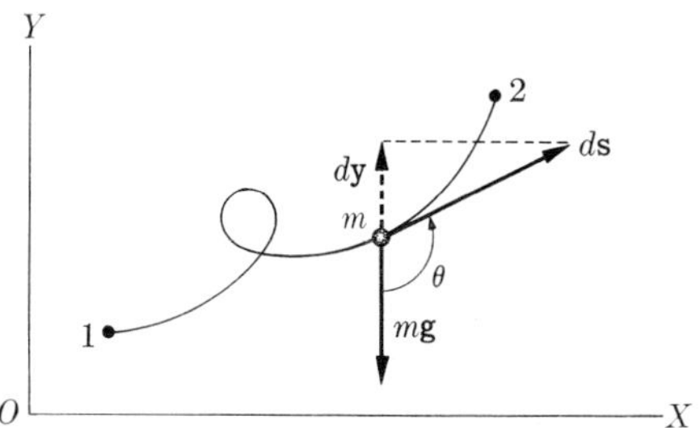

FIG. 9–17. A mass m follows a complicated two-dimensional path between points 1 and 2. The path lies in a vertical plane. The projection dy (onto the vertical axis) of an element of displacement ds is shown.

But since $\cos\theta\, ds = -dy$, as seen from Fig. 9–17, we have

$$W = mg \int_1^2 -dy = mg(y_1 - y_2). \qquad (9\text{–}50)$$

It is seen that the work by the gravitational force is independent of the path from (1) to (2) because it depends only on the end coordinates y_1 and y_2. Therefore, change in potential energy is a useful concept for the work done by the gravitational force:

$$\Delta V = -W = mg(y_2 - y_1). \qquad (9\text{–}51)$$

The change in potential energy can be expressed as the difference between two terms, that is,

$$\Delta V = V_2 - V_1, \qquad (9\text{–}52)$$

and the two terms can be chosen to be

$$V_2 = mgy_2, \qquad V_1 = mgy_1, \qquad (9\text{–}53)$$

which corresponds to the arbitrary choice that $V = 0$ at $y = 0$. A more general choice would be

$$V_2 = mg(y_2 - y_0),$$
$$V_1 = mg(y_1 - y_0), \qquad (9\text{–}54)$$

which corresponds to the choice that $V = 0$ at $y = y_0$.

Now consider the other forces. The force of constraint (the normal component of the force by the track) does no work, as seen earlier. The friction force does work that must be evaluated by a line integral along the path. Designate this work by W_{fr}.

Finally, remember that the total work (or work by the resultant of all forces) equals the gain in kinetic energy; therefore

$$W(\text{gravity}) + W_{\text{fr}} = \Delta T, \qquad (9\text{–}55)$$

or

$$-(V_2 - V_1) + W_{\text{fr}} = T_2 - T_1, \quad (9\text{–}56)$$

or

$$V_2 + T_2 = V_1 + T_1 + W_{\text{fr}}. \qquad (9\text{–}57)$$

It is interesting to note that the force of constraint must take part in the proof that total work equals change in kinetic energy, since the sum of *all* forces entered into the proof. The effect of the constraint force is felt in changing the direction of the velocity even though it can never itself change the magnitude of the velocity. The work by friction will be *negative* since the force is opposite to the motion. If friction is negligible, there is conservation of mechanical energy, that is,

$$V_2 + T_2 = V_1 + T_1. \qquad (9\text{–}58)$$

Equation (9–57) can be written out in terms of velocities, positions, etc.:

$$mgy_2 + \frac{mv_2^2}{2} = mgy_1 + \frac{mv_1^2}{2} + \int_1^2 F_{\text{fr}}\, ds. \qquad (9\text{–}59)$$

The last term can be written $-\bar{F}_{\text{fr}}L$, where $\bar{F}_{\text{fr}}$ is the average friction force and L is the total path length.

In the above, the power of the work-energy method begins to be evident. It would be a formidable task indeed to apply Newton's laws directly to the motion along the path in Fig. 9–17. On the other hand, we have obtained only the relationship between the magnitude of the velocity and the position. The time-dependence of either of these quantities is much more difficult to obtain. However, many important properties of the motion are known when the velocity-position relation is known.

9–17 ENERGY IN CENTRAL FORCE PROBLEMS

Examples of central forces that have already been noted are: (a) gravitational force,

$$F_G = G\,\frac{mm'}{r^2}, \tag{9–60}$$

where r is the distance from m to m'; (b) electrical force due to charges at rest,

$$F_E = K\,\frac{qq'}{r^2}; \tag{9–61}$$

and (c) spring forces, e.g., a spring that follows Hooke's law,

$$F_{sp} = -k(r - r_0), \tag{9–62}$$

where r_0 is the unstretched length.

A convenient choice of coordinates is a polar system with its origin at the point toward which the central force is directed. If one of the two interacting objects is much more massive than the other, the more massive object can be assumed to be fixed in position and used as the origin. For example, in the analysis of the motion of an artificial earth satellite, the earth can be assumed to be a fixed center of attraction for the artificial satellite.

If the two objects have comparable masses, each object moves appreciably. The center toward which the forces are directed is located on the line of centers at the point that divides the line of centers into segments r_1 and r_2, given by

$$m_1r_1 = m_2r_2, \tag{9–63}$$

as developed in Section 7–9.

With the above choice of coordinates, a central force has only a radial component F_r. The work

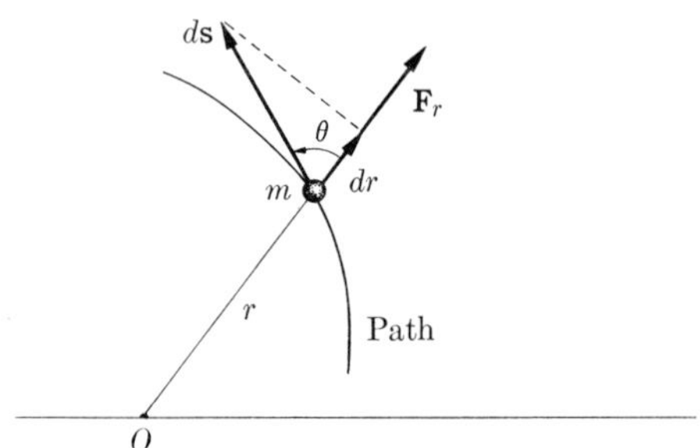

Fig. 9–18. A mass m that experiences a central force $\mathbf{F}_r$. The radial component dr of an elementary displacement ds is shown.

done by the central force is therefore

$$W = \int F_r \cos\theta\, ds. \tag{9–64}$$

But $\cos\theta\, ds$ is just dr (see Fig. 9–18). Consequently, the work integral becomes

$$W = \int_1^2 F_r\, dr. \tag{9–65}$$

If F_r is a function of r alone, the work integral above is the same in form as in the case of rectilinear motion with a force that depends only on position (Section 9–6). We saw that the value of the integral is independent of path under these circumstances. Since the work is independent of path, the potential energy concept can be used for central forces. Thus

$$\Delta V = V_2 - V_1 = -\int_1^2 F(r)\, dr, \tag{9–66}$$

where we have changed notation slightly in order to indicate that the force is a function of r alone.

The total energy of the system will now be considered. The work by the resultant force equals the gain in kinetic energy regardless of whether cartesian or polar coordinates are used, since only the resultant velocity appears in the final equation (9–46). In polar coordinates the expression for the composition of the magnitude of the velocity is simply

$$v^2 = v_r^2 + v_\theta^2 = v_r^2 + (\omega r)^2. \qquad (9\text{–}67)$$

If the only force on m is the central force, the gain in kinetic energy equals the work done by the central force. But this work is expressible as change in potential energy. Hence Eq. (9–30) is applicable (that is, $V_2 + T_2 = V_1 + T_1$). Or, in different notation, we have

$$V(r) + T = \text{constant}, \qquad (9\text{–}68)$$

where the notation indicates that V is a function of r. This equation states that the *total* mechanical energy remains constant.

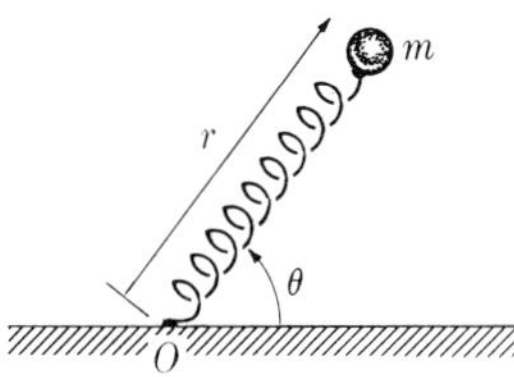

FIG. 9–19. A mass m that experiences a central force exerted by a spring.

In the case of a *spring* attached to a pin (Fig. 9–19), the force is given by Eq. (9–62) for an ordinary spring. The work and change in potential energy are then given by

$$-(V_2 - V_1) = W_{12} = \int_{r_1}^{r_2} F_r\,dr = \int_{r_1}^{r_2} -k(r - r_0)\,dr = -\frac{k}{2}\left[(r_2 - r_0)^2 - (r_1 - r_0)^2\right]. \qquad (9\text{–}69)$$

The potential energy terms might be chosen as $V_1 = (k/2)(r_1 - r_0)^2$ and $V_2 = (k/2)(r_2 - r_0)^2$ or, at any distance r,

$$V = \frac{k}{2}(r - r_0)^2, \qquad (9\text{–}70)$$

in which case $V = 0$ at $r = r_0$.

It is again emphasized that the choice of the position for zero potential energy is completely arbitrary. In this case, for example, it might be equally convenient to choose $V = 0$ at $r = 0$. In order to do this, a constant C is added to V:

$$V = \frac{k}{2}(r - r_0)^2 + C.$$

The constant is evaluated by setting $V = 0$ at $r = 0$ with the result that

$$V = \frac{k}{2}(r^2 - 2rr_0), \qquad (9\text{–}71)$$

when the above particular choice for the zero of potential energy is made. Either Eq. (9–70) or Eq. (9–71) can then be used in an equation for energy conservation such as Eq. (9–58). In particular, if we substitute Eq. (9–70) into Eq. (9–58), the result is

$$\frac{k}{2}(r_2 - r_0)^2 + \tfrac{1}{2}mv_2^2 = \frac{k}{2}(r_1^2 - r_0^2) + \tfrac{1}{2}mv_1^2. \qquad (9\text{–}72)$$

Spring forces that have a nonlinear law for force versus change in length will, of course, have a different dependence of potential energy on position.

If the masses at each end of the spring are comparable in magnitude, both ends of the spring move. The work integrals could be performed separately for each end of the spring and the result would be as above with r corresponding to the total length of the stretched spring. The potential energy is then the internal potential energy of the system, and hence the kinetic energy in the conservation of energy equations would be the sum of the kinetic energies of the two masses.

Both *gravitational* and *electric* forces depend on r as $1/r^2$. The change in potential and work for either case is therefore of the form

$$-(V_2 - V_1) = W_{12} = \int_{r_1}^{r_2} -C\frac{dr}{r^2} = C\left(\frac{1}{r_2} - \frac{1}{r_1}\right), \qquad (9\text{–}73)$$

where C is Gmm' in the gravitational case.

The usual choice for potential energy is

$$V = -\frac{Gmm'}{r}, \qquad (9\text{–}74)$$

which corresponds to $V = 0$ at $r = \infty$. Again, other choices can be made, but the above is most convenient since it results in a single term. Note that with the above choice the gravitational potential energy is negative for all values of r. For ease of calculation, it is often convenient to express the constants in terms of g and the earth's radius as follows: At the surface of the earth, the force by the earth on m is $mg = Gmm'/R_e^2$ or $Gm' = gR_e^2$, where R_e is the radius of the earth. Then Eq. (9–74) can be written

$$V = -mgR_e^2/r, \qquad (9\text{–}75)$$

and the force can be written

$$F = -mgR_e^2/r^2, \qquad (9\text{–}76)$$

and so forth for any equation based on universal gravitation. Mechanical energy is conserved, if there is no friction. If, in addition, $m' >> m$, the change in kinetic energy of m' is negligible, and we have

$$\frac{v_2^2}{2} - G\frac{m'}{r_2} = \frac{v_1^2}{2} - G\frac{m'}{r_1}, \qquad (9\text{–}77)$$

where the v's are the resultant velocities, as usual.

If m is comparable with m', the energy-conservation principle is most easily applied to the two-body system. The kinetic energy of the system is the sum of the kinetic energies of the parts, and the potential energy is given by Eq. (9–75) with r the distance between the masses.

9–18 SYSTEMS WITH TWO OR MORE CONSERVATIVE FORCES

It has already been proved that the work by several forces is the sum of the work terms for each force. A direct consequence of this is that changes of potential energy are additive. That is, if two or more conservative forces act on a body, the total change in potential energy is the sum of the potential energy changes due to the individual forces.

Furthermore, if the zero of potential energy is chosen at the same position for all the forces, the potential energies themselves can simply be added.

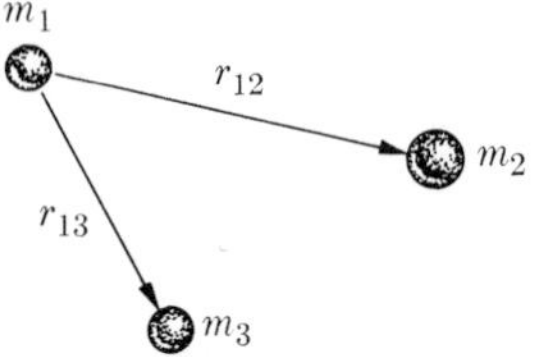

FIG. 9–20. Three masses isolated in space.

Example 6. Consider three masses isolated in space and arranged as in Fig. 9–20. Find the potential energy of m_1 due to m_2 and m_3.

Solution: Since the potential energies are additive, if we choose a common zero (at infinity in this case), we have

$$V_1 = -Gm_1\left(\frac{m_3}{r_{13}} + \frac{m_2}{r_{12}}\right).$$

Example 7. Find the potential energy of the planet Saturn due to its rings, assuming that the rings have a mass M that is effectively concentrated at a distance R from the planet, as in Fig. 9–21.

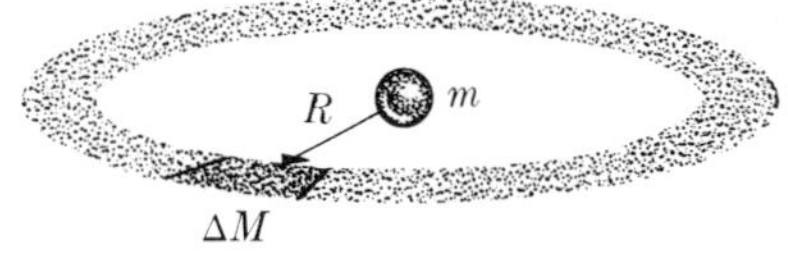

FIG. 9–21. A mass m at the center of a ring-shaped mass M.

Solution: The potential energy of m due to a segment of the ring ΔM is $\Delta V = -Gm\Delta M/R$, where in this case the ΔV means V due to ΔM (*not* a change in V). The total V is then $\sum \Delta V = \sum - Gm\Delta M/R = -GmM/R$.

9–19 COLLISIONS AND EXPLOSIONS

In Chapter 4, it was found that momentum is conserved during interactions involving systems with internal forces alone. The conservation principle followed directly from the definition of mass. The net effect of outside forces was negated by the type of support, e.g., a low-friction horizontal table or track, or the effect of outside forces was assumed to be small during the interaction.

The latter condition can now be understood in terms of impulse. The change in momentum of one of the interacting objects equals the impulse of the interaction force [Eq. (9–5)]. The magnitude of the force varies during the interaction, but the average value is simply the impulse J (or the change in momentum $p_f - p_0$) divided by the time duration of the interaction. Thus, if the time of interaction is short, the average force is large for a given momentum change. Thus, the degree of approximation in neglecting outside forces during an interaction is determined by the brevity of the interaction for a given momentum change.

Momentum conservation applies to all interactions. What about energy? We have also postulated that energy is always conserved. But energy conservation includes heat energy, etc., in addition to mechanical energy. In interactions of macroscopic bodies, some of the mechanical energy is always "converted" into heat energy. For example, even in the interaction of objects due to action at a distance, there is usually generation of heat; in the case of electromagnetic forces, there are induced currents; in the case of gravitation, there are "tides" in the solid material (as well as in the oceans).

However, there are many cases in which the energy transformation to heat, sound, etc. is negligible. Such interactions are called *elastic* or *perfectly elastic.* In an elastic interaction, mechanical energy is conserved, since, by definition, there is no transformation to other forms. In the submicroscopic realm, elastic collisions predominate. Atomic and molecular collisions at ordinary temperatures are usually elastic. In fact, you will learn later that heat energy is attributable to molecular or atomic motion, and therefore heat cannot be developed in such collisions. In the macroscopic realm, springlike forces can give nearly elastic interactions, e.g., carts with spring or rubber bumpers, hardened steel balls, etc. Electric, magnetic, and gravitational forces can also result in nearly elastic interactions.

In the above discussion, we see that the forces that give rise to elastic interactions are conservative forces, which is to be expected, since the definition of elastic collision stated that there is no dissipation of mechanical energy.

In consequence of our definition of elastic interaction, we have

$$\Sigma(T + V) = \text{constant} \tag{9–78}$$

at all times during an elastic interaction. In most cases, the overall change in potential energy is zero from a time before the interaction to a time after the interaction, and we can write

$$\Sigma T_f = \Sigma T_0 \tag{9–79}$$

for kinetic energy both after and before the interaction. The subscripts indicate original and final values.

Given the initial velocities (and the masses), Eq. (9–79) has two unknowns in two-body interactions, the final velocities. But momentum is conserved in *all* interactions, and therefore another relation containing the final velocities can be written:

$$\Sigma \mathbf{p}_f = \Sigma \mathbf{p}_0. \tag{9–80}$$

The result is two equations, which means that the problem can be solved if there are only two unknowns. In the case of two-body interactions, these equations are written

$$\tfrac{1}{2}m_A v_{Af}^2 + \tfrac{1}{2}m_B v_{Bf}^2 = \tfrac{1}{2}m_A v_{A0}^2 + \tfrac{1}{2}m_B v_{B0}^2 \tag{9–81}$$

and

$$m_A \mathbf{v}_{Af} + m_B \mathbf{v}_{Bf} = m_A \mathbf{v}_{A0} + m_B \mathbf{v}_{B0}. \tag{9–82}$$

Equation (9–82) can be written in component form. If more than two bodies interact, terms can simply be added to the above. The algebra of solving the two equations for two velocities is laborious. Particular cases are left for problems.

In the case of *partially elastic* interactions, the energy equation must include the dissipative term. The general energy equation will then be

$$T_0 + V_0 = T + V + W_R, \tag{9-83}$$

where W_R is the energy dissipated from the beginning of the interaction (subscripts 0) until the time at which T and V on the right-hand side are determined. The momentum conservation equations are unchanged.

A collision type of interaction is *completely inelastic* if the objects stick together after the collision. In this case, the momentum conservation equation alone provides the solution, if the initial conditions are given:

$$\sum(m\mathbf{v})_0 = (\sum m)\mathbf{v}_f. \tag{9-84}$$

The energy equation can then be used to find how much mechanical energy was dissipated.

9-20 SUMMARY

The *impulse* $\mathbf{J}$ by a force is defined by

$$\mathbf{J} \equiv \int \mathbf{F}\, dt.$$

From Newton's second law, we find that the impulse by the resultant force is the change in momentum, that is,

$$\int \sum \mathbf{F}\, dt = \mathbf{p}_f - \mathbf{p}_0.$$

The *work* W by a force $\mathbf{F}$ is defined by a line integral along the path of motion; thus

$$W \equiv \int \mathbf{F} \cdot d\mathbf{s} = \int |\mathbf{F}|\, |d\mathbf{s}| \cos\theta,$$

where $\mathbf{F} \cdot d\mathbf{s}$ is a scalar product between the vectors (θ is the angle between $\mathbf{F}$ and $d\mathbf{s}$).

In the *case of rectilinear motion*, the work is independent of path if the force depends only on the position (not on the direction of motion, for example). The work done by friction forces does depend on the path between two points, since the friction force depends on the direction of motion.

It is convenient in some cases to reformulate the work integral in terms of force, velocity, and time as follows:

$$W = \int \mathbf{F} \cdot \mathbf{v}\, dt.$$

The integral is then an ordinary integral. The product $\mathbf{F} \cdot \mathbf{v}$ is the *power* P.

When the work by a force is independent of the path between two points, it is useful to define the difference in potential energy between the two points as the negative of the work along a path between the points:

$$V_2 - V_1 = -\int_1^2 \mathbf{F} \cdot d\mathbf{s}.$$

If the force is exerted by a spring, the difference in potential energy is

$$V_2 - V_1 = \tfrac{1}{2}kx_2^2 - \tfrac{1}{2}kx_1^2.$$

If the force is the gravitational force near the earth, the difference in potential energy is

$$V_2 - V_1 = mg(h_2 - h_1).$$

The work by the resultant force is found to be (regardless of the nature of the individual forces)

$$\int_1^2 \sum \mathbf{F} \cdot d\mathbf{s} = \tfrac{1}{2}mv_2^2 - \tfrac{1}{2}mv_1^2.$$

The terms of the form $\frac{1}{2}mv^2$ are defined as kinetic energy:

$$T \equiv \tfrac{1}{2}mv^2.$$

The principle of conservation of energy can be stated in the form that the total energy of a system changes by the amount of work done on the system by outside agents plus the amount of energy introduced into the system by an outside agent. If only mechanical work and energy, including friction, are involved, the conservation principle can be stated in the form

$$W - Q = V_2 - V_1 + T_2 - T_1,$$

where W is the work done on the system by an outside agent and Q is the energy transformed to heat by friction forces.

Turning explicitly to *motion in two dimensions*, we see that the sum of the work contributions by individual forces is equal to the work by the resultant of the forces.

The condition that a force is conservative and, therefore, can have its work represented by a change in potential energy is, in general,

$$\frac{\partial F_x}{\partial_y} = \frac{\partial F_y}{\partial_x},$$

where the derivatives are partial derivatives.

The work by the *resultant force* is shown to be equal to the change in kinetic energy, just as in the case of rectilinear motion:

$$\int_1^2 \Sigma \mathbf{F} \cdot d\mathbf{s} = \tfrac{1}{2}mv_2^2 - \tfrac{1}{2}mv_1^2.$$

The work can again be divided into work by conservative forces, which can be expressed in terms of change in potential energy, and work by nonconservative forces, which represents a change in the mechanical energy of the system. In the case of motion near the earth over small distances, we can write

$$mgy_2 + \tfrac{1}{2}mv_2^2 = mgy_1 + \tfrac{1}{2}mv_1^2 + W_{\text{fr}},$$

where W_{fr} represents the work by friction, which is usually negative since the force due to friction is usually opposite to the direction of motion.

More generally, it is shown that any central force that is a function of r alone is a conservative force. Consequently, the work by such a force can be represented by a change in potential energy. An example of a central force exerted by a spring is treated in this chapter. The frequently occurring case of an inverse square central force results in

$$\tfrac{1}{2}v_2^2 - G\frac{m'}{r_2} = \tfrac{1}{2}v_1^2 - G\frac{m'}{r_1}$$

for the gravitational case when there are no dissipative (nonconservative) forces.

When two or more conservative forces occur, the method of potential energy is particularly useful because the potentials are scalars and can be added algebraically.

The use of two conservation principles, energy and linear momentum, in interaction problems such as collisions and explosions is discussed. The reader is reminded that linear momentum is always conserved when no resultant outside force acts on the system, regardless of the nature of the internal forces of interaction among parts of the system.

Problems

You will find that these problems provide a review of the topics of previous chapters.

1. A person pushes for ten minutes on a ship of mass 10^4 metric tons (10^7 kg) that is initially at rest. The ship has a speed of 1 cm/sec at the end of the ten-minute interval.

(a) How large was the impulse given to the ship?

(b) What was the average force exerted by the person, assuming that water resistance is negligible at these velocities?

2. A gust of wind that lasts 20 sec strikes the side of a boat of mass 500 kg. The boat, which was initially at rest, is given a sideways velocity of 0.5 cm/sec as a result of the gust. If the force by the wind increased from zero linearly with time for 15 sec and decreased to zero linearly for 5 sec, (a) find the impulse by the gust on the boat. (b) Find the maximum force exerted on the boat. (c) Make a graph of F versus t, and find the area under the curve. Does the area agree with (a)? Water resistance is negligible at these velocities.

3. A rocket weighing 10^4 n is fired vertically upward from the earth. Its motor provides a vertically upward thrust of 10^6 n for 20 sec, followed by a thrust that decreases linearly with time from 10^6 n to zero in the next 100 sec.

(a) Find the total impulse given to the rocket.

(b) Find the velocity of the rocket after 120 sec by using the results of (a). Assume that the mass of the rocket stays approximately constant.

4. In simple harmonic motion, the force can be written $F = -kA \cos 2\pi ft$, where A is the amplitude of the motion, k is the restoring force constant, and f is the frequency.

(a) Calculate the impulse from this force between $t = 0$ and $t = \tau/4$, where τ is the period.

(b) Find the velocity at $t = \tau/4$ from the impulse, assuming that $v = 0$ at $t = 0$. Compare this result with the result obtained from the usual equations of simple harmonic motion. (Note: $2\pi f = \sqrt{k/m}$.)

5. A boy moves a sled by pulling on the rope with a force of 20 n. The rope makes an angle of 30° with the ground.

(a) How much work does the boy do on the sled while pulling the sled 5 m over level ice?

(b) If the sled moves at constant velocity and its mass is 12 kg, what is the coefficient of friction between sled and ice?

(c) What is the minimum coefficient of friction between the ice and the boy's shoes if his mass is 20 kg? Is this the static or the sliding coefficient of friction?

6. A mass of 20 kg is moved by a horizontal push of 2 n a distance of 5 m at constant velocity along a horizontal surface. How much work is done (a) by the agent exerting the push, (b) by the friction force, (c) by the gravitational pull of the earth, (d) by the normal force exerted by the horizontal surface, and (e) by the total force exerted by the horizontal surface?

7. An artificial satellite is in a circular orbit around the earth. How much work is done by the earth on the satellite, if the satellite is above the atmosphere?

8. Find the work done by the force $F = F_0 + kx$, which acts at an angle θ, such that $\cos \theta = (1 - x/x_0)$, on an object that moves from x_1 to x_2 along the x-axis. The units of k are force/length.

9. An object of mass 3 kg is (a) lifted vertically from the floor to a height of 2 m above the floor and (b) then lowered to a point 1.5 m above the floor. Calculate the work done by the earth on the mass in (a), in (b), for the total motion, and for motion directly from floor level to the 1.5-m level.

10. A box of mass 40 kg is pushed up an inclined board of length 5 m. The height of the incline is 3 m. Find the work done by friction when the box is pushed from the bottom to the top of the incline and then permitted to slide back to the midpoint. The push on the box is parallel with the incline, and the coefficient of friction is 0.3.

11. Derive an expression for the work done by a spring that follows Hooke's law when the free end of the spring moves from x_1 to x_2 (in the direction of the spring axis), where x is the length of the spring and x_0 is the length of the undistorted spring.

12. A boat is being towed through the water at constant velocity $\mathbf{v}$. The water resistance force is kv^2, where k is a constant.

(a) Find the work done by the resisting force during the time t_1 to t_2 by using the ordinary integral method of Section 9–7.

(b) Draw a graph to illustrate the integration, and shade in the area which represents the work.

(c) What power is required to tow the boat?

13. A spring that follows Hooke's law is initially compressed by an amount x_1. It is allowed to expand and is then stretched by an equal amount x_2. Thus $x_1 = -x_2$, and the change in potential energy is zero [Eq. (9–20)]. Show, in terms of work, how this result comes about.

14. Using the length y of a spring as coordinate, derive an expression for the change in potential energy when y changes from y_1 to y_2. (Assume Hooke's law.)

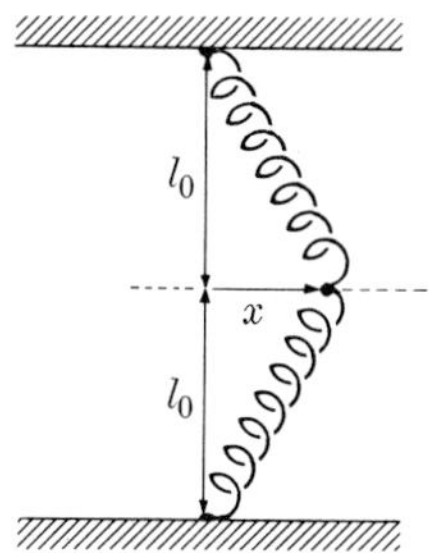

FIGURE 9–22

15. It was shown in an earlier chapter that the spring system pictured in Fig. 9–22 results in a restoring force $F = -kx^3$ for small x. Derive an expression for the change in potential energy for small values of x.

16. A mass m rests on a table of height h. (a) What is the potential energy of the mass m? The mass is lifted to a height y above the table. Calculate the change in potential energy (b) using the table top as the origin of coordinates, and (c) using the floor as the origin.

17. A rocket of mass m is fired vertically away from the earth.

(a) Calculate the change in gravitational potential energy of the rocket when it rises to a height r (measured from the center of the earth), where $r - r_0$ is not small compared with the radius of the earth r_0.

(b) Is it possible to choose $V = 0$ at $r = 0$?

18. Would it be possible to derive the work-kinetic energy relationship of Eq. (9–25) by considering individual forces (A, B, C, etc.) one at a time and then adding the results, i.e., by saying that $W_A = (mv_2^2/2)_A - (mv_2^2/2)_A$, etc., and then adding?

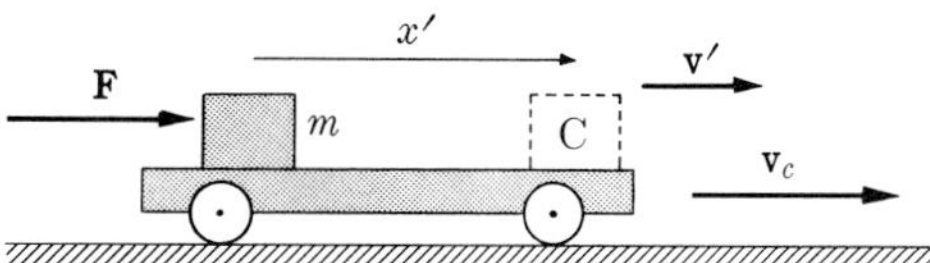

FIGURE 9–23

19. Consider the work done by a constant force F on a mass m, sliding on the frictionless surface of a car C (Fig. 9–23). The mass starts at rest relative to C and attains a speed of v' relative to C after moving a distance x' relative to C. The car moves with constant velocity v_c relative to the earth. It was shown in an earlier chapter that F is the same in all inertial frames.

(a) Are both the car and the earth inertial frames? Is $F' = F$?

(b) Is the initial kinetic energy the same in both frames? Is the final kinetic energy the same?

(c) Calculate the change in kinetic energy and the work in the "moving" frame (the car).

(d) Transform the expressions for $\Delta T'$ and for W' to the "fixed" frame (the earth), and show that $\Delta T = W$. [Remember that $x = x' + v_c t = x' + v_c(2x'/v')$].

20. A block of mass m is moved horizontally on a frictionless table, starting and ending at rest.

(a) How much work was done on the block?

(b) How much work was done starting and stopping the block? Explain your answer to (a) in terms of your answer to (b).

21. A man pushes a lawn mower weighing 10 kg over level ground. He pushes at an angle of 30° with the horizontal. When he pushes with a force of 10 n, the velocity is constant. Assuming that the friction force opposing the motion remains constant, independent of velocity and how hard the man is pushing, how much work *does he do* in 10 m if: (a) the

velocity remains constant? (b) the velocity increases from 0 to 2 m/sec? (c) the velocity decreases from 2 to 1 m/sec?

22. An object of mass 2 kg is moving in a straight line with a velocity of $\sqrt{2}$ m/sec. What is the velocity of the mass (a) after 6 joules of work are done on it? (b) after it has done 1 joule of work on another object?

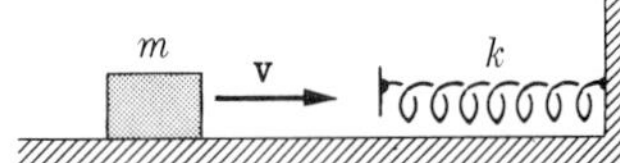

FIGURE 9–24

23. A 1-kg object slides along a table with velocity **v** and collides with a weightless spring (Fig. 9–24). The spring constant is $\frac{1}{2}$ n/cm. The object compresses the spring by a maximum displacement of 2 cm. What was the original velocity of the object?

24. A mass m is placed on a spring scales. The spring is compressed by an amount d when the system comes to equilibrium. Show that $mgd \neq \frac{1}{2}kd^2$, where k is the spring constant. Account for the energy.

25. A simple pendulum is displaced by 60° from the vertical and then released from rest. The length of the pendulum is 30 cm, and the mass of the bob is 0.1 kg.

(a) What is the velocity of the bob as it passes through the lowest point in its path?

(b) Compare this exact result with the result which can be obtained by using the expressions for simple harmonic motion.

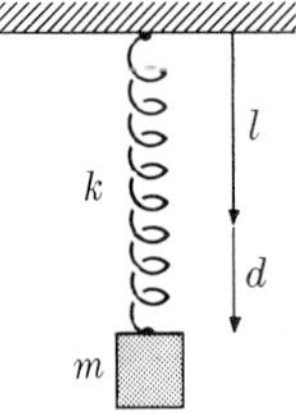

FIGURE 9–25

26. A mass m is placed on the free end of a spring of constant k (Fig. 9–25).

(a) Calculate the work done by each outside force when the mass is allowed to stretch the spring from its unloaded length l to its equilibrium length $l + d$.

(b) From energy considerations, find the maximum displacement of m if it is allowed to "fall" after it is hooked onto the free end of the spring.

27. Repeat Problem 26 for a spring that has a force law $F = -kx^3$.

28. A 70-kg man sits in a loop at one end of a rope. The rope passes over a frictionless pulley, and he holds the other end.

(a) How much work does the man do in raising himself 10 m by pulling on the rope, if he starts and stops at rest?

(b) What is the tension in the rope?

(c) What is the tension when he accelerates or decelerates by 0.1 m/sec² at the beginning or end of his motion?

(d) Does he do work at a constant rate?

29. A mass m is rotating in a vertical circle on the end of a string. Prove that the tension in the string at the lowest point equals the tension at the top point plus 6 mg.

30. By using the *kinematics* of projectile motion, show that the conservation of energy is correctly stated as $(mv_0^2)/2 = (mv^2)/2 + mgy$, where v_0 is the initial velocity and v is the velocity at any height y above the initial point.

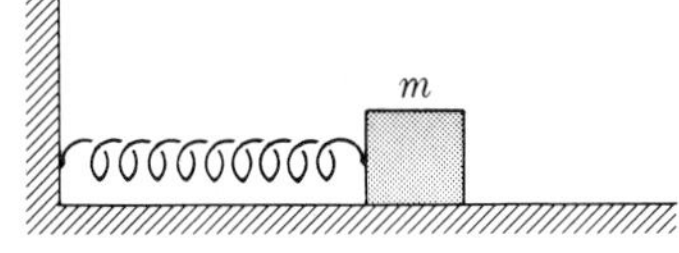

FIGURE 9–26

31. By using the kinematical equations for the simple harmonic motion of a mass on a spring, $x = A \sin \omega t$ and $v = \omega A \cos \omega t$, show that the sum of the potential energy and the kinetic energy remains constant, independent of time or position (Fig. 9–26).

32. If a 70-kg high jumper raises his center of mass 3 ft (90 cm) in clearing the bar and accomplishes this with an effective crouch of 30 cm, what average force does he exert on the ground during his spring?

33. How high can a pole vaulter raise his center of gravity due to his kinetic energy alone, if he can attain a speed of 7 m/sec while running with the pole? Since the pole-vaulting record is about 4.8 m, a

vaulter actually raises his center of mass about 3.8 m. How much work must he do with his arm and other muscles while in midair?

34. A block slides on a frictionless circular track. The plane of the circle is vertical (Fig. 9–27).

(a) What is the critical speed at the top if the block just stays on the track?

(b) Use conservation of energy to find its speed at the bottom and at a point halfway to the bottom.

(c) If its mass is m, find the resultant force on the block at the top, midpoint, and bottom.

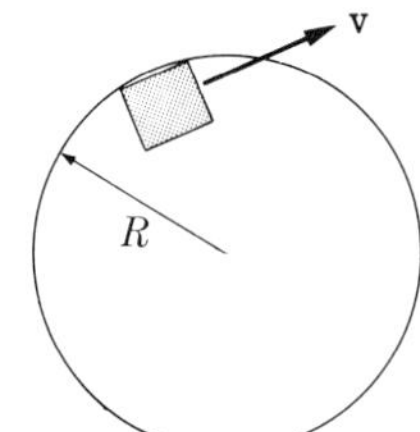

FIGURE 9–27

35. From what height h must the block m in Fig. 9–28 start from rest in order to complete the loop, assuming that friction is negligible?

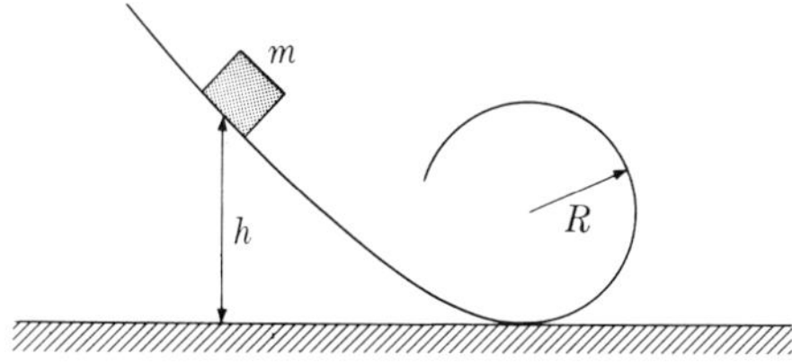

FIGURE 9–28

36. A boy of mass m is seated on a hemispherical mound of ice as shown in Fig. 9–29. If he starts sliding from rest and the ice is assumed to be frictionless, where is the point P where the boy leaves the mound?

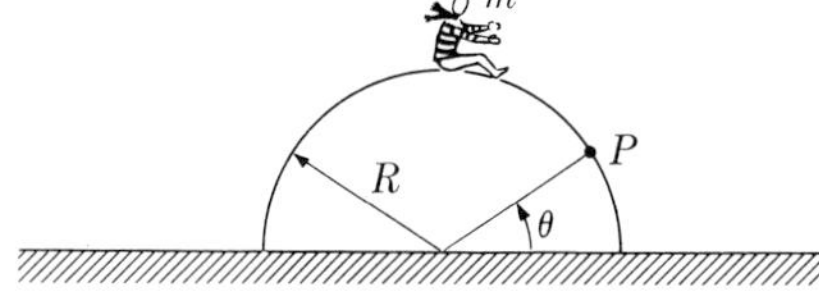

FIGURE 9–29

37. A mass of 2 kg falls *in air* a distance of 19.6 m, starting from rest, and attains a speed of 9.8 m/sec. Discuss the energy exchanges that occurred.

38. How much work is required to raise a 100-kg object from the surface of the earth to a distance above the surface equal to the earth's radius (6.4×10^6 m)? to an infinite distance?

39. Calculate the escape velocity for a rocket fired vertically from the earth, neglecting the effect of the atmosphere.

40. One of the Pioneer moon rockets reached a height of about 125,000 km. With what velocity did it strike the earth's atmosphere ($r = 6500$ km) on its return, neglecting the effect of the moon? Assume that the rocket was fired straight up.

41. Set up the problem of finding the work required to get a rocket to the point on the way to the moon at which the gravitational force changes its direction toward the moon. (Mass of moon = $\frac{1}{80}$ mass of earth. Distance to moon 3.6×10^8 m.) Where is the point of change?

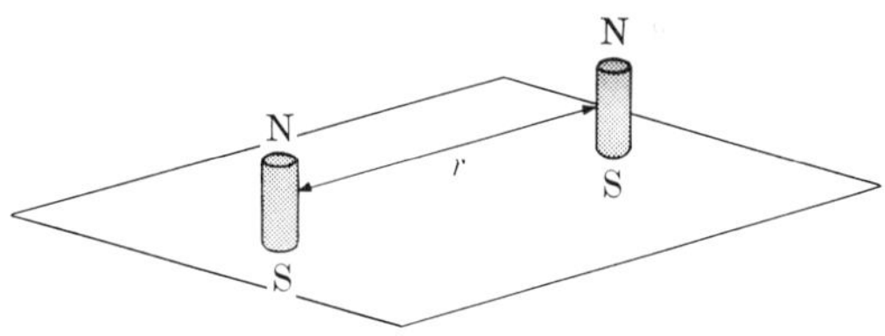

FIGURE 9–30

42. The force between two magnets is k/r^3, where k is a constant if the motion is confined to a plane, as shown in Fig. 9–30, and if the separation is greater than a few magnet lengths. (a) Find the potential energy as a function of separation if the magnets repel each other. (b) Where did you choose the zero of potential energy?

43. With what velocity would the moon strike the earth if v_θ of the moon suddenly became zero? The distance of the moon from the earth is roughly 400,000 km. Did you assume the earth fixed?

44. Neglecting air resistance, propulsion inefficiency, etc., how much work is required to put a satellite of mass 100 kg in a circular orbit 3200 km above the earth's surface? Assume that the launching site is at the north pole so that the earth's rotation plays no role? How much less is the work if the launching is at the equator and the path is toward the east?

45. Find the height of a satellite (in circular orbit in the equatorial plane) that remains over *the same point* on the earth at all times.

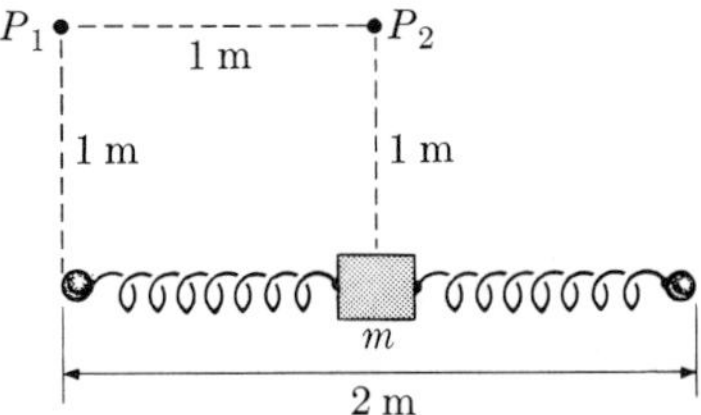

FIGURE 9–31

46. Two identical springs are connected to a mass m that is free to move in a horizontal plane, as shown in Fig. 9–31. The springs are unstretched in the position shown. The spring constants are 5 n/m, and the mass is 2 kg. The mass is displaced to point P_1 and launched with a velocity of 2 m/sec in a direction such that it passes through P_2.

(a) Find the change in potential energy from P_1 to P_2.

(b) Find the speed of the mass at P_2.

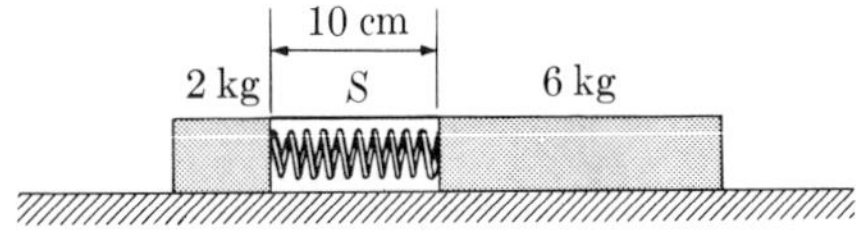

FIGURE 9–32

47. Two masses, 2 kg and 6 kg, are held at a separation of 10 cm against the forces of a compressed spring, as shown in Fig. 9–32. The normal length of the spring is 30 cm, and its force constant is 20 n/m. Friction is negligible. After the connecting string S is burned, find the velocities of the masses when their separation is (a) 20 cm, and (b) 30 cm.

48. A collision between two carts, equipped with a spring bumper and latch as indicated in Fig. 9–33, conserves mechanical energy even though the carts proceed with a common velocity after the collision. How much is the spring compressed if it obeys Hooke's law? The measured quantities are v_0, m, M, and K.

49. A spring of negligible mass supports a platform of mass M gm which deflects the spring d cm when at rest (Fig. 9–34). The spring obeys Hooke's law.

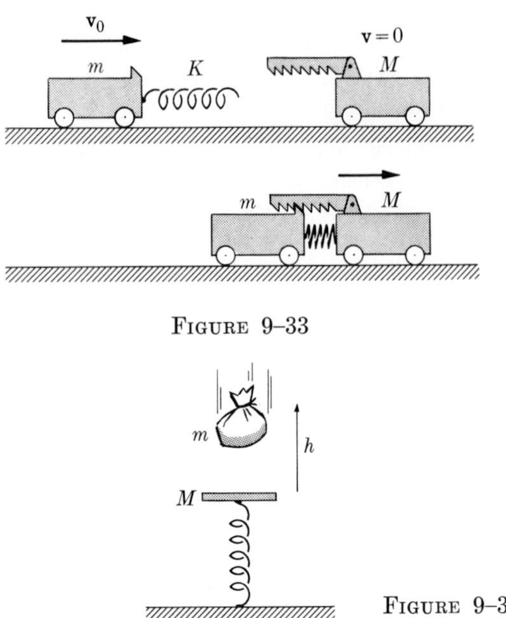

FIGURE 9–33

FIGURE 9–34

(a) A bag of shot of mass m is dropped onto the platform from a height h, making an inelastic impact. Find the maximum deflection of the spring. What are the amplitude and period of the subsequent vibrations?

(b) A steel ball of mass m replaces the bag of shot, and the collision is elastic. Find the deflection, amplitude, and period, assuming that the ball is removed after the first collision.

50. A 1-kg object falls freely from rest for 1 sec. At the end of 1 sec it is struck by a 100-gm pellet that was traveling horizontally at 55 m/sec at the moment of impact. The pellet remains embedded in the block, and they strike the ground at the end of the next second. How far was the block displaced from its vertical path? Use $g = 10\ \text{m/sec}^2$.

51. A billiard ball strikes symmetrically between two stationary balls and is brought to rest. Use a vector diagram to show that kinetic energy and momentum are conserved if the struck balls move away at 45° from the line of flight of the cue ball.

52. Make a vector diagram showing that momentum and kinetic energy are conserved in a collision of a moving object and a stationary object of equal mass when the lines of flight after collision are at right angles.

53. When elastic spheres collide, the contact force acts in the direction of the line between their centers (Fig. 9–35). In what direction is (a) the impulse, and (b) the *change* in momentum? Make a diagram of an off-center collision between an elastic sphere in motion and an identical sphere at rest, showing the directions of the momentum changes of each. Assume that the time of contact is very short.

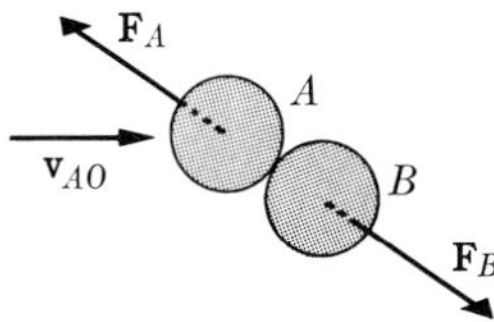

FIGURE 9–35

54. Make momentum diagrams for the effect of the collision of Problem 53 (a) on each sphere separately, and (b) on the system.

55. Make diagrams similar to those in Problem 54 for the off-center collision of identical elastic spheres, both of which were moving before the collision.

56. Consider the moon and earth as a system revolving about a common point along their line of centers. The momentum of the moon changes by 2 mv during half a lunar month ($\frac{1}{2}$ a revolution). How is momentum conserved in this system?

57. One type of subatomic particle, the tau meson, spontaneously "explodes" into three pi mesons.

(a) Prove that the pi mesons must have their momenta in the same plane if the tau meson "explodes" while at rest.

(b) Assume that in a particular case the pi mesons are emitted symmetrically in an explosion of a tau meson at rest. Find their velocities if the energy release is 1.2×10^{-4} erg and the mass of a pi meson is 2.5×10^{-25} gm.

(c) What would be the effect if the tau meson of (b) was moving when it exploded?

58. A proton of mass m and velocity v strikes another proton at rest. How much of the original KE do the protons retain if the collision is head-on and completely inelastic? How much of the original KE is available for creation of new particles (the two protons continue to exist)?

59. Repeat Problem 58 for the case where the protons meet in a completely inelastic head-on collision, each of them having the same speed v before the collision.

60. A bullet of mass m and velocity v passes through a pendulum bob of mass M and emerges with velocity $v/2$ (Fig. 9–36). The pendulum bob is on the end of a *string* of length l. What is the minimum value of v such that the pendulum bob will swing through a complete circle?

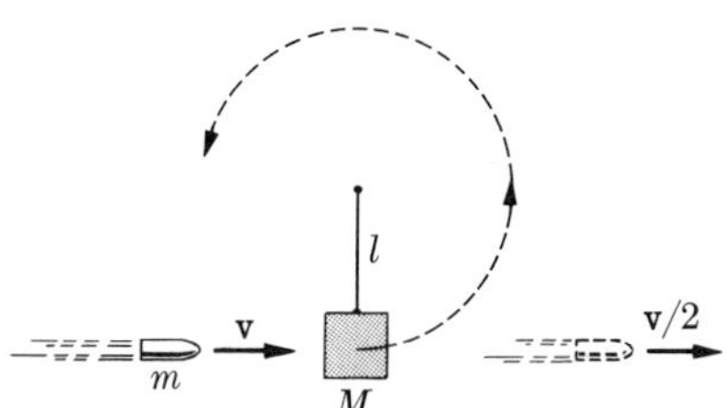

FIGURE 9–36

61. Repeat Problem 60 when the string is replaced by a rod of negligible mass.

62. A certain mass m experiences an attractive central force that is constant.

(a) Derive an expression for the potential energy as a function of the distance r from the center of attraction.

(b) What point did you choose as the zero of potential energy?

(c) Given the initial position r_0 and the magnitude of the initial velocity v_0, find the magnitude of velocity at some other distance r.

63. A mass m rests on a horizontal surface with coefficient of friction μ between m and the surface. Assume that the static coefficient is the same as the sliding coefficient. The mass is connected to a spring with Hooke's law constant k and executes "simple harmonic motion" of decreasing amplitude. From conservation of energy, show that the amplitude of motion decreases by $2\mu mg/k$ in each half period of the motion. Make a graph of the position versus time.

64. A block is pushed along a horizontal surface on which the friction varies as $(6x)$n, where x is in meters,

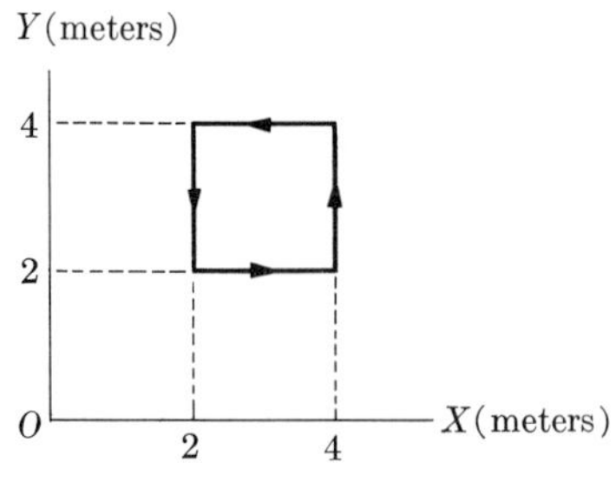

FIGURE 9–37

but is independent of y. Find the work done by friction if the block goes around the path shown in Fig. 9–37.

65. Suppose that the force in Problem 64 is *not* a friction force. Find the work done as the block goes around the path of Fig. 9–37 (a) if the force is always directed parallel to the positive OX-axis (b) if the force is always directed parallel to the positive OY-axis, and (c) if the force is always in the direction of motion. (d) Which of the forces is conservative?

66. In the case of a simple pendulum (Fig. 9–38), we saw that the resultant force has a component in the direction of motion, $F_\theta = -mg \sin \theta$.

(a) Show that the force can be written $F_\theta = -mg \sin (S/l)$.

(b) Find the work done on the pendulum as it goes from S_0 to $S = 0$ by integrating the force along the direction of motion.

67. A mass of 5 kg rests on a horizontal frictionless surface. It is fixed to a spring of constant $k =$ 20 n/m as in Fig. 8–20 and is oscillating with an amplitude of 0.5 m.

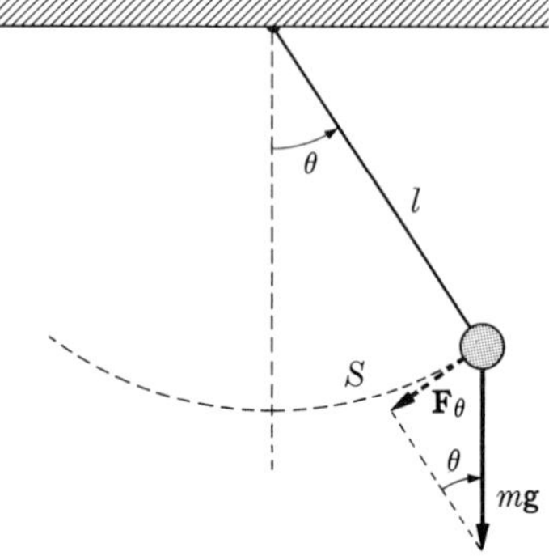

FIGURE 9–38

(a) Write the kinematical equations of motion if $x = 0$ and v is positive at $t = 0$.

(b) Find the equations of motion after a ball of putty of mass 2.5 kg is dropped onto the mass (i) at the midpoint of the motion, and (ii) at the end point of its motion.

68. A mass M with initial velocity V collides elastically with a mass m that is initially at rest.

(a) Find the new velocity of m and then take the limiting case of $m \ll M$.

(b) When M is much greater than m, as above, the velocity of M is not changed significantly by the collision. Therefore, either M or the laboratory can be used as an inertial frame. Analyze the collision from the point of view of M as the reference system and then transform the results to the laboratory system. Compare with the result of (a).

10

Gravitation, Angular Momentum, and Satellites

10–1 INTRODUCTION

In Section 5–4, the law of universal gravitation was considered in the special case of objects with dimensions small compared with their separations. This condition, for example, prohibited the treatment of motion of satellites within a few earth radii of the surface of the earth. In this chapter, we will consider the case of attraction in the proximity of spheres and even inside spheres.

In addition, we will introduce another conservation law, angular momentum, and apply the results to central force problems in general.

Finally, general features of central force motion will be determined from considerations of energy and angular momentum conservation.

10–2 THE UNIVERSALITY OF GRAVITATION

The moon represents to us the most easily observed astronomical object. How is the motion of the moon about the earth to be explained? Is the explanation or understanding to be found in the laws of mechanics that have been constructed to predict mechanical processes on the surface of the earth? If the answer is affirmative, then indeed the range of validity of the laws has been enormously extended. We present here a thumbnail calculation which bears a close relationship to Newton's inquiry, although exact historical accuracy is not claimed.

The motion of the moon is a nearly circular orbit about the earth. According to our mechanical laws, circular motion requires a centripetal force, directed inward along the radius of motion. Thus, the motion of the moon could be explained if the earth exerted a force on the moon directed exactly toward the earth. Is this a sensible postulate? Certainly it is, because the earth exerts such a force upon objects at its surface. Surface gravitation is known by everyone, hence it must not be said to be Newton's discovery.

The big step is to assert that the surface gravitation that we experience personally extends outward into the heavens. It must also be decided how the extension goes. Does the gravitational force remain constant or does it diminish as we recede from the earth? Newton used as a trial a reduction in force, and hence in acceleration, according to the inverse square law. The gravitational acceleration at the earth's surface, 6350 km from the center of the earth, is 9.8 m/sec^2. The law of inverse squares, then, gives the gravitational acceleration of the moon toward the earth as $a_{\text{m}}/9.8 = 6350^2/385{,}000^2$, where a_{m} is the gravitational acceleration of the moon caused by the earth and 385,000 km is the radius of the moon's orbit. Solving for a_{m}, we obtain $a_{\text{m}} = \frac{1}{360}$ m/sec^2. This prediction is now to be tested against the observed acceleration. The acceleration of a particle in circular motion is $a = 4\pi^2 r/\tau^2$ where the period τ is 27.3 days or 2.36×10^6 sec. The resulting value of acceleration is $\frac{1}{374}$. The agreement is within the accuracy of our figures. Note that the analysis has apparently been of a kinematic nature. No direct mention is made of the mass of the moon. However, we remember that the equality of inertial and gravitational mass is implicit in the assumption of the universality of g. Hence the above agreement indicates the universality of the gravitation law and of the equivalence of inertial to gravitational mass.

The motion of all objects in the solar system is found to agree with the assumption of the universality of Newton's law of gravitation. It seems reasonable, then, to assume that the law is valid also on the stellar scale and to use it as a tool in finding masses of double stars, etc.

At the beginning of this section we proposed, as Newton proposed, to extend the laws of known terrestrial validity to the astronomic scale. The success of the extension must come as a surprise. There could never have been a guarantee that in the study of material systems so light that we can hold them in our hands we might not overlook or miss a modification that is required when the motions of the ponderous bodies of the universe are to be described. It should be noted also that the crude calculations we presented were only a small portion of the whole picture. Actually, this was a field where observation had far outrun theoretical analysis. The motions of the planets had been observed and recorded with the finest precision. Here was an open body of data of a refined nature waiting to be analyzed. The Newtonian analysis was equal to the task of correlating the precise data with very few exceptions, such as that of the precession of the perihelion of Mercury. It is worthy of remark that such success was not encountered when physicists turned from the very large to the very small. Classical physical theory failed miserably when it was applied to the analysis of atomic structure.

10–3 EFFECT OF FINITE SIZE

Thus far it has been assumed that objects with spherical symmetry attract other masses as if all the mass of the spherical object were concentrated at its center. That is, we have used Newton's law of universal gravitation (Chapter 5),

$$F_G = G\,\frac{mm'}{r^2}, \tag{5–5}$$

as if m and m' were point masses concentrated at the center of the actual masses. For example, in the treatment of rocket and satellite motion in Chapter 9, it was implicitly assumed that r is to be measured from the center of the earth to the rocket. On the other hand, in the motion of the members of the solar system, the question of the effect of finite size of the masses is relatively unimportant, since the dimensions of the masses are very small compared with their separations. Therefore, the success of Newton's laws in describing the motion of the planets allows us to conclude (a) that the law of universal gravitation is valid for masses whose dimensions are small compared with their separation, and (b) that gravitational forces add vectorially (effect of sun *plus* neighboring planets on the motion of a planet).

From the above, we see that the method of analysis for predicting the gravitational force between finite objects with separations comparable to their dimensions is to divide the finite objects into elements of volume that are small compared with the separation of the objects. The total gravitational force can then be found by summing (vectorially) the forces between the elements of volume. For simplicity, we start with the case of the attraction between a mass of negligible size and a finite object. Thus, the summation will extend over one object only. For further simplicity, we choose the case of a spherically symmetric mass distribution for the finite object. Finally, we start with the simplest case of spherical symmetry, that of the force on a small mass located *inside* a hollow sphere.

A convenient way to find the total effect of a spherically symmetric object is to first divide the object into concentric spherical shells of small thickness compared with the radii of the shells. We let R be the radius and ΔR be the thickness of such a shell (Fig. 10–1). The procedure will then be to subdivide the shell into elements of volume sufficiently small so that we can use the law of attraction between point masses [Eq. (5–5)]. The attraction by the shell will then be found by summation over its elements. Finally, the summation will be extended by adding the

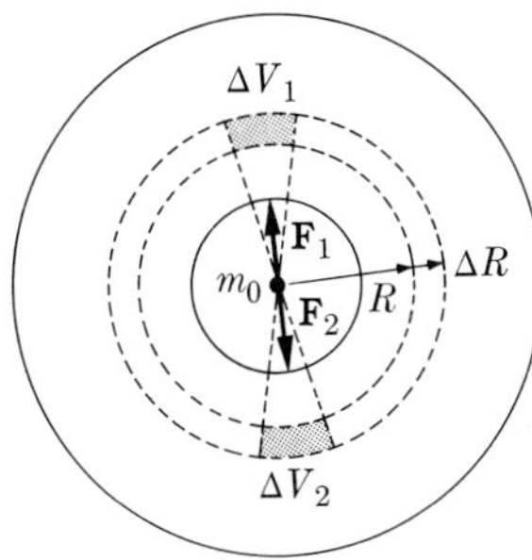

FIG. 10-1. A mass m_0 at the center of a hollow sphere. A shell of radius R and thickness ΔR is constructed. The volumes ΔV_1 and ΔV_2 are then constructed by extending vertical cones out from m_0.

effects of the individual shells in order to find the attractive force by the entire sphere.

Consider the simple case of a small mass m_0 located at the center of a hollow sphere (Fig. 10-1). We first select a spherical shell of radius R and thickness ΔR as an element of volume and then proceed to subdivide this shell into elements of volume, all of whose dimensions are small compared with R. This subdivision is accomplished by constructing a narrow conical surface with its vertex at m_0. This cone will define an element of volume ΔV (element of mass $\Delta m = \rho \Delta V$) where the cone cuts through the spherical shell, for example, ΔV_1 in Fig. 10-1. Since $\Delta R \ll R$, all the mass of the element ΔV_1 can be considered to be concentrated at the distance R from m_0. Consequently, the force between Δm_1 and m_0 is simply

$$F_1 = G\,\frac{\Delta m_1 \cdot m_0}{R^2} = G\,\frac{\rho\,\Delta V_1 m_0}{R^2},$$

where ρ is the density. Next, a second element volume ΔV_2 is selected by constructing a conical surface with a cone that is vertical to the first cone (Fig. 10-1). In this special case (where m_0 is centered in the hollow sphere), $\Delta V_2 = \Delta V_1$, and therefore the force F_2 due to element ΔV_2 is equal but opposite to F_1. Consequently, the sum of the forces by ΔV_1 and ΔV_2 is zero. The summation over all the shell can be accomplished by pairing off volumes in the above manner. If the volume elements ΔV_1 are chosen to cover one hemisphere, the pair elements ΔV_2 will cover the other hemisphere. Thus the total force is zero. There is no net gravitational force on a small mass m at the center of a spherically symmetric mass distribution, since the force by each thin shell from which the hollow sphere can be constructed is zero.

The above result can be generalized to the case of a small mass m_0 in any position within the hollow sphere. The sphere is again divided into thin, concentric spherical shells as the first stage in constructing elementary volumes. This time, it is convenient to limit the other dimensions of the elementary volume by considering the volumes cut out by the sides of a square pyramid with m_0 as the vertex (Fig. 10-2). For the sake of clarity, the finite shell thickness ΔR is not shown in Fig. 10-2. The faces of the pyramid will cut off a block of sides Δx and Δy (and thickness ΔR). If one face of the pyramid is chosen to lie in the plane of a great circle, as shown in the figure, the edge Δx cut off by it will *not* be normal to the line r from m_0 to the element, but will be tilted at angle θ relative to the normal.

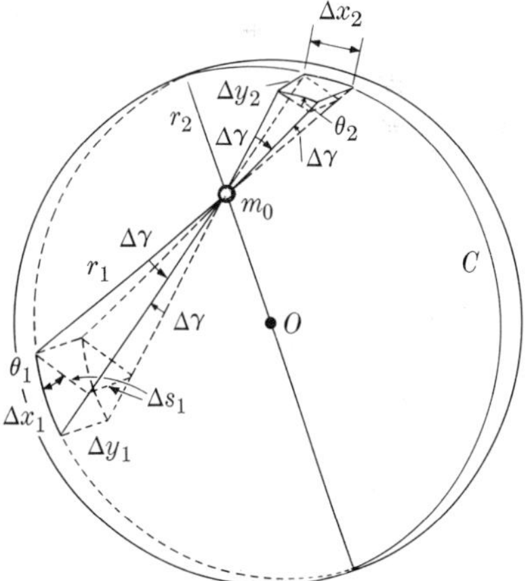

FIG. 10-2. A mass m_0 inside a hollow spherical shell. The thickness Δr of the shell is omitted for the sake of clarity. Vertical square cones are extended outward from m_0 and intercept elements of volume in the spherical shell.

The other edge Δy will be normal to r in the limit of vanishingly small Δy. Consider the element of sides Δx_1 and Δy_1 and thickness ΔR, cut out by the sides of a square pyramid in the spherical shell as shown. Its mass Δm_1 is $\rho \Delta R \Delta x_1 \Delta y_1$, since the volume of the element is $\Delta R \Delta x_1 \Delta y_1$ (and ρ is the density). The arc $\Delta s_1 = r_1 \Delta\Upsilon$, and therefore $\Delta y_1 = \Delta s_1 = r_1 \Delta\Upsilon$ and $\Delta x_1 = \Delta s_1/\cos\theta_1 = r_1(\Delta\Upsilon)/\cos\theta_1$. Finally, we have

$$\Delta m_1 = \rho\,\Delta R r_1^2(\Delta\Upsilon)^2/\cos\theta_1. \tag{10–1}$$

The gravitational force on m_0 due to Δm_1 is

$$\Delta F_1 = \frac{Gm_0\,\Delta m_1}{r_1^2} = Gm_0\rho\,\Delta R(\Delta\Upsilon)^2/\cos\theta_1. \tag{10–2}$$

In place of immediately summing over all Δm's, we consider a second element Δm_2 cut out by a square pyramid that extends in the sense opposite to that of the first pyramid. If this pyramid has the same angles $\Delta\Upsilon$, the force contribution by Δm_2 will be

$$\Delta F_2 = \frac{Gm_0\,\Delta m_2}{r_2^2} = Gm_0\rho\,\Delta R(\Delta\Upsilon)^2/\cos\theta_2. \tag{10–3}$$

In the limit as $\Delta\Upsilon \to 0$, the angles θ_1 and θ_2 are measured from the same chord and therefore become equal. Hence, $\Delta F_1 \to -\Delta F_2$ as $\Delta\Upsilon \to 0$, and the force contribution by the elements Δm_1 and Δm_2 cancel.

The entire shell can be covered by letting the square pyramids move about with m_0 as center. Therefore, the total force is zero. The only restriction is that ρ is constant over the shell.

In the case of a hollow sphere, the above argument can be applied to a succession of concentric thin shells for each of which the gravitational force vanishes for an object inside. Therefore, the gravitational force due to a hollow sphere is zero on an object inside the hollow sphere. Since it was required that ρ be constant only over the surface of each shell, the density ρ can vary with distance from the center of the sphere, and the force will still be zero inside.

In the case of a solid sphere, it follows that the gravitational force on a particle inside the sphere is due entirely to the sphere with radius equal to the distance of the object from the center.

The next problem—that of the force on an object outside a sphere—is also attacked by considering first a thin spherical shell. There is no convenient trick you can use to avoid integration in this case. However, the integration is much more easily performed for the potential energy. The potential energy ΔV* due to an element of mass Δm is [see Eq. (9–51)]

$$\Delta V = -Gm_0\,\Delta m/r, \tag{10–4}$$

where the dimensions of m_0 are assumed to be small compared with r and the potential energy is chosen to be zero at infinity. Consider a zone on the surface of the shell, all of which lies at a distance between r and $r + dr$ from m_0, as shown in Fig. 10–3(a). The area of the zone ΔA approaches the inner circumference times the width Δs as Δr approaches zero:

$$\Delta A = (2\pi r\sin\alpha)\,\Delta s, \tag{10–5}$$

where r, α, and Δs are defined in Fig. 10–3.

In order to express Δs in terms of Δr, we see from Fig. 10–3(b) that $\Delta r = \Delta s\sin(\theta + \alpha)$. (We have used the theorems for alternate interior angles and for angles whose sides are perpendicular.) But $\sin(\theta+\alpha) = \sin\beta$, and from the law of sines we have $\sin\beta = D(\sin\alpha)/R$. Finally, then, $\Delta r = \Delta s\,D(\sin\alpha)/R$, which allows us to rewrite Eq. (10–5) as

$$\Delta A = 2\pi rR\frac{\Delta r}{D}\cdot \tag{10–6}$$

---

* Here, ΔV means the contribution to the potential energy by a mass element Δm. Do not confuse this use of the notation ΔV with our more frequent use of ΔV to indicate difference of potential energy for two different positions of the masses in a system.

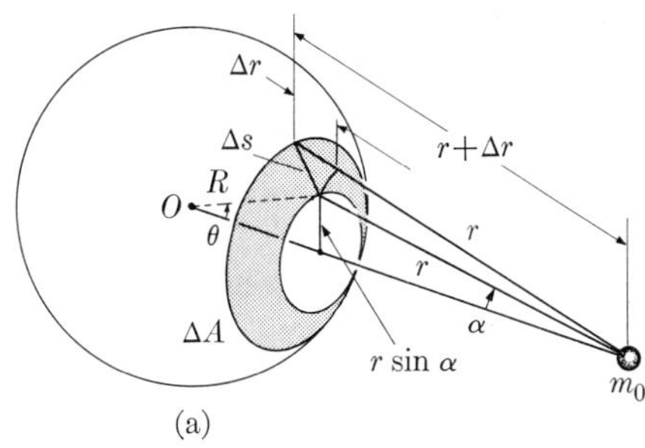

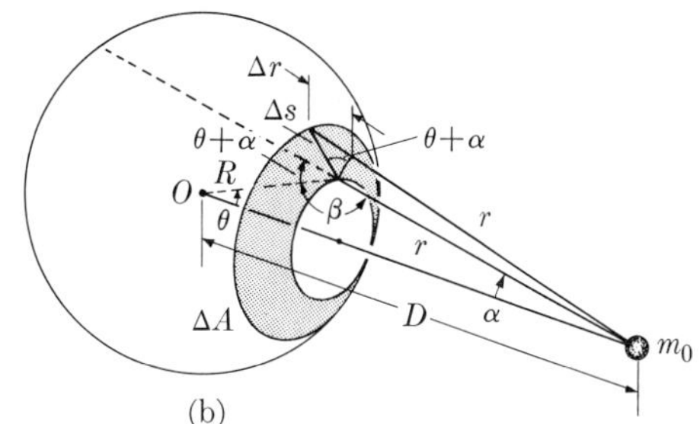

FIG. 10–3. A mass m_0 that is outside a spherical shell of thickness Δr. The finite thickness is omitted for the sake of clarity. An element of area ΔA at a distance r from m_0 is in the form of a ring on the shell. The right-hand figure shows the details of the geometric relationships among the angles.

Therefore, the mass Δm of the zone (of thickness ΔR and density ρ) can be written

$$\Delta m = \rho\,\Delta A\,\Delta R = \rho 2\pi r R\,\Delta R\,\frac{\Delta r}{D}. \qquad (10\text{–}7)$$

The potential energy of m_0 due to the zone is found by substituting Eq. (10–7) in Eq. (10–4) (the r's cancel):

$$\Delta V = -Gm_0\rho 2\pi R\,\Delta R\,\frac{\Delta r}{D}. \qquad (10\text{–}8)$$

The effect of the entire shell can be obtained by summing over all zones, which we recognize as the process of integration when $\Delta r \to 0$, that is,

$$V = \int_{D-R}^{D+R} -Gm_0\rho 2\pi R\,\Delta R\,\frac{dr}{D}, \qquad (10\text{–}9)$$

where dr is the only variable. Consequently, the integral is simple to evaluate:

$$V = -\left(Gm_0\rho 2\pi R\,\frac{\Delta R}{D}\right)\int_{D-R}^{D+R} dr$$
$$= -Gm_0\rho(4\pi R^2\,\Delta R)/D. \qquad (10\text{–}10)$$

The quantity $4\pi R^2\,\Delta R$ is the volume of the entire shell, and $\rho 4\pi R^2\,\Delta R$ is its mass m. The final result is therefore

$$V = -\frac{Gm_0 m}{D}, \qquad (10\text{–}11)$$

which shows that *the potential energy is the same as it would be if all the mass of the shell were concentrated at its center.*

A solid sphere can be built up of shells. Therefore, the potential energy of a mass that is outside a sphere is the same as it would be if all the mass of the sphere were concentrated at its center. The density can vary with R, since the only condition in the derivation was that the density must be constant over a spherical shell.

If m_0 is also spherically symmetric, it is tolerably obvious that the potential energy is the same as if *both* masses were replaced by point masses at their centers.

Since the potential energy is the same as for point masses in the above case of spherical symmetry, the force law must also be the same.

Example 1. Find the gravitational force law for a mass m inside a solid sphere of uniform density ρ and with radius R.

Solution: Let r be the distance of m from the center of the sphere, where $r < R$ (Fig. 10–4). Divide the mass M into two parts, M_b that lies outside the surface of radius r and M_a that lies inside the surface of radius r. Then the net interaction between m and M_b is zero. The interaction between m and M_a is the same as if M_a were concentrated at its geometric center, i.e., the law of interaction of point masses holds for M_a and m. The net force of interaction is then $F = GmM_a/r^2$. If the density ρ of the sphere is

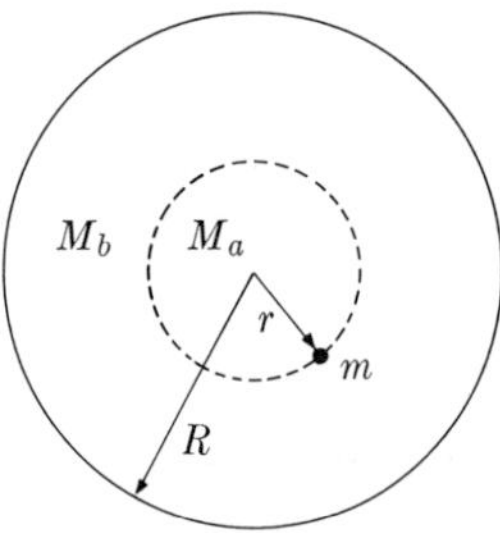

FIG. 10–4. A mass m inside a solid sphere. The mass is at a distance r from the center.

uniform, then the mass of any portion of the sphere is proportional to the volume of that portion, that is,

$$\frac{M_a}{M} = \frac{\frac{4}{3}\pi r^3}{\frac{4}{3}\pi R^3},$$

where r is the radius of M_a and R is the radius of the whole sphere M. The result is $M_a = (r^3/R^3)M$. Substituting this expression for M_a into the first equation, we have

$$F = G\frac{m\dfrac{r^3 M}{R^3}}{r^2},$$

or

$$F = G\frac{mMr}{R^3}, \tag{10–12}$$

which is an expression for the force law in terms of the mass and radius of the whole sphere. The force is no longer of the inverse-square form. The force of interaction is directly proportional to r, the distance between the center of M and the point m. A summary of the force law is given in the graph of Fig. 10–5 of the force of interaction versus the distance for points inside and outside the sphere.

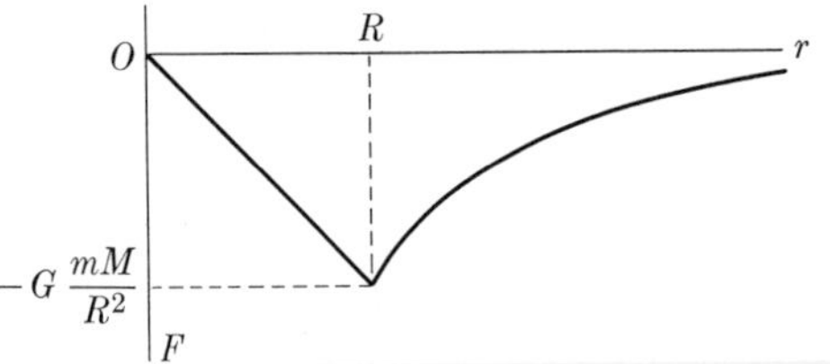

FIG. 10–5. Graph of the force on a mass m that is inside a uniform sphere of mass M and radius R as a function of distance from the center.

10–4 CONSERVATION OF ANGULAR MOMENTUM

It is desirable to review our notation at this time. The position of mass m is specified by polar coordinates r, θ, as in Fig. 10–6. But let us now consider a path that is *not* necessarily circular. The velocity v is tangent to the path. The convenient components of v are v_r (along r with θ held constant) and v_θ (perpendicular to r, that is, in the direction of increasing θ with r held constant). For the special case of circular motion, v_θ is sometimes denoted by v_T.

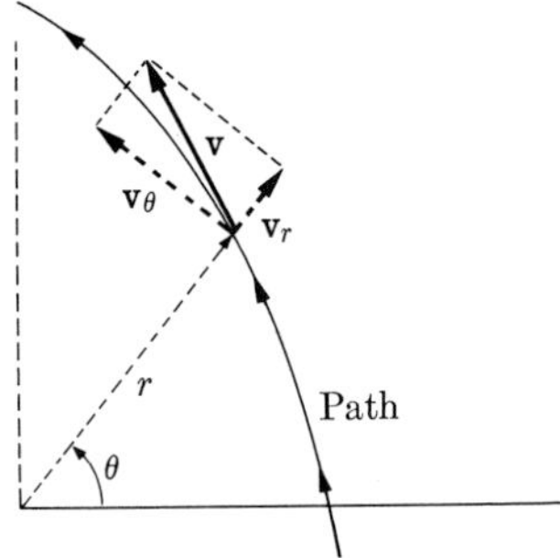

FIG. 10–6. Resolution of the velocity $\mathbf{v}$ of an object into polar components $\mathbf{v}_r$ and $\mathbf{v}_\theta$.

A new concept that leads to a third conservation law in the case of central forces will now be developed. We first derive *Kepler's law of equal areas.* Consider the effects of successive applications to mass m of impulses directed always along a line through point O. The impulses are to be delivered at equal time intervals, but the time *duration* of each impulse is to be vanishingly small. Figure 10–7 shows a part of the possible motion of m, with impulses J delivered at points 1, 2, 3′ at equal time intervals.

We shall prove that triangles $O12$, and $O23'$ have equal areas, independent of the magnitude of J_2 (that is, independent of the size of Δv_2).

The areas are $r_2h_1/2$ and $r_2h_2/2$, respectively.

In the diagram, an object at 1 has velocity v_1 and travels to 2 during the interval t_0. If no force acted, it would continue to 3 during the next interval t_0. However, an impulse ($\mathbf{J}_2$),

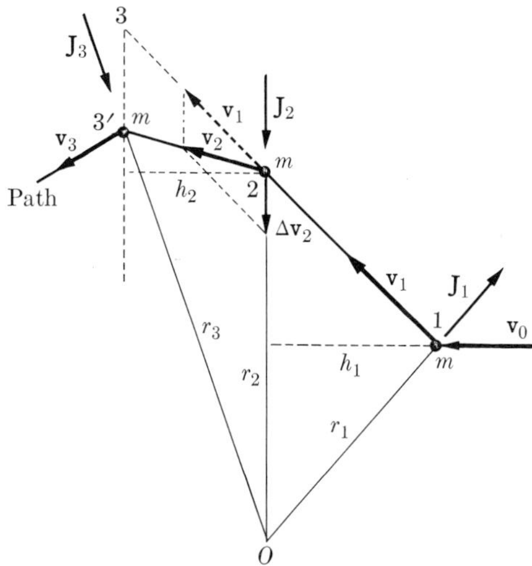

FIG. 10–7. An object enters the field of view of the diagram from the right with velocity $\mathbf{v}_0$. It experiences instantaneous impulsive central forces $\mathbf{J}_1$, $\mathbf{J}_2$, and $\mathbf{J}_3$ at points 1, 2, and 3, respectively. As a result, the direction and magnitude of the velocity are changed instantaneously at the points of application of the impulses.

directed toward O, changes its velocity by $\Delta\mathbf{v}_2$. The new direction is given by $\mathbf{v}_2 = \mathbf{v}_1 + \Delta\mathbf{v}_2$, as shown. It will therefore travel to $3'$ during t_0. Note that $33'$ is parallel to $\Delta\mathbf{v}_2$ and hence to r_2. Why? Triangles $O21$ and $O3'2$ have the common base r_2 and heights h_1 and h_2, respectively. But, since $33'$ is parallel to r_2, and 23 is parallel and equal to 12, the right triangles with 23 and 12 as hypotenuses are identical. Therefore, h_1 equals h_2, and the triangles $O21$ and $O3'2$ have the same areas.

Since the time interval t_0 can approach zero and since there was no limitation on the magnitude of the impulsive force in the above, a continuous central force of any kind will also give Kepler's equal area law, i.e., when a particle experiences a force directed always toward the same point, *the line from the point to the object sweeps out equal areas in equal times.*

We now consider the mathematical way of describing the equal area law in the case of a continuous force. The equal area law was proved above for a continuous central force. In this case the path of m is a smooth curve. For a small angular motion $\Delta\theta$, the area is approximately (Fig. 10–8)

$$\Delta A = r\,\Delta s/2 = rv_\theta\,\Delta t/2,$$

or

$$\Delta A/\Delta t = rv_\theta/2. \qquad (10\text{–}13)$$

Equation (10–13) becomes the exact equation

$$dA/dt = rv_\theta/2, \qquad (10\text{–}14)$$

as Δt, and hence $\Delta\theta$, approach zero.

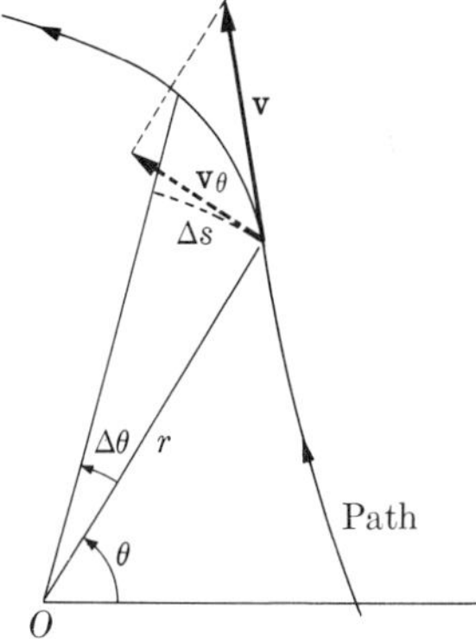

FIG. 10–8. An object moving under the influence of a nonuniform but continuous central force.

Since it was proved earlier that the rate at which the radius vector sweeps out area is constant, we have

$$dA/dt = \text{constant} = rv_\theta/2, \qquad (10\text{–}15)$$

or simply,

$$rv_\theta = \text{constant}. \qquad (10\text{–}16)$$

The *conservation of angular momentum* can be obtained from the above kinematical equation. If we multiply rv_0 by the mass m of the object, we obtain the dynamical quantity mrv_θ, which is called *moment of momentum* or *angular momentum*, l, that is,

$$l \equiv mrv_\theta = rp_\theta = m\omega r^2 = \text{constant}, \tag{10–17}$$

where r, v_θ, p_θ, and ω may be variables. In words, the angular momentum about O remains constant, if the resultant force on m is always in the direction of O, where point O is a fixed point in an inertial frame.

We have just described the *third conservation principle.* A fourth conservation principle, the conservation of mass, has been implicit throughout. The latter is an independent law of classical physics and chemistry, based on observation of physical and chemical changes.

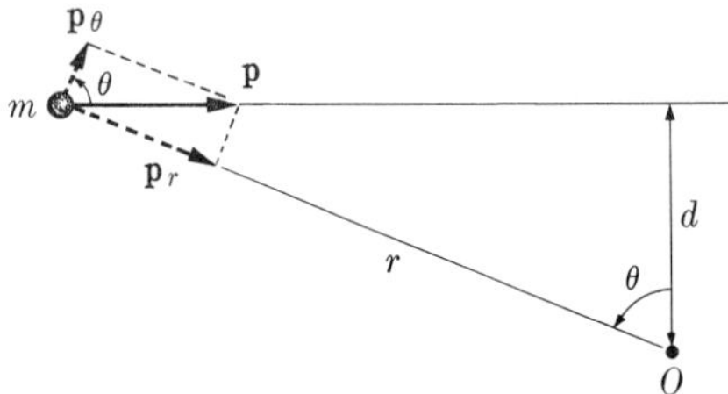

Fig. 10–9. The mass m experiences a central force directed toward O. The straight-line extension of the momentum p of the mass at a given point in its path passes within a distance d of the attracting center.

In collision or scattering problems (in which one object approaches from a large distance the object with which it interacts), it is convenient to express the initial angular momentum in terms of the "impact parameter" d, the distance of closest approach if the distant object were to move in an undeflected straight-line path (Fig. 10–9). From the diagram, we see that the initial angular momentum can then be written

$$l = rp_\theta = rp\cos\theta = pr\cos\theta = pd. \tag{10–18}$$

The expression $l = pd$ is valid for any point of the trajectory, where d is a variable, but it is chiefly useful as a way of obtaining the initial value of angular momentum.

Example 2. A mass m rotates at angular velocity ω_0 in a circle of radius r_0 on a horizontal frictionless table (Fig. 10–10). The string that provides the centripetal force passes through a hole as shown. The mass is pulled into a new circular path of radius $r_0/2$ by a pull P. Find the new angular velocity and the work done by P. Check the work by integration.

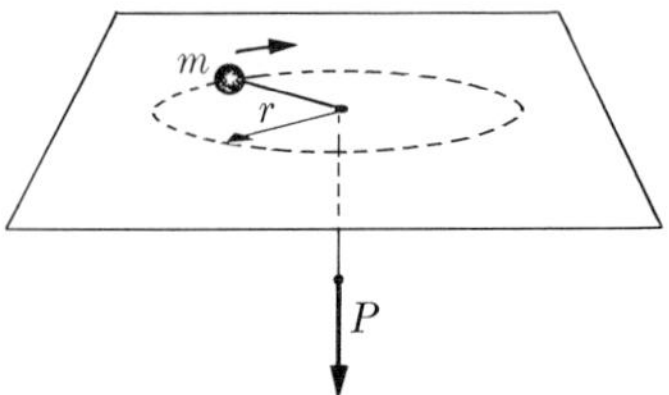

Fig. 10–10. A mass m moving on a frictionless horizontal plane experiences a central force exerted by a string that passes through a hole in the plane. A pull P is exerted on the string.

Solution: (a) Since the force on m is a central force, angular momentum is conserved, that is, $m\omega_0 r_0^2 = m\omega_f(r_0/2)^2$ [Eq. (10–17)]. The result is $\omega_f = 4\omega_0$ or, in terms of speed, $v_f = 2v_0$.

(b) The work equals change in kinetic energy: $W = \Delta T = (mv_f^2/2) - (mv_0^2/2) = \frac{3}{2}mv_0^2$.

(c) By integration,

$$W = \int_{r_0}^{r_0/2} F_r\,dr = \int_{r_0}^{r_0/2} -m(v^2/r)\,dr,$$

since the required force is $F_r = mv^2/r$. The velocity is a variable. It can be expressed in terms of r from conservation of angular momentum: $mvr = mv_0r_0$ or $v^2 = v_0^2r_0^2/r^2$. The integral becomes

$$W = mv_0^2r_0^2\int_{r_0}^{r_0/2} -\frac{dr}{r^3} = mv_0^2r_0^2\left(\frac{1}{2r^2}\right)_{r_0}^{r_0/2} = \frac{3}{2}mv_0^2,$$

which checks with (b).

A few words of explanation are necessary. The line integral was evaluated as an ordinary integral because the force is conservative. The minus sign comes from the fact that F is directed inwards. The speed v appearing in the above integral was the component v_θ, although the subscript was omitted.

10-5 ANGULAR MOMENTUM AS A VECTOR

The vector properties of Eq. (10-17) and many of the preceding equations were ignored. In Eq. (10-17), the quantities r, v_θ, p_θ, and ω may all be considered as vectors. Or it is more usual to write the vector equations in terms of v and p themselves as follows:

$$\mathbf{l} \equiv m\mathbf{r} \times \mathbf{v} = \mathbf{r} \times \mathbf{p} = m\mathbf{r} \times \boldsymbol{\omega} \times \mathbf{r}, \tag{10-19}$$

where the $\times$ indicates the vector or cross product. The spatial relationships are shown in Fig. 10-11. The angular momentum vector is perpendicular to the plane of motion in the simple example considered here. The conservation of angular momentum therefore requires consideration of direction as well as magnitude.

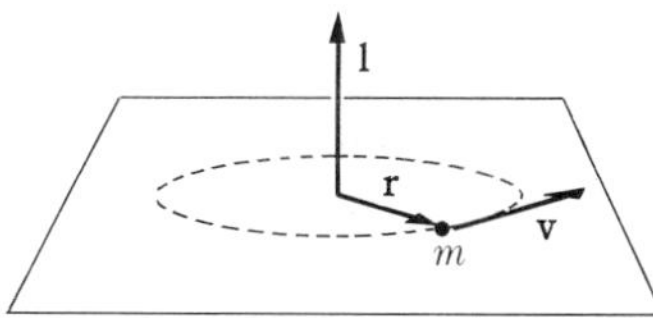

Fig. 10-11. The radius vector **r**, the velocity vector **v**, and the angular momentum vector **l** for a mass moving in a plane.

Equation (10-19) is written as follows in terms of magnitudes only:

$$l = mrv \sin \alpha = rp \sin \alpha, \tag{10-20}$$

where α is the angle between the **r** and the **v** or **p** vectors. These reduce to Eqs. (10-17), since $v \sin \alpha = v_\theta$ and $p \sin \alpha = p_\theta$.

As an example, in central force motion the direction and the magnitude of the angular momentum remain constant, meaning that the plane of motion remains fixed.

10-6 SATELLITE MOTION

In Section 10-3, it was shown that an object A with a spherically symmetric mass distribution attracts another mass as if all the mass of A were concentrated at the center of the sphere. Since the force of gravity at the surface of the earth varies by only a few tenths of a percent over the earth's surface, it can be concluded that the mass distribution within the earth has approximate spherical symmetry. When we desire an accuracy no greater than a few tenths of a percent, it can therefore be assumed that the mass of the earth is concentrated at the center, so far as external gravitational effects are concerned.

In earlier sections, we considered two special cases of satellite paths: a circle and a straight line vertically upward. The latter is an incomplete periodic path only because the earth gets in the way. We found all features of the circular motion, including position as a function of time. For the vertical straight line path we found only the relationship between height and velocity. The question of position as a function of time is left to the problems.

When conservation of angular momentum is utilized in the analysis, certain features about the more general orbit, the elliptical orbit, can be obtained. The conservation of angular momentum gives the magnitude of one component, v_θ, of the velocity as a function of distance, while the conservation of energy gives the magnitude of the velocity itself as a function of distance. In both cases, it is necessary to know the velocity in question at one distance in order to find it at other distances. In particular, the equation for conservation of energy is

$$mv_1^2/2 - Gmm'/r_1 = mv_2^2/2 - Gmm'/r_2, \tag{10-21}$$

which can be written

$$v_1^2 - 2gR_e^2/r_1 = v_2^2 - 2gR_e^2/r_2, \tag{10-22}$$

and the equation for conservation of angular momentum is

$$mv_{\theta 1}r_1 = mv_{\theta 2}r_2 \qquad \text{or} \qquad v_{\theta 1}r_1 = v_{\theta 2}r_2. \tag{10-23}$$

If more than one mass, m', affects the motion of m appreciably, the potential energy terms in Eq. (10–21) simply become a sum over contributions by each m'. But the angular momentum of m is no longer a constant, since the resultant force is not a central force.

Returning to the case of one attracting object, we can ascertain the direction of v at any distance if v is known at one distance, since the magnitudes of v and of one component are determined by Eqs. (10–22) and (10–23), respectively.

Example 3. A satellite is put in orbit just above the earth's atmosphere with a velocity $\sqrt{1.5}$ times the velocity for a circular orbit and initially parallel to the earth's surface. What is the maximum distance of the satellite from the earth while it is in orbit?

Solution: The velocity for a circular orbit near the earth can be found from simple dynamics of circular motion:

$$F = ma \text{ gives } mg = mv^2/R_e \qquad \text{or} \qquad v = \sqrt{gR_e}.$$

The initial energy divided by m is therefore

$$v_1^2/2 - gR_e^2/r_1 = 1.5gR_e/2 - gR_e^2/R_e = -gR_e/4.$$

Therefore, energy conservation leads to

$$v_1^2/2 - gR_e^2/r = -gR_e/4.$$

Since the initial orbit velocity is parallel to the earth's surface, it is perpendicular to r, and therefore $v_{\theta 1} = v_1 = \sqrt{1.5\,gR_e}$. Momentum conservation

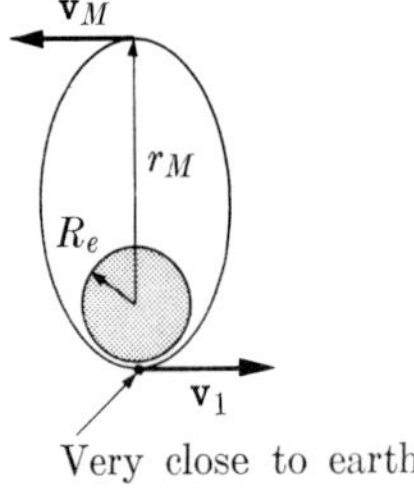

FIG. 10–12. Path of the satellite of Example 3 that is placed in orbit with initial velocity $\mathbf{v}_1$, which is greater than the velocity for a circular orbit.

then gives $(\sqrt{1.5\,gR_e})\ R_e = v_\theta r$. At the maximum distance r_M the velocity is again parallel to the earth's surface (Fig. 10–12), and hence $v_{\theta M} = v_M$. Therefore, there are two equations in two unknowns: $\sqrt{1.5\,gR_e} = v_M r_M/R_e$ and $(v_M^2/2) - (gR_e{}^2/r_M) = -gR_e/4$.

Upon solving for the unknowns, we find $r_M = 3R_e$ and $v_M = \sqrt{1.5\,gR_e}/3$.

The ideas in this section are valid for central forces with any dependence on distance, as well as for forces of repulsion and attraction. The momentum conservation equation is the same for all cases of central force. The potential energy in the law of energy conservation depends on the particular force law and must be determined from the definition, $-\Delta V =$ work, for each different force law.

10–7 SUMMARY

The validity of the universal law of gravitation on the astronomical scale is determined from the observation of the motion of the moon and the planets.

It is shown that the gravitational attraction by an object with a spherically symmetric mass distribution is the same as it would be if all its mass were concentrated at its center, so long as the attracted mass is outside. The gravitational attraction on a mass located inside a hollow, spherically symmetric mass distribution is shown to be zero. A consequence of the above two results is that a mass located in the interior of a spherically symmetric mass distribution experiences the same force as it would if all the mass of the sphere of radius r were concentrated at the center, where r is the distance of the object from the center of the mass distribution.

The law of gravitational attraction between two masses is

$$F = G\,\frac{mm'}{r^2},$$

where G is a constant, m and m' are the masses, and r is their separation.

It is shown that Kepler's law—that the radius vector from the sun to any planet sweeps out equal areas in equal times—is a special case of the law of conservation of angular momentum for an object moving under the influence of *any* central force. The law can be stated in the form

$$l \equiv mrv_\theta = m\omega r^2 = \text{constant},$$

where l is the angular momentum. In vector notation, we have

$$\mathbf{l} = m\mathbf{r} \times \mathbf{v} = m\mathbf{r} \times \boldsymbol{\omega} \times \mathbf{r}.$$

The application of the laws of conservation of energy and of momentum to the motion of satellites is discussed.

Problems

The earth's radius is about 6400 km. The moon's orbit has a radius of about 400,000 km.

1. Derive the law of Kepler that states that the square of the period of revolution of a planet is proportional to the cube of the orbital radius in the special case of a circular orbit: $\tau^2 = (4\pi^2/Gm')r^3$.

2. Do the moon and the planets follow the law of Kepler given in Problem 1? Is the equation the same for the moon and the planets?

3. What would be the period of a satellite revolving about the earth in an orbit $\frac{1}{4}$ the radius of the moon's orbit? The moon's period is about 28 days.

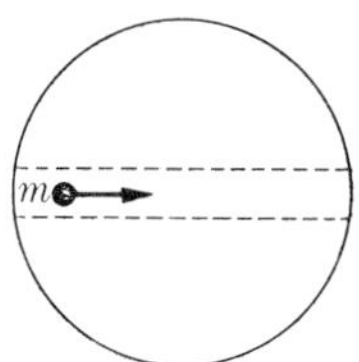

FIGURE 10–13

4. Suppose a hole were drilled completely through the earth along a diameter (Fig. 10–13).

(a) Show that the force on a mass m at a distance r from the center of the earth is $F = -mgr/R_e$, if we assume that the density is uniform.

(b) Show that the motion of m would be simple harmonic with a period of about 90 min.

(c) Write the equations for position, velocity, and acceleration as functions of time, with numerical values of the constants.

5. Show that the frictionless motion of a mass in a hole drilled as a chord through the earth (Fig. 10–14) would be simple harmonic. Find the period.

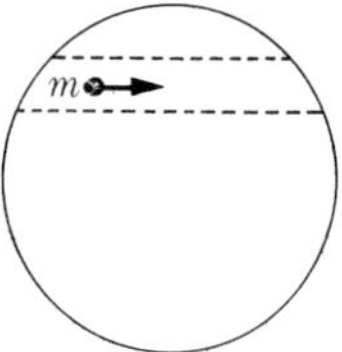

FIGURE 10–14

6. A cart rolls on a frictionless straight track that is tangent to the earth at its surface. Prove that the motion is simple harmonic for small amplitudes and find the period (Fig. 10–15).

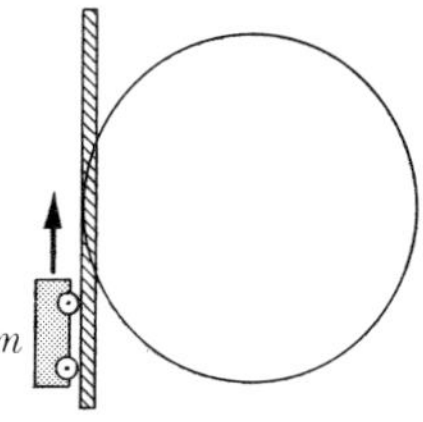

FIGURE 10–15

7. (a) Show that the potential energy of a mass m at the surface of the earth is $-mgR_e$.

(b) Where was the arbitrary choice of position of zero potential energy?

(c) Show that the difference in potential energy $(V_r - V_{R_e})$ as a mass m moves in from the surface of the earth inside the hole of Fig. 10–13 is $mg(r^2 - R_e^2)/2R_e$.

(d) Finally, show that the potential energy inside the hole is $(mg/2R_e)(r^2 - 3R_e^2)$.

8. A mass m is dropped from a great height h above the hole in Fig. 10–13.

(a) With what velocity would m pass the center of the earth?

(b) Would the motion be simple harmonic?

(c) Would the motion be periodic? Give reasons for your answers.

9. Suppose that gravitation were an inverse cube law.

(a) Would the derivation of the first part of Section 10–3 be valid?

(b) How would the force depend qualitatively on position inside the shell?

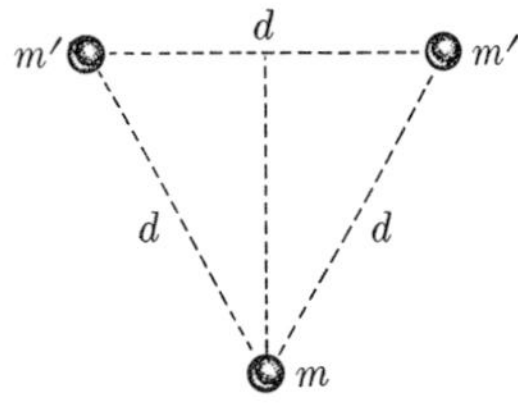

FIGURE 10–16

10. Prove that the gravitational force on m of two equal masses, m', is *not* the same as it would be if both masses were concentrated at a point midway between them. Consider the special case of Fig. 10–16.

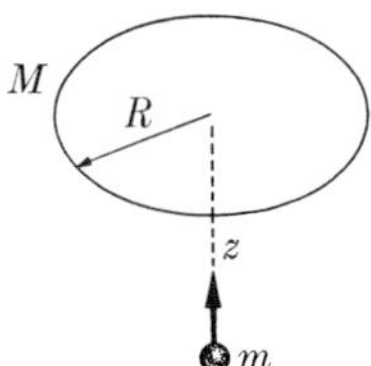

FIGURE 10–17

11. (a) Find the potential energy of a star of mass m located at the center of a ring-shaped nebula of total mass M and radius R (Fig. 10–17).

(b) With what velocity would a star pass through the ring if it approached the nebula along the axis, starting at rest from a distance z?

12. Prove that the gravitational force is zero on a mass m placed anywhere between two infinite parallel

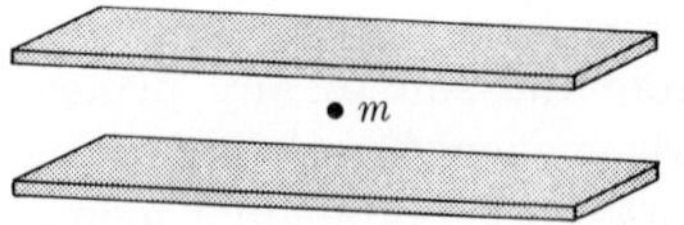

FIGURE 10–18

slabs of material if the slabs are the only material in the vicinity of m (Fig. 10–18).

13. In Fig. 10–10, let m of 0.5 kg be initially rotating at $\frac{1}{2}$ revolution per second at a radius of 0.3 m.

(a) What will its angular and linear velocity be after it is allowed to pull the string slowly out to a radius of 0.9 m?

(b) Suppose the force P in (a) was provided by fluid friction (for example, a light metal disk pulled upward through heavy oil). How much work was done on the oil?

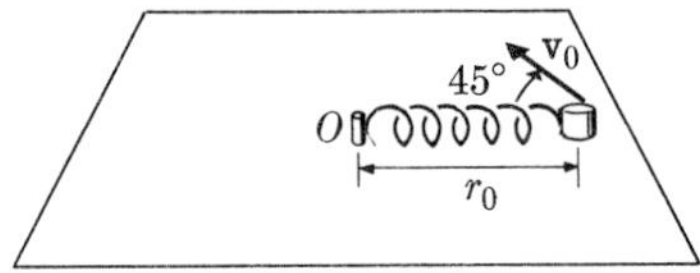

FIGURE 10–19

14. A mass fixed to one end of a spring moves on a horizontal frictionless surface, as shown in Fig. 10–19. The other end of the spring is fixed to a pivot O as shown. The normal length of the spring r_0 is 30 cm. If the mass is started as indicated, with $v_0 = 50$ cm sec, what is v_θ when the mass is 25 cm from O?

15. Suppose that the spring constant in Problem 14 was 2 n/m and the mass was 0.5 kg. Find the distances of nearest approach to O and greatest departure from O. [*Hint:* What is the relationship between v_θ and v at the start? at minimum distance from O? at maximum distance from O?]

16. Airplanes move in circular orbits around the earth at much lower velocities than the velocities of satellites. Explain this by drawing a force diagram and deriving an equation relating the forces, radius of path, and the velocity.

17. (a) Would the angular momentum of m in Problem 10 remain constant as it moved under the

influence of the combined effects of the two m' masses? (b) Would its mechanical energy remain constant?

18. Two positively charged particles repel each other with an inverse square law of force, $F = Kqq'/r^2$, (Section 5–5).

(a) Show that the potential energy is $V = +Kqq'/r$, if $V = 0$ at $r = \infty$.

(b) A particle of mass m and charge $+q$ is projected with velocity $\mathbf{v}$ from a large distance directly toward a particle of mass M and charge $+q'$. If $M \gg m$ and therefore M remains essentially stationary, find the distance of closest approach of m to M (Fig. 10–20).

FIGURE 10–20

19. Suppose mass m of Problem 18 is not initially directed toward M, but would miss M by distance d, if it continued along a straight line path (Fig. 10–21).

(a) What is the initial angular momentum and the initial total energy of m?

(b) Find an expression for the distance of closest approach by noting that $v = v_\theta$ at that distance.

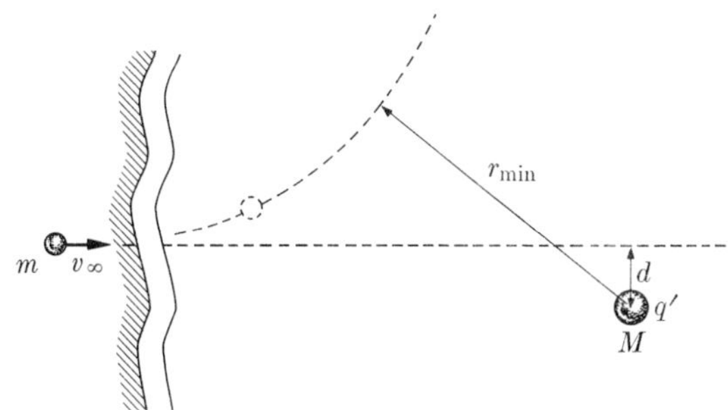

FIGURE 10–21

20. A meteor at a large distance from the earth has a velocity $\sqrt{2\,gR}$ and an impact parameter $\sqrt{2}R$, where R is the radius of the earth. How close to the earth will the meteor come?

21. A space platform of mass m is in a circular orbit O of radius R around the moon. In order to land on the earth, the pilot changes his speed so that his new orbit will be tangent to the moon as shown in Fig. 10–22 (neglecting the effect of the atmosphere).

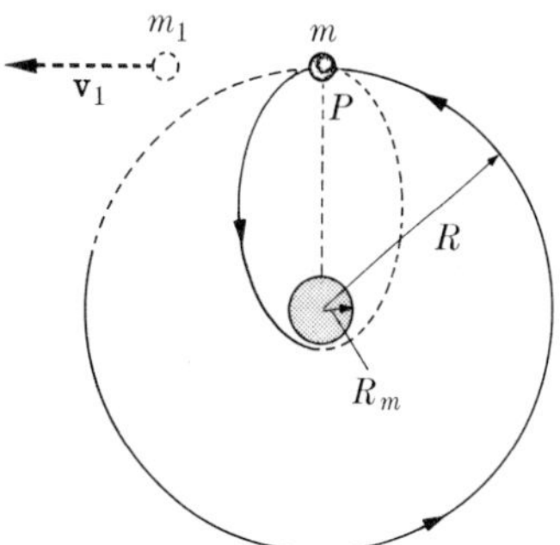

FIGURE 10–22

He changes speed by shooting a mass m_1 forward in his direction of motion at point P. Given m, m_1, R, R_m, M_m, and G, find the initial velocity $\mathbf{v}_1$ of m_1.

22. A rocket is fired vertically from the earth toward the moon. The fuel is used up soon after the rocket leaves the earth. At what point in its path toward the moon is the acceleration of the rocket zero? Is the velocity also zero at this point? (The mass of the moon is about 81 times smaller than the mass of the earth, and its distance is about 400,000 km.)

23. Show how to calculate the minimum departure velocity that the moon rocket must have in the preceding problem in order to reach the moon.

24. Show how to calculate the velocity at which the rocket of Problems 22 and 23 arrives at the moon.

25. (a) Neglecting the effect of the moon, show that a rocket falling from rest at height r_0 has a velocity at r given by

$$v = \sqrt{2Gm'\left(\frac{1}{r} - \frac{1}{r_0}\right)}.$$

(b) Show that the time to fall from r_0 to r_f is

$$t = \int_{r_0}^{r_f} \frac{1}{\sqrt{2Gm'}} \frac{dr}{\sqrt{\dfrac{1}{r} - \dfrac{1}{r_0}}}.$$

(c) The result of the integration is

$$t = \frac{r_0^{3/2}}{R\sqrt{2g}}\left(-\sqrt{\frac{r_f}{r_0}}\sqrt{1 - \frac{r_f}{r_0}} + \sin^{-1}\sqrt{\frac{r_f}{r_0}}\right).$$

Find the time required for the moon to fall to the earth, if it were suddenly stopped in its path by the impact of a high-speed meteor. [*Hint:* for $r_0 \gg r_f$, use series expansions to show that $t \simeq \frac{2}{3} r_f{}^{3/2}/(R\sqrt{2g})$.]

26. Assume that a satellite is launched in such a way that it begins its free flight just above the atmosphere (R from the earth's center) with its initial velocity tangent to the circle of radius R. Notice that $v_0 = v_{\theta 0}$.

(a) Show that the maximum distance r_m of the satellite from the center of the earth will be $r_m/R = v_0^2/(v_{es}^2 - v_0^2)$, where $\sqrt{2gR}$ has been replaced by v_{es}, the escape velocity. Make a graph of r_m/R versus v_0^2 for $(v_{es}^2/2) < v_0^2 < v_{es}^2$.

(b) If $v_0 > v_{es}$, the satellite will have a final velocity v_∞ along a line whose perpendicular distance to the center of the earth is d. (If the motion were reversed, d would be called the impact parameter). Show that $(d/R)^2 = v_0^2/(v_0^2 - v_{es}^2)$.

27. A mass is set into rotation in a vertical circle on the end of a string. Does the string sweep out equal areas in equal times? Explain.

11

Center of Mass: Noninertial Reference Frames

11-1 INTRODUCTION

In most of our analysis thus far, we have studied the motion of one object whose mass is small compared with the masses with which it interacts. As a result, it has been possible to assume that only the motion of the small mass is appreciably affected by the interactions.

Certain properties of the motion of interacting bodies of comparable masses have been established. For example, we noted that linear momentum is always conserved in the absence of external forces in the plane of motion. In the case of conservative interaction forces, mechanical energy is also conserved. In order to facilitate further application of the conservation principles and of Newton's laws, this is a convenient place to introduce the concept of center of mass.

It has been emphasized repeatedly that all the analysis thus far has been based on the use of inertial coordinate systems. In these systems, all forces are interaction forces, i.e., there is always a real object B exerting the force in question on the object A. This chapter will treat some ideas and uses of noninertial coordinate systems.

11-2 CENTER OF MASS

The cartesian coordinates of the center of mass are defined by

$$X = \frac{\sum m_i x_i}{\sum m_i}, \qquad Y = \frac{\sum m_i y_i}{\sum m_i}, \tag{11-1}$$

where the summations are to be carried out over all the individual masses m_i. The coordinates of the ith mass are x_i and y_i. The denominators in Eq. (11-1) are simply the total mass of the system. In case of a continuous distribution of the masses m_i, the summations become integrals.

The distance of the ith mass from the center of mass can be found from Eq. (11-1). If there are only two masses and if we choose the origin of coordinates at the center of mass ($X = 0$ and $Y = 0$), we have

$$m_1 x_1 = -m_2 x_2, \qquad m_1 y_1 = -m_2 y_2, \tag{11-2}$$

or, in polar coordinates,

$$m_1 r_1 = -m_2 r_2. \tag{11-3}$$

If there are no external forces on the system of particles, the *conservation of linear momentum* can now be stated as follows: the velocity of the center of mass remains constant. The proof of this statement follows immediately from the result of differentiating Eq. (11-1) with respect to time, giving

$$V_x = \frac{\sum m_i v_{ix}}{\sum m_i}, \qquad V_y = \frac{\sum m_i v_{iy}}{\sum m_i}. \tag{11-4}$$

But we know that the sum of the momenta components, $\sum m_i v_{ix}$, of interacting particles remains constant, and therefore V_x and V_y remain constant.

If there are external forces on the system, these forces must be exerted directly on parts of the system. From application of Newton's laws to the ith mass, we have

$$F_i = m_i \frac{d^2 x_i}{dt^2}, \tag{11-5}$$

where F_i is the resultant external force on the ith mass. If we now sum over all masses, we obtain

$$\Sigma F_i = \Sigma m_i \frac{d^2 x_i}{dt^2} = (\Sigma m_i) \frac{d^2 X}{dt^2} \qquad (11\text{–}6)$$

from Eq. (11–1).

It is seen from Eq. (11–6) that *Newton's second law is applicable to a system where the acceleration is the acceleration of the center of mass of the system.*

11–3 INTERACTION OF TWO POINT MASSES

If the interaction is due only to a contact collision, the objects must collide at their common center of mass. Hence the angular momentum is zero about the center of mass.

If the force extends to finite distances (e.g., if springs or magnets provide the force of interaction), then the objects interact at finite separations. Then the angular momentum about the center of mass need not be zero when there is to be an interaction. We distinguish two cases: the masses are bound to closed orbits by the force; the objects collide or they "explode" away from one another.

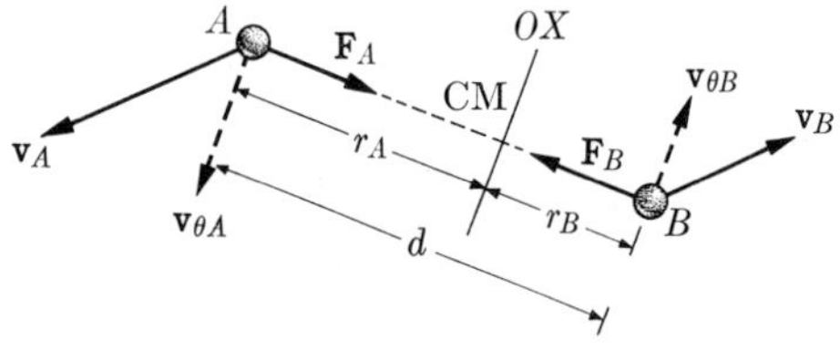

FIG. 11–1. Two masses A and B whose force of interaction is along the line joining them. The center of mass is designated by CM.

Bound orbits. Consider objects A and B which move as shown in Fig. 11–1. If it is assumed that the center of mass was initially at rest, it will continue at rest in the absence of outside forces. Then the total linear momentum is always zero, or

$$m_A v_{XA} = -m_B v_{XB} \quad \text{or} \quad m_A v_{\theta A} = -m_B v_{\theta B}. \qquad (11\text{–}7)$$

The total angular momentum (which is constant), $L = l_A + l_B$, becomes

$$L = m_A v_{\theta A} r_A + m_B v_{\theta B} r_B = m_A v_{\theta A} (r_A - r_B). \qquad (11\text{–}8)$$

Since the r's are oppositely directed $r_A - r_B = d$ (Fig. 11–1) and

$$L = m_A v_{\theta A} d = m_B v_{\theta B} d = \text{constant}. \qquad (11\text{–}9)$$

Collisions. If one object is initially at rest, all the momentum (linear and angular) resides originally in the moving object. The momenta of the system are therefore

$$P = m_A v_{A0} \quad \text{and} \quad L = m_A v_{A0}\, a, \qquad (11\text{–}10)$$

where a is the perpendicular distance between the direction of v_{A0} and the line of the center of mass, as shown in Fig. 11–2.

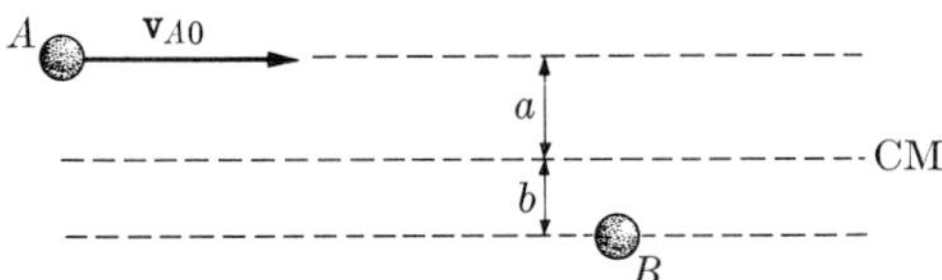

FIG. 11–2. A system of two objects A and B in which B is initially at rest and A has an initial velocity $\mathbf{v}_{A0}$ as shown. The center of mass lies along CM.

As B is set in motion by the force of interaction, both linear and angular momenta are conserved. Therefore

$$m_A v_A + m_B v_B = m_A v_{A0} \qquad (11\text{–}11)$$

and

$$m_A \omega r_A^2 + m_B \omega r_B^2 = m_A v_{A0}\, a, \qquad (11\text{–}12)$$

where ω is the angular velocity about the center of mass, that is, $d\theta/dt$ (see Fig. 11–3).

Example 1. A child on a moving swing reaches out as he passes a neighboring swing that is at rest and

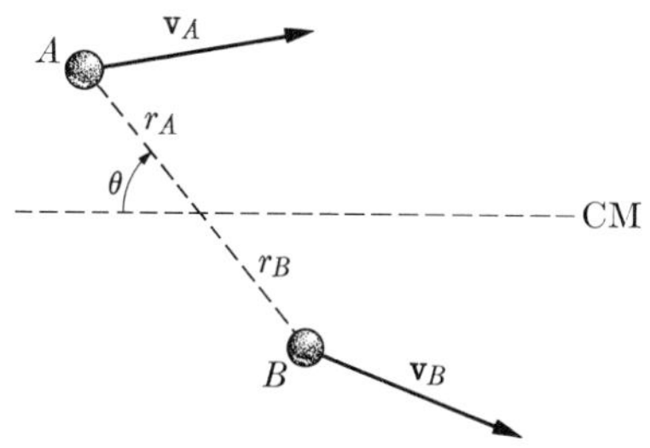

FIG. 11–3. The system of Fig. 11–2 when B has been set in motion by the force of interaction with A.

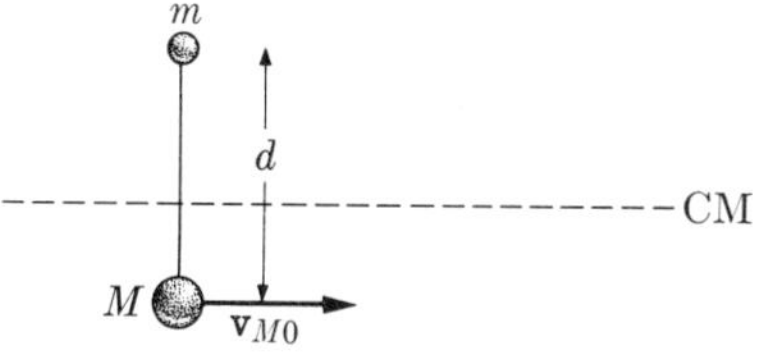

FIG. 11–4. The child M and the adjacent swing m are rigidly joined at the instant depicted in the drawing (Example 1). The drawing is a view from above.

seizes this swing firmly at arm's length. Find the motion of the system (considered as two point masses) immediately after the "collision."

Solution: Use the notation of Fig. 11–4, which is a view from above. The child has mass M, and the second swing has mass m. Their separation is d, as shown. The velocity of the child just before the "collision" is v_{M0}. From conservation of linear momentum, $Mv_{M0} = (M + m)V$, where V is the velocity of the center of mass. Also, the center of mass remains along the line labeled CM. The distances of M and m from the center of mass, r_M and r_m, are in the ratio $r_M/r_m = m/M$ [from Eq. (11–3)], and their sum is $r_M + r_m = d$. The conservation of angular momentum gives $Mv_0r_M = Mr_M^2\omega + mr_m^2\omega$, where ω is the angular velocity about the center of gravity. The angular velocity can immediately be found in terms of the given quantities: $\omega = Mv_0r_M/(Mr_M^2 + mr_m^2)$, where $r_m = Md/(m + M)$ and $r_M = md/(m + M)$. Therefore, the motion is completely described by the velocity of the center of mass,

$$V = Mv_{M0}/(M + m),$$

and the angular velocity about the center of mass as given above.

11–4 SYSTEMS OF MORE THAN TWO BODIES

In Section 11–2, it was shown that the center of mass of any number of masses moves at constant velocity if there are no external forces. It was also shown that the effect of external forces can be described by applying Newton's laws to the motion of the center of mass of the system.

Finally, if the forces between the masses are central forces and there are no external forces, the angular momentum of the system remains constant. To prove this, we need only note that any change of linear momentum of m_1 due to interaction with m_2 must be accompanied by an equal and opposite change in momentum of m_2. The accompanying *angular* momentum changes are also equal and opposite because both linear momentum changes are along the same line and therefore have the same perpendicular distances to any chosen axis. Consequently, the total angular momentum is unchanged by central force interactions among the mass elements of a system.

If external forces are exerted on the system by the entrance into the system of a *new* interacting mass, the *total* angular momentum of the original system plus the new particle must remain constant. Why? If the new particle approaches the system along a direction that is not toward the center of mass, it brings additional angular momentum into the composite system, just as in the case of a two-particle interaction.

The actual analysis of the general aspects of multiparticle interactions by the use of the conservation laws is a simple extension of the two-body examples, with one important difference: since there are only three conservation laws for the motion of the objects, there can be only three unknowns in a problem that is to be solved by use of the conservation principles.

11–5 NONINERTIAL REFERENCE FRAMES

You are reminded, first of all, that an inertial reference frame is one in which Newton's laws are valid when only interaction forces are considered. We have shown (Section 7–5) that any frame which moves with uniform velocity of translation relative to an inertial frame is itself an inertial frame, but that a frame which is accelerated relative to an inertial frame is *not* itself an inertial frame. In Section 7–5 it was also mentioned that it is customary to assume that a frame fixed relative to the distant stars is a basic inertial frame. This choice is consistent with the experimental observations that Newton's laws predict to a high degree of accuracy the motion of objects in this reference frame. The sun itself can be used as the origin of such a coordinate system, with the other stars simply determining a "fixed" orientation for the direction of the axes.

Since the radial acceleration of the earth in its orbital motion is only 0.006 m/sec^2, the earth itself can be used as an approximation to an inertial system for any motion with accelerations and distances on the usual scale. Again, the reference frame, with earth as origin, should have a fixed orientation relative to the stars if effects of the earth's motion are to be minimized.

Finally, the diurnal rotation of the earth about its axis gives rise to a radial acceleration that is a function of latitude (and altitude). The maximum acceleration, which is at the latitude of the equator, is 0.034 m/sec^2. A coordinate system which has its origin *and* the direction of its axes fixed relative to the earth (and which therefore rotates relative to the stars) is the "laboratory system" that we use in everyday analysis. Again, for many purposes this frame is an adequate approximation of an inertial frame. In the case of motion over short distances, as we shall see in a moment, the inertial force resulting from the acceleration of the reference frame is concealed as a simple alteration in gravitational force.

11–6 LINEARLY ACCELERATED REFERENCE FRAMES

We let OXY represent an inertial cartesian coordinate system, and let $O'X'Y'$ represent a cartesian coordinate system that has an acceleration $a_{O'}$ in the x-direction relative to the OXY system (Fig. 11–5). Suppose that a mass m experiences a force F, where F is an ordinary interaction force, i.e., a force exerted by a second object. For example, F may be due to a stretched spring or to a string that passes over a pulley and supports a weight.

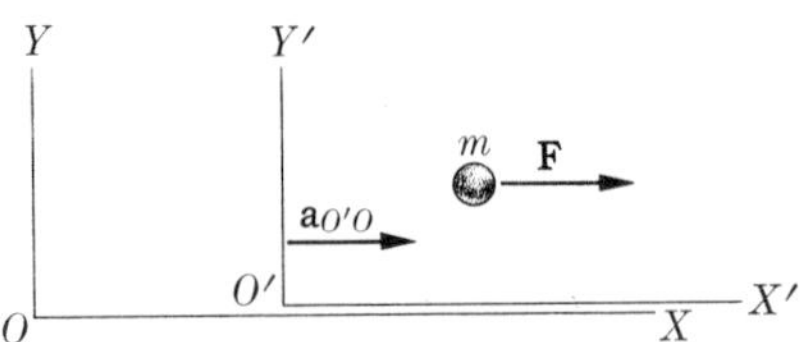

FIG. 11–5. A mass m experiences an interaction force **F** when observed from an inertial reference frame OXY. A second frame $O'X'Y'$ is accelerated relative to the inertial frame.

In the OXY system, we then have

$$\sum F = ma, \tag{11–13}$$

where a is the acceleration measured in the inertial system OXY.

The kinematical transformation to the O' system is, as usual,

$$x = x' + O', \tag{11–14}$$

where we have let O' stand for the x-component of the origin of the primed system, measured from the inertial system. Upon differentiating Eq. (11–10) twice with respect to time, we have

$$a = a' + a_{O'}. \tag{11–15}$$

Newton's second law, Eq. (11–9), can then be written

$$\sum F = ma' + ma_{O'} \tag{11–16}$$

or

$$(\sum F) - ma_{O'} = ma'. \tag{11–17}$$

It is seen that Newton's second law can be used in the accelerated reference frame, if we add a term, $-ma_{O'}$, to the interaction forces. The term $ma_{O'}$ is called a force (an *inertial force*), since its effect on the *motion* of m is exactly the same as an interaction force, according to the accelerated observer.

The above treatment is easily generalized to accelerations in any relative direction. In the compact notation of vectors, we write

$$(\sum \mathbf{F}) + m\mathbf{a}_{O'} = m\mathbf{a}'. \qquad (11\text{–}18)$$

Example 2. An object hangs on a string from the ceiling of an airplane that is flying horizontally with acceleration a_p. Analyze the problem from the point of view of an observer (a) on the ground and (b) in the plane.

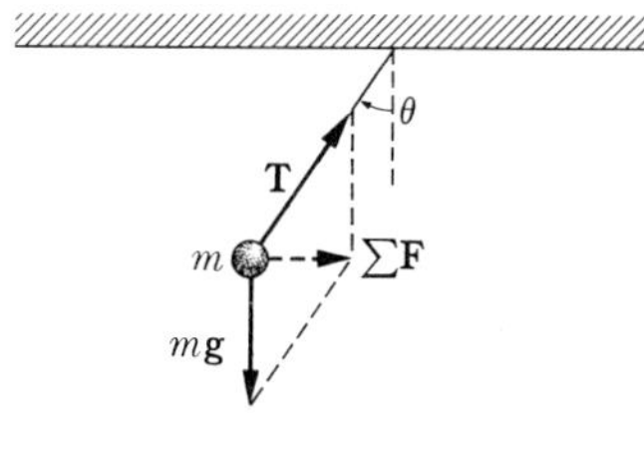

FIG. 11–6. The forces on m according to a ground observer (Example 2).

Solutions: (a) The interaction forces are T and mg (Fig. 11–6). Therefore $\sum \mathbf{F} = \mathbf{T} + m\mathbf{g} = m\mathbf{a}$, and when the object comes to rest relative to the plane, the acceleration of the object equals the acceleration of the plane, as seen from the ground. Then $\tan\theta = ma/mg = a/g$. (b) An observer in the plane finds that the object comes to rest in his reference frame, i.e., the acceleration is zero relative

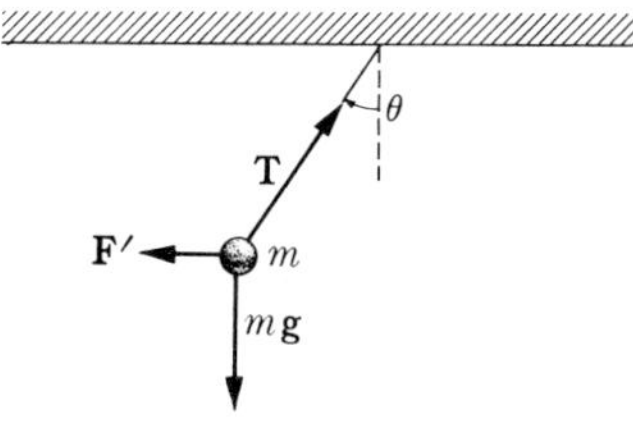

FIG. 11–7. The forces on m according to a plane observer (Example 2).

to the plane. He *must* assume that there are three forces, T, mg, and F' (Fig. 11–7), if Newton's laws are to hold in his system. He might attribute F' to some kind of action by some mysterious object at a distance behind the plane. Whatever its cause, he would evaluate the force by stating that $\sum \mathbf{F} = \mathbf{T} + m\mathbf{g} + \mathbf{F}' = 0$ or $F' = mg\tan\theta$. On the other hand, if he is experienced in physics and if *he knows the value of* m, he would attribute the mysterious force to an acceleration of his system and include an inertial force in his analysis. Furthermore, by measuring T he would find that F' is in fact horizontal. He would then write F' as an inertial force and have

$$T + mg + ma = 0 \text{ or } \tan\theta = ma/mg = a/g.$$

Note that he cannot find m from his own observations.

If the observer in the plane performs experiments in which objects are accelerated relative to the plane, he will write $\sum \mathbf{F} + m\mathbf{a}_p = m\mathbf{a}'$, where $\mathbf{a}'$ is the acceleration that he observes for the object and $\mathbf{a}_p$ is the acceleration of the plane.

It is interesting to note that the string in the above example will assume the same angle θ if the plane climbs at angle θ at *constant* velocity. The observer can, however, determine the acceleration of the plane uniquely if he knows the value of m and measures T as well as the angle θ.

Suppose that the observer's system is accelerated and he has no information on the local value of g. He cannot distinguish between the inertial force and gravitational force on a mass located at a given point in his system when his observations are confined to his system. For example, if a mass of 2 kg is hung from a spring balance and has a "weight" of 9.8 n, the observer can say only that $mg + ma_s = 9.8$ n or $g + a_s = 4.9\ \text{m/sec}^2$, where a_s is the acceleration of his laboratory. He cannot distinguish between the cases in which his laboratory is at the earth's surface and accelerating downward at $4.9\ \text{m/sec}^2$ or is at a distance of $\sqrt{2}\,R_e$ from the center of the earth and unaccelerated, or any other combinations satisfying $g + a_s = 4.9\ \text{m/sec}^2$.

It should be noted, however, that the observer can, in principle, determine g independently of a_s by taking measurements at various positions in his laboratory. The magnitude and direction of g will vary with position in the laboratory, but a_s will be constant.

11–7 COORDINATE FRAMES ROTATING AT UNIFORM ANGULAR VELOCITY

Object at rest in rotating system. If a mass m is at rest in the rotating system, it must have an interaction force or a resultant of all interaction forces given by

$$\sum F = ma_r = m\omega^2 r, \tag{11–19}$$

as seen by a stationary observer. But according to an observer on the rotating system, the mass is at rest. Hence, he says that the sum of the forces must be zero. Since the sum of the interaction forces is *not* zero, he must include an inertial force $m\omega^2 r$ in his analysis. This inertial force is sometimes called the centrifugal force and is directed outward from the center of rotation.

Example 3. Consider the example of a car rounding a curve on a banked road, from the point of view of an observer in the car.

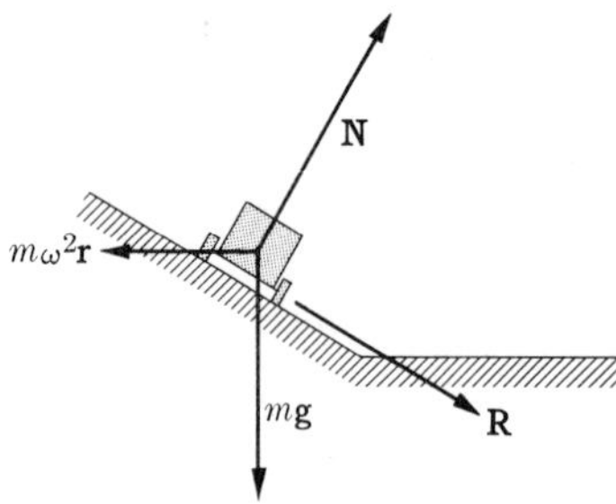

FIG. 11–8. The forces on a car rounding a banked curve according to an observer in the car (Example 3).

Solution: Since the car is at rest relative to the observer, the sum of interaction and inertial forces is zero. The forces are shown in Fig. 11–8, where N and R are the road's normal and friction forces on the car.

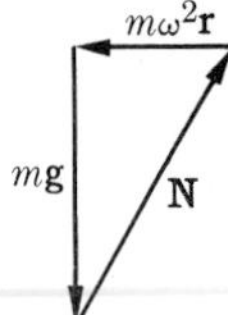

FIG. 11–9. Vector diagram for Example 3 in the case of an ideally banked curve (for the velocity in question) according to an observer in the car.

If the road is ideally banked, then $R = 0$ and the vector diagram is simply that shown in Fig. 11–9. Otherwise, $R = \mu N$ must be included in the vector sum.

Object in motion in rotating system. It is simpler to approach this problem kinematically. If an object has a displacement $\Delta\mathbf{S}'$ according to the rotating observer, the displacement $\Delta\mathbf{S}$ according to a stationary observer is found by the usual method of vector addition (Fig. 11–10). Since the primed coordinate system has different displacements for every point, we must be careful to add the particular displacement $r'\,\Delta\theta$ of the point of the system at the moving object to $\Delta\mathbf{S}'$ in order to obtain $\Delta\mathbf{S}$. Thus we have

$$\Delta\mathbf{S} = \Delta\boldsymbol{\theta} \times \mathbf{r}' + \Delta\mathbf{S}'. \tag{11–20}$$

Dividing this equation by Δt, taking the limit, and using proper vector notation, we obtain

$$\frac{d\mathbf{S}}{dt} = \frac{d\boldsymbol{\theta}}{dt}\,\mathbf{r}' + \frac{d\mathbf{S}'}{dt} \qquad \text{or} \qquad \mathbf{v} = \boldsymbol{\omega} \times \mathbf{r}' + \mathbf{v}'. \tag{11–21}$$

This is the equation for relating velocities of a given object as seen by the two observers, one rotating relative to the other. When $v' = 0$, we have $\mathbf{v} = \boldsymbol{\omega} \times \mathbf{r}$, as expected.

The relationship between accelerations of the object is a little more complex. The special case in which $v' = 0$ has already been discussed. For

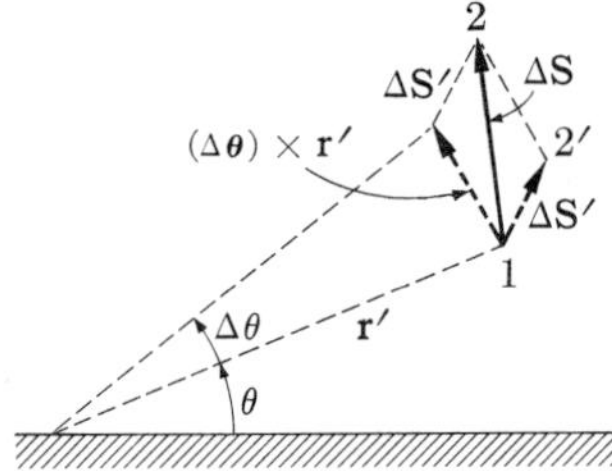

FIG. 11–10. An object moves from 1 to 2′ according to an observer in a rotating system, while the object moves from 1 to 2 according to an observer in a fixed system.

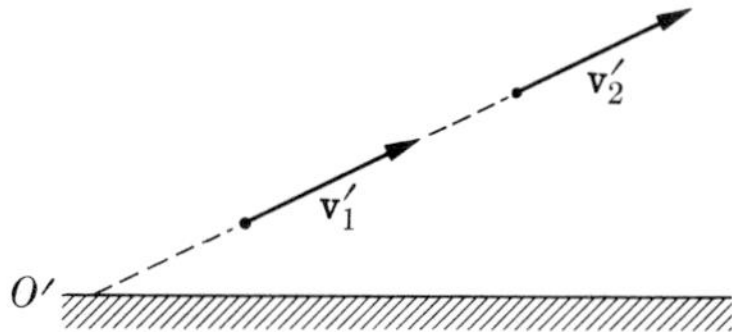

FIG. 11-11. An object moving at constant velocity in the radial direction ($\mathbf{v}_2' = \mathbf{v}_1'$) as observed in a system rotating about O'.

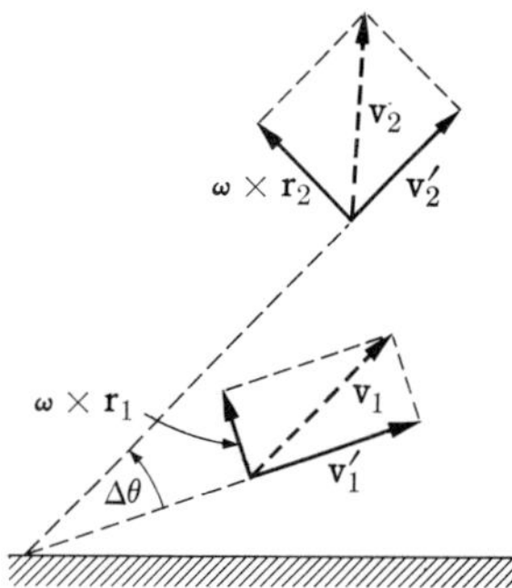

FIG. 11-12. The object of Fig. 11-11, as seen by an observer in a fixed system, has velocities $\mathbf{v}_1$ and $\mathbf{v}_2$.

this case, Eq. (11-19) gives $a = \omega^2 r$, or, in vector notation,

$$\mathbf{a} = \boldsymbol{\omega} \times (\boldsymbol{\omega} \times \mathbf{r}). \tag{11-22}$$

Next, consider another special case, one in which the velocity is radial and constant in the rotating system (Fig. 11-11). Now consider the velocity observed from the nonrotating system. It will change in direction due to the rotation of the system, and it will change in magnitude and direction due to the change in the θ-component. The relationships (shown in Fig. 11-12) can be written vectorially as

$$\mathbf{v}_1 = \mathbf{v}_1' + \boldsymbol{\omega} \times \mathbf{r}_1, \qquad \mathbf{v}_2 = \mathbf{v}_2' + \boldsymbol{\omega} \times \mathbf{r}_2. \tag{11-23}$$

By subtracting one equation from the other and using delta notation, we have

$$\Delta\mathbf{v} = \Delta\mathbf{v}' + \Delta(\boldsymbol{\omega} \times \mathbf{r}). \tag{11-24}$$

The magnitude of $\Delta\mathbf{v}'$ is $v'\,\Delta\theta$ (Fig. 11-13), or, vectorially, $\Delta\boldsymbol{\theta} \times \mathbf{v}'$. The $\Delta(\boldsymbol{\omega} \times \mathbf{r})$ term has both θ- and r-components, as shown in Fig. 11-14. Its θ-component is approximated by simply writing $|\Delta\omega r| = |\omega\,\Delta r|$, which becomes exact in the limit as $\Delta\theta \to 0$. Its r-component is $\omega r\,\Delta\theta$ (Fig. 11-15).

Assembling the above information, we have

$$(\Delta v)_\theta = \Delta\theta\, v' + \omega\,\Delta r, \qquad (\Delta v)_r = -\omega\, r\,\Delta\theta. \tag{11-25}$$

Dividing these relations by Δt and taking limits, we obtain

$$\left(\frac{dv}{dt}\right)_\theta = \frac{d\theta}{dt}\, v' + \omega\,\frac{dr}{dt}, \qquad \left(\frac{dv}{dt}\right)_r = -\omega r\,\frac{d\theta}{dt}, \tag{11-26}$$

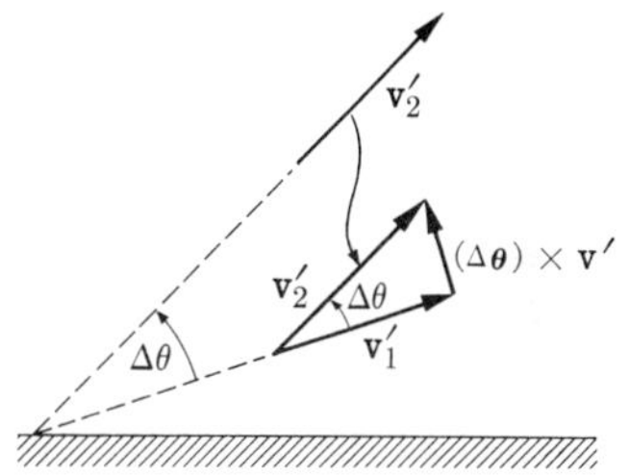

FIG. 11-13. Graphical illustration of $\Delta\mathbf{v}' = \mathbf{v}'\,\Delta\boldsymbol{\theta}$.

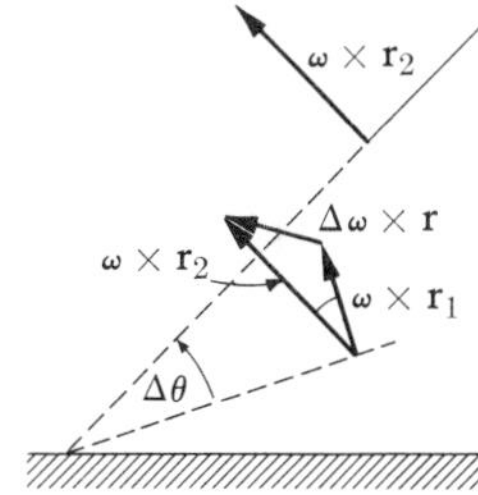

FIG. 11-14. Graphical representation of the change in ωr.

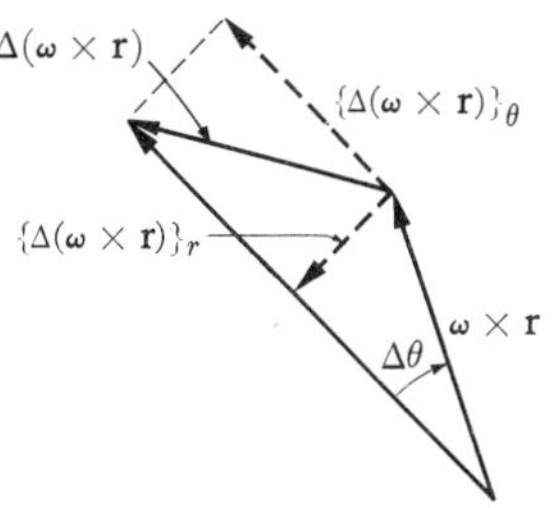

FIG. 11-15. The polar components of the change in ωr.

or, in terms of the usual definitions,

$$a_\theta = 2\omega v', \qquad a_r = -\omega^2 r. \qquad (11\text{–}27)$$

In vector notation, Eqs. (11–27) are written

$$\mathbf{a} = 2\boldsymbol{\omega} \times \mathbf{v}' + \boldsymbol{\omega} \times (\boldsymbol{\omega} \times \mathbf{r}). \qquad (11\text{–}28)$$

The dynamics of the motion, as analyzed by the nonrotating observer, can now be obtained by multiplying through by m and by using the definition of force:

$$\begin{aligned} \textstyle\sum F_\theta &= ma_\theta = m2\omega v', \\ \textstyle\sum F_r &= ma_r = -m\omega^2 r. \end{aligned} \qquad (11\text{–}29)$$

That is, the resultant of the interaction forces must have a radial component *and* a θ-component. For example, if an object slides outward at constant radial speed on a rod that is rotating (Fig. 11–16), the rod must exert a force F_θ in the direction of rotation and a force F_r in the direction of the axis. (The force F_r would be a friction force that is made to increase with r by means of some clever device.)

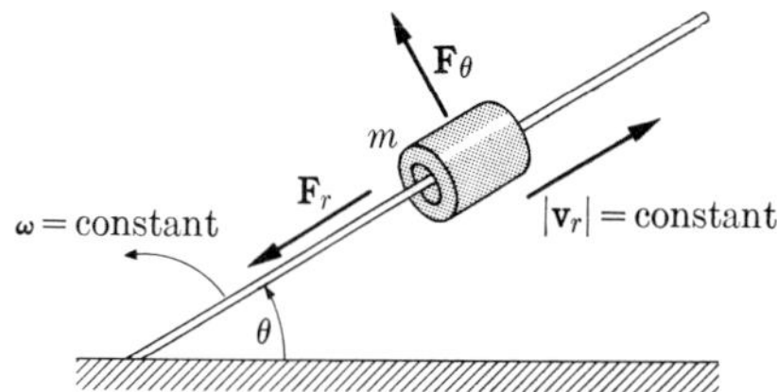

FIG. 11–16. A mass m that moves outward at constant speed relative to a rod that is rotating at constant speed.

The *rotating observer* finds that v = constant and $a = 0$. Therefore

$$\textstyle\sum F' = 0, \qquad (11\text{–}30)$$

but, since he finds that there are interaction forces whose resultant is *not* zero, he must hypothesize inertial forces whose resultant is equal and opposite to the resultant of the interaction forces. The simplest hypothesis is a single inertial force with components $-m2\omega v$ and $+m\omega^2 r$, which are called Coriolis and centrifugal forces, respectively. His dynamical equations are

$$\begin{aligned} \textstyle\sum F'_\theta &= \textstyle\sum \mathfrak{F}'_\theta - 2m\omega v = 0, \\ \textstyle\sum F'_r &= \textstyle\sum \mathfrak{F}'_r + m\omega^2 r = 0, \end{aligned} \qquad (11\text{–}31)$$

where $\mathfrak{F}$ is used to designate interaction force.

The above results can be extended for more general types of motion. If the velocity, according to the rotating observer, is constant but not radial, it can be treated just as above with the same results. If the motion is accelerated even in the rotating system with acceleration a', this acceleration is simply added to the expression (11–28), giving

$$\mathbf{a} = \mathbf{a}' + 2\boldsymbol{\omega} \times \mathbf{v}' + \boldsymbol{\omega} \times (\boldsymbol{\omega} \times \mathbf{r}). \qquad (11\text{–}32)$$

11–8 SUMMARY

The center of mass of a system of particles is defined by

$$X = \frac{\sum m_i x_i}{\sum m_i}, \qquad Y = \frac{\sum m_i y_i}{\sum m_i},$$

where X and Y are the cartesian components of the center of mass. It is shown that the center of mass moves at constant velocity in the absence of a resultant external force on the system.

General features of the motion of two point masses that interact with a force directed along their line of centers can be predicted from the conservation of linear momentum and the conservation of angular momentum. It proves convenient to describe the motion in terms of a motion of translation of the center of mass plus rotation of the line of centers about the center of mass. The extension of the conservation principles to systems of more than two objects is demonstrated.

The description of motion with noninertial reference frames is considered, and it is found necessary to introduce fictitious forces, i.e., noninteraction forces, in order to use Newton's laws.

In the case of a linearly accelerated reference frame we must introduce the fictitious force $-m\mathbf{a}_{O'}$, where $\mathbf{a}_{O'}$ is the acceleration of the reference frame relative to an inertial reference frame. In the case of an object at rest in a rotating reference frame, a fictitious force $m\omega^2 r$ directed outward from the center of rotation must be introduced by the observer in the rotating reference frame if he wishes to use Newton's laws. Again, we mean that the reference system is accelerated (in this case, rotating) relative to a known inertial frame. If an object is in motion relative to a rotating frame, a second fictitious force, the Coriolis force, must be introduced by the rotating observer. The Coriolis force is a tangential force of magnitude $2m\omega v'$, where v' is the velocity observed by the rotating observer. The direction of the Coriolis force is most easily specified by the vector relationship $2m\boldsymbol{\omega} \times \mathbf{v}'$.

Problems

1. Find the coordinates of the center of mass of the system of point masses in Fig. 11–17. Does your answer depend on the state of motion of the masses?

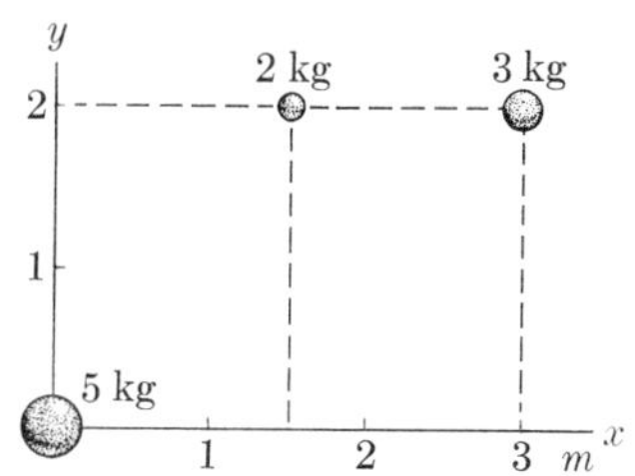

FIGURE 11–17

2. Find the center of mass of the moon-earth system, given that $m(\text{earth})/m(\text{moon}) = 81$ and their separation is 400,000 km. Where does the center of mass lie relative to the earth's surface (radius of earth = 6400 km)?

3. Describe the path of the moon-earth system about the sun, given that mass (sun)/mass(earth) = 330,000, distance to sun = 1.5×10^8 km, and radius of sun = 7×10^5 km. What is the path of the moon about the sun? of the earth about the sun?

4. Assume that the masses of Problem 1 are initially at rest. Due to forces of interaction, they start moving when released. If the 2-kg and 3-kg masses collide at point ($x = 4$, $y = 3$), where is the 5-kg mass at that moment? What can you say qualitatively concerning the interaction forces?

5. Masses of 2 kg and 5 kg are attracted to one another by an inverse-square law. If they are released from rest with a separation of 2 m, where will they collide? If their collisions are partly inelastic, where will they ultimately come to rest?

6. Assume that the masses of Problem 1 attract one another and that their velocities when in the positions of Fig. 11–17 are as shown in Fig. 11–18. They collide inelastically and are stuck together at $t = 5$ sec. Where are they at $t = 5$ sec?

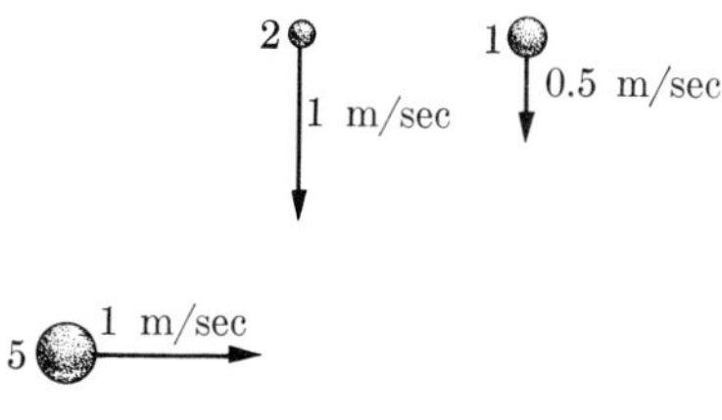

FIGURE 11–18

7. An acrobat of mass 40 kg is balanced on the end of a pole of negligible mass of length 3 m (Fig. 11–19). If the floor is horizontal and *frictionless*, where will the acrobat land if the pole slips? Where will he land if his colleague, of mass 50 kg, grasps the

FIGURE 11–19

lower end of the pole just as it starts to slip? (Assume that the masses of the men are concentrated at the ends of the pole.)

8. Two masses connected by a light rod are at rest on a horizontal frictionless surface, as shown in Fig. 11–20. A third object of mass 0.5 kg approaches the system with velocity $\mathbf{v}_0$, as shown, and strikes the 2-kg mass. What is the ensuing motion (a) if the colliding masses stick together, and (b) if the 0.5-kg mass bounces off at 90° with velocity $\mathbf{v}_f = 1$ m/sec, as shown?

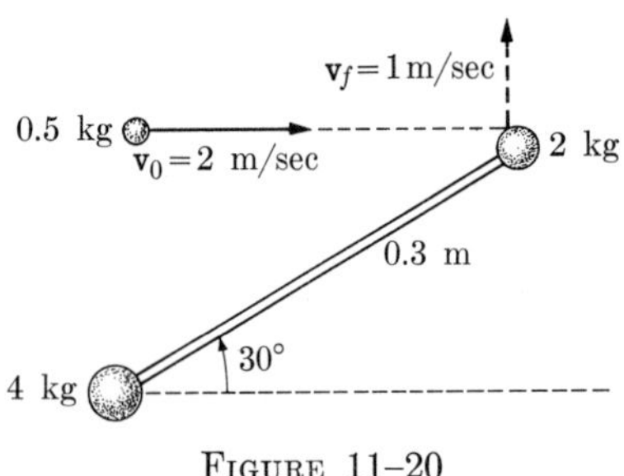

FIGURE 11–20

9. Two mountain climbers, tied together with a 10-m rope, occupy positions as shown in Fig. 11-21. Climber B slips and slides off the 45° ledge with velocity 8 m/sec. Assuming that A exerts a negligible force on the cliff as he is pulled off and that the rope is inelastic and inextensible, find the subsequent motion of the two climbers.

10. How would the observer in the airplane in Example 2 conclude from his measurement of the magnitude as well as the direction of the tension in the string that the acceleration of the plane is horizontal? Can he draw any such conclusion if he does not already know the mass of the object, i.e., can he determine both the mass of the object and the acceleration of the plane?

11. A mass m is placed on a frictionless horizontal table in a laboratory that experiences a uniform rectilinear acceleration a_L. Using the accelerated laboratory as the reference frame, write Newton's second law for the mass and derive the equations for velocity and displacement.

12. Is Newton's third law applicable to inertial forces? Explain. Is the first law applicable? Explain.

13. Which kind of mass appears in the inertial force expression ma_L, where a_L is the acceleration of the reference frame relative to an inertial system? Which kind of mass appears in the gravitational force mg? If we postulate the indistinguishability of the two forces, what are we postulating about mass?

14. An observer in a rotating laboratory discovers that a 2-kg mass suspended from a short string at point A in his laboratory deflects the string 15° from the vertical. He moves the string to point B, which is 2 m from A, and finds that the string now hangs at an angle of 30°. Where is the center of rotation of the laboratory, and what is the angular velocity of rotation?

15. How can an observer in an accelerating laboratory distinguish rectilinear acceleration from rotational acceleration?

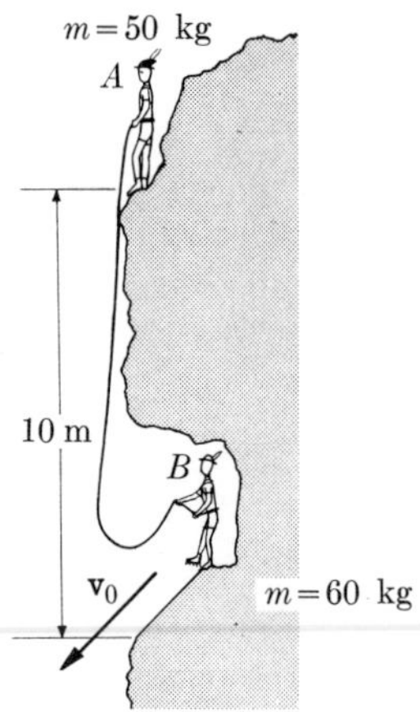

FIGURE 11–21

16. The inertial force on an object at rest in a rotating laboratory is a central force. How would you distinguish it from a central force due to gravitational attraction?

17. A mass m is free to slide on a rod that rotates at constant angular velocity ω. A spring of unstretched length l_0 and constant k is connected between the axis and the mass (Fig. 11–22).

(a) Using a coordinate system which rotates with the rod, show that the equilibrium radius, r_0, for m is given implicitly by $k(r_0 - l_0) = m\omega^2 r_0$.

(b) Using Newton's second law and the results of (a), show that if the mass is displaced to a new radius r and released, then

$$-k(r - r_0) + m\omega^2(r - r_0) = ma'_r,$$

where a'_r is the acceleration measured in the rotating system.

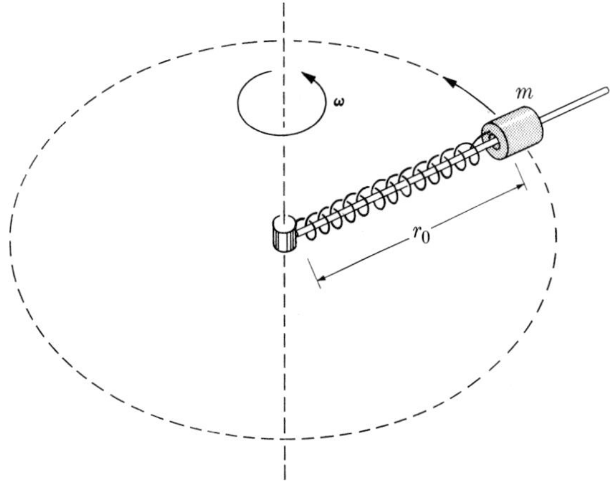

FIGURE 11–22

(c) Show that the displaced mass will execute simple harmonic motion with period $2\pi\sqrt{m/(k - m\omega^2)}$.

12

Summary in Deductive Form

12–1 INTRODUCTION

You may feel that you have been learning a vast number of distantly related subjects. This impression could be due to the fact that our approach has been inductive at times—purposely in order not to give a false picture of the development of a science. General laws do not usually come to the minds of scientists as inspirations from which many additional ideas can be deduced. The growth of the ideas leading to the generalizations and idealizations that we call laws is usually slow and indirect. Perhaps more importantly, most students find it more difficult to start with a completed generalization than to start with simple cases and build up to the generalization.

But once the general laws are formulated, we tend to forget the background development, which depended on special cases, and, instead, deduce the special cases from the generalization. This sort of economy of intellectual effort is necessary if we are to keep from becoming enmeshed in an impossibly complex network of detail.

In this chapter, we shall summarize what we have done thus far in our presentation of mechanics. Then we shall present a summary in a more nearly deductive form. We hope that you will thereby gain perspective for your future approach to mechanics.

12–2 DEVELOPMENT OF MECHANICS IN THIS TEXT

First of all, the methods for describing the motion of objects were developed. It was necessary to define length and time, since they are the tools used in the description of motion. From there, the development of kinematics was largely an exercise in mathematics in which quantities such as $d\mathbf{s}/dt$ were given names (in this case "velocity") corresponding to the physical problem at hand. The additional touch of physics was the definition of standards for the units of length and time, following the choice of these two quantities as the fundamental quantities for the description of motion.

The other kinematical quantities, velocity and acceleration, were then defined in terms of length and time. The basic equations of kinematics are simply the definitions of velocity and acceleration.

In order to extend the discussion to dynamics, in which the causes of motion are developed, a third fundamental quantity, inertial mass, was introduced (in the absolute system of units). The definition of inertial mass is much less straightforward than that of length and time, since the concept of force is used implicitly. The law of conservation of momentum is a direct consequence of the observations leading to the definition of mass.

Newton's laws, which relate forces and motion, were then introduced and applied to various types of problems. The second and third laws are closely connected with the definition of mass.

The time integral of force (impulse) was introduced, and its relationship to momentum was developed. Impulse is most useful in a discussion of interactions of the collision or explosion type.

The line integral of force along a path of motion (work) was analyzed. The concepts of kinetic and potential energies evolved in the analysis of the line integrals of resultant and conservative forces, respectively. The law of conservation of energy was introduced after the tools of work and energy had been developed.

Finally, the necessary alterations in the ideas of classical mechanics, dictated by the requirement of the constancy of the velocity of light, will be developed in the discussion of special relativity.

12–3 DEVELOPMENT OF MECHANICS IN DEDUCTIVE FORM

It is possible to start with Newton's second law as the basis for deducing most of what we have done in mechanics. To this end, it is useful to write the second law in the general form

$$\sum \mathbf{F} = \frac{d\mathbf{p}}{dt}, \tag{12–1}$$

where $\sum \mathbf{F}$ represents the vector sum of all the external forces acting on an object or system of objects. If an inertial reference frame is chosen, all the forces are interaction forces. If a non-inertial frame is chosen, there will also be inertial forces, which must be included.

The quantity $\mathbf{p}$ is the momentum, which is defined by

$$\mathbf{p} \equiv m\mathbf{v} \tag{12–2}$$

where m is the inertial mass of the chosen object or system and $\mathbf{v}$ is the velocity of the object or of the center of mass of the system.

In its turn, the velocity $\mathbf{v}$ is defined by

$$\mathbf{v} \equiv d\mathbf{s}/dt, \tag{12–3}$$

where $\mathbf{s}$ is the vector specifying the position of the object or of the center of mass of a system relative to the chosen coordinate system. We note, in passing, that the units of $\mathbf{s}$ and t are chosen to be two of the fundamental units of mechanics. The third unit, mass, is a little more complex. In the present (deductive) approach, the definition of mass is implicit in Eq. (12–1).

In the so-called closed systems that we have studied, the mass m is constant (in classical physics), and Eq. (12–1) becomes simply

$$\mathbf{F} = m\, d\mathbf{v}/dt. \tag{12–4}$$

(Rocket motion is an example of a special sort of system that will not be reviewed here.) Because of its frequent use, $d\mathbf{v}/dt$ is given a name, "acceleration," and a symbol $\mathbf{a}$. Thus

$$\mathbf{a} \equiv d\mathbf{v}/dt. \tag{12–5}$$

From the above we see that the forces acting on a system determine the kinematical quantity $d\mathbf{v}/dt$. The determination of the other kinematical quantities, $\mathbf{v}$ and $\mathbf{s}$, which are required in the complete specification of the motion, follows various patterns, depending on the nature of the forces. The problem of determining the motion from a given $d\mathbf{v}/dt$ is purely mathematical. Particular cases will, however, be reviewed here.

If the *forces are constant*, $d\mathbf{v}/dt$ is constant (Eq. 12–4). Letting $d\mathbf{v}/dt = \mathbf{a} =$ constant, we obtain by integrations

$$\begin{aligned} \mathbf{v} &= \mathbf{v}_0 + \mathbf{a}t, \\ \mathbf{s} &= \mathbf{s}_0 + \mathbf{v}t + \tfrac{1}{2}\mathbf{a}t^2, \end{aligned} \tag{12–6}$$

where $\mathbf{v}_0$ and $\mathbf{s}_0$ are the constants of integration evaluated from the initial conditions. The vector equations (12–6) can be written in component form.

If the *forces are known functions of time*, the resultant force can be expressed as a function of time, that is, $\sum \mathbf{F}(t) = \mathbf{f}(t)$, and the equations of motion can be obtained by the integrations

$$\begin{aligned} \mathbf{v} &= \frac{1}{m}\int \mathbf{f}(t)\, dt = \mathbf{v}(t), \\ \mathbf{s} &= \int \mathbf{v}(t)\, dt. \end{aligned} \tag{12–7}$$

If the *forces are functions of position*, the problem of finding the motion is usually more difficult, and, in fact, it is not always possible to find the motion analytically (methods of approximation must be used). Certain cases that can be solved are treated in this text. One of these is the case in which

$$|\sum \mathbf{F}| = f(x), \tag{12–8}$$

where the direction of the x-axis has been appropriately selected. If it is remembered that $dv/dt = d^2s/dt^2$, then the component form of Eq. (12–4) gives

$$f(x) = m\frac{d^2x}{dt^2}. \qquad (12\text{–}9)$$

The mathematical problem is now one of solving a differential equation. This cannot be done by following a single prescription for all cases.

We considered the special case in which

$$f(x) = -kx. \qquad (12\text{–}10)$$

Equation (12–9) then becomes

$$m\frac{d^2x}{dt^2} = -kx, \qquad (12\text{–}11)$$

whose solution can be written in terms of sine or cosine functions; for example,

$$x = A\sin\left(2\pi\sqrt{\frac{K}{m}}\,t + \theta_0\right). \qquad (12\text{–}12)$$

This motion is called simple harmonic motion. The velocity can be obtained by differentiation of Eq. (12–12).

Another special case that was analyzed was the one in which $|\sum\mathbf{F}|$ is constant but the direction is a special function of position such that $\sum\mathbf{F}$ is always directed toward one point. In polar-coordinate notation,

$$F_r = \text{constant},\ F_\theta = 0. \qquad (12\text{–}13)$$

The resulting motion is uniform circular motion, described by

$$\begin{aligned} r &= \text{constant}, \\ v_r &= 0, \\ a_r &= \omega^2 r, \\ \theta &= \theta_0 + \omega t, \\ \omega &= \text{constant}, \end{aligned} \qquad (12\text{–}14)$$

where r and θ are polar coordinates with r measured from the point toward which $\sum\mathbf{F}$ is directed and ω is defined as $d\theta/dt$.

Finally, the general case of a *central force* was treated. The complete description of the motion was not developed, i.e., the position and velocity were not obtained as functions of the time. However, a relationship between the component of velocity v_θ (directed perpendicularly to r) and r itself was derived, namely,

$$rv_\theta = \text{constant}. \qquad (12\text{–}15)$$

The *integral with respect to time* of the resultant force was considered. This integral, which is called impulse, can be formulated from Eq. (12–1), giving

$$\int \sum\mathbf{F}\,dt = \int d\mathbf{p}. \qquad (12\text{–}16)$$

The integral is usually treated as a definite integral, in which case we have

$$\int_1^2 \sum\mathbf{F}\,dt = \mathbf{p}_2 - \mathbf{p}_1. \qquad (12\text{–}17)$$

The most fruitful application of this integral is to systems in which the resultant external force is zero or to systems in which internal forces are much larger than the resultant external force. The internal forces in the latter case are usually forces due to relatively violent collisions or explosions that have short time durations. During that short time, the impulses by external forces may be negligible compared with the impulses by internal forces.

If the external forces (or their resultant) on a system can be neglected, the total impulse on the system is zero, since all the internal forces cancel one another. Consequently, for the system we have

$$\mathbf{p}_2 = \mathbf{p}_1$$

or, if $\mathbf{p}_i$ represents the momentum of the ith component of the system, then

$$\left(\sum\mathbf{p}_i\right)_2 = \left(\sum\mathbf{p}_i\right)_1, \qquad (12\text{–}18)$$

which is a statement of conservation of momentum. Note that in the present chapter, this conservation law has been deduced from Newton's laws whereas in our earlier, more logical treatment, it was considered to be an experimentally determined law connected with the definition of mass.

The *line integral* of the resultant force, taken along the path of motion of the object, was shown to give

$$\int_1^2 \Sigma \mathbf{F} \cdot d\mathbf{s} = \tfrac{1}{2}mv_2^2 - \tfrac{1}{2}mv_1^2. \quad (12\text{–}19)$$

The terms on the right are called kinetic energy terms, which we abbreviate by

$$T = \tfrac{1}{2}mv^2,$$

giving

$$\int_1^2 \Sigma \mathbf{F} \cdot d\mathbf{s} = T_2 - T_1. \quad (12\text{–}20)$$

The line integrals of individual forces (i.e., the work by the forces) were then considered, and it was found that, in certain cases, the results are independent of the path between any two points. Such forces are called conservative forces, and the value of the integral is called change in potential energy (with a negative sign). Thus, for a conservative force $\mathbf{F}_c$, we have

$$\int_1^2 \mathbf{F}_c \cdot d\mathbf{s} = -(V_2 - V_1), \quad (12\text{–}21)$$

where $V_2 - V_1$ is the change in potential energy. The terms V_2 and V_1 can be called the potential energies at (2) and (1), respectively.

On the other hand, *nonconservative* forces were found to depend on the path and to result in the increase of some form of energy such as heat. For example, the work by a friction force F_R would be

$$\int_1^2 \mathbf{F}_R \cdot d\mathbf{s} = -Q, \quad (12\text{–}22)$$

where the minus sign appears because $\mathbf{F}_R$ is always opposite to $d\mathbf{s}$.

We can now rewrite Eq. (12–20) in terms of the work by the individual forces:

$$\int_1^2 \Sigma \mathbf{F} \cdot d\mathbf{s} = \int_1^2 \mathbf{F}_A \cdot d\mathbf{s} + \int_1^2 \mathbf{F}_B \cdot d\mathbf{s} + \cdots = T_2 - T_1. \quad (12\text{–}23)$$

But each of the forces is either conservative or nonconservative, and its work can be represented in the manner of Eq. (12–21) or Eq. (12–22). All the potential energy terms can be represented by functions of position. Letting the sums of the potential energy terms be represented by V_2 and V_1, we have for Eq. (12–23)

$$-(V_2 - V_1) - Q_a - Q_b - \cdots = T_2 - T_1. \quad (12\text{–}24)$$

When the terms are rearranged, there results

$$T_1 + V_1 = T_2 + V_2 + Q_a + Q_b + \cdots, \quad (12\text{–}25)$$

which is a statement of the law of *conservation of energy*, i.e., the total energy of a system remains constant.

The energy conservation principle is found to be a powerful tool in obtaining the velocity as a function of position in situations in which the motion is complicated but the forces are conservative.

12–4 FORCE LAWS

The principal omissions in the above outline are the various force laws. To date, the law of universal gravitation, the laws of electrical interaction, etc., cannot be deduced from a single basic law. Thus the force laws stand as several additional independent ideas.

On the other hand, it is believed that force "laws," such as Hooke's law for an ideal spring, the "law" for sliding friction, etc., can be derived from the basic laws of interatomic forces, which are electrical in character.

12–5 SUMMARY

The principal ideas of elementary mechanics have been treated from the deductive point of view wherever possible. It was found that nearly all the ideas could be deduced from Newton's laws. However, there were certain flaws in the logic of the above procedure; for example, the definition of the basic quantity mass did not appear in a clear-cut way. It is hoped that the above outline will help the student to recognize the general pattern of what has been done thus far in our treatment of elementary mechanics.

13

Special Relativity

13–1 INTRODUCTION

The usefulness of the definitions of length, coordinate system, and time interval given in Chapter 1 was demonstrated in the topics in classical mechanics which followed. Such questions as what is meant by "rest" and "simultaneity" did not present fundamental difficulties in the solution of problems, even though they may have remained interesting topics for speculation. We did show care in our choice of a coordinate system when we wished to deal only with interaction forces. Such a coordinate system is called an inertial frame. But there was no preference for any particular inertial frame. The success of a system of physical definitions and laws is determined by its ability to make predictions that agree with experiment, and from this standpoint Newtonian mechanics is both valid and powerful.

The breakdown of classical mechanics occurs when the velocities of material objects become comparable with the velocity of light. While this is a rare occasion in gross mechanical systems, it is common in particle and atomic physics. Electrons with speeds easily produced in the laboratory require 1000 times the force for deflection that is predicted by classical theory. Unstable particles decaying in high-speed flight "live" many times longer than is predicted by classical theory. It would be impossible to explain, on the basis of Newtonian mechanics, these and many other examples of high-speed motion which can be observed in the laboratory today. Newtonian mechanics was revised by relativity before the above examples were at hand. The development of this revision (it was done by Einstein, beginning in 1905) from a historical point of view is the topic of this chapter.

13–2 NEWTONIAN RELATIVITY IN SPACE

Consider the situation in which two distinct observations are made of the same physical process. A man on a train moving at constant velocity throws a ball directly upward and watches it rise and fall, as in Fig. 13–1. The trajectory which he observes is vertical rectilinear motion. A second observer standing on the ground outside the train watches the same process. If he is careful to observe the ball and is not distracted by the moving train, he observes a parabolic trajectory, as in Fig. 13–2.

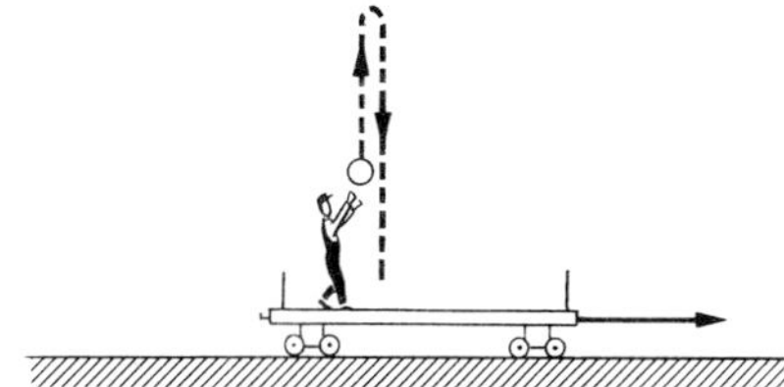

Fig. 13–1. The motion of a ball thrown vertically upward from a moving train, as observed by the man on the train.

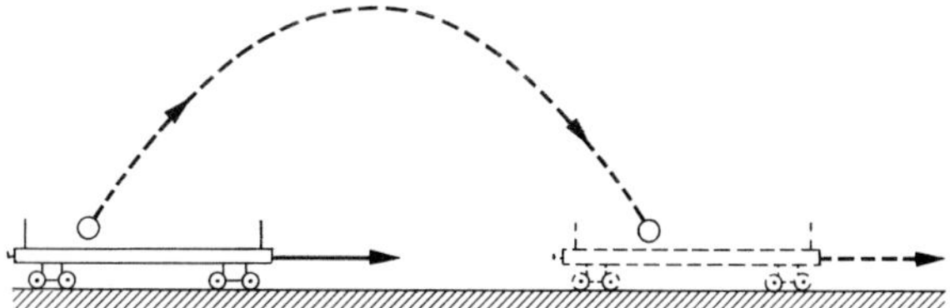

Fig. 13–2. Motion of the ball of Fig. 13–1, as seen by an observer at rest on the ground.

Here, then, are two quite different descriptions of the same event. Which is correct? The answer must be that both descriptions are equally valid and that a discrepancy need not arise if we admit that the observer himself is a necessary, important, and integral part of the system. We have seen earlier that if we extend the observations to include dynamic quantities such as force, momentum, etc., there is still no preference for either frame of reference. It was only when one reference frame was accelerating relative to another that we could distinguish one frame from another. In applications of Newton's law, we preferred, for most purposes, a frame in which only interaction forces were required, i.e., an inertial frame.

13-3 GALILEAN TRANSFORMATION

In early chapters, transformation equations were developed specifically for the transformation of velocity among inertial frames. To briefly review transformations between two inertial frames, we will go back to the basic quantities, length and time.

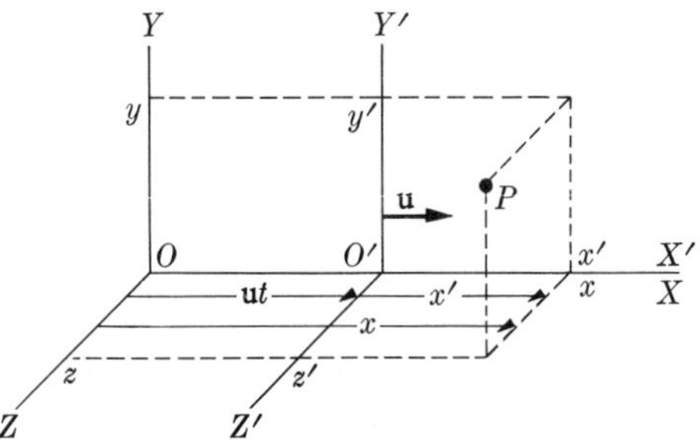

FIG. 13-3. A point P that is at rest in the $O'X'Y'$ system. The $O'X'Y'$ system is moving at uniform velocity u in the OX direction relative to the OXY system. The two systems coincided at $t = 0$.

Choose the spatial orientation of cartesian axes so that the relative motion is parallel to the X-axis. Choose the positions so that the axes coincide at $t = 0$. Then the relative position of the frames at time t is as shown in Fig. 13-3. The primed system is moving to the right at uniform velocity u relative to the unprimed system. Point P is a position in space at instant t. From the figure we see that

$$x = x' + ut, \qquad y = y', \qquad z = z', \tag{13-1}$$

which are the component equations for the vector transformation that we have earlier written as $\mathbf{S} = \mathbf{S}' + 0'0$. We now include the transformation for time that has been implicitly assumed previously,

$$t = t'. \tag{13-2}$$

By differentiation we obtain immediately the Galilean or Newtonian transformation for velocity,

$$v_x = v'_x + u, \qquad v_y = v'_y, \qquad v_z = v'_z, \tag{13-3}$$

which is a special case of relative velocities as treated earlier.

Example 1. Return now to the problem of the ball thrown upward from a moving train, and let the train be the primed system. The train velocity is then u, if we choose the earth as the second system. The equations of motion of the ball, as seen from the train, are

$$y' = v_0t - \tfrac{1}{2}gt^2, \qquad x' = z' = 0.$$

Using the transformation equations (13-1) to transform to the earth system, we have

$$y = y' = v_0t - \tfrac{1}{2}gt^2, \qquad x = x' + ut = ut,$$
$$z = z' = 0,$$

which are familiar equations for a parabolic trajectory, as observed from the earth.

13-4 NEWTONIAN TIME

Even though our classical definition of time is based on a method of comparison (the size of one time interval compared with another), there remains in the definition a presumption that there is "a uniform time" which pervades all parts of any system of reference. Certainly the definition could not account for a discrepancy in time measurements which are performed in different inertial frames. In the Galilean transformation, space coordinates are transformed, and the time coordinate is left unchanged. A summary of this attitude is contained in a statement by Newton: "Absolute, true, and mathematical time, of itself, and from its own nature, flows equably without regard to anything external, and by another name is called duration." It is implicit in the above that information can be communicated at velocities so large compared with the velocities of the objects under study that no problem of defining simultaneity arises. But, when we admit that light signals constitute our most rapid means of communication, we anticipate complications in describing the motion of objects when their velocities approach that of light.

13–5 VELOCITY OF LIGHT

One of the first challenges to the definitions in classical mechanics stemmed from the interpretations of the measurements of the velocity of light. The question of whether or not light is transmitted with a definite velocity was asked long before the nature of light was known. When measurements showed that light is propagated with a definite velocity, then still more vital questions were raised. It is now our purpose to show how the propagation of light is connected with the problems of mechanics. But first we must discuss some properties of light in a qualitative way.

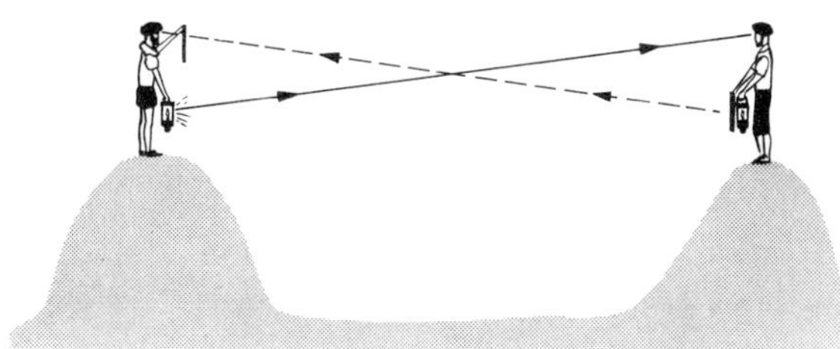

FIG. 13–4. Galileo and his assistant attempting to measure the velocity of light.

An early attempt to measure the transmission time for light signals was made by Galileo. In an experiment (Fig. 13–4), he stationed an observer on each of two mountaintops. Both observers were equipped with hooded lanterns. The first observer lifted the hood on his lantern, initiating a light signal. The second observer was instructed to lift his hood the instant that he saw the signal. Then the first observer measured the interval of time between the initiation of the first signal and his receipt of the second. The results were typical of exploratory experiments, namely, only an upper limit could be given for the time of transmission. This upper limit was determined by the experimental limitations and was probably of the order of $\frac{1}{2}$ sec at the best. Subsequent measurements, operationally the same as this but performed with essentially a much higher shutter speed, give the value of light velocity as about 3×10^8 m/sec.

If the observers in Galileo's experiment had been stationed a diameter of the earth apart (1.3×10^7 m), the transmission time from the first observer to the second and back would have been

$$t = \frac{d}{c} = \frac{2.6 \cdot 10^7 \text{ m}}{3 \cdot 10^8 \text{ m/sec}} \simeq 0.1 \text{ sec},$$

still far less than the reaction time of the observers. Electronic timers now in common use can measure time intervals as small as 10^{-9} sec. During this time, light travels a distance $d = ct = 3.10^8 \cdot 10^{-9} = 0.3 \text{ m} = 30 \text{ cm}$. Mechanical, electronic, and astronomic methods of measuring the velocity of light provide an intriguing topic for reference reading. However, the point to be made here, without further development, is that the velocity of light is finite and unvarying with time within the error of experiment.

13–6 THE NATURE OF LIGHT

Light signals can be propagated in the best laboratory vacuum and indeed in a far better vacuum, that of outer space. Another easily demonstrated property of light signals is that of rectilinear propagation: if the path of light travel is unobstructed by opaque obstacles or changes in medium, then light travels with uniform velocity in a straight line. Sharp shadows are a common illustration of rectilinear propagation. Two historical models of the structure of light were proposed and used to explain these facts of light propagation. They are the corpuscular model and the wave model, both of which remain in force today.

With the corpuscular model, light may be considered to be a stream of tiny, "bright" particles emitted by a source of light and received by a detector, e.g., the eye. One attractive feature of this model is that it directly explains reflection. Light reflects from a surface at an angle equal to the angle of incidence (Fig. 13-5).

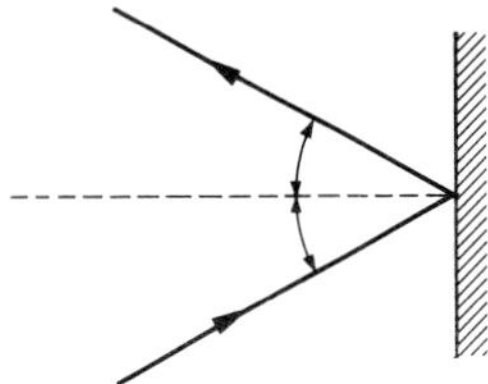

FIG. 13-5. The angle of reflection equals the angle of incidence for reflected light.

Material particles impinging on a wall obey the same rule. On the other hand, many properties of light are not so easily explained by a particle model; for example, the interference and polarization effects are very difficult to explain with a particle model. The decrease in velocity upon entering a refracting medium is even more difficult to explain. A further difficulty of the corpuscular model is that the observed deflection of a light beam due to gravitational attraction is extraordinarily minute.

We now turn to the wave model. Wave motion (such as a surface water wave or a wave in a string) is transmitted with a definite velocity characteristic of its medium. Also, while material may participate in wave motion, the wave itself is not material and would not be deflected in the gravitational field. This fact alone makes a wave theory of light extraordinarily attractive. In addition, further researches on the nature of light proved that light can undergo refraction, diffraction, interference, and polarization—all specifically wave phenomena. Therefore, the wave nature of light can be considered well established, with one severe difficulty remaining: light propagation is supported by a perfect vacuum. Even though the wave model succeeds in so many respects, the analogy fails here. In all other examples of wave motion the motion is supported by identifiable media whose properties can be used to predict the wave velocity. By analogy with mechanical waves, it was suggested that vacuum itself must be fitted with elastic and inertial constants which serve to explain the wave motion of light. Vacuum is then no longer a vacuum but is pervaded by a substance called the ether. A vast literature in physics develops the properties of this substance. However, the ether theory failed; its failure is described in the following sections.

13-7 THE ETHER AS A MEDIUM FOR LIGHT PROPAGATION

The propagation of light waves by their medium, the ether, was presumed to proceed in the same way as any other type of wave motion in its medium. One important prediction was that motion of the ether relative to the observer should affect the velocity, just as in any other type of wave motion. However, experience with other types of waves leads us to assume that motion of the source does not affect the *velocity* of the waves that the source emits. In the case of light, De Sitter justified this assumption by observations of the light emitted by double stars. Double stars revolve about their common center of gravity, and hence each star alternately moves toward and away from the earth. According to the observations, there is *no* resulting effect on the velocity of the light that the double stars emit.

If the ether is the medium that propagates the light waves, the velocity of light *relative* to the ether must be a fixed quantity, just as with any wave motion. We are then left with only the question of the effect of relative motion between the observer and the ether on the observed velocity of light. Letting $\mathbf{c}$ represent the fixed velocity of light relative to the ether, $\mathbf{c}_0$ the velocity of light relative to the observer, and **v** the velocity of the observer relative to the ether, we have

$$\mathbf{c}_0 = \mathbf{c} - \mathbf{v}. \qquad (13\text{–}4)$$

The velocity $-\mathbf{v}$ is sometimes called the ether wind velocity.

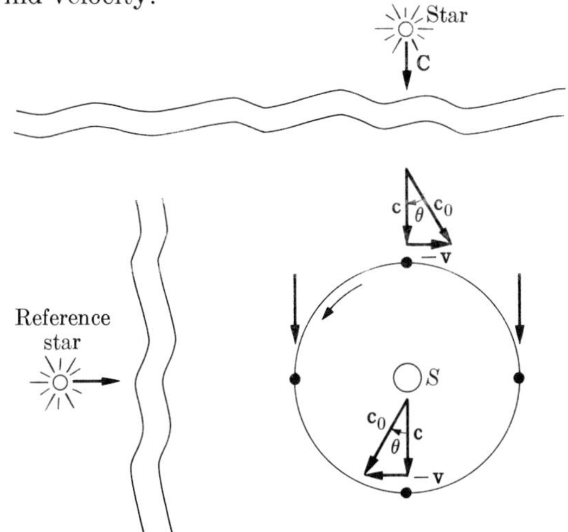

FIG. 13–6. Illustration of an aberration of starlight due to the orbital motion of the earth.

The orbital velocity of the earth provided a convenient way of testing the above effect of the ether as the medium for light propagation. The distant stars provide convenient sources whose *directions* are approximately fixed. If we make the natural assumption that the ether is fixed relative to the stars, and observe a star that lies in the plane of the orbit of the earth, the velocities will be related as shown in Fig. 13–6. In the figure, we are looking down on the plane of the orbit. The star is far away, and hence the light beams from the star are parallel in all parts of the orbit. But the velocity of the observer on the earth changes direction throughout the year. The effect on the velocity of light *relative* to the observer is shown in the figure. The observed direction of the star is in the direction of c_0, and hence it varies with the time of year. A reference star in a direction as shown might be used as the comparison for measurement of the angles θ.

The predicted angle θ is $\tan^{-1} v/c \simeq v/c$, which is $(30 \text{ km/sec})/(3 \times 10^5 \text{ km/sec}) = 10^{-4}$ rad $= 0.0057°$. The observed angles, called the aberration of starlight, agree with this prediction. *Therefore, the ether is indeed at rest relative to the stars.* Furthermore, the ether cannot be dragged along locally as a sheath by the earth because the ether wind $(-v)$ would then be zero at the point of observation (the earth).

Note that the aberration of starlight is a so-called first-order effect since it depends on v/c to the first power.

Michelson-Morley experiment. Although the motion of the earth through the ether was proved by the aberration-of-starlight experiment, it would be interesting to demonstrate the effect of the ether wind in an experiment confined to the laboratory. The ether wind must affect the *magnitude* of the velocity of light, if it affects its direction. The change in magnitude, however, is a second-order effect, depending on $(v/c)^2$, and hence is much more difficult to measure.

The measurement was accomplished by Michelson and Morley, by means of a clever experiment, one of the crucial experiments in the development of physics. Michelson had developed a device called an interferometer that can measure differences of length to within a fraction of a wavelength of light (by interference effects). With this device, it would be possible to detect the second-order effect of the ether wind on the velocity of light in the laboratory. The expected change in the light's time of flight could be measured in terms of change in number of wavelengths.

The transit time for a round trip by a light beam moving perpendicular to the ether wind is compared with the time for a round trip parallel to the wind (Fig. 13–7). The light beam is actually split by a 45° half-reflecting mirror M_0 into a transmitted beam (1) and a reflected beam (2). Each beam is reflected back toward the mirror M_0, where (1) is half-reflected and (2) is half-transmitted to the observer.

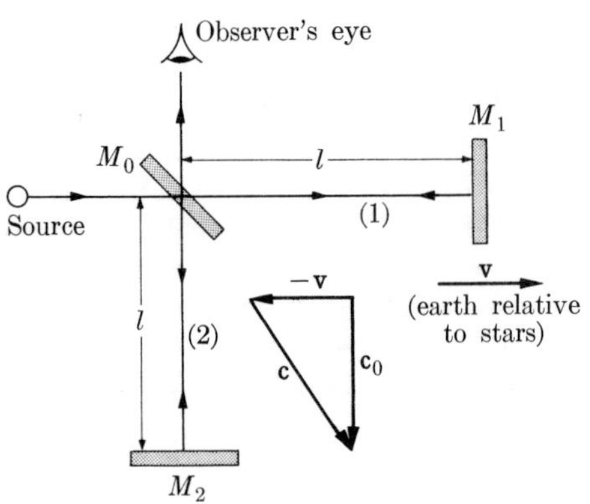

FIG. 13-7. Schematic diagram of the Michelson-Morley apparatus to detect the motion of the earth relative to the ether.

Both beam (1) and beam (2) travel the same path from the source to M_0 and from M_0 to the observer. Hence, only the paths from M_0 to M_1 and M_2 need be analyzed.

Consider first the transit time for beam (1). From the result of the experiment on the aberration of starlight, it is assumed that the velocity of the earth relative to the stars is also the velocity of the earth (and hence the apparatus) relative to the ether. Since all the pertinent velocities referring to beam (1) are parallel, the vector equation (13-4) for composition of velocities becomes simply $c_0 = c - v$ for the outgoing trip and $c_0 = c + v$ for the return. The total time is therefore

$$t_1 = \frac{l}{c - v} + \frac{l}{c + v} = \frac{2cl}{c^2 - v^2}$$
$$= \frac{2l}{c}\frac{1}{1 - v^2/c^2} \simeq \frac{2l}{c}\left(1 + \frac{v^2}{c^2}\right), \qquad (13\text{-}5)$$

where the binomial expansion has been used for the last step, since $v^2/c^2 \ll 1$.

For path (2), the velocity composition is shown in Fig. 13-7. We see that the magnitudes of the velocities are related by $c_0 = \sqrt{c^2 - v^2}$. For the return trip to M_0, the velocity diagram is simply reflected about the $-v$ vector, and the magnitude of c_0 is therefore the same. The total time for beam (2) is therefore

$$t_2 = 2\frac{l}{\sqrt{(c^2 - v^2)}}$$
$$= \frac{2l}{c}\frac{1}{\sqrt{(1 - v^2/c^2)}} \simeq \frac{2l}{c}\left(1 + \frac{1}{2}\frac{v^2}{c^2}\right), \qquad (13\text{-}6)$$

where the binomial expansion has again been used for the last step, since $v^2/c^2 \ll 1$.

The difference in times is approximately

$$\Delta t \simeq \frac{l}{c}\left(\frac{v^2}{c^2}\right). \qquad (13\text{-}7)$$

This analysis is exactly the same as our earlier analysis for two men rowing boats on a river, one to a point downstream and back, the other to a point across the stream and back. The river current corresponds to the ether wind, and the speed of the boat in still water (i.e., relative to the water) corresponds to the speed of light relative to the ether.

The key points in the observational technique by Michelson and Morley were (a) to observe wave interference effects between the two beams, which makes possible the determination of these small Δt's and (b) to rotate the apparatus, interchanging the roles of (1) and (2) so that a change in interference effect could be observed, if there really were a Δt. In addition, the rotation doubles the predicted Δt.

We can use some of the terminology of periodic motion in order to obtain a rough idea of the interpretation of Δt in terms of the wavelength of the light. Use is made of so-called interference effects. The period of the light wave is about 2×10^{-15} sec. If the distance l is 11 m, the time difference (Eq. 13-7) is $2\,\Delta t = 7 \times 10^{-16}$ sec, since v is 30 km/sec. Therefore, the effect predicted is that the time difference for the two beams shifts by $(7 \times 10^{-16})/(2 \times 10^{-15}) \simeq \frac{1}{3}$ the period of the light. This corresponds to $\frac{1}{3}$ of a wavelength, or $\frac{1}{3}$ of an interference band. The experimental precision was about $\frac{1}{100}$ of a band.

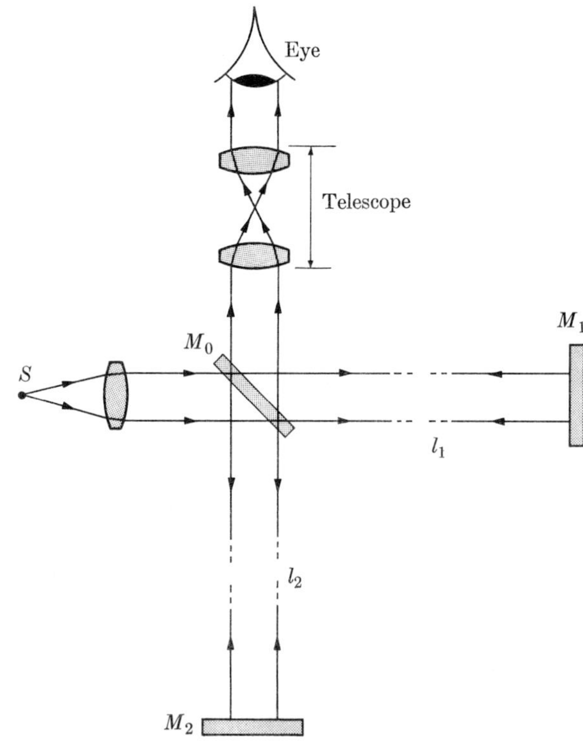

FIG. 13–8. Paths of light rays in the Michelson-Morley experiment.

Before giving the experimental results, we will describe briefly the theory of the Michelson interferometer. The optical features of the interferometer, as designed for this experiment, are shown in Fig. 13–8. The main feature that is brought out in this figure is the finite cross section of the beams of light.

If the path lengths were exactly the same for both beams of light and also the same for all rays in each beam, there would be so-called constructive interference over the area of the beam, and the observer would see a uniform disk of light. That is, all the waves would arrive "in phase," crests coinciding with crests and troughs with troughs. The effects would add (Fig. 13–9) and give a bright image.

Now suppose that M_2 is moved $\frac{1}{4}$ wavelength closer to M_0. The path $2l_2$ would then be short-

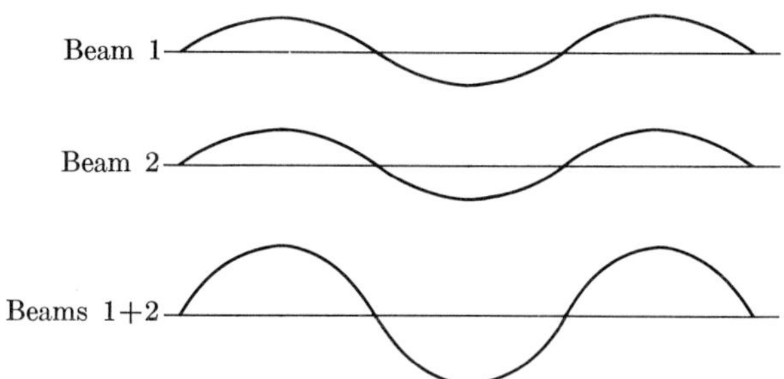

FIG. 13–9. The addition of light waves that are in phase.

ened by $\frac{1}{2}$ wavelength, and the interference would be destructive, since the beams are now "out of phase" (Fig. 13–10). The result would be a dark image.

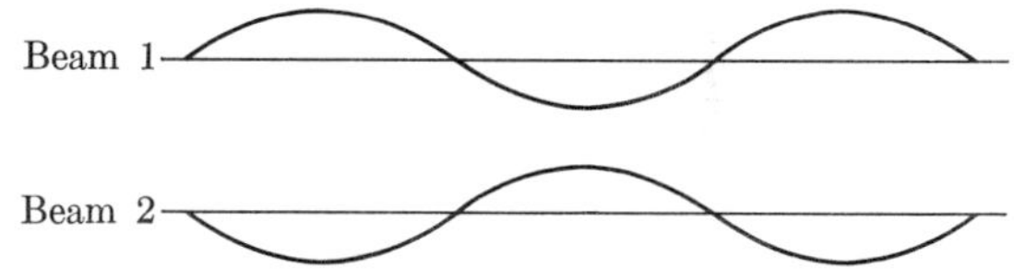

FIG. 13–10. The addition (algebraic) of light beams that are completely out of phase.

It would be very difficult to judge changes in l_2 of less than $\frac{1}{4}$ wavelength by this method. Consequently, one of the mirrors is permitted to be out of perpendicularity to the beam by a few wavelengths. The result is that the light's path length is not the same over the cross section of the beam. There will be alternating regions of constructive and destructive interference. The observer will see interference bands as in Fig. 13–11.

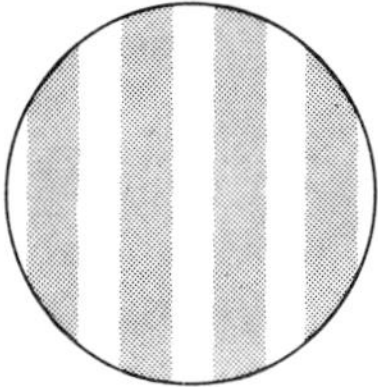

FIG. 13–11. Observed interference pattern when one mirror is not perpendicular to the light beam.

Now when one mirror is moved, the bands will move across the field of view. It is possible to observe a motion of the bands equal to $\frac{1}{100}$ of a band width and hence to detect a motion by the mirror of $\frac{1}{200}$ of a wavelength of light.

Returning now to the use of the interferometer in the Michelson-Morley experiment, a change in resultant velocity results in a change in transit time, which in turn results in a change in number of wavelengths in a given path length. This change would produce the same effect as the movement of a mirror, that is, a shift in the bands. We have seen that the expected effect was a shift by $\frac{1}{3}$ of a band when the apparatus was rotated so that the two paths, l_1 and l_2, were interchanged relative to the ether wind.

The astonishing result was that the observed shift was much smaller than $\frac{1}{3}$ of a band. Furthermore, extended observations showed that the small shifts that were observed were random in character and hence averaged out to zero!

There is no ether wind! But the aberration of starlight gives equally strong evidence that there is an ether wind. The conclusion must be that the ether model for light propagation is false. Although the invention of ether may have appeared drastic to begin with, the abolition of ether, which is now demanded, gives rise to the assumptions of relativity which are no less challenging to the imagination.

13–8 THE POSTULATES OF SPECIAL RELATIVITY

In the foregoing it has been shown that the measured velocity of light is independent of motion by the observer. The above conclusion must be accepted as a summary of experimental evidence, even though one is surprised that the propagation of light is quite unlike the propagation of sound in this respect. If an observer moves about in air, which carries sound waves, the observed velocity of sound depends on the velocity of the observer, and this variation can be computed by the vector rules for velocity addition. But if an observer moves about in space and measures the velocity of light, he will obtain the same value for the velocity of light, regardless of his motion. It will be our purpose in the following sections to show that this one fact, connected with the measurement of the velocity of light and quite apart from any other details about the property of light itself, requires an essential modification of the basic rules of classical mechanics. The rules for the measurement of time and space intervals must be changed. We begin by setting down the postulates of special relativity.

One postulate is based on the contradictions of the ether model. It is a statement that effects of the ether on the velocity of light cannot be detected. The usual statement is that the measured speed of light is independent of motion of the source and/or the observer.

The second postulate is that the basic laws of physics are unchanged by motion of the observer with uniform velocity relative to the apparatus (even at high velocities).

An alternative way of expressing the above is to postulate that no experiment can be performed that will distinguish one reference frame from another if their relative motion is at constant velocity.

We now turn to some of the interesting consequences of these two hypotheses. The approach will be a mixed one. We shall first directly deduce the time interval dilation and length contraction equations. The advantage will be that an impression of reality and insight will result. Then, the less direct but more general method of the Lorentz transformations will be described and used.

13–9 DILATION OF TIME INTERVALS

Let two separate laboratories be established for the performance of a velocity-of-light measurement. Each laboratory contains an observer and a set of apparatus. The set of apparatus consists of a light source, a meter stick, a mirror, and a

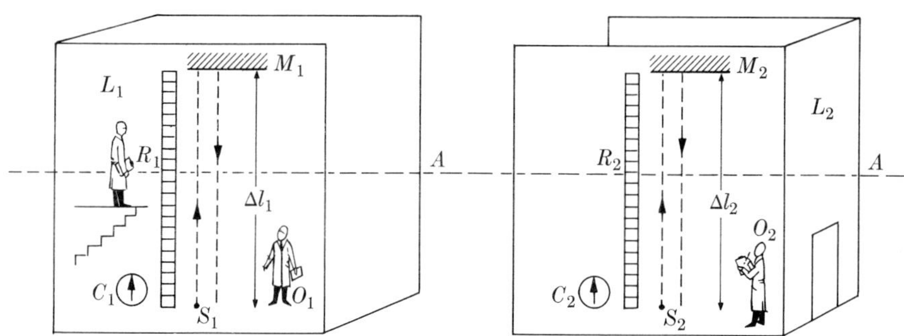

FIG. 13–12. Two laboratories that are equipped to measure the time required for a light pulse to travel from a source to a mirror and return.

clock. The measurement is performed as follows: The observer releases a flash of light from the source S, directed toward the mirror M. With his clock C, he measures the time of emission of the flash and the time at which the flash returns from the mirror and arrives again at the position S. The time of flight of the light flash from S to M and back to S is Δt. The measured length of the course C, from S to M is Δl. Then the velocity of light is

$$c = \frac{2\,\Delta l}{\Delta t}. \tag{13–8}$$

Now, two laboratories, L_1 and L_2, are set up in identical fashion (Fig. 13–12). The subcript "1" will be used to designate apparatus and measured quantities associated with L_1. The observer is an integral part of the experiment and will be designated O_1. The subscript "2" will be used similarly in the case of L_2.

The first measurements are made with the *laboratories at rest* relative to one another. Each observer measures his own source-mirror distance and time of round-trip flight for his light flash. The two observers compare results and find that $\Delta l_1 = \Delta l_2$, $\Delta t_1 = \Delta t_2$, and $c = 2\,\Delta l_1/\Delta t_1 = 2\,\Delta l_2/\Delta t_2$, just as expected. Furthermore, observer O_1 asks O_2 to repeat his experiment in L_2, while O_1 looks on from L_1. When O_1 reads off the length Δl_2 and time Δt_2 on O_2's meter stick and clock, he agrees with O_2. Finally, O_1 uses his own meter stick and clock to measure the distance Δl_2 and time interval Δt_2 of O_2's experiment. He again agrees with O_2's findings. In order to indicate that O_1 is using his own instruments but measuring objects and events in *another laboratory*, we shall use the notation $\Delta\tau_1$ and $\Delta\lambda_1$ for such measurements.

At this time, it is desirable to be *very* explicit about the manner in which the instruments are read, since we shall soon see that the results of a measurement depend on the way in which the measurements are made. The instruments are read by means of light beams that must travel from the source of illumination to the instrument and then to the eye of the observer or to the recording device. We have seen that light signals do *not* travel with infinite velocity. The finite time delays in transmission of the information cannot be ignored. The delay in transmission between the source of illumination of the instrument and the instrument itself can be eliminated by having the sources at the instruments themselves.

The above experiment has been carefully designed to simplify the problems of reading the instruments. The light pulse whose velocity is to be measured returns to its starting point. Thus only *one* timing mechanism (clock) is required in each laboratory. One might suggest that the time of flight of the light pulse could be measured for a one-way trip with a single timer by simply sending an electric signal back to the timer from the receiver, but this is unsatisfactory because the transit time of the electric signal introduces a delay. We may think that we know how to correct for the delays, but we cannot be sure, at this stage, when moving systems are introduced. The second important feature of the experiment is that the paths from S to M and back are perpendicular to a line drawn between corresponding elements in the two laboratories. This means that observer O_1 need only place his eye at the midpoint level AA^1 when reading the meter sticks R_1 or R_2 in order to be sure that his measurement of distances Δl_1 or Δl_2 is not affected by the finite time of travel of the light from the meter stick to his eye. Furthermore, O_1 can measure the length Δl_2, using his own meter stick, by simply sighting along perpendicular lines, first at S_2 then at M_2. (When either laboratory is in motion, O_1 needs a helper in measuring Δl_2 in terms of R_1, so that they can readily take simultaneous readings of the positions of M_2 and S_2.)

In view of the above discussion of the methods for making the measurements, we can be assured that the previously mentioned agreements in the various measurements of time intervals and lengths are valid.

The next measurements are made with one laboratory moving at constant velocity v relative to the other. Again, each observer makes measurements in his own laboratory with his own instruments. They report results to each other and find that they are identical, just as when there was no motion.

We at last come to the crucial experiment: observer O_1 again abandons his own experiment and observes the experiment that O_2 is performing but the laboratory is now moving relative to O_1. Observer O_1 first measures the distance S_2M_2 by sighting perpendicular to his own ruler R_1 and finds that he still agrees with O_2 on this distance. *But* O_1 now disagrees with O_2 on the distance that the light pulse travels. Observer O_1 finds that the light path is two sides of a triangle, since the mirror M_2 moves to the location (2) of Fig. 13–13, while the light pulse travels from S_2 to M_2, and

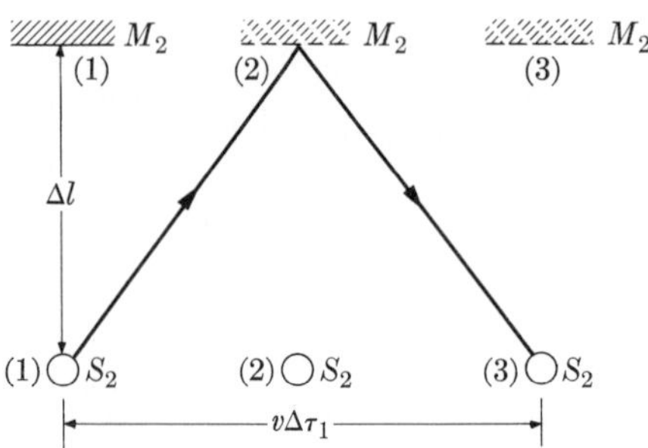

FIG. 13–13. The path of the light beam as seen by the "stationary" observer.

since S_2 moves to point (3), while the pulse returns to S_2 from M_2. While the light traveled to M_2 and back, the source S_2 moved a distance $v\,\Delta\tau_1$, according to O_1's observations. Therefore the length of path traveled by the light according to O_1 is

$$2\sqrt{\Delta l^2 + (v\,\Delta\tau_1/2)^2}, \tag{13–9}$$

whereas O_2 still measures the path as $2\,\Delta l$.

According to postulate, the two observers must agree on the velocity of the light. Since they disagree on the path length, they must also disagree on the time interval. The amount of disagreement is easily found, since O_2 obtains the velocity of the light from

$$c = \frac{2\,\Delta l}{\Delta t_2} \tag{13–10}$$

and O_1 obtains the velocity from

$$c = \frac{2\sqrt{\Delta l^2 + (v\,\Delta\tau_1/2)^2}}{\Delta\tau_1}. \tag{13–11}$$

By equating Eqs. (13–10) and (13–11) and solving for $\Delta\tau_1$, we have

$$\Delta\tau_1 = \frac{\Delta t_2}{\sqrt{1 - (v^2/c^2)}}. \tag{13–12}$$

The times the two observers measure for the same physical event differ by the factor $\sqrt{1 - (v^2/c^2)}$, if our basic postulates are correct.

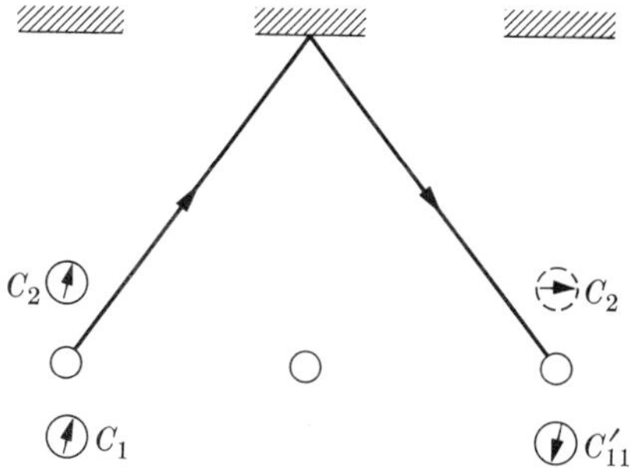

FIG. 13–14. Illustrating the use of two clocks by O_1 as a means of minimizing the distance between the event to be observed and the observing instrument (clock) for both the initial event and the final event.

We guarantee that there are no hidden flaws in our argument by noting that O_1 could actually use two clocks in his measurement, one, C_1, located at the position of S_2 when the light signal was dispatched and the other, C_{11}, at the position of S_2 when the signal had returned (Fig. 13–14). Observer O_1 had previously synchronized his two clocks by stationing himself halfway between them and noting that they read the same. Since O_1 uses clocks that are synchronized, that are at rest, and that are located at the positions where the physical events in question occur, there can be no errors due to the transmission time of signals from the position of an event to a clock.

In view of the above analysis, the only conclusion that O_1 can make is the following: *the clock of O_2 runs slowly when it is in motion relative to O_1.* In principle, this conclusion could be verified directly.

For example, O_1 can directly observe the clock of O_2 at two points as it passes by his (O_1's) clocks. In principle, O_1 can take at each station a single flash photograph that includes both his clock and the moving clock and simply read the clocks in the photographs. Or O_1 can station himself at one clock and his helper at the other clock and make visual comparions of C_2 with C_1 and with C_{11}.

If O_2 abandons his experiment and observes the experiment of O_1, observer O_2 will conclude that the clock of O_1 runs slowly. (The only change from the foregoing analysis is the sign of v, but since v finally appears only as v^2, the result is the same.) It is because of this equivalence of the two laboratories that we have chosen the notation of subscripts 1 and 2 to identify the laboratories, measurements, etc.

However, now that the point of equivalence has been made, we shall turn to the notation usually employed. Primes are used to designate the reference frame, observer, measurements, etc. that are at rest relative to the experiment in question. Unprimed symbols are then used for the measurements made by an observer who studies the experiment of the system that is moving relative to him. He uses his own instruments for the measurements.

Thus primed quantities represent measurements by an observer at *rest* relative to the experiment, while unprimed quantities represent measurements of the same experiment by an observer who sees the apparatus in motion. The usual phraseology is (a) "moving observer" and moving system" for the observer and system who "move" along with the experiment (they are at rest relative to the experiment) and (b) "rest observer" and "rest system" for the observer and system who see the primed system in motion. This phraseology may seem confusing at first. However, since it stems from discussions of actual experimental situations instead of "thought experiments," it will be clearer to you after real examples have been discussed. We will state rest or moving relative to a specified object whenever uncertainty might arise.

In the above notation, the time-dilation expression becomes

$$\Delta t = \frac{\Delta t'}{\sqrt{1 - v^2/c^2}}, \tag{13–13}$$

where $\Delta t'$ is the time interval measured by the moving observer (i.e., moving with the experiment) and Δt is the time interval measured by the rest observer for the same physical event, but using his own timer.

The above expression is frequently written

$$\Delta t = \gamma\, \Delta t', \tag{13-14}$$

where, for the sake of compactness, we have simply let

$$\gamma \equiv 1/\sqrt{1 - (v^2/c^2)}. \tag{13-15}$$

The factor γ is often called "the relativistic factor." We shall see later that the factor γ is always greater than one for material objects. Another frequently used abbreviation is $\beta \equiv v/c$, which leads to

$$\Delta t = \Delta t'/\sqrt{1 - \beta^2}. \tag{13-16}$$

As an illustration of time dilation, we consider another thought experiment. If the clock in the moving system is a pendulum clock, the period of the pendulum is longer when the clock is in motion since it must run slower than a clock at rest. Thus, when the rest observer used his two synchronized clocks, C_1 and C_{11}, to measure the period, his result, Δt, differs from the period, $\Delta t'$, measured by the observer moving with the pendulum, by the amount given in Eq. (13–13). The "experiment" is depicted in Fig. 13–15.

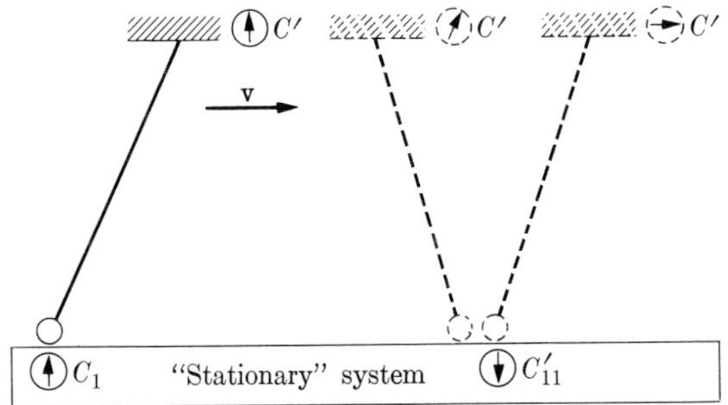

FIG. 13–15. A pendulum swing timed by two observers, one moving with the pendulum support, the other stationary in the laboratory.

Consider the possibility of observing time dilation of a clock. Air resistance limits the velocity of macroscopic bodies to relatively low values, but artificial satellites above the earth's atmosphere escape this limitation. It has been shown earlier that satellites in orbit near the earth have a velocity of 8000 m/sec. Assuming that rockets fired from satellites in the near future might have velocities 100 times as great, we find a relativistic factor

$$\gamma = \frac{1}{\sqrt{1 - (8 \times 10^5/3 \times 10^8)^2}} = \frac{1}{\sqrt{1 - 7 \times 10^{-6}}}.$$

Using the binomial expansion, we have $\gamma \simeq 1 + \frac{1}{2}7 \times 10^{-6}$, that is, the time dilation factor is a few parts per million. At the satellite velocity itself the effect would be $(100)^2$ times smaller, or a few parts in 10^{10}. Accuracy of this sort is possible with atomic frequency-controlled clocks. The satellite also has an acceleration of about g, relative to the earth observer but this does not appreciably affect the above calculation (the effect of acceleration is treated in general relativity).

Finally, we turn to actual observations of time dilation. In order to have large effects, the velocities must be comparable with c. At present, such velocities can only be obtained in the submicroscopic realm of individual atoms, of constituents of atoms, or of created particles. But we cannot build a clock with one atom. Fortunately, there are unstable atoms that mark off time intervals by disintegrating in an easily detectable manner. These are radioactive atoms. Consider, for example, radium (element number 88), which is itself a particular type of radioactive atom. Each atom of radium disintegrates after a different length of time, but the *average* time for every sample of many atoms is the same (within the inherent statistical error). The average is 2300 years. If we wish to use radioactive decay as a "clock," we simply observe the average decay time for the number of atoms dictated by our desired statistical accuracy and find the mean time. The statistical accuracy depends on $1/\sqrt{n}$, where n is the number of events. Therefore 1% accuracy requires 10,000 events.

In the subatomic realm, particles are found that also disintegrate spontaneously, just as radioactive atoms do. These subatomic particles do not exist as stable constituents of matter. They are produced in high-energy collisions between particles, for example collisions of cosmic rays with atoms of air, or collisions of particles that are given high velocities in accelerators with nuclei of atoms of a "target." These unstable particles are produced copiously, and they are emitted at high velocities if the collision energy is high enough. The largest of the cyclotron accelerators and all the new superaccelerators in nuclear physics laboratories produce streams of these unstable particles. The particle that is produced most copiously is called a pi-meson (π-meson), which has a mean life at rest of 2×10^{-8} sec in the charged form, or $\sim 2 \times 10^{-16}$ sec in the neutral form. The relativistic increase in the lifetime of the charged π-mesons is an everyday observation in all the accelerator laboratories of the world. In some cases, the research workers depend on the relativistic increase to get the particles from the accelerator target to the observation equipment before the particles disintegrate.

Example 1. An experimenter wishes to study a beam of π-mesons of velocity $0.9c$. How far can he place his apparatus from the target where the π-mesons are produced and still expect to get a reasonable number of π-mesons?

Solution: If he neglects relativistic effects, he would say that $\Delta x = v\,\Delta t = 0.9 \times 3 \times 10^8 \times 2 \times 10^{-8} = 5$ m, but, when relativistic time dilation is taken into account, there results (Eq. 13–13), $\Delta t = \Delta t'/\sqrt{1 - 0.9^2} = 2.3\,\Delta t'$. Since $\Delta t'$ is the time interval measured by an observer moving with the π-meson, it is the rest lifetime of 2×10^{-8} sec. Therefore, in the laboratory system of reference, the mean life is $\Delta t = 2.3 \times 2 \times 10^{-8} = 4.6 \times 10^{-8}$ sec, and the particles travel an average distance of $\Delta x = v\,\Delta t = 12.5$ m. This result pleases the experimenter, because he was forced to work at a distance greater than 10 m due to radiation-shielding problems.

The mean life of π-mesons at rest is measured directly by introducing a solid material in their path. They are brought to rest (by collisions with the electron clouds around the atoms) in a time that is short compared with their lifetime. Thus a measurable number of mesons can be brought to rest. The time delay between their entrance into the stopping material and the emission of the products of their decay can be measured electronically, giving the above result of 2×10^{-8} sec for the lifetime at rest.

All inertial frames of reference are equivalent as far as the velocity of light and physical laws are concerned. However, *one* frame has special significance when time intervals are measured, namely, the frame in which the device that generates the time interval in question is at rest. An observer in this particular frame finds a smaller value for the interval than an observer in any other inertial frame. The interval measured by this preferred observer is called the *proper time.*

13–10 LENGTH CONTRACTION

It was noted in the previous section that observers in relative motion agree on the measurement of lengths at *right angles to the motion.* In fact, the orientation of the apparatus was deliberately chosen to be transverse to the motion, so that we could concentrate on the question of time intervals. We now consider the problem of lengths measured in the direction of the relative motion. This problem was implicitly introduced in the discussion of the distance of travel of the π-meson in Example 1.

The experiment of Example 1, as seen by the laboratory observer, is shown in Fig. 13–16. The

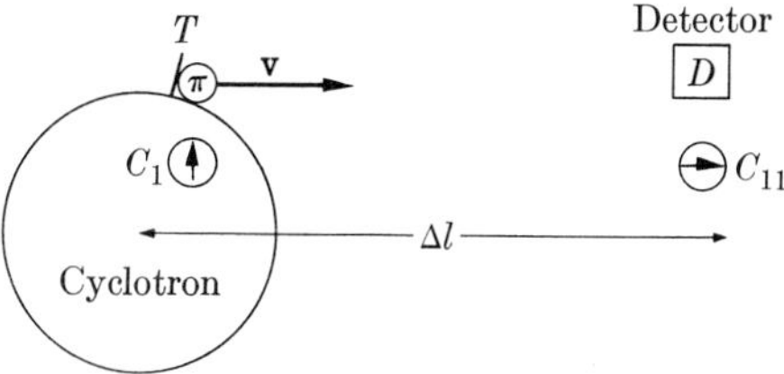

FIG. 13–16. An unstable particle (clock) flies at velocity **v** from its point of birth T toward a particle detector D.

π-meson has a lifetime $\Delta t'$ at rest, and therefore it has a lifetime $\Delta t = \gamma \, \Delta t'$, according to the laboratory observer; i.e., his clocks C_1 and C_{11} will measure an interval Δt between the creation of the meson at the target T and its decay in flight at D. We need not be concerned with the fact that different π-mesons will travel different distances before decay. The time $\Delta t'$ can be that of any particular π-meson, or it can be the average for a large number of π-mesons.

The observer can also measure the distance Δl in the laboratory and thus compute the velocity of the meson,

$$v = \frac{\Delta l}{\Delta t} = \frac{\Delta l}{\gamma \, \Delta t'} . \tag{13–17}$$

An observer who is at *rest relative to the meson* observes the laboratory in motion to the left with velocity v. His measurement of the time of flight from T to D is $\Delta t'$, in terms of notation of the first analysis. (Note that in order to keep our notation common to the discussions from the point of view of both observers, we are not, for the moment, exchanging primes when we change observers.) The observer on the π-meson now calculates the distance Δl_π according to

$$\Delta l_\pi = v \, \Delta t'. \tag{13–18}$$

Comparing Eq. (13–17) with Eq. (13–18, we have

$$\Delta l_\pi = \frac{\Delta l}{\gamma} , \tag{13–19}$$

where Δl is the distance from target to detector measured by a laboratory observer and Δl_π is the distance between the same two points calculated by the observer moving with the π-meson.

In order to be systematic in our notation, we must *really* identify ourselves with the observer moving with the π-meson. The laboratory then becomes the moving system, and it was agreed that quantities fixed in the moving system would be labeled with primes. Therefore, since the target and detector are fixed in the now-moving system, we must label Δl of Eq. (13–19) with a prime. The π subscript can then be removed from the Δl_π, leaving

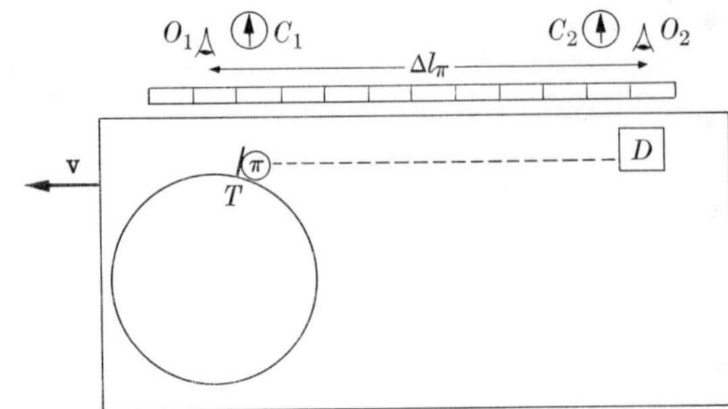

FIG. 13–17. The measurement of distance by observers moving with the velocity of the π-meson.

$$\Delta l = \frac{\Delta l'}{\gamma} , \tag{13–20}$$

which is the equation for space contraction in the direction of motion.

If the π-meson observer wishes to measure the distance TD directly, he must, in principle, station another observer in his laboratory at a position such that one observer, O_1, is adjacent to T at the same instant that the other observer, O_2, is adjacent to D (Fig. 13–17). Each observer has a clock and each makes his observation at the same instant according to these clocks. The clocks were, of course, synchronized before the measurement was made. Alternatively, a single observer could have set up compact flash cameras so that they would be opposite T and D simultaneously. He would then trigger them simultaneously at the right moment. These photographs would show images of the observer's ruler superimposed on images of the target and detector.

Note that the above operation of measurement is quite different from taking a *single* photograph of the target, entire ruler, and detector. In order to take a single photograph in the usual way, the camera could *not* be adjacent to *both* points of measurement. The finite time of travel of light from the observation points would alter the results. Therefore, in order to make a simple direct measurement, two mechanisms or observers are required as above, so that observations can be made simultaneously at each point by an observer adjacent to the point in question. By "adjacent," we ideally mean coincident with the point in question.

Articles have appeared recently in the research literature showing the effect of determining the shape of a moving object by taking a single photograph of the object or by visual observation by a single observer. In these articles, it is implicitly assumed that the illumination of the object is continuous and therefore that the object is seen by light pulses that arrive at the single observer or camera at the same instant. Since this procedure is operationally quite different from the customary one that we have used, the results are quite different. In fact in such a photograph there is no contraction in the direction of motion, but there *is* a distortion of a three-dimensional object such as a cube.

There are no better examples of actual observations of length contraction than the type above of the π-meson. To illustrate this, we might consider another sort of example. Suppose that two satellites pass each other in opposite directions. The velocity of each is about 8000 m/sec, if they are near the earth. Observers on S measure the length of S' (Fig. 13–18). The length of S' was measured to be 10 m while it was at rest on the firing pad. Relative to S, the velocity of S' is about 16,000 m/sec. Applying Eq. (13–20), we have

$$\Delta l = \Delta l'\sqrt{1 - (1.6 \times 10^4/3 \times 10^8)^2}\,,$$

$$\simeq \Delta l'\left[1 - \frac{1}{2}\left(\frac{1.6}{3}\right)^2 10^{-8}\right],$$

$$= \Delta l'(1 - 1.4 \times 10^{-9}).$$

Since $\Delta l'$ is 10 m, the observed length Δl is $10 - 1.4 \times 10^{-8}$ m. The contraction is about 100 atom diameters and is therefore unobservable by presently available methods.

Just as in the case of the measurement of time intervals, the frame in which the object to be measured is at rest has special significance. Length measure in this frame is a maximum and is called the *proper length*.

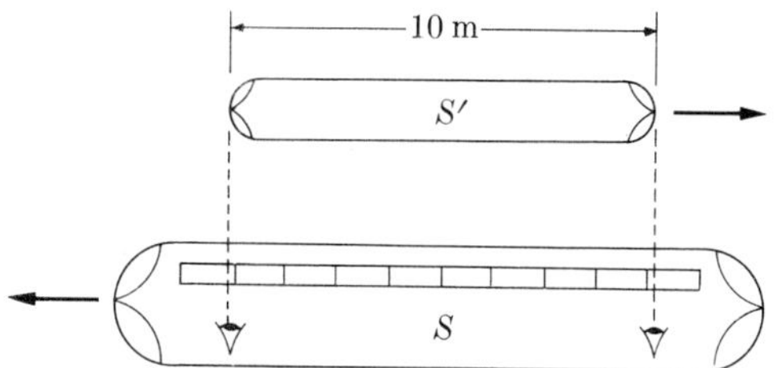

FIG. 13–18. Measurement of the length of an object S' as it moves past a length-measuring system S.

13–11 POINT TRANSFORMATIONS

In the preceding sections the transformations of time and space *intervals* were developed from the postulates of Einstein. The interdependence between the two was evident when it was shown that time dilation according to one observer corresponded to space contraction according to the other observer. It is possible, in principle, to continue the development along the same lines and find the equations for transformation of clock synchronization and for velocities. However, there is another approach to the entire question of transformations that is more general (although less intuitive, since the time and position transformation properties appear in the same equation).

The method of point transformations is the method that we have already used many times in our Galilean transformations. In place of keeping time or position fixed, we examine the concept of points in space and time, i.e., the position of an object at a particular *instant* of time.

What is the criterion that a point transformation satisfies the postulates of relativity? Since the present question is purely one of kinematics, the pertinent postulate is that the velocity of light is independent of motion of the observer. Consider a light pulse originating at the origin of a cartesian coordinate system at time $t = 0$.

The pulse travels outward in all directions at velocity c. At time t it will therefore form a spherical surface of radius $R = ct$. In cartesian components, $R^2 = x^2 + y^2 + z^2$, and therefore we have

$$R^2 = x^2 + y^2 + z^2 = c^2t^2 \qquad (13\text{–}21)$$

for the equation describing the propagation of the light pulse.

Now consider an observer in a second cartesian system that coincided with the first system at $t = 0$ but is moving at uniform velocity v in the OX-direction (Fig. 13–19). We shall label the second system and all its attributes with primes on the symbols. Remember that the designations "rest" and "moving" are entirely relative. For the sake of convenience of expression, we shall usually call the unprimed system the rest or laboratory system and the primed system the moving system.

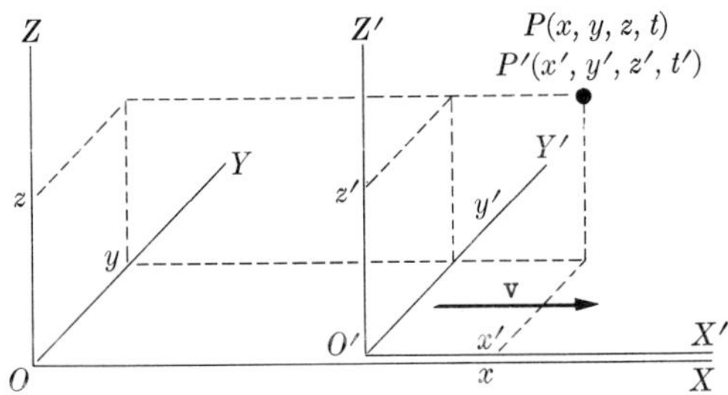

FIG. 13–19. A point P whose coordinates are to be specified at a given instant by observers in relative motion at constant velocity. Since the observers may disagree on the instant of time as well as on the position, it is necessary to give coordinates and time in both cases. The point is fixed in the system $O'X'Y'$, which was coincident with OXY at $t = 0$ and moves at constant velocity $\mathbf{v}$ in the OX-direction relative to OXY.

The Galilean transformation was given by Eqs. (13–1) and (13–2). If Eq. (13–21) is transformed to the moving system by means of the Galilean transformation, it is found that the form of the equation is *not* the same in primed coordinates, x', y', z', t', as it was in the unprimed coordinates. This means that the pulse of light does *not* appear the same to the two observers, a result in conflict with Einstein's postulate.

It is necessary to modify the Galilean transformation. The simplest modification to try is a multiplicative constant γ for the x-transformation:

$$x = \gamma(x' + vt'), \qquad (13\text{–}22)$$

where γ must reduce to unity for ordinary velocities. But, clearly, the moving observer will not find himself at the center of the spherical pulse unless his time measurements are a function of position as well as of time. We assume a linear dependence on position and also include a multiplicative factor for time; thus

$$t = M(t' + Nx'). \qquad (13\text{–}23)$$

When the transformations (13–22) and (13–23) are substituted in Eq. (13–21), it is found that the requirement that the moving observer also see the pulse as a spherical surface centered on his origin of coordinates, that is, the requirement

$$(R')^2 = (x')^2 + (y')^2 + (z')^2 = c(t')^2, \qquad (13\text{–}24)$$

can be met if

$$M = \gamma = \frac{1}{\sqrt{1 - v^2/c^2}}$$

and

$$N = \frac{v}{c^2}\cdot$$

Thus the relativistic transformation (called the Lorentz transformation) is given by

$$\begin{aligned} x &= \gamma(x' + vt'),\\ y &= y',\\ z &= z',\\ t &= \gamma(t' + vx'/c^2). \end{aligned} \qquad (13\text{–}25)$$

If we consider the problem from the point of view of the observer in the primed system, we would simply interchange primed for unprimed quantities and change the sign of v:

$$\begin{aligned} x' &= \gamma(x - vt), \\ y' &= y, \\ z' &= z, \\ t' &= \gamma(t - vx/c^2). \end{aligned} \qquad (13\text{–}26)$$

As indicated in the beginning of this section, these are *point* transformations and therefore are perfectly general. Pure time or length transformations are made by keeping the appropriate length or time coordinate constant. First, we consider the two special cases treated earlier.

Pure time dilation. To avoid effects of position, consider a succession of events taking place at a *fixed* position (x', y', z') in the moving system, for example, a periodic succession, such as a running clock, or simply two events, such as the birth and death of a radioactive particle. The last of Eqs. (13–25) is the most direct transformation, since x' is a constant. We then have

$$\begin{aligned} \Delta t \equiv t_2 - t_1 &= \gamma\left[(t'_2 - t'_1) + \frac{v}{c^2}(x'_2 - x'_1)\right] \\ &= \gamma(t'_2 - t'_1) = \gamma\,\Delta t', \end{aligned}$$

which is the same as our earlier result, as expected. Remember that in order to measure Δt, the fixed observer must, in principle, use two synchronized clocks. These clocks must be placed so that they are adjacent to the primed clock at times t_1 and t_2. Any equivalent method such as detectors (located at the two points in question) that send signals to a central time clock might be used. The observer can correct for the finite time of transmission of the signals so long as all the recording devices are fixed in his system.

Pure length contraction. To avoid effects of time, consider the measurement of two positions taken at the same instant of time. The length to be measured is fixed in the primed system and is to be observed from the unprimed system. Since it is t that is to be held constant, the first part of Eq. (13–26) is most appropriate. We have

$$\begin{aligned} \Delta x' \equiv x'_2 - x'_1 &= \gamma[x_2 - x_1 - v(t_2 - t_1)] \\ &= \gamma(x_2 - x_1) \equiv \gamma\,\Delta x, \end{aligned}$$

which is the same as our earlier result, as expected. The unprimed observer must make the measurement by a process equivalent to having two observers, one at x_1 and the other at x_2, who make simultaneous observations of opposite ends of the object fixed in the primed system.

13–12 SIMULTANEITY

We have seen above that there are experimental problems in mechanics in which the object of research is not the measurement of the velocity of light but, nevertheless, the velocity of light enters the problem as an unavoidable factor. In taking length measurements, we look at rulers. To make time measurements, we look at clocks. The process of seeing requires the transmission of either emitted or reflected light from the instrument to the eye, and the information is delayed by the transmission time of light. If a clock is 30 cm away, we see the clock as it was 10^{-9} sec ago, just as we may observe the position of a distant star as it was 1000 years ago but not as it is today. The finite velocity of light imposes a finite delay in the process of locating and timing mechanical events. This finite delay time modifies, as we shall see, the customary notions of synchronism and simultaneity, which are absolute notions in classical mechanics. We have been able to avoid complicated questions of simultaneity in the discussion of time dilation and space contraction. We now consider two events occurring at different points in *both* systems. By an "event" we mean some physical occurrence such as—to choose dramatic examples—a lightning stroke or an explosion. Observers in different frames of reference can record the time at which the event occurred and where. Remembering the preceding section, we are prepared to expect that the observers may not agree on where

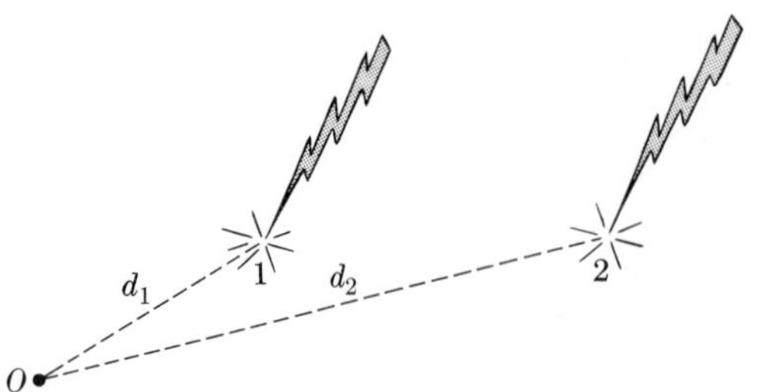

FIG. 13–20. Two lightning bolts strike the earth, one at 1 and the other at 2.

or when the event took place. In this section we relate the position and the motion of an observer to his ability to place an event in space and time.

Let us consider an example. Two lightning bolts strike the earth at two different positions (Fig. 13–20). Whether or not an observer classifies the strikings as simultaneous depends on his position relative to the points of striking. The information that bolt 1 has struck the earth arrives at O delayed by $t_1 = d_1/c$, while the information that bolt 2 has struck the earth arrives at O delayed by $t_2 = d_2/c$. Observers at different stations will disagree on the time interval separating the two events. The variability may be eliminated if we agree on a standard method of determining simultaneity. We insist that a qualified observer be stationed at the same distance from each of the events (Fig. 13–21). If signals from event 1 and event 2 reach him at the same time, he declares events 1 and 2 to be simultaneous. This is the defining operation for the determination of simultaneity.

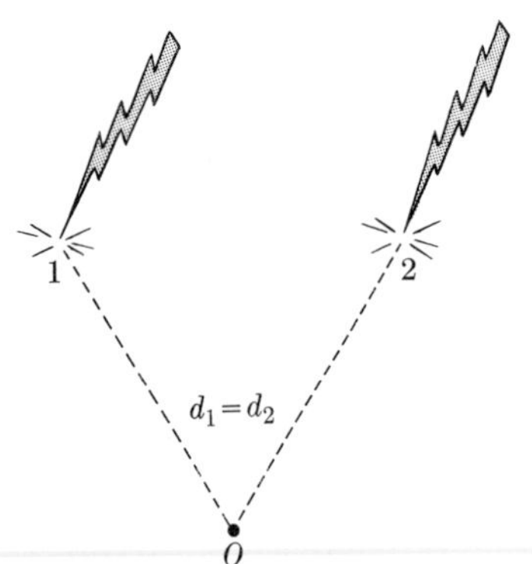

FIG. 13–21. Position of an observer O, relative to points 1 and 2, that is best suited for determining the relative time of occurrence of events at 1 and 2.

A similar question arises when we attempt to set two clocks in synchronism. If an observer plans to use two clocks in an experiment, he wants to be assured that the two clocks give the same reading at the "same" time. The information that the hand of the clock is pointed in a given direction is delayed in the transmission of light from the dial to the eye. Suppose that an observer sets two clocks to read the same at the same glance when he is at a, where $d_2 > d_1$ (Fig. 13–22). Then if he moves to b, where $d_1 > d_2$ (Fig. 13–23), the same clocks, left untouched, will appear out of synchronism. Clock 2 will appear advanced relative to clock 1. This ambiguity is resolved if the observer is always required to stand midway between his clocks when he sets them in synchronism.

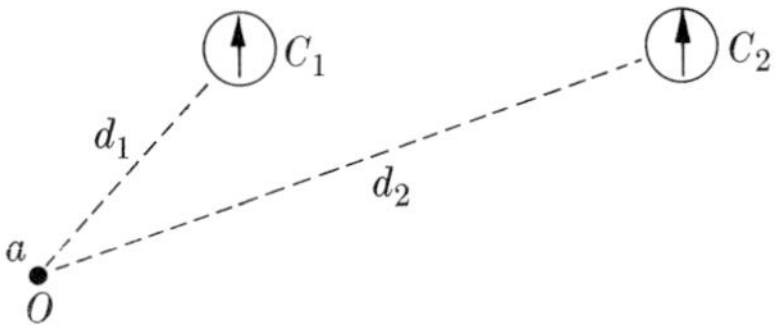

FIG. 13–22. Two clocks that are set to read the same according to observer O.

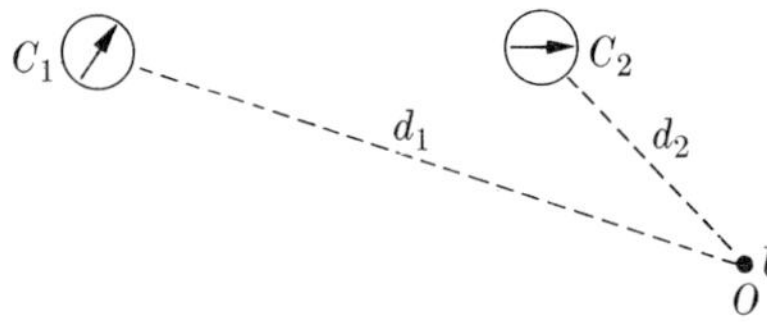

FIG. 13–23. The appearance of the two "synchronized" clocks of Fig. 13–22, when viewed from a position b that differs from the position of the observer a from which the clocks appeared to be synchronized.

We now ask whether or not observers in different frames of reference can agree on the matter of synchronism and simultaneity. The answer is that they cannot. To illustrate the point qualitatively, we imagine again a cross observation between two laboratories in relative uniform motion.

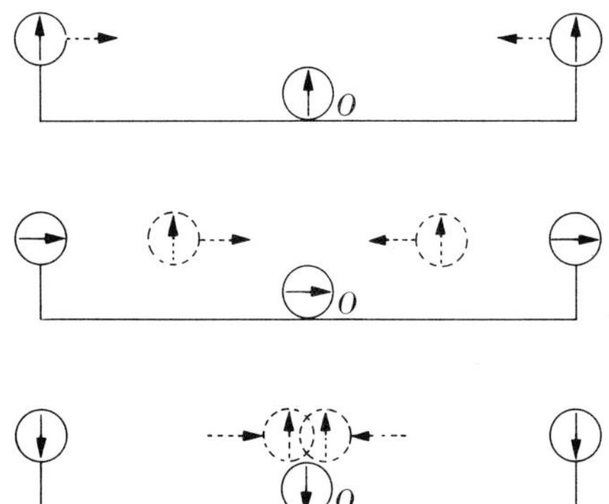

FIG. 13–24. Synchronization of clocks by an observer midway between the clocks and at rest relative to the clocks.

An observer at rest performs an experiment to establish synchronism between a pair of clocks. He arranges that each clock will be illuminated by a flash at 12:00 noon. We shall denote this time by t_0. He is stationed appropriately midway between the clocks, and the success of the experiment is indicated by the fact that the two images cross at his position, that is, the clocks will both read 12:00 and will arrive simultaneously at O. We note that a clock at O will not read 12:00 at the same glance, but rather 12:00 + $l_1/2c$, as in Fig. 13–24. This, however, is an expected classical effect, which we can correct for.

Now let an observer O' in a moving laboratory interpret this experiment (Fig. 13–25). We contrive that O' is coincident with O when it is 12:00 noon in the stationary system. The clocks are equidistant from O. They are also equidistant from O', although, of course, this observer's measure of the distance would not be $l/2$. The clocks are illuminated by a flash at 12:00 noon local time. Within the time that the flashes require for transit from the clocks of O to observer O', the latter will have moved.

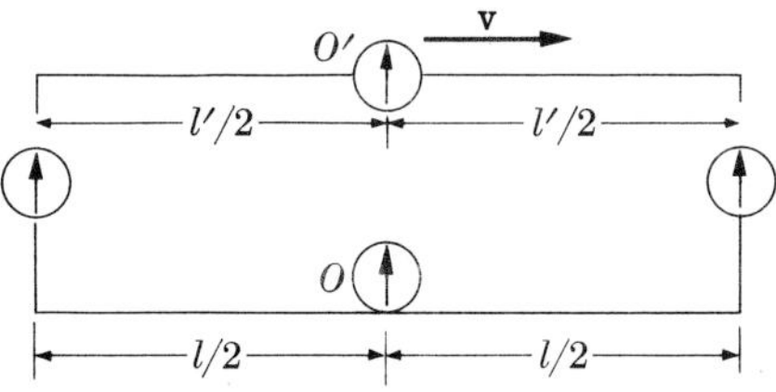

FIG. 13–25. An observer O' equidistant between two clocks, but in motion relative to the clocks, tests the clocks for synchronism.

The sequence of drawings in Fig. 13–26 shows the passage of the images of the two end clocks through space. The instant of illumination is t_0, the first image arrives at O' at time t_2', *both* images arrive at O at time t_3, and the second image arrives at O' at time t_5. Remember that observer O' deliberately arranged to be midway between the clocks at time t_0, the prearranged time at which O planned to illuminate the end clocks. Thus, observer O' had satisfied the criterion for testing the simultaneity of events occurring at the positions of the end clocks. But since the images of the clocks arrived at O' at different times, t_2' and t_5', observer O' is forced to conclude that the end clocks did *not* read the same time at the same instant (since they read the same time at different instants, according to O').

The above test for simultaneity was also a test of the synchronization of the two clocks. Observer O' found that the clocks of O were not synchronized and the error was $t_5' - t_2'$. If the end clocks had been continuously illuminated, observer O' could have simply "read" both clocks at the same instant (according to him) in order to test their synchronization. The result of this sort of observation at time t_5' is shown in Fig. 13–26(c). In order to arrive simultaneously at O', the light (i.e., image) from the forward clock must have left later by a time $t_5' - t_2'$ than the light from the rear clock. Thus, O' concludes that the forward clock is set too fast relative to the rear clock. If O' had looked at the two clocks simultaneously when at the midpoint, the result would have been as shown in Fig. 13–26(b), that is, he would have found that the rear clock was set too slow and the forward clock too fast by the same amounts, namely, $t_5' - t_2'/2$. He could have made this observation at any time with the same result. The center point was chosen only because of symmetry. The diagrams in Fig. 13–26 show

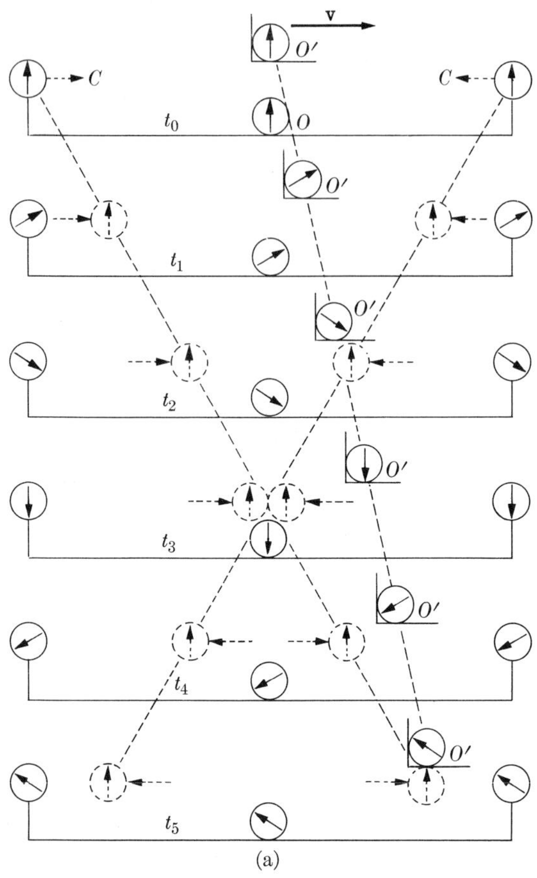

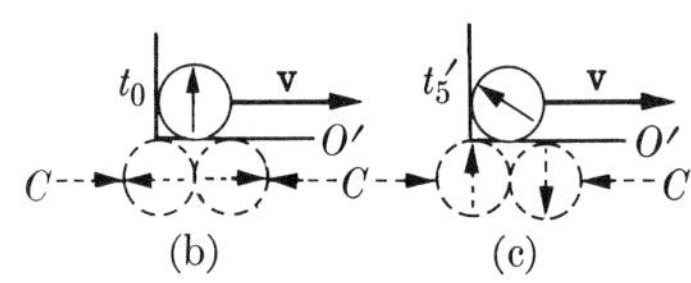

FIG. 13-26. (a) A moving observer O' and two stationary clocks that send out images of their faces at the same instant according to a stationary observer. The flight of the two images and of the moving observer through space is shown at five different instants of time. The images arrive at O' at different times. (b) Observer O' glances at the two clocks (at the same instant according to him) when he is at the midpoint. They do not read the same. (c) Observer O' glances at the two clocks when he is at position 5. The clocks do not read the same.

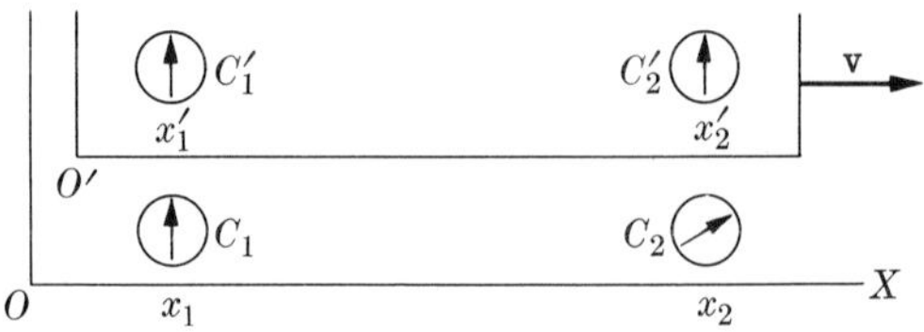

FIG. 13-27. Two events are simultaneous at x_1' and x_2' according to observer O'. Observer O finds that the events are not simultaneous according to his synchronized clocks C_1 and C_2 that are very close to the positions where the events occur.

the times as seen by local observers stationed at each clock. We should remember that the clocks of O also *run* slowly according to O', which is different from the question of synchronization.

With the point transformations as tools, the quantitative analysis of the questions of synchronization and simultaneity is straightforward. For the sake of variety, consider events that are simultaneous in the *primed* system. For example, suppose that clocks synchronized in the primed system are placed at different positions, x_1' and x_2', and send out flashes of light at the same instant of time t'. If the laboratory observer has placed synchronized clocks directly adjacent to each of the primed clocks (Fig. 13-27), they can be observed or photographed in the light of flashes that were simultaneous according to the primed observer. Since x_1 and x_2 are given, it is most convenient to use the last part of Eq. (13-26) twice, once for each clock. We have

$$t_1' = \gamma\left(t_1 - \frac{vx_1}{c^2}\right) \quad \text{and} \quad t_2' = \gamma\left(t_2 - \frac{vx_2}{c^2}\right),$$

and, remembering that $t_1' = t_2'$, we obtain

$$t_2 - t_1 = \frac{v}{c^2}(x_2 - x_1). \qquad (13\text{-}27)$$

It is seen that the flashes are *not* simultaneous according to the laboratory observer. According to his clocks the flash from 2 came after the flash from 1. In fact, he could have made a simple visual observation by stationing himself midway between the points 1 and 2. He would then have seen the flash from 1 before he saw the flash from 2.

The conclusion is that there is no such thing as absolute simultaneity. Events that are simultaneous for one inertial system are not simultaneous in another inertial system, that is in uniform relative motion (with a velocity component along the line of separation of the clocks).

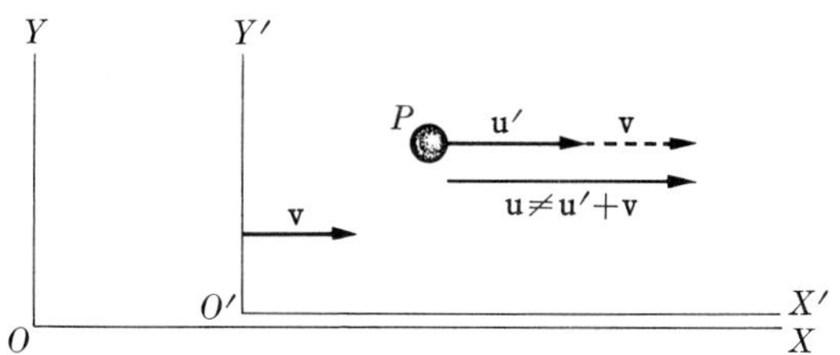

FIG. 13–28. A point P has a velocity u' parallel to the OX-axis when measured by observer O'.

13–13 VELOCITY TRANSFORMATION

Thus far an object was at rest in one system. Do different observers agree on velocity if an object is in motion in both systems? The answer is "no," even at low velocities. The concept and equations for relative velocities have been used frequently in our study of Newtonian mechanics. Is the relativistic transformation the same as the Galilean transformation for velocities?

We must now be very careful in our analysis because three velocities will be involved. We consider an object P that is moving with velocity u' as measured in the primed system. The primed system is moving with velocity v relative to the unprimed system. Finally, u is the velocity of the object as measured by O in the unprimed system. All velocities are positive toward positive x. We consider only the special case of u, u', and v parallel to the x-axis. The Galilean velocity transformation is then

$$u = u' + v. \tag{13–28}$$

We now use the relativistic point transformation and derive the relativistic velocity transformation. Since the velocities are all constant, we can simply use

$$u = \frac{x_2 - x_1}{t_2 - t_1} \quad \text{and} \quad u' = \frac{x'_2 - x'_1}{t'_2 - t'_1},$$

in place of the definitions of the velocities in terms of derivatives. (See Fig. 13–28.)

If we substitute the transformations of Eqs. (13–25) into our definition of u above, and make use of the definition of u', we find that

$$u = \frac{u' + v}{1 + (vu'/c^2)}. \tag{13–29}$$

Similarly, we can substitute Eqs. (13–26) in the definition of u' and find that

$$u' = \frac{u - v}{1 - (uv/c^2)}, \tag{13–30}$$

as expected, since it is necessary only to reverse v.

In the limit of low velocities, the relativistic expressions reduce to the usual relative velocity equations. In the limit of high velocities, we see that $u \leq c$, no matter how closely v' and v approach c. In the limit of $u' = v = c$, we find that $u = c$.

Example 2. A rocket is traveling toward the moon with velocity $0.6c$. When it is halfway to the moon, it fires a message rocket back toward the earth with velocity $0.8c$ relative to the primary rocket. What is the velocity of the message rocket as seen by an earth observer? Assume that the recoil effect is negligible.

Solution: In our regular notation, we write $v = 0.6c$ and $u' = -0.8c$. Therefore the velocity relative to the earth is found to be $-0.385c$, the minus sign indicating that the rocket is coming toward the earth. Note that the result is quite different from the "common sense" result of $-0.2c$.

Everyday experiments in all nuclear research laboratories confirm the correctness of the relativistic transformation of velocities.

Our use of the term relative velocity is apt to be ambiguous in some cases. Ordinarily we simply mean the velocity of object A as observed from object B or reference frame B. This velocity can never be greater than c, according to Eq. (13-29). But it is also possible to speak of the velocity of A relative to B as observed from C. If A and B are traveling in opposite directions, their relative velocity, *as viewed from* C, can be as large as $2c$.

13-14 RELATIVISTIC MASS INCREASE

Since special relativity is restricted to observers moving at uniform relative velocities, Newton's laws are postulated to apply in the usual form in which only interaction forces occur. In consequence, momentum conservation holds during the interaction of objects. The mass of objects can therefore be compared quantitatively by observing velocity changes during the interaction of the objects. Let an interaction experiment be contrived with two particles (which are to collide elastically) contained separately in laboratories which are in uniform relative motion (Fig. 13-29). Particle 2 is shot downward in L_2 toward L_1. Particle 1 is shot upward in L_1 toward L_2. When the laboratories are directly opposite each other, the collision occurs (Fig. 13-30). Then the particles retreat from each other as L_2 passes along to the right (Fig. 13-31). The particles are chosen to be identical so that $m_2 = m_1$, as reported by the separate observers. They are given identical initial velocities, that is, $v_2 = v_1$, as measured in the systems in which the particles reside. Neither laboratory can be preferred over the other as a suitable reference for physical observations. We could as well consider L_1 to be stationary and L_2 to be moving with velocity v toward the right, or L_2 to be stationary and L_1 to be moving with velocity $-v$ to the left. Since there is perfect symmetry between these two conditions, we must expect identical results in the two laboratories. That is, each observer reports that his particle recoils with a final velocity equal and opposite to the original velocity. We then have $u_1 = -v_1$, $u_2 = -v_2$, and, from the original conditions, $|u_1| = |u_2|$. Now let O_1 in L_1 view the trajectory of particle 2. Since the velocity of particle 2 in L_2 is perpendicular to the relative motion of the two laboratories, there is no observed length contraction along the direction of particle motion in the laboratory. Therefore, if a transverse course is marked out in L_2 for the measurement of the velocity of particle 2, both observers will agree on the length of that course in L_2, that is $l = l'$.

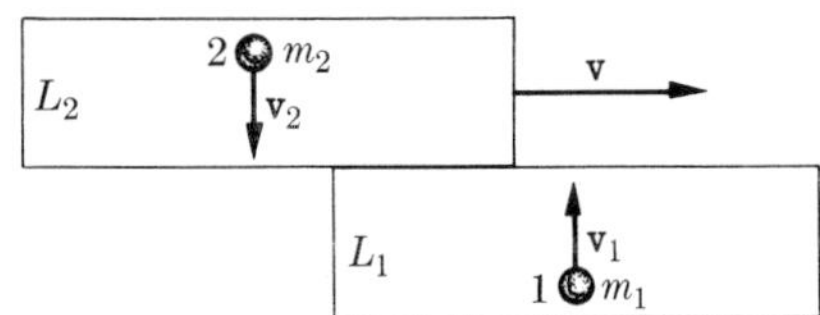

FIG. 13-29. A collision experiment between masses m_1 and m_2. The observers agree that each will give his mass the velocity $|v_1| = |v_2|$ as measured within his own system.

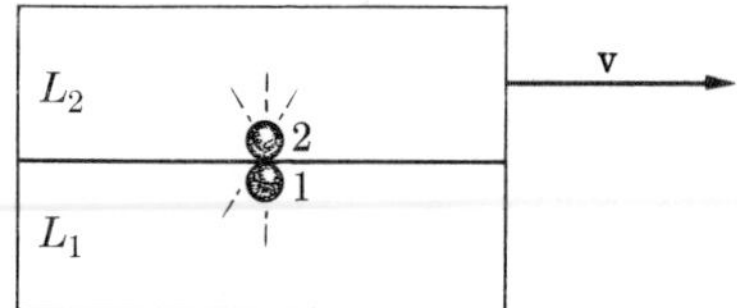

FIG. 13-30. The masses collide elastically.

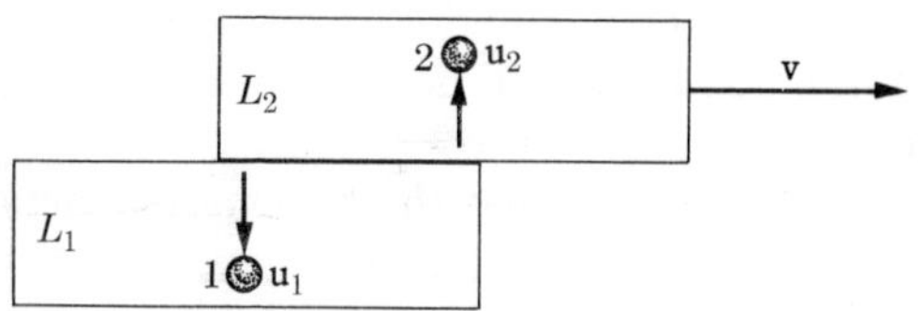

FIG. 13-31. The masses rebound. Each observer finds a recoil velocity u as measured within his own system.

We now consider the conservation of the transverse component of momentum. The time required for particle 2 to travel from one end of the transverse course to the other is $\Delta t'$, as measured by O_2, and Δt_1 as measured by O_1. Since the clocks in the two systems run at different rates, these time intervals are related by the usual expression, $\Delta t_1 = \gamma\, \Delta t'$. The transverse velocity of particle 2, as measured by O_1, is then

$$v_{\perp} = \frac{l}{\Delta t_1} = \frac{l'}{\Delta t_1} = \frac{l'}{(\gamma\ \Delta t')}\ \frac{v_2}{\gamma},$$

which is less than the velocity v_2 measured by O_2. Then the change in velocity of particle 2, as it approaches collision and recoils, is $2\,v_2/\gamma$, or, since $v_2 = v_1$, the velocity change is $2v_1/\gamma$. On the other hand, the velocity change of particle 1, upon collision, is $2v_1$, according to O_1. If momentum is to be conserved in the collision, the change in momentum of particle 1 must equal the change in momentum of particle 2. If the changes in velocities of the two particles are unequal, the masses of the two particles must be unequal, even though particles 1 and 2 are identical at rest. The transverse momentum-conservation law, in terms of the observation of O_1, is

$$2v_2m_2 = 2v_1m_1,$$

or

$$2v_1\,\frac{m_2}{\gamma} = 2v_1m_1,$$

and

$$m_2/\gamma = m_1.$$

The transverse velocity can be made so small that, in the limit, when we station ourselves in L_1, particle 1 is at rest relative to us. Then we call the mass of particle 1 the "rest" mass of the particle m_0, that is, $m_0 = m_1$. Particle 2 is at rest in L_2 but is in motion relative to L_1. Let the mass of particle 2 be simply m, that is, let $m = m_2$ representing the mass of the particle in motion. Then $m/\gamma = m_0$, or

$$m = \frac{m_0}{\sqrt{1 - v^2/c^2}}\cdot \qquad (13\text{–}31)$$

The last equation expresses the mass of a moving particle in terms of the "rest mass" m_0 of the particle and the velocity v of the particle. A particle which has a mass m_0 when at rest, with respect to an observer, has a mass greater than m_0 when it is in motion relative to an observer. Thus, as the velocity of the particle increases, the observer will find it more difficult to deflect or accelerate the particle. As the velocity of the particle, relative to the observer, approaches the velocity of light, the mass of the particle approaches infinity. The mass velocity relationship is contained in the graph of Fig. 13–32.

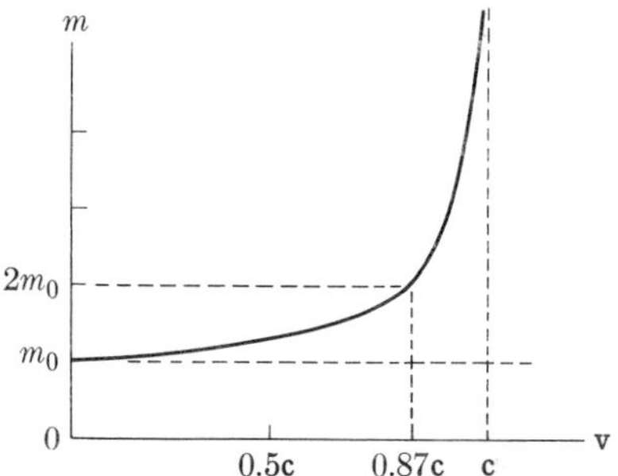

FIG. 13–32. The variation of mass with velocity of the mass relative to the observer.

At velocities below $v = c/2$, the mass is nearly equal to m_0. Beyond $v = c/2$, the value of the mass approaches infinity, where the line $v = c$ is the asymptote (Fig. 13–32). This relationship demonstrates the impossibility of causing a material particle to travel at speeds equal to or greater than the velocity of light relative to any observer. As $v \to c$, $m \to \infty$, and the force required for further acceleration also goes to infinity. The continued application of a force causes primarily a mass increase, while the velocity remains nearly constant. When the particle velocity is small, the application of a force to a material particle causes the velocity to change, while the mass of the particle remains nearly constant.

13–15 MASS AND ENERGY

When the classical expression for kinetic energy is derived, the work required to set a material particle into motion is computed, assuming that the particle mass remains constant. At high velocities, this condition no longer holds. The expression for Newton's second law, $\sum F = ma$, does not provide for a variation in mass. It is necessary to use the momentum formulation of the second law,

$$\sum F = \frac{d(mv)}{dt}, \tag{13–32}$$

which reduces to $\sum F = ma$ for $m =$ constant. If the mass is variable, the derivative becomes

$$\frac{d(mv)}{dt} = m\frac{dv}{dt} + v\frac{dm}{dt}, \tag{13–33}$$

and therefore

$$F = m\frac{dv}{dt} + v\frac{dm}{dt} \tag{13–34}$$

becomes the expression for Newton's second law of motion.

Work is defined by

$$dW \equiv F\,ds\cos\theta, \tag{13–35}$$

which becomes (if F is parallel to ds so that $\cos\theta = 1$)

$$dW = \left(v\frac{dm}{dt} + m\frac{dv}{dt}\right)ds. \tag{13–36}$$

Also, since $v = ds/dt$, the work performed during the displacement ds can be expressed in terms of the instantaneous values of mass and velocity and the increments in mass and velocity for the interval:

$$dW = v^2\,dm + mv\,dv. \tag{13–37}$$

It is convenient to let $\beta = v/c$. In terms of β, we have

$$v = \beta c,$$
$$dv = c\,d\beta,$$
$$m = \frac{m_0}{(1-\beta^2)^{1/2}},$$
$$dm = \frac{m_0\beta\,d\beta}{(1-\beta^2)^{3/2}}.$$

Substituting these expressions for v, dv, m, and dm into the equation for dW, we have

$$dW = \frac{c^2 m_0\beta^3\,d\beta}{(1-\beta^2)^{3/2}} + \frac{m_0\beta c^2/d\beta}{(1-\beta^2)^{1/2}}$$

or

$$dW = m_0c^2\beta(1-\beta^2)^{-3/2}\,d\beta. \tag{13–38}$$

This is the work performed by an applied force on an object of rest mass m_0 and velocity v, corresponding to an infinitesimal change in velocity of the object. The work performed during a finite change in velocity is found by integration as follows:

$$W = m_0c^2\int_0^{\beta_1}(1-\beta^2)^{-3/2}\beta\,d\beta,$$
$$W = m_0c^2[(1-\beta^2)^{-1/2}]_0^{\beta_1}. \tag{13–39}$$

When the limits are substituted in Eq. (13–39), we have

$$W = \frac{m_0c^2}{\sqrt{1-\beta^2}} - m_0c^2, \tag{13–40}$$

where the subscript has been dropped from the β, since the result is valid for any value of β. We recognize that the term

$$\frac{m_0}{\sqrt{1-\beta^2}} = m$$

is just equal to the instantaneous mass of the particle when its velocity is equal to βc. Then the work performed on the object to set it into motion (Eq. 13–40) can be written

$$W = mc^2 - m_0c^2 \tag{13–41}$$

or

$$W = (m - m_0)c^2 \tag{13–42}$$

(simply the *change in mass* of the object times the square of the velocity of light). The terms appearing in Eq. (13–41) can be defined in much the same way as they are in classical mechanics. The work performed in setting the object into motion (in the absence of friction) is called the kinetic energy of the object. But the kinetic energy, the energy of motion, is now equal to the difference of two terms, even when the initial velocity is zero, that is,

$$T = mc^2 - m_0c^2,$$

where T represents kinetic energy. The term

$$m_0c^2 \equiv W_0 \qquad (13\text{–}43)$$

is called the energy of the particle at rest, or the "rest energy." We then have

$$mc^2 = W_0 + T, \qquad (13\text{–}44)$$

which is the sum of the kinetic energy and rest energy of the object. This is called the "total energy" W_T of the object:

$$mc^2 \equiv W_T. \qquad (13\text{–}45)$$

Finally, we write an expression for the total energy of a material object:

$$W_T = W_0 + T. \qquad (13\text{–}46)$$

We have introduced through these definitions an idea which is foreign to classical mechanics and which requires a further remark. A particle at rest (with respect to an observer) is said to have a rest energy equal to

$$W_0 = (9 \times 10^{-16}\, m_0) \text{ joules}, \qquad (13\text{–}47)$$

where m_0 is in kg. In the statement of the theorem of the conservation of energy, it was remarked that energy of any form must be convertible into the others. That is, if m_0c^2 is regarded as energy which is "frozen" into matter, its identification as energy would have no meaning in physics. Experimentally, matter can be annihilated, and, when it is, new forms of energy, radiation, kinetic energy, heat, etc. appear in a net amount equal to m_0c^2. Therefore, m_0c^2 is indeed admissible as a form of energy.

In the above, it has been shown that increase in kinetic energy is equivalent to increase in mass. Relativity predicts that an increase in potential energy also results in an increase in mass (with c^2 as the proportionality factor). Thus the relativistic equation governs the energy release in an "atomic" reactor or bomb and in many examples of mass conversion in elementary particle reactions. When the theorem of the conservation of energy is extended to embrace rest energy, it replaces and nullifies the historical theorem of the conservation of matter. Matter can be created or destroyed, literally. Matter is a form of energy, and, according to the modern view, energy is conserved and matter is not.

It is left as an exercise in the problems to show that when the momentum p is defined the same way as in Newtonian mechanics, namely,

$$p \equiv mv, \qquad (13\text{–}48)$$

the relation between total energy and momentum is

$$W_T^2 \equiv p^2c^2 + m_0^2c^4. \qquad (13\text{–}49)$$

13–16 SUMMARY

In classical mechanics we have implicitly assumed that observers in different inertial frames of reference agree in their measurements of length and time. For example, if a certain bar is at rest in one inertial frame, an observer in another inertial reference frame was assumed to find the same result for the length of the bar as an observer in the first frame. Operationally, the moving observer was presumed to take the obvious precaution of measuring the positions of the ends of the bar at the same instant (or to make suitable corrections). The transformations of coordinates and time based on the classical assumptions are reviewed.

The contradictions in measurements related to the velocity of light are presented. Einstein's hypotheses of special relativity remove the contradictions.

The dilation of time intervals and the contraction of lengths in the direction of motion seen from moving reference frames,

$$\Delta t = \frac{\Delta t'}{\sqrt{1 - v^2/c^2}},$$

$$\Delta l = \Delta l'(\sqrt{1 - v^2/c^2}),$$

are shown to follow directly from the hypothesis of the constancy of the velocity of light.

The general description of transformations of position and time between inertial systems, Lorentz transformations, is $\gamma \equiv 1/\sqrt{1 - v^2/c^2}$:

$$x = \gamma(x' + vt'), \qquad x' = \gamma(x - vt),$$

$$y = y', \qquad y' = y,$$

$$z = z', \qquad z' = z,$$

$$t = \gamma\left(t' + \frac{vx'}{c^2}\right), \qquad t' = \gamma\left(t - \frac{vx}{c^2}\right).$$

(The primes refer to observations by an observer fixed in the primed system, which is moving at uniform velocity v relative to the unprimed system.) The cartesian axes are chosen to be coincident at $t = 0$, and v is parallel to the x-axis.

The question of simultaneity is discussed in general terms and an example is discussed in detail.

The velocity transformation for the special case of a point moving with velocity u' parallel to the x-axis in the primed system is shown to be

$$u = \frac{u' + v}{1 + (vu'/c^2)},$$

where u is the velocity in the unprimed system.

It is shown that the conservation of momentum requires that the mass m of an object moving at velocity v relative to the observer is

$$m = \frac{m_0}{\sqrt{1 - v^2/c^2}},$$

where m_0 is the mass when the object is at rest relative to an observer.

The work integral of the resultant force (the integral that leads to the idea of kinetic energy $\frac{1}{2}mv^2$ in classical mechanics) leads to the expression

$$W = \frac{m_0c^2}{\sqrt{1 - v^2/c^2}} - m_0c^2 = mc^2 - m_0c^2,$$

when the variation of mass with velocity is included. Kinetic energy T is then

$$T = mc^2 - m_0c^2.$$

The equivalence of mass and energy is suggested by the result that

$$W = (m - m_0)c^2.$$

The rest energy W_0 is

$$W_0 = m_0c^2,$$

and the total energy W_T is

$$W_T \equiv W_0 + T = mc^2.$$

The equivalence of mass and energy is equally valid for potential energy, that is, W_T includes potential energy, in general.

The relationship between energy and momentum is

$$W_T^2 = p^2c^2 + m_0^2c^4.$$

Problems

In atomic physics, energies are often expressed in units of the electron volt, which is the energy acquired by a particle of electronic charge when accelerated through a potential difference of one volt. For present purposes, it is sufficient to know that one electron volt of energy equals 1.6×10^{-19} joule. In your numerical calculations, when $v/c < 0.1$, you can approximate the relativistic factor γ by using the binomial expansion:

$$\gamma = 1/\sqrt{1 - v^2/c^2}$$
$$= (1 - v^2/c^2)^{-1/2} \simeq 1 + \tfrac{1}{2}v^2/c^2.$$

When $v/c > 0.9$, another approximation is useful:

$$\gamma = 1/\sqrt{(1 + v/c)(1 - v/c)} \simeq 1/\sqrt{2(1 - v/c)}.$$

1. A ball is thrown upward with a velocity v_0 at an angle of 45°.
(a) Write the equations for the cartesian components of displacement relative to the earth.
(b) Transform coordinates to an observer moving on the earth with velocity v parallel with the plane of motion of the ball, and find the displacement components of the ball in this new system.
(c) Find equations for the path in both cases above.

2. What is the apparent motion of a star due to aberration, (a) if it lies in the plane of the earth's orbit? (b) if it is in the direction of the axis of the earth's orbit?

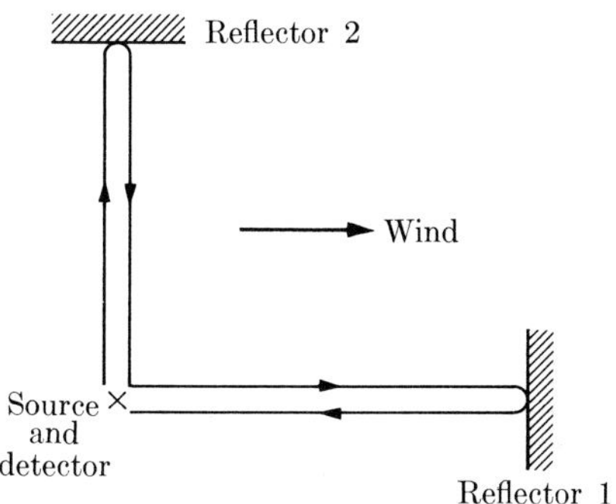

FIGURE 13–33

3. As a science project a group of students decides to use the Michelson-Morley method for determining wind velocity, by sending sound signals over two paths as in Fig. 13–33. The velocity of sound is 300 m/sec. What minimum wind velocity could they detect if $l = 100$ m and they can measure $\Delta t \geq 0.001$ sec?

4. A jet plane is flying horizontally, low over a city, at a speed of 1800 km/hr. If the tail light of the jet flashes with a period of 2 sec, what is its period according to observers in the city?

5. A rocket ship departs from a satellite platform and passes the earth at a constant velocity of $0.8c$ on a trip to Mars that passes the moon en route.
(a) What is the duration of the earth-to-moon passage (4×10^5 km) according to an observer on the earth? (The earth observer makes the obvious correction for the time of flight of a light signal back from the moon.)
(b) What is the distance according to the rocket pilot?
(c) What is the passage time according to an observer in the rocket?

6. The average lifetime of a neutron, as a free particle at rest, is 15 min. It disintegrates spontaneously into an electron, proton, and neutrino. What is the average minimum velocity with which a neutron must leave the sun in order to just reach the earth? The sun-earth distance is 1.5×10^{11} m.

7. What was the distance to the earth according to the neutron in Problem 6?

8. Show that the Galilean point transformations *do not* make the velocity of light invariant with the velocity of the observer, that is, show that $x^2 + y^2 + z^2 = c^2t^2$ does not transform to the same form with primed quantities.

9. Derive Eqs. (13–26) from Eqs. (13–25) by solving Eqs. (13–25) for the primed quantities.

10. Show that the Lorentz transformations *do* make the velocity of light invariant with the velocity of the observer, that is, show that when the Lorentz transformation is used $x^2 + y^2 + z^2 = c^2t^2$ has the same form in the primed quantities.

11. Use the Lorentz transformation equations to find the time dilation factor for a clock *fixed* in the unprimed system but viewed by the primed observer. Explain the result.

12. Repeat Problem 11 for the length contraction factor. Explain the result.

13. A meter stick is held at an angle of 45° with respect to the direction of motion in a moving coordinate system. What are the length and orientation, measured in the laboratory system, if the moving system has a velocity $0.8c$?

14. A velocity of light measurement is carried out in a moving system by setting up a path *parallel* to the direction of motion. The time is measured for a round-trip path (just as in Section 13–9 for the transverse path). Use the Lorentz transformations to describe the experiment according to the fixed-laboratory observer.

15. Jet planes pass over Detroit and Boston at the same instant, according to their synchronized chronometers. Both have velocities of 1800 km/hr toward the east.
(a) If the first jet passed over Detroit at 12:00 noon, according to an observer at rest in Detroit, at what time was the second jet over Boston, according to an observer at rest in Boston? Boston and Detroit use the same local time in winter. They are separated by about 1200 km, and Boston is nearly due east of Detroit.
(b) Repeat for rocket ships of speed $0.5c$.

16. A rocket ship is traveling directly away from the earth at velocity v. Light pulses are sent out toward the rocket from the earth f times per second, that is, the light pulses are spaced by $1/f$ sec according to an earth observer. Derive an expression for the time interval or the frequency according to the rocket observer (a) as received, (b) corrected for distance.

17. Derive one of the velocity transformation equations [(13–29) or (13–30)] from the Lorentz transformations and (a) the definitions for constant velocity, (b) the derivative form of definitions.

18. Prove that the relativistic velocity transformation reduces to the Galilean velocity transformation at low velocities.

19. A pulse of light is sent back toward the earth from a rocket that is traveling away from the earth with velocity $0.1c$. Find the velocity of the light pulse relative to earth, using the velocity transformation. Why is this the expected result?

20. A three-stage rocket is fired from the earth with velocity $0.5c$ relative to the earth. Each successive stage is fired with velocity $0.5c$ relative to its "mother." What is the velocity of the final stage?

21. A neutron of Problem 6 disintegrates while en route to the earth and gives off an electron which reaches the earth with a velocity $0.4c$. What was its velocity relative to the residue of the disintegration? (The main residue is a proton which is too heavy to change velocity appreciably because of the disintegration.)

22. Calculate the percent increase in the mass of the earth due to its orbital velocity of 30 km/sec.

23. Electrons with a velocity of $0.8c$ experience a force of 5×10^{-14} n at right angles to their path while traveling through a certain electric field. The rest mass of electrons is 9×10^{-31} kg. Compare the radius of the path of the electrons calculated classically with the radius calculated relativistically. (This sort of experiment was the first demonstration of relativistic mass increase.)

24. When μ-mesons decay, the decay fragments are an electron of average total energy 5×10^{-12} joule and two neutrinos. If an electron of this energy is emitted in the direction of flight by a meson whose velocity is $0.9c$, what is the velocity of the electron as seen by a stationary observer? Find the electron's velocity if emitted backward along the line of flight of the μ-meson.

25. Neutral π-mesons have an average life of about 10^{-16} sec and a rest mass of 2.5×10^{-28} kg. What must be their velocity in order to travel 1 mm, on the average, before decaying?

26. Show that the relativistic expression for kinetic energy reduces to the usual expression, $\frac{1}{2}mv^2$, when $v/c \ll 1$. (Use a binomial expansion.)

27. At low velocities the explicit relationship between momentum p and kinetic energy T is $T = p^2/2\,m$. Verify this relationship.

28. Momentum is defined the same way relativistically, namely, $p \equiv mv$. However, m is now a function of velocity: $m = \gamma m_0$. Show that the relativistic relationship between momentum and *total* energy W_T is

$$W_T^2 = p^2c^2 + m_0^2c^4,$$

or that the relativistic relationship between kinetic energy and momentum is

$$(T + m_0c^2)^2 = p^2c^2 + m_0^2c^4.$$

29. The decay fragments of neutral π-mesons are two pulses of "light" of short wavelength. Consider a case where the pulses are emitted forward and backward along the line of flight. What are the velocities of the pulses in the case of a π-meson of velocity v directed toward the earth, as seen by an observer (a) on the meson? (b) on the earth?

30. (a) What is the momentum of the meson in Problem 29, as seen from the meson? from the earth? (Let its rest mass be m_0.)

(b) What is the relation between the momenta of the light pulses in Problem 29, as seen from the meson? from the earth?

(c) What is the total energy of the meson of Problem 29, as seen from the meson? from the earth?

(d) What is the energy of each light pulse of Problem 29, as seen from the meson?

(e) Use the definition of momentum and the relativistic expression for total energy to show that $W_T = pc$ for a particle of zero rest mass. (The relationship between energy and momentum for light pulses is also $W = pc$.)

(f) With the help of $W = pc$ for light, find the energies of the light pulses of Problem 29, as seen from the earth.

31. All the neon lights in a city flicker in unison 120 times per second (if we make the unrealistic assumption of equivalent transmission delays to each).

(a) What is the flicker period according to an observer in a jet plane flying low over a city at a speed of 1800 km/hr?

(b) Which is larger, the dilation effect or the synchronization effect?

(c) Have you assumed in your analysis that the observer in the jet always watched the same light?

14

Rigid Bodies

14–1 INTRODUCTION

From the utilitarian standpoint, the extension of particle mechanics to the mechanics of gross objects is achieved quite literally by regarding the finite object as a set of particles. The kinds of properties to be described determine the assumptions made about the relationships of the particles to one another. For example, a rigid body is assumed to be made up of a set of particles that cannot move relative to one another. This assumption is incorporated into the mechanical theory as a *constraint* placed upon the particle set. From experience, it is clear that the assumption of absolute rigidity is quite satisfactory for many problems. For example, much is learned and little is lost in the study of the motion of a stone by assuming it to be absolutely rigid. Nevertheless, the assumption, even though a good one for many purposes, is an approximation; a stone can be deformed.

When the deformation of objects is of interest and must be accounted for, then the assumption of rigidity is relaxed, and we go to another level of approximation. For example, if the object is elastic, then the rigid constraining forces among particles are replaced by springlike forces. If the object is plastic, or fluid, compressible or incompressible, and so on, still other models must be used.

The extension of particle mechanics to the mechanics of rigid bodies is the subject of this chapter. The reader should be prepared to discover more than a formal recapitulation of the particle laws. New phenomena are to be encountered which are not exhibited by a point mass.

14–2 DESCRIPTION OF A RIGID BODY

For the greatest portion of this work, a simplification is made by considering *plane* rigid bodies, bodies whose masses are essentially confined to two dimensions. In many cases, the extension of the rules devised for a plane body to a three-dimensional body will be self-evident. From time to time, when it illuminates the plane body description, the extension will be mentioned in the discussion.

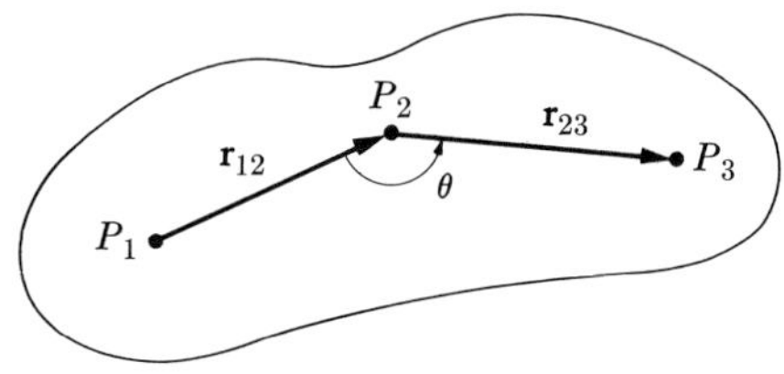

FIG. 14–1. The points P_1, P_2, and P_3 are fixed on the extended object.

The rigid-body constraint is established by considering a set of coordinate points on the body, such as P_1, P_2, and P_3, in Fig. 14–1. Then it is demanded that the relative positions of the points do not change. For example, it can be said that $|r_{12}| =$ constant, $|r_{23}| =$ constant, $\theta =$ constant. Or, in coordinate language, we have the conditions

$$\begin{aligned} x_2 - x_1 &= \text{constant}, \\ y_2 - y_1 &= \text{constant}, \\ x_3 - x_2 &= \text{constant}, \\ y_3 - y_2 &= \text{constant}, \\ x_3 - x_1 &= \text{constant}, \\ y_3 - y_1 &= \text{constant, etc.} \end{aligned}$$

All the body coordinates may change when the body moves in space, but they are still subject to the constraints stated.

14–3 TRANSLATION OF A RIGID BODY

A rigid body is said to undergo a *pure translation* when the displacements, $\Delta\mathbf{S}$, of all coordinate points are the same (Fig. 14–2). The displacements $\Delta\mathbf{S}$ are identical in magnitude and direction whether they are infinitesimal or finite.

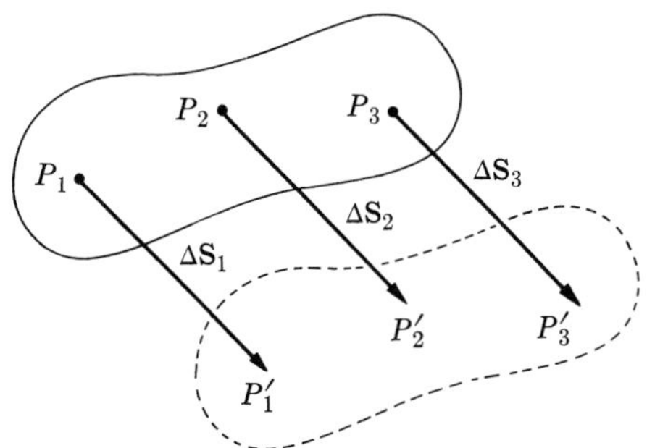

FIG. 14–2. Pure translation of a rigid body.

14–4 ROTATION OF A RIGID BODY

A rigid body is said to undergo a pure rotation provided that any one point (x_0, y_0) on the body, or on an imagined extension of the body, remains fixed in space (Fig. 14–3). For this particular point (x_0, y_0) the displacement vector is zero. As shown in the examples of Fig. 14–3, the displacement of the point (x_0, y_0) is zero. The paths of all other body coordinates are circular arcs about the stationary point (x_0, y_0).

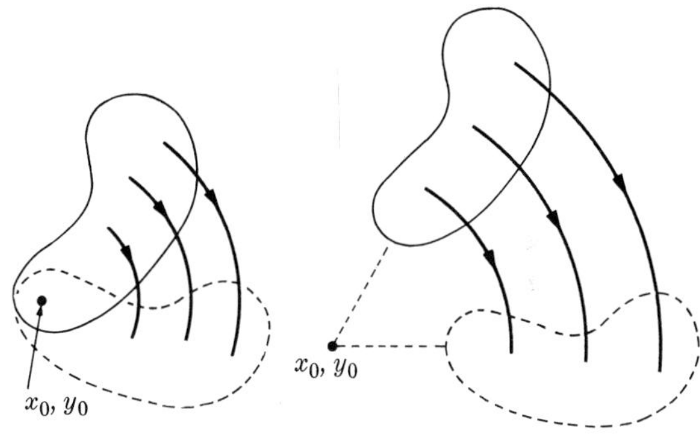

FIG. 14–3. Pure rotation of a rigid body about point x_0, y_0.

14–5 MIXED DISPLACEMENTS

Any arbitrary displacement of a rigid body can be regarded as composed of a pure rotation plus a pure translation (Fig. 14–4). Consider that a rigid body is displaced from the unprimed to the primed position. We first translate the object by $\Delta\mathbf{S}_T$ such that one point on the object, P_1, coincides with the primed position P_1'. Then the whole object is rotated about point P_1' until all coordinates lie at the primed position. All motion can be so decomposed and recomposed.

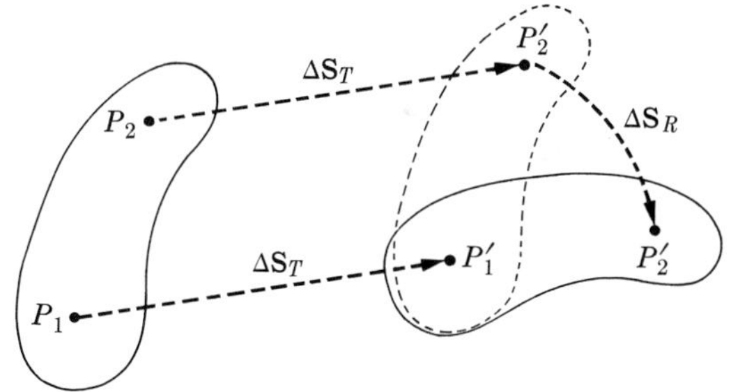

FIG. 14–4. Movement of a rigid body resolved into a pure translation plus a pure rotation.

14–6 KINEMATICS OF ROTATION

Let an object rotate about a *fixed* body coordinate P_0, as in Fig. 14–5. All the linear displacements of the body points are different, either in magnitude or direction or both. However, all the angular displacements are identical. For example, consider points 1 and 2. The angle between the

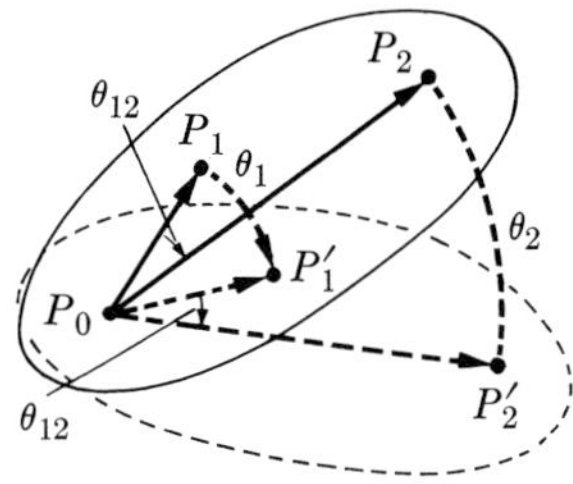

FIG. 14–5. Rotation of a rigid body about P_0.

lines P_0P_1 and P_0P_2 is θ_{12}. Since θ_{12} is invariable, then for any displacement, $\theta_1 = \theta_2$ (the proof is left to the reader).

Furthermore, all lines drawn on an object rotate by equal amounts, whether or not they extend through P (see Fig. 14–6). Since the angle θ_{ab} is invariable, then for any displacement, $\theta_a = \theta_b$ (the proof is left to the reader).

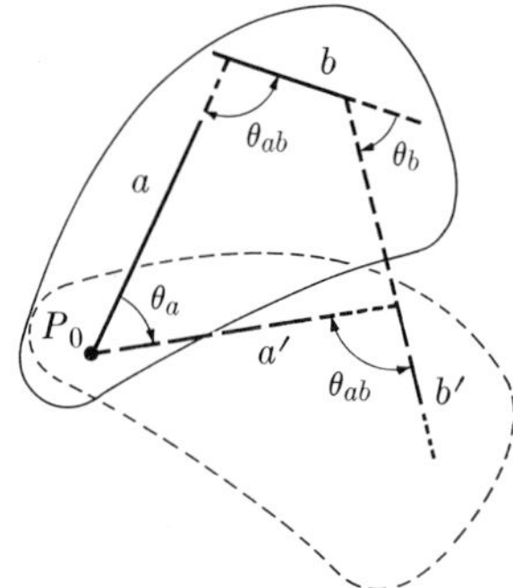

Fig. 14–6. Rotation of any line b on a rigid body in terms of the rotation of a line a through the center of rotation.

This identity of angular displacements for all lines demonstrates that the description of this kind of motion by means of angular variables is invaluable in rigid-body kinematics. The instantaneous angular velocity of a *line* is defined as

$$\omega = \frac{d\theta}{dt}, \tag{14–1}$$

and since $d\theta_1 = d\theta_2$, etc., for all lines, then $\omega_1 = \omega_2$, etc., for all lines; that is, the angular velocities of all lines are identical. In a similar way, it is seen that the angular accelerations, $\alpha = d\omega/dt$, of all lines are the same.

The relationships between linear and angular variables are the same as for the circular motion of a point; namely,

$$s = r\theta,$$
$$v_\theta = r\omega,$$
$$a_\theta = r\alpha, \tag{14–2}$$

where s is arc length, v_θ is the velocity, and a_θ is the component of acceleration perpendicular to r. In a typical analysis of rotational motion, the angular variables would be used, in view of the fact that their values apply universally to the whole object. If, then, a knowledge of the linear quantities is desired, they are obtained from the above conversion equations.

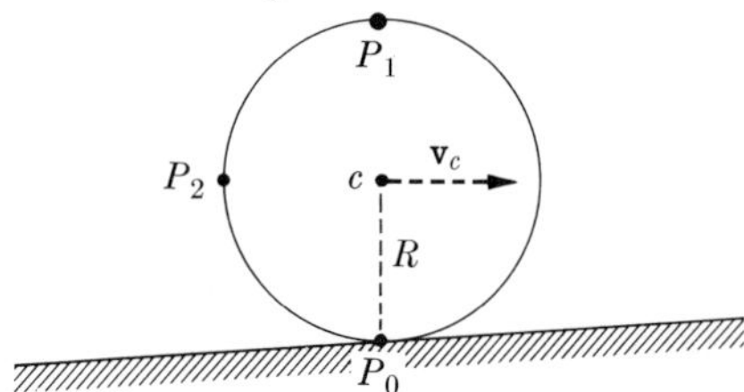

Fig. 14–7. Rolling without slipping results in rotation about the instantaneous axis P_0.

Example 1. *Rolling without slipping.* A wheel rolls on a straight line without slipping. The linear velocity of the center of the wheel is v_c. What are the velocities of the points P_1 and P_2 (Fig. 14–7)?

Solution: Since the wheel does not slip, the instantaneous point of contact with the ground P_0 is stationary. Therefore, the wheel can be considered to be in instantaneous pure rotation about P_0. The angular velocity of the radius line drawn from P_0 to c is

$$\omega = \frac{v_c}{R}.$$

This value of ω pertains to all lines on the wheel. For point P_1 the radius is the wheel diameter. The velocity v_1 is $v_1 = \omega 2R$ or $v_1 = (v_c/R)2R = 2v_c$. For point P_2 the radius is $\sqrt{2}R$ inclined at 45° from the vertical. The velocity v_2 is $v_2 = \omega\sqrt{2}\,R = \sqrt{2}\,v_c$ in the direction shown in Fig. 14–8.

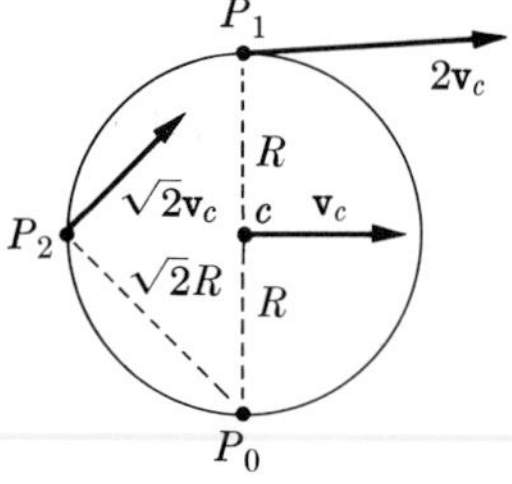

Fig. 14–8. Linear velocity of typical points on a rolling circle.

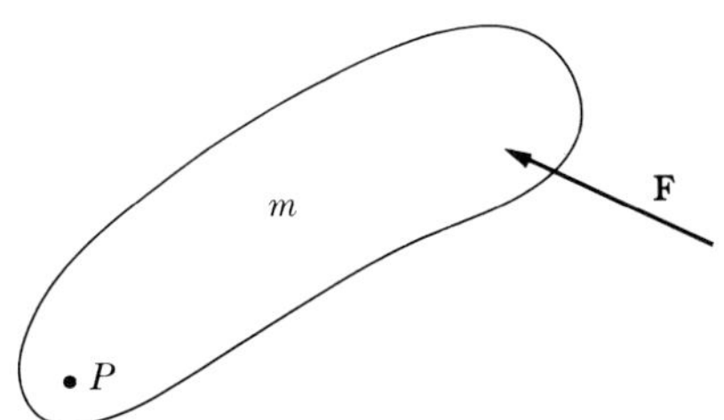

Fig. 14–9. Force **F** acting on a rigid body.

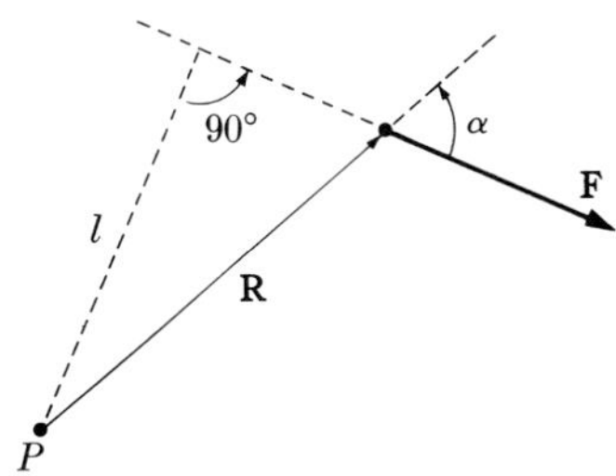

Fig. 14–10. Geometrical construction illustrating the moment of force **F** about point P.

14–7 MOMENTS

The general problem of rigid-body mechanics is now posed to the reader. Given (as illustrated in Fig. 14–9) a rigid body of arbitrary size and shape, let a force **F** of arbitrary magnitude and direction be applied at some point on the object. What is the ensuing motion? One of the facts of rigid-body mechanics is seen at once: we are dealing with space distributions of the usual mechanical quantities such as force, mass, acceleration, momentum, and so on. Not so evident is the fact that very simple characteristics of these distributions can contain all the relevant information required in the solution of most problems. The distribution characteristics referred to are moments. Examples of moments important to further development are given later as definitions. But first we list with commonly employed terminology.

1. Moment of force: torque.
2. First moment of mass: center of mass.
3. Second moment of mass: moment of inertia.
4. Moment of momentum: angular momentum.

Once the technique of moment calculation is established, it will be seen that the list could easily be extended. However, the four examples given are those of first importance.

1. *Torque.* When a force **F** acts at some point in space, the moment τ of the force referred to some other coordinate point P at distance R is defined by

$$\tau = FR \sin \alpha, \tag{14–3}$$

where the quantities are represented in Fig. 14–10. The moment of force **F** about the point P can be constructed in the following way: the perpendicular line l is constructed from the point P to the line containing **F**. The length l is called the lever arm or moment arm. Then the torque of **F** about P is the product Fl or $FR \sin \alpha$.

Another representation is illustrated in Fig. 14–11. Let the force **F** be resolved into components parallel and perpendicular to the position vector. Then the perpendicular component is $F_\theta = F \sin \alpha$, and the torque can be written $\tau = F(\sin \alpha)R$ as before. The parallel component of the force does not contribute to the torque. Stated in another way, the perpendicular lever arm of F_θ is R identically, while the lever arm of F_R is zero.

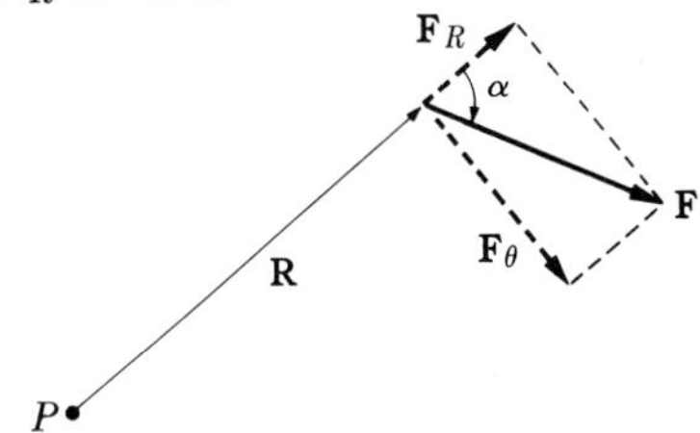

Fig. 14–11. Geometrical construction illustrating the moment of force **F** about point P.

It is possible to represent torque in cartesian component form. In cartesian coordinates, **R** is resolved into components R_x and R_y, and the force into components F_x and F_y, as in Fig. 14–12. The lever arm for the component F_y is R_x, and the torque is clockwise or negative, following the

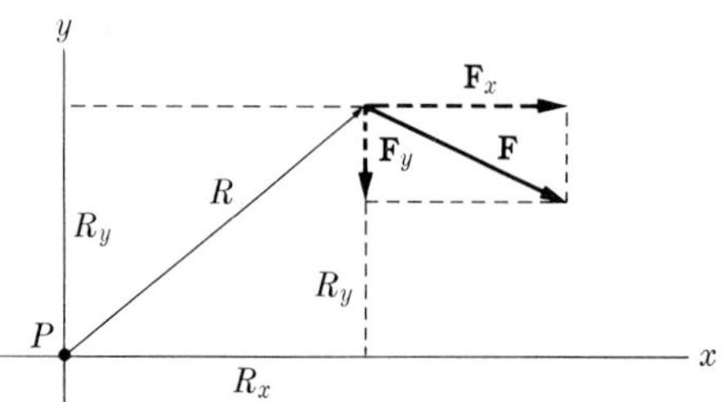

FIG. 14–12. Geometrical construction illustrating the moment of force **F** about point P in terms of cartesian components.

usual convention. The lever arm for the component F_x is R_y, and the sense is also clockwise or negative. The net torque is the sum of the two terms, or

$$\tau = -F_y R_x - F_x R_y. \tag{14–4}$$

The vector property of torque is evident from Eq. (14–3) or Eq. (14–4). We recognize them as vector products and write

$$\tau = \mathbf{R} \times \mathbf{F}, \tag{14–5}$$

with τ, therefore, perpendicular to the RF-plane and in the sense given by the usual right-hand screw rule.

A special combination of forces, called a force couple, is frequently encountered in rigid-body mechanics. A force couple is a pair of equal and opposite forces acting along parallel lines displaced by a perpendicular distance l (Fig. 14–13). The vector sum of the forces in a couple is zero:

$$\sum \mathbf{F} = 0.$$

It can be shown that the torque exerted by a

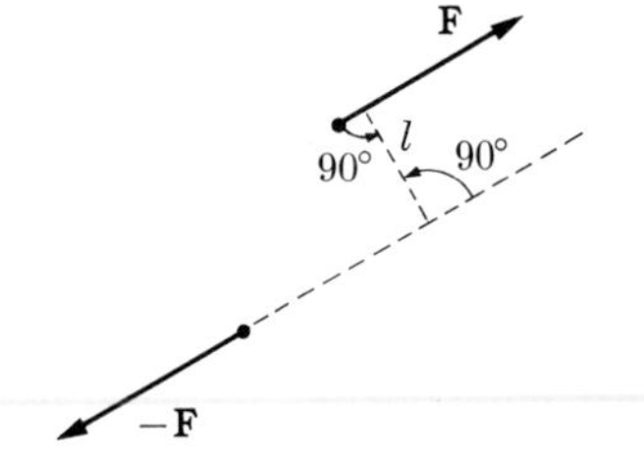

FIG. 14–13. Equal and opposite forces acting on a rigid body.

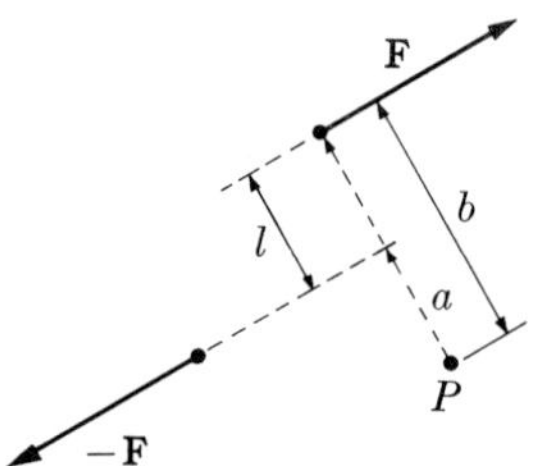

FIG. 14–14. Moment arms about P for equal and opposite forces.

force couple about *any* point is space is given by

$$\tau = Fl, \tag{14–6}$$

where F is the magnitude of either force and l is the perpendicular distance between the two lines of action. For the general case, the construction is shown in Fig. 14–14, where the point P is at a perpendicular distance a from $-F$ and b from F. The proof of the theorem is left to the reader. The problem is to compute the torque exerted by the couple about the point P.

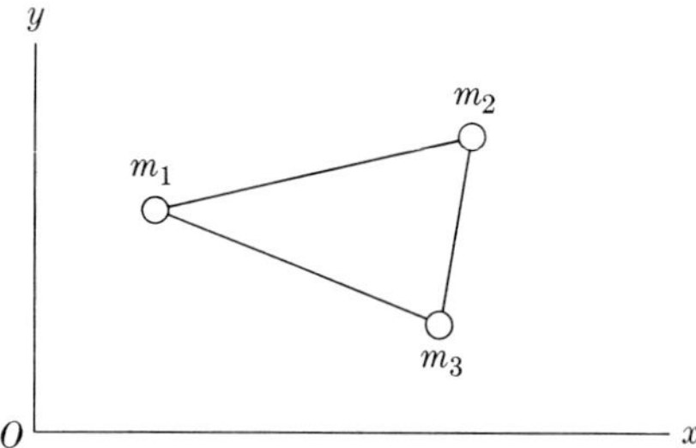

FIG. 14–15. A rigid body made up of three mass points.

2. *Center of mass.* For illustration consider a simple rigid body that is constructed of a set of three mass points, m_1, m_2, m_3 (Fig. 14–15). The locations of the mass points that are referred to a set of coordinate axes are (x_1, y_1), (x_2, y_2), (x_3, y_3). We now develop a characteristic of the mass distribution by defining the mass moments of the particles and of the system considered as a whole. The moment of m_1 that is referred to the y-axis is the product of m_1 times the distance x_1 of m_1 from the y-axis, that is,

$$M_1 \equiv m_1 x_1.$$

The total moment M_x of the system that is referred to the y-axis is the sum of all such products, or

$$M_x \equiv m_1x_1 + m_2x_2 + m_3x_3.$$

In this sum, each mass is said to be "weighted" by its distance from the y-axis. In an exactly similar manner, the moment of the system that is referred to the x-axis is the sum

$$M_y \equiv m_1y_1 + m_2y_2 + m_3y_3.$$

We now define the center of mass of the system. The system is to be represented by an equivalent single particle where the equivalence is twofold. The mass of the single particle equals the mass of the whole system, that is,

$$m = m_1 + m_2 + m_3,$$

and the mass moment of the single particle equals the total mass moment of the system. Let the coordinates of the single mass particle be called X and Y. Then from the defining relationships we have

$$mX = m_1x_1 + m_2x_2 + m_3x_3$$

and

$$mY = m_1y_1 + m_2y_2 + m_3y_3.$$

The coordinate points X and Y of the mass center can be written explicitly as

$$X = \frac{m_1x_1 + m_2x_2 + m_3x_3}{m_1 + m_2 + m_3} \tag{14–7}$$

and

$$Y = \frac{m_1y_1 + m_2y_2 + m_3y_3}{m_1 + m_2 + m_3}. \tag{14–8}$$

The position (X, Y) is called the mass center of the system (Fig. 14–16). For some attributes of the rigid-body problem, the complex system of particles can be wholly replaced by an equivalent particle at the mass center, with consequent simplification. This is particularly the case in statics and in translational motion.

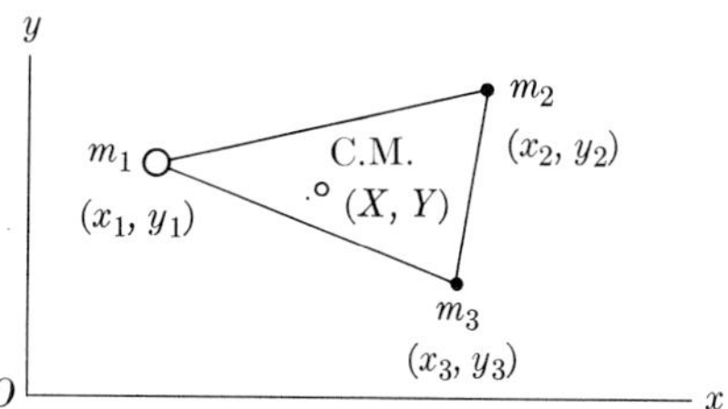

FIG. 14–16. The center of mass of the three mass points is at (X, Y).

For a general set of n particles, labeled with the running index i, the expression for the mass center is written using the summation notation:

$$X \equiv \frac{\sum_{i=1}^{n} m_ix_i}{\sum_{i=1}^{n} m_i}, \qquad Y \equiv \frac{\sum_{i=1}^{n} m_iy_i}{\sum_{i=1}^{n} m_i}. \tag{14–9}$$

It is frequently useful to regard a rigid body as a continuous distribution of mass rather than as a set of discrete particles. For this description, a density function is used. Mass density is defined as the local ratio of mass to volume at any coordinate of an object, that is,

$$\rho \equiv \lim_{\Delta V \to 0} \frac{\Delta m}{\Delta V} = \frac{dm}{dV}. \tag{14–10}$$

Then the total mass is found by integration rather than by discrete summation:

$$m = \int_V \rho \, dV. \tag{14–11}$$

For a plane object it is sufficient to define a surface density of mass, i.e., mass per unit area, as illustrated in Fig. 14–17. Consider an element of the object of size $\Delta A m^2$ at the point (x, y). In general, the mass contained in the element

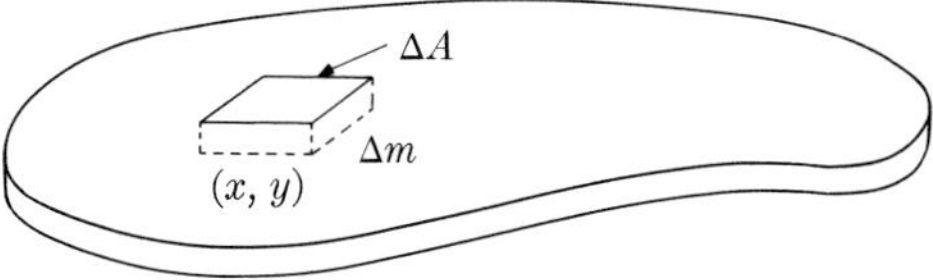

FIG. 14–17. An element of area ΔA of mass Δm in a rigid body.

depends on the location of the element. The local average density of mass, σ_{av}, is defined as the ratio of Δm to ΔA. The point density is the limiting value of the ratio as ΔA approaches zero:

$$\sigma \equiv \lim_{\Delta A \to 0} \frac{\Delta m}{\Delta A} = \frac{dm}{dA}. \tag{14–12}$$

The density σ is a function of the body coordinates, if the mass distribution is nonuniform. The total mass is then found by integrating $\sigma(x, y)\, dA$ over the whole object, that is,

$$m = \int_A dm = \int_A \sigma(x, y)\, dA. \tag{14–13}$$

When the plane object is uniform in surface mass density, σ is constant and may be taken outside the integral, leaving simply

$$m = \sigma \int dA = \sigma A. \tag{14–14}$$

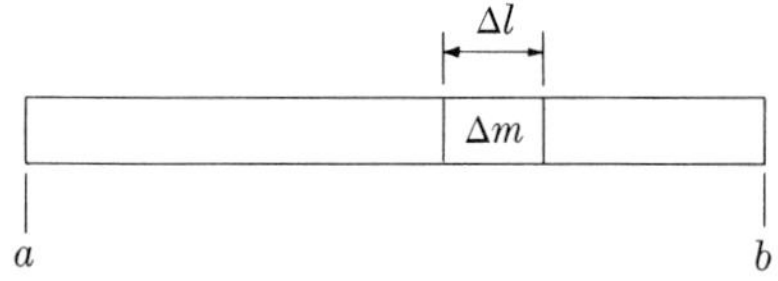

FIG. 14–18. An element of length Δl of mass Δm in a rod.

Similarly, a linear distribution of mass such as a rod can be assigned a linear mass density λ. The average linear density is the mass Δm contained in the segment of length Δl (Fig. 14–18), and the point linear density is the limiting value of the ratio $\Delta m/\Delta l$ at any point as Δl approaches zero; that is,

$$\lambda \equiv \frac{dm}{dl}. \tag{14–15}$$

In turn the mass of the element dl is

$$dm = \lambda\, dl,$$

and the total mass of the rod is

$$m = \int_a^b \lambda\, dl. \tag{14–16}$$

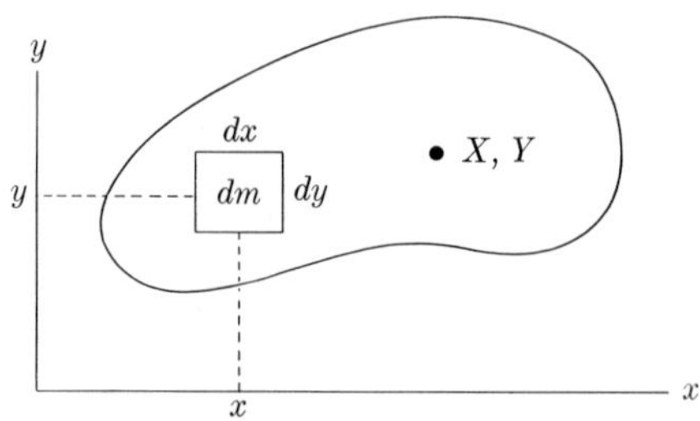

FIG. 14–19. An element of area described with cartesian coordinates.

When the continuous-mass description is used, the mass center definition is rewritten in integral form as follows: the components of the first moment of the element of mass dm are (Fig. 14–19)

$$x\, dm = x\sigma\, dA = x\sigma\, dx\, dy,$$
$$y\, dm = y\sigma\, dA = y\sigma\, dx\, dy.$$

Referring to the definitions for the center of mass coordinates for discrete particles, X and Y of the center of mass become

$$X = \frac{\int x\, dm}{\int dm} = \frac{\int x\sigma\, dA}{\int \sigma\, dA} = \frac{\iint x\sigma\, dy\, dx}{\iint \sigma\, dy\, dx},$$

$$Y = \frac{\int y\, dm}{\int dm} = \frac{\int y\sigma\, dA}{\int \sigma\, dA} = \frac{\iint y\sigma\, dx\, dy}{\iint \sigma\, dy\, dx}. \tag{14–17}$$

Example 2. For the purpose of illustration, we will compute the mass center of a right triangular area of constant density (Fig. 14–20). Since the mass density

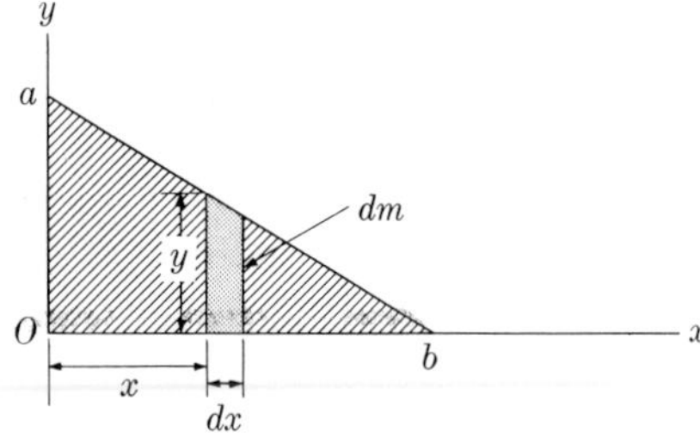

FIG. 14–20. An element of mass in a triangular object.

σ is constant, the mass of the strip of width dx and height y at the distance x from the y-axis is

$$dm = \sigma\, dA = \sigma y\, dx.$$

(It should be noted that, in setting up the element of mass, we have implicitly integrated over dy and obtained as a result the factor y.) The x-coordinate of the mass center becomes

$$X = \frac{\int x\, dm}{\sigma \int dm} = \frac{\sigma \int xy\, dx}{\sigma \int y\, dx},$$

where y is given by the equation of the bounding line as

$$y = a - \frac{a}{b}\, x.$$

Using this substitution, we obtain for X

$$X = \frac{\sigma \int_0^b x\left(a - \frac{a}{b}\, x\right) dx}{\sigma \int_0^b \left(a - \frac{a}{b}\, x\right) dx}.$$

The integral is performed between the limits $x = 0$, $x = b$. The result is

$$X = \frac{\sigma ab^2/b}{\sigma ab/2} = \frac{b}{3}\cdot$$

(It will be noted that the denominator is just the mass density times the total triangular area, as expected.) Similarly, we can find that

$$Y = \frac{a}{3}\cdot$$

3. *Moment of inertia.* As an illustration of the calculation of higher moments, we choose the second moment of mass, called the moment of inertia. The second moment of the particle m_1 about the y-axis is

$$I_1 \equiv m_1 x_1^2.$$

The total second moment, the *moment of inertia* of the system, is (see Fig. 14–21)

$$I = m_1 x_1^2 + m_2 x_2^2 + m_3 x_3^2. \qquad (14\text{–}18)$$

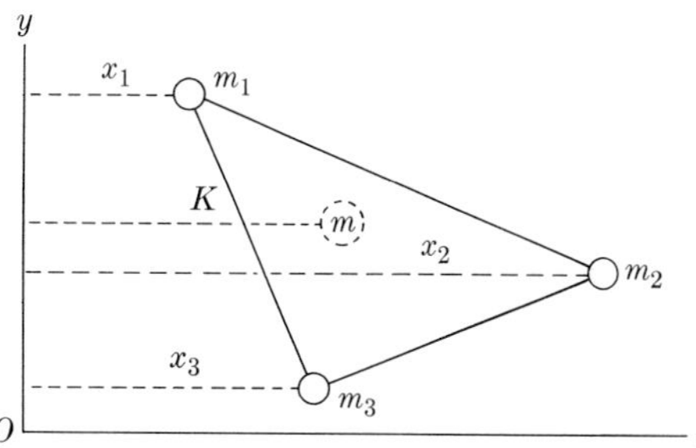

FIG. 14–21. A rigid body consisting of point masses m_1, m_2, and m_3 rotates about the y-axis. The moment of inertia would be the same if a mass $m = \Sigma m$ were at $x = K$.

In a manner similar to the definition of center of mass, a radius of gyration, K, is defined such that a single particle having the same mass m as the total system has the same moment of inertia as the whole system, if the total mass m is placed at the radius K. From the definition, we have

$$mK^2 \equiv m_1 x_1^2 + m_2 x_2^2 + m_3 x_3^2,$$

or

$$K^2 = \frac{m_1 x_1^2 + m_2 x_2^2 + m_3 x_3^2}{m_1 + m_2 + m_3}\cdot \qquad (14\text{–}19)$$

The extension to a continuous mass distribution is made in the same way as for the definition of the center of mass. The result is

$$K^2 \equiv \frac{\int x^2\, dm}{\int dm} \qquad (14\text{–}20)$$

for the radius of gyration about an axis contained in the plane of the flat, rigid body. The y-axis is chosen along the axis of rotation.

When the axis of rotation is *perpendicular* to the plane of a flat, rigid body, we have

$$I = \int r^2\, dm \qquad (14\text{–}21)$$

and

$$K^2 = \frac{\int r^2\, dm}{\int dm} \qquad (14\text{–}22)$$

for the moment of inertia and radius of gyration, where r is the distance from the axis of rotation to the element of mass dm. The quantities I and K will be discussed further in Section 14–9. At this point, however, the reader may wish to compute I and K for the triangular area of Example 14–2.

4. *Angular momentum.* The angular momentum of particles was discussed in Section 10–4. The ideas will be briefly reviewed here, and then they will be extended to rigid bodies.

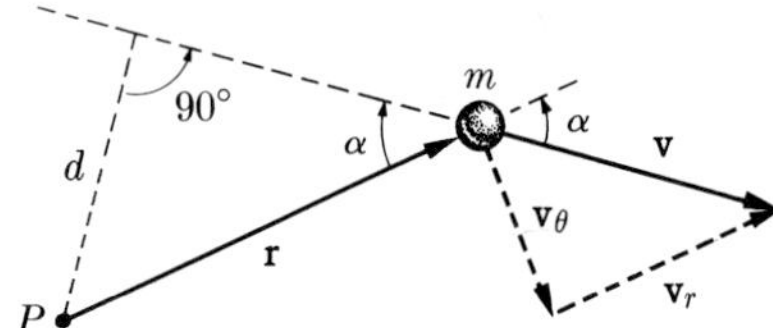

FIG. 14–22. Mass m is moving at velocity $\mathbf{v}$.

A particle of mass m travels at velocity $\mathbf{v}$ along a line at a perpendicular distance d from the point P (Fig. 14–22). The linear momentum of the particle is defined by $\mathbf{p} = m\mathbf{v}$. The angular momentum of the particle about the point is defined as

$$l = mvd, \tag{14–23}$$

the product of linear momentum times the distance d.

From the geometric construction given, it can be seen that

$$l = mvr \sin \alpha, \tag{14–24}$$

where $\mathbf{r}$ is the position vector and α is the angle between $\mathbf{r}$ and $\mathbf{v}$. The angular momentum is a vector quantity, which can be written

$$\mathbf{l} = m\mathbf{r} \times \mathbf{v}. \tag{14–25}$$

Let a set of particles composing a rigid body be labeled m_1, m_2, m_3 (see Fig. 14–23). The system is in rotation about the point P, or, in fact, about the axis drawn through P normal to the paper.

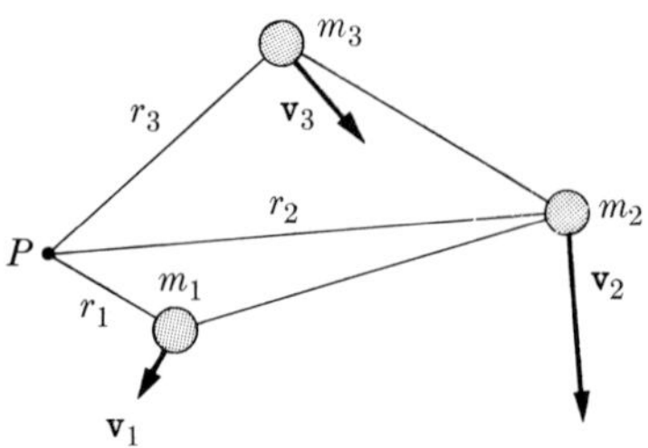

FIG. 14–23. The velocities of three masses that constitute a rigid body in rotation about P.

Since the velocity of each particle is perpendicular to its radius vector, the total angular momentum L, of the set about P is

$$L = m_1v_1r_1 + m_2v_2r_2 + m_3v_3r_3.$$

The angular velocity of each particle is the same, namely, ω. Thus we have $v_1 = \omega r_1$, $v_2 = \omega r_2$, and $v_3 = \omega r_3$. By substitution, the angular momentum can be written in terms of ω as

$$L = \omega\left(\sum_i m_i r_i^2\right). \tag{14–26}$$

From earlier definitions, it is evident that the term in parentheses is just the total moment of inertia of the system of particles about the axis through P. If the distribution of mass is continuous, the summation in parentheses (Eq. 14–26) is replaced by an integral representing the moment of inertia. Thus, in general, there results

$$L = I\omega. \tag{14–27}$$

With this illustration, it can be seen how some simple interrelationships among the various moment distributions can be drawn. The moment distributions defined in this section form the mathematical basis of the physics of rigid bodies now to be presented.

14–8 DYNAMICS OF TRANSLATION

In Section 11–2, it was proved that Newton's second law for a system of interacting bodies is simply as follows:

$$\sum F_x = (\sum m)\frac{d^2X}{dt^2}, \qquad \sum F_y = (\sum m)\frac{d^2Y}{dt^2}. \tag{14–28}$$

A rigid body is simply a special case of an assemblage of interacting particles. Hence, Eqs. (14–28) are applicable, and we see that the motion of the center of mass is the same as if all the external forces acted on a single mass point whose mass is the sum of the individual masses.

Since $(\sum m)(dx/dt)$ is the component of total momentum P_x, the law of motion can be written

$$\sum \mathbf{F} = \frac{d\mathbf{P}}{dt}, \tag{14–29}$$

where $\mathbf{P}$ is the total momentum or the "momentum of the center of mass."

Qualitatively, we realize that when external forces are applied to the rigid-body system as a whole, complex reactions occur. An external force will cause a state of acceleration in which the acceleration of each component may be different. Under acceleration, each component is subjected not only to external forces but also to internal forces in the form of stresses due to the constraints. While this is a complex problem, we are not trying to analyze it in detail. In order to understand the motion of the system, it is necessary to classify all forces which occur into only two kinds.

Consider in detail an example in which two mass points are connected by a weightless bar, as in Fig. 14–24. An external force is applied at some point and in some direction on the bar, as shown. The effect of the force is then transmitted through the bar and is imparted in some ratio to the mass points. The forces transmitted to m_1 and m_2 are called $(F_1)_{\text{ext}}$ and $(F_2)_{\text{ext}}$. In principle, we could find the ratio of the two forces, which would depend on the point of application and on the relative magnitude of the masses. Whatever the division, however, we know that

$$\mathbf{F}_{\text{ext}} = (\mathbf{F}_1)_{\text{ext}} + (\mathbf{F}_2)_{\text{ext}}.$$

We designate such forces as these external forces. Other forces are also brought into play. Forces of action and reaction are set up within the system. These are forces of constraint which hold the particles at a fixed separation. Such forces, called internal forces, since they are internal to the system as a whole, may occur on and by each component. The net effect, then, is as if there were external forces acting on parts of the system and a change in the internal forces. But the internal forces cancel, leaving only the external force contribution to $\sum \mathbf{F}$.

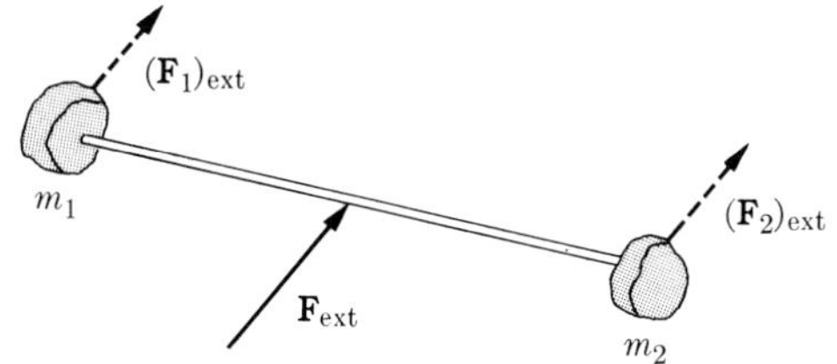

FIG. 14–24. The external force $\mathbf{F}_{\text{ext}}$ on a rigid body can be replaced by forces (shown as dashed lines) acting on the constituents of the rigid body.

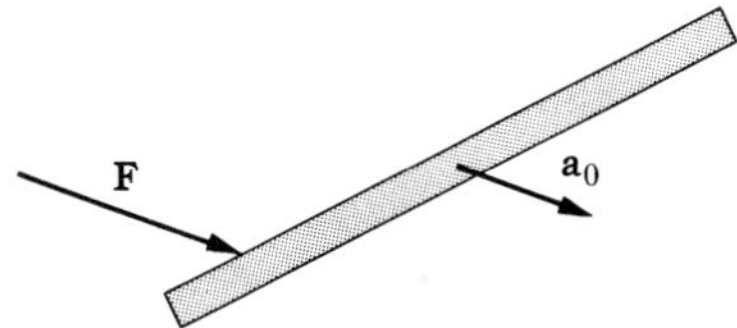

FIG. 14–25. The acceleration $\mathbf{a}_0$ of the center of mass produced by a force $\mathbf{F}$.

Example 3. A force $\mathbf{F}$ is applied to a uniform stick of mass m, as in Fig. 14–25. What is the acceleration of the mass center?

Solution: The mass center of a uniform stick coincides with the geometric center. From Eq. (14–28) we have simply $\mathbf{a}_0 = \mathbf{F}/m$, regardless of where and in what direction the force is applied.

This extraordinarily simple law is exact. However, it is evident that the motion of the system is not fully described by this law of translation. There will also be a rotation of the stick in the general case. The theorems to be presented in the following sections apply to rotational motion.

14–9 DYNAMICS OF ROTATION

Generally, when a rigid body is subjected to external forces, both rotational and translational accelerations result. The theorems just derived complete the formal treatment of the translational motion. The applications of Newton's laws to rotation are now to be made. Before the more general problems are considered, a very restricted example of rotation, that of a single constrained particle, is reviewed to show the kinds of transformations that are involved.

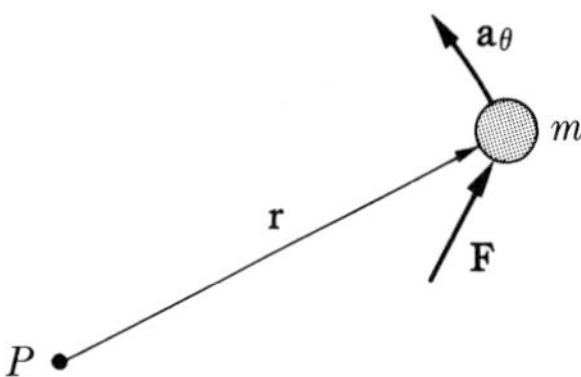

FIG. 14–26. The acceleration $\mathbf{a}_\theta$ produced by a force $\mathbf{F}$ on a mass m that is constrained to circular motion about P. An additional force, a constraint on P, is not shown.

Let a single particle of mass m be constrained to rotate at distance r about the point P (Fig. 14–26). A force $\mathbf{F}$ is applied to the particle. Then the tangential acceleration is given implicitly by

$$F_\theta = ma_\theta.$$

Letting both sides of the equation be multiplied by the radius of motion r, we have

$$F_\theta r = mra_\theta. \qquad (14\text{–}30)$$

But the product of tangential force times radius arm is the torque τ about the center of motion, and a_θ can be written as αr, where α is the angular acceleration. Equation (14–30) then becomes

$$\tau = mr^2\alpha,$$

or

$$\tau = I\alpha, \qquad (14\text{–}31)$$

since $I \equiv \sum mr^2$.

Alternatively, it is possible to write the right side of Eq. (14–30) as $mr\,dv_\theta/dt$ or $d(mrv_\theta)/dt$. But since the angular momentum l is just mrv_θ, we have

$$\tau = \frac{d\mathbf{l}}{dt}. \qquad (14\text{–}32)$$

That is, torque equals the time rate of change of angular momentum. This expression for the second law applied to rotational motion is of exactly the same form as the linear momentum formulation of the second law,

$$\mathbf{F} = \frac{d\mathbf{p}}{dt}. \qquad (14\text{–}33)$$

In the rotational form, torque occupies the position of force; angular momentum, the position of linear momentum.

Returning to Eq. (14–31), we note that it also is similar in form to the linear expression for the second law,

$$\mathbf{F} = m\mathbf{a},$$

where, in the rotational expression, torque occupies the position of force; moment of inertia, the position of simple inertia; and angular acceleration, the position of linear acceleration.

This one-particle example of some of the possible transformations draws together many of the formal definitions which were put forward in the earlier sections, namely, torque, angular momentum, and moment of inertia. From a physical standpoint, however, literally nothing has been accomplished, for we have done nothing except to rewrite old expressions in novel forms. Nothing is gained in generality. However, it will emerge from the proofs to follow that Eqs. (14–31) and (14–32) have a general validity for rigid-body motion. It will be seen that the torque, angular momentum, and moment of inertia quantities are *in general* related as in Eqs. (14–31) and (14–32).

We now show that, for an arbitrary rigid body subjected to external forces, the time rate of change of angular momentum of the body about any fixed axis equals the torque applied to the body measured about the same axis. Let a rigid

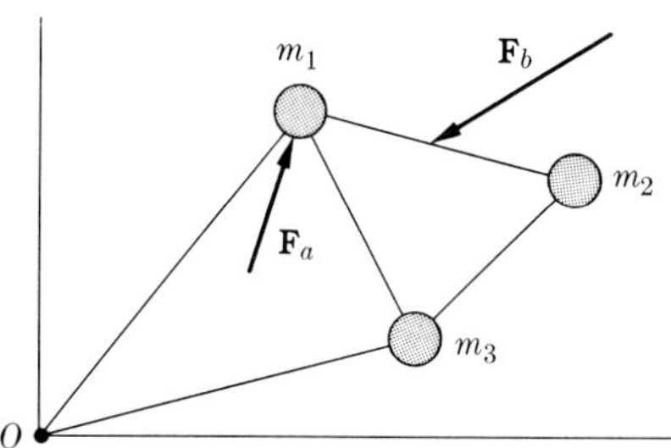

FIG. 14–27. Two forces act on a rigid body composed of three point masses. The body is constrained to rotate about O. (There must also be a force at O.)

body that is free to rotate about O be composed of the mass particles m_1, m_2, and m_3, as in Fig. 14–27. The angular momentum of any particle about the origin is

$$l_i = m_i(v_{xi}y_i - v_{yi}x_i), \tag{14–34}$$

where (x_i, y_i) are the particle coordinates and (v_{xi}, v_{yi}) are the components of the particle velocity. The total angular momentum of the rigid body is, by definition, the sum of the angular momenta of its components:

$$L = \sum_i m_i(v_{xi}y_i - v_{yi}x_i). \tag{14–35}$$

The time rate of change of total angular momentum is found by differentiation, giving

$$\frac{dL}{dt} = \sum_i m_i\left(\frac{dv_{xi}}{dt}\,y_i + v_{xi}\,\frac{dy_i}{dt} - \frac{dv_{yi}}{dt}\,x_i - v_{yi}\,\frac{dx_i}{dt}\right).$$

The terms in parentheses can be identified as particle velocity and acceleration, and the expression can be written as

$$\frac{dL}{dt} = \sum_i m_i(a_{xi}y_i + v_{xi}v_{yi} - a_{yi}x_i - v_{yi}v_{xi}).$$

The velocity products cancel, giving simply

$$\frac{dL}{dt} = \sum_i m_i(a_{xi}y_i - a_{yi}x_i). \tag{14–36}$$

The mass-acceleration products can now, as before, be related to the applied forces. Again it is to be noted—and this is the central point of the proof—that the applied external forces give rise to a complex set of internal forces, i.e., stresses, within the body. While we are considering body components individually, both external and internal forces must be considered alike in computing the acceleration of any individual component. However, when we consider the body as a whole system and perform the sum over all components, all the internal forces must vanish, for they occur in exactly equal and opposite action-reaction pairs. Thus we specify again that the force on any component is split into two kinds, $(F_i)_{\text{int}}$ (the net internal force) and $(F_i)_{\text{ext}}$ (the external force acting on the same component). We have from the second law

$$m_i a_{xi} = (F_{xi})_{\text{ext}} + (F_{xi})_{\text{int}},$$
$$m_i a_{yi} = (F_{yi})_{\text{ext}} + (F_{yi})_{\text{int}}.$$

Equation (14–36) can therefore be written

$$\frac{dL}{dt} = \sum_i [(F_{xi})_{\text{ext}}y_i - (F_{yi})_{\text{ext}}x_i] + \sum_i [(F_{xi})_{\text{int}}y_i - (F_{yi})_{\text{int}}x_i].$$

The second sum occurring in the above equation vanishes, since all the internal forces occur in equal and opposite pairs and therefore their torques also occur in equal and opposite pairs. We then have the expression

$$\frac{dL}{dt} = \sum_i [(F_{xi})_{\text{ext}}y_i - (F_{yi})_{\text{ext}}x_i],$$

where the sum is by definition the total torque exerted by the external forces, computed about the same axis that is used for the calculation of the angular momentum. Thus, we have

$$\frac{dL}{dt} = \tau \tag{14–37}$$

for this general case. It is important to note that

the expression holds for any fixed axis, but that torque and angular momentum are to be computed about the same axis.

The angular momentum of a set of particles has been shown to be equal to

$$L = \sum_i m_i r_i^2 \omega,$$

where ω is the common angular velocity of all components about an axis, r_i^2 is the square of the radial distance of a component from the axis, and m_i is the mass of the component. The sum of the products $m_i r_i^2$ is the moment of inertia I of the object, and therefore the angular momentum can be written

$$\mathbf{L} = I\boldsymbol{\omega}. \tag{14-38}$$

If an object is pivoted so that one point can be regarded as stationary, then the radial distance r of any component from the axis is constant, and the moment of inertia is therefore a constant, defined quantity. This is a special case of constrained rotation. For this case the time rate of change of angular momentum (since I is constant) is

$$\frac{dL}{dt} = I\frac{d\omega}{dt} \quad \text{or} \quad \frac{dL}{dt} = I\alpha.$$

However, we have shown that the time rate of change of angular momentum equals the applied torque. We therefore have the expression for rotation of a rigid body about a fixed axis,

$$\tau = I\alpha. \tag{14-39}$$

A review of the derivations of the equations will be of value. The review should be inspected for these points: the manner in which the rigid body definition is used (nonrigid bodies are not governed by all these equations), the use of the rules of rigid-body kinematics, the role played by the forces of internal constraint, and the fact that the laws utilize both the second and third laws of Newton. The final simplicity of the laws of rotational dynamics is quite remarkable in view of the evident complexity of the problem which has been solved.

While it will not be shown here, it is not difficult to prove that the equations hold for another case of special importance. As they have been derived, the equations are valid only for the case of a fixed reference axis. Employing the definition of mass center, we can show that the equations hold for a rotational axis through the mass center of a free rigid body. Thus, in principle, the dynamic problem is fully solved. Knowing the forces applied to a body, and their torques, we can find the translation of the mass center of the body and the rotation about the mass center. This is the point of departure for an advanced course in rigid-body mechanics. Here we confine our attention mostly to illustrations of rigid bodies which are pivoted on a fixed rotational axis.

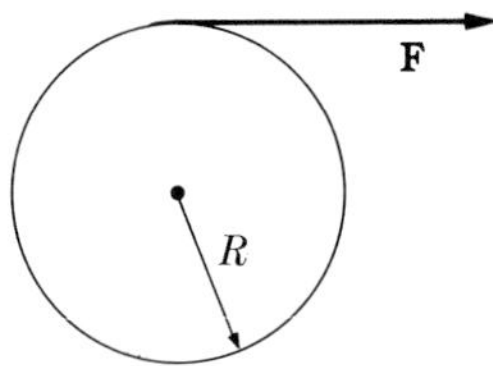

FIG. 14-28. A force **F** is applied tangentially at the rim of a disk.

Example 4. A disk of mass m is pivoted at its center. The radius of the disk is R. A string is wrapped on the disk rim, and a force **F** is applied to the string in a tangential direction (Fig. 14-28). What is the angular acceleration of the disk, and what is the linear acceleration of the string?

Solution. The moment of inertia is found by integration (Eq. 14-21). Let the disk have a surface density of σ kilograms per square meter. We divide the disk into rings of radius r, width dr, and area $2\pi r\, dr$ (Fig. 14-29). All elements on the ring are at the distance r from the center. The mass of the element is $dm = \sigma 2\pi r\, dr$. The moment of inertia of the element is evaluated from Eq. (14-21) as

$$I = \int r^2\, dm = 2\pi\sigma \int_0^R r^3\, dr = \frac{\pi\sigma R^4}{2}.$$

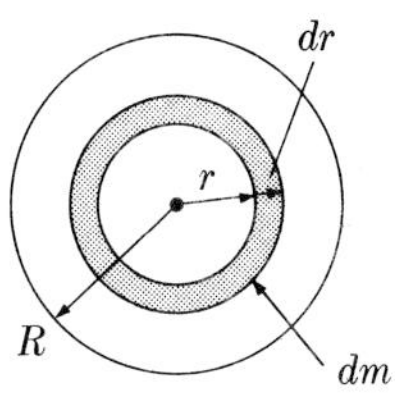

FIG. 14–29. The element of mass dm is chosen to be a ring, as shown.

Since the total mass is σ times the total area, we have $m = \sigma\pi R^2$, and the moment of inertia can be written

$$I = \tfrac{1}{2}mR^2 \qquad (14\text{–}40)$$

(which is the expression for the moment of inertia of any cylinder about its axis).

Since the total torque about the center is FR, Newton's second law applied to rotation (Eq. 14–39) gives

$$FR = \tfrac{1}{2}mR^2\alpha,$$

or the angular acceleration is

$$\alpha = \frac{2F}{mR}\cdot$$

The tangential acceleration of a point on the rim is

$$a_\theta = \alpha R = \frac{2F}{m}\cdot$$

The moment of inertia is usually computed about a line through the mass center, particularly in the case of symmetrical objects. While derivations for some of these are requested in the problem section, the answers for the familiar shapes are given here for convenience.

1. A disk of radius R and mass m. The moment of inertia about an axis through the center normal

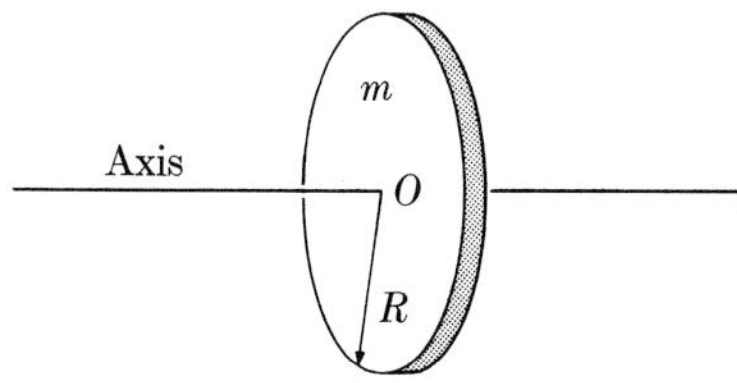

FIG. 14–30. The disk rotates about axis O through its center.

to the face of the disk (Fig. 14–30) is

$$I = \tfrac{1}{2}mR^2. \qquad (14\text{–}40)$$

2. A right circular cylinder of radius R and mass m. The moment of inertia about the cylindrical axis (Fig. 14–31) is

$$I = \tfrac{1}{2}mR^2. \qquad (14\text{–}40)$$

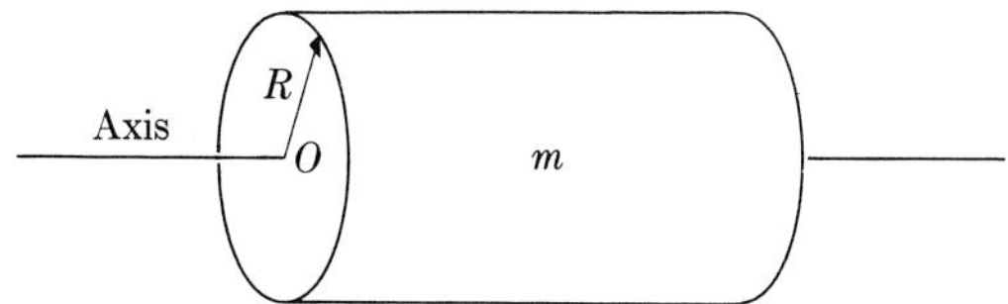

FIG. 14–31. The cylinder rotates about the axis O through its center.

3. The moment of inertia of a rod of length L about a line through the center (Fig. 14–32) is

$$I = \tfrac{1}{12}mL^2. \qquad (14\text{–}41)$$

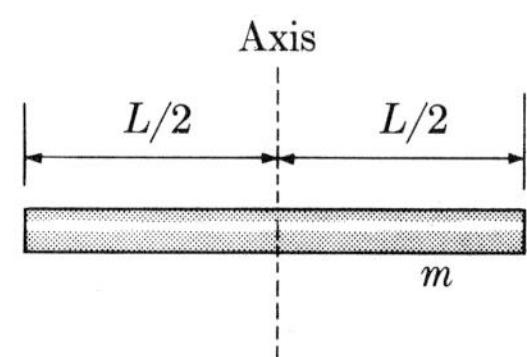

FIG. 14–32. A rod rotates about an axis perpendicular to its length.

4. The moment of inertia of a sphere of radius R about its diameter (Fig. 14–33) is

$$I = \tfrac{2}{5}mR^2. \qquad (14\text{–}42)$$

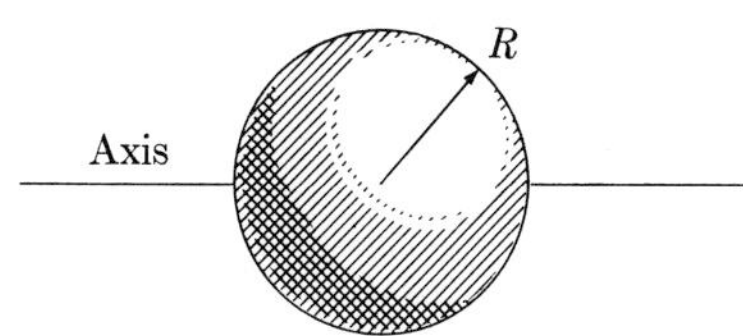

FIG. 14–33. A sphere rotates about a diameter.

In addition, it will be useful to know a theorem for moments of inertia about parallel axes.

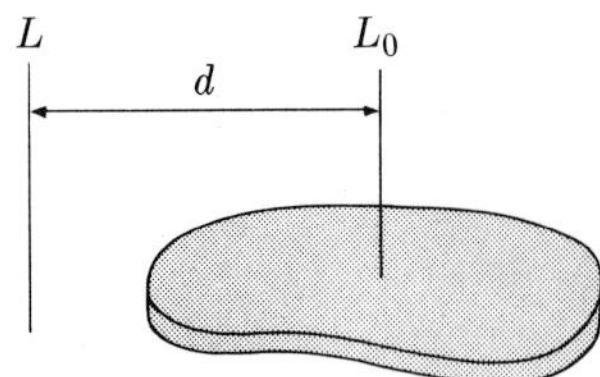

FIG. 14–34. Axes L and L_0 are parallel.

Given the moment of inertia I_0 about a line L_0 through the mass center, the moment of inertia of the object about any other line L parallel to L_0 and at a distance d from L (Fig. 14–34) is

$$I = I_0 + md^2. \tag{14–43}$$

The proof is reserved for the problem section.

14–10 EQUILIBRIUM CONDITIONS FOR A RIGID BODY

The laws of rigid-body dynamics single out the two agents which cause a change in velocity: the force, which causes a change in translational velocity, and the torque, which causes a change in angular velocity. For a free rigid body we showed that

$$\sum \mathbf{F}_{\text{ext}} = m\mathbf{a}_0, \tag{14–44}$$

where $\mathbf{a}_0$ is the acceleration of the center of mass. For a pivoted body, we showed that

$$\sum \tau_{\text{ext}} = I\alpha, \tag{14–39$'$}$$

where the external torque and moment of inertia are computed relative to the pivot point. Stated, but not proved, is the free-body rule for rotation,

$$\sum \tau_{\text{ext}} = I_0\alpha, \tag{14–45}$$

where the rotational quantities are computed relative to an axis through the mass center.

In particle mechanics the condition for mechanical equilibrium is that the sum of the external forces applied to the particle is zero:

$$\sum \mathbf{F}_{\text{ext}} = 0.$$

The rule follows from the condition that the particle acceleration is zero (since the velocity is either constant or permanently zero) for equilibrium. This condition is then applied to the solution of force problems in statics. For a static system it is usual that the system is at rest, although it is evident that a system in uniform rectilinear motion obeys the same rules.

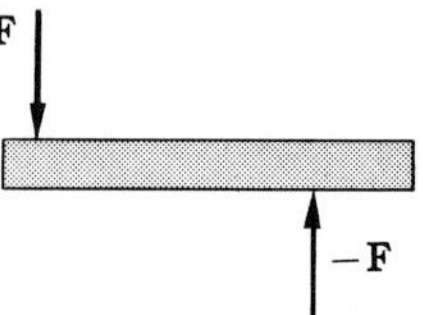

FIG. 14–35. A force couple acting on a rigid body.

A simple illustration can show that the zero-force condition is not sufficient to guarantee an equilibrium situation for a rigid body (Fig. 14–35). For example, a rigid body subjected to a couple experiences no net external force, yet the body is in a state of angular acceleration.

Since rotational equilibrium is defined by the condition that there be no rotation or that there be rotation at constant angular velocity, it is obvious that the condition for rotational equilibrium is

$$\sum \tau = 0 \tag{14–46}$$

about any axis whatsoever.

In statics, it is customary to use the term moment of force in place of torque, but the two are synonymous. The term *center of moments* is then used to indicate the arbitrary choice of a point that is to be considered as the center in calculating torques or moments. The center of moments may or may not be a physical pivot point.

Thus a complementary statement of the first law of translational motion can be formulated in terms of the new definitions which have been put forward: a body in a state of rest or of uniform angular velocity will remain in a state of rest or of uniform angular velocity unless acted upon by outside torques. The natural motion of a spinning body, in the absence of all outside influence, is to remain spinning at a constant rate and with the direction of the axis constant.

It can be seen that the formulation of the equilibrium condition for a rigid body is not so simple as in the case of particle mechanics. For a particle, it suffices to say that in equilibrium the particle acceleration is zero, thus giving a purely kinematic description of the system. In contrast, a rigid body need not, under the conditions stated, have a zero acceleration of its components. A wheel in rotation on a frictionless axle has zero translational acceleration of the body as a whole, and zero angular acceleration. However, the body components are in a state of centripetal acceleration. The centripetal acceleration in the equilibrium state is supported solely by internal forces.

14–11 CENTER OF GRAVITY

Considerable advantage is to be gained by replacing, whenever it is possible, a set of forces by a single force. For example, in particle mechanics a set of forces is usually replaced by the resultant, the vector sum of the forces in the set. There is a simplification of this kind to be found for a rigid body acted on by the gravitational force.

Consider a body of components m_1, m_2, m_3, rigidly constrained and subjected to the pull of gravity (Fig. 14–36). Each body component ex-

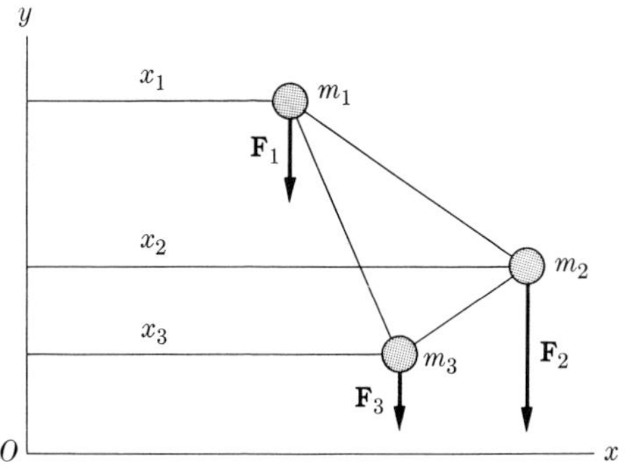

FIG. 14–36. A rigid body composed of three point masses. The forces indicated are the gravitational forces on the masses. The Oy-axis is vertical.

periences a force equal to its own weight, $F_i = m_i g$, where the forces on the components are parallel to one another.

For translational effects, we have found that the force set can be replaced by the sum of forces. Since the forces are parallel, the sum is obtained by simple vector addition, giving

$$\mathbf{W} = m_1\mathbf{g} + m_2\mathbf{g} + m_3\mathbf{g}$$

or

$$\mathbf{W} = (m_1 + m_2 + m_3)\mathbf{g},$$

where $\mathbf{W}$ is the single weight-vector which represents the resultant gravitational force. It is in the direction of its components.

It is also possible to find a point fixed relative to the body such that if the single weight vector were applied at that point, the rotational effect of W would be the same as the combined effects of the components. This point is called the *center of gravity*. With knowledge of foresight, its coordinates are called X and Y. The condition then is that the torque exerted by W about any point in space is to be the same as the net torque exerted by the pull of gravity on the constituents. If we choose the center of moments as the y-axis, the torque of the weight vector is

$$\tau = WX = (m_1 + m_2 + m_3)gX,$$

and the net torque of the components is

$$\tau = m_1gx_1 + m_2gx_2 + m_3gx_3.$$

Since X is defined by equating the two, we have

$$X = \frac{m_1x_1 + m_2x_2 + m_3x_3}{m_1 + m_2 + m_3}. \quad (14\text{–}47)$$

The coordinate X determines a line on the body which contains the point of center of gravity. The determination of any other line will locate the center of gravity at the intersection of lines. By rotating the whole mass system 90° and proceeding in a fashion like that for X, we find that

$$Y = \frac{m_1y_1 + m_2y_2 + m_3y_3}{m_1 + m_2 + m_3}. \quad (14\text{–}48)$$

The coordinates X and Y determine the single point at which the total weight vector is to be applied. From an inspection of the result, it is seen that the center of gravity coincides exactly with the center of mass, in this special case where $\mathbf{g}$ is assumed to be constant over the region occupied by the body.

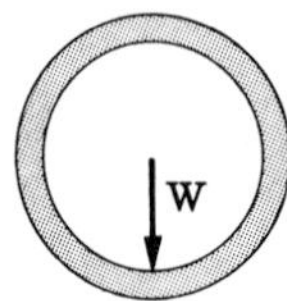

FIG. 14–37. A uniform ring has its center of gravity at the center.

Since the weight vector is applied at the mass center, it can also be seen that the weight exerts no torque about the mass center. Thus the weight vector alone will always cause pure translational acceleration of a free body. Finally, it must be remembered that the center of gravity is a point where there may be no mass at all. For example, the center of gravity of a mass in the form of a ring is at the center of the ring (Fig. 14–37). This is the point at which the weight vector is said to act on the ring.

14–12 APPLICATIONS OF RIGID-BODY MECHANICS

The equations developed above are sufficient for the solution of many problems in rigid-body mechanics. Selected problems will now be presented in order to illustrate techniques of solution. They are (a) a static system, (b) a rolling body, and (c) an oscillating body. Of course, the list can be extended indefinitely. Following the solutions of selected problems we shall discuss the energy and the momentum for systems containing rigid bodies.

Example 5. A block of 10-kg mass is placed on a board of 20-kg mass, as shown in Fig. 14–38. The board is supported at its ends. What are the forces at the supporting points A and B?

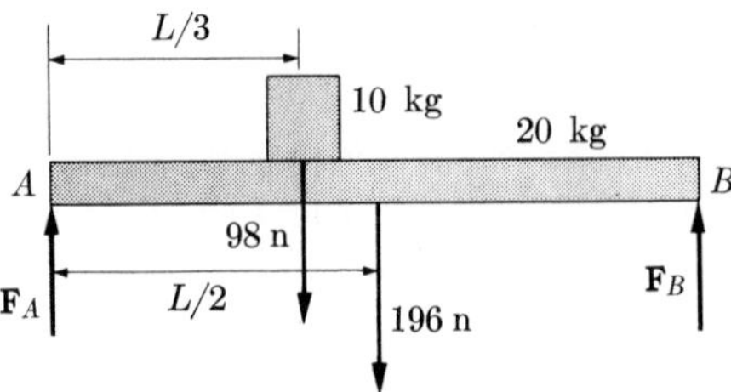

FIG. 14–38. A system of two rigid bodies (Example 5).

Solution: We select the board itself as the system and consider the case of equilibrium. The board is subjected to four forces, the upward forces by the end supports, F_A and F_B, the downward force of 98 n acting at $L/3$ from point A, and the downward force of 196 n acting at $L/2$ from point A (at the center of gravity of the board). From the condition for translational equilibrium $\sum \mathbf{F} = 0$, we have

$$F_A + F_B - 196 - 98 = 0$$

or

$$F_A + F_B = 294 \text{ n}.$$

The condition for rotational equilibrium is that the sum of the torques about any point is zero. We choose the point A for convenience, and from the condition $\sum \tau = 0$, we have $98(L/3) + 196(L/2) - F_B L = 0$. Solving for the forces, we obtain $F_B = 130.7$ n and $F_A = 163.3$ n. Exercises of a like nature are presented in the problem section.

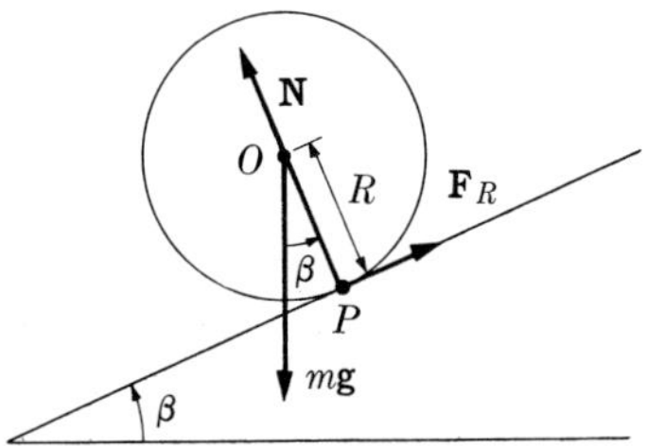

FIG. 14–39. A disk rolling on an inclined plane (Example 6).

Example 6. A disk of mass m and radius R is placed on a plane surface that is inclined at an angle β relative to the horizontal (Fig. 14–39). What is the acceleration of the disk, if it is assumed that the disk rolls without slipping? The instantaneous point of contact P between the disk and the plane is the only point on the disk that is instantaneously at rest. The line through P and perpendicular to the direction of motion is therefore regarded as an instantaneous axis about which the disk executes a motion of pure rotation.

Solution: The disk experiences two outside forces, the gravitational force mg, exerted at the center of gravity, and the force by the plane, exerted at P. The force exerted by the plane is represented by components N and F_R in the figure. We first find the torque about P exerted by the outside forces. The forces exerted by the plane act at point P, and, therefore, they have zero torque about that point. Therefore the resultant torque about P is $\sum \tau_p = mgl = mgR \sin \beta$. We wish to apply Newton's law for rotation, $\sum \tau_p = I_P\alpha$, but we know I_0 and not I_P. However, since we do know the moment of inertia about an axis through the center of mass, $I_0 = mR^2/2$, we can use the theorem of Eq. (14–43), $I_P = I_0 + md^2$, and obtain $I_P = 3mR^2/2$. Then by substitution in $\sum \tau_p = I_P\alpha$, we obtain $mgR \sin \beta = \frac{3}{2}mR^2\alpha$ or $\alpha = \frac{2}{3}g \sin \beta/R$.

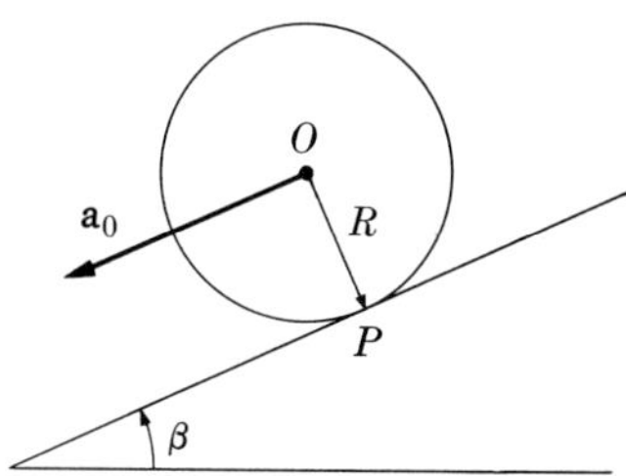

Fig. 14–40. The acceleration $\mathbf{a}_0$ of the center of mass of the rolling disk.

The linear acceleration, $a_0 = R\alpha$, of the center of mass is perpendicular to a radius from P to O. Therefore the acceleration is parallel to the inclined plane, as shown in Fig. 14–40. We see that its magnitude is $a_0 = \frac{2}{3}g \sin \beta$, which is less than it would be ($a = g \sin \beta$) for a disk sliding down a frictionless incline without rotation.

Example 7. A torsion pendulum consisting of a disk of mass m and radius R is suspended horizontally from its center by a wire fixed to an overhead support (Fig. 14–41). When given an angular displacement about O in a horizontal plane by an amount

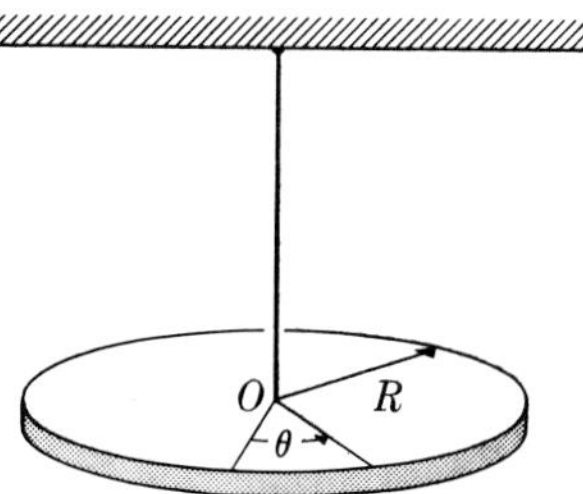

Fig. 14–41. A disk suspended at its center on a vertical wire.

θ from the equilibrium orientation, the wire exerts a restoring torque that is proportional to the angle; that is,

$$\tau = -\kappa\theta. \tag{14–49}$$

The torque constant K has the units n-m/rad. If the disk is given an angular displacement θ about O and then released, what is the resulting motion?

Solution: Since the torque by the wire on the disk is the only torque, it is the resultant torque. We set it equal to $I_0\alpha$, by the second law, and have $-K\theta = I_0\alpha$. Substituting the second derivative of the angle variable for α, we obtain the following differential equation:

$$-K\theta = I_0 \frac{d^2\theta}{dt^2} \quad \text{or} \quad \frac{d^2\theta}{dt^2} = -\left(\frac{K}{I_0}\right)\theta. \tag{14–50}$$

The general solution of this form of differential equation was discussed in Chapter 8. The solution is of the form

$$\theta = \theta_m \sin(2\pi ft + \phi_0), \tag{14–51}$$

where θ_m is the angular amplitude and ϕ_0 can be determined from the initial conditions. The frequency f can be found by substitution of Eq. (14–51) into Eq. (14–50), with the result

$$f = \frac{1}{2\pi}\sqrt{K/I_0}. \tag{14–52}$$

Thus the motion is analogous to linear simple harmonic motion, with the linear spring constant replaced by the torsion constant and the mass term by the moment of inertia.

Example 8. The physical pendulum consists of a rigid body suspended on a frictionless bearing point

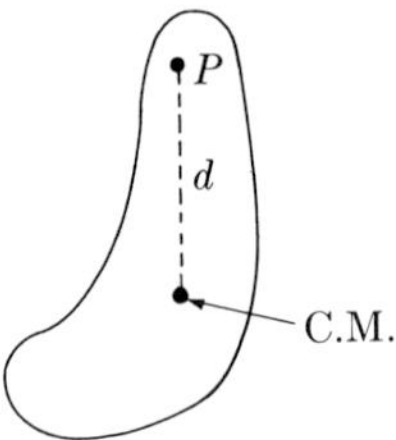

FIG. 14-42. The normal position of a physical pendulum (Example 8).

at a distance d above its center of mass (Fig. 14-42). The body is rotated slightly and released, thereby setting it into oscillation. What is the moment of inertia about the pivot in terms of the frequency f?

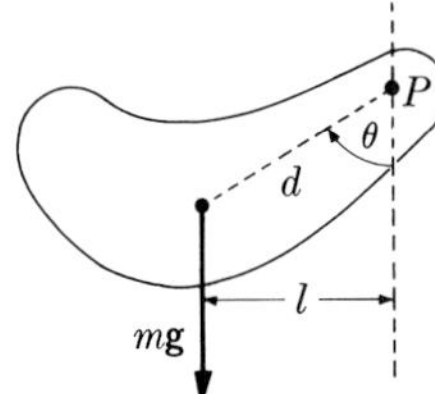

FIG. 14-43. The physical pendulum of Example 8 displaced from its normal position.

Solution: Let the moment of inertia about the pivot be I_P. When the center of mass is displaced away from the vertical line through the support (Fig. 14-43), a restoring torque $\tau = mgl$ is set up about the point of support. There will be a consequent angular acceleration α, and the second law will lead to $\tau = mgd \sin \theta = I_P\alpha$. Since $\alpha = d^2\theta/dt^2$, we have the differential equation

$$I_P \frac{d^2\theta}{dt^2} = mgd \sin \theta.$$

This equation is of the same form as one for a simple pendulum and leads to elliptic integrals as solutions. We now consider the simple case of small amplitude, just as we did for the simple pendulum. The simplifying approximation is $\sin \theta = \theta$, which gives the simplified differential equation

$$\frac{d^2\theta}{dt^2} = \frac{mgd}{I_P}\,\theta.$$

This is the differential equation of simple harmonic motion, whose solution is

$$\theta = \theta_m \sin (2\pi ft + \phi_0), \tag{14-53}$$

where θ_0 is determined by the initial conditions, and the frequency is given by

$$f = \frac{1}{2\pi}\sqrt{mgd/I_P} \tag{14-54}$$

(from which I_P is obtained).

A particular point on the physical pendulum is defined as the center of oscillation of the pendulum. This is the point at which all the pendulum mass can be concentrated without changing the frequency of the pendulum. If the mass were concentrated at such a point, at distance h below the point of support, we would have a simple pendulum whose frequency would be $f = 1/2\pi\sqrt{g/h}$. Thus the distance h is found by equating the physical pendulum frequency to that of a simple pendulum of length h (an equivalent simple pendulum). The result is

$$h = \frac{I_P}{md}\cdot \tag{14-55}$$

14-13 WORK AND ENERGY

In analogy with the procedure followed in the mechanics of particles, mechanical work, a scalar function that is useful in a discussion of the energy of rigid bodies, can be defined.

For pure translatory motion, there is no difference between the case of a mass point and that of an extended rigid body. Work is specified by the defining equation

$$dW = \mathbf{F} \cdot d\mathbf{s}, \tag{14-56}$$

where W is the work done by the force $\mathbf{F}$ during a displacement $d\mathbf{s}$.

The same methods are of interest here as were of interest in the case of mass points. If we consider the work by the *resultant force* (where $d\mathbf{s}$ is the displacement of the center of mass), the concept of kinetic energy will appear just as in the case of a point mass (Section 9-6). The result is

$$\int_A^B (\Sigma\mathbf{F}) \cdot d\mathbf{s} = \left(\frac{mv_0^2}{2}\right)_B - \left(\frac{mv_0^2}{2}\right)_A, \tag{14-57}$$

where v_0 is the velocity of the center of mass.

We also saw that certain forces are conservative, i.e., the work done by these forces was independent of the path between two points. Since this work is path independent, it is convenient to replace the work by change in *potential energy.* The change in potential energy therefore depends only on the initial and final positions of the object (i.e., of its center of mass in the case of rigid bodies). The work by nonconservative forces is path dependent and can be included either as work terms or as energy-transformation terms. The left side of Eq. (14-57) can then be separated into terms due to the various forces and the resulting expression labeled the equation of *conservation of energy* (Eq. 12–25). In the above, the effects of translational motion have been reviewed.

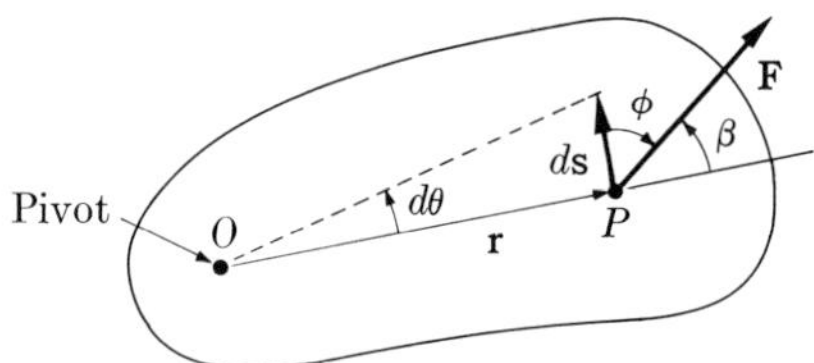

FIG. 14–44. Rotation $d\theta$ about O. A force $\mathbf{F}$ acts at point P.

We now consider a case of rotation about a fixed axis. Suppose a force $\mathbf{F}$ is applied to a rigid body at a point at a distance $\mathbf{r}$ from the pivot, as in Fig. 14–44. The work performed by the force $\mathbf{F}$ while the point P on which it acts is displaced by $d\mathbf{s}$ is $dW = \mathbf{F}\cdot d\mathbf{s}$ or

$$dW = |\mathbf{F}|\,|d\mathbf{s}|\cos\phi, \qquad (14\text{–}58)$$

as usual. Using the complementary angle β between $\mathbf{F}$ and $\mathbf{r}$, we can rewrite Eq. (14–58) as

$$dW = |\mathbf{F}|\,|d\mathbf{s}|\sin\beta. \qquad (14\text{–}59)$$

Also, since the displacement is necessarily perpendicular to $\mathbf{r}$, it can be simply expressed in terms of the radius vector and the angular displacement as

$$|d\mathbf{s}| = |\mathbf{r}|\,d\theta. \qquad (14\text{–}60)$$

The work expression becomes

$$dW = |\mathbf{F}|\,|\mathbf{r}|\sin\beta\,d\theta. \qquad (14\text{–}61)$$

Using the definition of torque exerted by $\mathbf{F}$ about the pivot,

$$\tau = |\mathbf{F}|\,|\mathbf{r}|\sin\beta, \qquad (14\text{–}62)$$

we can write the work definition as

$$dW = \tau\,d\theta. \qquad (14\text{–}63)$$

This is a reformulation of the definition of work, which has the result of torque replacing force and angular displacement replacing linear displacement in the basic definition.

The concept of *rotational kinetic energy* can be developed in the same way as translational kinetic energy by considering the work done by the *resultant* torque. Since the resultant torque on a body is equal to the moment of inertia about the pivot point times the angular acceleration, the work expression becomes

$$dW = I\alpha\,d\theta.$$

Substituting for α its definition, $d\omega/dt$, we have

$$dW = I\,\frac{d\omega}{dt}\,d\theta.$$

But $d\theta/dt$ is simply the angular velocity ω and so we obtain

$$dW = I\omega\,d\omega.$$

The work expression can now be integrated between the limits ω_0 and ω_f to obtain the work required to increase the angular velocity from ω_0 to ω_f. We have

$$W = \int_{\omega_0}^{\omega_f} I\omega\,d\omega$$

or

$$W = \tfrac{1}{2}I\omega_f^2 - \tfrac{1}{2}I\omega_0^2. \qquad (14\text{–}64)$$

As before, we identify this amount of work as the change in kinetic energy of the body resulting from its changing angular velocity. We therefore call the individual terms on the left side of Eq. (14–64) the kinetic energy of rotation T_R, that is,

$$T_R \equiv \tfrac{1}{2}I\omega^2. \tag{14–65}$$

The form of the rotational kinetic energy expression is identical with that for translational kinetic energy, with inertial mass replaced by moment of inertia and translational velocity by angular velocity.

In cases of conservative torques, such as the torsion spring of Example 7, a change in potential energy ΔV can be defined as the negative of the work done by the torque. The definition is meaningful and useful because the work is independent of the path, and hence the change in potential energy is dependent only on the end points of the motion. The potential energy V at a point is a meaningful term when a particular choice of reference angle and corresponding potential energy has been made. In Example 7, the obvious choice is $V = 0$ at $\theta = 0$, with the result

$$V = \tfrac{1}{2}k\theta^2. \tag{14–66}$$

The work by the resultant of all forces can be divided into work by conservative forces and work by nonconservative forces. The former can be expressed as a change in potential energy $-(V_2 - V_1)$ and the latter by terms Q_A, Q_B, etc., that depend on the path. Equation (14–64) then becomes

$$-(V_2 - V_1) - Q_A - \cdots = T_2 - T_1$$

or

$$V_1 + T_1 = V_2 + T_2 + Q_A + \cdots,$$

which is the familiar statement of conservation of energy. The statement of the energy-conservation principle asserts that the total of the energy of all forms possessed by a closed mechanical system is constant, or that the energy added to a system by work or other methods equals the change in total energy of the system.

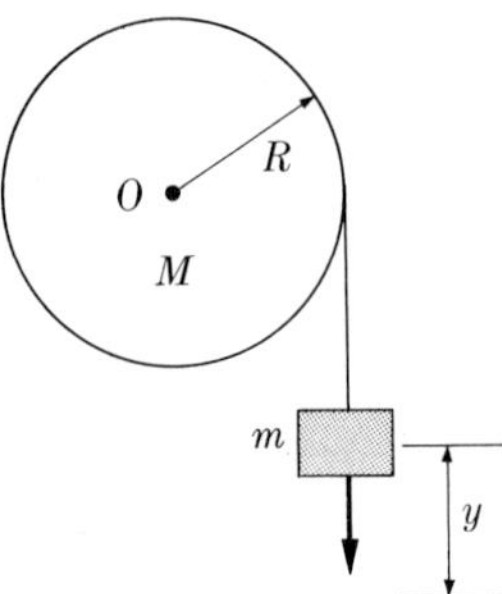

FIG. 14–45. A mass m supported on a string that is wrapped around the disk M. The disk is free to rotate about O.

Example 9. A disk of mass M and radius R is mounted on a frictionless pivot at its center (Fig. 14–45). A string is wrapped around the rim of the disk, and to its free end is attached a mass m. The string unwraps without slipping. What is the velocity of m after falling from rest a distance y?

Solution: The effect of outside agents on the Mm system is most easily treated in terms of change in gravitational potential energy, mgy. The resulting increase in energy of the system appears exclusively as kinetic energy (of translation and rotation). The equation for conservation of energy is $\Delta V = \Delta T_T + \Delta T_R$, which becomes

$$mgy = \tfrac{1}{2}mv^2 + \tfrac{1}{4}MR^2\omega^2.$$

But since $v = R\omega$ *in this particular case,* we have

$$mgy = \tfrac{1}{2}mv^2 + \tfrac{1}{4}Mv^2,$$

which can be solved for v in terms of the given quantities.

14–14 CONSERVATION OF ANGULAR MOMENTUM

The angular momentum of a rigid body about a given axis was shown (Section 14–7) to be

$$L = I\omega. \tag{14–27}$$

This expression followed from the definition of angular momentum or moment of momentum of a point mass, mvr or $mr^2\omega$, which, when summed over all the mass elements constituting a rigid body, becomes

$$L = \sum mr^2\omega = \omega\sum mr^2 = \omega I,$$

where we have made use of the fact that ω is the same for all elements and have taken it outside the summation sign.

Since the second law for rotational motion is

$$\sum \boldsymbol{\tau} = \frac{d\mathbf{L}}{dt},$$

it is a direct consequence of the second law that the angular momentum of a system is constant when the resultant external torque is zero. Therefore

$$L = I\omega = \text{constant} \qquad (14\text{–}67)$$

when $\sum\tau = 0$. This is the basis for the law of conservation of angular momentum, which can be stated: When the resultant external torque on a system is zero, the angular momentum of the system is conserved, i.e., it remains constant.

Whether or not the resultant external torque is zero depends on our choice of the physical system. As the choice of system is made more inclusive, external torques may become internal torques. Since the choice of system is at our disposal, the use of the law of conservation of angular momentum can be made a matter of convenience. Two illustrations of the use of angular-momentum conservation will now be given.

Example 10. Two blocks each of mass m are free to slide (except for the constraint of strings) along a weightless bar (Fig. 14–46). The bar is horizontal and pivoted about a vertical axis at a point midway between the blocks. The blocks can be drawn in toward the center without exerting any torque, by pulling downward on the strings at the axis, as shown. The body is in rotation at angular velocity ω, with the blocks at distance r from the center. What is the angular velocity after the blocks have been pulled inward to a radius $r/2$?

Solution: The initial angular momentum is $L_1 = I_1\omega_1 = 2mr^2\omega_1$. The final angular momentum is $L_2 = I_2\omega_2 = 2m(r^2/4)\omega_2$. Since there are no external torques, angular momentum is conserved, and L_1 and L_2 are equal. Upon equating the two angular momenta, we find that $\omega_2 = 4\omega_1$.

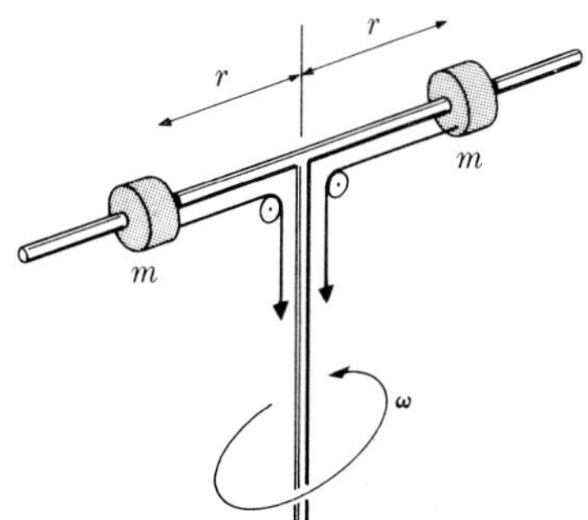

FIG. 14–46. The system of Example 10.

Note that the energy of the system has *not* been conserved in the process, since work has been done on the system by outside forces. The result is an increase in the kinetic energy of the system. It is left as an exercise for the student to show that the increase in kinetic energy is $3mr^2\omega_1$. It is a good review exercise to verify, by integrating $\mathbf{F}\cdot d\mathbf{s}$ directly, that this is also the work done by the external forces.

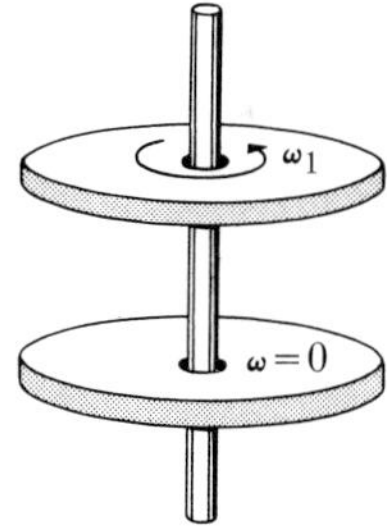

FIG. 14–47. The system of disks of Example 11.

Example 11. Consider two identical disks, each of mass m and radius R, mounted on frictionless bearings on a vertical axle as in Fig. 14–47. The disks are kept in their vertical positions by some type of frictionless device. The upper disk is set into rotation at angular velocity ω_1, and the lower disk is initially at rest. The vertical support of the upper disk is now removed, permitting the upper disk to fall onto the lower disk. There is friction between them, and they finally rotate at the same angular velocity.

What is the final angular velocity? The situation may be described as a rotational collision.

Solution: The problem could be solved by considering the two disks separately, if we assumed a particular form for the friction torque. However, when we consider the two disks together as a system, the problem is simplified because there are no external torques on the chosen system. Therefore angular momentum is conserved for the two-disk system, and we can write $I\omega_1 = (I + I)\omega_2$. Consequently the final angular velocity is $\omega_1/2$. Note that the collision is inelastic. Energy has been transformed into heat, etc., during the collision. The student can verify that one-half the initial kinetic energy of the upper disk has been lost as mechanical energy during the collision. Since no special form of interaction force has been assumed, this result is independent of the way the coupling was accomplished. For example, it could have been done suddenly by equipping the surfaces with teeth. The student should consider the question, How does the change in *potential* energy of the upper disk, due to its change in vertical height, enter the problem and why?

14-15 ROTATION IN THREE DIMENSIONS

The laws of rigid-body mechanics have been developed for motion in a plane, with forces lying in the same plane. The laws of motion of such systems have mostly been expressed in terms of scalar equations. For more general systems, which require a three-dimensional description, the quantities such as torque, angular velocity, and angular acceleration are more conveniently represented in vector form. A partial analysis in terms of vector quantities will be made here, leaving the more difficult parts of the analysis for other texts.

We consider the motion of a disk rotating about an axis through the center and normal to the faces of the disk (Fig. 14-48). An infinitesimal angular displacement $d\theta$ is measured in magnitude by the angle traversed by a radial line. Magnitude alone does not, however, fully describe the state of motion, because the instantaneous plane of the disk can have any orientation in

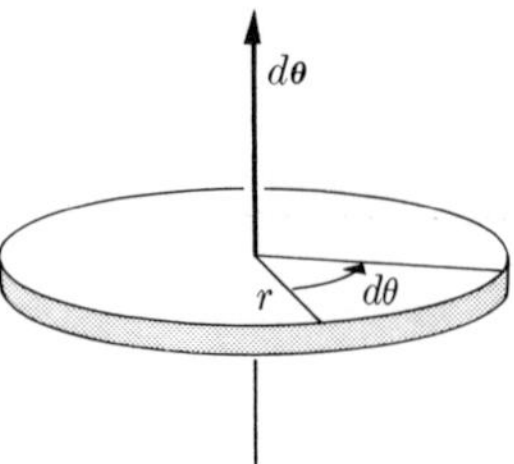

FIG. 14-48. The vector representing an infinitesimal angular displacement $d\boldsymbol{\theta}$.

space. For descriptive purposes, a suitable direction line is the instantaneous axis of rotation. The displacement vector $d\boldsymbol{\theta}$ is chosen to lie in the direction of the axis of rotation. Its sense is given by the right-handed screw rule. In component form, the differential angular displacement vector $d\boldsymbol{\theta}$ can be described by cartesian components $d\theta_x$, $d\theta_y$, and $d\theta_z$, as in Fig. 14-49. Note that we have avoided a discussion of finite angular displacements. This was deliberate, since vectors describing finite angular displacements do not follow the vector algebra that you have learned thus far, whereas the infinitesimal displacements do follow it.

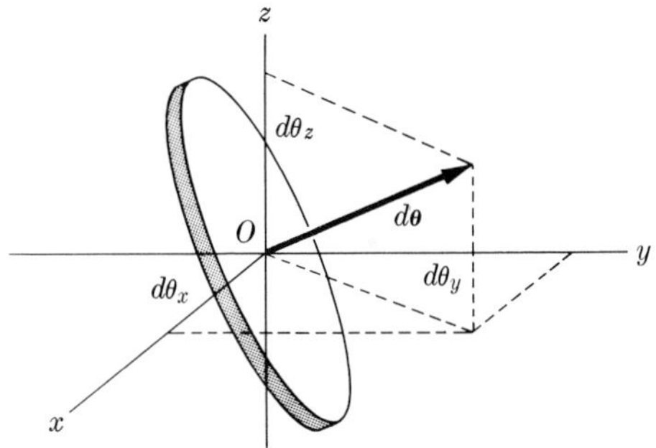

FIG. 14-49. Cartesian components of an angular displacement $d\boldsymbol{\theta}$.

The angular velocity vector is already defined, since

$$\boldsymbol{\omega} \equiv \frac{d\boldsymbol{\theta}}{dt}. \tag{14-68}$$

Therefore the angular velocity is also in the direction of the instantaneous axis of rotation.

We now consider changes in angular velocity. If the axis remains fixed in direction, a change in angular velocity can lie only along the same axis as the angular velocity itself. Only the magnitude of the angular velocity vector changes (Fig. 14–50). This is the case that we have already analyzed in earlier sections by means of scalar equations. Just as significant as a change in rate of rotation is a change in the direction of the axis of rotation. A tilting of the axis of rotation of the disk, such as depicted in Fig. 14–52, corresponds to a change in angular velocity, $d\boldsymbol{\omega}$, as portrayed in the figure. A torque is required to change the angular velocity, whether it be a magnitude change or a direction change. It is easily observed experimentally that a twisting effort (torque) is required to change the direction of the axis of a rotating body. The unexpected part of the experimental observation is the *direction* in which the torque must be exerted to effect a given change in direction of the axis of rotation.

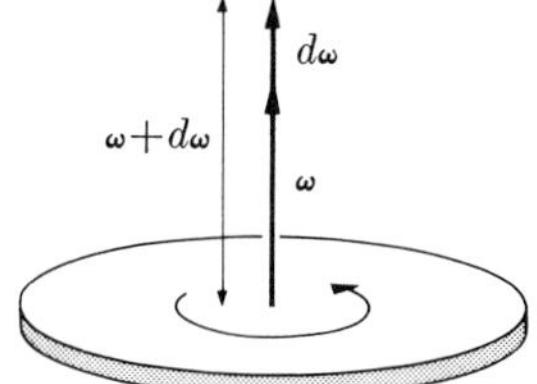

FIG. 14–50. Angular velocity vector.

Quantitatively, we define the change in the angular velocity in terms of angular acceleration:

$$\boldsymbol{\alpha} = \frac{d\boldsymbol{\omega}}{dt}, \tag{14–69}$$

where we see that the angular acceleration is in the direction of the *change* in angular velocity. Thus, in the case of a change in magnitude of the angular velocity, the angular acceleration is in the direction of the rotational axis (Fig. 14–51), but in the case of a change in direction with no change in magnitude, the instantaneous angular acceleration is perpendicular to the axis of rotation (Fig. 14–52). The situation is analogous to point-mass motion in rectilinear motion and in uniform circular motion, respectively.

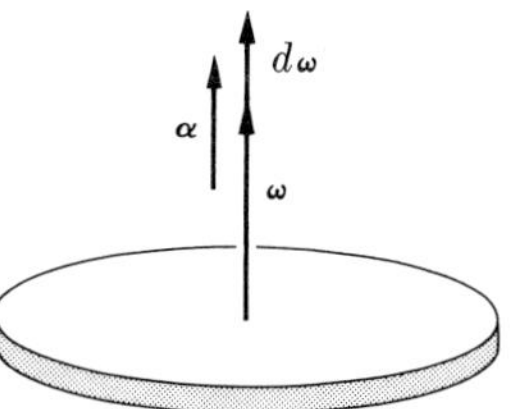

FIG. 14–51. The angular acceleration in the case of a change in the magnitude of the angular velocity.

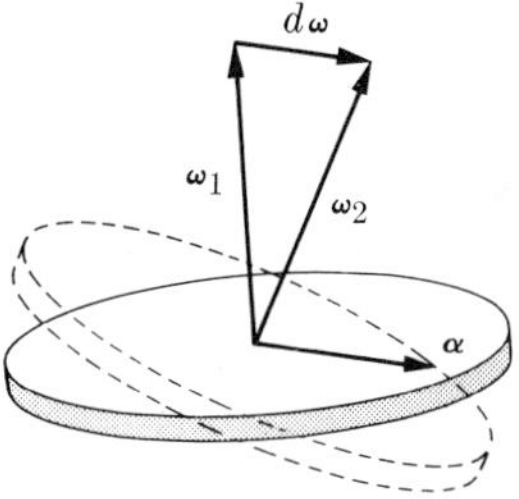

FIG. 14–52. The angular acceleration in the case of a change in the direction of the angular velocity.

We now give a brief review of torque as a vector quantity. Torque is a vector quantity whose direction is defined by the plane of the force $\mathbf{F}$ and the radius vector $\mathbf{r}$ from the axis to the point of application of the force. The torque vector is normal to the plane so defined. For example, if $\mathbf{F}$ and $\mathbf{r}$ are both contained in the xy-plane, as in Fig. 14–53, the torque vector is in the z-direction. We have already seen that, in general,

$$\boldsymbol{\tau} = \mathbf{r} \times \mathbf{F}. \tag{14–70}$$

The definitions that we have given are consistent with the rotational motion form of the second law. Of course, they were chosen to be consistent with the second law, which can be written as

$$\boldsymbol{\tau} = I\boldsymbol{\alpha} \quad \text{or} \quad \frac{d\mathbf{L}}{dt}, \tag{14–71}$$

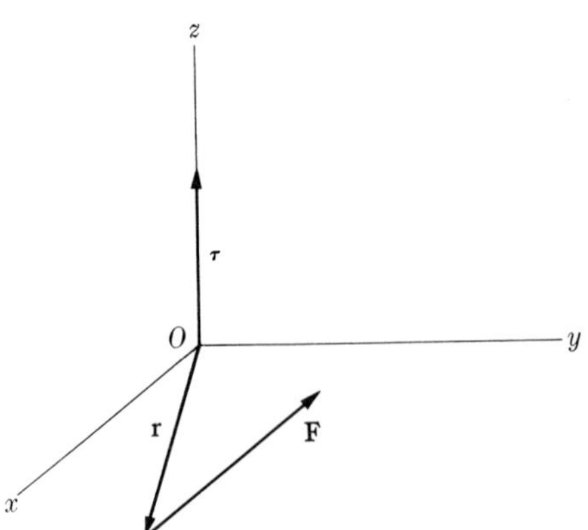

FIG. 14–53. The torque $\boldsymbol{\tau}$ due to a force lying in the Oxy-plane.

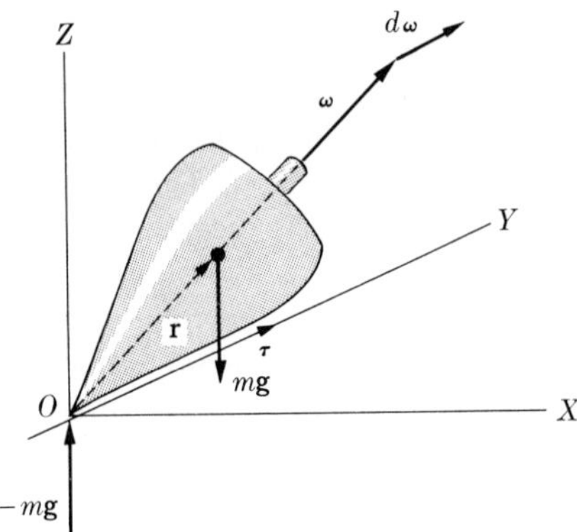

FIG. 14–54. A top spinning with its axis in the OXZ-plane at the instant of observation. Since the OXZ-plane is vertical, the torque τ is in the OY direction and, therefore, $d\omega$ is in the OY direction, as shown.

showing that the torque and the angular acceleration are codirectional.

The derivation of these vector equations for the general case proceeds along much the same lines that we have followed here.

14–16 PRECESSION

From the descriptive part of the analysis given above, the nature of the motion of a symmetrical top can be shown qualitatively. The motion of the top is necessarily a three-dimensional effect, except for the case in which the axis is vertical. A symmetrical rigid body is assumed to be spinning with angular velocity $\boldsymbol{\omega}$ about the axis of symmetry (Fig. 14–54). The top is supported by a floor in the XY-plane, the point of support being chosen as the origin of the coordinate system. We consider the instant when the angular velocity vector lies in the XZ-plane.

Two forces act on the body, a downward force $m\mathbf{g}$ at the center of gravity and an equal force upward at the point of support. The forces are equal if the center of mass is not accelerated in the vertical direction. The resultant force will be zero but the resultant torque is not zero. The torque, $\mathbf{r} \times m\mathbf{g}$, lies in the direction of the Y-axis, as shown. If the top were not spinning, we would certainly expect the effect of the torque to be a "falling" motion of the top, which it would indeed be. The top would simply topple over with increasing angular velocity, the angular velocity vector and its increase both lying in the direction of the torque (the direction of the Y-axis). If the top is spinning about its axis when it is placed in the position of Fig. 14–54 and then is released, the ensuing motion is complex. In the next paragraph, we consider a special case in which the top is given a particular initial motion.

Suppose the top has an initial spin angular velocity $\boldsymbol{\omega}$ at an angle θ from the vertical, as shown in Fig. 14–55. We choose the instant in which the spin lies in the XZ-plane. The torque

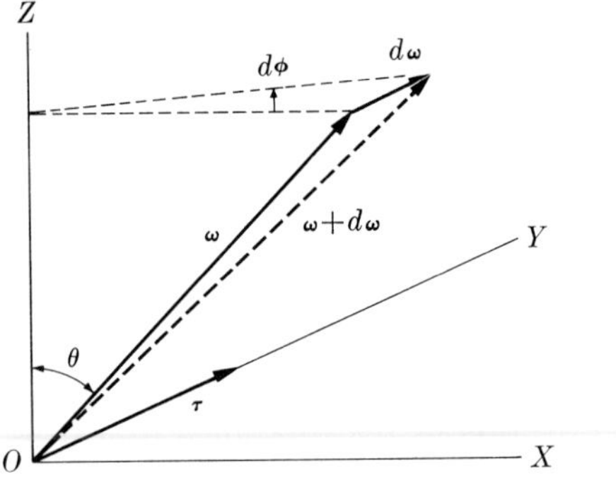

FIG. 14–55. Vector diagram for the spinning top at the instant the axis is in the OXZ-plane.

is along the OY-direction as before, but this time the top already has angular momentum. The change in angular velocity $d\boldsymbol{\omega}$ is in the direction of the torque, which is perpendicular to the spin angular momentum. Thus the *magnitude* of the spin component of angular velocity will not change; only its direction will. The change in direction is in the direction of the torque (Fig. 14–55).

Quantitatively, we have, from Eqs. (14–71) and (14–69),

$$d\boldsymbol{\omega} = \frac{\boldsymbol{\tau}}{I}\, dt. \tag{14–72}$$

From Fig. 14-55, it is seen that

$$|d\boldsymbol{\omega}| = \omega \sin\theta \, d\phi \tag{14–73}$$

for a small angle $d\phi$. Eliminating $d\boldsymbol{\omega}$ between Eqs. (14–72) and (14–73) and solving for torque, we obtain

$$\tau = I\omega \frac{d\phi}{dt} \sin\theta, \tag{14–74}$$

which give a precession rate, $d\phi/dt$, in terms of τ, I, ω, and θ. As the axis of rotation is displaced slightly along the Y-axis, the plane containing the gravitational force and the pivot point is carried along with the spin axis $\boldsymbol{\omega}$. The next slight change in angular velocity is then normal to this new plane. As we follow successive changes in the direction of the angular velocity, they are seen to describe a circle, as in Fig. 14–56, assuming the

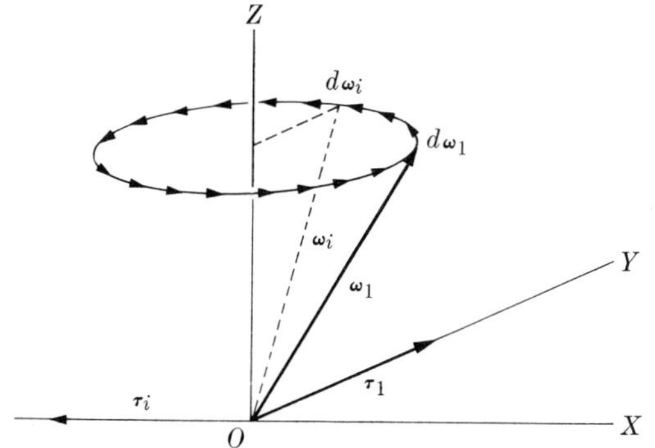

FIG. 14–56. Precession of the spin angular velocity about the OZ direction.

steady state. The steady state could be established by giving the spin axis an initial precessional angular velocity equal to the value given by Eq. 14–74. The axis of the top then describes a cone. This part of the motion is called precession. In principle, the top will never fall out of this conical path if friction is negligible. The situation is analogous to uniform circular motion under the influence of a force that depends on r, for example, the inverse square gravitational force. It was necessary that the object in circular motion be given an initial velocity just equal to the steady-state velocity for a circular path.

If the angular velocity of spin diminishes (due to friction, for example), the precessional velocity must increase according to Eq. (14–74).

We note that, for the torque due to gravitation, the sin θ-factor in Eq. (14–74) drops out when we substitute $\tau = mg \sin\theta$.

In the case of a spinning top, the contact with the horizontal supporting surface cannot be an infinitely fine point. Consequently there are additional small torques due to the finite radius of curvature of the point and to the finite friction with the surface. As a result, there is an initial decrease in angle θ that results in the so-called sleeping top, a stable orientation of the axis in the vertical direction.

Additional examples of precession are the nosing up or nosing down of an airplane when a turn is made in a horizontal direction. The effect is due to the spin angular momentum of the rotating engine and propeller. A motorcycle at high speed will tilt to the right and turn to the right only if the driver pushes on the "wrong," or right-hand, handle bar.

14–17 CONSERVATION OF ANGULAR MOMENTUM OF SYSTEMS OF RIGID BODIES

The total angular momentum of a system of rigid bodies consists in part of (a) angular momentum of each body due to the motion of its center of mass relative to the center of mass of the system, and (b) spin angular momentum of each body. The former is referred to as orbital angular momentum in cases in which the bodies move in closed paths or orbits. For example, in the solar system, each planet has orbital angular momentum due to its revolution about the sun and spin angular momentum due to its rotation on its axis.

If no outside forces act on a system of rigid bodies, both the total linear momentum and the total angular momentum must remain constant, as we have seen. There can be actual collisions or merely interactions due to long-range forces such as gravitation between the bodies. The momenta of individual bodies may change. In the case of angular momenta, there can even be interchanges between ordinary and spin angular momenta.

If an object enters the system from a large distance, the easiest way to analyze the momentum problem is to include the entering object as part of the system. Its initial orbital angular momentum as part of the system is given by $l = pd$ (Eq. 10–18), where d is the distance of closest approach to the center of mass of the entire system if the object were to move always on the line of its initial velocity at infinity.

The conservation of angular momentum includes the direction as well as the magnitude properties of angular momentum, just as in the case of linear momentum conservation.

Examples of the conservation of linear and of angular momentum in systems of mass points have been considered in earlier chapters. Therefore, we shall here consider only examples that include specific rigid-body properties, namely, spin effects.

Example 12. A lecture demonstrator sits at rest at the center of a turntable, as in Fig. 14–57. He holds a spinning wheel in his hands. What happens if he inverts the axis of the wheel?

Solution: The angular momentum $\mathbf{L}_0$ of the system is initially $I_1\boldsymbol{\omega}$, where I_1 is the moment of inertia of the wheel. Suppose the vector $\mathbf{L}_0$ is directed upward. When the wheel is inverted, its angular momentum becomes $-I_1\omega$ if upward is considered positive and if we write $I_1\omega$ as a scalar component so that signs indicate direction. In order to conserve the total angular momentum of the system, the man must acquire angular velocity ω_2 such that $I_2\omega_2 = 2I\omega_1$, where I_2 is the moment of inertia of the man. Then the final angular momentum of the system is the same as its initial angular momentum.

FIG. 14–57. Lecture demonstrator holding a spinning wheel.

Example 13. A boy of mass M runs through a turnstile that is initially at rest. Assuming that the change in velocity of the boy from v_0 to v_f (Fig. 14–58) is entirely due to his interaction with the turnstile, what is the angular velocity of the turnstile after this encounter? A plane view is shown in Fig. 14–58. The initial angular momentum of the system—boy plus turnstile—about the turnstile pivot

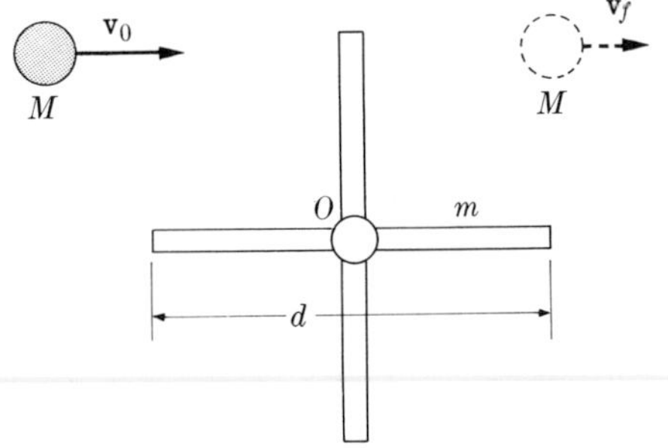

FIG. 14–58. Top view (schematic) of the boy and turnstile of Example 13.

O is $Mv_0\, d/2$. The final angular momentum of the system is $(Mv_f\, d/2) + (md^2/12)\omega$, where ω is the final angular velocity of the turnstile. The final and initial angular momenta can be equated in order to find the value of ω. (The total mass of the turnstile is m.)

14–18 SUMMARY

Any displacement of a rigid body can be described by a motion of pure translation plus a motion of pure rotation. The translatory motion can be analyzed in the same way as for point particles, and therefore all the earlier results developed for point particles apply directly to the motion of the center of mass of the rigid body.

The kinematical quantities used to describe rotation are the same as those used earlier to describe circular motion of a point mass, namely, θ, ω, and α, respectively, for the angular displacement, velocity, and acceleration. They are interrelated by the differential relations of their definitions

$$\omega \equiv \frac{d\theta}{dt}, \qquad \alpha \equiv \frac{d\omega}{dt}$$

or by the inverse or integral relations.

The center of mass is defined in the same way as for a group of point masses, namely, the cartesian coordinates are X and Y, which become the following for a continuous mass distribution:

$$X \equiv \frac{\int x\, dm}{\int dm}, \qquad Y \equiv \frac{\int y\, dm}{\int dm}.$$

The moment of force or torque about a point O is defined as

$$\boldsymbol{\tau} \equiv \mathbf{R} \times \mathbf{F},$$

where $\mathbf{R}$ is the vector from O to the point of application of the force. In cartesian components, the torque is

$$\tau = F_y R_x - F_x R_y.$$

The torque by two equal and opposite forces whose lines of action are separated by the perpendicular distance l (called a force couple) is

$$\boldsymbol{\tau} = \mathbf{l} \times \mathbf{F}.$$

The second moment of mass leads to the idea of moment of inertia I, which is defined by

$$I \equiv \int r^2\, dm.$$

The radius of gyration is defined by

$$K^2 \equiv \frac{\int r^2\, dm}{\int dm}.$$

It is shown that the dynamics of translation of the center of mass are the same as for a point mass.

The dynamics of rotation are similar to those of translation.

The rotational motion follows laws of the same form as Newton's laws of translational motion, with angular quantities replacing the linear motion quantities. The second law becomes

$$\sum \tau = I\alpha,$$

or, in terms of angular momentum, L,

$$\sum \tau = \frac{dL}{dt},$$

where L is

$$L = I\omega.$$

The derivation of the last equation is presented in detail.

The moments of inertia of certain regular objects of uniform density are: $MR^2/2$ for a cylinder about its axis, $ML^2/12$ for a rod about a transverse axis through the center, and $\frac{2}{5}MR^2$ for a sphere about a diameter as axis. If the moment of inertia of an object about an axis 0 is I_0, the moment of inertia about a parallel axis at perpendicular distance d is

$$I = I_0 + Md^2,$$

where m is the mass of the object.

The conditions for equilibrium of a rigid body are

$$\sum \mathbf{F} = 0, \qquad \sum \tau = 0.$$

The gravitational force can be replaced by an equivalent single force acting at the center of gravity. The center of gravity's distance from a given reference point is

$$X_{\text{cg}} = \frac{\sum m_i g_i x_i}{\sum m_i g_i},$$

which is the same as the position of the center of mass in the special case that g is uniform over the region occupied by the parts of the object.

Angular harmonic motion resulting from a linear restoring torque is considered in an example. The period is

$$T = 2\pi\sqrt{I/K}$$

where K is the restoring torque constant, $K = -\tau/\theta$. The frequency of a pendulum with mass distributed over distances comparable with the distance to the support, a physical pendulum, is derived.

The work done by forces and the resulting changes in various forms of energy during the translation of a rigid body are found to be the same as for point masses. If the forces also result in torques, the work done by the torques is

$$W = \int \tau \, d\theta.$$

The work by the *resultant* torque equals the gain in kinetic energy of rotation:

$$W = \int \sum \tau \, d\theta = \tfrac{1}{2}I_2\omega_2^2 - \tfrac{1}{2}I_1\omega_1^2.$$

Torques that depend only on the angular displacement give rise to changes in energy that depend only on the initial and final angles, and therefore the energy changes are conveniently described in terms of change in potential energy.

In the absence of an external resultant torque, the total angular momentum of a system remains constant.

The three-dimensional characteristics of the motion of a symmetrical rigid body are treated for the case of spin about the axis of symmetry with a motion of precession added by the effect of an external torque whose axis is different from the spin axis. The frequency of precession $d\phi/dt$ is given by

$$\tau = I\omega \frac{d\phi}{dt} \sin\theta.$$

Conservation of angular momentum of systems that possess both spin angular momentum and angular momentum due to angular motion of the center of mass (orbital angular momentum) is discussed.

Problems

1. Prove that the angular displacements of all lines drawn on a plane rigid body are the same when the body is rotated in the plane of the body.

2. A force is applied at the point $x = 3$, $y = 4$ m. The force is 10 n directed vertically upward. What is the torque exerted about the origin? about the point $x = 3$ m, $y = 0$?

3. Prove that the torque exerted by equal and opposite forces that act along lines separated by a distance b is Fb about any point in the plane of the forces (see Fig. 14–14). These forces constitute a *couple.*

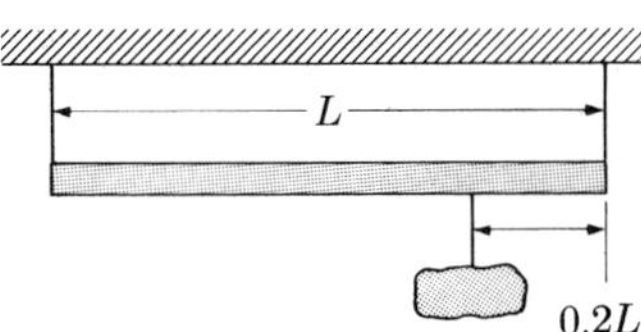

FIGURE 14–59

4. The mass of the uniform stick in Fig. 14–59 is 10 kg. The mass of the suspended object is 4 kg. What are the tensions in the supporting strings?

5. A half-disk (Fig. 14–60) has a mass m and radius R. The surface mass density is uniform. Find the center of mass of this object.

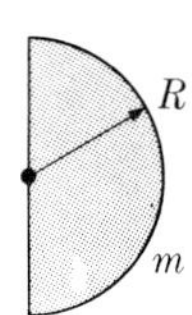

FIGURE 14–60

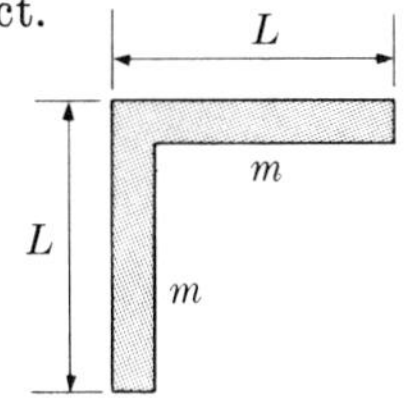

FIGURE 14–61

6. Two uniform sticks, each of mass m and length L are joined at right angles, as shown in Fig. 14–61. Find their center of mass.

7. Three identical mass particles are disposed at the vertices of a 30°–60° triangle. Find the center of mass.

8. A uniform door of height 2.5 m and width 1.0 m weighs 50 n. It is hung vertically on hinges that are 25 cm from the top and bottom. The bottom hinge exerts *no* vertical force on the door. Find the forces exerted by the door on the hinges.

9. A ladder is inclined against a wall at an angle of 30° from the vertical. The ladder is uniform and weighs 100 n. Assuming that the wall is frictionless and that the coefficient of static friction between ladder and floor is $1/(2\sqrt{3})$, how high can a boy of mass 500 n climb before the ladder begins to slide (a) if he climbs at constant velocity? (b) if he climbs with an upward acceleration $g/2$?

10. (a) Given that the angular acceleration of a certain object is constant, show by integration that the equations of motion are

$$\omega = \omega_0 + \alpha t,$$
$$\theta = \theta_0 + \omega_0 + \tfrac{1}{2}\alpha t^2.$$

(b) Given that $\alpha = 30$ rad/sec^{-2}, $\theta_0 = 0$, and $\omega_0 = -10$ rad/sec^{-1} when $t = 0$, find the angular velocity and angular displacement when $t = 4$ sec.

11. A rigid body starts from rest and rotates about a fixed axis with constant angular acceleration. Each point on the body experiences a tangential acceleration a_θ and a radial acceleration a_r. Prove that $a_r/a_\theta = 2\theta$, where θ is the angular displacement at any instant.

12. A uniform disk has mass m and radius R.

(a) Find the moment of inertia about a normal line through the center of the disk.

(b) Find the moment of inertia about a diameter.

13. Find the moment of inertia of a uniform sphere about a diameter.

14. A stick has a mass m and length L. The linear mass density λ is uniform over the length of the stick.

(a) Find the moment of inertia about the normal line through the center.

(b) Find I by direct integration for a normal line through one end.

(c) Show that the result of (b) agrees with the parallel-axis theorem for moments of inertia.

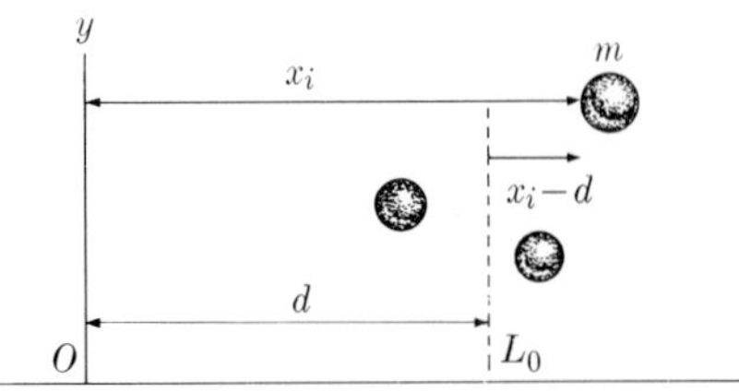

FIGURE 14–62

15. A line L_0 through the mass center of a system of particles is at a distance d from the y-axis, as shown in Fig. 14–62. The particles lie in the xy-plane. The moment of inertia of the system about L_0 is by definition

$$I_0 = \sum_i m_i(x_i - d)^2.$$

The distance d is given by the definition for mass center

$$d = \frac{\sum_i m_i x_i}{\sum_i m_i}.$$

Finally, the moment of inertia about the y-axis is, by definition,

$$I = \sum_i m_i x_i^2.$$

Show that

$$I = I_0 + md^2,$$

which is a special case of the parallel-axis theorem for moments of inertia given in the text.

16. A string is wrapped around the rim of a uniform disk of mass M and radius R. The disk is mounted on a frictionless pivot at its center so that the disk is in a vertical plane (Fig. 14–63). The free end of the string is attached to a mass m. The system is in the earth's gravitational field. Find the acceleration of the mass m and the tension in the string.

17. The pulley in an *Attwood* machine is a disk of mass m and radius R. Objects of unequal masses, m_1 and m_2, are suspended at either end of a string that passes over the top of the pulley (Fig. 14–64). The string does not slip on the pulley. Find the accelerations and tensions.

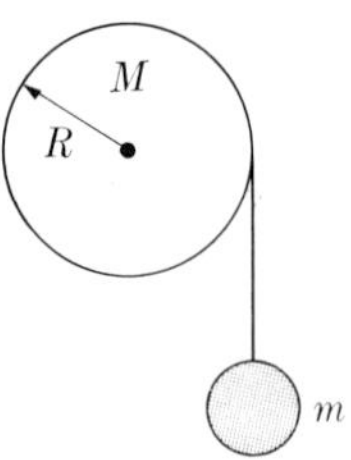

FIGURE 14–63

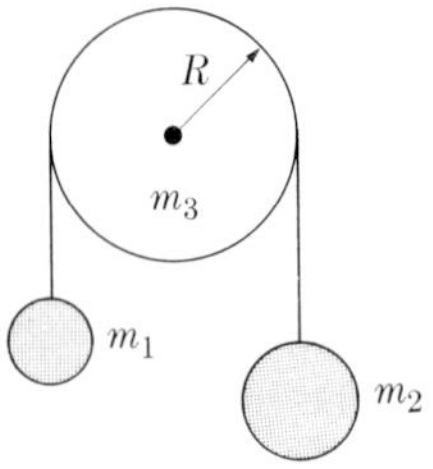

FIGURE 14–64

18. A uniform sphere of radius R and mass m rolls down an inclined plane without slipping. The plane is inclined at angle β with the horizontal.

(a) Find the linear and angular accelerations of the sphere.

(b) Using energy conservation, find the velocity after the sphere, starting from rest, has descended a distance d along the plane.

(c) Repeat the above exercises for a solid disk and for a ring.

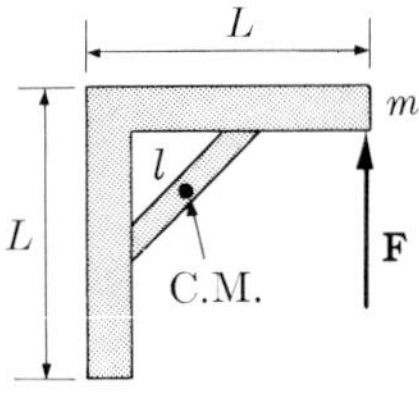

FIGURE 14–65

19. The rigid body of Problem 6 is pivoted about its center of mass, with the axis perpendicular to the plane of the bars (Fig. 14–65). The mass of bar l is negligible.

(a) Find the initial angular acceleration when a force F is applied, as shown.

(b) Repeat the problem for the case in which the body rests flat on a horizontal frictionless surface, with the pivot removed.

20. A cylinder of mass m and radius R rolls down an inclined plane without slipping. The total kinetic energy can be written $T = \frac{1}{2}I_P\omega^2$ when the motion is considered to be pure rotation about the point of contact P with the plane. Prove that the expression $T = \frac{1}{2}I_0\omega^2 + \frac{1}{2}mv_0$ (where I_0 is the moment of inertia about the center of mass and v_0 is the translational velocity of the center of mass) is equivalent to the first expression for the kinetic energy.

21. Find the velocity of a solid cylinder at the lowest point of a vertical circular track if the cylinder just barely maintains contact with the inside of the track as it passes the highest point. Assume that rolling friction is negligible and that the cylinder rolls without slipping.

22. What is the minimum coefficient of static friction required for a solid cylinder to roll without slipping on a plane inclined at an angle θ with the horizontal?

23. A uniform stick of mass m and length L is pivoted at one end, as in Fig. 14–66. The stick is initially at rest in an upright vertical position before it is given a slight displacement that causes it to fall.

(a) What is the velocity of the free end when the stick reaches the downward vertical position?

(b) What is the acceleration of the center of mass when the stick is horizontal?

(c) Can you easily calculate the time for the motion from vertically upward to vertically downward? Explain.

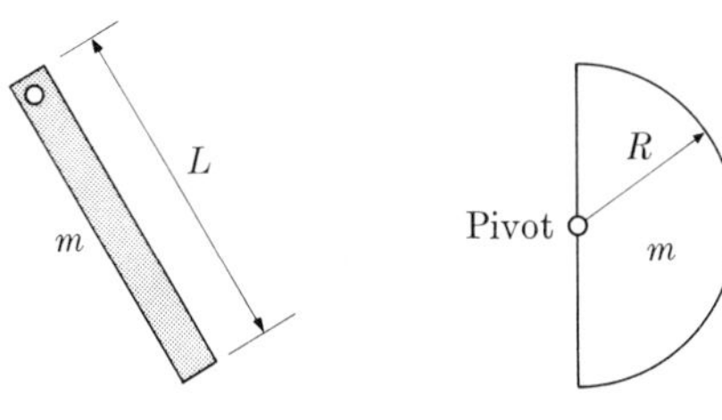

FIGURE 14–66 FIGURE 14–67

24. With what frequency does a uniform stick, pivoted as in Fig. 14–66, oscillate for small amplitudes about the downward vertical position?

25. A half-disk is pivoted about a frictionless horizontal axis at its center of curvature, as in Fig. 14–67.

(a) Compute the angular acceleration as a function of angular position.

(b) Find the maximum angular velocity of the disk if released from rest from the position shown.

26. Find the period of oscillation of the half-disk in Fig. 14–67 for small amplitude oscillations about the equilibrium position. It is pivoted at point P, on a horizontal axis.

27. Suppose a stick is pushed at right angles against the rim of the half-disk in Fig. 14–67. If the coefficient of sliding friction between stick and disk is μ, how much force must be exerted by the stick to make the half-disk rotate at constant angular velocity?

28. In the problem of Example 10, prove that energy is conserved. To do this compute the work done by the external forces when the masses are pulled inward and compare the result with the change in kinetic energy calculated from the velocities.

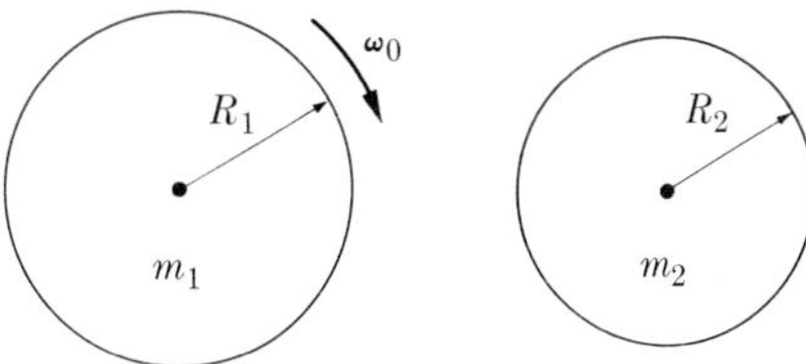

FIGURE 14–68

29. Two disks (Fig. 14–68) are mounted on frictionless pivots. Disk 1 is given an initial angular velocity ω_0 and disk 2 is at rest. The pivot points are shifted so that the rims are in contact, and after an initial period of partial slipping, the disks rotate with no slippage between the rims. Find the final angular velocities in terms of the given quantities ω_0, m_1, R_1, m_2, and R_2.

30. Suppose that disk 1 in Fig. 14–68 is mounted vertically above disk 2 and is lowered until it rests with its full weight on disk 2. If disk 1 has initial angular velocity ω_0 and disk 2 is initially at rest, how long does it take disk 2 to come up to its final velocity? Let the coefficient of sliding friction between the two disks be μ.

31. A uniform stick of length 1 m, pivoted at its upper end, is struck by an impulsive force of 100 n that lasts for $\frac{1}{50}$ sec (Fig. 14–69).

(a) If the stick was at rest before it was struck, what is the change in angular momentum of the stick?

(b) Does the stick reach the vertically upright position in its ensuing motion?

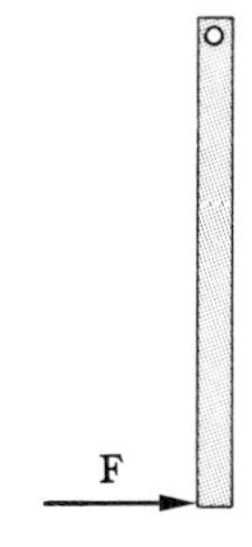

FIGURE 14–69

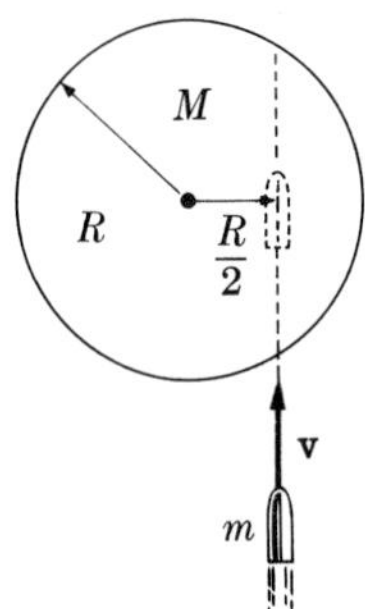

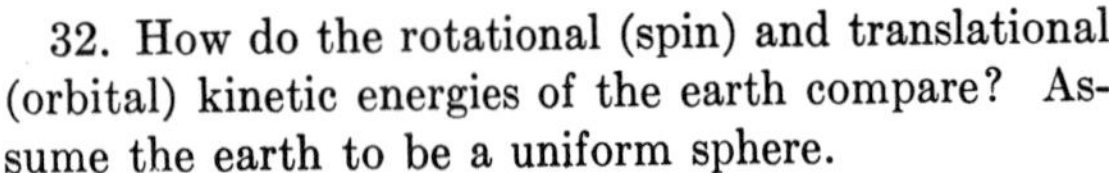

FIGURE 14–70

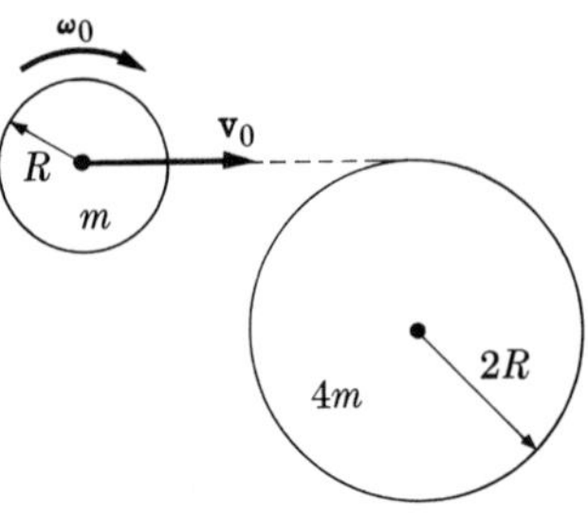

FIGURE 14–71

32. How do the rotational (spin) and translational (orbital) kinetic energies of the earth compare? Assume the earth to be a uniform sphere.

33. A constant torque of 40 n-m is applied to an object of moment of inertia 3 kg-m^2. How much work is done in one minute?

34. What would be the final velocity of the boy-turnstile system in Example 13 if the boy had clung to the turnstile bar with his feet clear of the ground?

35. A cylindrical disk of mass M and radius R rests flat on a frictionless horizontal table. A bullet of mass m is fired with velocity v in a horizontal plane and strikes the edge of the disk along a line directed half a radius from the center, as in Fig. 14–70. Find the resulting motion of the disk (a) if the bullet sticks to the rim of the disk, (b) if the bullet penetrates to a point P halfway through the disk before stopping, (c) if the bullet bounces off elastically at an angle of 90° from the original path.

36. Two circular disks are supported flat on a frictionless horizontal surface, as shown in Fig. 14–71. The initial conditions of motion are shown in the figure. If the collision is inelastic, both in translation and in rotation, find the final motion of the system.

15

Temperature, the Gas Laws, and Heat

15-1 THE NATURE OF THERMODYNAMICS

The domain of the science of thermodynamics includes all natural processes in which *temperature* is an essential variable. Mechanical systems can easily be contrived in which the temperature variable is of no interest whatever, and thus, to a limited extent, a science of mechanics can be divorced from a science of thermodynamics. However, a brief exploration can reveal a wealth of examples of even the simplest mechanical systems in which temperature cannot be ignored. For example, if a block is set in motion along the floor and then released, it quickly comes to rest. As it does so, its kinetic energy decreases. What has been the fate of the kinetic energy originally given to the block? What physical changes have occurred while the block was being brought to rest? The principal physical change that can be observed is an increase in the temperature of both the block and the floor.

The laws of thermodynamics place a process such as that of the preceding example into an analytical, predictive framework. Another kind of question can be asked. Can the above process be reversed? That is, can the temperature of the block and floor decrease with a resulting increase in the kinetic energy of the block? Practical experience says no, but what kind of physical reasoning leads to this negative answer? These questions will emerge in the following discussion as questions that lie at the heart of thermodynamics.

Thermodynamics is based on two important laws, commonly called simply the first and the second laws of thermodynamics. The first law is merely a general statement of energy conservation; the second is related to the directionality of thermal processes. These laws will be introduced as soon as the quantities that they govern have been defined and explored.

Temperature is the fundamental quantity that is added to the body of scientific quantities in order to develop thermodynamics. All other additional quantities introduced by thermodynamics are related to the basic notion of temperature.

Besides the construction of definitions and the abstract formulation of laws, one further element is required in the discussions to follow, namely a concrete physical system that can be used to illustrate the operation of the laws and deductions. Such systems exist in great abundance in the fields of physics and chemistry. Because of its simplicity and educational value, the system chosen for principal study is that of a confined gas. The student may expect, therefore, to learn something about the thermodynamic behavior of gases as well as something about the general ideas of thermodynamics itself.

15-2 TEMPERATURE

The idea of temperature is usually derived from our sense of feeling; that is, objects are found to be hot or cold to touch. We can also judge temperature without direct physical contact. For example, we feel bathed in warmth when exposed to a fire or to sunlight, or we feel cooled when exposed to open sky on a clear night. Although physical sensation provides an excellent clue to the construction of physical quantities, it seldom provides a means of quantitative measure. There are obvious limitations to reliance on our sensations. Objects that have coarse temperature gradations can be ordered by our senses unambiguously from cold to cool to warm to hot, but ordering becomes difficult when the gradation is fine. Even if ordering is possible, the reduction of order to quantitative measure is hopeless, and physics relies on quantitative measurement. We conclude, then, that the subjective notion of temperature is clear to all of us, but there remains the vital step of deciding how the *measurement* of temperature is to be achieved.

The quantitative definition of temperature is arbitrary, just as with all other fundamental quantities. We first note that changes in the temperature of objects as perceived by sensation are often accompanied by other physical changes that can be measured quantitatively:

(a) A body when heated or cooled may suffer a change in size. For a given change in temperature from t_1 to t_2, there may be a change in volume ΔV. Such volume changes for most solids and liquids are difficult to perceive directly. The relative change of volume of a liquid such as alcohol or mercury can, of course, be readily observed in a glass container by the trick of permitting a relatively large volume of the liquid to change volume only along a narrow channel (the usual thermometer). In contrast to liquids and solids, gases under constant pressure experience large changes in volume with changes in temperature.

(b) If a substance is confined to a fixed volume, there is a change in the forces exerted on the constraining walls when the temperature is altered. It is common to express the force exerted by an extended object in terms of force per unit area; this is called the *pressure*. The change in pressure due to temperature variation follows directly from the change in volume that would occur if the substance were not restricted to a constant volume.

(c) Resistance to the flow of electric current in a metal is altered when the temperature of the metal is changed.

(d) The radiation of energy varies with change in temperature and becomes visible at temperatures such that the energy lies in the region visible to the eye. The color of a substance changes from red to white to blue as it is heated through the range of incandescent temperatures. For example, the temperature of a star can be measured by analyzing the color of its light.

(e) The rates at which chemical reactions proceed can depend on the temperature of the reactants.

The changes in properties listed above (there are many others) usually have the appearance of continuous change with temperature. There are other changes that are abrupt, for example:

(1) The discontinuous changes of state from solid to liquid and from liquid to gas are characteristic of particular temperature changes.

(2) Ferromagnetic materials have strong magnetic properties below a certain temperature characteristic of the particular material.

(3) The rate of reaction of some chemical processes can become explosive at certain temperatures.

The definition of the unit for measuring change in temperature depends on three fundamental choices: a particular temperature-dependent property, a particular substance that displays the chosen property, and the functional dependence of the temperature on the chosen property. All three choices are arbitrary.

The choice of functional dependence is that of a linear relationship with the temperature, but this means that almost all other properties except the selected one will *not* be linear in temperature. The temperature-dependent property chosen as the standard for temperature measurements is the volume of a gas at constant pressure, with hydrogen chosen as the particular gas, that is, substance. Actually, it is the change in volume that is chosen, and the change in standard temperature is defined as directly proportional to the change in volume under standard atmospheric pressure. (The details will be developed in Section 15–3.) An instrument designed to measure temperature is called a thermometer.

15–3 THE LAW OF GAY-LUSSAC; THE CENTIGRADE AND KELVIN SCALES

Let a gas confined to a container support a freely moving piston, as in Fig. 15–1. In particular, the gas is chosen to be hydrogen. The space above the piston is evacuated, so that the pressure exerted on the gas by the piston is just w/A, where w is the weight of the piston and A is its area. The mks units of pressure are newtons per square meter. Since the weight of the gas is negligible, the total force, and hence the pressure, at the bottom of the container must be the same as at the top (for mechanical equilibrium). We must, in addition, assume a property of fluids, namely, that the pressure at a point is independent of direction. Then it can be concluded that the pressure on all the walls is the same (for a fluid of negligible mass).

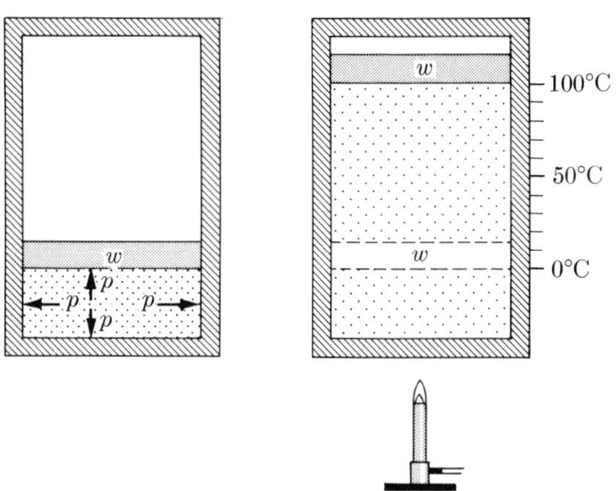

FIG. 15–1. Displacement of a piston of weight w due to the increase in temperature of the gas.

As the gas expands or contracts, the position of the piston changes in a manner that maintains constant pressure. The height of the piston above the floor of the cylinder is a direct measure of the gas volume.

When the temperatures of the gas and the container are increased, as by the application of a Bunsen flame, the gas expands and the piston rises. The amount of gas expansion (measured by the piston level) is to be taken as a *linear measure of the increase in temperature of the gas.*

For a quantitative scale, we require a zero mark and a unit size. Let the gas thermometer be immersed in water that is under standard atmospheric pressure $(0.76 \times 13.6 \times 10^{-3} \times 9.8 \text{ n/m}^2)$. While the water is frozen, the flame is applied to the system, and a change in volume of the gas may be observed. From the instant when the first water appears until the instant when the last of the ice disappears, the gas volume is observed to remain constant! By definition, the temperature is constant throughout the melting process, since the volume of the gas remains constant. Another constant point of reference is the volume when the container is immersed in water, or better, the steam from water boiling at standard pressure. From the time of onset of boiling until the time at which all the water has changed to steam, the volume of the gas in the cylinder and hence the temperature are observed to remain constant.

These convenient landmarks of melting and boiling water are chosen as fixed points on the thermometer scale. The melting point is chosen as zero "degrees," the boiling point is chosen as 100 degrees, and the distance that the piston moves between these two points is divided equally into 100 parts. The scale so defined is called the *centigrade or celsius scale* of temperature measurement. The zero of this scale and the size of the unit are defined as described above.

It should come as no surprise to the student that the volume of hydrogen gas is a linear function of temperature in degrees centigrade, since the functional dependence has been operationally defined so that it will be linear. The relationship in equation form is

$$V = V_0(1 + \alpha t) \text{ m}^3, \qquad (15\text{–}1)$$

where V is the volume at temperature t, t is the temperature in degrees centigrade, V_0 is the volume at $t = 0°\text{C}$ (0 degrees centigrade), and α is a constant with the dimension of reciprocal degrees centigrade. The constant α is called the coefficient of thermal expansion.

A comparison of the thermal behavior of different gases in the category of the so-called permanent gases (hydrogen, helium, nitrogen, etc.) leads to new physical information beyond the arbitrary process of definition. This new information is that the value of α for all the different gases is remarkably close to the same numerical value for all. This universal value of α for the permanent gases is about

$$\alpha = \tfrac{1}{273}(°\mathrm{C})^{-1}. \qquad (15\text{–}2)$$

The law of Gay-Lussac is the above result, Eq. (15–1), including its universality.

The universality of α suggests one reason for the adoption of a permanent gas as the working substance and V as the measured quantity in the choice of the standard thermometer. The choice of hydrogen as the specific gas can be seen to be a matter of finer distinction. This latter point will be discussed later, but one item of clarification should be stated immediately. The equivalence of the constant α for various gases is more exact the lower we make the pressure. Therefore, we agree that our standard thermometer shall correspond to the extrapolated behavior at low pressures.

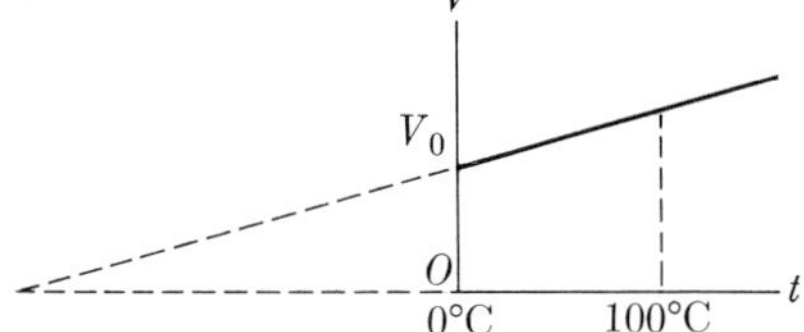

Fig. 15–2. The volume as a function of temperature in °C.

The scale of temperature can be extrapolated in both directions, in a formal way, by simply adding evenly spaced marks above and below the 0 to 100° range defined above. The result is indicated graphically in Fig. 15–2. A glance at the V vs t graph in Fig. 15–2 will suggest an obvious extension in the definition of temperature; namely, we ask if the point on the extrapolated curve denoting zero gas volume has any natural significance. Certainly a negative volume has *no* significance. Therefore, zero temperature may be taken as a new landmark on the temperature scale. It should be mentioned that certain difficulties may occur when one tries to operate a hydrogen gas thermometer down to zero volume, but these technicalities need not be considered here. The measurements of very low and very high temperatures in themselves constitute extensive fields of research and theory.

Continuing our formal line of reasoning, we can see (Eq. 15–1) that the zero-volume intercept occurs at $t = -273°\mathrm{C}$. This temperature value is given the name *absolute zero*, and is chosen as the zero of the kelvin (K) scale. The size of the unit on the kelvin scale remains the same as that on the centigrade scale. Denoting the reading on the kelvin scale as T and on the centigrade scale as t, we have

$$T = t + \frac{1}{\alpha} \qquad (15\text{–}3)$$

or

$$T = t + 273°\mathrm{K}. \qquad (15\text{–}4)$$

The expansion law for gases can be rewritten in terms of the kelvin scale by substituting t from Eq. (15–4) into Eq. (15–1), giving

$$V = V_0 \alpha T. \qquad (15\text{–}5)$$

If we now let the subscript 0 denote values at zero centigrade, that is, $V = V_0$ and $T = T_0$ at $t = 0°\mathrm{C}$, we have $T_0 = 1/\alpha$ and Eq. (15–5) can be written

$$V = V_0 \frac{T}{T_0}\cdot \qquad (15\text{–}6)$$

This result is plotted in Fig. 15–3.

The arbitrary nature of the definitions of temperature has been emphasized above. It must

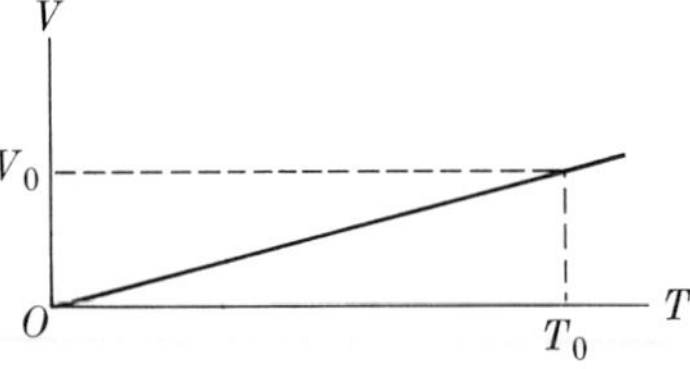

Fig. 15–3. The volume as a function of temperature in °K.

not be thought, however, that the gas laws and the associated gas thermometer were suddenly born out of such straightforward logic. Experiments using ordinary thermometers had already shown the equivalence of α for different gases. In fact, Gay-Lussac had already deduced the linear relationship between gas volume and temperature from measurements with the mercury thermometer. It must be remembered, however, that a temperature scale based on the expansion of mercury relative to glass will agree exactly with the standard gas thermometer only at the end points of 0 and 100°C. The law of Gay-Lussac is, therefore, highly accurate only when the gas-thermometer scale is used. The gas thermometer was adopted as the standard for the reasons given earlier.

Not only is the choice of the relative separation of the scale divisions a "natural" choice in terms of the gas thermometer, but the choice of the zero at $t = -273$°C is also a "natural" choice. Within a small fraction of a degree, the latter is the lowest temperature that can be achieved in nature. More will be learned about the point $T = 0$°K in the discussion of the second law of thermodynamics.

A note should be added. It is customary to discuss the definition of the standard temperature scale in terms of the change in *pressure* of a gas that is held at constant volume. We shall see in what follows that the two methods give exactly the same results in the limit of low pressure, and we remember that the limit at low pressure is chosen for the definition. Therefore in the above discussion we chose the constant *pressure* device because of its simplicity.

15–4 BOYLE'S LAW; THE IDEAL GAS

One of the objectives of this introductory discussion is the definition of the properties of an "ideal" gas. There are several ingredients in this definition, and when they have all been discussed, a summary will be given. One rule that the ideal gas is defined to obey exactly is the law of Gay-Lussac. Another of the conditions on the behavior of an ideal gas is that it exactly obey the experimental law of Boyle:

$$pV = k \tag{15–7}$$

for a fixed temperature T and a fixed mass m of gas. In the above, p is the pressure, V is the volume, and k is a constant.

Expressed in words, Boyle's law says that for a fixed mass of gas held at constant temperature, the product of pressure and volume is a constant k, which will be shown to depend on the mass and temperature of the gas. A simple dimensional analysis shows that k has the dimensions of energy. Boyle's law is quite accurate even for real gases, that is, gases at ordinary pressures, unless the gases are near their points of liquefaction. A series of curves showing the $pV = k$ relationship is shown in Fig. 15–4, where for a given mass of gas, the temperatures T_1, T_2, and T_3 are progressively increasing. The curves are hyperbolas.

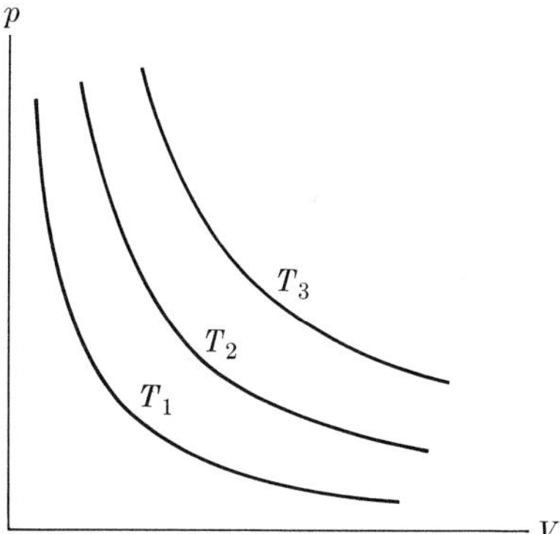

Fig. 15–4. Pressure as a function of volume for three different temperatures.

15–5 EQUATION OF STATE

The laws of Gay-Lussac and Boyle for permanent gases contain relations among the gas attributes such as pressure p, volume V, and temperature T. It is appropriate here to reflect for a moment on the nature of these quantities and on the nature of the relations among them. It is recognized that these attributes of the gas cannot be changed arbitrarily. For example, in order to change the volume a certain amount, the pressure must be changed by a certain amount when other conditions are kept constant. None of the quantities p, V, T, or m can be changed alone, i.e., without affecting the value of at least one of the others.

A gas whose physical attributes are fully described is said to occupy a given state. It is found from experiment that the state of the gas is fully determined when any three of the four variables, p, V, T, and m, are given. One equation relating these four variables must, then, exist. Such an equation is called an equation of state of the gas (or substance other than a gas). The equation of state of an ideal gas is found by combining the laws of Boyle and Gay-Lussac.

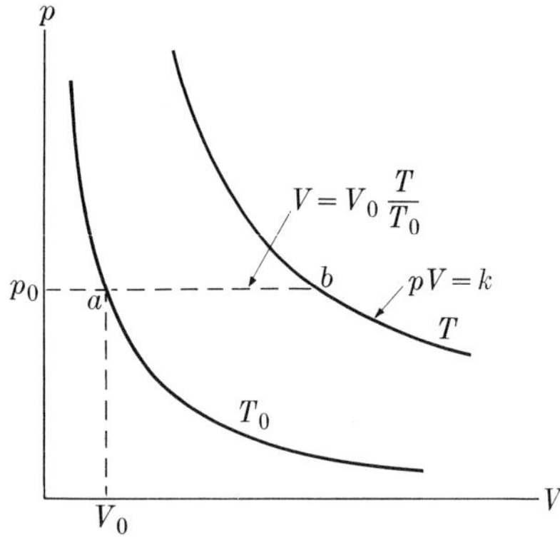

FIG. 15–5. Pressure, volume, and temperature changes in a process that carries the gas from condition a to condition b.

In deriving the equation of state, we can start with Boyle's law, $pV = k$ at constant T. In Fig. 15–5, Boyle's law is represented for two different temperatures T and T_0 for the same mass of gas (where $T > T_0$). Such curves are called isotherms, and a process carried out at constant temperature is called an isothermal process.

In the law of Gay-Lussac, we have a particular process (namely, a process at constant pressure) for reaching one of these isothermal curves starting from the other. In the figure such a process is represented for pressure p_0. Such a process is called isobaric, and the curve is called an isobar. The equation representing the process is, of course,

$$V = V_0 \frac{T}{T_0} \qquad (p = \text{constant}),$$

the law of Gay-Lussac.

Now a single equation combining both relationships can be found, a relationship that will describe the condition (state) of the gas for all values of p, V, and T. In order to obtain this equation, consider the following form for Boyle's law,

$$pV = p_0 V,$$

which is certainly valid since the law holds for all pressures, including the particular value, p_0. Using the law of Gay-Lussac, we can express the volume V in terms of V_0 by considering a process at constant pressure, that is, an expansion in which the temperature increases. Specifically, we have

$$V = V_0 \frac{T}{T_0}.$$

By substitution as follows, we have

$$pV = p_0 V = p_0 V_0 \frac{T}{T_0}, \qquad (15\text{–}8)$$

where the factor $p_0 V_0 / T_0$ may be considered as a constant that is characteristic of the mass of the particular sample of gas. We can set this constant equal to C, giving

$$\frac{p_0 V_0}{T_0} = C. \qquad (15\text{–}9)$$

The temperature dependence of the Boyle constant k is seen to be linear and simply given by

$$k = CT, \qquad (15\text{–}10)$$

where T is the absolute temperature as usual.

The equation of state of the ideal gas can then be written

$$pV = CT, \qquad (15\text{–}11)$$

or in terms of relative values [rearranging factors in Eq. (15–8)],

$$\frac{pV}{T} = \frac{p_1V_1}{T_1} = \frac{p_0V_0}{T_0}. \qquad (15\text{–}12)$$

This last equation demonstrates the equivalence of a constant-pressure gas thermometer to a constant-volume gas thermometer, since the two quantities appear in exactly the same way.

15–6 AVOGADRO'S LAW

The equation of state as deduced above, $pV = CT$, gives a relationship among the quantities p, V, and T. The role that the mass of gas assumes is lacking. The constant C must be related to the mass of gas, and this relationship must be discovered by experiment. The result of experiment is that one gram-molecular weight of gas (one mole) at standard temperature and pressure (zero degrees centigrade and one atmosphere) occupies a volume of 22.4 liters regardless of the kind of gas. It is customary to designate the particular value of the constant C for one mole of gas by

$$R = C \quad \text{(for one mole)}. \qquad (15\text{–}13)$$

From experimental results, as indicated above,

$$R = \frac{p_0V_0}{T_0}, \qquad (15\text{–}14)$$

where V_0 is 22.4 liters when the pressure is 1 atm and the temperature is 0°C. The units of R will, of course, depend on the choice of units for the other quantities. The commonly used scale for temperature is the kelvin scale, on which T_0 is 273.15°K. Standard atmospheric pressure is taken as 1.013×10^5 n/m^2. When these values are substituted into Eq. (15–14), the result is

$$R = 8.3 \text{ joules/mole °K}. \qquad (15\text{–}15)$$

Moreover, by experiment it can be shown that the gas constant C is directly proportional to the mass of gas. Therefore, we use the mole as the unit quantity of gas and let N represent the quantity of gas measured in moles. When this is done, the constant C can be written

$$C = NR = 8.3\, N \text{ joules/°K}, \qquad (15\text{–}16)$$

and the complete equation of state relating the four variables, p, V, T, and N, becomes (for an ideal gas)

$$pV = NRT. \qquad (15\text{–}17)$$

Since the laws of both Boyle and Gay-Lussac are included in the above equation, this equation of state can be said to contain all the properties of the ideal gas, as presented thus far. Equations of state for real gases or other physical systems can be functionally quite different from the above.

Many times it is convenient to use quite different units for the quantities appearing in the equation of state, particularly when using the form of Eq. (15–12). For example, the volume can be measured in units of the volume occupied by one mole at standard temperature and pressure (molal volume), and the pressure can be measured in units of standard atmospheres.

15–7 TEMPERATURE OF A SUBSTANCE

The measurement of temperature involves the following procedure: The thermometer to be used is placed in contact with the substance whose temperature is to be measured. The reading of the thermometer will change, in general, from its value before it was placed in contact with the substance. When the thermometer has come to a steady final reading, we assume that it reads the temperature of the substance in question. It is assumed that the approach of the reading to a final steady value is a natural process ending with a condition of so-called thermal equilibrium between the thermometer and the substance. In this sense, thermal equilibrium means temperature uniformity.

We also assume that the thermometer itself, or the act of measurement, has a negligible effect on the temperature of the object whose temperature we set out to measure, or that a suitable correction can be made.

15–8 HEAT AND CALORIMETERS

Let two objects having dissimilar temperatures be placed in contact, as in Fig. 15–6. Upon contact, the temperatures, T_1 and T_2, of each object begin to change, the higher one decreasing and the lower one increasing. Finally, a state of equilibrium is reached in which a single temperature T_3 obtains for the entire system. A study of the results of experiments of the above sort leads to certain rules of regularity and to the fundamental notion of physical *heat*.

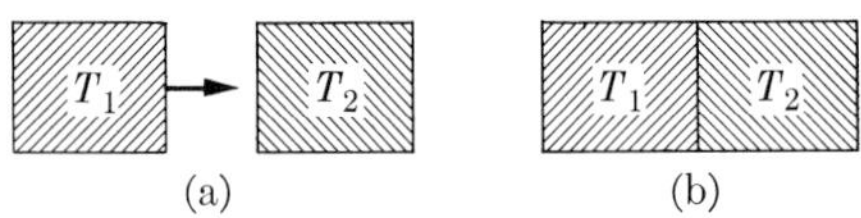

FIG. 15–6. Two objects are placed in thermal contact.

Practically speaking, the above experiment would be very unproductive as stated because the relative effect of the environment of the two blocks would be marked. A more practical system for experiment than the one above is the calorimeter, for example, the water calorimeter, in which the two objects in question come quickly to their common temperature, thereby minimizing the effects of the environment. In the case of the water calorimeter, one of the objects is a container with water at temperature T_1 and the other is a second object, which, if a solid, is conveniently brought to a measurable temperature T_2 by immersion in a water bath (Fig. 15–7). The object at temperature T_2 is then transferred to the calorimeter and the final temperature T_3 of the mixture is measured.

When a series of experiments is performed in which the initial temperatures are given different values, a striking regularity is discovered;

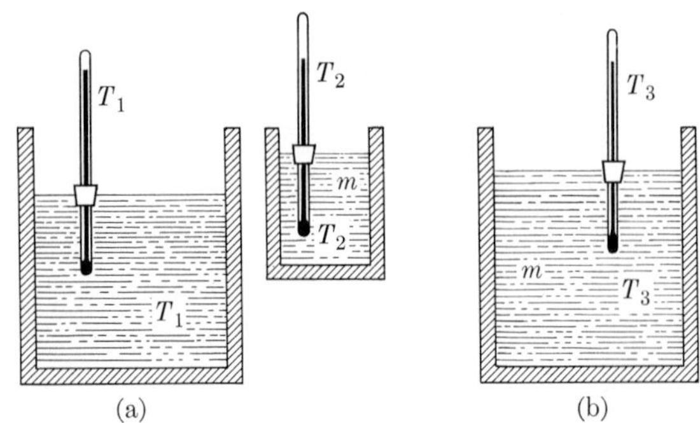

FIG. 15–7. Object m at temperature T_2 is placed in a liquid at temperature T_1, resulting in the final temperature T_3.

namely, the temperature *changes* of the blocks are in a constant ratio, that is,

$$T_3 - T_1 = c(T_2 - T_3).$$

It will be convenient for the discussion that follows to use two constants, c_a and c_b, in place of one. Thus, we write

$$c_a(T_3 - T_1) = c_b(T_2 - T_3). \tag{15–18}$$

By its nature, the calorimeter experiment suggests an interpretation that is at once attractive but also deceptive. We give here the classical interpretation that there is implicit in the calorimeter result a principle of conservation pertaining to a physical quantity called heat. Every object is assumed to have a temperature, which is a measure of how hot the object is. In turn the object is said to be hot because it "contains heat," and the greater the heat content of a given object, the higher its temperature. Now, it can be ascertained that the law of calorimetry can be explained by saying that the hotter object loses heat and the cooler object gains heat. Moreover, the restriction must be applied that heat lost equals heat gained, that is, heat is conserved. The quantity of heat transferred is measured by either side of the calorimeter equation (15–18). The right-hand side of this equation is identified with the heat Q_G gained by the water (assuming that the water was initially the cooler element),

$$Q_G = c_b(T_2 - T_3). \qquad (15\text{–}19)$$

The heat Q_L lost by the test object is identified with the left-hand side,

$$Q_L = c_a(T_3 - T_1). \qquad (15\text{–}20)$$

Then the calorimeter law is obtained by equating the heat gained to the heat lost; that is,

$$Q_L = Q_G, \qquad (15\text{–}21)$$

in agreement with Eqs. (15–18) through (15–20).

In the above, we have assumed that a quantity called heat is conserved for a particular sort of process, namely, heat exchange in a closed system in which no other processes occur. The quantity of heat was defined to be proportional to the change in temperature. The conservation theorem expressed by Eq. (15–21) is perfectly valid under the restricted conditions stated above. It is dangerous to generalize the above ideas in what seemed to the early scientists an obvious direction. The extension might read as follows: "Heat is a kind of indestructible fluid possessed by an object. The amount of fluid and the capacity of the substance to hold this thermal fluid determine the temperature of the object. When objects at different temperatures are in contact, heat fluid flows from the hotter to the colder object. However, the total amount of fluid is an invariable, that is, a conserved quantity, the amount lost by one object being equal to the amount gained by the other." This invention of the heat fluid, called caloric, and the theorem of the conservation of caloric constitute a generalization that does not stand the test of further experiment. We are to encounter situations in which heat is *not* conserved.

Returning to the restricted conditions under which Eq. (15–21) is valid, we continue the discussion of heat and the thermal properties of substances. Using more general notation for the loss or gain of heat by an object, we have

$$\Delta Q = C\,\Delta T, \qquad (15\text{–}22)$$

where ΔQ is the heat gain or loss, ΔT is the temperature change, and C is called the "heat capacity" of the object. When the terms in Eq. (15–22) are rearranged, the definition of C is given explicitly as

$$C = \frac{\Delta Q}{\Delta T}. \qquad (15\text{–}23)$$

The units for heat in the mks system are the kilogram calorie or, for brevity, the kilocalorie (kcal). Therefore the units of heat capacity are kilocalorie per degree centigrade. The kilocalorie will be defined in a moment.

Water is adopted as the standard calorimetric substance. Thus it is agreed that a unit mass of water (one kilogram) requires one kilocalorie of heat when its temperature is changed by 1°C at a temperature centered on 15°C. In other words, the heat capacity of 1 kg of water at 15°C is, by definition, one unit. The heat capacity of any other object can then be measured in terms of the standard by the method of calorimetry. It is found that the heat capacity of any given substance is directly proportional to its mass. The constant of proportionality c is called the specific heat of the material; that is, the specific heat is defined as the heat capacity per unit mass.

Finally, then, the quantity of heat required to change the temperature of an object of mass m can be written

$$\Delta Q = mc\,\Delta T, \qquad (15\text{–}24)$$

with the quantities measured in the following units: ΔQ in kcal, m in kg, c in kcal/(kg · C°), and ΔT in °C.

The value of the specific heat is characteristic of the particular substance. By definition the specific heat of water is unity. A perusal of tables in handbooks will show one that the specific heat of water is large compared with that of other substances; for example, the specific heat of a metal is typically of the order of

TABLE 15-1

Material	Specific heat, kcal/kg·C°
Aluminum	0.22
Copper	0.093
Iron	0.12
Glass	0.12
Mercury	0.033
Ice	0.5

0.1 kcal/(kg · C°). Table 15-1 gives the specific heat for a few substances.

In summary, the definition of temperature and the results of calorimetric experiments have led to the definition of the quantity called heat. An arbitrary definition of the heat unit, called the kilocalorie, is devised. (It should be mentioned that a small calorie is also used that is defined as the quantity of heat required to raise the temperature of 1 gm of water by 1°C. It is therefore $\frac{1}{1000}$ of 1 kcal.) Much of the discussion that follows pertains to this physical quantity called heat. However, it is not the only thermal quantity of importance. Others will be introduced, particularly in more specialized texts.

One property of heat, a property that has already been noted, is of vital importance. This is the experimental observation that heat of itself always flows from hot to cold bodies. This observation may, at first glance, appear to be so self-evident from experience that its importance is missed. Actually, this idea is so important that it forms the foundation for the second law of thermodynamics, as we shall see later.

15-9 CHANGE OF STATE; LATENT HEAT

In the definition of the fixed points on the temperature scale at 0 and at 100°C, it was mentioned that the temperature of water remains fixed while it is changing its physical form from solid to liquid or from liquid to vapor. Since the temperature remains constant even while heat is being added to or subtracted from water during the above process, the equations and ideas of the preceding section [with the exception of Eq. (15-21)] clearly do not apply. The processes of physical change noted above are called *changes of state*.

It is found that heat must be added or subtracted from a substance in order to change its state and, furthermore, that the temperature does not change during the change of state. In order to utilize the calorimetric idea of heat conservation, a new concept must be introduced, the concept of the latent heat involved in a change of state. Quantitatively, the latent heat L is defined as the quantity of heat required to change the state of unit mass of the substance. Thus the heat ΔQ required to change the state of a mass m is simply

$$\Delta Q = mL. \tag{15-25}$$

The temperatures at which changes of state occur are called melting or freezing points, boiling or condensation points, etc. The latent heat and the temperature at which changes of state occur depend on the pressure. The values are usually given for standard atmospheric pressure, as in Table 15-2.

Once again it is necessary to recognize the restricted nature of our assumption of conservation of heat energy. Heat interchanges during changes of state can be included in the calorimetric equations only if the pressure on the system is kept constant and if no other types of energy interchanges occur.

A few additional facts are the following: In the case of solids, changes of state from one crystalline form to another can sometimes occur. The latent heats and the temperatures at which changes of state occur depend on pressure. For example, it is well known that as the boiling point of water becomes lower so does the pressure. This is a common experience when one cooks at high altitudes where the pressure is lower than at sea level. It is less well known that at a pressure of about 0.6% of standard atmospheric pressure,

TABLE 15–2

Temperatures and Latent Heat of Changes of State
(at standard atmospheric pressure)

Material	Melting point, °C	L (fusion), kcal/kg	Boiling point, °C	L (vaporization), kcal/kg
Water	0	79.7	100	540
Mercury	−39	2.8	357	65
Helium	—	—	−268.6	6.0
Nitrogen	−210	6.1	−196	48

the boiling point *and* the melting point of water coincide at 0.01°C. This is the so-called triple point, at which ice, water, and water vapor are in equilibrium.

15–10 HEAT TRANSFER

The heat quantity Q has been defined on the basis of an elementary calorimetric experiment. Now that the nature and method of measurement of Q have been set forth, it is possible to observe additional physical laws which pertain to this quantity. It is important both to the specification of the nature of heat and to the analysis of more advanced experiments to study the laws of heat transfer.

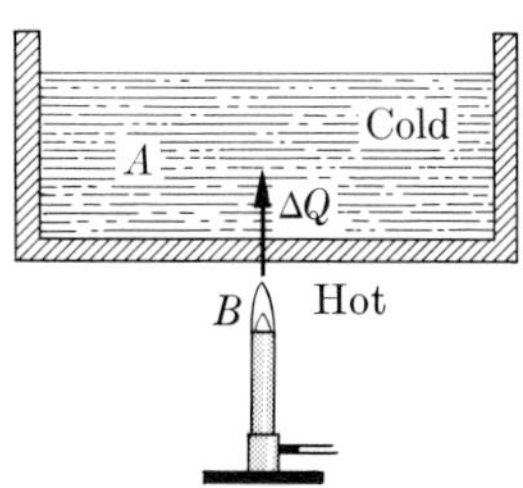

Fig. 15–8. Transfer of heat ΔQ from B to A.

How, operationally, do we "add heat" to an object? The operation is simple indeed. If the object to be heated is a vessel of water A, we bring into its vicinity a hotter object, such as a Bunsen flame B (Fig. 15–8). The transfer of heat from B to A occurs solely because the temperature of B is greater than the temperature of A. We identify the cause of heat transfer as the temperature difference ΔT between the objects. The rate of heat transfer, that is, number of kilocalories transported per unit time, depends, in the example presented here, in a very complex way on the temperature difference, since several different mechanisms for heat transfer are involved. They are conduction, convection, and radiation. Refined experiments can be constructed in which the different mechanisms are effectively isolated. The results of such experiments are presented below.

Conduction. Let two objects have temperatures T_1 and T_2. Let the intervening space be filled with a material substance (Fig. 15–9). It can be observed that heat is transported from the hot to the cold object through the material medium, and such a process is called heat transport by conduction. The rate of conduction depends on the temperature difference, the geometry of the system, and the nature of the material substance itself. We do not ask here why heat is conducted but only how.

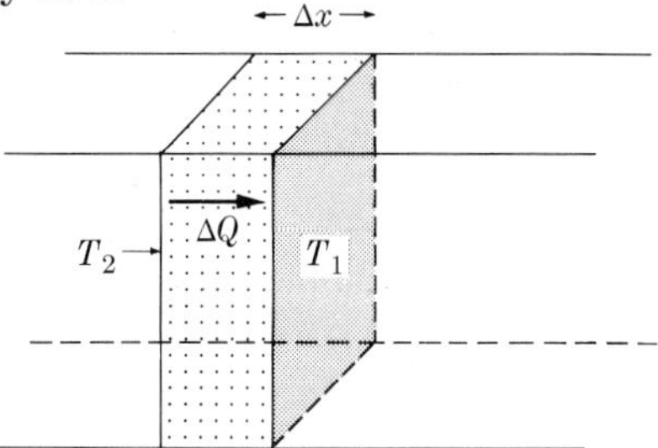

Fig. 15–9. Transfer of heat ΔQ through the layer Δx.

For the simplest geometric arrangement, let the two objects of different temperatures have plane faces separated by a flat slab between the faces. Each face of the slab is to have a uniform temperature, one face at T_2, the other at T_1, where $T_2 > T_1$.

The time rate of heat flow, dQ/dt, is found experimentally to be directly proportional to the temperature difference between the slab faces, directly proportional to the area, and inversely proportional to the slab thickness Δx, that is,

$$\frac{dQ}{dt} = KA\,\frac{\Delta T}{\Delta x}\,\frac{\text{kcal}}{\text{sec}}. \qquad (15\text{–}26)$$

The coefficient K is called the coefficient of heat conductivity. It has the dimensions kcal/(m · sec · C°), and its magnitude is a characteristic of the conducting medium. Many materials fall into two distinct classes according to their heat conductivity. Metals are good conductors of heat with K in the range 0.001 to 0.01, whereas nonmetals are poor conductors with K in the range 10^{-6} to 10^{-4} mks units.

Radiation. If the conducting material slab in Fig. 15–9 is removed and if the intervening space between the faces with temperatures T_2 and T_1 is made a perfect vacuum, heat transport is still observed. The law of heat transport across the vacuum, however, is very different from that for material conduction, and new properties of the system become important to the rate of heat transport. The mechanism for heat transport through the vacuum is called radiation. In more advanced studies, the heat radiation (called infrared radiation) is found to be identical in fundamental nature with light radiation, radio signals, and others of a large class called electromagnetic radiation. In this purely descriptive treatment we are again interested only in the systematic rules for the radiation process and not in the detailed mechanism of the process.

The optimum geometric arrangement for studying radiation transfer is different from that for conduction. We place an object with temperature T_2 in an enclosure at temperature T_1, as in Fig. 15–10. The central object is suspended by a thin nonconductor to ensure that the process of thermal conduction from central object to wall is a negligible factor. The rate of heat transport is observed to be proportional to the surface area A of the central object, to the difference between the fourth powers of the absolute temperatures of the object and the wall, and to a constant ϵ (called emissivity) that is dependent on the nature of the surface of the central object. We have

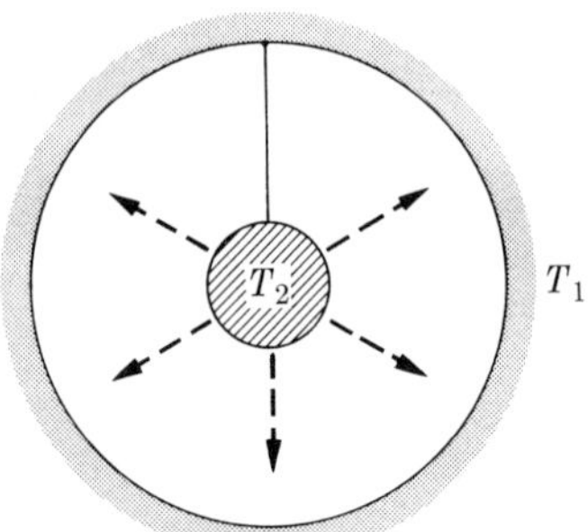

FIG. 15–10. Heat transfer from T_2 to T_1 by radiation.

$$\frac{dQ}{dt} = \epsilon\sigma A(T_2^4 - T_1^4), \qquad (15\text{–}27)$$

where the universal constant, σ, called the Stefan-Boltzmann constant, has the value

$$\sigma = 5.67 \times 10^{-5}\,\frac{\text{erg}}{\text{cm}^2\cdot\text{deg}^4\cdot\text{sec}}. \qquad (15\text{–}28)$$

For heat conduction, the temperatures can be given either on the centigrade or on the kelvin scale, since temperatures appeared only as a difference. But in the present case, radiation transfer of heat, the temperatures appearing in Eq. (15–27) must be on the kelvin scale. The units are cgs units, the erg being $1/10^7$ joule.

The coefficient ϵ is a dimensionless number which characterizes the surface quality and has a range of values between zero and unity. If we apply an extremely dull black finish (such as a coating of fine soot) to the surface, then the value of ϵ approaches unity. An ideal radiator, whose surface is characterized by the value unity for ϵ, is called a perfect "blackbody." By contrast, for a shiny mirror surface, ϵ approaches zero. Thus for the radiation process, a mirror surface has an insulating effect. We have here the rules for the construction of a Dewar flask or Thermos bottle, which is a double-walled container whose surfaces are shiny (minimum radiation) with the interwall space evacuated of air (minimum conduction).

A few words about the radiation mechanism will increase the students' understanding of the radiation law. The container wall to which the central object radiates heat also radiates heat to the object. Thus the two terms $\epsilon\sigma A T_2^4$ and $-\epsilon\sigma A T_1^4$ can be interpreted as the difference between the heat radiated from the object to the wall (first term) and the heat radiated from the wall to the object (second term). The net rate of heat transport is the difference between the two terms. As the two temperatures become more nearly equal, the two terms balance each other such that when $T_2 = T_1$, the *net* rate of heat transport from one to the other vanishes. However, the radiation process has not ceased. We simply have the equilibrium case where the radiations in both directions are equal, making the *net* transport zero.

Convection. No formal laws of heat transport by convection are presented here because the convective process does not lend itself to simple geometric arrangements and analysis. A descriptive remark is offered. It is common knowledge that air rises when heated above the temperature of the surrounding air. Heat transport is thereby accomplished quite literally through the transport of the heated mass (Fig. 15–11).

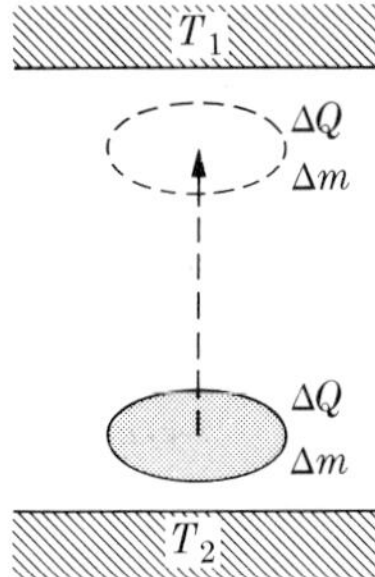

FIG. 15–11. The transfer of heat ΔQ by the motion of mass Δm (convection).

15–11 SUMMARY

Various effects of temperature on properties of materials are discussed. A scale of temperature is defined in terms of the change in volume of hydrogen gas with change in temperature, with the boiling point of water and the freezing point of water under standard conditions chosen as references. In the centigrade system, the boiling point is chosen to be 100° and the freezing point zero. The scale is then chosen to be linearly dependent on the volume of hydrogen gas at constant pressure as the gas density approaches zero. Thus, the temperature t in centigrade degrees is given implicitly (the law of Gay-Lussac) by

$$V = V_0(1 + \alpha t),$$

where α is a constant. It is found that α is the same for all gases in the limit as the density of the gases approaches zero. The measured value of α is about $\frac{1}{273}$ per °C. Since the volume law extrapolates to $V = 0$ at $t = -273$, a second temperature scale is defined using the same size intervals but with the zero shifted from the melting point of ice to $1/\alpha \simeq -273$. The latter zero is called absolute zero, and the temperature scale based on the above system is called the kelvin scale.

A second result of the observation of the behavior of gases is Boyle's law,

$$pV = \text{constant},$$

when the temperature is kept constant. When the two above laws are combined, there results the equation of state

$$pV = CT, \qquad \text{or} \qquad pV = RT,$$

where R is the constant for one mole of gas and

has the value 8.3 joules/°K. An ideal gas is defined as a gas that would follow the above laws exactly. Other properties of the ideal gas will be defined later.

The heat capacity of substances is defined in terms of the amount of heat energy required to raise the temperature by one degree. Water is chosen as the standard, with the heat capacities of other substances referred to water. When inert substances are left in close contact, it is found that they come to the common temperature (if they are well insulated from their environment). The results of experiments in which substances initially at different temperatures are placed together and allowed to come to a common final temperature can be interpreted in terms of heat capacities and the conservation of heat energy. Experiments of the above sort are called calorimetry experiments. The heat energy unit is the *calorie*, defined as the heat required to raise the temperature of 1 gm of water 1°C (or kelvin).

When a substance changes state, heat is absorbed or emitted without any change in temperature. The heat per gram of substance required in a change of state is the *latent heat.*

Heat can be transferred by conduction. It is found from experiment that the rate of heat transfer dQ/dt is given by

$$\frac{dQ}{dt} = KA\,\frac{\Delta T}{\Delta x},$$

where A is the area of the surface through which the heat is transferred, $\Delta T/\Delta x$ is the temperature gradient in the direction of heat transfer, and K is a constant characteristic of the substance.

Heat transfer by radiation follows the law

$$\frac{dQ}{dt} = \epsilon\sigma A(T_2^4 - T_1^4),$$

where ϵ is a property of the surfaces called emissivity, A is the area of the surface of the radiating object, T_2 is the temperature of the surface of the radiating object and T_1 of the surrounding surface, and σ is a universal constant of value 5.67×10^{-5} erg/cm$^2 \cdot$ deg$^4 \cdot$ sec.

Heat transfer by convection is a complicated effect depending on the flow of fluid between surfaces at different temperatures.

Problems

1. What is the pressure at standard temperature of 10 gm of molecular hydrogen confined to a volume of 10 liters?

2. A bubble of air is made at the bottom of a lake. The water temperature at the bottom is 4°C. The bubble rises 20 m to the lake surface, where the temperature is 24°C. What is the ratio of the volume at the surface to the volume at the bottom? Hydrostatic pressure is given by the rule $p = p_0 + h\rho g$ where p is the pressure at depth h, p_0 is the surface, or atmospheric, pressure, ρ is the mass density of the liquid, and g is the gravitational acceleration.

3. An extreme idealization of the earth's atmosphere assumes that the temperature of the air is constant, say $T = 300$°K, at all altitudes. Then the Boyle condition would pertain. Consider that the atmosphere is representable by a uniform column of air. At the base of the column we have a pressure p_0, the surface atmospheric pressure. At some level h above the surface we have a pressure p, at the base of a thin slab (Fig. 15–12). At $h + dh$ we have a pressure $p - dp$, the difference in pressure being due to the weight of the air contained in the slab of thickness dh. Call ρ the density of air at pressure p.

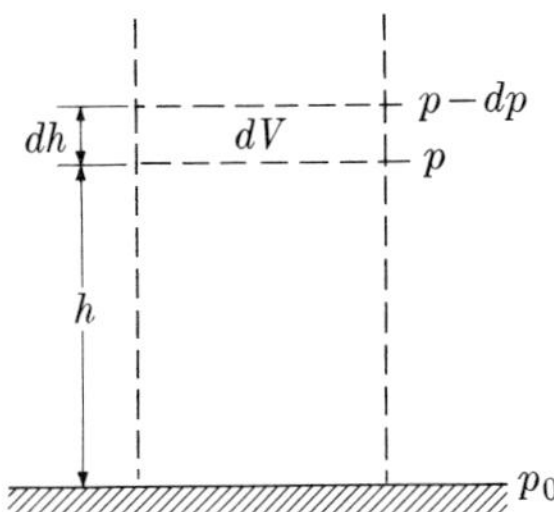

FIGURE 15–12

Then the pressure difference dp is

$$dp = -\rho g\, dh$$

where g is the gravitational acceleration. The product $\rho g\, dh$ is the gravitational weight of a slab of unit area. We also have the gas law

$$pV = nRT \qquad \text{or} \qquad pV = \frac{m}{M} RT,$$

where m is the mass of gas, and M is the molecular weight. This can be written

$$p = \frac{m}{V}\frac{1}{M} RT \qquad \text{or} \qquad p = \frac{\rho}{M} RT.$$

Combining the equations for p and dp, deduce the differential equation for pressure

$$\frac{dp}{p} = \frac{Mg\, dh}{RT}.$$

Integrate this equation, to obtain the expression

$$\frac{p}{p_0} = e^{-(Mg/RT)h}.$$

The molecular weight of air is about 29 gm/mole. How high in the atmosphere do we have to go to encounter a pressure of $\frac{1}{2}p_0$? At what altitude do we encounter a good laboratory vacuum, that is, $p = 10^{-9}p_0$? What is the pressure at the peak of the highest mountain? Actually the gas condition is more nearly adiabatic than isothermal. Can you deduce the atmospheric law corresponding to this rule? What depth of water is required to give the same pressure as the atmospheric air?

4. A 2 kg mass of metal has a specific heat of 0.1 kcal/(kg·°C). What is the heat capacity of the object? Let the metal be heated to 90°C. It is then dropped into a body of water 1 m^3 in volume at 24°C. The whole system is isolated so as to prevent the absorption or escape of heat. What is the final, or equilibrium, temperature of the system?

5. Two plane faces spaced 1 centimeter apart are maintained at different temperatures, $T_2 = 100$°C and $T_1 = 0$°C. A fairly good conductor of heat is placed between the faces, filling the space. It has a thermal conductivity of 0.001 kcal·sec^{-1}·deg^{-1}·m^{-1}. What is the rate of heat conduction per unit surface area? Let the conductor be removed. What is the rate of heat transfer per unit area by radiation through the intervening vacuum? Assume the faces to be perfect emitters. At what value of T_2 is the transmission of heat through the conductor equal to the "transmission" of heat through the vacuum?

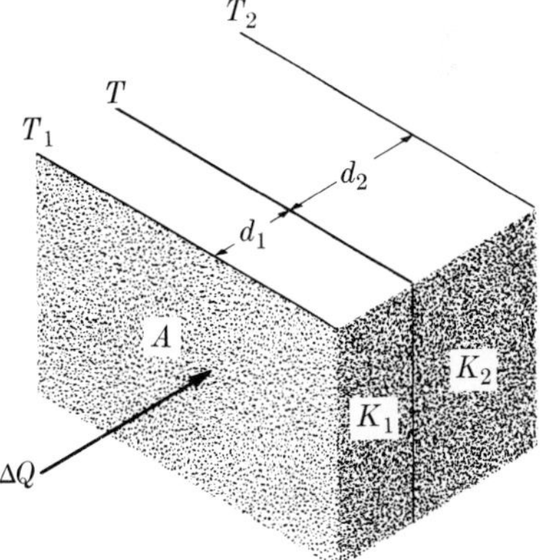

FIGURE 15–13

6. Heat is conducted through a compound wall as in Fig. 15–13. Part of the wall is of thickness d_1 and has a conductivity K_1. The other part is of thickness d_2 and has a thermal conductivity K_2. The outer faces are held at temperatures T_1 and T_2 as shown. Let the interface temperature be T'. Solve for T' in terms of the given data. Assume in the steady case that the heat transfer through either part of the wall is the same. Is this true? Why?

Set up the heat transfer equation separately for each portion of the wall. Show that the heat transfer through the compound wall can be written

$$\frac{\Delta Q}{\Delta t} = \frac{A(T_2 - T_1)}{(d_1/K_1) + (d_2/K_2)}.$$

7. Find the surface area of the tungsten filament of a 100-watt light bulb. The emissivity is $\epsilon = 0.25$. The temperature is 2000°K.

8. Let a blackened object of initial absolute temperature T_1 be suspended in outer space, such that the surroundings can be characterized by a temperature of absolute zero. The radiation law for the object is then

$$\frac{dQ}{dt} = \sigma A T^4.$$

Also, the relationship between heat loss and temperature change is

$$dQ = mc\, dT,$$

where m is the mass and c is the specific heat of the object. Show that the differential equation for "cooling" can be written

$$\frac{dT}{T^4} = \frac{\sigma A}{mc}\, dt.$$

Integrate this equation to obtain the law of cooling (the temperature-time equation):

$$\frac{1}{T^3} = \frac{-3\sigma A t}{mc} + \frac{1}{T_1^3}.$$

The block is made of copper. It has a radius of 10 cm and it is coated with lampblack. The initial temperature is 1000°K. How much time is required to cool to 300°K?

9. An ideal gas is enclosed in a chamber of volume V at a pressure $2p_0$, where p_0 is atmospheric pressure. The container is punctured so as to allow the gas to leak out slowly until the pressure is p_0. How much work is done by the escaping gas? Where does the energy come from?

16

The First Law of Thermodynamics

16–1 INTRODUCTION

The function of the first law of thermodynamics is the identification of the heat quantity Q as a form of energy and the formulation of the principle of energy conservation in a way that is applicable to thermal (temperature-dependent) processes. While the reader, with his modern technological background, will be prepared for a speedy acceptance of the first law, he should consider carefully the very considerable break in scientific thinking which was required for its deduction. Chapter 15 contains a very small portion of what once was termed the science of heat. A brief review of the chapter, in which the quantity Q is defined, will show that there is no *a priori* reason why Q must be regarded as a form of energy. No such assumption is implied in the definition of the quantities called temperature, heat capacity, and specific heat.

So long as physical systems are so contrived that heat transfer is isolated from the processes of heat production and heat conversion (the conditions assumed in Chapter 15), the actual connection between heat and the other branches of science is blocked from view. It is interesting that it was not the physicists of yesterday who extended the subject of heat into its modern form of thermodynamics. Figuring largely in the evolution of the law were engineers and medical doctors who were evidently more anxious than physicists to see the broader context of the subject. We do not follow the historical development here, because it cannot be done briefly without losing the real point. Nevertheless, an excellent literature exists on the history of the first law, and the student is referred to the library on this subject. We proceed immediately to a logical construction.

Unless otherwise stated, it will always be assumed that the processes that will now be discussed are reversible. The conditions for reversibility are that there is no friction and that the processes are carried on slowly enough that equilibrium conditions are maintained at all times except for infinitesimal departures of quantities from equilibrium values. The second condition guarantees that we can describe the state of a material in terms of its pressure, temperature, etc.

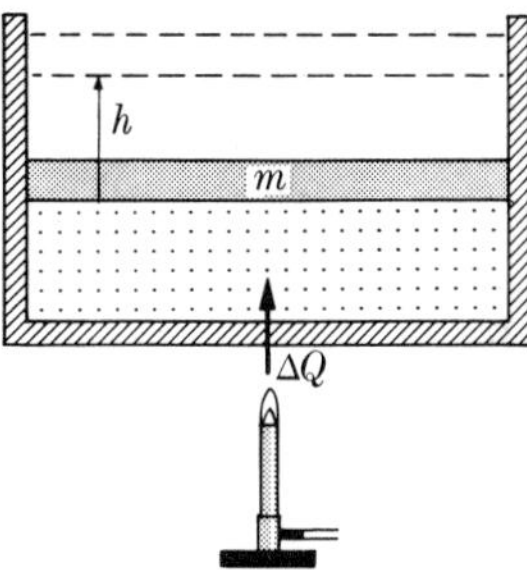

FIG. 16–1. Heat transfer ΔQ resulting in an expansion of the substance that receives ΔQ.

Consider again the system in which a gas is confined at constant pressure. This system is, in fact, the physical thermometer set forth in Chapter 15. A Bunsen flame is applied to the gas chamber. The confined gas is heated, and it expands, raising the piston weight as in Fig. 16–1. There are two distinct and identifiable physical changes that attend the addition of heat ΔQ to the system. Letting the system include the weight and the gas in the chamber, we see that physical changes are specifically:

(a) The temperature of the gas has risen, presumably in a way that can be described through the definition of a specific heat of the gas in the chamber.

(b) The piston has been raised, and this in itself requires the performance of mechanical work mgh, where m is the piston mass, g is the gravitational acceleration, and h is the height through which the piston is moved.

There is an obvious connection between the heat ΔQ and energy; the injection of heat into the system has resulted in the performance of work. It has been assumed that we have an idealized system such that the chamber walls do not affect the thermal aspects of the problem.

There is an advantage here in developing a more careful formulation of our choice of system, for it has two components. One component is the gas itself; the other is the piston. If the gas is regarded as the system under study, then the description of the process goes somewhat differently; namely, the gas absorbs heat from one outside element (the flame) but performs work on another outside element (the piston). The designation of the gas alone as the thermal system is typical of thermodynamic analysis.

If heat is to be identified as a form of energy, then, in the example given above, the effect of ΔQ must be divided into two parts. *Part* of the effect of heat addition has been the resultant temperature increase of the gas. This part is called ΔU, the *change in internal energy* of the gas. This is the portion of ΔQ retained by the gas system. The other part of ΔQ has escaped the gas system. This is ΔW, the work performed by the gas on the piston. *A quantitative statement of this partition of the added heat energy becomes the first law of thermodynamics.* Before proceeding to the exact statement of the law, we present an essential groundwork in two areas: (1) an experimental measurement of work-to-heat conversion and (2) the formal methods of computing work for confined-gas systems.

16-2 THE MECHANICAL EQUIVALENT OF HEAT

Experimentally, there is no evident reason why work cannot be transformed into heat with 100% efficiency. Systems can be easily contrived in which, with the performance of work, there is *no other effect* than a heating of the system. The same cannot be said for the reverse process, the conversion of heat into work. The efficiency of this latter process is a topic under the second law of thermodynamics, which will be presented later.

In Chapter 15, a specific way of heating an object was described. A hotter object was brought close by, and heat ΔQ was transferred. This is the method of heating the object portrayed in Fig. 16-1. By a second method, no hotter object is involved at all and no heat is transferred. A second object is brought into contact with the first and the objects are vigorously rubbed against each other. Heat is not necessarily transferred from one object to the other; both get hot. Heat is generated in the process, where none existed before. Mechanical work is required in this second process. The experimental problem proposed is this: What amount of work ΔW is required to cause a definite temperature change equivalent to the addition of heat ΔQ? This *equivalent* amount of work is called the mechanical equivalent of heat. Since mechanical work is measured in an energy unit, the experiment must succeed in ascribing an energy equivalent to the kilogram calorie of heat.

The physicist Joule contrived the first careful experiment on the ratio of the work unit to the

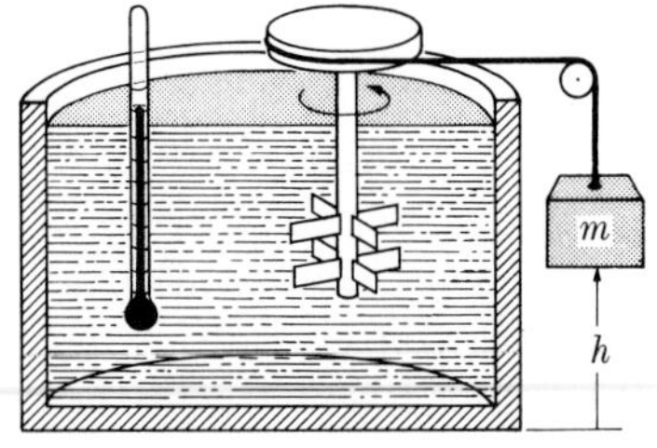

FIG. 16-2. Schematic diagram of apparatus to measure the mechanical equivalent of heat.

heat unit. In principle, a set of rotating paddles is immersed in a jar of water, as in Fig. 16–2. The paddles are driven by a falling weight through a shaft-string-pulley arrangement. When the weight falls there is an agitation of the liquid. After the mechanical process has ended, that is, when the weight has stopped and the water has ceased swirling, we find only two changes in the system: the weight has lost potential energy in the amount

$$\Delta W = \Delta PE = mgh \text{ joules}, \qquad (16\text{–}1)$$

and the temperature of the water has risen by Δt. We have neglected the fact that the weight had kinetic energy. If the kinetic energy changed appreciably *during* the downward motion of m, this effect can be taken into account. To cause the same temperature rise by the addition of heat, we require an amount of heat

$$\Delta Q = mc\,\Delta T \text{ kcal}. \qquad (16\text{–}2)$$

The expressions for ΔW and ΔQ contain only directly measurable quantities, which give the following value for the ratio of mechanical to heat energy units:

$$J = \frac{\Delta W}{\Delta Q} = 4180\,\frac{\text{joules}}{\text{kcal}}. \qquad (16\text{–}3)$$

The student is urged to put sample data which he believes would be typical into the above equations. The results will show how difficult the accurate measurement of ΔT must be in practice by the above method. Or, if the student is an experimentalist by temperament, he may try boiling a glass of water by stirring it.

With the measured value of J at our disposal, the partition problem of the preceding section, the splitting of ΔQ into work, ΔW, and into internal energy, ΔU, can be put onto a quantitative basis.

16–3 MECHANICAL WORK

The definition of mechanical work is reviewed here in a form which is useful in the study of confined gases. Let a confined gas expand by moving a piston, as in Fig. 16–3. In the expansion the piston moves a distance dy. The work performed is

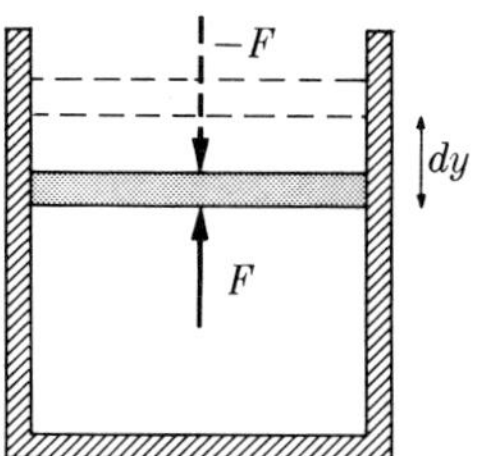

Fig. 16–3. The motion of a piston (expansion of a gas) under equilibrium conditions.

$$dW = F\,dy \text{ joules}. \qquad (16\text{–}4)$$

An external force, $-F$, must always be exerted on the piston if the piston is to move at constant velocity. In fact, we usually assume that the process is slow enough that equilibrium conditions are always maintained; that is, all the gas is at the same temperature, etc. From the definition of pressure,

$$F = pA,$$

where p is the gas pressure in newtons per square meter and A is the area of the piston surface in square meters. Then by substitution,

$$dW = pA\,dy.$$

Also, $A\,dy$ is just the change in volume, dV of the gas, and therefore we have the relationship

$$dW = p\,dV \text{ joules}. \qquad (16\text{–}5)$$

Work is therefore expressible in terms of the gas characteristics p and V.

Example 1. Let a gas expand against a piston under the conditions implied for Boyle's law, an isothermal expansion. What is the work performed in an expansion from V_1 to V_2?

When an isolated gas expands and does work, the performance of work is observed to result in a decrease in gas temperature. Thus to maintain constant

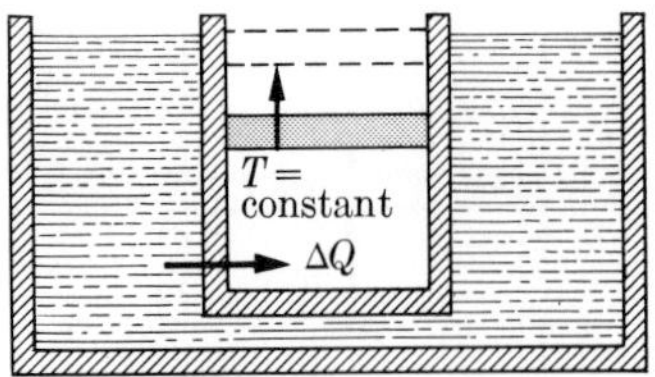

Fig. 16-4. Absorption of heat ΔQ from the environment when a gas is allowed to expand.

temperature, heat must be supplied to the gas at just the correct rate to prevent cooling. This can be accomplished in practice by placing the gas container in a bath of very large heat capacity, say a large water bath, as in Fig. 16-4. Then any cooling of the gas is attended by a heat flow from bath to gas tending to keep the temperature of the gas constant. It is further presumed that the expansion is performed extremely slowly so that the heat transfer can be accomplished with a vanishingly small temperature difference between gas and bath. This is one of the practical implications of Boyle's law.

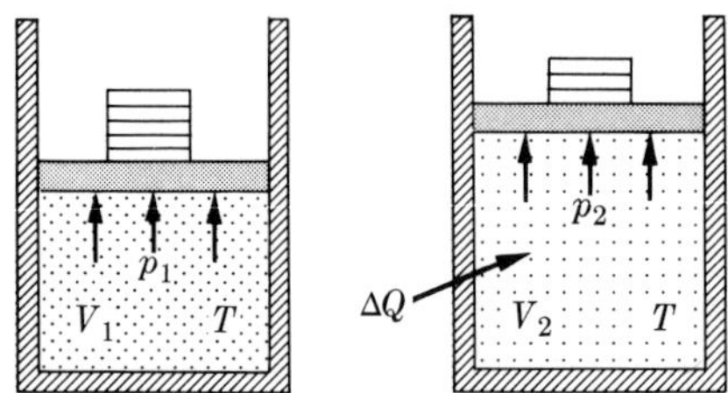

Fig. 16-5. Schematic representation of the slow expansion of a gas realized by successive removal of small weights on the piston.

How can a gas at constant temperature expand? It does so only if the confining pressure is reduced. This can be accomplished in principle by loading the piston with a great number of small weights (Fig. 16-5). As the weights are gradually removed from the piston, the pressure is reduced in small stages and the gas expands, doing work on the *remaining* weights, which are lifted. A pause between the removal of each weight ensures that time is allowed for heat transfer from bath to gas, enabling the temperature of the gas to remain constant. These are the precautions required in a proper Boyle expansion. The expansion is termed *isothermal* to denote that temperature is held constant.

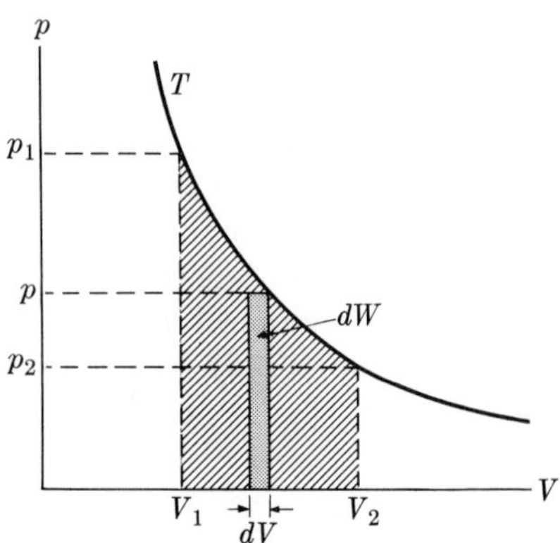

Fig. 16-6. Pressure versus volume for the expansion of a gas at constant temperature. Work dW is done during the expansion dV at volume V.

In Fig. 16-6 a representation of the state of the gas at any stage of the process is given by a graph of p versus V.

The work done in an expansion dV is

$$dW = p\,dV,$$

and the work done in expansion from V_1 to V_2 is the definite integral

$$\Delta W = \int_{V_1}^{V_2} p\,dV. \qquad (16\text{-}6)$$

We can see in the figure that the work ΔW is the area under the p-V curve bounded by the vertical lines $V = V_1$ and $V = V_2$. The functional dependence of p on V for the gas is given approximately by assuming an ideal gas, for which $pV = NRT$ (Eq. 15-17). Then

$$\Delta W = \int_{V_1}^{V_2} \frac{NRT\,dV}{V},$$

and since T is constant, it can be taken outside the integral, with the result

$$\Delta W = NRT \int_{V_1}^{V_2} \frac{dV}{V}. \qquad (16\text{-}7)$$

By integrating, we obtain

$$W = NRT \log_e \frac{V_2}{V_1}. \qquad (16\text{-}8)$$

Also, since

$$p_1 V_1 = p_2 V_2,$$

we can express ΔW in terms of the pressure limits; that is,

$$\Delta W = NRT \log_e \frac{p_1}{p_2}. \qquad (16\text{–}9)$$

The example illustrates in a special case (T = constant) the way that a confined gas can be harnessed to perform mechanical work.

16–4 INTERNAL ENERGY

Consider a system such as a gas to which heat ΔQ is added. From the foregoing discussion, it is evident that the gas may in turn perform external work. Part of the energy ΔQ which has been added to the system has left the system in the form of external work ΔW. If the principle of energy conservation is to be applied to the process, we must account for the difference between ΔQ and ΔW. We say that an amount of the energy ΔU, called internal energy, has been deposited into and retained by the gas itself. The temperature increase of the gas is physical evidence of the absorption of internal energy by the gas. As long as it remains a gas, the principal manifestation of an increase in internal energy is the increase in temperature. There are, as we have seen, other possible effects due to a change in internal energy, some attended by no temperature change at all. Examples are changes of state as discussed in Chapter 15.

A change in state involves a change in internal energy. For example, when heat is added to melting ice, the principal result is that a definite amount of ice is converted into liquid water. Through calorimetric experiments we can find that the addition of 80 kcal of heat is required for the conversion of each kilogram of ice into water. Contrarily, the same amount of heat is given up by each kilogram of water that freezes into ice at 0°C. Therefore the surroundings are heated when water freezes. The energy which is absorbed by the melting solid is evidently retained by the system and is regarded as fixed into a form of internal energy. From such examples, we see that a change in internal energy may be manifested by a change in temperature or a change in the intrinsic structure of the system. The processes described are illustrative of the nature of internal energy.

16–5 STATEMENT OF THE FIRST LAW OF THERMODYNAMICS

Let an amount of heat ΔQ be absorbed by a substance. Suppose also that the substance performs an amount of work ΔW upon its surroundings. Then the first law of thermodynamics states that the change in internal energy of the substance equals the difference between ΔQ and ΔW. In equation form,

$$\Delta U = \Delta Q - \Delta W, \qquad (16\text{–}10)$$

or

$$\Delta U = \Delta Q - p\,\Delta V. \qquad (16\text{–}11)$$

This is the result of applying the principle of energy conservation to thermal processes. The first law contains the formal definition of the quantity called internal energy, since ΔQ and ΔW have been previously defined and their units related. It is, of course, assumed that identical units are used for U, Q, and W in Eq. (16–11), either a mechanical unit, e.g., the joule, or a thermal unit, e.g., the kilogram calorie. The conversion to uniform units is accomplished by using the mechanical equivalent of heat, J, of Eq. (16–3).

The operation of the first law is illustrated in a series of applications which follow. The applications treated in order are: (a) the specific heats of an ideal gas, (b) the expansion and compression of an ideal gas, and (c) the operation of the Carnot heat engine.

16–6 SPECIFIC HEAT OF AN IDEAL GAS AT CONSTANT VOLUME; INTERNAL ENERGY

We can now subject the descriptive quantity called internal energy to an analytical treatment. The specific heat of a substance is defined as the heat absorbed per kilogram of substance per degree temperature change; namely,

$$c \equiv \frac{1}{m}\frac{\Delta Q}{\Delta T}. \tag{16–12}$$

If c is dependent on temperature, Eq. (16–12) defines an average value. The definition in more general form is, therefore,

$$c \equiv \frac{1}{m}\frac{dQ}{dT}. \tag{16–13}$$

The fate of the heat added to a gas depends on the constraints which are applied to the gas during the addition of heat. If the gas is held at fixed volume, then no work can be performed by the gas. The first law then reduces to

$$\Delta Q = \Delta U, \tag{16–14}$$

and we see that the heat added to the gas equals the change in internal energy. We denote the specific heat of a substance at constant volume by affixing the subscript V and write

$$c_V = \frac{1}{m}\left(\frac{\Delta Q}{\Delta T}\right)_V. \tag{16–15}$$

From the relationship derived above we can write

$$c_V = \frac{1}{m}\frac{\Delta U}{\Delta T} \tag{16–16}$$

or

$$\Delta U = mc_V\,\Delta T. \tag{16–17}$$

The change in internal energy of a gas equals the mass times the *specific heat at constant volume* times the temperature change. For solids and liquids where the thermal expansion is usually very small, the condition of constant volume is automatically quite well satisfied regardless of pressure, and Eq. (16–17) is generally applicable. From what we have deduced so far, the validity of Eq. (16–17) for gases is restricted to heating at constant volume.

We must now appeal to experiment in order to learn the way internal energy depends on volume.

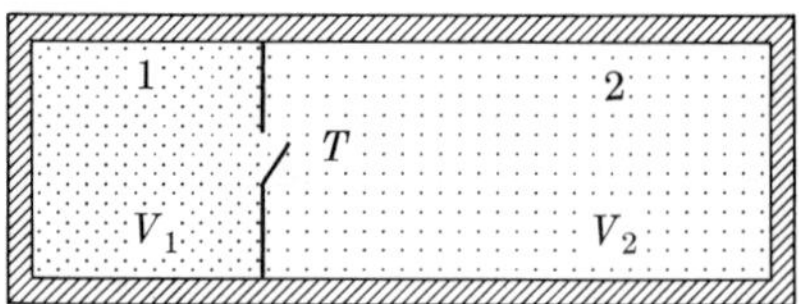

FIG. 16–7. The free expansion of a gas into the evacuated volume V_2.

The result is that, to a good approximation, the internal energy is volume independent. The experimental method is that of a *free expansion*, as follows.

Let a gas be confined in a section of a dual chamber, as in Fig. 16–7. Chamber 1 is filled with gas at temperature T. Chamber 2 is separated from chamber 1 by a membrane and is evacuated to a perfect vacuum. Now the membrane is broken, and the gas expands from a volume V_1 to volume $V_1 + V_2$. The whole system is insulated so that heat is neither added to nor taken from the gas. Therefore, ΔQ is zero. Also, since the walls of the chamber are rigid, no work is performed by the gas. (The gas can exert a force upon the chamber walls, but there is no displacement as required in the performance of work.) Therefore, ΔW is zero. From the above conditions and the first law of thermodynamics, $\Delta Q = \Delta U + \Delta W$, we have as a consequence for this process

$$\Delta U = 0; \tag{16–18}$$

that is, the initial and final internal energies are equal.

The experimental result is that the temperature of a gas undergoing free expansion usually changes. The necessary conclusion is that the internal energy of a *real* gas depends on its volume as well as on its temperature. We therefore extend our analysis.

The internal energy may conceivably depend on all the variables which together fully determine the state of the gas. These are p, V, and T. Thus, generally, we may write

$$U = U(p, V, T) \tag{16–19}$$

to denote that internal energy is a function of the variables p, V, and T. However, there is always one equation of state connecting the variables p, V, and T. This equation may be used to eliminate any one of them. Let the internal energy be written $U = U(T, V)$, where p has been eliminated by using the equation of state. We now use the rules of differential calculus to find the differential of a function of two independent variables and have

$$dU = \left(\frac{\partial U}{\partial T}\right)_V dT + \left(\frac{\partial U}{\partial V}\right)_T dV, \qquad (16\text{–}20)$$

where the derivative with respect to either variable is performed with the other held constant. We identify the derivative with respect to temperature ($V =$ constant) with the definition of the specific heat at constant volume,

$$c_V = \frac{1}{m}\left(\frac{\partial U}{\partial T}\right)_V \cdot \qquad (16\text{–}21)$$

Therefore, by substitution, we have

$$dU = mc_V\,dT + \left(\frac{\partial U}{\partial T}\right)_T dV,$$

and since $dU = 0$ for the process of free expansion, we have

$$mc_V\,dT = -\left(\frac{\partial U}{\partial V}\right)_T dV$$

or

$$dT = -\frac{1}{mc_V}\left(\frac{\partial U}{\partial V}\right)_T dV. \qquad (16\text{–}22)$$

Thus, even though dU equals zero for the process, there can be a change in internal energy with volume, $(\partial U/\partial V)_T\,dV$, compensated for by a change of internal energy with temperature. If so, the temperature will change by an amount expressed in Eq. (16–22). As the gas pressure in a free-expansion experiment is made lower and lower, the change in temperature approaches zero. We therefore say that

$$\left(\frac{\partial U}{\partial V}\right)_T = 0 \qquad (16\text{–}23)$$

is a property of an ideal gas. *The internal energy resident in an ideal gas is independent of the gas volume* and is therefore given by Eq. (16–17).

Most real gases are cooled during a free expansion. This phenomenon is commonly utilized as one of the steps in cooling gases to their condensation temperature. The kinetic theory explanation of the above features of internal energy will be given in Chapter 18.

16–7 SPECIFIC HEAT OF AN IDEAL GAS AT CONSTANT PRESSURE

In practice the mechanical load applied to a gas may be varied in any manner whatever when the gas is heated. In the example given above, the container walls are held fixed and the volume cannot change. Another case of interest is that in which the pressure is held constant. The gas is loaded with a constant-weight piston which is free to move. When the gas is heated, it expands against the piston and performs work. The specific heat is defined for this process by

$$c_P \equiv \frac{1}{m}\left(\frac{dQ}{dT}\right)_P \cdot \qquad (16\text{–}24)$$

From the first law of thermodynamics we have the expression for dQ,

$$dQ = dU + p\,dV.$$

For an ideal gas, the first term can be written in terms of c_V, that is,

$$dU = mc_V\,dT,$$

as deduced in the preceding section. Then

$$dQ = mc_V\,dT + p\,dV. \qquad (16\text{–}25)$$

The second term is transformed through the use of the equation of state for an ideal gas,

$$pV = NRT.$$

The differential of this expression is

$$p\,dV + V\,dp = NR\,dT, \qquad (16\text{–}26)$$

from which we write

$$p\,dV = NR\,dT - V\,dp. \qquad (16\text{–}27)$$

However, since pressure is held constant in the present case, $dp = 0$ and (16–27) becomes

$$p\,dV = NR\,dT. \qquad (16\text{–}28)$$

This expression is substituted into Eq. (16–25) with the result

$$dQ = mc_V\,dT + NR\,dT. \qquad (16\text{–}29)$$

We use this expression to find

$$\left(\frac{dQ}{dT}\right)_p = mc_V + NR, \qquad (16\text{–}30)$$

and the specific heat at constant pressure,

$$c_p = \frac{1}{m}\left(\frac{dQ}{dt}\right)_p,$$

becomes

$$c_p = c_V + \frac{N}{m}\,R. \qquad (16\text{–}31)$$

This result shows that the specific heats of an ideal gas at constant pressure and at constant volume differ by a constant amount. It can be readily understood that c_p should be greater than c_V. For a given number of calories added to a gas at constant pressure, only part of the heat appears in the form of increased internal energy or increased temperature. The rest is used in the performance of work and is lost from the system.

Another expression for Eq. (16–31) is found in the literature, in which the unit of mass is not the kilogram but rather the mole. Then the specific heat is written as the heat capacity per mole of substance, C, rather than the heat capacity per kilogram of substance, c. In this system, $dQ = nC\,dT$, where n is the number of moles of gas. Then

$$C_p = \frac{1}{n}\left(\frac{dQ}{dT}\right)_p, \qquad C_V = \frac{1}{n}\left(\frac{dU}{dT}\right)_v,$$

and

$$C_p = C_V + R. \qquad (16\text{–}32)$$

(When using this system remember that the molar quantities of different substances have different masses.)

The expression derived for the difference in C_p and C_V can be used to compute the ratio of C_p to C_V, a number which is useful in a later development. By definition, we let

$$\gamma = \frac{C_p}{C_V}\cdot \qquad (16\text{–}33)$$

Utilizing Eq. (16–32) and Eq. (16–33), we can write

$$\gamma = 1 + \frac{R}{C_V}$$

or

$$\gamma = 1 + \frac{n}{m}\,\frac{R}{C_V}\cdot \qquad (16\text{–}34)$$

The dimensionless number γ is a measurable and characteristic quantity for all gases. In the next section, it will be found that γ is a constant that appears in so-called adiabatic expansions.

16–8 COMPRESSION AND EXPANSION OF GASES

Depending on the constraints which are applied, the compression or expansion of a gas can take place along any line in the p-V diagram. For an ideal gas the only rule which governs all paths is the equation of state,

$$pV = mRT.$$

In general all quantities may vary.

One special case has already been explored in which the value of T is held constant. You will recall that experimentally this condition is achieved by placing the gas chamber in a large thermal bath which can impart heat to the gas or extract it as needed to hold the temperature constant when the volume changes. This constraint gives the Boyle relationship between temperature and volume,

$$pV = K \qquad (T = \text{constant}).$$

The Boyle equation (plus the Gay-Lussac law) specifies a family of curves in the p-V diagram called isothermal curves or simply isotherms (Fig. 16-8). A gas which is compressed or which expands along one of these curves is said to undergo isothermal expansion or isothermal compression.

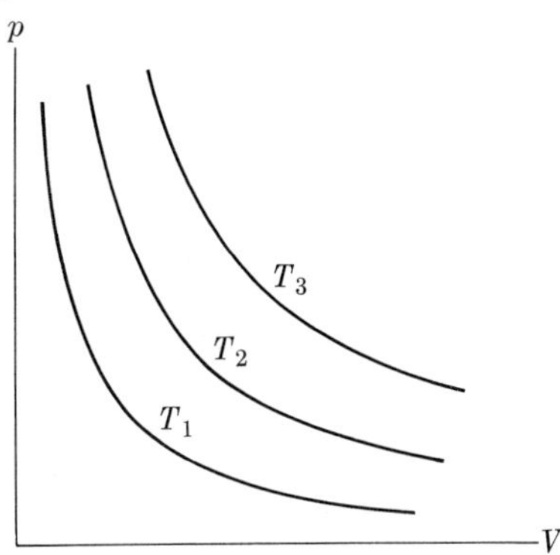

FIG. 16-8. Pressure as a function of volume for three different temperatures.

Another case of special interest is called *adiabatic* expansion or compression. The constraint applied to a gas for an adiabatic change is that *no heat* is added to or subtracted from the gas, i.e., for an adiabatic process,

$$\Delta Q = 0.$$

This constraint may be achieved by surrounding the gas container with insulating material or, better, by surrounding it with a vacuum. In practice, adiabatic processes can be well approximated, even with poor insulation, if the expansion or compression is rapid compared with the rate of heat exchange with the surroundings. For example, a sudden sharp stroke on an air pump will give rise to an adiabatic change, even though heat conduction will soon thereafter modify the condition of the gas. It can be said that, in practice, an extremely slow expansion is nearly isothermal and an extremely fast expansion is nearly adiabatic.

Assume then that the heat exchange has been suitably reduced so that we may assume the condition of no heat exchange. We wish to know the pressure-volume relationship for the gas in this condition. It is evident at the outset that the temperature of the gas will be affected by a volume change. Isotherms will be crossed, since in compression, all the work done on the gas goes into the form of internal energy. In expansion, all the work done by the gas is at the expense of internal energy. It is therefore of interest to find the volume-temperature and pressure-temperature relationships.

From the first law of thermodynamics,

$$\Delta Q = \Delta U + \Delta W,$$

and the adiabatic condition,

$$\Delta Q = 0,$$

we have for an adiabatic process the equation

$$\Delta U = -\Delta W.$$

Also, for an ideal gas there is an expression for dU in terms of the specific heat at constant volume, which we have already discussed, namely, Eq. (16-17),

$$dU = mc_V\,dT.$$

Equating the two expressions, we have

$$mc_V\,dT = -p\,dV. \qquad (16\text{-}35)$$

When, furthermore, the equation of state for the ideal gas is used to express p in terms of V and T, we have

$$mc_V\,dT = -NRT\,\frac{dV}{V}\cdot \qquad (16\text{-}36)$$

An algebraic rearrangement of terms gives the differential equation for the adiabatic gas law,

$$\frac{dT}{T} + \frac{NR}{mc_V}\,\frac{dV}{V} = 0. \qquad (16\text{-}37)$$

It will be recalled from the previous section that

$$\frac{NR}{mc_V} = \gamma - 1,$$

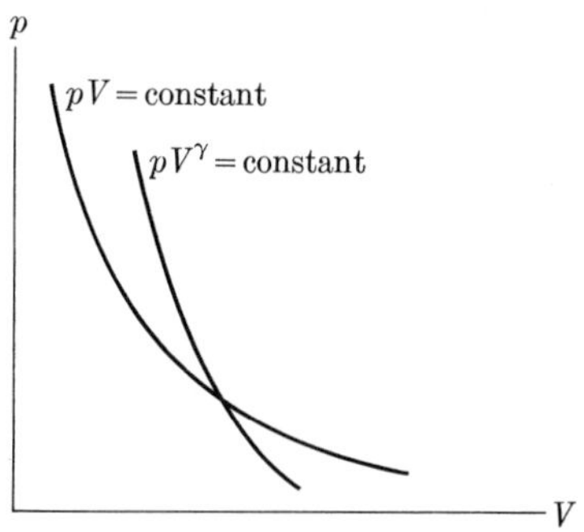

Fig. 16-9. Comparison of an isothermal with an adiabatic expansion.

where (Eq. 16-33)

$$\gamma \equiv \frac{C_p}{C_V}.$$

Using this relationship, we write Eq. (16-37)

$$\frac{dT}{T} + (\gamma - 1)\frac{dV}{V} = 0. \tag{16-38}$$

This equation can be readily integrated to give

$$\log_e T + (\gamma - 1)\log_e V = \text{constant},$$

or

$$TV^{(\gamma-1)} = K. \tag{16-39}$$

This is the desired temperature-volume relationship for an adiabatic change. Using the equation of state, it can be shown that the pressure-volume relationship is

$$pV^\gamma = \frac{K}{NR} = K'. \tag{16-40}$$

An analysis of the adiabatic curves shows that at every point in the p-V diagram they are steeper than the isothermal curves (Fig. 16-9). A gas compressed adiabatically exhibits both a pressure and a temperature increase. The increase in pressure is caused not only by the volume reduction but also by the increase in temperature. From the standpoint of energy, all the work performed in compressing a gas adiabatically appears in the form of increased internal energy, and hence the gas becomes hotter,

$$-dW = dU = mc_V\,dT.$$

A gas expanding adiabatically performs work, and since no heat is added to the system, all the work performed is done at the expense of the internal energy originally resident in the gas. Therefore the gas must become colder upon adiabatic expansion.

16-9 THE CARNOT HEAT ENGINE

The groundwork has been laid in the foregoing sections for the design and analysis of a heat engine. A heat engine is a device which converts heat energy into mechanical energy, that is,

$$\Delta Q \to \Delta W.$$

The practical usefulness of this subject is readily apparent, since our whole economy is supported mainly by heat engines. However, we also discover in the analysis of this subject a further understanding of the nature and quality of heat energy. In the discussion of the second law, we are led, finally, to a distinction between high-grade and low-grade energy forms.

The heat engine to be constructed is of a cyclic kind. By this we mean that the engine returns periodically to the same state. The processes are all to be reversible, that is, we assume that there is negligible friction and that the changes are made slowly enough that departures from equilibrium conditions are negligibly small. To

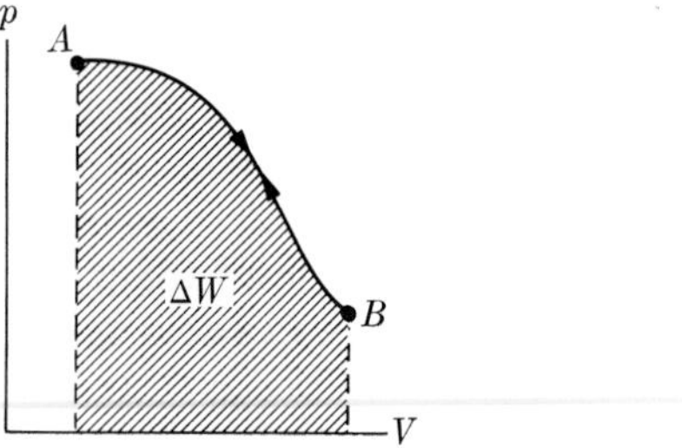

Fig. 16-10. A cyclic process in which no net work is done, if the process is reversible.

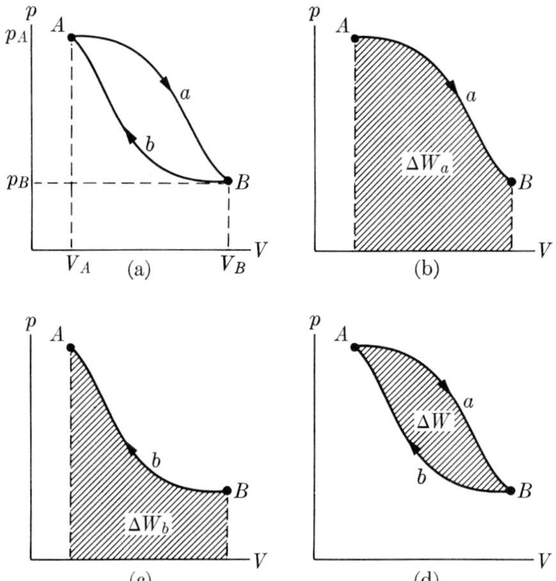

FIG. 16–11. A cyclic process (a). The work done during two portions of the cycle is shown in (b) and (c). The net work during the entire cycle is shown in (d).

see the way that work is obtained in a cyclic process, refer to the p-V diagram for a gas. Let a gas expand against a piston from the state A to the state B along the path A-B in the p-V diagram of Fig. 16–10. Work in amount ΔW (the area under the p-V curve) is performed *by* the gas in the expansion process. Now, if the gas were compressed from B to A along the same path, the same amount of work ΔW is performed *on* the system. This is a cyclic process, for we have gone from A to A, but there has been no net work delivered by the system. However, if the expansion and compression paths are not identical, then net work may be done. Consider the cycle portrayed in Fig. 16–11(a). Let the gas begin in the condition p_A, V_A and expand along path a to the condition p_B, V_B. During expansion the gas performs an amount of work ΔW_a equal to the area under the a curve, between the V_A and V_B lines. Then the gas is compressed to the original condition p_A, V_A along the path b. The net work required for compression is ΔW_b, which is the area under the curve b bounded by the V_A and V_B lines. By suitable choice of paths, we have made ΔW_b less than ΔW_a. The net work performed on the outside world by the gas is ΔW, the difference between ΔW_a and ΔW_b, that is,

$$\Delta W = \Delta W_a - \Delta W_b. \tag{16–41}$$

In the graphical representation, ΔW is exactly the area bounded by the paths a and b. The work performed in *any* closed cycle is the area in the p-V diagram bounded by the closed path.

In this section we will inspect a specific closed path (Carnot cycle) for the following kinds of information: (1) How is such a closed-cycle engine achieved in principle? (2) What is the source of energy for the performance of work ΔW? (3) What is the efficiency of the engine?

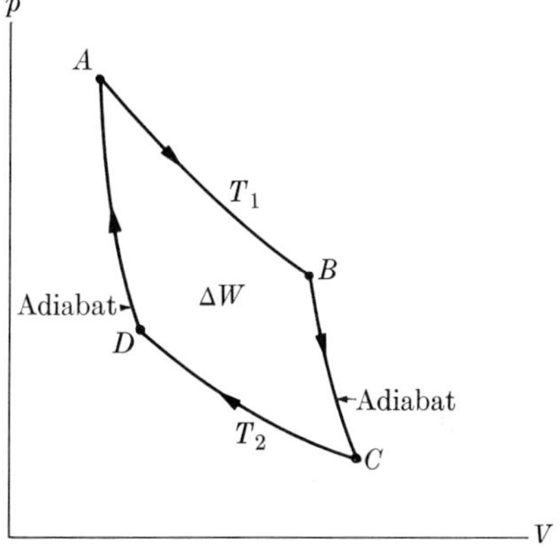

FIG. 16–12. The Carnot cycle.

The Carnot cycle utilizes a closed path made up of four branches; two branches are isothermal curves, two are adiabatic curves (Fig. 16–12). The first expansion from A takes place along an isothermal curve, at constant temperature T_1, to the point B. At B the gas expands adiabatically to the point C, and in so doing the gas cools down to the new temperature T_2. At C the gas is compressed isothermally at temperature T_2 to the point D. At D the gas is further compressed adiabatically, and therefore heated, to the point

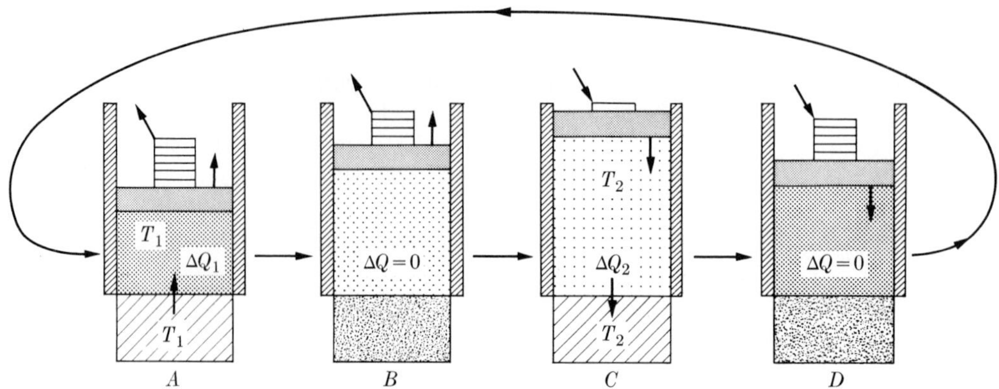

FIG. 16–13. Schematic representation of the experimental procedure in carrying out a Carnot cycle.

A at temperature T_1. The point D must be so chosen that the adiabat which contains point D also contains point A, thereby closing the cycle. At A the gas may expand again, and thereafter the cycle is repeated. For every cycle, an amount of work ΔW is performed, equal to the area bounded by the paths.

In practice the cycle must be achieved in the following way (Fig. 16–13): At point A the gas is placed in good contact with a reservoir of heat at the temperature T_1. By reservoir we mean a body of such large heat capacity that whatever heat ΔQ we draw from it, its temperature will change by only a negligible amount. While in contact with the heat reservoir, weights are gradually removed from the piston and the gas expands, performing work on the weights that remain. As the gas expands, performing work, it would naturally cool, but the slightest temperature drop causes heat to flow from the reservoir into the gas. Thus heat energy is continually supplied to the gas by the reservoir during the isothermal expansion. At B the gas cylinder is shifted from the reservoir to a block of heat-insulating substance. As further weights are removed, the gas expands, performing work but absorbing no heat. The gas cools during this expansion, doing work at the expense of its own internal energy. When point C at the temperature T_2 is reached, the adiabatic expansion is ended. The chamber is then shifted to the thermal reservoir at the temperature T_2, and the compression cycle is begun. Weights are added to the piston, and the work done on the gas would go into increase of internal energy. However, the slightest temperature increase results in the transport of heat from the gas into the cold reservoir. At the point D, the chamber is shifted again to an insulating block. Compression is continued, causing a heating of the gas, until the temperature T_1 is reached. Then the chamber is shifted again to the high-temperature reservoir, at which point the entire cycle can be repeated.

The energy exchanges which take place during the complete cycle can be identified at once. During expansion at temperature T_1, the engine absorbs an amount of energy ΔQ_1 from the hot reservoir. Absorption of heat energy takes place only during this isothermal phase, since the engine is insulated during the adiabatic phase. During the isothermal compression at temperature T_2, the engine ejects (exhausts) an amount of heat energy ΔQ_2. During the complete cycle the machine performs mechanical work, ΔW. The three energy quantities are designated as follows:

$$\Delta Q_1 = \text{heat taken in,}$$
$$\Delta Q_2 = \text{heat exhausted,}$$
$$\Delta W = \text{work output.}$$

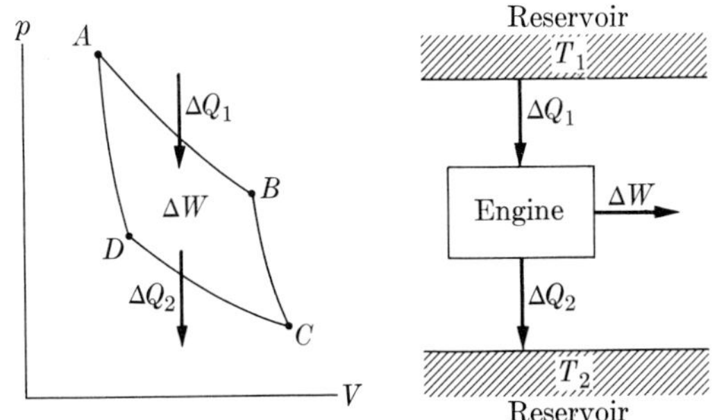

FIG. 16–14. Graphical and schematic representation of the energy transfers during a cyclic process.

The schematic flow diagram of Fig. 16–14 illustrates these energy exchanges. The efficiency of the engine E is defined as the output work divided by the heat intake; that is,

$$E \equiv \frac{\Delta W}{\Delta Q_1}\cdot \qquad (16\text{–}42)$$

Energy conservation as expressed generally by the first law is

$$\Delta Q = \Delta W + \Delta U.$$

In the complete cycle, the internal energy does not change, since the gas begins at the condition A and returns to the same condition A. Therefore we have

$$\Delta Q = \Delta W, \qquad \text{or} \qquad \Delta Q_1 - \Delta Q_2 = \Delta W. \qquad (16\text{–}43)$$

The engine efficiency (Eq. 16–42) can then be written

$$E = \frac{\Delta Q_1 - \Delta Q_2}{\Delta Q_1} \qquad (16\text{–}44)$$

or

$$E = 1 - \frac{\Delta Q_2}{\Delta Q_1}\cdot \qquad (16\text{–}45)$$

Only one restriction has been put on the nature of the working substance in the heat engine in deriving Eq. (16–45), the restriction that the internal energy has returned to its inital value after completing a closed cycle. Thus we are presumably not even limited to a gas as the working substance.

We can see that a perfect engine, $E = 1$, can be achieved only if the exhaust energy ΔQ_2 is zero. This is not a very striking conclusion, and it could have been stated immediately on the basis of the energy conservation principle.

In order to draw further conclusions, we now return to the ideal gas as the working substance.

The branch *A-B*. During an isothermal expansion, the gas temperature and therefore the internal energy of an ideal gas do not change; that is, $T = T_1$ (a constant) and $\Delta U = 0$. Therefore the work performed equals the energy absorbed,

$$\Delta W_1 = \Delta Q_1. \qquad (16\text{–}46)$$

The work ΔW_1 is computed by integrating $p\,dV$ along the branch, A-B. Using the ideal gas law, the pressure-volume relationship is

$$p = \frac{NRT_1}{V} \qquad (T_1 = \text{constant}).$$

The work integral becomes

$$\Delta W_1 = NRT_1 \int_{V_A}^{V_B} \frac{dV}{V}$$

or

$$\Delta W_1 = NRT_1 \log \frac{V_B}{V_A}\cdot \qquad (16\text{–}47)$$

Therefore, by Eq. (16–46), we have

$$\Delta Q_1 = NRT_1 \log \frac{V_B}{V_A}\cdot \qquad (16\text{–}48)$$

The other heat exchange occurs in the other isothermal process, the compression from C to D. Obviously, the resulting heat exchange ΔQ_2 would be given by Eq. (16–48) with a change in subscripts and sign:

$$\Delta Q_2 = -NRT_2 \log \frac{V_D}{V_C} = NRT_2 \log \frac{V_C}{V_D}\cdot \qquad (16\text{–}49)$$

The ratio of ΔQ_2 to ΔQ_1, which appears in the efficiency expression (Eq. 16–45) therefore becomes

$$\frac{\Delta Q_2}{\Delta Q_1} = \frac{T_2}{T_1}\left[\frac{\log(V_C/V_D)}{\log(V_B/V_A)}\right].$$

The factor in parentheses is equal to one (the proof is left to the problems). Therefore, we have

$$\frac{\Delta Q_2}{\Delta Q_1} = \frac{T_2}{T_1}, \tag{16–50}$$

and the efficiency of the Carnot cycle (Eq. 16–45) can be written

$$E = \frac{T_1 - T_2}{T_1}. \tag{16–51}$$

The criterion for a perfect engine is seen to be the stringent requirement that the exhaust temperature must be made equal to absolute zero. It will be recalled that the specialization made in this calculation is that the working substance is an ideal gas. Using only the first law of thermodynamics, we can compute efficiencies specifically from the given properties of the working substance. When the second law of thermodynamics is incorporated into the theory (in Chapter 17), the efficiency equations derived for the Carnot engine will be found to have a much more general validity and significance.

The progression in the development of the first law has taken place along the following line: First we rely on the definition of mechanical work ΔW, upon which the concept of energy is founded. We then show that the previously defined heat quantity ΔQ can be identified dimensionally and physically as an energy quantity, with the experimentally measured conversion constant J, where $\Delta W = J\,\Delta Q$ joules. With this equivalence demonstrated, the next step is the statement of energy conservation, for which purpose a *new* quantity, internal energy, is defined by

$$\Delta U \equiv \Delta Q - \Delta W.$$

Formally, ΔU is defined as the difference between heat transferred and work performed. Physically, ΔU is identified as the energy resident in the thermodynamic system itself.

In conclusion, more can now be said about the false theory of heat conservation. Heat is a *form* of energy, and as such need *not* itself be conserved. The true conservation principle applies to total energy. Thus we need only say that if heat is created or destroyed, the accounts must be settled by finding an equivalent amount of energy transfer to another form. In the very restricted systems described in the calorimetric experiments, heat was the *only* form of energy involved and therefore it had to be conserved. Thus the more general theory includes the calorimetric rules as a special case. Indeed, it can be said that the general principle of energy conservation was born with the statement of the first law. The technique of the first law is the definition of suitable physical quantities such that the conservation principle can be stated mathematically.

Another general interest in thermodynamic theory, beyond the conservation principle, is a search for so-called path-independent physical quantities. A brief illustration of what is meant by path independence is given here as a demonstration of the nature of the quantities we have defined.

A path-independent function of a system is one that depends only on the initial and final conditions of the system and is independent of the way the transfer between conditions is made. Thus if the function is $f(x, y)$, and if $f(x, y)$ is path-independent, then

$$\int_A^B df = f_B - f_A. \tag{16–52}$$

This is mathematically equivalent to saying that df is an exact differential. We now test some of the thermodynamic quantities that we have discussed for path independence.

First, ΔW is *not* a path-independent function. If we perform the integral of dW from point A to

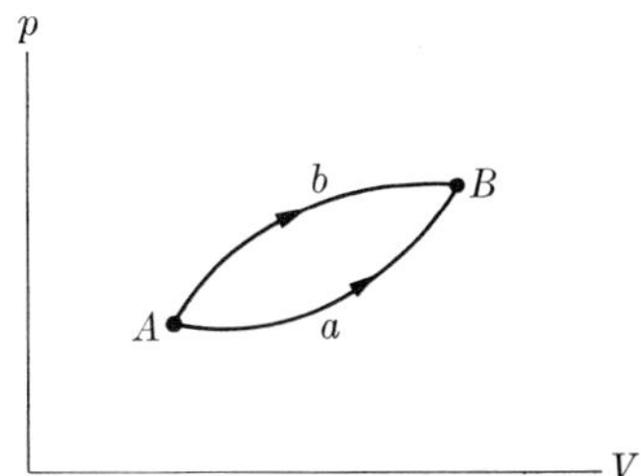

FIG. 16–15. Two different ways for going from state A to state B.

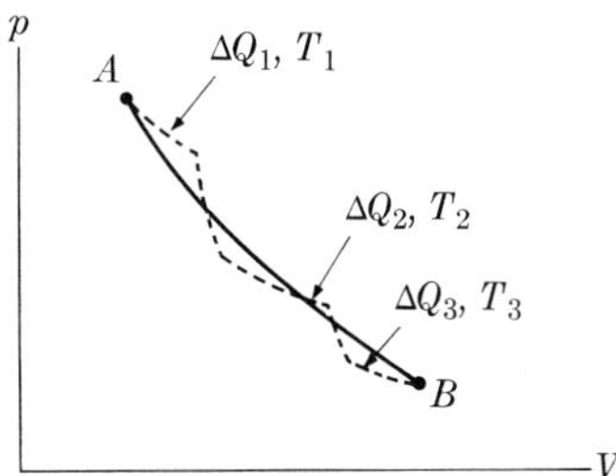

FIG. 16–17. Approximation of any path by a series of isothermal and adiabatic processes.

point B, we obtain

$$\int_A^B dW = \int_A^B p\,dV \neq W_B - W_A.$$

This result is clearly seen graphically (Fig. 16–15), since the integral is the area under the p-V curve. It is seen at once that if the path is b, rather than a, then $\Delta W_b > \Delta W_a$. The areas under the two curves are different. Thus the work performed in reaching state B from state A depends not only on the states themselves but also on the *way* B is reached from A. In fact B can be reached from A by doing no work at all (Fig. 16–16).

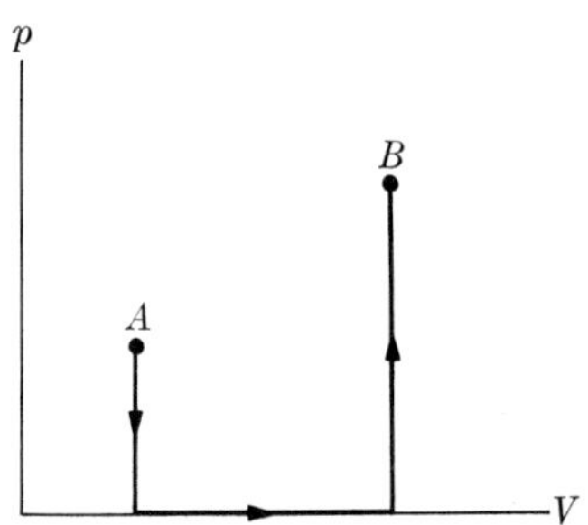

FIG. 16–16. Idealized scheme for going from state A to state B without performing work.

Similarly, it is meaningless to say that a substance contains a given amount of heat Q, given its conditions P, V, N, and T. Let us say that we are to reach the state B from A by creating heat (Fig. 16–17).

Generally, the calculation is complex, although the mechanics of the calculation can be formulated. Divide the curve into a series of tiny isothermal expansions, followed by tiny adiabatic expansions, such that the curve is exactly followed; then you will see that heat is absorbed only during the isothermal parts. For example during step 1, ΔQ_1 is absorbed at T_1, then ΔQ_2 is absorbed at T_2, etc. The total heat absorbed is

$$\Delta Q_1 + \Delta Q_2 + \Delta Q_3 + \cdots$$

We have also shown that the heat absorbed in isothermal expansions is identically the work done in the expansions. Consequently,

$$\Delta Q = \Delta W_1 + \Delta W_2 + \Delta W_3 + \cdots$$

However, this second series is just the area under the path, and it is path-dependent. Thus, the heat absorbed in reaching state B from state A depends on the way that the state is reached and is not a simple characteristic of the state. This is an added argument against the notion of heat as an invariable fluid.

However, the story is different with internal energy. For example, for the ideal gas,

$$dU = mc_V\,dT,$$

and

$$\int_A^B dU = mc_V(T_B - T_A) = U_B - U_A. \tag{16–53}$$

The initial and final energies depend on the initial and final temperatures and not on the means by which B was reached from A. Internal energy U is thus termed a "characteristic function," whereas heat Q is not. However, by inference from the first law, we have discovered a new characteristic function. Since $dU = dQ - dW$, then $dQ - dW$ is a characteristic function. While both dQ and dW are path-dependent quantities, their difference is path-independent. In advanced studies, an important part of the development is the construction of other characteristic functions of thermodynamics.

Early in Chapter 15, we proposed summarizing a complete specification of the ideal gas. These are the specifications: The law of Gay-Lussac is followed perfectly:

$$V = V_0(1 + \alpha t) \qquad (P = \text{constant}),$$

where α is constant. The law of Boyle is followed perfectly:

$$pV = K \qquad (T = \text{constant}),$$

where K is a constant. Deduced from the laws of Boyle and Gay-Lussac is the equation of state for an ideal gas:

$$pV = NRT,$$

where R is constant. The specific heat c_V of an ideal gas at constant volume is constant. It is temperature-independent and volume-independent. From this, the internal energy of an ideal gas can be written as a function dependent solely on temperature:

$$\Delta U = mc_V\, \Delta T.$$

These are the characteristics of an ideal gas. Real gases in dilute form (far from the condensation point) follow these laws quite accurately, and in many instances the ideal and real gas behavior can be considered identical to a good degree of approximation. However, near the liquefaction point, the deviations of real gas behavior from ideal behavior become so great that the use of the ideal laws would be completely inappropriate.

16–10 SUMMARY

The observations that lead to the idea of exchanges between heat energy and mechanical energy are presented. Thus, we are led to the idea of heat as a form of energy.

The direct conversion of mechanical energy to heat energy, with the consequent possibility of determining the relationship between the two energy scales, joules and calories, is described. The result is

$$1 \text{ cal} = 4.18 \text{ joules}.$$

The interchanges between heat and mechanical work or energy, with particular emphasis on the case of an ideal gas, are developed. The work done by an expanding gas on its surroundings, for example, on a movable piston, is

$$\Delta W = \int_{V_1}^{V_2} p\, dV.$$

For an ideal gas kept at constant temperature, the resulting work can be written

$$\Delta W = NRT \log (V_2/V_1),$$

where V_2 and V_1 are the final and initial volumes.

In addition to heat energy and mechanical energy or work, it is found that the possibility of a change in the internal energy of a substance without a change in temperature must be taken into account in an assessment of the energy interchanges. The first law of thermodynamics is a statement of the conservation of energy, including the above forms of energy, viz.,

$$\Delta U = \Delta Q - \Delta W,$$

where ΔU is the change in internal energy when heat energy ΔQ is added and the substance does work ΔW on its surroundings. The work term can be written $p\, \Delta V$.

The specific heat of an ideal gas at constant volume c_V can be related to the change in internal energy of the ideal gas with the result

$$\Delta U = mc_V\, \Delta T.$$

In the case of a real gas, on the other hand, it is found that the internal energy usually depends on the volume as well as on the temperature, that is,

$$\Delta U = mc_V\, dT + \left(\frac{\partial U}{\partial T}\right)_V dV.$$

When a specific heat at constant pressure c_p is defined, it is found that

$$c_p - c_V = (n/m)R,$$

where n is the number of moles and m is the mass of the sample of gas. The above is again for an ideal gas. The ratio of the two specific heats defined above is customarily represented by γ, where

$$\gamma = c_p/c_V = 1 - (n/m)(R/c_V).$$

An adiabatic process is a process in which there is no heat interchange with the environment. It is shown that, for an ideal gas,

$$TV^{(\gamma-1)} = \text{constant}$$

or

$$pV^{\gamma} = \text{constant}$$

during an adiabatic expansion.

The Carnot cycle is a closed cycle of changes in a substance, a cycle in which two of the processes are at constant temperature (isothermal) and two are under conditions of thermal insulation from the environment (adiabatic). It is shown that the net work done during any closed cycle is the area enclosed by the graph of the cycle in the coordinates, pressure and volume. When a Carnot cycle operates in the direction of isothermal expansion at the higher temperature, work is done on the surroundings, accompanied by a net transfer of heat from the higher temperature reservoir to the lower temperature reservoir. The efficiency is defined as the ratio of the work output to the heat absorbed from the higher temperature reservoir (both expressed in the same units),

$$E = \Delta W/\Delta Q_1.$$

It is shown that the efficiency can be expressed in the form

$$E = 1 - \Delta Q_2/\Delta Q_1,$$

which, in the case of an ideal gas, becomes

$$E = (T_1 - T_2)/T_1$$

where the T's are the temperatures of the reservoirs.

The properties of an ideal gas are summarized at the end of the chapter.

Problems

1. A rod is swirled in a liter jar of water at a constant torque of 0.1 n·m at a rate of 10 cycles/sec. Is this vigorous stirring? How long do we work for the temperature to rise 10°C?

2. A mole of monatomic ideal gas is allowed to undergo adiabatic expansion from $V = 1\text{m}^3$ to $V = \infty$. The initial temperature is 300°K. How much work is done? What is the final temperature? Allow the same gas to expand isothermally from $V = 1\text{m}^3$ to $V = \infty$. How much work is done? Where did the energy come from?

3. A mole of ideal gas at $T = 300°\text{K}$ expands isothermally so that $V_2/V_1 = 2$. How much work is done?

4. How much work is done by the rising bubble in Problem 2, Chapter 15?

5. How do the values of specific heat and heats of combustion yield information about the highest temperatures to be achieved in chemical reactions? Data on these values are to be found in handbooks. We allow 1 gm of H_2 to combine with the appropriate amount of O_2. Assuming the combustion to take place in a rigid container, what is the final temperature of the water vapor? (The oxygen-hydrogen combination is a so-called exotic fuel in rocket technology.)

6. When water is boiled under atmospheric pressure, the energy required to transform 1 kg of liquid water to 1 kg of water vapor is 540 kcal. What is the initial volume of the liquid water? What is the final volume of the water vapor? Due to the expansion of water in the conversion process, work is performed. How much work is done in the expansion? How much of the 540 kcal goes into the change in internal energy of the water? What would be the energy required to boil water in vacuum, assuming that the change in *internal* energy is independent of p and T?

7. A liter of monatomic ideal gas at standard temperature and pressure is expanded isothermally to a volume of 2 liters. How much work, in joules, is performed by the gas?

The expansion is continued under adiabatic conditions until the volume is 3 liters. How much work is done by the gas? What is the temperature of the gas?

The gas is now compressed, first isothermally and then adiabatically, so that the original condition is reached. How much work is done in each of the compressions? What was the total work delivered by the engine in the complete cycle?

8. Show that the last step in the derivation of Eq. (16–49) is justified; that is, that $\log (V_C/V_D)/\log (V_B/V_A)$ is one.

9. Unless new materials are discovered in solid-state research, it is safe to say that the highest conceivable temperature of a hot metallic reservoir is 3000°K (white heat). Also the lowest useful exhaust temperature is about 300°K (room temperature). What is the best efficiency of a heat engine running between these two temperatures? Assume some appropriate figures for the source and exhaust temperatures of a gasoline engine, and compute the ideal efficiency of such an engine.

10. Let the heat source temperature of an engine be $T_1 = 1500°\text{C}$ and the exhaust temperature be $T_2 = 500°\text{C}$. Which of these, increasing T_1 by 100°C or decreasing T_2 by 100°C, would result in a greater improvement in efficiency?

11. Given the efficiency equation

$$E = \frac{T_1 - T_2}{T_1},$$

compute the change in efficiency with an increase in T_1, holding T_2 constant. Compute the change in efficiency with decrease in T_2, holding T_1 constant. Form the ratio of these derivatives and discuss whether $+dT_1$, or $-dT_2$ is more effective in efficiency improvement.

12. Consider an ideal gas that is carried through the cycle indicated in Fig. 16–18. The initial conditions p_1, V_1, and T_1 are specified (at point A). The other given quantities are p_2, V_2, and the gas constants R and $C_V = (\frac{3}{2})R$ for one mole.

(a) How many moles of gas are there?

(b) Find the temperatures at points B, C, and D in terms of the given quantities.

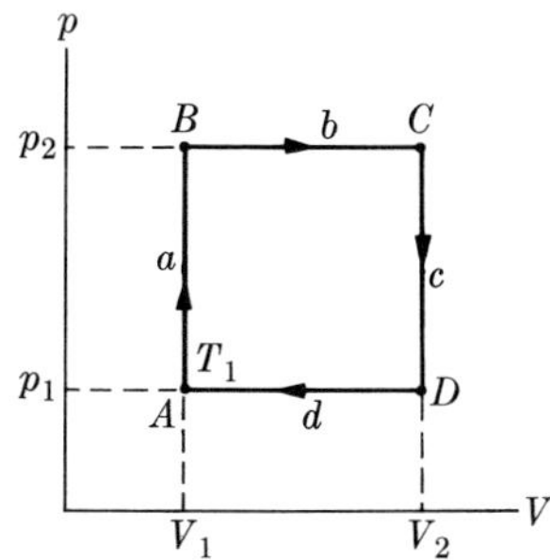

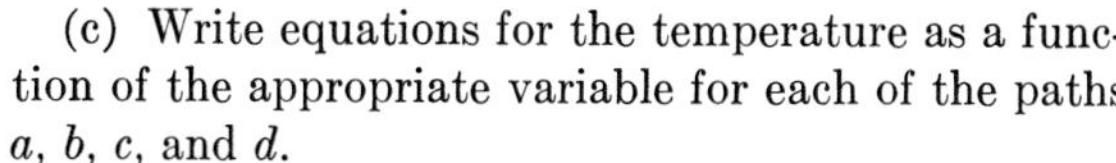

FIGURE 16–18

(c) Write equations for the temperature as a function of the appropriate variable for each of the paths a, b, c, and d.

(d) How much work is done *by* the gas in each of the four parts of the cycle? What is the net work by the gas?

(e) How much heat is absorbed or emitted in branches a and c?

(f) How much heat is emitted or absorbed in branches b and d?

(g) What is the change in internal energy for each part of the cycle?

(h) Find the efficiency of the cycle and compare it with the efficiency of a Carnot cycle operating between the extreme temperatures of the present cycle.

13. Consider an ideal gas that is carried through the cycle shown in Fig. 16–19. The given conditions

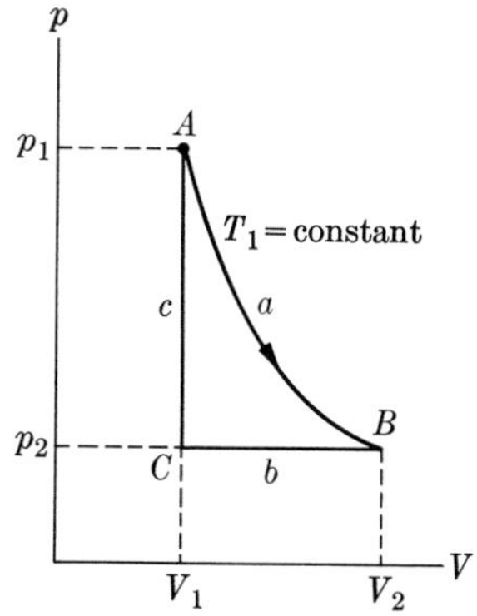

FIGURE 16–19

are p_1, V_1, and T_1, as well as V_2 and the gas constants R and $C_V = (\frac{3}{2})R$. Carry through the same sort of analysis as requested in Problem 2.

14. Using the gas laws presented in this chapter, show that the change in pressure per unit change in volume is greater for an adiabatic change than for an isothermal change by the factor γ. Show specifically that

$$\frac{dp}{dV} = -\frac{p}{V} \text{ isothermal}$$

and that

$$\frac{dp}{dV} = -\gamma\frac{p}{V} \text{ adiabatic.}$$

17

The Second Law of Thermodynamics

17-1 INTRODUCTION

There are universal principles that evidently apply to thermal processes and that are not contained in the first law. The first law requires an exact balance in energy conversion. However, the intrinsic directionality of energy conversion and of energy transfer in thermal systems is not mentioned by the first law. Consider some of the evidence for this directionality.

To use the example in the introduction to Chapter 15, a block slides to rest along a floor, causing heat production in the block and floor. We do not observe the reverse reaction—a sudden cooling of the floor and block—resulting in motion of the block. Similarly, when a hot object and a cold object are placed in contact, the cold object becomes hotter and the hot object becomes cooler, but we do not observe the reverse reaction.

Mechanical energy is fully convertible to heat energy. No examples can be found in which the reverse occurs, that is, complete conversion of heat to mechanical energy. We have presented one case in evidence, the Carnot engine, in which the efficiency is demonstrated to be less than unity. Although it is true that the demonstration of one case does not constitute a general proof, the construction of other kinds of cycles also leads to the inevitability of a finite exhaust energy in the form of heat.

The second law asserts the complete generality of these specific observations, namely, that no exceptions have ever been found. There are several statements of the second law, each closely connected with the rules stated above. It is possible to show the logical equivalence of the statements; since they do not contain different principles, they are to be taken as representations of a single law.

17-2 STATEMENTS OF THE SECOND LAW

First statement: Heat flows spontaneously from a hot to a cold object; it is impossible to transfer heat from a colder to a hotter object without other changes occurring in the system.

Second statement: It is impossible to convert heat into work without other changes occurring in the system.

These statements are to be used as logical references in the calculations which follow. It is possible to translate the verbal statements into mathematical form, and before continuing with the reading, the student may wish to consider how he would set about such a task.

17-3 THE CARNOT REFRIGERATOR

It is the purpose of this section to consider the mechanism and rules for transferring heat from colder to hotter objects, the process which, according to the second law, cannot occur spontaneously. The basic refrigeration device is a heat engine run in reverse. We consider specifically the Carnot cycle, the analysis having already been presented in Section 16-9. The Carnot refrigerator follows the cycle $ADCBA$ of Fig. 17-1, where AD and CB are adiabats, and DC and BA are isotherms.

The gas, while isolated from heat sources, first expands against the piston load. The work of expansion is done at the expense of internal energy, and, consequently, the gas cools to the temperature T_2 at point D. Thereupon, the expansion proceeds along an isothermal curve, and the gas *absorbs* an amount of heat ΔQ_2 from the *cold* reservoir. At point C expansion ceases and compression begins. The first compression step is adiabatic, and the work done on the gas causes the temperature to increase to T_1. At B, the gas container is placed on the high-temperature reservoir. Upon further thermal expansion, heat ΔQ_1 is deposited *into* the *hot* reservoir until the initial condition is reached, whereupon the cycle is repeated.

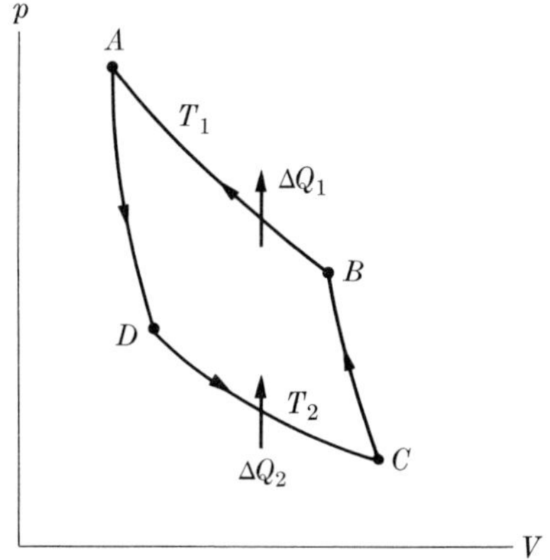

FIG. 17–1. A "reversed" Carnot cycle transfers heat from a reservoir of a lower temperature to one of a higher temperature.

The analysis of energy transfers given in Chapter 16 applies directly to the refrigeration process, provided that the device is operated in a reversible fashion. That is, it must operate infinitely slowly, with zero-temperature differences in any part of the cycle, and with no friction.

Along the isothermal curves, the mechanical work equals the amount of heat absorbed or exhausted (according to the first law). It follows that ΔQ_1 and ΔQ_2 have the same ratio as the absolute temperatures of the reservoirs, as before (Eq. 16–50),

$$\frac{\Delta Q_1}{\Delta Q_2} = \frac{T_1}{T_2}. \tag{17–1}$$

It is evident that more heat is delivered to the hot reservoir than is extracted from the cold reservoir. To drive the system, however, an *external* source of mechanical energy is required.

The work supplied to the refrigerator from the outside for one cycle of operation is (since $\Delta U = 0$)

$$\Delta W = \Delta Q_1 - \Delta Q_2. \tag{17–2}$$

It is not customary to define an efficiency for the system, but rather we may define so-called "coefficients of performance." If, for example, the desired action is the deposit of heat into the hot reservoir, the useful output of the device is ΔQ_1. The required input to make the device operate is ΔW. Thus the coefficient of performance is

$$C_{\mathrm{I}} \equiv \frac{\Delta Q_1}{\Delta W}$$

or

$$C_{\mathrm{I}} = \frac{\Delta Q_1}{\Delta Q_1 - \Delta Q_2}, \tag{17–3}$$

which, from Eq. (17–1), becomes

$$C_{\mathrm{I}} = \frac{T_1}{T_1 - T_2}. \tag{17–4}$$

The device described here is called more appropriately a "heat pump" than a refrigerator when the coefficient of performance is defined as above. An energy-flow diagram is shown in Fig. 17–2.

The heat delivered to the hot reservoir equals the sum of the work done on the engine and the

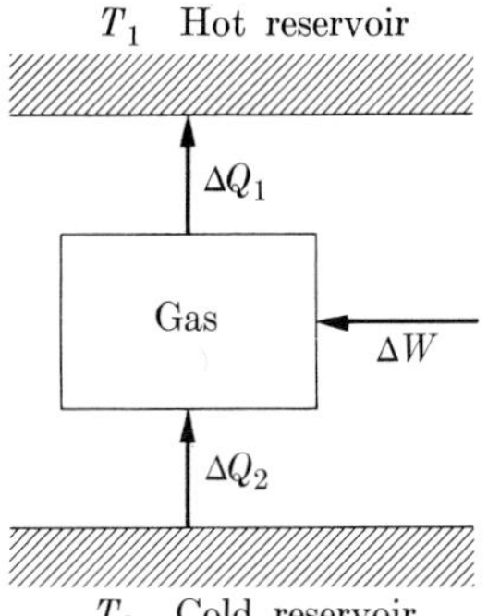

FIG. 17–2. Energy flow diagram for a refrigeration process.

heat absorbed by the engine. As $T_2 \to T_1$, the work required for a given ΔQ_1 becomes less and less. If a reservoir of heat at a temperature not far below the desired temperature of a house is available in winter (for example, water from an underground source), it might be economical to use a heat pump to extract heat from the reservoir in order to heat the house.

When the function is refrigeration, the useful task is the extraction of heat ΔQ_2 from the cold reservoir, while the mechanical input to the machine is still ΔW. The coefficient of performance is now chosen as

$$C_{\text{II}} \equiv \frac{\Delta Q_2}{\Delta W}, \tag{17–5}$$

which becomes

$$C_{\text{II}} = \frac{T_2}{T_1 - T_2}. \tag{17–6}$$

Since the coefficient of performance is zero when $T_2 = 0$, a refrigeration device can cool an object such that it can approach, but not reach, absolute zero.

The ordinary household refrigerator is used to transfer heat from a cold object (the interior of the refrigerator) to a warm object (the air of the room). The rate of heat transfer must be equal to the heat flow by conduction through the walls of the refrigerator if the interior temperature is to be constant.

17–4 EXTENSIONS OF THE CARNOT THEOREM

Theorem: A reversible Carnot engine, using any working substance at all, has the same efficiency as a Carnot engine whose working substance is an ideal gas; that is,

$$E = \frac{T_1 - T_2}{T_1}, \tag{17–7}$$

independent of the working substance. Thus, the specialization made in the derivation of the efficiency equation, through the use of the ideal-gas law $pV = NRT$, was not essential. The

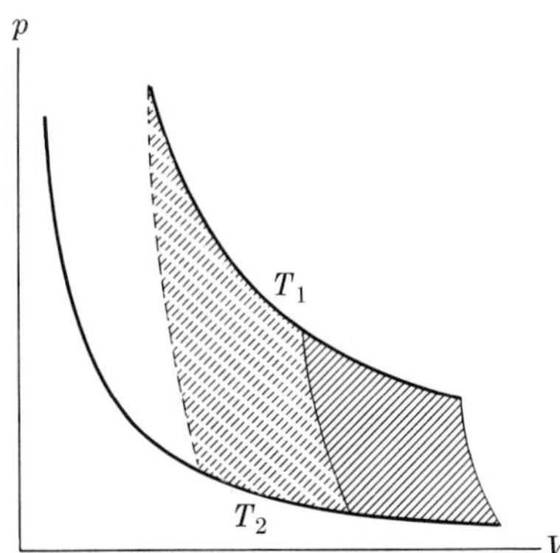

FIG. 17–3. Variation of the area enclosed and hence of the work per cycle for two different amplitudes of the cycle.

proof of this statement is made by using the second law of thermodynamics and the refrigeration principle.

Consider that we have two engines, engine A and engine B, both of which are reversible. Both operate between the same reservoirs at temperatures T_1 and T_2. We assume for the purposes of proof that the efficiencies of A and B are *not* equal; i.e., suppose $E_A \neq E_B$. However, we arrange that the mechanical work of each machine per cycle is the same; i.e.,

$$\Delta W_A = \Delta W_B.$$

This condition can always be made to apply since the work output of an engine depends on the *size* of the engine. For example the work output or input for the cycle depicted in Fig. 17–3, operating always between the same temperatures, can be varied arbitrarily by varying the size of the stroke (Δp and ΔV). Finally, it is assumed that engine A uses an ideal gas and that engine B uses a material of any property whatever. Now let the devices be arranged so that one acts as a heat engine whose output is used to drive the other as a refrigerator, as shown in the energy-flow diagram of Fig. 17–4.

First we let engine B drive refrigerator A. It is implicit in this arrangement that A *is a reversible* engine so that it can be used in this

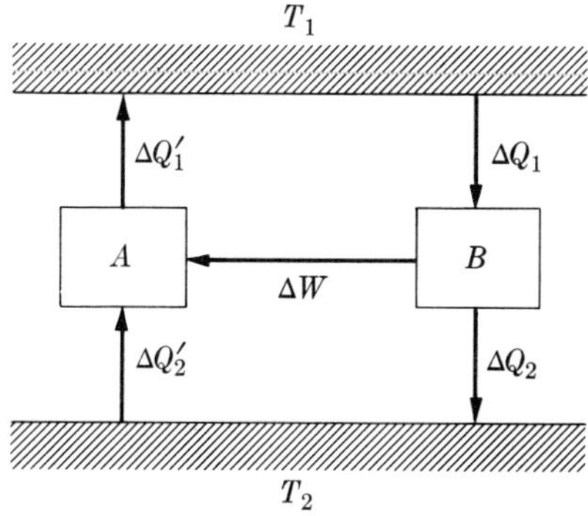

FIG. 17-4. Energy-flow diagram for a system in which engine B supplies the mechanical work ΔW to run engine A backward.

fashion. We assume that the efficiency of the engine is greater than the efficiency of the refrigerator, i.e.,

$$E_B > E_A.$$

The working of the device is as follows: Engine B absorbs heat ΔQ_1 from the hot reservoir, performs work ΔW, and rejects heat ΔQ_2 into the cold reservoir. The refrigerator B accepts work ΔW, extracts heat $\Delta Q_2'$ from the cold reservoir, and deposits heat $\Delta Q_1'$ into the hot reservoir. Under the assumptions given, we have for engine A the efficiency equation,

$$E_A = \frac{\Delta W}{\Delta Q_1'} = \frac{\Delta Q_1' - \Delta Q_2'}{\Delta Q_1'} \quad \text{(first law)}, \tag{17-8}$$

and for engine B,

$$E_B = \frac{\Delta W}{\Delta Q_1} = \frac{\Delta Q_1 - \Delta Q_2}{\Delta Q_1} \quad \text{(first law)}. \tag{17-9}$$

Assuming that $E_B > E_A$, we have

$$\frac{\Delta W}{\Delta Q_1} > \frac{\Delta W}{\Delta Q_1'}, \tag{17-10}$$

from which it follows that

$$\Delta Q_1' > \Delta Q_1; \tag{17-11}$$

that is, more heat is delivered to the hot reservoir than is taken from it! Also we have the condition

$$\Delta Q_1' - \Delta Q_2' = \Delta Q_1 - \Delta Q_2. \tag{17-12}$$

Since it has already been shown that $\Delta Q_1' > \Delta Q_1$, it follows that

$$\Delta Q_2' > \Delta Q_2. \tag{17-13}$$

Thus, more heat is extracted from the cold reservoir than is delivered to it. The net heat transfer from cold to hot is

$$\Delta Q_n = \Delta Q_1' - \Delta Q_1 \quad \text{to the hot,}$$
$$\Delta Q_n = \Delta Q_2' - \Delta Q_2 \quad \text{from the cold.}$$

The expressions for ΔQ_n are equal (Eq. 17-12) and positive. The net action of the system is a transfer of heat ΔQ_n from the cold to the hot reservoir during each cycle. There is no other change in the system, since the engines return to their initial condition at the end of every cycle. This result is in conflict with the second law, and therefore the original assumption that $E_B > E_A$ is false. Consequently,

$$E_B \not> E_A. \tag{17-14}$$

We can now interchange the two engines and prove, in exactly the same manner, that

$$E_A \not> E_B. \tag{17-15}$$

Since E_A is not greater than E_B, and since E_B is not greater than E_A, then it follows that

$$E_A = E_B, \tag{17-16}$$

and the original theorem is proved.

Now, it was asserted at the outset that engine A is a Carnot engine using an ideal gas, for which the efficiency has been shown to be

$$E_A = \frac{T_1 - T_2}{T_1}.$$

Therefore we have

$$E_B = \frac{T_1 - T_2}{T_1}. \tag{17-17}$$

However, the working substance in B was allowed to have any character. Therefore the efficiency has been shown, for a reversible Carnot cycle, to be independent of the equation of state of the substance. The efficiency equation, therefore, is a general law of nature applying to an engine working between two thermal reservoirs. It is not a specific attribute of a single device.

Theorem: The efficiency of an *irreversible* Carnot engine is always less than the efficiency of a *reversible* Carnot engine.

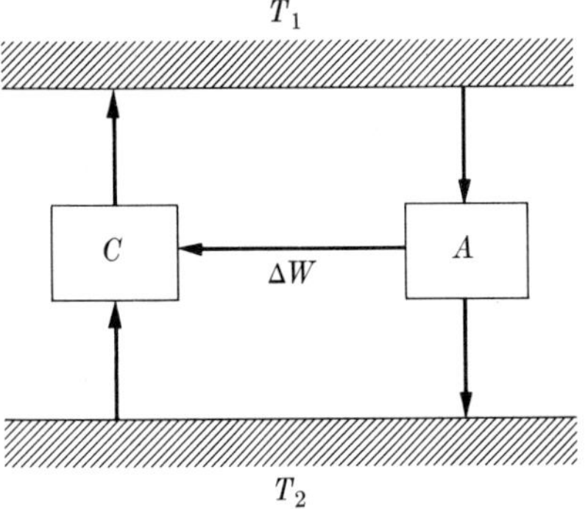

Fig. 17–5. Energy-flow diagram for a system in which engine A drives engine C.

Using the results of the foregoing section, we have shown that if C is a reversible Carnot engine (using any working substance), then there would be a violation of the second law if the efficiency of engine A were greater than the efficiency of engine C when A drives C, as in Fig. 17–5. We therefore have

$$E_A \ngtr E_C. \tag{17–18}$$

The converse cannot be shown in this case, since we allow A to be irreversible. (It may, for example, have friction in its moving parts, or it may operate at speeds such that equilibrium conditions of p, V, and T are not approximated.) Therefore it is impossible to interchange A and C in the diagram. Note that we have *not* proved that $E_A < E_C$, because equality of efficiencies is still consistent with the conclusion of Eq. (17–18). We have therefore shown that either $E_A = E_C$ or $E_A < E_C$ or, generally,

$$E_A \leq E_C. \tag{17–19}$$

17–5 THE THERMODYNAMIC TEMPERATURE SCALE

Our first step in the introduction to heat was the definition of physical temperature, or the specification of how a thermometer is to be constructed and used. The ideal-gas thermometer was selected for the definition of a temperature scale. It was seen from the derivations that were given that the ideal-gas thermometer is a useful device in the development of thermodynamic logic. However, at least one of the conventions used in the creation of the thermometer remains quite unsatisfactory from a physical point of view. This is the need of seeking a real gas that corresponds as closely as possible to the ideal-gas fiction.

The theorems just developed for the Carnot heat engine offer, in thought if not in practice, a way of escaping this difficulty. It was shown that the efficiency of a reversible Carnot engine is independent of the working substance in the engine and that the efficiency depends on the reservoir temperatures and nothing else. Thus it is proposed at this stage to turn the logic of thermodynamics back on itself and to create a new temperature definition. Given a Carnot device acting between two temperatures T_1 and T_2, the efficiency is

$$E = 1 - \frac{T_2}{T_1}.$$

One temperature can be adopted as a standard reference temperature, say $T_1 = T_R$, and the other can then be regarded as unknown, say $T_2 = T_x$. Then we can write

$$T_x = (1 - E)T_R. \tag{17–20}$$

Thus if we measure the engine efficiency, we have determined the temperature T_x in terms of T_R.

The Carnot engine is regarded, then, as a standard thermometer, and its performance is independent of the working substance with which it is filled. The absolute zero on this new scale is readily found by inspection. The temperature T_x of the low temperature reservoir is zero when the efficiency E of the engine is unity. The size of the temperature unit is determined, as before, by choosing the two fixed points of the melting of ice and of the boiling of water and by dividing the interval between them into 100 equal parts. From the above point of view, the Carnot cycle may be regarded as a defining operation, from which all other thermodynamic phenomena may be deduced.

17–6 ENTROPY

For heat energy to be convertible into useful forms, such as mechanical work, it must reside in a reservoir at a temperature higher than the temperature of the environment. The environmental temperature at the surface of the earth is roughly 300°K. Thus for a heat engine to work on the earth, the lowest exhaust temperature is of the order of 300°K. Suppose that we have at our disposal a kilogram of water at the temperature of our environment, and that this water possesses heat energy due to its temperature. Assuming that the specific heat of ice is 0.5, the water contains about 250 kcal of heat energy. In principle, the work equivalent of this heat energy is about a half-million joules. Yet, in fact, no net mechanical energy is extractible from the water, since the environment is at the same temperature. When the water is used as the hot reservoir of an ideal engine, the hot reservoir temperature is 300°K, but the exhaust reservoir temperature is the same. Even a perfect thermodynamic engine would have zero efficiency for the conversion of the heat energy in this water into useful work. Thus the heat energy possessed by objects at the environmental temperature is completely unavailable to us for useful purposes. Such heat energy is called degraded energy.

On the other hand, the heat energy of a kilogram of water at 600°K is (partially) available to us for the production of useful work. In fact, about 50% of the heat energy at 600° is available for conversion into work if the environmental temperature is 300°K. It is appropriate to say, then, that the heat of an object at higher temperatures is of a higher grade than the heat possessed by objects at lower temperature. It is only through temperature differences that work energy can be obtained from heat energy. This fact, that temperature differences support our activities and our life processes, is an alarming one, for we also know that heat is naturally transported from hot to cold. Thus, the temperature differences that are useful to us are in themselves self-destructive. The ultimate reduction of all temperatures to a common value is called the "heat death" of the universe. The heat death does not mean that the universe has lost all its energy; rather it means that when all heat energy is contained in objects at the same temperature, the heat energy is unavailable.

Notice that our discussion has been confined to thermal and mechanical energy interchanges. In a general treatment, chemical, nuclear, and other forms of potential energy would also be included. These forms of energy are, of course, available for conversion to other forms even when the substances in question are initially at the environmental temperature. However, these forms of available energy are due to organization. When energy is extracted, the degree of organization diminishes and the available energy decreases.

The grading of heat energy is described by a thermodynamic quantity called entropy. Just as in the case of work, the definition is made in terms of the differential of the quantity. The change in entropy function, dS, for an object is defined as the ratio of the element of influx of heat, dQ, to the temperature of the object; namely,

$$dS \equiv \frac{dQ}{T}, \qquad (17\text{–}21)$$

when the heat transfer is made by a reversible

process. For a given reversible change of heat in a reservoir, the entropy change is less the higher the temperature of the reservoir. Thus, high-grade heat energy is characterized by a low entropy change for a given heat exchange. The statement of the second law of thermodynamics can be formulated in terms of the entropy function: *if* the entropy of a system changes at all, the change is always positive. The natural directionality of heat processes is toward higher entropy of the system as a whole, corresponding to the degradation of the heat energy.

Consider the process of heat conduction, which is irreversible. We have previously specified the directionality of conduction by saying that heat flows from hotter to colder objects. The directionality of conduction can also be specified by stating that the entropy of the system must increase. The proof follows. If two objects at different temperatures, T_1 and T_2, are placed in contact, heat is assumed to be transported from one to the other, for example, from 1 to 2. Since the process of heat conduction is irreversible, we must devise a *reversible* process that has the same end results for objects 1 and 2, in order to find the entropy change. A portion of a Carnot cycle will accomplish the desired heat transfer. Heat in amount dQ is absorbed from 1 by an isothermal expansion of the Carnot engine at temperature T_1 while in thermal contact with 1. The engine is removed from 1 and further expanded adiabatically until its temperature is T_2. It is then placed in thermal contact with 2 and compressed isothermally until heat in amount dQ has been delivered to 2. The process is shown graphically in Fig. 17–6. The final result for objects 1 and 2 is the same as if the transfer of dQ had been by conduction, but the change in entropy can now be found. The total entropy change of the reservoirs is

$$dS = \frac{dQ}{T_2} - \frac{dQ}{T_1}, \tag{17–22}$$

where the minus sign derives from the fact that dQ in the definition (Eq. 17–21) of entropy is

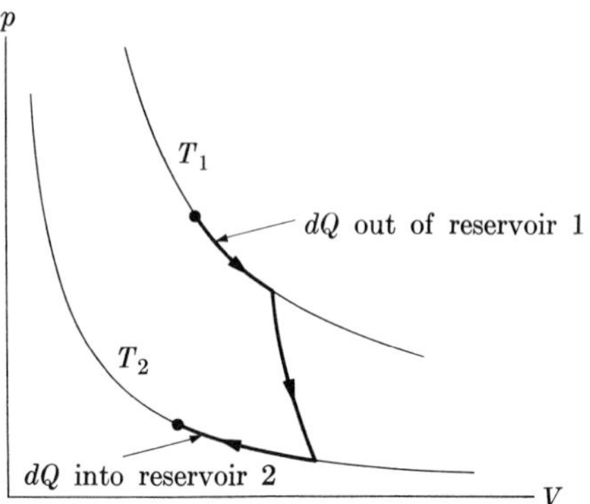

FIG. 17–6. Transfer of heat dQ from the high to the low-temperature reservoir by a portion of a Carnot cycle.

heat influx. If the change of entropy is positive, the first term in (17–22) must be the larger, since T_2 must be less than T_1, and therefore the heat flows from the reservoir with a higher temperature to the one with a lower temperature.

The properties of entropy for *reversible* processes will now be explored. First, consider a complete Carnot cycle. If the cycle is made up of finite changes, it is necessary to write Eq. (17–21) in the integral form

$$S_b - S_a = \int_a^b \frac{dQ}{T}, \tag{17–23}$$

in order to find the change in entropy in going from one state to another. During the adiabatic changes, $dQ = 0$ and there is no entropy change. During the isothermal changes, the T of the integrand is constant and the integral of (17–23) becomes simply

$$S_b - S_a = \frac{Q_b - Q_a}{T}. \tag{17–24}$$

Letting ΔS_1 and ΔQ_1 represent entropy change and heat influx, respectively, at temperature T_1, we have

$$\Delta S_1 = \frac{\Delta Q_1}{T_1}. \tag{17–25}$$

For the isothermal change at temperature T_2,

$$\Delta S_2 = \frac{-\Delta Q_2}{T_2}; \tag{17–26}$$

the minus sign comes from the fact that heat leaves the engine at temperature T_2. The total change of entropy of the working gas in the complete cycle is, therefore,

$$\Delta S = \Delta S_1 + \Delta S_2 = \frac{\Delta Q_1}{T_1} - \frac{\Delta Q_2}{T_2}, \tag{17–27}$$

but, since we earlier showed that

$$\frac{\Delta Q_1}{T_1} = \frac{\Delta Q_2}{T_2}$$

for a Carnot cycle, it follows that the left side of Eq. (17–27) is zero. Consequently, the entropy change of the working gas in a complete Carnot cycle is zero. Mathematically, we write

$$\oint dS = \oint \frac{dQ}{T} = 0 \tag{17–28}$$

for a complete Carnot cycle.

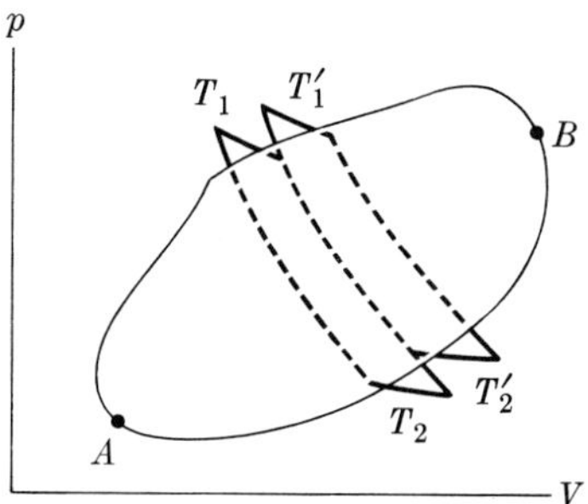

FIG. 17–7. Composition of any cycle by a summation of Carnot cycles.

Turning now to a closed cycle of arbitrary shape, as shown in Fig. 17–7, we see that such a cycle can be compounded of the end portions of adjoining elementary Carnot cycles of the sort shown by dashed lines in the figure. By making the elementary Carnot cycles vanishingly narrow, the arbitrary cycle can be perfectly represented in the limit. Since, for the ends of each Carnot cycle

$$dS = dS_1 + dS_2 = \frac{dQ_1}{T_1} - \frac{dQ_2}{T_2} = 0, \tag{17–29}$$

the entropy change for the complete arbitrary cycle must be zero. Thus

$$\oint dS = \oint \frac{dQ}{T} = 0$$

for any complete reversible cycle.

One further result is of immediate interest, namely, that the change in entropy between any two states A and B on a reversible path must be independent of the particular choice of reversible path. This result follows from the fact that the two reversible paths between A and B (as in Fig. 17–7) constitute a closed reversible cycle for which

$$\oint dS = \int_A^B dS + \int_B^A dS' = 0, \tag{17–30}$$

and hence

$$\int_A^B dS = \int_A^B dS', \tag{17–31}$$

where the prime indicates, say, the upper path and the unprimed quantity the lower path. Consequently, we can say that the entropy of one state relative to another is a function of the states only; that is, it is independent of the method of going from one state to another.

Therefore, the entropy difference between states can be found by utilizing any reversible mechanism for going from one state to the other. In the case of a process that is actually irreversible, we can find the entropy change by devising a reversible process that carries the system between the same two states. The entropy difference between states can then be found by calculating the entropy change during the selected reversible process. This was the method used in our opening example of heat flow by conduction. It is found that, in all cases so far investigated, the entropy increases during an irreversible process.

Example 1. Find the entropy change during the free expansion of an ideal gas from volume V_1 to volume V_2.

Solution: During the free expansion there will be no change in temperature of an ideal gas (as seen in Chapter 16). A reversible process that will carry the gas between the same two states is an isothermal expansion from volume V_1 to volume V_2 against a piston that exerts a pressure on the gas that is within dp of the equilibrium pressure at all times. During the expansion, heat ΔQ must be provided in order to maintain the gas at constant temperature. From the first law, $dQ = dW$, since the internal energy remains constant. The work can be computed from

$$dW = p\,dV = NRT\frac{dV}{V},$$

where the equation of state of the ideal gas has been used. The change in entropy ΔS is, therefore,

$$\Delta S = \int_1^2 \frac{dQ}{T} = \int_1^2 \frac{dW}{T} = NR\int_1^2 \frac{dV}{V} = NR\log\left(\frac{V_2}{V_1}\right).$$

17–7 PERPETUAL MOTION

Man's attempts to achieve perpetual motion are fascinating. Some of the less noble characteristics of men, such as dreams of quick wealth, have resulted indirectly in the advancement of science. The comparison of the immensity of the effort to achieve perpetual motion versus the totality of failure provides us with a logical foundation for the first and second laws of thermodynamics. Machines have been designed that were intended to provide us with useful work output greater than the energy input. We designate these as perpetual-motion machines of the first kind, denoting that a successful performance would be in conflict with the first law. A second and more subtle class of machines admits the equality of energy input and work output, and thus leaves the first law unchallenged. However, the design usually does not provide suitable reservoirs at different temperatures and thus is in conflict with the second law: there can be an admission that output is less than input, but not by the factor dictated by the Carnot limit, $1 - (T_2/T_1)$. Machines in conflict with the second law are classified as perpetual-motion machines of the second kind.

The failure of machines of either kind to perform as advertised amounts to a body of evidence supporting the validity of the two laws. Viewed in this way, the laws become sweeping statements that specify the limits we can approach in the realm of energy conversion. Thus the laws are the statements of *negative* principles: we *cannot* by cleverness ever create more energy than is supplied and we cannot by any cleverness improve on the Carnot efficiency. The laws are mathematical summaries of our failure to do otherwise.

17–8 SUMMARY

Two possible statements of the second law of thermodynamics are: (a) it is impossible to transfer heat from one object to another at a higher temperature without the occurrence of other changes in the system, (b) it is impossible to convert heat into work without the occurrence of other changes in the system.

The Carnot "refrigerator" consists in a Carnot cycle in which the direction of operation is reversed from that of an engine, that is, the net effect is the absorption of mechanical energy and transfer of heat from the cold to the hot reservoir. If the purpose of the device is to transfer heat to the hot reservoir, the effectiveness of the device can be specified by the ratio of heat transferred to mechanical energy absorbed,

$$C_{\mathrm{I}} \equiv \frac{\Delta Q_1}{\Delta W} = \frac{\Delta Q_1}{\Delta Q_1 - \Delta Q_2}$$

or

$$C_{\mathrm{I}} = \frac{T_1}{T_1 - T_2}.$$

When used in the above fashion, the device might be called a heat pump, since it is the amount of heat deposited in the higher temperature reservoir that is involved. When the device is used as a refrigerator, the coefficient of performance can be specified by the amount of heat extracted from the reservoir of lower temperature compared with the amount of mechanical energy required,

$$C_{II} \equiv \frac{\Delta Q_2}{\Delta W} = \frac{T_2}{T_1 - T_2}.$$

It is shown that a reversible Carnot engine, using any substance as the working material, has the same efficiency as the ideal gas engine. The proof utilizes the second law and the idea of a Carnot engine using an ideal gas coupled mechanically to a Carnot engine using another working substance. The temperature reservoirs are common to the two engines.

The thermodynamic temperature scale is defined in terms of the efficiency of a Carnot device

$$T_x = (1 - E)T_R,$$

where T_x is the unknown temperature of a reservoir and T_R is the temperature of a reference reservoir. The scale is the same as the ideal-gas thermometer scale, but it has the advantage of principle that any substance can be used for the Carnot device.

The concept of entropy is developed as a quantity that can be used to indicate the relative availability of heat energy. The change in entropy is

$$dS \equiv \frac{dQ}{T},$$

where dQ is the heat influx to a reservoir at temperature T. The second law can be expressed in the form that the entropy of a system always increases if there is any change at all in the entropy.

It is shown that the entropy change in a complete Carnot cycle or in any closed, reversible cycle is zero. It follows that the entropy change between any two states, when the change takes place along reversible paths, is independent of the path.

Perpetual motion machines are briefly discussed.

Problems

1. How high would you be raised into the air if all the thermal energy resulting from a 1°C drop in your body temperature were transformed into mechanical energy? Would the above process be possible according to the second law? the first law?

2. How much work is required to pump 1 kcal of heat from the outdoors at 0°C into a house at 27°C, using a Carnot refrigerator?

3. How much work is required to freeze 1 kg of ice cubes with a refrigerator that operates between 0 and 27°C?

4. Prove, using the type of argument illustrated in this chapter, that no refrigerator can have a coefficient of performance greater than that of a reversible Carnot refrigerator.

5. Prove that the size of the degree defined by the ideal-gas thermometer is the same as that defined by the Carnot-cycle thermometer.

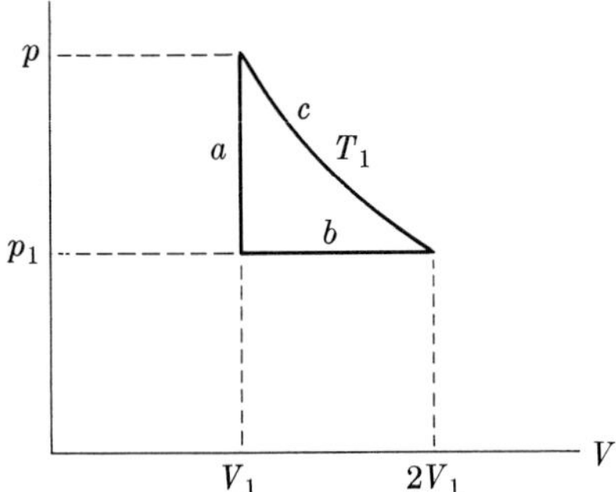

FIGURE 17–8

6. Calculate the entropy change along paths a and b in Fig. 17–8. Calculate the entropy change along the isothermal path c, and show that the result is equal to the sum of the entropy changes along a and b.

7. A perpetual-motion machine was designed, as in Fig. 17–9. The wooden disk D is pivoted at O and makes a watertight joint with the container walls. The A portion of the disk experiences a buoyant force in the water while the B portion experiences a net downward force due to gravity. Why will the disk not rotate? Is this a perpetual-motion machine of the first or of the second kind? Suppose we assert that the machine will somehow run because it converts heat energy from the water into mechanical energy. What type of perpetual motion machine would this be? Will it operate in this manner?

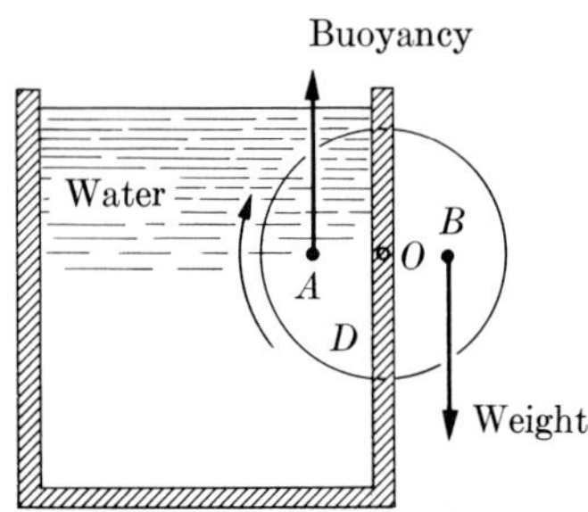

FIGURE 17–9

8. A perpetual-motion machine was designed, as shown in Fig. 17–10. It was asserted that the pivoted arms A, which can swing only from 0 to 90° relative to radii of the wheel, will give rise to a larger torque on one side than on the other because the moment arms are longer on one side. Criticize the ideas of the designer in terms of the laws of thermodynamics. The designer does not believe such a generalized argument. Criticize the design in terms of the simple mechanical argument of torques.

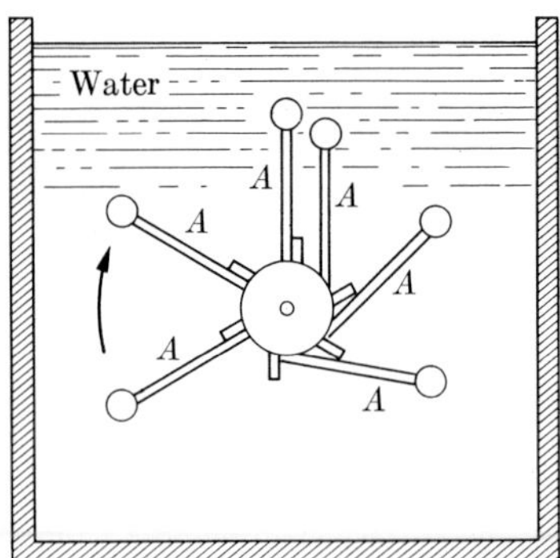

FIGURE 17–10

18

Kinetic Theory of Heat

18–1 INTRODUCTION

In the preceding chapters, it was found that heat energy can be included in the principle of conservation of energy, if the concept of temperature is introduced. We now examine the question of whether the introduction of the concept of temperature was a necessity or simply a convenience. The inclusion of heat energy in the discussion of energy conservation implies that the finite size of real objects is being recognized. (Heat energy was found to involve internal energy of some kind, the existence of which suggests that the object in question cannot be considered to be a point.) We now inquire into the properties that a finite object possesses that may lead to a more fundamental understanding of heat as a form of energy. To this end, certain details of the structure of matter must be examined.

In chemistry, you have been introduced to certain aspects of the molecular and atomic theory of matter as a means of understanding chemical properties and chemical reactions. In this chapter, we shall see how the ideas of atomic and molecular constitution of matter can be used to help us understand some of the physical properties of matter.

18–2 THE PRESSURE OF AN IDEAL GAS

In the discussion of heat and thermodynamics, we found that gases were particularly easy to describe, especially in the limit of low pressures. The limiting case was considered to be that of an idealized gas. It seems reasonable, therefore, to first attempt to understand the thermodynamic properties of an ideal gas in terms of the molecular model of a gas. Our procedure will be one of assuming a molecular model with certain properties, calculating the behavior of a gas constructed according to the assumed model, and, finally, comparing the calculated behavior with the experimental results, i.e., the gas laws, etc.

The simplest model is that of molecules (a) that have dimensions negligible compared with their mean separation, (b) that make completely elastic collisions with the walls of the container with negligible energy transfer to the walls, and (c) that make completely elastic collisions with each other. What is the dynamic behavior of a gas of such molecules when confined to a fixed volume? For simplicity, we choose a cubically shaped container and we choose cartesian coordinates coinciding with three of the edges of the container (Fig. 18–1).

Consider a particular molecule within this container, letting its position be x, y, z and its

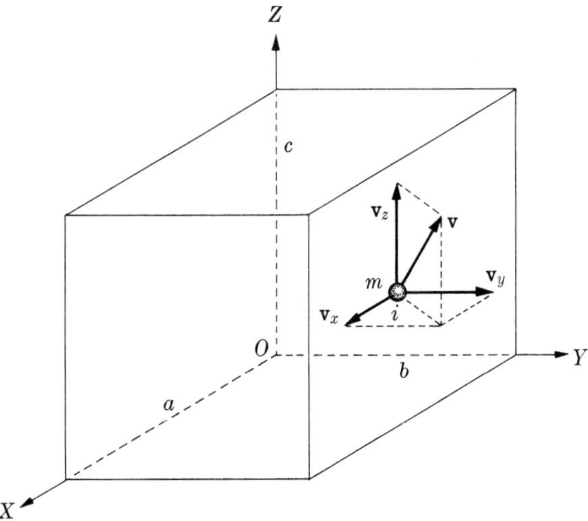

Fig. 18–1. Cartesian components of velocity of a molecule m in a rectangular-shaped box.

velocity be **v** as shown in Fig. 18–1. Excepting the instants of intermolecular collision, each molecule will have different position coordinates and different velocities. The problem of treating the dynamics of each molecule would be formidable indeed because of the large number of molecules. Therefore, we instead exploit the fact of the large numbers of molecules, within a macroscopic volume, and argue that time variations of properties such as velocity must be very small under constant conditions of pressure, temperature, and volume when *averages are taken over all molecules within the volume.*

In particular, let us consider the velocity. If the velocity of the ith molecule is resolved into cartesian components (Fig. 18–1), we have

$$v_i^2 = v_{ix}^2 + v_{iy}^2 + v_{iz}^2, \tag{18–1}$$

where v_i is the magnitude of the velocity. Because of intermolecular collisions, the magnitude and direction of the velocity of each molecule will change with time. (Note that only the direction of **v** is changed in collisions with the walls, according to our condition (b). We note further that the simplest model for container walls that will satisfy (b) is perfectly smooth walls, with no molecular structure evident. This apparently contradictory idealization will be discussed later.) The changes of velocity will be essentially random and because of the high collision rate, the values of the three *components* of the velocity of a given molecule will be essentially equal when averaged over even a rather short time interval (an interval long compared with the time between collisions). Thus, we have

$$\overline{v_i^2} = \overline{v_{ix}^2} + \overline{v_{iy}^2} + \overline{v_{iz}^2}, \tag{18–2}$$

where

$$\overline{v_{ix}^2} = \overline{v_{iy}^2} = \overline{v_{iz}^2}. \tag{18–3}$$

Furthermore, the random nature and high rate of the collisions will result in time averages that are the same for all molecules (i.e., all molecules of the same mass). Consequently, we can drop the subscript i in the equations for time averages and write simply

$$\overline{v^2} = 3\overline{v_x^2} = 3\overline{v_y^2} = 3\overline{v_z^2}. \tag{18–4}$$

What is the pressure exerted by such gas on the walls of the container? We fix our attention on the walls normal to the OX-axis. The time-averaged effect of collisions is uniform over the walls for the reasons given above. (We further assume that the height of the vertical walls is small enough so that vertical variations due to the earth's gravitation are negligible.) The pressure on the walls is due to the forces exerted by individual molecules during their collisions with the walls. The individual forces change rapidly with time during the collisions and these individual impulses are scattered randomly in time and position over the face of the wall. We again exploit the large size of the number of events even in a short interval of time and over a small (but macroscopic) area of wall. The result is that the *average* force on the wall will vary remarkably little with time.

The time-averaged force is simply equal to the change in momentum per unit time of the incident molecules,

$$\overline{F} \equiv \frac{\int_0^\tau F\,dt}{\tau} = \frac{\Delta mv}{\tau}, \tag{18–5}$$

where we have used the impulse formulation of Newton's second law, $\int F\,dt = \Delta mv$, to obtain the value of the force averaged over the interval τ.

The change in momentum Δmv during a time τ is simply the momentum change *per collision* times the number of collisions during time τ. Since the velocities of the molecules vary from molecule to molecule, it is necessary to consider the molecules separately and then integrate over all molecules. If there are dn molecules per unit volume, with velocity component v_x to $v_x + dv_x$, the number in time τ striking a wall that is normal

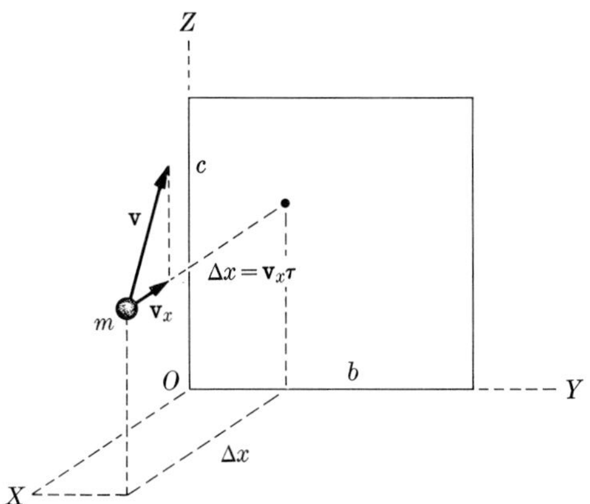

FIG. 18–2. All molecules with velocity component v_x will strike the OZY-wall of the box in time τ if they are at a distance $\Delta x = v_x\tau$ from the wall.

to v_x will be the number contained in a layer Δx of thickness $v_x\tau$ (see Fig. 18–2). (We note that particles that hit side walls before hitting the wall in question will simply be "reflected," with v_x unchanged.) The number of molecules of velocity v_x striking the wall in time τ will be

$$\frac{v_x\tau bc}{2}\,dn, \tag{18–6}$$

because only half the molecules with component v_x will have v_x in the direction toward the wall in question. The momentum change during the "reflection" from the wall will be

$$2mv_x. \tag{18–7}$$

The total momentum change by all molecules striking the wall in time τ will therefore be

$$(\Delta mv)_T = \int (2mv_x)\,\frac{v_x\tau bc}{2}\,dn, \tag{18–8}$$

which becomes (since m, b, c, and τ are constants)

$$(\Delta mv)_T = m\tau bc\int_0^{n_0} v_x^2\,dn, \tag{18–9}$$

where n_0 is the total number of molecules striking the wall during τ. But, by definition,

$$\overline{v_x^2} = \frac{\int_0^{n_0} v_x^2\,dn}{n_0}, \tag{18–10}$$

where n_0 is the total number of molecules per unit volume. Therefore,

$$(\Delta mv)_T = bcm\tau n_0\overline{v_x^2}. \tag{18–11}$$

The average force [from Eqs. (18–5) and (18–11)] becomes

$$\overline{F} = bcmn_0\overline{v_x^2},$$

or the pressure ($p \equiv \overline{F}/bc$)

$$p = mn_0\overline{v_x^2}. \tag{18–12}$$

But in terms of velocity itself (Eq. 18–4) we have

$$p = \frac{mn_0\overline{v^2}}{3}. \tag{18–13}$$

Finally, the total number of molecules n in the container is n_0V, where V is the volume, and Eq. (18–13) can be written

$$pV = n\,\frac{m\overline{v^2}}{3}. \tag{18–14}$$

A few comments concerning the collisions with the walls are in order. It is certainly contradictory to assume a molecular model for the gas but not for the walls. If we assume a molecular model for the walls, they cannot be smooth in the sense of "reflecting" the gas molecules. Second, as we shall see later, the molecules of the wall must also be pictured as in motion—vibrational motion in their case. Therefore, we cannot even say that the energy of the gas molecules remains the same in individual collisions with the walls. The answer to both apparent difficulties comes again from the consideration of average effects. From symmetry, the changes (during a collision) in the velocity components of the gas molecules parallel to the walls will be as often in one direction as in another. Consequently, the average will be the same as if there were no change in the parallel component, which was assumed in our derivation. As for the second apparent difficulty, there certainly are energy interchanges between the molecules of the gas and the molecules of the walls during their individual collisions, but, since macroscopic equilibrium has been assumed, there can be no *net* energy transfer in either direction, on the average, so long as the walls are fixed. The apparent need for a macroscopic change in momentum of a particular wall is answered by remembering that there is an opposite wall that would experience an equal and opposite change in momentum if the two were not rigidly interconnected.

18–3 TEMPERATURE AND SPECIFIC HEAT

We now confront the results predicted by our simple kinetic-theory model with experimental results. In Chapter 15, the definition of temperature in terms of the expansion of an ideal gas led to the equation of state of an ideal gas, which is

$$pV = RT \tag{18–15}$$

for one mole of gas, if R is the gas constant per mole. We see that our kinetic-theory model agrees with experiment, if we assume that

$$\frac{nm\overline{v^2}}{3} = RT; \tag{18–16}$$

that is, if we assume that temperature is proportional to the average *kinetic energy* of translation, $m\overline{v^2}/2$, of the molecules, we have

$$\frac{m\overline{v^2}}{2} = \frac{3}{2}\frac{R}{n}T, \tag{18–17}$$

where n is the number of molecules per mole.

The success of the above kinetic-theory model of a gas in predicting an equation of state that agrees with experiment for an ideal gas is a strong argument in favor of the basic accuracy of the assumed model.

The *specific heat* is defined as dQ/dT. If we identify the change in heat energy dQ with the change in kinetic energy $d(nm\overline{v^2}/2)$ of the gas particles (in a constant volume process so that none of the heat goes to external work), we get (Eq. 18–17),

$$dQ = d\left(\frac{nm\overline{v^2}}{2}\right) = \frac{3}{2}R\,dT. \tag{18–18}$$

But $C_v = dQ/dT$ for this process, and hence

$$C_v = \tfrac{3}{2}R \tag{18–19}$$

for the kinetic theory prediction of C_v per mole of an ideal gas. The result agrees with experiment for monatomic gases, giving us added confidence in the kinetic-theory model. Polyatomic gases will be discussed later.

18–4 DIRECT MEASUREMENT OF VELOCITIES

The evidence presented in the preceding material is not complete since other models might also lead to the correct equation of state for ideal gases. The prediction of Eq. (18–17) for the average squared velocity can be tested directly by measuring the velocities of particles in a gas. We expect a distribution of velocities but, if the distribution is found, the averages can be obtained.

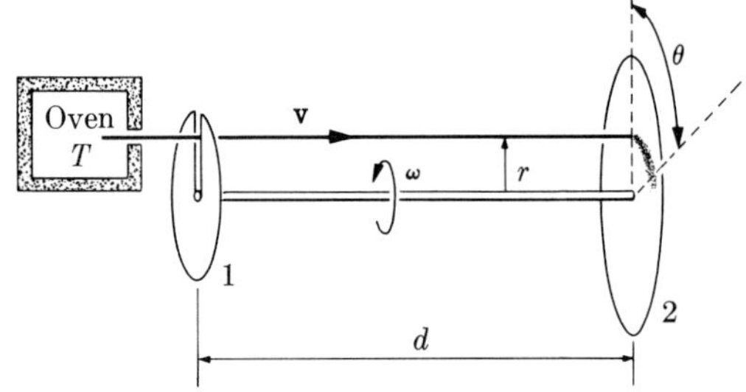

Fig. 18–3. Schematic diagram of apparatus to determine the velocities of molecules.

One of the experimental methods that has been used to measure the velocity distribution is shown schematically in Fig. 18–3.

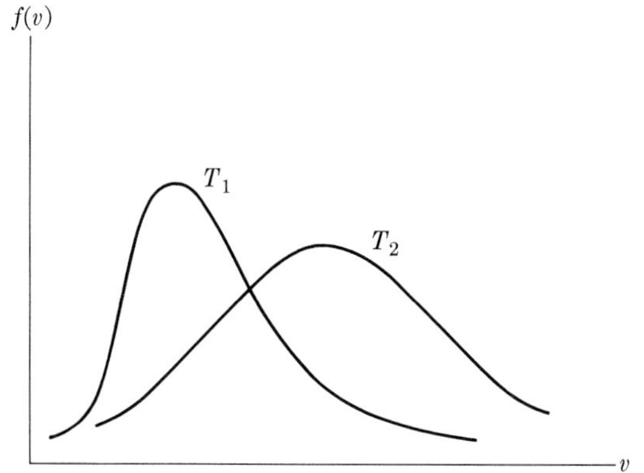

FIG. 18–4. The velocity distributions of molecules for two different temperatures, where $T_2 > T_1$.

A "gas" of vaporized metal, for example, mercury, is formed by raising the temperature of the oven to a suitable value T. Some of the gas escapes through a small hole into an evacuated chamber where it passes through a slot in a rotating disk 1. Another disk, 2, on the same shaft intercepts the beam of atoms, but at varying angles θ, depending on the speed of the atom. The density of the deposit can be measured and therefore the relative number of atoms, $f(v)\,dv$ with velocity v to $v + dv$ can be measured. (The total number of atoms is $\int_0^\infty f(v)\,dv$.) The results of the experiment are shown in Fig. 18–4, where $f(v)$ is plotted as a function of v and T, where $T_2 > T_1$. The average of the velocity squared can be obtained from the curves by the calculation,

$$\overline{v^2} = \frac{\int_0^\infty v^2 f(v)\,dv}{\int_0^\infty f(v)\,dv}. \qquad (18\text{–}20)$$

The result agrees with the theory, Eq. (18–17), thus giving quite direct confirmation of kinetic theory. A more detailed theory actually predicts the form of $f(v)$, called a Maxwellian distribution, and the prediction agrees with the experimental distributions such as Fig. 18–4.

18–5 BROWNIAN MOTION

Less direct but very striking evidence for the kinetic model is obtained by observation of microscopic particles, for example, smoke particles "suspended" in a gas. If the particles are suitably small, the rate of collisions of gas molecules is small enough on a given particle so that fluctuations in the collision frequency and intensity produce random wandering of the particles. The wandering is dependent on the velocities and number of colliding molecules. Since the molecular velocities are known from theory (verified by experiment), the number of molecules can be found from observations of the motion of the microscopic particles. In this way, Avogadro's number (the number of molecules per mole of gas) was first determined.

Another related effect on suspended microscopic particles is a dependence of the number of particles on vertical height. This effect is brought about by the gravitational force on the particles and results in a decrease of particles with height.

18–6 REAL GASES (MOLECULAR MODEL)

The properties of an ideal gas are satisfactorily described by the simple kinetic-theory model presented above. In order to describe real gases, the finite size of the molecules and the effect of possible forces of attraction might be added to our model. (There must still be a dominant force of repulsion at small separations, since collisions result in a rebound.)

The changes that might be hypothesized in the *equation of state* are (a) a term subtracted from the volume because of the finite volume occupied by molecules themselves, and (b) a term added to the pressure because of the net attraction of the molecules in the gas toward the main body of gas for a molecule at the "surface" of the gas. The latter is expected to depend on the gas density squared, one factor for the magnitude of the force on a boundary molecule, and the second factor for the number of boundary molecules that feel the effect. Since density varies inversely with volume, the form of the equation of state changes as follows

$$pV = NRT \rightarrow \left(p + \frac{a}{V^2}\right)(V - b) = NRT, \tag{18–21}$$

where b is the volume of the molecules and a is a constant dependent on the long-range force of attraction. Equation (18–21) is called van der Waals equation of state. The above equation of state gives a good description of gases at high pressure, even including the condensation to the liquid state. For low pressures, that is, large V, the correction terms become negligible and van der Waals equation goes over to the ideal-gas equation.

The *condensation of a gas* to the liquid state is predicted qualitatively from the above model by simply remarking that when the temperature is lowered, the molecules lose kinetic energy, and when the pressure is increased, the average separation becomes smaller. We may then expect a condition of reduced temperature and increased pressure when the force of attraction between molecules becomes sufficient to cause coalescence, particularly of the slower molecules of the gas. The faster molecules that are left behind in the gas must be slowed down by the abstraction of heat before they in turn can coalesce with other molecules. Thus, the latent heat that must be abstracted in order to produce condensation is qualitatively understood.

The *vaporization of a liquid* is, of course, the opposite. The kinetic energy of the liquid molecules must be increased by raising the temperature until the kinetic energy is comparable with the potential (binding) energy of boundary molecules in the liquid. The faster molecules escape, thus cooling the remaining liquid unless heat is supplied from outside.

The *freezing of a liquid* corresponds to the change to a still more ordered state of the material in which the potential energy is even more negative than for the liquid. Again, it is preferentially the slower molecules of the liquid that first coalesce into the fixed structure of a solid. This accounts for the latent heat of fusion, the need to abstract heat from a liquid, even at the constant temperature of the freezing point, in order to produce fusion.

The *change in temperature of a real gas upon free expansion* can also be understood. We have assumed long-range forces of attraction in the above. During the free expansion (or any expansion, for that matter) of such a gas, the average separation of the molecules increases. The result is an increase in the potential energy associated with the force of attraction. For an isolated gas, this increase in potential energy can come only from a decrease in kinetic energy; that is, such a gas should become cooler during a free expansion. It is observed experimentally that most gases are indeed cooled by free expansion. Thus, even for a gas (except an ideal gas), the *internal energy* is not determined by temperature alone but also by the volume.

18–7 LIQUIDS AND SOLIDS

It has already been indicated that potential energy plays an important role in our understanding of liquids and solids. On the other hand, the temperature is measured by the kinetic energy alone, since by definition, temperature can be measured with an ideal-gas thermometer. The ideal gas has only kinetic energy. To measure the temperature of a liquid or a solid, we would place the gas of the thermometer in contact with the liquid or solid. The gas would interact with the liquid or solid by molecular collisions at the walls. The interchanges during collisions are conditioned *only by the kinetic energies.*

Within the liquid or solid, however, there are forces of attraction that keep the solid or liquid intact (except for evaporation or sublimation from the surface). Potential energy is associated with these binding forces. In mechanics, we found that the average potential energy was equal to the average kinetic energy for the case of a linear binding force. We also found that any binding force could be approximated by a linear force over small distances. Consequently, we might expect the addition of a *given amount* of internal energy to a solid or liquid to be less effective in raising the temperature (kinetic energy) than in the case of ideal gases, since potential energy must also be supplied to the solid or liquid. In general, such is indeed the case.

The above effect is an example of equipartition of energy, of which more will be said in Section 18–8. There must, however, be a force of repulsion between atoms or molecules at sufficiently small distances; otherwise, solids, liquids, and even molecules would contract toward zero volume as the temperature is decreased.

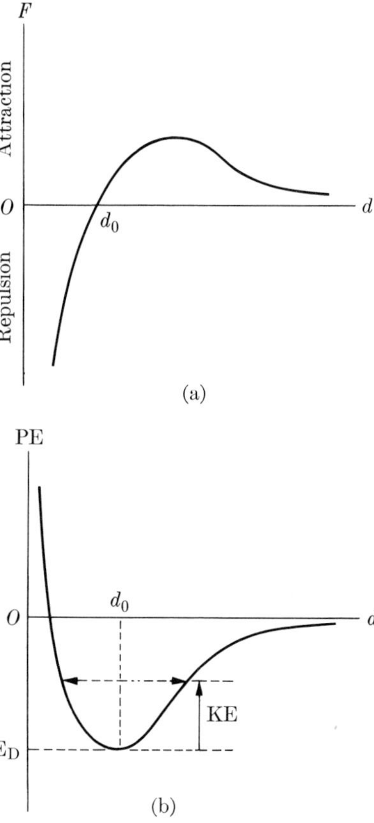

FIG. 18–5. (a) The force of attraction versus separation for the atoms in a diatomic molecule. (b) The potential energy corresponding to the force in (a).

18–8 MOLECULAR GASES; EQUIPARTITION OF ENERGY

In the case of solids, it has been pointed out that we expect an equal division of internal energy between kinetic and potential energy. This is an example of what is called equipartition of energy and results in a less rapid rise of temperature with added internal energy than would result if only kinetic energy were involved.

In the case of an ideal gas at constant pressure, we have seen that kinetic theory agrees with experiment for the rise in temperature accompanying a given influx of heat for *monatomic* gases, that is,

$$C_v = \tfrac{3}{2} R \text{ per mole} \qquad \text{(Section 18–3)}.$$

What is the kinetic-theory model for a diatomic molecule? The form of the force and, more usefully, of the potential energy curve predicted for a diatomic molecule is shown in Fig. 18–5. The force is zero and the potential energy is a minimum at the equilibrium separation d_0. As a result of collisions, we should expect the atoms to be set into vibration about their equilibrium separation with excursions in d as shown by the dashed line at height KE above the minimum of PE in Fig. 18–5(b). The energy of vibration would be determined by the severity of the collision that induces vibration. An equilibrium state between vibration energy and translational kinetic energy would be expected. We *hypothesize* that the equilibrium state corresponds to an *equipartition* of energy among the various modes. Further, we assume that translational kinetic energy corresponds to three modes, corresponding to the fact that there are three components to velocity and we assume that kinetic and potential energy of vibration are two modes.

In addition to vibration, we expect that rotation of the molecule will be produced by collisions. If the model of the molecule consists of two atoms separated by d_0 (with the atoms vibrating about separation d_0, as in Fig. 18–6), we also expect rotation, which can be resolved into three components as shown. Classically, if the atoms are considered to have "frictionless surfaces," rotation about OY cannot be produced by collisions. Consequently, only two components of rotation are expected, that is, two more modes of energy absorption or emission during collisions.

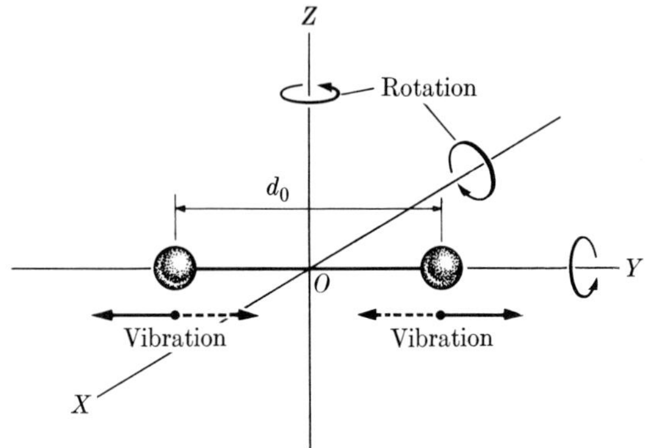

FIG. 18–6. The degrees of rotational and vibrational freedom of a diatomic molecule.

From the above discussion, we see that there are seven energy modes for a diatomic molecule. The usual phraseology is that there are seven *degrees of freedom.* Since the specific heat $(3/2)R$ was for atoms with three degrees of freedom, the hypothesis of equipartition of energy predicts

$$C_v = \frac{f}{2} R \qquad (18\text{–}22)$$

for the specific heat per mole of molecules that have f degrees of freedom.

The diatomic molecule is, therefore, expected to have $C_v = (7/2)R$, according to the preceding discussion. Experimentally, it is found that, at high temperatures, the specific heat does have this value; but at lower temperatures C_v falls to a value of $(5/2)R$ and at very low temperatures C_v becomes only the $(3/2)R$ of a monatomic gas! The interpretation of these results is that all degrees of freedom are excited only at high temperatures, vibration is *not* excited at moderate temperatures, and at very low temperatures not even rotation is excited. The explanation of this phenomenon of suppression of degrees of freedom constitutes one of the triumphs of quantum theory that you will study later.

18–9 THERMAL CONDUCTION; TRANSPORT PHENOMENA

The kinetic-theory model for *heat conduction* has been described implicitly in foregoing sections. The molecules at the boundary between a hot and a cold object interact by collisions. Since the average kinetic energy of the molecules of the hot object is higher than the average kinetic energy of the molecules of the cold object, there is a net transfer of energy from the hot to the cold object when averaged over many collisions of molecules at the boundary. The result is a flow of heat, that is, kinetic energy (and, due to equipartition, of potential energy as well), from the hot to the cold object. Heat conduction can be described as transport of thermal energy due to a temperature gradient.

Diffusion is transport of material due to a density gradient. For example, if a gas A is released near one wall of a container that is filled uniformly with gas B, gas A will gradually mix uniformly with gas B because of the motion of the molecules. The factors affecting the rate of diffusion will be the velocity of the molecules and their collision frequency, as well as the concentration gradient. The rate can be predicted from a kinetic-theory model and the result agrees with experiment.

A transport of momentum laterally between layers of gas moving past one another results in the resistance to flow called *viscosity.* Again, the kinetic theory predictions are in accord with experiment.

18–10 MOLECULAR THEORY INTERPRETATION OF THE FIRST LAW

In the preceding sections, the examples have *not* involved interchanges among various gross forms of energy, such as mechanical and thermal energy. We now turn to such examples. Consider the simple process of expansion of a gas as accomplished by motion of a piston. In collisions with stationary walls, the molecules of a gas exchange energy with the walls, but on the average there is no exchange of momentum with the walls. Even if the temperatures are different, so that there is a net transfer of energy of thermal agitation, there is no net momentum transfer because the directions are random. But if a wall is moving, there is a directed average effect in the direction of motion of the wall. Molecules that strike a receding wall rebound with a reduced velocity component in the direction of motion of the wall. The result is a cooling of the gas, unless heat is supplied as a means of maintaining the average velocity of the gas molecules at its original level. If no heat is provided, adiabatic cooling of the gas results. The work done moving the piston is at the expense of the random kinetic energy of the gas molecules.

On the other hand, in a free expansion the molecules do not strike a receding wall and, therefore, they retain their average kinetic energy unchanged by collisions. If the gas is ideal, no change in temperature occurs. We have already seen, however, that a real gas with, for example, an attractive force between molecules, must cool upon expansion because of the increase in internal potential energy of the gas.

If work is done against friction, energy is transferred to increased random motion of the molecules at the surfaces where the friction force occurs. In case of fluid friction there is transfer of energy from the gross mechanical energy of motion to the random molecular motion of thermal agitation. In the usual example given for determining the mechanical equivalent of heat, paddle wheels rotating in water are used to transfer mechanical energy to thermal energy. The overall result is the conversion of the gross, directed mechanical energy, due perhaps to falling weights, to the random mechanical energy of molecules. When objects collide, some of the kinetic energy of motion as a whole is changed to the random molecular motion of thermal energy of the objects.

18–11 MOLECULAR THEORY AND THE SECOND LAW

The statement of the second law in the form that heat by itself flows only in the direction of diminishing temperature can now be understood as a statistical law, in terms of the kinetic theory. In energy interchanges during collisions, faster molecules will always lose energy to slower molecules. Since the *average* molecular energy is greater when the temperature is greater, we expect a net flow of energy toward the lower temperature regions because of the energy interchanges during molecular collisions.

We must be very careful to admit in the above example that is is perfectly possible for the collisions to happen in such a manner that there is a preponderance of collisions between molecules of the hotter region that have lower velocity than the molecules of the cooler region with which they collide. The result would be a flow of heat from the cooler to the hotter object. If we look at sufficiently small regions for sufficiently short times, the above reversal of normal heat flow certainly occurs. But when we look at many small regions or watch one small region over a long period of time, it is *extremely* unlikely that the average or net result is flow of heat energy from the cooler to the hotter regions.

It is seen that the *second law* in the form discussed above becomes a *statement of probability* when the molecular-kinetic theory model is used to "understand" the second law in terms of first principles.

Let us turn now to a case in which gross interchanges of mechanical-heat energy occur in an irreversible manner according to the second law. For example, consider the mechanical equivalent of heat experiment in which a falling weight turns paddles in a water bath, resulting in a rise in temperature of the water. The kinetic theory description of the heating mechanism has already been given in the discussion of the kinetic theory interpretation of the *first law* (Section 18–10).

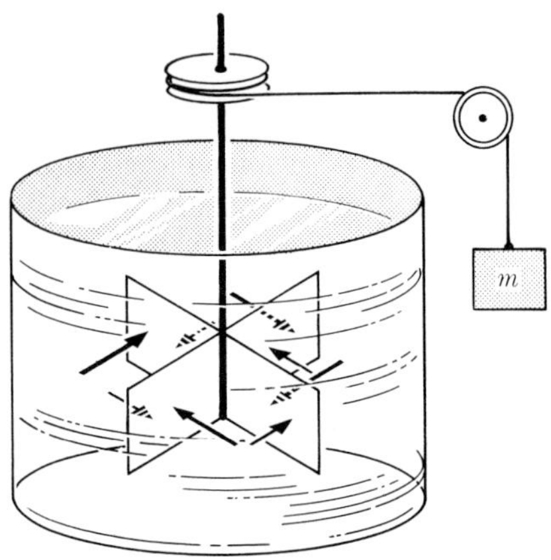

FIG. 18–7. Schematic diagram of a mechanical equivalent of a heat experiment. The arrows show representative velocities of molecules that strike the vanes.

Now suppose that, by chance, the water molecules striking one set of faces of the paddles have sufficiently higher velocity than the water molecules striking the other set of faces (Fig. 18–7). The result could be that m is raised back to its original height. The faster molecules of water will lose more energy in their collisions with the receding faces of the paddles than the slower molecules will gain in their collisions with the advancing faces. The result is that the water becomes cooler; mechanical energy is increased at the expense of heat energy. The law of conservation of energy (first law) is not violated.

Once again we must admit that the above would occur with a sufficiently small apparatus. In fact, Brownian motion is an example of *exactly* this sort of process. Smoke particles can be lifted vertically by a *local* preponderance of severity or number of collisions from below. The increase in potential energy of the particle comes at the expense of a local reduction of gas-molecule velocities, that is, cooling of the gas.

On a larger scale, however, the probability of the above result becomes extremely small. Thus, once again, the second law is to be understood as a probability statement.

A rather general qualitative statement of the second law, in terms of molecular theory, can be made in terms of order versus disorder. In our first example above, an unusually systematic *ordering of events* was assumed, namely, that there was a preponderance of collisions between fast molecules of the cooler region with the slow molecules of the hotter region. In the second example, an unusually systematic ordering was also assumed. It would be found, in general, that any process violating the second law requires a similar unlikely ordering of the inherent disorder of thermal energy.

Therefore, the qualitative statement might be that energy changes never go in the direction of a net increase in molecular ordering of the system as a whole.

18–12 MOLECULAR THEORY AND ENTROPY

Quantitatively, entropy is used to state the condition of the second law on the macroscopic scale. In the earlier sections it was found possible to express other macroscopic quantities of thermodynamics, such as temperature and heat, in terms of the average microscopic properties assumed for the kinetic-theory model. Can the same be done for entropy?

The answer is that entropy can also be quantitatively related with a concept derived from microscopic properties. The concept is the relative probability W, that among all possible microscopic states, a certain microscopic state will exist. The equation is

$$S = k \log W, \qquad (18\text{–}23)$$

where S is the entropy, W is the probability as defined above, and k is a constant of microscopic physics called the Boltzmann constant.

The methods of obtaining k and W from the kinetic-theory model are the subject of the division of physics called "statistical mechanics."

18–13 SUMMARY

A simplified model of macroscopic bodies is developed, starting from microscopic first principles in the sense of starting with idealized atoms or molecules as the smallest separate entities to be considered. An ideal gas of perfectly elastic, point-mass molecules is predicted to exert a pressure given by

$$pV = n\,\frac{m\overline{v^2}}{3}$$

where $\overline{v^2}$ is the average of the velocity squared of the molecules.

By comparison with the macroscopic observation of the equation of state of an "ideal" gas, it is seen that the macroscopic property, temperature, corresponds to the microscopic property, kinetic energy of the molecules. Quantitatively, we have

$$\frac{m\overline{v^2}}{2} = \frac{3}{2}\,\frac{R}{n}\,T,$$

where n is the number of molecules per mole.

The specific heat that is thereby predicted,

$$C_v = \tfrac{3}{2}R,$$

agrees with experiment for monatomic gases.

Direct measurement of molecular velocities of a gas gives results that are in agreement with the above model. Indirect confirmation of the essential correctness of the kinetic-theory model comes from observation of Brownian motion, from which Avogadro's number can be obtained.

When the additional properties of finite size and long-range forces of interaction are added to the microscopic model, van der Waals equation results,

$$\left(p + \frac{a}{V^2}\right)(V - b) = NRT,$$

an equation that describes quite well the state of real gases, even including their change to the liquid state. The dependence of internal energy of a real gas upon its volume is qualitatively understandable in terms of long-range forces. A qualitative understanding of some properties of liquids, solids, and changes of state is possible in terms of the kinetic-theory model. The classical microscopic model of the internal structure of polyatomic gases leads to the prediction that the specific heat should be

$$C_V = \frac{f}{2}\,R$$

where f is the number of degrees of freedom. Experimentally, it is found that the specific heat of polyatomic gases is dependent on temperature and is less than the above value except at high temperatures. Quantum theory is required in order to understand the variation of specific heat with temperature.

Descriptive interpretation of the observations on thermal conduction is given, in terms of kinetic theory. The first and second laws of thermodynamics are discussed in terms of the kinetic-theory model. The idea of probability must be included in the discussion of the interpretation of the second law in terms of kinetic theory.

Problems

The number of molecules per mole (Avogadro's number) is 6.02×10^{23}.

1. One cubic centimeter of water is $\frac{1}{18}$ of a mole. How many molecules does it contain? What is the volume occupied by one molecule? Picture each molecule as occupying a cubical volume; what is the length of the edge of the cube? What can you conclude from the above about the approximate diameter of a molecule?

2. Show that 1 cc of a gas at standard temperature and pressure contains about 3×10^{19} molecules. Assuming that the diameter of a molecule is about 2×10^{-8} cm, find the ratio of the volume of a molecule of a gas to its share of the volume of the container at standard temperature and pressure.

3. Using the information for number of molecules and their sizes from Problem 2, can you estimate the distance that a molecule would travel before making a collision with another molecule? [*Hint:* How thick must a layer of the gas be in order to contain enough molecules so that their combined cross-sectional area would just completely obscure the passage of an incident molecule, assuming that no molecule lies behind another?]

4. Prove that a perfectly elastic head-on collision between particles of the same mass results in a simple exchange of velocities; that is, if one mass has velocities v_1 and v_1' and the other velocities v_2 and v_2' before and after the collision, respectively, show that

$$v_1 = v_2' \quad \text{and} \quad v_2 = v_1'.$$

5. Since gas molecules that strike a wall experience a change in momentum that is always directed away from the wall, the wall should experience an equal and opposite change in momentum directed away from the gas. Why does the wall not move (accelerate) in the direction away from the gas?

6. Calculate the root mean square velocity ($\sqrt{\overline{v^2}}$) of a hydrogen molecule in a gas at standard conditions. (The mass of a molecule can be found from the molecular weight divided by Avogrado's number.) Can you find the velocity, or rather, the average velocity itself?

7. By how much must the temperature of a gas be raised above its initial temperature in order to double the average molecular kinetic energy? to double the root mean square velocity?

8. Assuming that all the molecules of a gas have the root mean square velocity, find the number of collisions per second on a wall area of 1 cm^2 in hydrogen gas under standard conditions. At the same temperature, show that the collision frequency with the wall is proportional to $1/m$ of the molecule, but that the momentum change during collision is proportional to m and therefore the pressure is independent of mass. Is the above a proof that all gases exert the same pressure under the same conditions?

9. Calculate the numerical value of the specific heat per gram of an ideal gas.

10. In the case of sodium at 300°C, at what angle θ will molecules of root mean square velocity strike disk 2 in the apparatus of Fig. 18–3? The gram atomic weight of sodium is 23.

11. What are the units of $f(v)$ in Eq. 18–20? Tell how you would find $\overline{v^2}$ from one of the graphs in Fig. 18–4.

12. Imagine a fluctuation in which 10 gas molecules strike a smoke particle nearly head-on from the same side, with no other collisions occurring during that short interval of time. What is the diameter of a smoke particle that will be given a change in velocity of 1 mm/sec in the above process? Assume nitrogen gas (gram molecular weight 28) at 300°K and assume density 2 gm/cm^3 for the smoke particle.

13. In a gas at standard temperature and pressure, how large is b compared with V in van der Waals equation (18–21) for molecules of diameter 2×10^{-8} cm? At what pressure would the molecules be closely packed, that is, simultaneously touch their neighbors on all sides? (Neglect the a/V^2 term for this calculation.)

14. Describe the equilibrium state between a liquid and its vapor (gas) qualitatively on the kinetic theory model. Why is the equilibrium vapor pressure an increasing function of temperature?

15. The energy of dissociation of the hydrogen molecule is about 7×10^{-19} joule. Assuming equipartition of energy, and that each molecule has average energy, at what temperature will hydrogen molecules dissociate?

16. In a mixture of a monatomic gas and a diatomic gas in equilibrium, which molecules have the higher average energy? the higher average translational energy? Give quantitative ratios in both cases.

17. Compare quantitatively the changes in internal energy of monatomic with diatomic gases (a) when the temperature of each is raised by ΔT, and (b) when each does an amount of work ΔW by expansion.

18. If a piston moves very slowly during the adiabatic expansion of a gas, the gas molecules lose very little energy when they collide with the receding piston. Why does the gas cool as much as it does during a fast expansion?

19. A cylinder with cross section of 10 cm^2 contains a gas at normal temperature and pressure at the instant that the piston is 10 cm from the floor of the cylinder. The cylinder is moving with a velocity of 1 cm/sec and the expansion is isobaric. Assuming a monatomic gas, with each molecule possessing the root mean square speed, find the change in energy per collision of each molecule with the moving piston. How many collisions must occur per second in order to provide the power to move the piston when it is 10 cm from the floor?

20. Xenon gas (gram atomic weight 131) at normal temperature and pressure is confined in a cubic container of volume 22.4 liters (22,400 cm^3 or 28 cm in size). What is the total kinetic energy of the gas? Suppose that, by chance, all the atoms of the xenon acquire a velocity in the same direction. Could this happen due to collisions between xenon atoms? collisions with the walls? Find the recoil velocity of the container if its mass is the same as that of the xenon. Can the xenon have the same total energy that it had before its velocities became ordered? What is the new temperature of the xenon? Is its temperature definable?

21. In an average sample of gas, there will be as many molecules with velocities directed in the upper hemisphere as directed in the lower hemisphere. In other words, the probability is one-half that a given molecule will be traveling upward. What is the probability that all the molecules in a cubic centimeter of gas will be moving upward at the same instant? How small a sample of gas would you have to examine in order to have one chance in about a million of finding all the molecules moving upward?

22. Consider a sample of gas containing four molecules that are labeled. How many combinations are there with two moving upward and two moving downward? with three moving upward? with four moving upward? The above results are the relative probabilities of the above states. Plot a graph of the relative entropies of the above states. Which has the greatest entropy?

19

The Electrostatic Force

19–1 INTRODUCTION

Forces are a fundamental element in the theory of mechanics. Usually, when the force law governing a system is found, the solution of the physics problem is reduced to a problem in mathematics. It is not surprising, then, with the utility and theoretical importance of forces so well established, that whole branches of physics have grown around the study of the origin of forces in nature. Today, a system of classification prevails which separates all forces into four major kinds, according to their origin. These classes are, broadly: (a) gravitational, (b) electromagnetic, (c) nuclear, and (d) weak interactions.

(a) *Gravitational mass* m is the source of the gravitational force. In the universal law of gravitation for the interaction of two material objects,

$$|\mathbf{F}| = G\,\frac{m_1 m_2}{r^2}. \tag{19–1}$$

The product $m_1 m_2$ suggests to us that the "cause" of the force lies in the masses of the objects. The force is proportional to the mass of each object, there is no force if either mass is zero, and the force depends on no other intrinsic characteristics of the objects. The force so described is therefore put into a special class because of its origin in mass, and is called the gravitational force. The gravitational constant G is peculiar to this class, and its value is 6.67×10^{-11} mks unit. It is found that the inertial mass and the gravitational mass are identical within present experimental accuracy.

(b) The source of the *electromagnetic* force is the *electric charge*. Many of the particles of which the universe is made up are electrified in their natural state, and the amount of electrification is described by the charge q which the particle possesses. For illustration, we write down the *Coulomb law* of interaction for two charged particles at rest. It is

$$|\mathbf{F}| = k\,\frac{q_1 q_2}{r^2}, \tag{19–2}$$

where $\mathbf{F}$ is directed along the line that passes through both charges. This law is exactly similar to the gravitational law. Here the cause, or source, of the force is contained in the electric charges of the two bodies. The interaction is proportional to the product of the charges. The geometric dependence is still of the inverse-square form. If the bodies are in relative motion, an additional force arises between them. This is called the magnetic force, although its source is still fundamentally the electric charge. Therefore the electric force and the magnetic force are grouped together in the same class, and are often combined and called the electromagnetic force. If the same bodies possess mass, there is also a gravitational force operating between them, but it is usually very small compared with the electromagnetic force.

It is the electromagnetic force that binds electrons to the atomic nucleus and binds atoms together to form molecules. Thus the electromagnetic force governs all chemical interactions. The electromagnetic force binds atoms or molecules together to form solids or liquids. Forces of cohesion, forces of contact, the force in a spring, and gas pressure are all electromagnetic in origin.

(c) The third class of forces is not so evident in ordinary experience. Specifically nuclear, this force binds protons and neutrons together in the atomic nucleus: the force is neither electrical nor gravitational. This force is of such "short range" that its effect does not extend beyond the nuclear surface. (Gravitational and electrical forces are called "long range," since their effects can be important for macroscopic distances.) The short-range nuclear force is negligible even at distances equal to an atomic diameter. However, within its range of 10^{-15} m, the nuclear force is much greater than either the electromagnetic or the gravitational force of interaction. The large magnitude of the nuclear force is strikingly demonstrated in the "production of nuclear energy."

(d) The fourth class of forces is associated with beta decay of radioactive nuclei.

Our treatment of interaction forces is mostly classical, that is, the concept of fields will be used to describe the interactions, but the quantization of the fields will not be treated in detail. It is the hope of physicists that ultimately the interaction of objects can be described by a single field theory which embraces at once all the separate theories of today. Such a unified picture has not yet been developed, even though striking similarities and relationships can be seen among the different kinds of forces. We now return to electric forces.

19–2 SOME PROPERTIES OF THE ELECTRIC CHARGE

Macroscopic quantities of matter usually are nearly electrically neutral. This initially neutral matter can often be electrified simply by rubbing it in contact with some other substance. For example, a comb drawn through dry hair becomes electrified and so does the hair. The manifestations of the electrification are evident, since the strands of hair bristle and stand apart. The comb now can attract to itself light objects such as dust particles or fragments of paper. This is a simple demonstration that matter can have a power of attraction for other matter which is independent of gravitational action. Electrified bodies are said to possess a net electric charge.

Experiments on electrification, such as the one just described, can be contrived to demonstrate the behavior of material with respect to charge and some properties of charge itself. It is found that charge can be transferred from one object to another. If an electrified comb is touched to a pith ball, the ball becomes electrified and has a new power of attraction. The charge can also be transferred to metallic objects. One notable distinction among different kinds of matter can be observed at once. When electricity is deposited on a metallic object, it is quickly distributed over the entire object. If one end of a long copper bar is electrified, the other end becomes electrified almost at once. Charge is said to flow along the bar. Such materials are called *electrical conductors.* If charge is deposited onto amber, glass, or synthetic resins, it may remain locally fixed to the point of deposit for hours. Such substances are called *electrical insulators.* It is remarkable that the difference between most conductors and most insulators is so great and so clear-cut. Only a few substances lie in a border region. They are called *electrical semiconductors.*

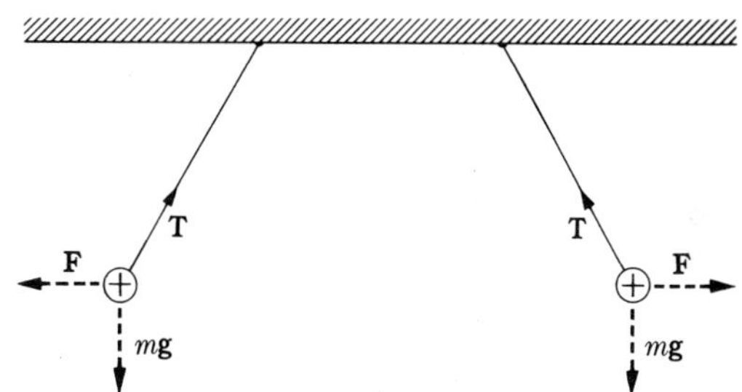

FIG. 19–1. Equilibrium positions of two charged pith balls hanging from threads. The force **F** is the electrostatic force.

Let a device for the measurement of electric-charge effects be constructed. It may consist of a pair of tiny, light pith balls suspended by threads from an overhead support. If a rod of glass is rubbed with a silk cloth, the glass becomes electrified. When some of this electric charge is deposited on each of the pith balls, the balls are repelled from each other (Fig. 19–1).

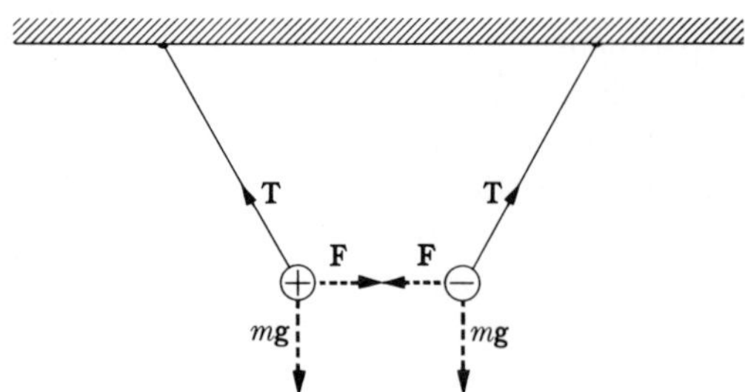

FIG. 19–2. Equilibrium positions of two charged pith balls hanging from threads. The force **F** is the electrostatic force.

The phenomenon of repulsion is quite different from the gravitational force which always causes attraction. If amber is rubbed by cat's fur, and if some of the charge of the rubbed amber is deposited on each neutral pith ball, then the balls are again repelled. Now, if the charge of the amber is placed on one originally neutral ball, and if the charge on glass is placed on the other neutral ball, we discover a force of attraction (Fig. 19–2). The conclusion from these observations is that the charge generated on glass by silk and the charge generated by fur on amber are of different kinds. Each kind of charge repels its own kind. But the different kinds attract each other. If the experiments are repeated with different materials, we find that the classification of charge into *two kinds* is sufficient as well as necessary. One kind, that is generated on glass, is called *positive charge*, the other is called *negative charge*. The utility of the mathematical labeling will become apparent later. For the above discussion, we could just as well have called the charges north and south charges or black and white charges.

There are other general properties of the electric charge which are known from extensive laboratory experience. First, charge is a scalar physical quantity. We do not observe a changed electrostatic effect by "pointing" a charge in different directions. Therefore, charges are additive according to the scalar rules. Second, charge is always conserved. No observation has ever taken place in which a net charge was created where there was none before, nor has total charge been annihilated. An annihilation process, the addition of equal positive and negative charges to give neutrality, does not contradict this statement, since the mixture of different charges on the macroscopic scale can in principle and in practice be again purified into the two separate kinds.

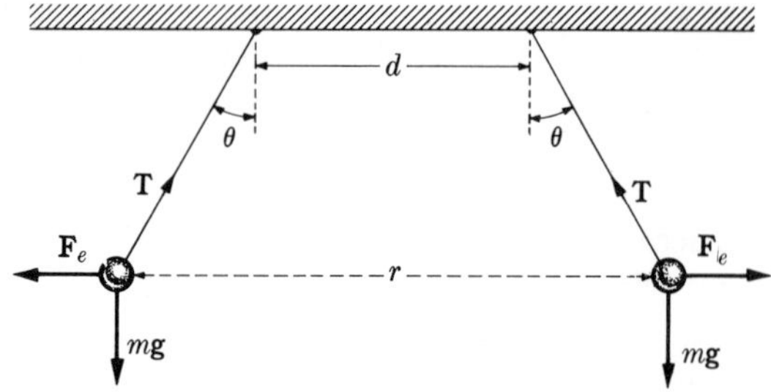

FIG. 19–3. The quantities to be measured if the dependence of the electrostatic force $\mathbf{F}_e$ on separation r of the charged objects is to be measured. In practice the distance d between supporting points of the threads would be varied as a means of changing r, with charge kept constant.

19–3 THE COULOMB LAW FOR POINT CHARGES

In 1784 André Coulomb established the inverse-square law of electrostatic interaction by experimental means, using a torsion balance. In principle, the pith-ball arrangement we have shown could also be used for this demonstration. We place charges on the two balls and observe the effect of the interaction. The measurement of the angle of deflection yields the electrical force on a pith ball in terms of the gravitational force. From the elementary laws of mechanics, we have for the electric force (Fig. 19–3)

$$F_e = mg \tan \theta.$$

By varying the distance of separation of the points of support d, we observe a different deflection. Upon measuring F_e as a function of the equilibrium separation of the charges r, we find that

$$F_e \sim \frac{1}{r^2} \qquad (19\text{–}3)$$

if the pith balls are small compared with r. Therefore, the force between a given pair of charges is inversely proportional to the square of the distance between the charges. The electrical forces on either ball are the same in magnitude and oppositely directed. The summary of the above experimental evidence is now presented in equation form, called the Coulomb law of interaction,

$$F_e = k\,\frac{q_1 q_2}{r^2}, \tag{19–4}$$

where q_1 and q_2 represent the magnitudes of the separate charges. The charge dependence was not established by Coulomb, for he had no independent means of judging the strength of the charge. The length r is the distance between the centers of the charges. The law holds strictly only when the dimensions of the charge distributions, α_1 and α_2, are made very small compared with r (Fig. 19–4). Analytically, we say that the law holds for *point charges.*

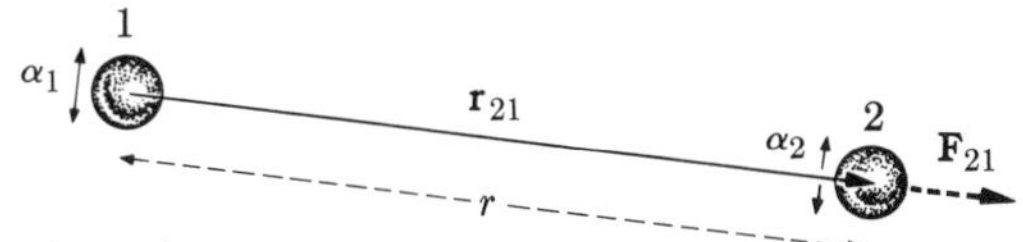

FIG. 19–4. Quantities involved in the specification of Coulomb's law of force between charges.

19–4 UNITS

Since electric charge is a concept that lies outside the field of mechanics, a fourth fundamental unit must now be introduced. In the cgs system the unit of charge is chosen as the additional unit. The size of the unit is defined by setting $k = 1$ in Eq. (19–4). The unit is called the statcoulomb.

In the mks system, electric current is chosen as the fourth basic quantity. The size of the unit of current (ampere) is defined in terms of the force between two currents, as we shall see later. Electric charge is then a derived quantity (ampere-sec) and is called a coulomb. Since the units of all quantities except k in Eq. (19–4) have been chosen independently, the value of k is fixed by these choices as

$$k = 8.9874 \times 10^9\,\frac{\text{n}\cdot\text{m}^2}{\text{coul}^2} \tag{19–5}$$

which can be approximated by 9×10^9 for most numerical calculations.

There is also a usefulness for later work in expressing k as a special combination of constants,

$$k = \frac{1}{4\pi\epsilon_0},$$

where 4π is a geometric factor and ϵ_0, called the *permittivity of vaccuum,* is

$$\epsilon_0 = 8.85 \times 10^{-12}\,\frac{\text{coul}^2}{\text{n}\cdot\text{m}^2}.$$

A vector formulation of the Coulomb law is written as follows:

$$\mathbf{F}_{21} = \frac{1}{4\pi\epsilon_0}\,\frac{q_1 q_2}{r^3}\,\mathbf{r}_{21}. \tag{19–6}$$

The direction of the vectors is shown in Fig. 19–4. The force exerted *on* q_2 *by* q_1 is F_{21}, the radius vector drawn *from* q_1 *to* q_2, is $\mathbf{r}_{21}$, and $\mathbf{F}_{21}$ is in the direction of $\mathbf{r}_{21}$. The inclusion of $\mathbf{r}_{21}$ in the numerator is compensated for in magnitude by writing the denominator as r^3. Then we still have the correct inverse-square law. Similarly, we have for the force on q_1:

$$\mathbf{F}_{12} = \frac{1}{4\pi\epsilon_0}\,\frac{q_1 q_2}{r^3}\,\mathbf{r}_{12}. \tag{19–7}$$

The senses of the forces $\mathbf{F}_{12}$ or $\mathbf{F}_{21}$ are determined by the signs of the charges. Like signs, either both positive or both negative, will give a positive product, and the force will have the same sense as the radius vector $\mathbf{r}$. Unlike signs will give a negative product, and the minus sign will reverse the force, making it opposite in sense to $\mathbf{r}$.

19–5 SUPERPOSITION. CHARGE DISPOSITIONS

The Coulomb law establishes the interaction of *point* charges at rest. On the other hand, it is often necessary to deal with charge distributions, a group of charges arranged in a particular way. For example, let a charge Q be distributed throughout a volume of such large extent that it is no longer true that the effective size of charge Q is small compared with the distance r from another charge q'. Then Q is not a point, but for simplicity let q' be a point. Then the calculation of the force between Q and q' requires another law that comes from observations of electrostatic forces. This is the law of addition or superposition.

It can be experimentally demonstrated that, for an assembly of charges such as shown in Fig. 19–5, the resultant force exerted by charges 1 and 2 on 3 is the vector sum of the forces which would be exerted by 1 on 3 and by 2 on 3 independently; that is,

$$\mathbf{F} = \mathbf{F}_{31} + \mathbf{F}_{32}. \qquad (19\text{–}8^*)$$

With this rule, and with the point charge law, we are equipped with the means to compute the interaction of finite charged bodies.

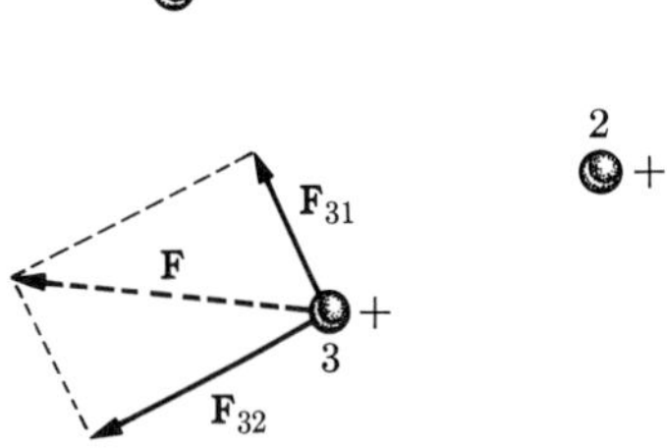

FIG. 19–5. The forces on charge 3 due to a like charge 2 and an unlike charge 1. The resultant force is the vector sum **F**.

*This result may seem intuitively obvious and universally true. In fact, it is neither. It must be tested for each type of force. It is *not* valid, for example, in the case of forces between atoms or in the case of nuclear forces.

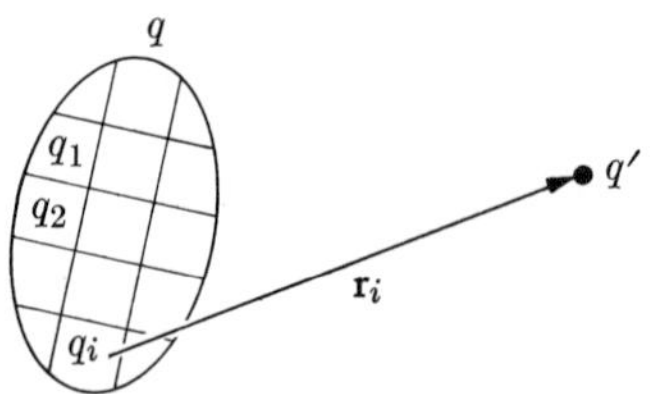

FIG. 19–6. The subdivision of an extended charge q into small segments q_i as a step in finding the resultant force on another charge q'.

Let the charge Q be divided into cells of such size that they can be regarded as points (Fig. 19–6). Each cell, according to the local quantity of charge and the size of the cell, will contain a charge q_i. The index i labels the cells and runs from 1 to n, where n is the total number of cells. (Actually, the array of cells is three-dimensional and we should therefore use two indices.) Call the external point charge q'. Then for the interaction of q and q' (both of which are now points) the Coulomb law pertains, i.e.,

$$\mathbf{F}_i = \frac{1}{4\pi\epsilon_0}\frac{q_i q'}{r_i^3}\,\mathbf{r}_i. \qquad (19\text{–}9)$$

The total force of interaction is then the result of summing vectorially over all cells,

$$\mathbf{F} = \frac{q'}{4\pi\epsilon_0}\sum_{i=1}^{i=n}\frac{q_i\mathbf{r}_i}{r_i^3}. \qquad (19\text{–}10)$$

Mathematically, the sum would become an integration, as we shall see in the next chapter.

Now let both charges be of finite extent. The second charge is Q' divided into cells labeled by j from 1 to m. Then the force between individual cells is

$$\mathbf{F}_{ji} = \frac{1}{4\pi\epsilon_0}\frac{q_i q_j}{r_{ij}^3}\,\mathbf{r}_{ji}. \qquad (19\text{–}11)$$

The force between Q and Q' is then found in principle, by a double sum or a double integration.

The above very detailed elaboration of the problem is intended to demonstrate the formal solution to the problem of forces between finite charges at rest.

A combination of the point charge law and the rule for force addition permits the solution, in a formal way, of the general problem of the interaction of electrical bodies at rest. Without further discussion, the solution of such problems could be declared routine. Instead, it will be shown in the following chapter that there exist for this class of problems some powerful theorems about electrical interaction which are not immediately self-evident from the Coulomb law and which can lead to a substantial insight into the general behavior of electrical systems. The development of the theorems is based on a geometrical interpretation of the Coulomb law and the introduction of the concept of the electric field.

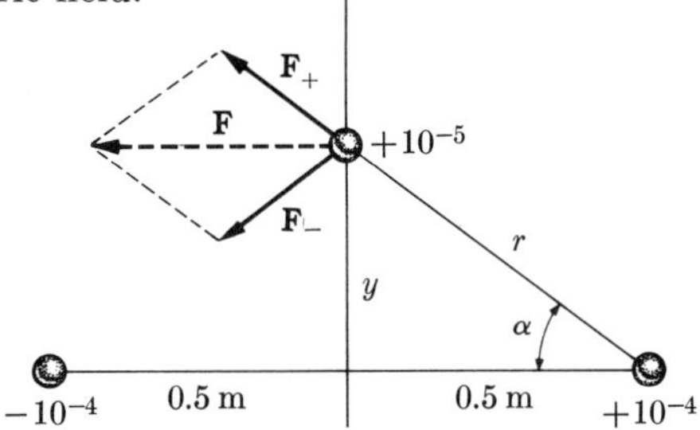

FIG. 19–7. The configuration of charges for Example 1.

Example 1. *Dipole.* Equal and opposite charges, $+10^{-4}$ coul and -10^{-4} coul, are placed a meter apart. Find the force exerted by these two particles on a third charged particle, $+10^{-5}$ coul, when the third particle is any place on a line drawn perpendicular to and bisecting the line drawn between the equal and opposite charges (Fig. 19–7).

Solution: The third particle experiences a repulsive force F_+ due to the positive charge and a force

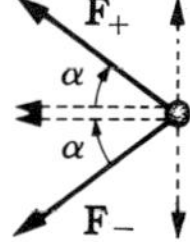

FIG. 19–8. The component method of adding the forces on the upper charge of Fig. 19–7.

of attraction F_- due to the negative charge. The forces F_+ and F_- are equal in magnitude. Resolve each force into horizontal and vertical components. The vertical components are equal and opposite and therefore cancel (Fig. 19–8). The horizontal components are equal but they add. Each horizontal component is

$$F_{\text{H}} = \frac{9\times 10^9 \times 10^{-4} \times 10^{-5}\cos\alpha}{r^2} = \frac{9\cos\alpha}{r^2}.$$

The net force $F = 2F_{\text{H}} = 18\cos\alpha/r^2$. But since $\cos\alpha = \frac{1}{2}r$, we have $F = 9/r^3$. Or since

$$r = \sqrt{y^2 + 0.5^2},$$

the final result is

$$F = \frac{9}{(y^2+0.5^2)^{3/2}}\ \text{n},$$

where y is the position of the third particle on the line measured from the origin. This is an exact result for point charges. At large distances, where $y \gg 0.5$ m, the force can be expressed approximately as

$$F = \frac{9}{y^3}\ \text{n}.$$

Thus, at suitably great distances, the force follows an inverse-cube dependence rather than the inverse-square law that would obtain between the third charge and either of the others separately. There are two interesting points to note here. First, we have described, in part, the interaction of an electrically "neutral" system (a dipole) with a point charge. Second, we have discovered a noninverse-square law. It is possible to arrange charges to give forces that fall off even more rapidly (or less rapidly).

19–6 SUMMARY

An inverse-square law of force is found to apply to electrically charged objects when their size is small compared with their separation. The law is Coulomb's law, which can be written

$$|\mathbf{F}| = \frac{1}{4\pi\epsilon_0}\frac{q_1 q_2}{r^2}.$$

The force can be either attractive or repulsive, depending on whether or not the charges are alike. The distinction between kinds of charges is made by the designations plus and minus. Thus, the q's in Coulomb's law can have plus or minus values.

The unit of charge is the coulomb in the mks system. Actually, the rate of flow of charge or current is chosen as the standard. The unit of current is the ampere. Thus, the mks system becomes the mksa system when the basic quantity (current) of electricity is included. The constant, $1/4\pi\epsilon_0$, is therefore an experimentally determined constant. Its value is

$$\frac{1}{4\pi\epsilon_0} = 8.9874 \times 10^9 \frac{\text{n} \cdot \text{m}^2}{\text{coul}^2}.$$

For values of charge that are easily obtainable experimentally, the electrical force is incomparably greater than the gravitational force between objects on the laboratory scale. The ratio is even greater on the atomic scale.

The electric force is additive vectorially. Therefore, the force between charge distributions can be found by vector summation or by integration.

Problems

Constants:

$$G = 6.67 \times 10^{-11} \text{ mks unit}$$
$$e = -1.6 \times 10^{-19} \text{ coul}$$
$$m_e = 9.0 \times 10^{-31} \text{ kg}$$
$$m_p = 1840\, m_e.$$

1. Why are pith balls used in the usual demonstration of electrostatic forces?

2. Two identical small pith balls are suspended by strings of equal length. The strings are attached to a support at a common point. The length of each string is 30 cm. The mass of each ball is 0.10 gm. Assuming that the charges are equal, what charge in coulombs must be placed on each ball such that the strings are deflected 30° from vertical? Will the angles be equal if the charges are unequal? Explain.

3. Let two small and equal packets of electrons be placed a meter apart. Each packet contains a gram of electrons. What electrical force in newtons is exerted by one packet upon the other? What is the gravitational force in newtons between the two packets?

4. In a simplified model of the hydrogen atom, we have a heavy stationary nucleus consisting of one proton. The proton has a charge of $+1.6 \times 10^{-19}$ coul (the mass of the proton is 1840 times the mass of the electron). The lighter electron executes a circular trajectory about the proton. The radius of the orbit is 0.53×10^{-10} m. (This is the classical Bohr radius r_0 in atomic theory.) The centripetal force required to sustain circular motion is the attractive force between the oppositely charged electron and proton. Compute the frequency of rotation of the electron in its orbit. (For comparison, the frequency of visible light emitted by atoms is roughly 10^{15} cps.)

5. Electric charges of $+1\mu$coul (microcoulombs) are placed at the vertices of an equilateral triangle of sides 10 cm in length. What is the force in newtons upon each charge?

6. Protons in the atomic nucleus are spaced about 10^{-13} cm apart. Since the electrostatic force is one of repulsion, another force must act to hold the protons together. What must be the least value of this attractive force between two protons such that the electric effect is just canceled? What is the gravitational force of attraction of two protons at this nuclear spacing?

7. What are the similarities and dissimilarities between the gravitational and electrical force laws

of interaction between a pair of charged massive particles? On what basis do we say that the two kinds of forces are distinct or unrelated?

8. One theory of the expanding universe assumes that the force of gravitational attraction is balanced by an electric force of repulsion due to inequality of + to − charges in the atom. Show, for example, that an inequality by about 1 part in 10^{18} would balance the gravitational force between two hydrogen atoms.

9. Find the force in Example 1 if the third charge is on the line through the 10^{-4} coul charges (but not between them). What is the result for large distances?

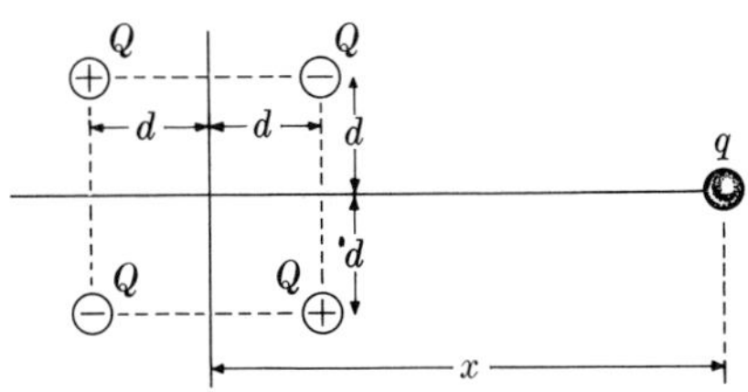

FIGURE 19–9

10. Find the force on a charge $+q$ due to the configuration of charges Q shown in Fig. 19–9. What is the result when $x \gg d$?

20

The Electrostatic Field

20–1 INTRODUCTION

The interaction of point electric charges, as expressed in the last chapter in terms of the Coulomb law, is representative of a particular physical point of view. This is called the action-at-a-distance picture of the interaction. Two charges exert a force, each upon the other, without contact and with only empty space intervening between them. We say that charge q_1 "acts at a distance" on q_2, and vice versa. In this statement there is no explanation of the process involved. Rather, the statement is simply an expression of the facts of observation. Action-at-a-distance is a universal phenomenon in nature. We are accustomed to the idea of "forces of contact" in practical experience, and this notion is often employed as an artifice in mechanics. However, when forces of contact are submitted to closer scrutiny, it is found that they are an artifice and nothing more. When we push on an object by what we call "contact" with the object, we are placing the molecules of our hand in close proximity with those of the object, so close in fact that electrical repulsion takes place. But on an atomic scale, there is still empty space intervening between the charges of the hand and those of the object. All action appears to be action at a distance.

There is another formulation of forces that was first introduced as a convenience but has since proved to be a necessity. This is the "field" formulation of the force problem. Let the electric field first be defined, and once the working definition is established, we will return to a discussion of the comparison of the field portrayal and the action-at-a-distance portrayal of physical forces.

20–2 DEFINITION OF THE ELECTRIC FIELD

Let a charge q_1 be fixed in space. Let q_2 be a point-test charge which may be moved from point to point in the space around q_1 (Fig. 20–1). At any of these points we can determine a magnitude and direction of the electric force upon q_2. The assembly of an infinite number of points about q_1 is called a "field" of points. Each point is characterized by the space coordinates that fix its position. *In addition*, each point can be characterized by the force exerted upon q_2 by q_1. Such a field of points, each labeled by a force vector, is called a "force field" (Fig. 20–2). Now if the field is to be definite, it should not depend on the way in which it is measured. As described so far, the force at each point depends on the value of the test charge q_2. In fact, the force is directly proportional to q_2. This dependence can be eliminated if it is specified that q_2 must always be a unit positive charge. Thus the force field is defined as the *force per unit positive*

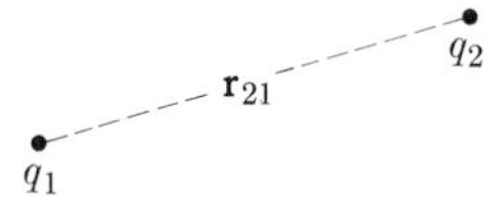

Fig. 20–1. A point test charge q_2 is used to explore the field in the vicinity of a charge q_1.

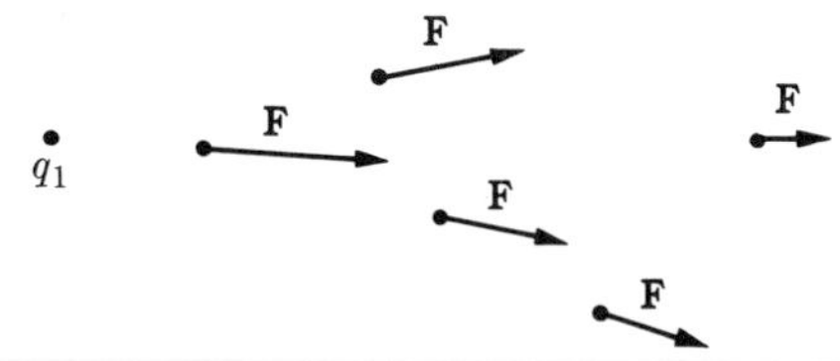

Fig. 20–2. Sample force vectors representing the force on a test charge at various points in the vicinity of a charge q_1.

charge at every point about q_1. An equivalent result is obtained if the force at each point is divided by the value of q_2. The adopted definition of the electric field E is therefore

$$\mathbf{E}(x, y, z) = \frac{\mathbf{F}}{q_2} \frac{\text{n}}{\text{coul}} \qquad (20\text{–}1)$$

where $\mathbf{E}$ is the electric field at any point, and $\mathbf{F}$ is the electric force experienced by q_2 at that point. It is impossible to portray the field at every point in space about q_1, for there is an infinite number of points. It is sufficient to show the field vector for sample points, as shown in Fig. 20–3.

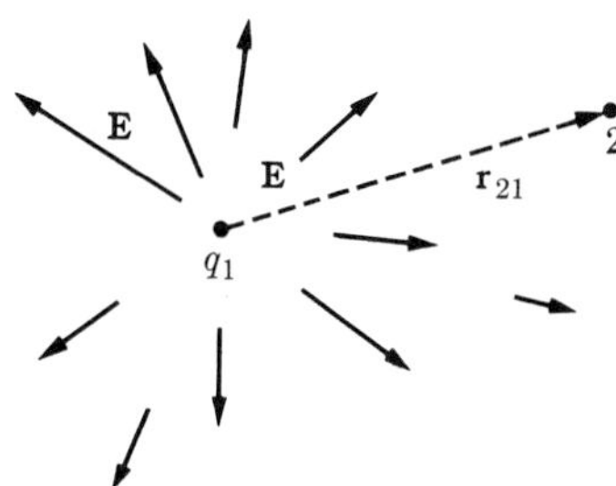

FIG. 20–3. Vectors representing the electric field intensity at various points in the vicinity of a charge q_1.

An equation for the field about a point charge q_1 can be found at once through the use of the Coulomb law. The force by q_1 on q_2 is

$$\mathbf{F}_{21} = \frac{1}{4\pi\epsilon_0} \frac{q_1 q_2 \mathbf{r}_{21}}{r_{21}^3}.$$

Since by definition,

$$\mathbf{E} \equiv \frac{\mathbf{F}_{21}}{q_2},$$

the electric field at a point (2) due to a point charge at (1) is

$$\mathbf{E} = \frac{1}{4\pi\epsilon_0} \frac{q_1 \mathbf{r}_{21}}{r_{21}^3} \frac{\text{n}}{\text{coul}}. \qquad (20\text{–}2)$$

In the last expression, it can be seen that the electric field depends only on the magnitude of the charge q_1 and the radius vector drawn from q_1 to the field point. The charge q_1 is called the source charge, since it is the source of the electric field. The test charge q_2 feels the influence of the field of q_1. From the definition of the field,

$$\mathbf{F}_{21} = \mathbf{E} q_2;$$

that is, the force experienced by q_2 is the product of the field at q_2 times the charge of q_2. This is an unbalanced picture which has separated the roles of the two charges into one which generates a field and one which experiences a force in the field. In point of fact, the charges are equivalent. The charge q_2 can be regarded as a source and q_1 as a test charge.

In general, the test charge must be vanishingly small, geometrically and electrically, so that it will not alter the distribution of charges whose field is to be measured. These induction effects due to finite size will be discussed later.

Although the electric field as utilized above is merely a useful mathematical construct for convenience in the analysis of electrostatic forces, it will be found to have reality as an independent entity when we come to the study of electromagnetic waves. We will see later that electromagnetic waves possess energy, momentum, and angular momentum of their own. Even in the simple problem of the force between moving charges, we shall see that the fields play an essential role in the conservation principles.

20–3 ELECTRIC FIELD DUE TO ARBITRARY CHARGE DISTRIBUTIONS

The electric field due to any distribution of charges can be found, in principle, by adding the effects of all the individual charges, that is,

$$\mathbf{E} = \sum \mathbf{E}_i = \frac{1}{4\pi\epsilon_0} \sum \frac{q_i}{r_i^3} \mathbf{r}_i \qquad (20\text{–}3)$$

or, in component form,

$$E_x = \sum (E_i)_x = \frac{1}{4\pi\epsilon_0} \sum \frac{q_i}{r_i^2} \cos_i (r, x), \text{ etc.,} \qquad (20\text{–}4)$$

where E_i is the field due to the ith charge and $\cos(r, x)$ is the cosine of the angle between r_i and the x-axis.

On the macroscopic scale, we picture the charge as a uniform distribution, and the summation then becomes an integration. In order to perform the integration, we introduce the concept of charge density. We consider first a volume distribution of charge, that is, a three-dimensional solid that has charge distributed throughout its volume. We now define the charge density ρ by

$$\rho \equiv \lim_{\Delta V \to 0} \frac{\Delta q}{\Delta V}, \tag{20–5}$$

where ΔV is a small element of volume which contains a net charge Δq. In calculus notation,

$$\rho \equiv \frac{dq}{dV} \text{ coul/m}^3. \tag{20–6}$$

Charge density is analogous to the mass density of mechanics.

The amount of charge dq in an elementary volume dV is, therefore,

$$dq = \rho\, dV. \tag{20–7}$$

The charge density ρ is a function of position alone in electrostatics, a fact that is represented by the notation $\rho(x, y, z)$ in case of cartesian coordinates. The element of volume dV can be expressed in coordinates convenient to a particular problem if the integration is actually to be carried out.

The total net charge Q is then

$$Q = \int dq = \iiint \rho(x, y, z)\, dV \tag{20–8}$$

where the integral is carried out over the entire volume. It will be a triple integral in general. In practice, there are usually degrees of symmetry that permit the integral to be expressed in terms of one or two coordinates alone, with consequent simplification. The integral (20–8) is used to fix any constants in the function $\rho(x, y, z)$ so that the total charge does come out to be Q as required. This is the process of normalization.

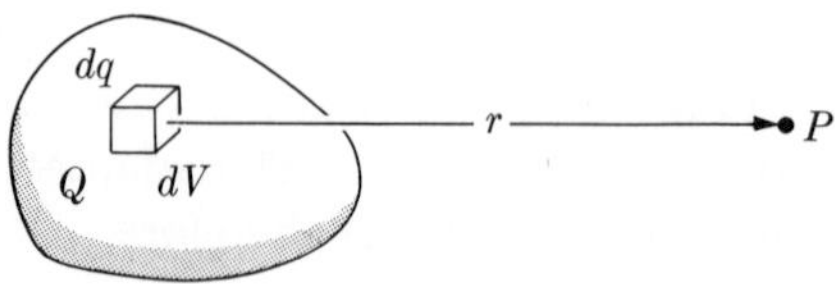

FIG. 20–4. Illustration of the quantities to be used in finding the electric field intensity at P due to an extended volume distribution of charge Q. The charge in a small volume element dV is dq.

Returning now to the problem of the electric field at P (Fig. 20–4) due to a volume distribution of charge, the summations (20–3) and (20–4) become the integrals

$$\mathbf{E} = \frac{1}{4\pi\epsilon_0} \iiint \frac{\rho \mathbf{r}}{r^3}\, dV, \tag{20–9}$$

or in components

$$\begin{aligned} E_x &= \frac{1}{4\pi\epsilon_0} \iiint \frac{\rho}{r^2} \cos(r, x)\, dV, \\ E_y &= \frac{1}{4\pi\epsilon_0} \iiint \frac{\rho}{r^2} \cos(r, y)\, dV, \\ E_z &= \frac{1}{4\pi\epsilon_0} \iiint \frac{\rho}{r^2} \cos(r, z)\, dV. \end{aligned} \tag{20–10}$$

A second type of charge distribution that is commonly encountered is a surface charge distribution. For example, we shall find later that the excess charge on a conductor resides exclusively on the surface. Surface charge density σ is defined by (going directly to calculus notation)

$$\sigma \equiv \frac{dq}{dS} \text{ coul/m}^2 \tag{20–11}$$

where dq is the charge in a surface element dS (Fig. 20–5).

Then the total net charge on the surface is

$$Q = \iint \sigma\, dS, \tag{20–12}$$

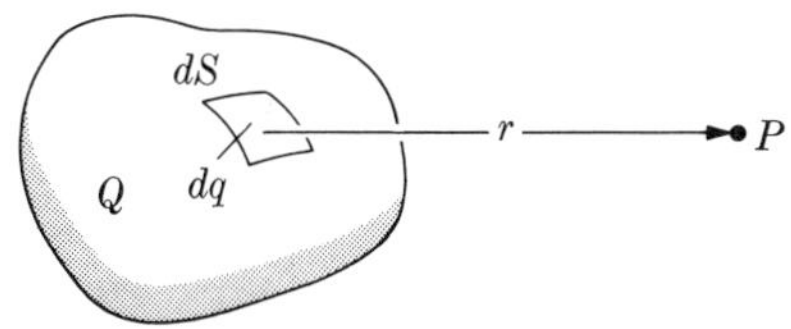

FIG. 20–5. Illustration of the quantities to be used in finding the electric field intensity at P due to an extended surface distribution of charge Q. The element of surface dS contains charge dq.

and the field at a point P is

$$\mathbf{E} = \frac{1}{4\pi\epsilon_0} \iint \frac{\sigma \mathbf{r}}{r^3}\, dS. \tag{20–13}$$

Finally, line density λ is a useful concept in some cases. It is defined by

$$\lambda \equiv \frac{dq}{dl} \text{ coul/m} \tag{20–14}$$

where, as before, the condition

$$Q = \int \lambda\, dl \tag{20–15}$$

must be satisfied by λ. The field is

$$\mathbf{E} = \frac{1}{4\pi\epsilon_0} \int \frac{\lambda \mathbf{r}}{r^3}\, dl. \tag{20–16}$$

Example 1. A wire of infinite length possesses a *uniform* linear charge density λ coulombs per meter. Find the electric field at any point about the wire.

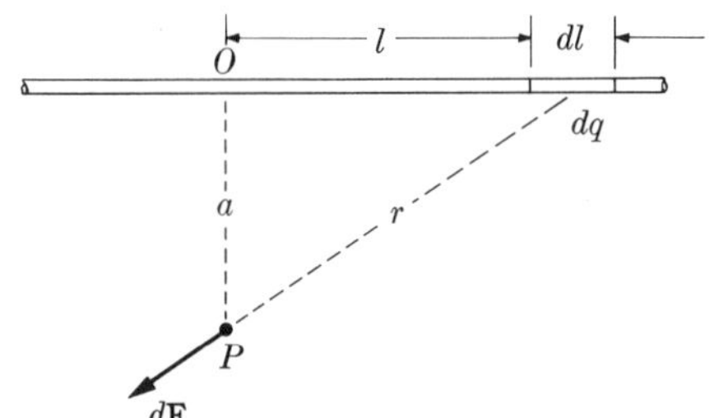

FIG. 20–6. Illustration of the quantities to be used in Example 2 for the calculation of the electric field intensity at P due to a long, thin straight line of charge. The point P is at a distance a from the line. There is charge dq in a length dl of charge.

Solution: Choose a point P at a distance a from the wire, as in Fig. 20–6. We now exploit the symmetry about line OP in setting up the integral. Choose an element dl at l meters from O along the wire. The contribution to the electric field at P due to the charge contained in dl is called dE. From the point charge law, we have

$$|d\mathbf{E}| = \frac{1}{4\pi\epsilon_0} \frac{dq}{r^2},$$

where r is measured from P to the coordinate of dl. Also $dq = \lambda\, dl$. By substitution

$$|d\mathbf{E}| = \frac{\lambda}{4\pi\epsilon_0} \frac{dl}{r^2}.$$

The integral of dl/r^2 is to be found. We now remark on the symmetry of this system. For every dl_1 on the right-hand side of the wire, we can find a mirror image dl_2 on the left (Fig. 20–7). The components of $d\mathbf{E}_1$ and $d\mathbf{E}_2$ along the wire are equal and opposite and therefore cancel. The components of $d\mathbf{E}_1$ and $d\mathbf{E}_2$ perpendicular to the wire are equal and add. Therefore, we eliminate the components along the wire and compute, for the total field, only the perpendicular component. At this stage we have already found the direction of the field at all points; it is radially outward from the wire.

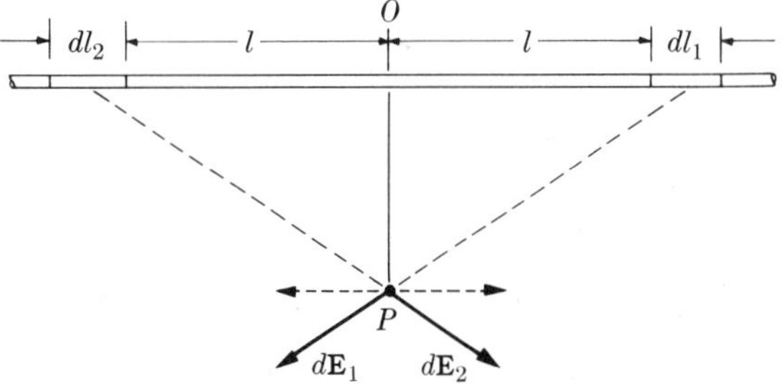

FIG. 20–7. The contributions of symmetrically located elements of charge on dl_1 and dl_2 to the field at P are $d\mathbf{E}_1$ and $d\mathbf{E}_2$, as shown. The components of dE that are parallel to the wire cancel, as shown, leaving only the components perpendicular to the wire.

The radial component of the field is (Fig. 20–8)

$$dE_r = dE \cos\theta = \frac{\lambda}{4\pi\epsilon_0} \frac{dl \cos\theta}{r^2}.$$

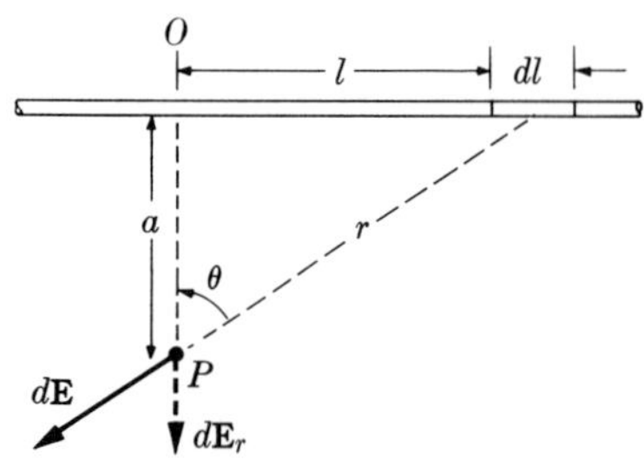

FIG. 20-8. Illustration of the quantities used in the integration to find the field **E** at point P due to a long, straight line of charge.

This equation is easily integrated when expressed in terms of θ. From Fig. 20-8, we see that $l = a \tan \theta$ and therefore $dl = a \sec^2 \theta \, d\theta$. Also, $r = a/\cos \theta$. The result is

$$dE_r = \frac{\lambda}{4\pi\epsilon_0} \frac{\cos\theta \, d\theta}{a}$$

or

$$E_r = \frac{\lambda}{4\pi\epsilon_0 a} \int_{-\pi/2}^{+\pi/2} \cos\theta \, d\theta = \frac{\lambda}{4\pi\epsilon_0 a} (\sin\theta)_{-\pi/2}^{+\pi/2}$$

or

$$E_r = \frac{\lambda}{2\pi\epsilon_0 a}. \tag{20-17}$$

This is an example of a field that varies inversely as the *first* power of the distance.

It would be possible to find the electric field at any point due to any distribution of charge by means of the integrals given above; however, there are other methods that are more powerful and that lead to a better insight into the nature of fields. Therefore, we shall now develop the ideas of these methods.

20-4 ELECTRIC LINES OF FORCE

As an aid to the visualization of the electric field, Faraday invented the notion of lines of force in the field. Subsequently, in the hands of Maxwell, the lines of force emerged as an important construct in the analysis of electric fields. Consider the force on a (positive) test charge in the field of a simple system of charges such as two equal and opposite charges (Fig. 20-9). If the coordinates of the charges are given, it is an elementary matter to compute the electric field at any point. The test charge will feel a force in the local direction of the field. If the charge is allowed to execute a series of small displacements at vanishingly low velocity in the direction of the field, it will trace the local direction of the field at every point along its line of motion. The locus of this natural motion of the test charge defines a line, and the force on the test charge is tangent to the line at every point (Fig. 20-10). Such a continuous, unbroken line whose tangent is everywhere the direction of the electric field at the point is called a *line of force.* Note that the line of force gives the direction of the electric field in space but not its strength. The strength of the field is less at points remote from the sources and greater at points close to the sources. The lines begin at positive charges and end at negative charges since the test charge experiences a resultant force in the direction of a charge when it is much closer to that charge than to any other charges. If a whole series of lines is found, we arrive at a *map of the direction of the field.* There are in fact an infinite number of lines which can

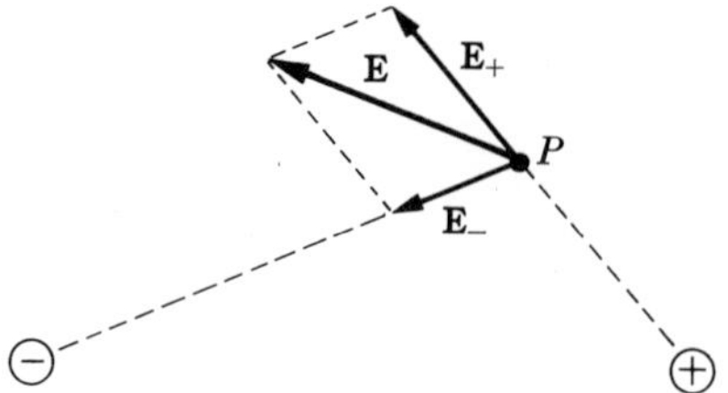

FIG. 20-9. The construction of the field **E** at point P due to two charges.

FIG. 20-10. The construction of a continuous line of force (dashed line) such that the electric field is everywhere tangent to the line.

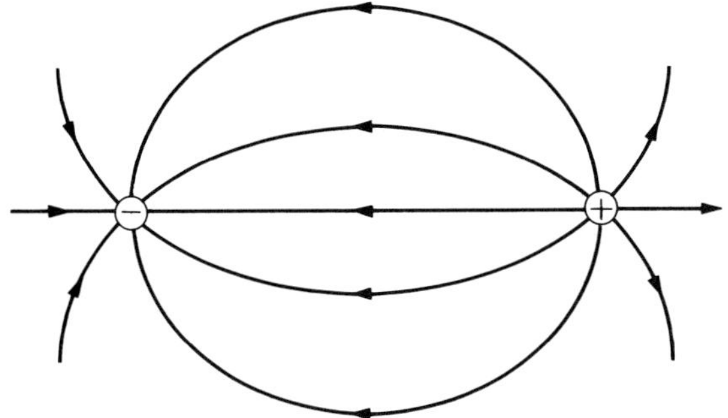

Fig. 20–11. Representative lines of force of the electric field due to two equal but unlike charges. Note that the lines begin on the positive charge and end on the negative charge.

be so defined. To show all the lines would not be very illuminating, for we would fill all the space with ink. Rather, a finite sample must be drawn with sufficient fineness to illustrate the directional properties of the field in all regions. The electric field lines are similar to the flow lines of a liquid that is discharged from holes at the positions of the positive charges and which flows into drains at the positions of the negative charges (Fig. 20–11).

We now return to the question of field strength, since the field has the property of magnitude as well as direction. Is there any connection between the directional lines and the strength of the field? Of course, the frequency of occurrence of the lines in a region could depend on our whims in the construction of the map. Nevertheless, if any pair of lines is followed, it can be seen that the lines become farther apart as we go away from the charges and are compressed closely together in bundles as we approach the charges. This suggests that a connection can be made between the spacing of the field lines, their dilution or concentration in space, and the field strength. Dilution should denote weak fields and concentration strong fields.

The connection between line concentration and field strength is made quantitative by the definition that the number of lines ΔN crossing an element of surface of area ΔS shall be equal to the average field strength over ΔS (if ΔS is perpendicular to E), that is,

$$\Delta N \equiv \overline{E}\,\Delta S.$$

In order to relate line density to E at a point, we must let $\Delta S \rightarrow 0$, thus, introducing the usual notation,

$$dN \equiv E\,dS, \tag{20–18}$$

still with the restriction that dS is perpendicular to E.

The vector nature of E has been ignored in Eqs. (20–17) and (20–18). Since ΔN or dN is a scalar, it must be that ΔS or dS is a vector and that the product on the right of (20–17) or (20–18) is a scalar or dot product. The *area element* $\Delta\mathbf{S}$ *or* $d\mathbf{S}$ *is a vector* whose direction is normal to the plane of the area element. In fact, the magnitude and direction of the area element are given by

$$\Delta\mathbf{S} = \Delta\mathbf{s}_1 \times \Delta\mathbf{s}_2 \qquad \text{or} \qquad d\mathbf{S} = d\mathbf{s}_1 \times d\mathbf{s}_2, \tag{20–19}$$

where the small **s**'s represent coordinates parallel to the edges of the area elements (Fig. 20–12). In general, $dS = ds_1\,ds_2 \sin\alpha$ for the magnitude of dS, but in most cases the coordinate axes will be mutually perpendicular and $\sin\alpha = 1$. In the case of closed surfaces, $d\mathbf{S}$ is chosen with the direction (that is, sense) of the outwardly directed normal.

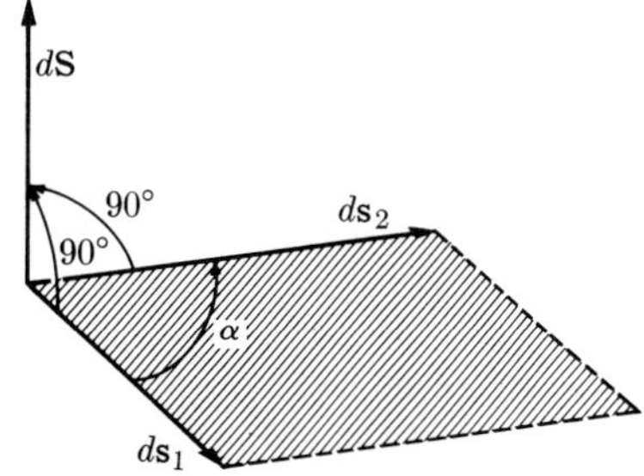

Fig. 20–12. Illustration of the vector representation of an element of area $d\mathbf{S}$ and its relationship to the vector elements of length $d\mathbf{s}_1$ and $d\mathbf{s}_2$ that define the edges of the area element (Eq. 20–19).

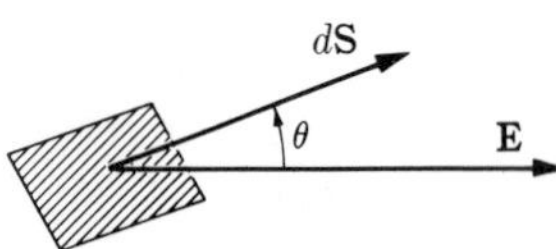

Fig. 20-13. An electric field vector **E** and an element of area $d\mathbf{S}$ at a point in space.

Returning now to the discussion of the relation between field lines and field intensity, Eq. (20-18) is properly written

$$dN \equiv \mathbf{E} \cdot d\mathbf{S} = |\mathbf{E}|\,|d\mathbf{S}| \cos \theta, \tag{20-20}$$

where θ is the angle between $d\mathbf{S}$ (that is, a normal to the area) and the field $\mathbf{E}$ (Fig. 20-13). This equation defines the "surface density" of lines dN through area $dS \cos \theta = dS'$, where the area dS' is perpendicular to the field (or lines), as shown in Fig. 20-14. The definition can be written more explicitly in the form

$$\frac{dN}{dS'} \equiv E; \tag{20-21}$$

dN/dS' is called the *flux density*, and N simply the *flux* of lines.

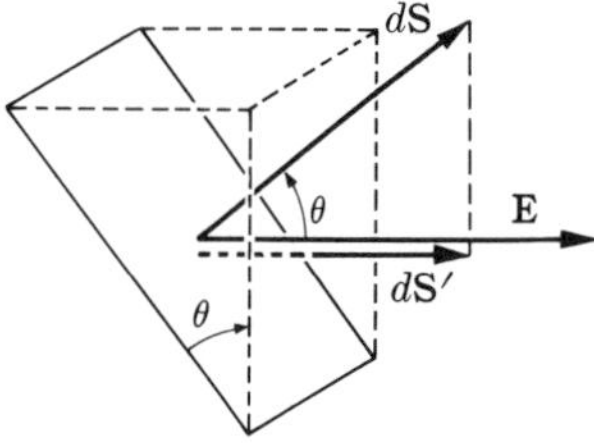

Fig. 20-14. An element of area $d\mathbf{S}$ at an angle θ relative to the field $\mathbf{E}$ at a point. The projection of the area $d\mathbf{S}$ on a plane perpendicular to $\mathbf{E}$ is represented by $d\mathbf{S}'$.

20-5 THE GAUSS THEOREM

The above ideas will now be used to develop one of the most useful general theorems for inverse square fields. We first consider the special, simple case of the field due to a point charge. As a further simplification, consider a closed spherical surface centered on the charge (Fig. 20-15). An element of area dS lying on the surface of this sphere is perpendicular to E. Therefore, the number of lines threading through dS is given simply by

$$dN = E\, dS.$$

The *total number* of lines N passing through the sphere is found by integration over the entire sphere. Since E is constant over the sphere (in this special case), we have

$$N = \iint E\, dS = E \iint dS = E\, 4\pi r^2, \tag{20-22}$$

where r is the radius of the sphere. But, for a point charge, we know that $E = q/(4\pi\epsilon_0 r^2)$ and therefore Eq. (20-22) becomes simply

$$N = \frac{q}{\epsilon_0}, \tag{20-23}$$

which is a direct result of: (a) the inverse square character of the field so far as the independence of r is concerned, and (b) the definition of dN so far as the particular proportionality constant $1/\epsilon_0$ is concerned.

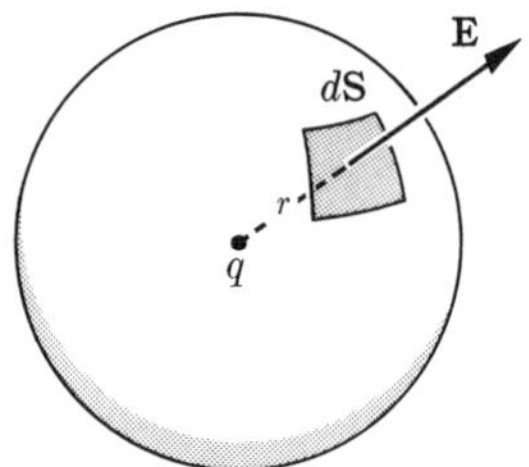

Fig. 20-15. The field **E** at the surface of a sphere of radius r centered on a charge q. The element of area $d\mathbf{S}$ lies on the surface of the sphere.

The above analysis will now be generalized in two respects. Let a point charge be placed at any position within a general closed surface. The electric field is directed at all points along radial lines drawn from q. At a sample point on the surface, the angle between $d\mathbf{S}$ and $\mathbf{E}$ is θ (Fig. 20-16). The electric flux through the area

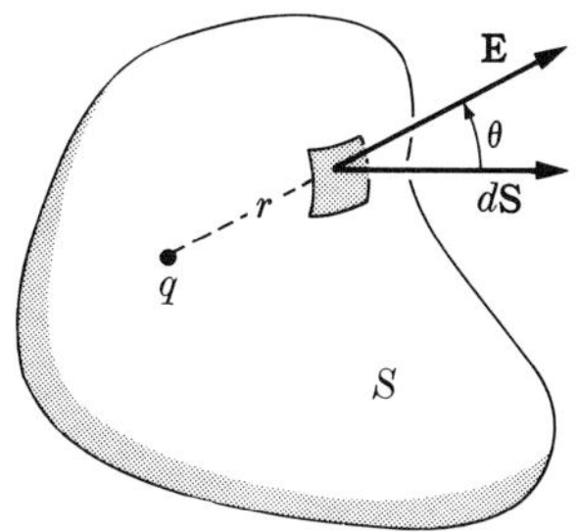

FIG. 20–16. A surface of any shape surrounding a charge q. The field is $\mathbf{E}$ at a point on the surface at distance r from the charge. The element of area $d\mathbf{S}$ at the point makes an angle θ with $\mathbf{E}$.

is $dN = \mathbf{E} \cdot d\mathbf{S} = E\,dS\cos\theta = E\,dS'$ as before. But in this general case, θ is not everywhere zero. Figure 20–17 shows the spatial relationships among q, dS, and dS'.

As we have remarked, the term $dS\cos\theta$ is dS', the projection of dS upon a surface normal to E. Now the strength of the electric field at this area element is given by

$$E = \frac{1}{4\pi\epsilon_0}\frac{q}{r^2}$$

so that

$$dN = \left(\frac{q}{4\pi\epsilon_0}\right)\frac{dS'}{r^2}. \tag{20–24}$$

The quantity dS'/r^2 has a special geometrical interpretation. Recall that the formal definition of angle is $\theta = s/r$, where s is the length of the arc (of a circle of radius r with center at the vertex of the angle) intercepted by the arms of the angle. By analogy, a *solid angle* Ω is defined by $\Omega \equiv S/r^2$, where S is the area intercepted by

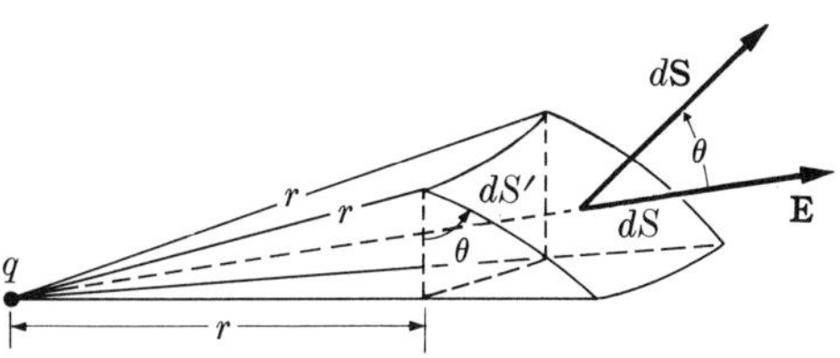

FIG. 20–17. The projection $d\mathbf{S}'$ of an element of surface area $d\mathbf{S}$. The projection is made in the direction of the field $\mathbf{E}$.

the surface of the cone or pyramid that delineates the solid angle on a sphere of radius r, with its center at the vertex of the solid angle. In Fig. 20–17, dS' is vanishingly small and the difference between a flat and a curved surface is negligible. Therefore, an element of solid angle $d\Omega = dS'/r^2$ is delineated by dS', as seen from q in the figure. Equation (20–24) becomes

$$dN = \frac{q}{4\pi\epsilon_0}\,d\Omega. \tag{20–25}$$

Now the integration over the whole surface requires integration over all directions of space about q, that is,

$$N = \frac{q}{4\pi\epsilon_0}\int d\Omega. \tag{20–26}$$

But $\int d\Omega = 4\pi$ for the total solid angle about a point. (We leave this as an exercise for the reader.) Finally, then,

$$N = \frac{q}{\epsilon_0} \tag{20–23}$$

just as in our special case. This computed result is in conformity with a simple expectation: Since the number of lines of force emanating from a point charge is fixed, the number of lines penetrating *any* closed surface about the point charge is quite independent of the size or shape of the surface.

An extension of the proof to cover a charge *distribution* within the closed surface requires only the principle of superposition. Consider two charges, q_1 and q_2, enclosed by the surface. The proof given above holds for a point charge at any position within the surface. The total flux for a charge q_1 would be $N_1 = q_1/\epsilon_0$ and for a charge q_2 at any point $N_2 = q_2/\epsilon_0$ so that $N = N_1 + N_2 = (q_1 + q_2)/\epsilon_0$, where $q_1 + q_2$ is still the net enclosed charge. Thus by addition the next flux due to any distribution of charges within the surface is $N = q/\epsilon_0$, where q is the *net* enclosed charge. This is one way of stating the Gauss law.

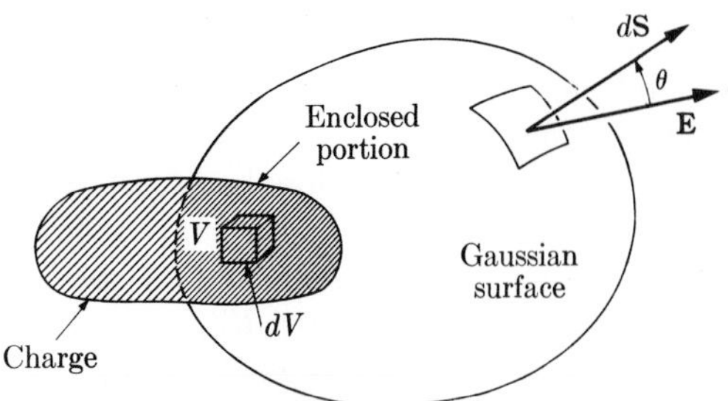

Fig. 20–18. Illustration of the quantities appearing in the general statement of Gauss' law in Eq. (20–27).

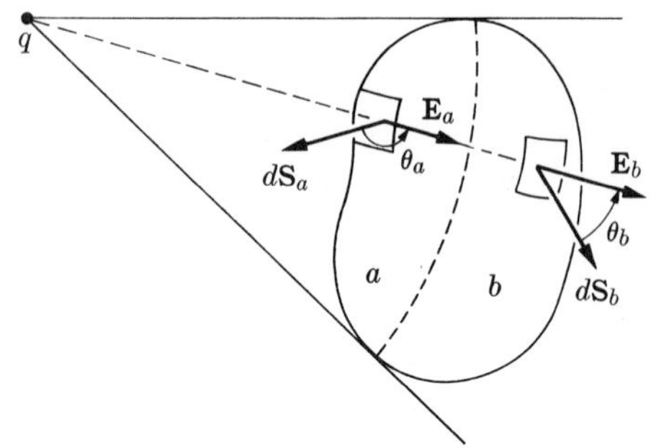

Fig. 20–19. Illustration of the application of Gauss' law to a surface that does *not* enclose a charge q.

A more sophisticated mathematical expression of the law is

$$\int_S \mathbf{E} \cdot d\mathbf{S} = \frac{1}{\epsilon_0} \int_V \rho \, dV = \frac{q}{\epsilon_0}, \tag{20–27}$$

where ρ represents the charge density in the volume element dV. The integral on the right is to include all the volume V enclosed by the closed surface S over which the integral on the left is performed (Fig. 20–18). In particular cases the integral on the right might include integrals over surfaces or along lines if the charge distribution within S is more conveniently described in terms of surface or line distributions.

For completeness, one further point must be made. It must be shown that there is no contribution to the net electric flux through a closed surface due to charges external to the surface. The proof follows the same method and construction as the one given above. Let a cone of lines be drawn from an external point source to the closed surface (Fig. 20–19). The lines are to be tangent to the surface, and they form a solid angle Ω subtended by the surface. The whole surface is then divided into two regions, region a in which the area elements dS_a are directed "toward" the source q and region b in which the area elements dS_b are directed "away" from q. The flux in region a penetrates the surface. It is therefore negative and it is equal to

$$N_a = -\frac{q}{4\pi\epsilon_0}\,\Omega_a.$$

The flux through region b is outward. It is positive and is equal to

$$N_b = +\frac{q}{4\pi\epsilon_0}\,\Omega_b.$$

The solid angle Ω subtended by both regions is the same, therefore, the inward flux and outward flux are equal and opposite, and the net flux is zero, i.e.,

$$N = N_a + N_b = 0.$$

Therefore, a source charge at any point outside a closed surface contributes no net flux through the surface. Parts of the above proof can be stated more formally by noting that dS is in the direction of the *outward* normal. Hence, we use the minus sign for the contributions dN to the flux from integration over certain parts of the surface. The surface can, of course, be less regular than in Fig. 20–19, with regions in which the lines from q cut the surface more than twice. But the final result will be the same.

The Gauss theorem serves as a useful guide to the understanding of the general properties of the electrostatic field. It also provides a method for the computation of the electrostatic field that is much simpler in cases of special symmetry than the method of direct integration over the contributing charges. We now turn to some examples.

What is the field inside a hollow, spherically symmetric charge distribution due to that charge alone? By symmetry, the field (if any) must be radial and dependent only on the distance r from the center of the sphere. Therefore, if we construct a Gaussian surface in the form of a concentric sphere of radius r lying inside the hollow sphere of charge, the field must be uniform in intensity and radial in direction anywhere on the Gaussian surface. Consequently, in evaluating the surface integral of the Gauss law (Eq. 20–27), the E factor can be taken outside the integral and, since $\cos\theta$ is unity, we have

$$|\mathbf{E}|\int_S |d\mathbf{S}| = \frac{q}{\epsilon_0} \quad \text{or} \quad |\mathbf{E}|4\pi r^2 = \frac{q}{\epsilon_0}.$$

However, the charge q enclosed by the Gaussian surface is zero (for any value of r less than the inside radius of the hollow sphere of charge), and hence **E** *must be zero anywhere inside.* It should be noted that this is the field due to the hollow charge alone. If there are other charges, the field inside the hollow sphere will not necessarily be zero.

We now turn to another case of spherical symmetry as an example of the use of the Gauss law. The example will be treated in apparently unnecessary detail in order to remind the reader of the methods of surface and volume integrals and in order to emphasize the meaning of the Gauss theorem.

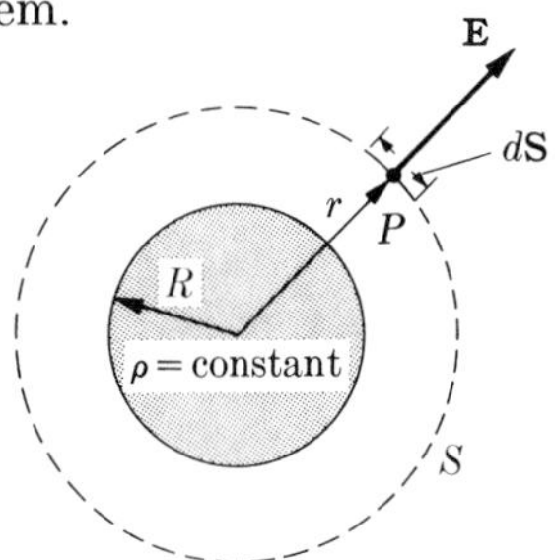

FIG. 20–20. Spherical Gaussian surface S of radius r concentric with a uniform spherical charge distribution q of radius $R < r$.

Example 2. Find the electric field due to a spherical charge of uniform charge density ρ of radius R (Fig. 20–20).

Field outside. Construct a concentric spherical Gaussian surface of radius r greater than R (Fig. 20–20). We now perform the integrals of Eq. (20–27) for the selected surface S enclosing the volume V,

$$\int_S \mathbf{E}\cdot d\mathbf{S} = \frac{1}{\epsilon_0}\int_V \rho\, dV.$$

First, consider the integral on the left, the integral that gives the total flux N through the surface,

$$N = \int_S \mathbf{E}\cdot d\mathbf{S} = \int_S |\mathbf{E}|\,|d\mathbf{S}|\cos\theta.$$

By symmetry, the field **E** must be everywhere normal to the Gaussian surface S that encloses the volume V, and it must be constant in magnitude over the surface. Therefore $\cos\theta$ is unity. Since $|\mathbf{E}|$ is constant, it can be taken outside the integral sign, and we have

$$N = |\mathbf{E}|\int_S |d\mathbf{S}| = |\mathbf{E}|S,$$

where S is the area of the spherical Gaussian surface, and therefore

$$N = |\mathbf{E}|4\pi r^2.$$

Turning now to the volume integral that gives the total charge q enclosed by the Gaussian surface [the integral on the right side of Eq. (20–27)], we take ρ outside the integral, since it is constant,

$$q = \int_V \rho\, dV = \rho\int_V dV = \rho V = \rho\,\tfrac{4}{3}\pi R^3,$$

where V is the volume of the sphere R, since there is no charge outside R.

In this case, the complete expression for the Gauss law has reduced to

$$|\mathbf{E}|4\pi r^2 = \frac{1}{\epsilon_0}\rho\,\tfrac{4}{3}\pi R^3$$

or

$$|\mathbf{E}| = \frac{1}{\epsilon_0}\rho\,\frac{1}{3}\frac{R^3}{r^2}\left(= \frac{1}{4\pi\epsilon_0}\frac{q}{r^2}\right)$$

for points outside the spherical charge. We note that the field is the same as if all the charge were concentrated at the center of the sphere.

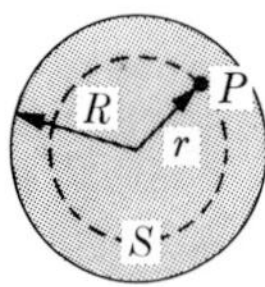

FIG. 20-21. Spherical Gaussian surface of radius r concentric with a uniform spherical charge distribution of radius $R > r$.

Inside the charge. In order to find the field at a point P inside the sphere R, we construct a Gaussian surface in the form of a concentric sphere of radius r and passing through point P (Fig. 20-21). From symmetry, the field must be normal to the spherical surface and constant in magnitude over the surface. It has already been shown that the field due to a hollow symmetrical shell of charge is zero inside the shell. Therefore, the field at P can be due only to the charge inside the sphere of radius r. From the law of Gauss, we then have

$$|\mathbf{E}|\int_S |d\mathbf{S}| = \frac{1}{\epsilon_0}\rho\int_V dV$$

or

$$|\mathbf{E}|4\pi r^2 = \frac{1}{\epsilon_0}\rho\,\tfrac{4}{3}\pi r^3$$

or

$$|\mathbf{E}| = \frac{1}{\epsilon_0}\frac{\rho}{3}r.$$

It is seen that the field at points inside the charge is directly proportional to the distance from the center. A graph of E as a function of r is shown in Fig. 20-22.

It will be illuminating to the reader to set up the above problem by the method of direct integration over the charges (Section 20-3). Once the direct integral has been correctly formulated, the power and simplicity of the Gauss theorem will become strikingly evident.

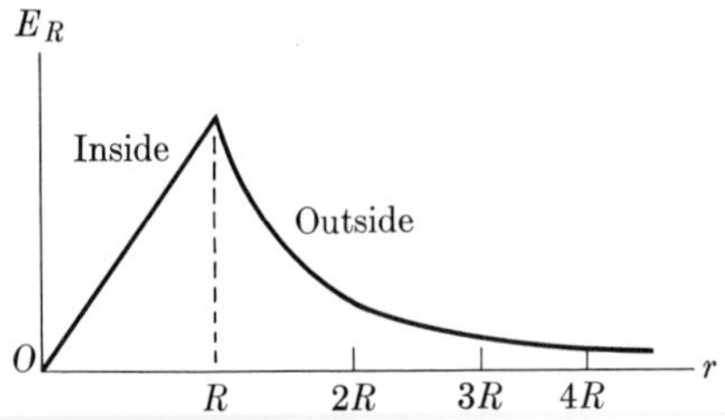

FIG. 20-22. The field intensity E versus distance r from the center of a uniform spherical charge distribution of radius R.

The symmetry arguments used above are equally applicable to the more general case of any charge distribution with spherical symmetry, that is, whenever ρ is a function of r alone. The only difference is that it will be necessary to carry out the volume integral of Eq. (20-27) in order to find the quantity of charge contained within a sphere of radius r.

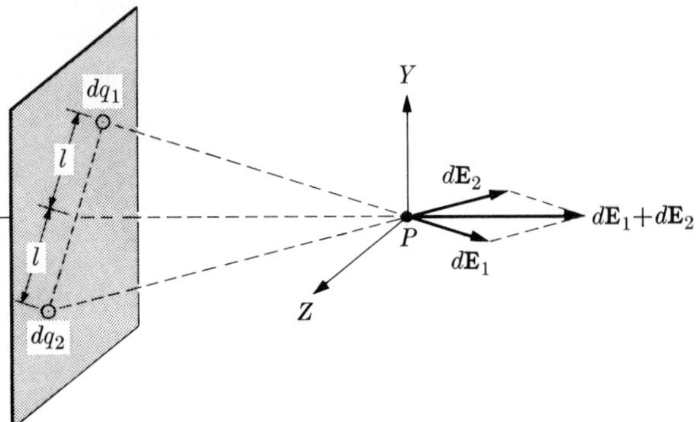

FIG. 20-23. Demonstration of the symmetry argument that the field due to a uniform infinite sheet of charge must be perpendicular to the surface.

Example 3. Compute the electric field due to an infinite plane with uniform density of positive charge. By symmetry (Fig. 20-23), the electric field lines must be everywhere normal to the plane which contains the electric charge. From the facts that all the field lines are parallel and that the field cannot vary with y or z, it follows at once that the field is uniform. The problem which remains is the computation of the strength of the uniform field.

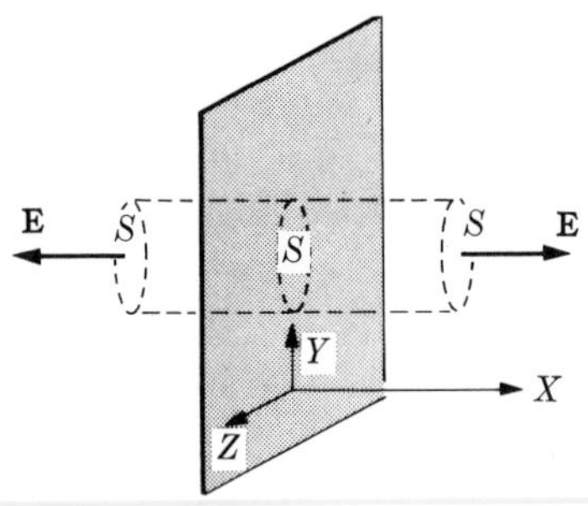

FIG. 20-24. A Gaussian surface in the form of a right circular cylinder perpendicular to a sheet of charge.

We construct a cylindrical volume of end area S with axis perpendicular to the plane (Fig. 20–24). Flux penetrates the two parallel ends of the volume but none penetrates the sides. The net charge enclosed by the volume is $q = \sigma S$ where σ is the surface charge density. The Gauss law then gives $\int E\, dS = E \times 2S = q/\epsilon_0 = \sigma S/\epsilon_0$ or

$$E = \frac{\sigma}{2\epsilon_0} \tag{20–28}$$

where E is directed away from the plane. If a cartesian coordinate system is chosen, as in Fig. 20–24, $E_y = E_z = 0$, and $E_x = +\sigma/(2\epsilon_0)$ or $E_x = -\sigma/(2\epsilon_0)$, depending on whether $x > 0$ or $x < 0$, respectively. Thus a graph of E versus x is as shown in Fig. 20–25.

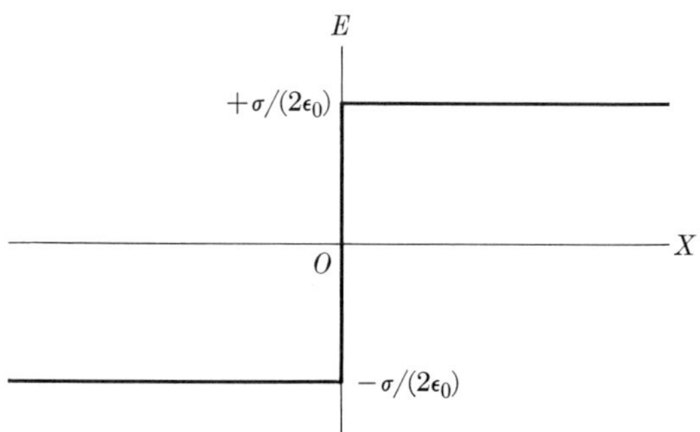

FIG. 20–25. Field versus position x along an axis perpendicular to a uniform, infinite sheet of charge, with the origin of coordinates at the sheet (Fig. 20–24).

It is now seen why the constant k in Coulomb's law was written with the factor 4π in the denominator. The result is that no numerical constants appear in the most frequently used expressions, such as Eq. (20–28).

A frequently occurring arrangement of charges is *two parallel sheets* of charge (Fig. 20–26) of opposite sign and equal densities with a separation that is small compared with the dimensions of the sheets. Thus the sheets can be considered of infinite extent for points between the plates or not too far outside the plates (and well away from the edges). From the principle of superposition, the resultant field will be zero outside the sheets and

$$E = \frac{\sigma}{\epsilon_0} \tag{20–29}$$

between the sheets.

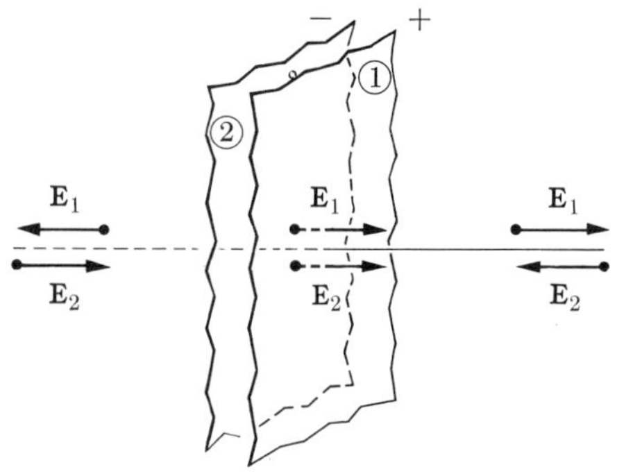

FIG. 20–26. The addition of field components $\mathbf{E}_1$ and $\mathbf{E}_2$ due to uniform infinite sheets of charge one and two, with the same magnitude of surface charge density but with opposite sign.

Another case of general importance is the field *near any charged surface*, that is, a surface that is not necessarily plane or infinite and over which the charge density need not be uniform. We again apply the Gauss law to a closed, approximately cylindrical surface (Fig. 20–27), but in this case the height Δt and the end areas ΔS must be permitted to approach zero so that the variations in magnitude and direction of the field over the surface of the cylinder will become negligibly small and so that the areas of the end faces will become equal.

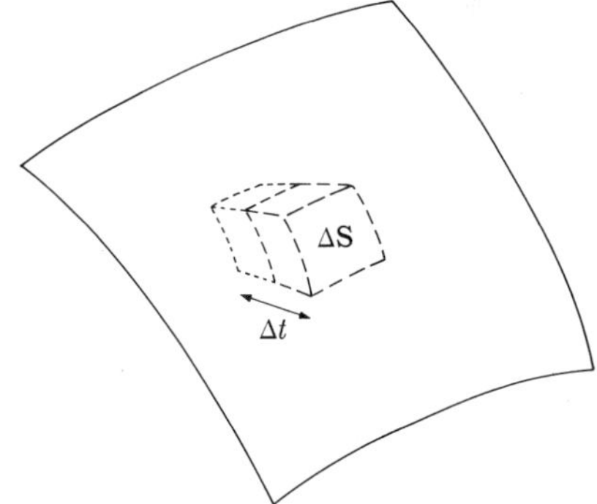

FIG. 20–27. Construction of a Gaussian surface that intersects a curved sheet of charge. The sides of the surface are constructed of elements that are everywhere perpendicular to the charge sheet. The ends of the surface are parallel to the charge sheet.

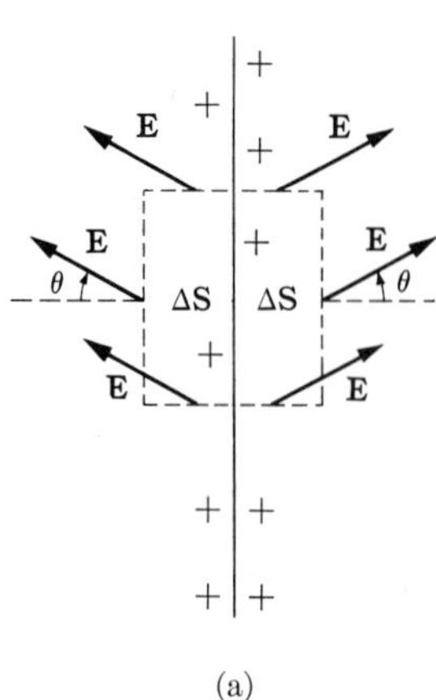

FIG. 20–28. (a) An isolated nonuniform plane sheet of charge viewed edge-on. The section of a Gaussian surface is represented by the dashed line. The Gaussian surface is in the form of a cylinder with end faces of area $\Delta\mathbf{S}$. The field $\mathbf{E}$ is at an angle θ with $\Delta\mathbf{S}$.

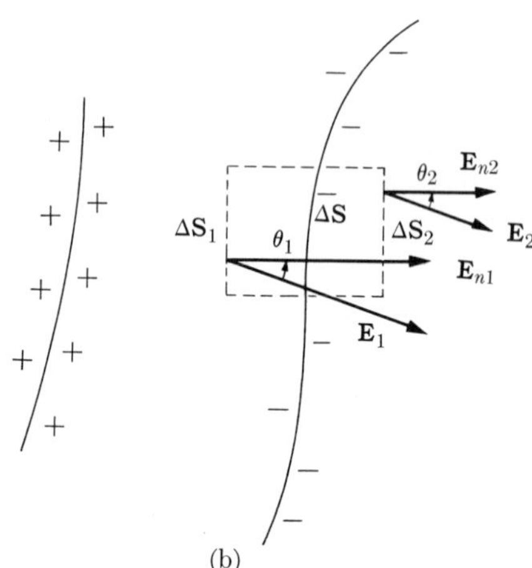

FIG. 20–28. (b) Similar to (a) except that the sheet of charge in question (right) is neither plane nor isolated (it is in the field of the sheet of positive charge).

We first consider the case of an isolated plane sheet of charge (Fig. 20–28a). Except in special cases, the field is not perpendicular to the surface and, therefore, it is not perpendicular to the end faces of the Gaussian cylinder. When we apply the Gauss law to the small cylinder, the side walls will not contribute to the net *outward* flux, since outwardly directed flux on one portion of a side wall will be canceled by inwardly directed flux on the opposite portion of the side wall. On the other hand, the flux is outward on both end faces in the present example and cannot cancel. The Gauss law

$$\int E\,dS\cos\theta = \frac{q}{\epsilon_0}$$

becomes

$$E\,\Delta S\cos\theta + E\,\Delta S\cos\theta = \frac{\Delta q}{\epsilon_0},$$

since the field must be symmetrical about the plane. Finally,

$$E\cos\theta = \frac{\Delta q}{2\epsilon_0\,\Delta S} = \frac{\sigma}{2\epsilon_0},$$

if we let σ represent the local charges density.

We now turn to a more general case, in which the charge sheet is neither plane nor isolated (Fig. 20–28b). In our example, the field on the left of the negative charge sheet is more intense than the field on the right. As before, the net flux outward through the side walls of the Gaussian cylinder is zero, and the Gauss law gives

$$E_2\,\Delta S_2\cos\theta_2 - E_1\,\Delta S_1\cos\theta_1 = \frac{\Delta q}{\epsilon_0\,\Delta S}.$$

Finally, if E is expressed in terms of its normal components E_n,

$$E_{n2} - E_{n1} = \frac{\sigma}{\epsilon_0}, \tag{20–30}$$

where $\sigma = \Delta q/\Delta S$ when $\Delta S \to 0$. Therefore, the normal component of the electric field changes by σ/ϵ_0 when passing from one side to the other side of any sheet of charge, the change depending on where the surface is crossed if σ is not constant over the surface.

It can also be shown that the tangential component of E does not change in passing through the sheet of charge. The proof is left until energy is discussed.

Additional examples of the use of the Gauss theorem are left for the Problems.

20–6 METALS IN ELECTROSTATICS

Metals as a group of elements have the special property of electrical conduction. This group is classified in the periodic table as the electropositive elements. In the free neutral atomic state, each atom has bound to it a number of electrons equal to the number of nuclear protons. In the aggregate solid or liquid states, some of the electrons become unbound and are not held to a definite atomic center. For the best conductors, as many as one electron per atom is so released and is free to move about in the whole body. The rest of the electrons remain bound. Nevertheless, the entire grouping of atoms and free electrons is normally neutral. A metal can be negatively charged by the addition of surplus electrons or positively charged by the removal of some of the free electrons, leaving a deficiency of negative charge. In most conceivable circumstances, the net charge on the metal, either the surplus or deficiency of negative charge, is extraordinarily small compared with the net *free* charge in the metal. It is this disparate relative size of the net versus the free charge which gives rise to the nearly absolute theorems which can be proved for conductors in electrostatics. The theorems are first asserted and then demonstrated in the discussion which follows:

1. The electric field interior to metals in an electrostatic system is zero.

2. The electric field at the surface of a metal is normal to the surface.

3. The net charge on a metal resides on the surface of the metal. The interior of a metal is always neutral.

Assume for the moment that the total free charge within the metal is in indefinitely large reserve. Then Theorem 1 is proved as follows: Let a metallic object be part of an electrostatic system. It may have a net charge, and the charge distribution may also be influenced by the presence of fields caused by adjacent systems. When the system was formed, charges were necessarily in motion, and fields generally may have penetrated the metals as well as the space around them. When equilibrium is reached, all motion of charge has ceased. However, if there is free charge within the metal, such free charge would continue to move under the influence of any remaining fields inside the metal. But motion has ceased, and therefore the interior field must be identically zero. From this we may add that there must always exist a particular distribution of charge on the metal such that the self-field of the charge and the externally applied fields combine to give a zero field, point by point, within the metal. The ingredients to the proof of zero interior field are: (a) free charge exists in great abundance in the metal, (b) the steady state has been reached, and (c) the indivisible unit of charge e is so small that we can assume a uniform charge distribution.

Presuming again the validity of our assumptions about electrical conductors, it also follows at once that the electric field at a metallic surface is normal to the surface. Assume, for the moment, that the field is not normal. Then the field has a tangential component. Charge on the metal surface is free to travel along the surface, and the charge would travel if there were a field component along the surface. But in a stationary system all motion has ceased. Therefore the tangential field must be zero. On the other hand, the metallic surface is a constraining boundary for free charge: the interior charge is not free to leave the surface (except at very high temperature or when extremely high fields are applied). Therefore, the field can have a normal component. Since the tangential component is zero, the total field is normal.

Finally, the theorem that all net charge on a metal is surface charge is a consequence of the theorem that the interior field is zero. For the proof, we construct a closed Gaussian surface within the metallic object, with this restriction: it must be interior to the object, but it may be

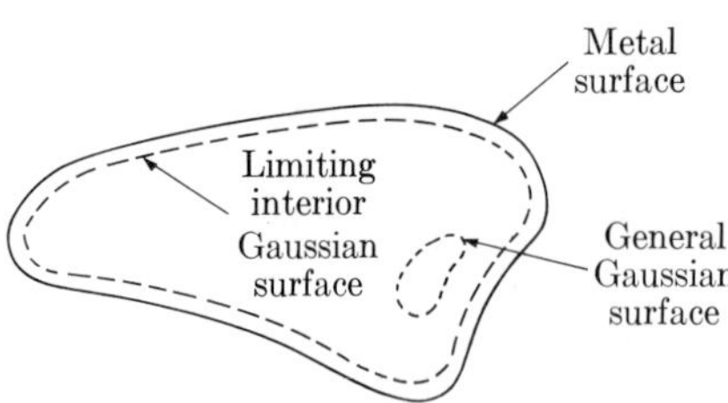

FIG. 20–29. Gaussian surfaces (dashed lines) lying within a conductor.

anywhere inside, it may be any size, and it may approach the metallic surface by an arbitrarily small distance (Fig. 20–29). We now apply the Gauss law to the constructed surface and the volume contained therein. Since E is everywhere zero inside the conductor, it is zero over the constructed surface. Hence the surface integral of E in Gauss' law is zero. The volume integral of charge must then be zero and, since the volume element dV is nowhere zero, the net charge must be everywhere zero within the enclosed volume. The volume enclosed by the Gaussian surface can be located anywhere within the conductor and it can be as large or as small as we wish. Therefore, since E is everywhere zero, the net charge must be zero everywhere within the conductor. Since the Gaussian surface can approach the metal surface arbitrarily closely, any net charge must reside on the metal surface.

The *field just outside the surface* due to charge on the conductor can be found from Eq. (20–30). Since there is no tangential component in the case of metals, we have $E_n = E$. Furthermore, E_1 of Eq. (20–30) is zero for metals, if we choose region 1 inside the metal. We finally have

$$E = \frac{\sigma}{\epsilon_0} \qquad (20\text{–}31)$$

near the surface of metals regardless of the shape of the surface. Equation (20–31) could also have been derived by direct application of the Gauss law to a small cylindrical surface, as in previous cases of fields at surfaces. In general the above result is only for conductors. If the surface is an infinite plane, the field is independent of distance.

Example 4. Check on the superabundance of charge in metals. The first question is: Are there limits to the net charge on a conductor? The answer is that when the electric field at the surface reaches about 10^6 n/coul, the charge begins to escape from the surface even in vacuum. From Eq. (20–31), the charge density corresponding to this field is $\sigma = \epsilon_0 E = 10^6/(36\pi \times 10^9) \simeq 10^{-5}$ coul/m^2. The charge e per electron is 1.6×10^{-19} coul and therefore the above corresponds to a density of elementary charges of $10^{-5}/(1.6 \times 10^{-19}) \simeq 6 \times 10^{13}$ per m^2. The size of an atom is about 10^{-10} m, or it occupies an area of about 10^{-20} m^2. Thus there are about 10^{20} atoms per m^2 of surface and, even in the case of a positively charged surface, where the surface charge is limited by the number of atoms, there is a superabundance of "free" charge by a factor of one million.

20–7 INDUCED CHARGES ON CONDUCTORS

The preceding section has been concerned with isolated conductors. We now consider the case of conductors located in a region where there is already an electrostatic field even in the absence of the conductor. When the conductor is first placed in the external field, the charges within the conductor experience forces. Consequently, the charges will move about in the conductor until the resultant field within the conductor due to the external field *plus* the field due to the charges on the surface of the conductor is zero. At this stage, electrostatic equilibrium obtains. Some examples follow.

In Fig. 20–30, a qualitative example is shown of an initially uncharged sphere that has been placed in an initially uniform field. There are several features that are instructive. (a) The field at large distances from the sphere is uniform, i.e., unaltered by introduction of the sphere. (b) The field must be normal at the surface of the conducting sphere. (c) The resultant field inside the conductor must be zero. This last condition means that the field due to the

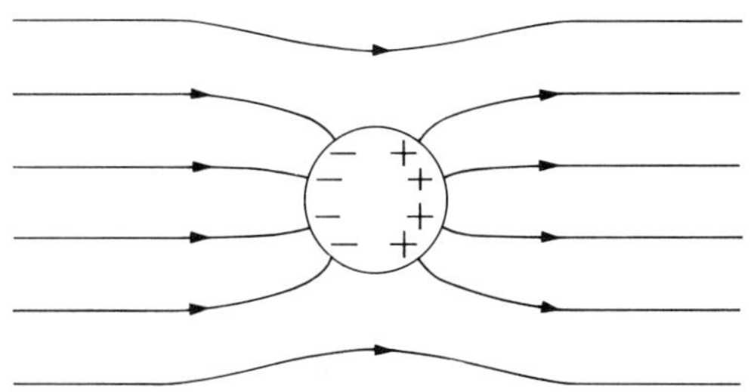

FIG. 20–30. The electric field resulting from placing an initially uncharged conducting sphere in an initially uniform electric field. The approximate distribution of induced charges is shown.

induced charges on the sphere alone would be uniform within the sphere and equal and opposite to the original external field. (d) The results would be the same if the sphere is hollow since there can be no net charge (induced or otherwise) within the solid conductor, and the conductor core can therefore be removed.

Electric shielding is accomplished by using a conductor to surround the object that we desire to shield from external fields. Stray fields from outside sources will then induce charges on the shielding conductor. These induced charges will give rise to fields that cancel the outside fields within the conductor and the region it encloses.

If an initially uncharged hollow conductor surrounds a charged object (Fig. 20–31), the total induced charge on the inner surface must just equal the surrounded charge. This statement is justified by considering a Gaussian surface surrounding the *inner* surface of the hollow conductor, as shown by the dashed line. The field is zero everywhere on this surface (the surface is inside a conductor) and hence it must enclose zero net charge. Therefore, the induced charge is equal and opposite to the surrounded charge. Since the hollow conductor was initially uncharged, its outer surface must have the same net charge (but opposite in sign) as its inner surface. The lines of force must end or start on the surface of the conductor as shown, that is, they cannot penetrate the conductor.

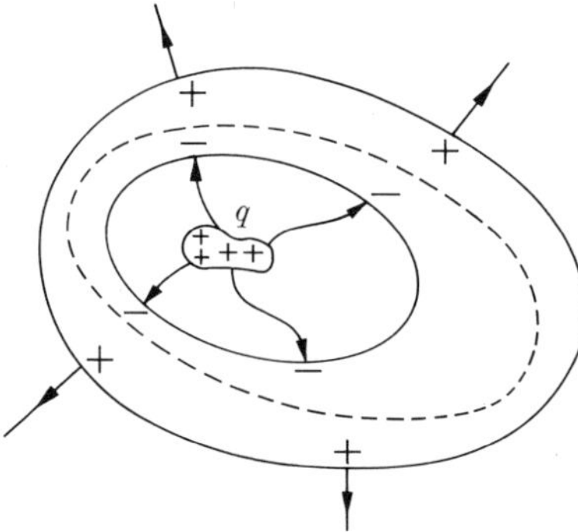

FIG. 20–31. A charge q is placed inside an initially uncharged conductor. The approximate distribution of the charge induced on the surfaces of the enclosing conductor is shown. A Gaussian surface is shown by the dashed line.

Example 5. An infinite slab of conductor of thickness t and initial charge $+Q$ per unit area is placed in a uniform field of original intensity E_0. Find the charge distribution on the slab and the electric field strength outside the slab.

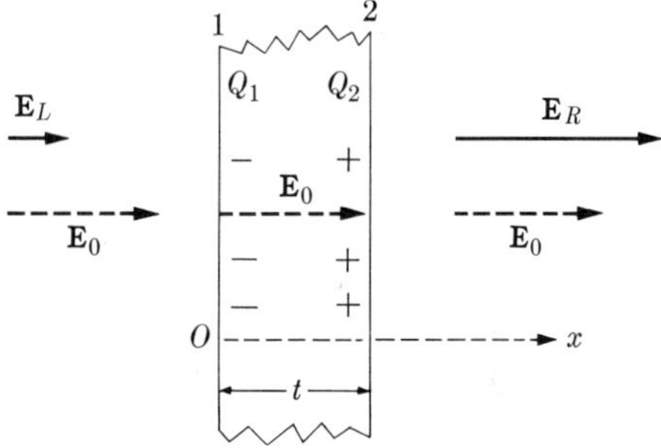

FIG. 20–32. An initially *charged* conducting slab is placed in a field that had uniform intensity $\mathbf{E}_0$ before the introduction of the slab. The resultant field intensity and the resultant charge separation on the conducting slab are shown.

Solution: Let Q_1 and Q_2 be the charge densities on faces 1 and 2, as shown in Fig. 20–32. Choose the x-axis as shown, with origin at surface 1. The field due to Q_1 and Q_2 must be $-E_0$ within the slab, in order to cancel the effect of the original field, E_0. Therefore, we have $Q_1/2\epsilon_0 - Q_2/2\epsilon_0 = -E_0$. Since $Q_1 + Q_2 = Q$, we can write Q_2 in terms of Q_1, giving $Q_1/2\epsilon_0 + Q_1/2\epsilon_0 - Q/2\epsilon_0 = -E_0$ or $Q_1 = (Q/2) - \epsilon_0 E_0$ and $Q_2 = (Q/2) + \epsilon_0 E_0$. The field on the right is therefore $E_R = E_0 + (Q_1/2\epsilon_0) + (Q_2/2\epsilon_0) = E_0 + Q/2\epsilon_0$, and the field on the left is $E_L = E_0 - Q/2\epsilon_0$. These last results could have been written down immediately from the fact that the *net* charge on the slab is always $+Q$ and therefore its contribution to the field outside the slab is always $Q/2\epsilon_0$ no matter how its charge is divided between the faces.

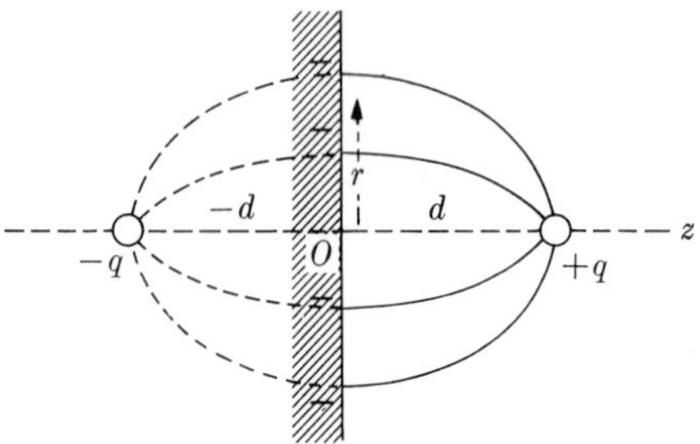

FIG. 20-33. A charge $+q$ is placed near a conducting plane sheet that is initially uncharged. The induced charge distribution on the plane and the original charge together give rise to a field distribution that is the same as that of a positive charge and an image (negative) charge, as shown.

The method of image charges is convenient for finding the field and induced charge distributions in some induction problems. As an example, suppose a point charge $+q$ is placed at distance d in front of an infinite plane conductor, as in Fig. 20-33. The lines of force must meet the conducting plane perpendicularly when equilibrium has been reached. This form of field is the same as the field due to equal and opposite charges separated by $2d$, as shown. The fictitious charge, $-q$, that will give the same effect as the charge induced on the plane, for the region to the right of the plane, is called an image charge. The field of the point charge, $+q$, plus its image, can easily be calculated.* From symmetry, the field will be a function only of z and r in Fig. 20-33. The field at the plane can be found and thus the induced charge density can be calculated. Details are left for the Problems.

* In the above discussion, it has been assumed that a field (a) of a form that behaves properly at the boundaries (in this case at the infinite plane) and (b) with a configuration that is known to be a possible solution is in fact *the* solution.

20-8 SURFACE AND VOLUME INTEGRALS

In general, a *surface integral* is a double integral, but in most of the problems that we shall encounter, it can be reduced to a single integral by proper choice of coordinates. Then the main problem of formulation is that of expressing the element of surface dS in terms of one coordinate.

As an example, let us consider the problem of finding the total charge on a plane surface if the surface charge density σ depends only on the distance r from a point O on the surface. Specifically, suppose that $\sigma = c$ coul/m^2 for $r < R$ and $\sigma = c/r^3$ for $r > R$.

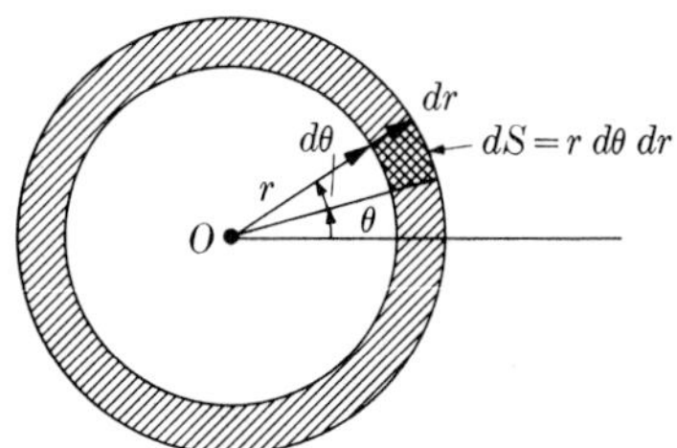

FIG. 20-34. The doubly crosshatched element of area is on a plane. A system of polar coordinates with axis at O is used. This formulation of an area element is useful when the quantity to be integrated is conveniently expressed in terms of polar coordinates. If the quantity is a function of r alone, the singly crosshatched area $2\pi r\,dr$ can be used.

Since σ depends only on r, the element of area dS which would be $r\,d\theta\,dr$ in general can be written $2\pi r\,dr$, just the area of the ring shown in Fig. 20-34. Then the total charge is found from

$$Q = \iint \sigma\,dS = \int_0^\infty \int_0^{2\pi} \sigma(r) r\,d\theta\,dr$$

$$= \int_0^\infty \sigma(r) 2\pi r\,dr.$$

Formally, we can say that we have integrated with respect to θ first, but, with experience, we simply set up dS as $2\pi r\,dr$ directly.

The integral then is evaluated in parts:

$$Q = \int_0^R c\,2\pi r\,dr + \int_R^\infty c\,2\pi\,\frac{dr}{r^2},$$

which gives

$$Q = 2\pi c\left(\frac{R^2}{2} + \frac{1}{R}\right).$$

In the same way, *volume integrals* are triple integrals, in general. But, again, in many problems the symmetry will be such that the integral can be formulated in one variable. As an example, if a volume distribution of charge has spherical symmetry, the density can be written as a function of r alone, $\rho(r)$. The total charge within a sphere of radius R is then obtained from the integral

$$Q = \int_0^\infty \rho(r) 4\pi r^2\,dr.$$

The formulation of dV as $4\pi r^2\,dr$ was accomplished by choosing a spherical shell of radius r and thickness dr as the element of volume. Over all of this shell, the charge density ρ is constant, since it depends only on r in this problem.

20–9 SUMMARY

The electric field concept is introduced as a means of describing the interaction between objects resulting from their electric charge. The intensity $\mathbf{E}$ of the electric field at a point is defined as the force per unit of positive charge on a test charge placed at the point, as the test charge is made vanishingly small

$$\mathbf{E} \equiv \frac{\mathbf{F}}{q} \quad \text{as} \quad q \to 0.$$

Since the principle of superposition is found to hold, the field due to a charge distribution is obtained by a vector summation or integration over the charges, giving rise to the field,

$$\mathbf{E} = \frac{1}{4\pi\epsilon_0}\sum_i \frac{q_i}{r_i^3}\,\mathbf{r}_i = \frac{1}{4\pi\epsilon_0}\iiint \frac{\rho\,dV}{r^3}\,\mathbf{r}.$$

Lines of force can be drawn representing the direction of the field by their direction, and the magnitude of the field strength by the number of lines per unit of area, $E = dN/dS$. The total number of lines N through a finite area is termed the flux. The Gauss theorem relates the total flux through a closed surface and the net charge q enclosed by the surface

$$\int \mathbf{E} \cdot d\mathbf{S} = \sum \frac{q}{\epsilon_0}.$$

In many cases Gauss' theorem enables us to calculate field strengths due to distributions of charge without the need for carrying out an integration. Symmetry arguments are usually invoked in such cases as an aid in applying Gauss' law. Some results that are derived using Gauss' law will now be listed.

The field interior to a hollow, spherically symmetric charge distribution is zero, if there are no other charges. The field exterior to a spherically symmetric charge distribution is the same as if all the charge were concentrated at the center of the charge distribution. The results in the above two statements can be used to find the field within a spherically symmetric, solid charge distribution.

The field due to a uniform, infinite plane sheet of charge is

$$E = \frac{\sigma}{2\epsilon_0}$$

where σ is the surface charge density. The field between two such sheets that have opposite charges is

$$E = \frac{\sigma}{\epsilon_0}$$

and zero outside.

The normal component of the field intensity changes by

$$\frac{\sigma}{\epsilon_0}$$

from one side of any sheet of charge to the other side. In this case there may be other charges in the region that contribute to the field.

The field at the surface of conductors is everywhere normal to the surface. The field within conducting material is zero. The net charge on conductors resides on surfaces of the conductor. The field immediately adjacent to the surface of a conductor is

$$E = \frac{\sigma}{\epsilon_0}$$

where σ is the local surface charge density.

When a conductor is placed in the region of a field arising from other charges, the surface charge on the conductor will become rearranged until the resultant field inside the conducting material is zero.

Problems

1. Two point charges 5 μcoul and -10 μcoul, are spaced 1 m apart. [Note: μcoul is the abbreviation for microcoulombs.]

(a) Find E at a point 0.6 m from the 5 μcoul and 0.8 m from the -10 μcoul charge.

(b) Where is the electric field zero due to these charges?

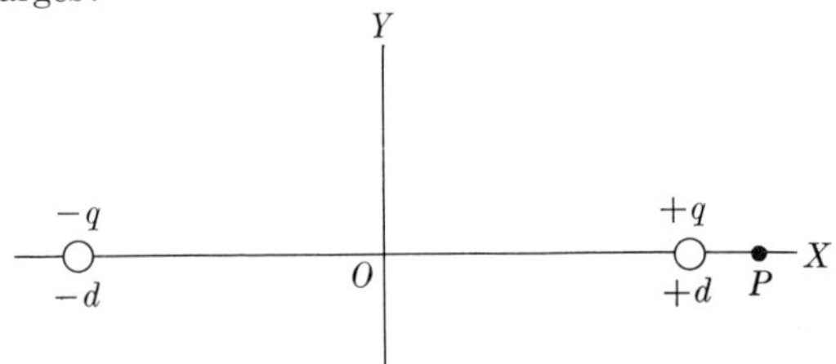

FIGURE 20–35

2. Two equal and opposite charges, $+q$ and $-q$, are spaced a distance $2d$ apart, as in Fig. 20–35.

(a) Prove that the electric field at a point P on a line drawn through the charges, called the x-axis, is

$$E_x = \frac{q}{4\pi\epsilon_0}\left[\frac{1}{(x-d)^2} - \frac{1}{(x+d)^2}\right],$$

where x is the distance from the center of the pair of charges to the field point.

(b) Show that in the limit when $x \gg d$, the expression for the field approaches an inverse cube law:

$$E_x = \frac{q\,d}{\pi\epsilon_0}\frac{1}{x^3}.$$

(c) Find a corresponding expression for points on the y-axis for $y \gg d$. Sketch the qualitative form of the field lines in space.

(d) Does E approach an inverse cube law more quickly as P moves outward along the x- or along the y-axis?

3. Charge is distributed uniformly on an infinite plane surface. The surface charge density is σ coulombs per square meter. Prove, *by direct integration*, that the electric field at any point in space is given by the formula

$$E = \frac{\sigma}{2\epsilon_0}$$

and that the field direction is normal to the plane. It will prove convenient to divide the plane into ring elements, such that all points on the ring are equidistant from the field point (Fig. 20–36). Note that the components of E perpendicular to OP cancel.

4. (a) Using the method and integral of Problem 3, find the electric field at a point on the axis of

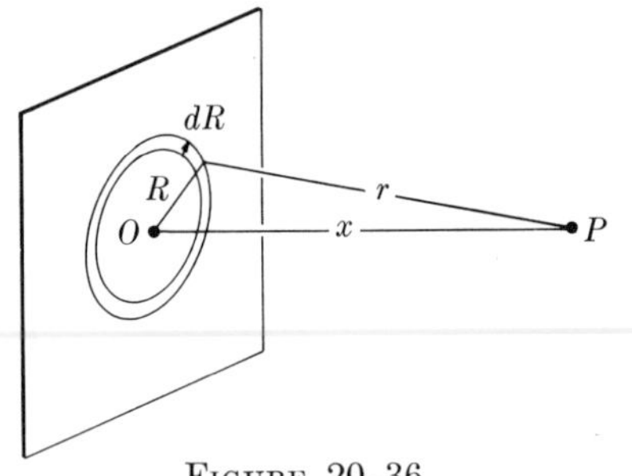

FIGURE 20–36

a circular disk of radius R with uniform charge density σ (Fig. 20–36).

(b) From the result in (a), show that in the limit as $x \to 0$, the equation reduces to the expression for an infinite plane surface, that is, $E \simeq \sigma/(2\epsilon_0)$ as $x \to 0$. Explain this result physically.

(c) Show that as $x \to \infty$, the general form of the field due to the disk approaches the Coulomb law for a point charge, that is, $E \simeq q/(4\pi\epsilon_0 x^2)$ as $x \to \infty$. What would be the result in directions other than the OX-direction?

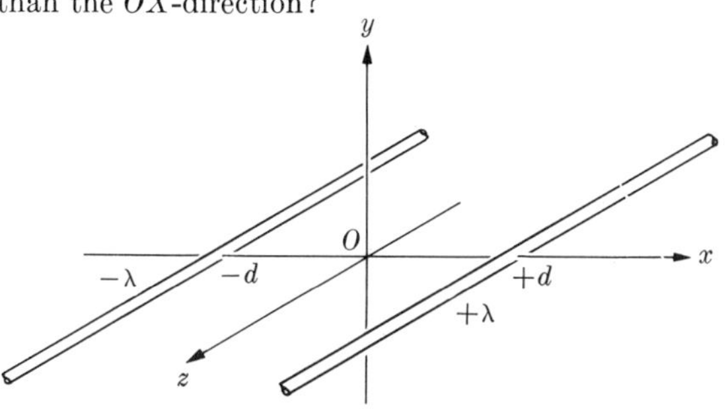

FIGURE 20–37

5. Two long, straight parallel wires have equal and opposite uniform charge densities, $\lambda_1 = -\lambda_2$. The wires are spaced a distance $2d$ apart (Fig. 20–37).

(a) Write an equation for the electric field for a point in the plane of the wires ($y = 0$) (Fig. 20–37).

(b) Write an equation for the field at a point on the y-axis ($x = 0$).

(c) Write approximate expressions for (a) and (b) when the distance to the field point is much greater than the spacing of the wires.

(d) Sketch the qualitative form of the field lines in the xy-plane.

(e) Find the mechanical force-per-unit length required to maintain the wire separation.

6. (a) Draw a diagram of the electric field lines for Problem 1. Make one line for each μcoul of charge, and place all lines in the plane of the paper. How many lines are there at large distances? How are they distributed?

(b) In what two ways is the diagram of (a) wrong, i.e., unrealistic?

7. In Fig. 20–38 find the field E at point P on the line d between a point charge $+q$ and an ∞ line charge $+\lambda$ ($d \perp$ the line charge).

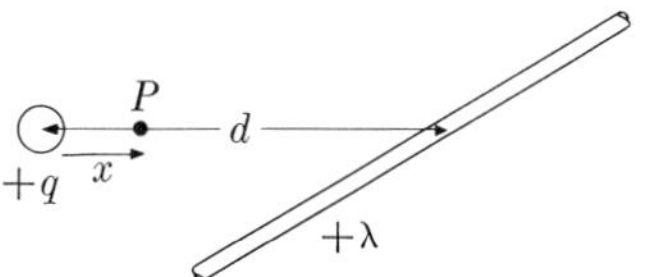

FIGURE 20–38

8. A hemispherical surface possesses a uniform surface charge density. Find the electric field intensity at the center of curvature of the hemisphere.

9. Find the momentum transferred to a stationary electron by a proton that passes the electron with constant velocity $\mathbf{v}_0$ with distance of closest approach d. It is a good approximation to assume that the proton is undeviated and that the electron moves a negligible distance during the encounter (Fig. 20–39). [*Hint:* Use the method of impulse, $\int \mathbf{F}\, dt = \Delta m\mathbf{v}$, and note that longitudinal components of the impulse cancel.]

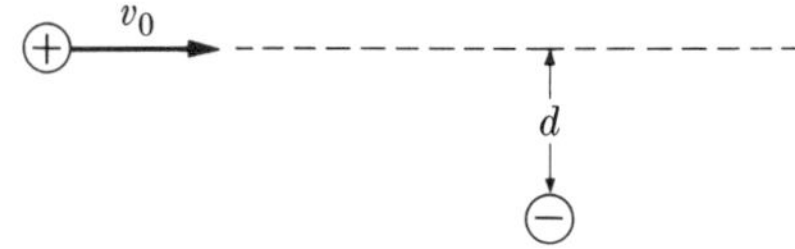

FIGURE 20–39

10. A point charge q resides on the axis of a disk of radius R, at a distance d from the disk (Fig. 20–40).

(a) Find the total flux N through the disk by integrating $\mathbf{E} \cdot d\mathbf{s}$ over the disk surface.

(b) Repeat the calculation by integrating over the cap of a sphere centered on q, with radius $\sqrt{d^2 + R^2}$, and with the edge of the cap coincident with the edge of the disk.

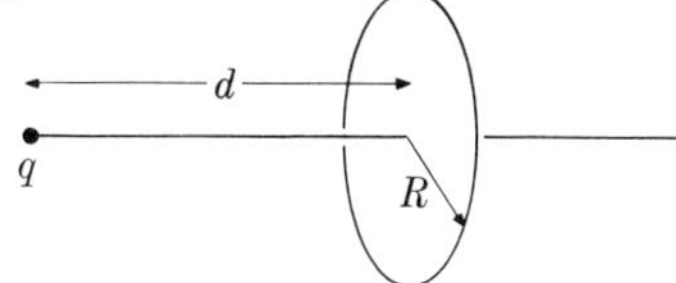

FIGURE 20–40

11. A nonconducting sphere of radius R contains a volume charge distribution of the form $\rho(r) = A/r$ for $r < R$ and $\rho = 0$ for $r > R$. Prove that $E = q/(4\pi\epsilon_0 R_2)$ at points $r < R$ and $E = q/(4\pi\epsilon_0 r^2)$ at points $r > R$.

12. A spherical shell of inner radius R_1 and outer radius R_2 contains a uniform charge density ρ. Find, by using Gauss' theorem, the electric field at all points in space, that is for $r < R_1$, $R_1 < r < R_2$, and $r > R_2$.

Sketch the graph of E as a function of r.

13. Charge is distributed in a spherical volume such that the charge density is proportional to the distance from the center of the sphere, within the radius R, i.e., $\rho = Ar$ for $(r < R)$, where A is a constant, and $\rho = 0$ for $(r > R)$.

(a) Using Gauss' theorem, prove that for points outside R we have the point charge law

$$E = \frac{q}{4\pi\epsilon_0 r^2}, \qquad (r > R).$$

(b) Prove that for field points within R, the expression for E is

$$E = \frac{Ar^2}{4\epsilon_0}, \qquad (r < R).$$

(c) Show also that the net charge in the sphere is

$$q = \pi A R^4$$

so that the electric field in (b) can be written

$$E = \frac{q\,r^2}{4\pi\epsilon_0 R_4}.$$

14. Find the field E at a distance r from a line charge of density λ coul/m, using Gauss' law. [*Hint:* Construct a Gaussian surface in the form of a right circular cylinder with its axis coincident with the line charge. Compare your result with Eq. (20–17).]

15. Find, by Gauss' theorem, the electric field for an infinitely long cylinder of radius R; the charge density within the cylinder is constant and equal to ρ. Outside R, $\rho = 0$. (See the hint to Problem 14.)

16. This is a problem on induced charges, and a special method of solution is shown. A point charge is placed at a distance d from the plane surface of an infinitely large piece of metal. From the properties of metals, we know that the field outside the surface at the boundary must be normal at all points to the surface. This condition can be made to hold if there existed an equal and opposite charge $-q$ at distance d behind the surface. This charge $-q$ is a fictitious charge called the image charge. Sketch the field *outside the metal* as if $-q$ were in place as shown.

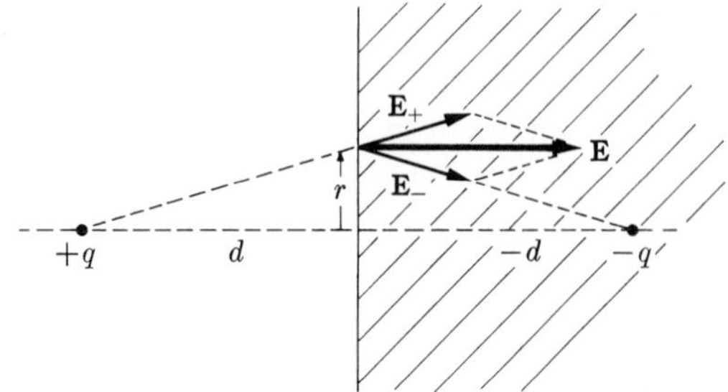

FIGURE 20–41

(a) Find the field intensity at the surface as a function of r (Fig. 20–41).

(b) Find the surface charge density σ as a $f(r)$ from your result of (a).

(c) Check your answer to (b) by integrating $\sigma\, ds$ over the entire surface to find the total charge induced on the surface. The result should be q.

17. Find the field in regions A, B, and C due to the infinite plane sheets of charge shown in Fig. 20–42.

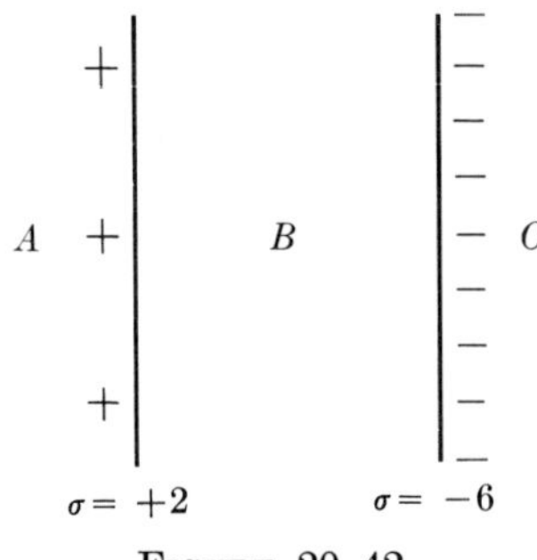

FIGURE 20–42

18. An infinite slab of charge of thickness t contains a uniform volume density of charge ρ. Find E at points inside and outside the slab.

19. Repeat Problem 18, but with volume charge density

$$\rho = \rho_0 \sin(\pi x/t),$$

where x is measured $\perp$ to the surfaces, and $x = 0$ at one face.

20. A certain distribution of parallel line charges (of infinite extent in the Z-direction) gives rise to an

electric field which at large distances from the origin can be well approximated by the following x- and y-components (where m is a constant):

$$\left.\begin{aligned} E_x &= \frac{m(x^2 - y^2)}{(x^2 + y^2)^2} \\ E_y &= \frac{2mxy}{(x^2 + y^2)^2} \\ E_z &= 0. \end{aligned}\right\} \text{for all values of } z$$

Use Gauss' law to compute the net charge per unit length which gives rise to this field. Explain. [*Hint:* To carry out the integral, it may be convenient to introduce polar coordinates and to use a cylindrical surface.]

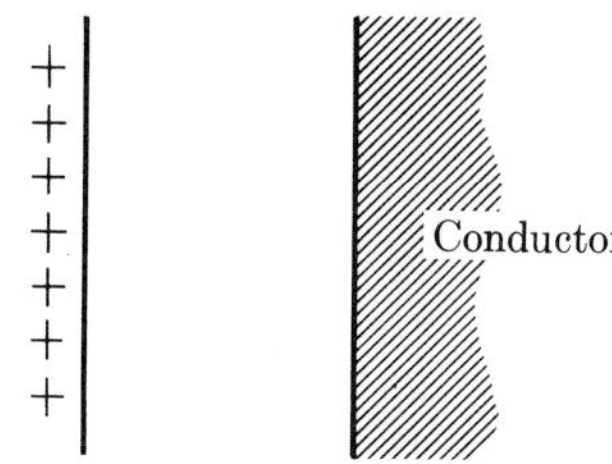

FIGURE 20–43

21. A uniform infinite sheet of charge of density σ is placed parallel to an infinite conducting slab of thickness t (initially uncharged).

(a) Find the induced charge density.

(b) Find E in the region between the charge sheet and the conductor. Where do the induced charges come from?

(c) Find the field and the induced charge density if the slab is semi-infinitely thick (Fig. 20–43).

22. Prove that the surface charge density must be the same on both sides of a charged, isolated conducting slab of thickness t and infinite area.

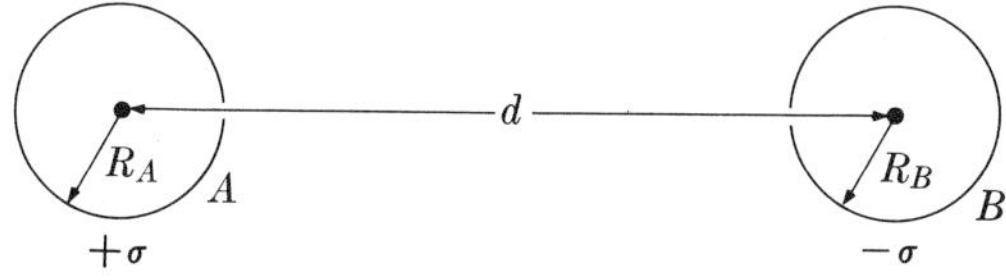

FIGURE 20–44

23. Find E inside A if A and B are spherical *nonconductors* with uniform surface charge density (Fig. 20–44).

24. An infinite plane surface has a *nonuniform* charge density given by $\sigma = a/r$, where r is measured from a fixed point O on the surface.

(a) Find E near the surface as a function of distance from O.

(b) Find E as a function of position along the line $r = O$ extending outward, perpendicular to the surface.

25. A spherically symmetrical charge cloud is found to give rise to an electric field which points radially outward from the center of the cloud and has the following strength at a distance r from the center

$$E_r = \frac{q_0}{4\pi\epsilon_0}\,\frac{(1 - e^{-\alpha r})}{r^2}.$$

Find the charge density $\rho(r)$ of the cloud. What is the total charge of the cloud? Plot $\rho(r)$ and E as functions of r.

26. Find the force-per-unit-area on one uniform infinite sheet of charge due to a parallel uniform infinite charge sheet.

27. An infinite slab of conductor of thickness t is placed between two infinite sheets of charge as shown in Fig. 20–45. The conductor has no *net* charge. Find (a) the surface charge densities induced on the slab, and (b) the field in each of the five numbered regions of Fig. 20–45. (c) Repeat for the case of $\sigma_b = +6\epsilon_0$.

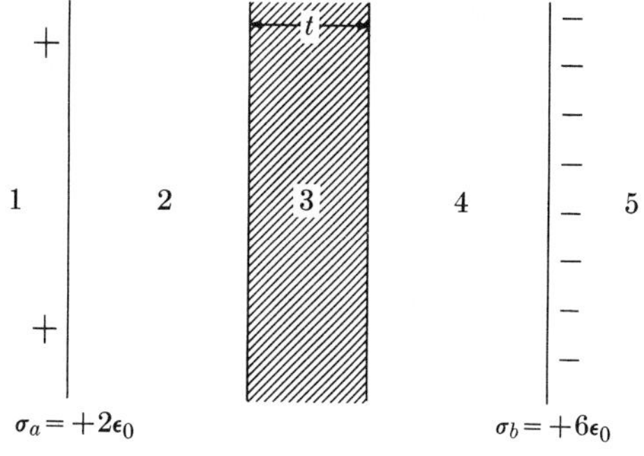

FIGURE 20–45

28. An isolated spherical nonconductor has a nonuniform distribution of surface charge and no charge inside the surface.

(a) Is $E = O$ inside the sphere? Explain.

(b) Construct a Gaussian surface just inside the charged surface? Is the *net* flux (total flux) zero through this Gaussian surface? Is the flux density zero everywhere on this Gaussian surface?

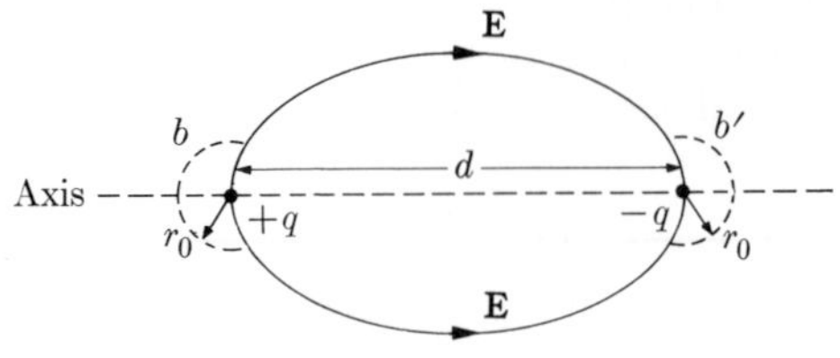

FIGURE 20–46

29. Two of the field lines due to two point charges are shown in Fig. 20–46. The selected lines leave the charges perpendicular to the line of centers. A Gaussian surface is constructed as a figure of revolution about the axis. Its outline follows the selected line of force between b and b' and then follows semicircular lines of radius r_0 centered on the charges, as shown by the dashed lines. Carry out the integral $\int \mathbf{E} \cdot d\mathbf{S}$ over the Gaussian surface for the case of $r_0 \ll d$.

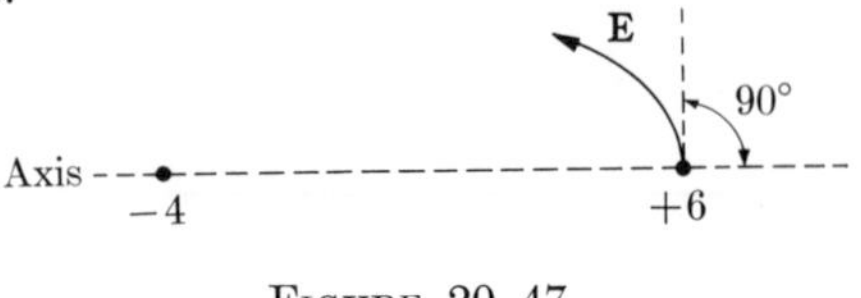

FIGURE 20–47

30. Use a technique modeled on Problem 29 to find where the line of force, shown starting from the +6 charge in Fig. 20–47, reaches the −4 charge, that is, find the angle between the line and the axis at the −4 charge.

21

The Electrostatic Potential and Energy

21–1 INTRODUCTION AND DEFINITIONS

It is possible to express the properties of the vector electric field in terms of a scalar potential field. There are several reasons why a translation of a vector problem into scalar language is a worthwhile venture. The first reason is the mathematical simplification which often occurs when this is done. Second, potential theory relates the electric force laws to the energetics of the electrical system, and energy is often a primary consideration, in itself, in the analysis of a problem. Finally, there is a practical point that in experimental practice, the electric field is seldom measured directly. Rather, potentials are measured and the electric field can be computed when the potential function is known.

The *definition of potential energy* is actually made in terms of *difference* in potential, as usual. That is, the difference in potential energy, $V_2 - V_1$, is defined by

$$V_2 - V_1 \equiv -W_{12} \equiv -\int_1^2 \mathbf{F} \cdot ds, \qquad (21\text{–}1)$$

where W_{12} is the work done *by the electric force* as the charge in question moves from point 1 to point 2. If another agent exerts a force on the charge so that it moves at constant velocity from 1 to 2, then $+W_{12}$ is the work done by the agent in question on the charge. The difference in potential energies will usually be expressed simply as ΔV. The *line integral* in Eq. (21–3) should be reviewed by referring to a mechanics text. *It is shown there that the above integral is independent of path for central forces, such as the present case.*

In the present subject, it is customary and convenient to define a quantity called simply *electric potential* as the potential energy per unit positive charge. Again, the actual definition is in terms of *difference* in electric potential $U_2 - U_1$. We have

$$U_2 - U_1 \equiv \frac{-W_{12}}{q_t}, \qquad (21\text{–}2)$$

where q_t is the positive test charge used in the evaluation of the work. The test charge must be considered as vanishingly small in order that its presence will not alter the charge distributions (by induction). Therefore, Eq. (21–2) is conveniently expressed in the differential form

$$U_2 - U_1 \equiv -\frac{dW_{12}}{dq_t}. \qquad (21\text{–}2')$$

21–2 ELECTROSTATIC POTENTIAL

Let a positive point test charge q_t be used to explore the electric field due to a source charge q. In practice the charge q_t must be held in place at any point by an external agent which exerts a force on q_t equal and opposite to the electric force experienced by q_t. If F_a, the applied force, is removed, the charge q_t would be a "free" charge and it would accelerate in the direction of the electric lines of force. Thus, in the exploration of a force field we need some outside agent to hold the test charge in place. If the test charge is to be moved about in the field in a deliberate manner, along some arbitrary path, the applied force will be adjusted from point to point so that it exactly counterbalances the local action of the electric field. When the charge is moved "against" the electric force, the external agent which carries the charge must perform work. When the charge is moved in the direction of the electric force, the electric system delivers work to the agent. This example illustrates the ability of an electric system to absorb and deliver energy. As an alternative to the definitions in Eqs. (21–1) and (21–2), the work done by the external agent could have been used. The only change would be in the sign of the work.

In the discussion above, it has been assumed that the electrostatic force is conservative and therefore that the concept of potential is meaningful. We remember from a mechanics course that central forces whose magnitudes are a function only of the distance between the interacting objects are conservative forces. Further, we remember that the resultant force due to the superposition of such forces is also conservative. Since the electrostatic force satisfies the above requirements, the concept of electrostatic potential is meaningful and useful.

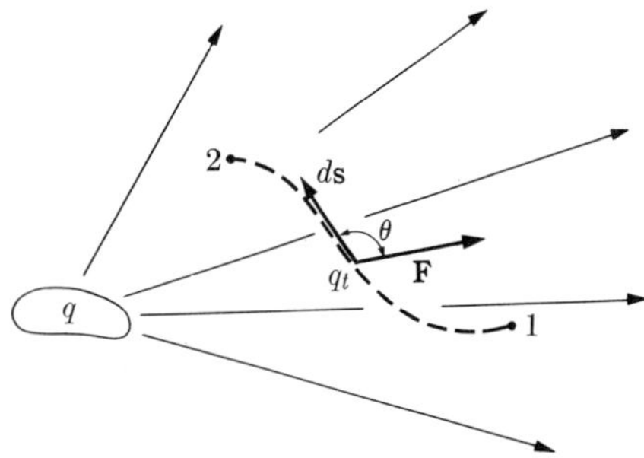

Fig. 21–1. A path from 1 to 2 is to be followed in calculating the line integral of the electrostatic force due to charge q on charge q_t. The force is **F** and the element of path is d**s**.

We now return to our example. Let q_t be moved from point 1 to point 2 (Fig. 21–1). An amount of work, W_{12}, is done by the electric force. This work is calculated by the line integral, $\int_1^2 \mathbf{F} \cdot d\mathbf{s}$, along the path followed in moving q_t from 1 to 2. But F is a conservative force, this integral is independent of path, and the work is describable as a change or difference in potential energy ΔV, or the work-per-unit-charge as a difference in electric potential ΔU. The difference in potential can be written as a line integral of the electric field E as follows:

$$\Delta U \equiv \frac{-W_{12}}{q} = -\int_1^2 \frac{\mathbf{F} \cdot d\mathbf{s}}{q} = -\int_1^2 \mathbf{E} \cdot d\mathbf{s}, \tag{21–3}$$

since E is defined by F/q. As before, the test charge q must be vanishingly small so that it will not cause induction effects. The change in potential in going from 1 to 2 is called the potential difference between 1 and 2.

The units of change in potential are joule/coulomb, which is called the *volt*.

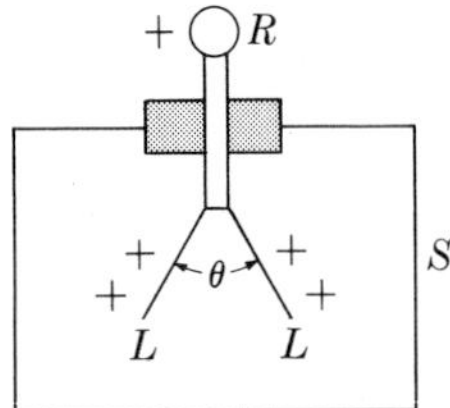

Fig. 21–2. Schematic diagram of an electroscope, a device for measuring electrostatic potential difference. The ball R, the vertical stem, and the leaves L are conductors that are in electrical contact. The leaves L are free to move and therefore separate, as shown, when they are charged. The above assembly of conductors is insulated from the case S by the insulating plug that is crosshatched. The case is a conductor if the electroscope is to be used for quantitative measurement.

The measurement of electrostatic potential can be made with instruments that utilize the force between charged objects for their operation. The most elementary is the electroscope, which, in its simplest form, consists of an insulated vertical rod R that supports two pieces of gold leaf L (Fig. 21–2) inside a case S. When R is placed in contact with a conductor, charge from the conductor flows onto R and thence onto the leaves L.

Since gold leaf is extremely flexible, the leaves separate, due to the force of electrical repulsion, and assume an angle θ, which is dependent on the amount of charge. We shall see later that the potential of an object of fixed geometry is directly proportional to the charge it contains. Thus if we can assume that the amount of charge drained off by the electroscope in the process of making the measurement is negligible, the angle θ can be a measure of the potential. If the charge drained off is not negligible, corrections can easily be made in terms of relative "capacitances," as we shall see later.

If a potential difference between two conductors is to be measured, R is connected to one and the shield S to the other. The shield S is a conductor that shields the gold leaves from extraneous electric fields if the instrument is used for quantitative measurements. The electroscope cannot ordinarily be used to measure the potential of a nonconductor or of a point in space because it requires a finite amount of charge for its operation. More sensitive potential measuring instruments are called electrometers. They can be either sensitive modifications of the above principle or they can be electronic devices.

The elementary unit of electric charge is carried by the electron, a fundamental constituent of matter. This is the least charge to be found in nature and it is a universal unit. All elementary charged particles in nature carry this same charge, either positive or negative. The unit is 1.6×10^{-19} coul.

A basic unit of energy is defined, using the above charge unit. It is called the electron-volt of energy. If an electron is transported through a potential difference of 1 v, it gains or loses 1 ev of energy. Thus an electron falling through a potential difference of 100 v gains 100 ev of energy. From Eq. (21–2), we can make the conversion from electron-volt units to the mks unit of energy. Setting $U_2 - U_1 = 1$ v, and $q = 1.6 \times 10^{-19}$ coul, W equals 1 ev and $W = 1.6 \times 10^{-19} \times 1 = 1.6 \times 10^{-19}$ joule. That is, 1 ev of energy equals 1.6×10^{-19} joule of energy, or

$$1 \text{ ev} = 1.6 \times 10^{-19} \text{ joule}.$$

We now consider the potential in particular cases.

21–3 POTENTIAL DUE TO A POINT CHARGE

We know that the field due to a point charge q is $\mathbf{E} = q\mathbf{r}/(4\pi\epsilon_0 r^3)$. The potential difference is therefore found from Eq. (21–3) as follows:

$$\Delta U = -\int_1^2 \mathbf{E} \cdot d\mathbf{s} = -\int_1^2 |\mathbf{E}| \cos\theta |d\mathbf{s}|$$

$$= -\int_1^2 \frac{q}{4\pi\epsilon_0 r^2} \cos\theta |d\mathbf{s}|.$$

But $\cos\theta \, ds$ is just dr (see Fig. 21–3) and therefore the integral becomes

$$\Delta U = -\frac{q}{4\pi\epsilon_0}\int_{r_1}^{r_2} \frac{dr}{r^2} = \frac{q}{4\pi\epsilon_0}\left(\frac{1}{r_2} - \frac{1}{r_1}\right) \tag{21–4}$$

or

$$U_2 - U_1 = \frac{q}{4\pi\epsilon_0 r_2} - \frac{q}{4\pi\epsilon_0 r_1}\cdot \tag{21–5}$$

Since our definition was only for potential difference, we still have the option of an arbitrary

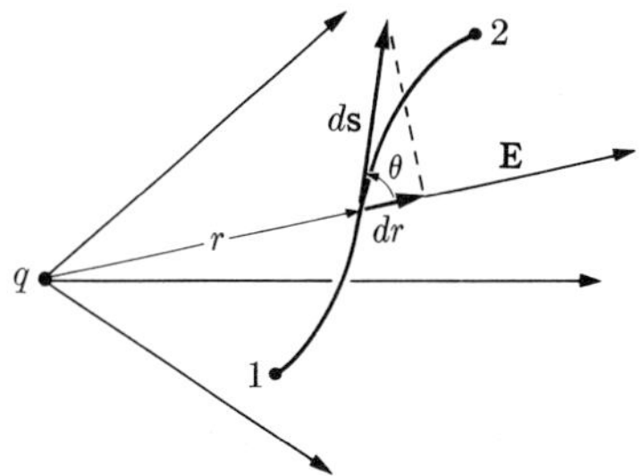

FIG. 21–3. The path of a line integral of the electric field from 1 to 2 is illustrated. The field is due to a point charge q and therefore is radial, as shown. The projection dr of the element of path ds onto the radial direction is shown.

choice of position for zero potential. In the case of the potential due to a point charge or any finite charge, it is customary and convenient to arbitrarily identify the terms in Eq. (21-5) as $U_2 = q/(4\pi\epsilon_0 r_2)$ and $U_1 = q/(4\pi\epsilon_0 r_1)$. This corresponds to the general case

$$U_r = \frac{q}{(4\pi\epsilon_0 r)} \tag{21-6}$$

for *the* potential at a distance r from a point charge (sometimes called the *absolute* potential). A *result* of this choice is that U at infinity is zero, which is easily seen from Eq. (21-6).

If the choice $U = 0$ at infinity is made, *the* potential at a point is the negative of the work per unit of positive charge done by the electric field on the positive charge as it is moved from infinity to the point in question.

Alternatively, we might have started with the arbitrary choice that $U_\infty = 0$. However, this second method involves the blind assumption that such a choice is useful, an assumption that is not valid for all types of electric fields. Therefore, the only satisfactory general procedure is to find the expression for the *difference* in potential and then, if desirable and possible, make a choice for definition of *potential.*

In the above calculation, the path independence of this particular line integral was apparent and, in fact, was essential in order to justify the use of the idea of a scalar potential. Thus, our earlier assertion that r-dependent central forces are conservative forces was verified for this special case.

21-4 POTENTIAL DUE TO A CHARGE DISTRIBUTION

We consider first the simplest example of a charge distribution—two point charges a and b. The contributions E_a and E_b made to the electric field by a and b add vectorially to give the resultant field E,

$$\mathbf{E} = \mathbf{E}_a + \mathbf{E}_b.$$

We now inquire into the nature of the potential difference between points 1 and 2 due to the two charges. From Eq. (21-3), we have

$$\Delta U = \int_1^2 (\mathbf{E}_a + \mathbf{E}_b) \cdot d\mathbf{s}$$

$$= \int_1^2 \mathbf{E}_a \cdot d\mathbf{s} + \int_1^2 \mathbf{E}_b \cdot d\mathbf{s}$$

or

$$\Delta U = \Delta U_a - \Delta U_b. \tag{21-7}$$

We see that the difference in potential is the algebraic sum of the potential differences due to each charge alone. Since this is a scalar sum, it is usually easier to calculate the potential distribution due to charges than it is to calculate the field distribution.

For the present case of two point charges, the potential difference (Eq. 21-7) can be formulated in terms of the charges and the distances from the charges by using Eq. (21-5), with the result

$$\Delta U = \frac{q_a}{4\pi\epsilon_0 r_{2a}} - \frac{q_a}{4\pi\epsilon_0 r_{1a}} + \frac{q_b}{4\pi\epsilon_0 r_{2b}} - \frac{q_b}{4\pi\epsilon_0 r_{2a}}\cdot$$

By extending the argument to any finite number of charges, the potential difference can be written

$$\Delta U = \sum_i \frac{q_i}{4\pi\epsilon_0 r_{2i}} - \sum_i \frac{q_i}{4\pi\epsilon_0 r_{1i}}\cdot \tag{21-8}$$

In many cases, it is convenient and possible to speak of *the* potential U at a point, which we define by

$$U = \sum_i \frac{q_i}{4\pi\epsilon_0 r_i}\cdot \tag{21-9}$$

Turning now to the potential difference between two points due to a continuous charge distribution of local density ρ, we can simply replace the summations with integrals,

$$\Delta U = \int_V \frac{\rho\, dV}{4\pi\epsilon_0 r_2} - \int_V \frac{\rho\, dV}{4\pi\epsilon_0 r_1}, \tag{21-10}$$

where the charge density ρ may be a function of position. The integrals in Eq. (21-10) are integrals over the charge distribution as viewed from points 2 and 1, respectively. Again, it is sometimes possible and convenient to speak of *the* potential U at a point where

$$U = \int_V \frac{\rho\, dV}{4\pi\epsilon_0 r}. \tag{21–11}$$

If a charge distribution is confined to a finite surface or a finite line, it is convenient to carry out the integrals of Eq. (21–11) in terms of surface charge density σ or line charge density λ, respectively, thus

$$U = \int_S \frac{\sigma\, dS}{4\pi\epsilon_0 r},$$

$$U = \int_l \frac{\lambda\, dl}{4\pi\epsilon_0 r}. \tag{21–12}$$

As mentioned earlier, the determination of the potential due to charges requires only scalar operations and therefore may be simpler than the determination of the field due to the charges. On the other hand, the potential cannot be found by integration over charge distributions if the charge distributions extend to infinity (see Problems). This may not seem to be a serious practical limitation, since any real charge distribution must be finite. However, there are cases in which the extension of a charge distribution in space is very great compared with the distances to the points that we are interested in, and consequently the effect is similar to that of an infinitely extended charge distribution. In cases like those above, it may be easier to first find the electric field (for example, by use of Gauss' law in situations with suitable symmetry) and then to obtain the difference in potential between points in the field by integration [Eq. (21–3)],

$$\Delta U = \int \mathbf{E} \cdot d\mathbf{s}.$$

21–5 EQUIPOTENTIALS AND LINES OF FORCE

In electrostatics, the potential is a function of the position coordinates alone. Thus a constant potential defines a surface or surfaces in space. Such a surface is called an *equipotential surface.* It is defined by $U =$ constant, if an absolute potential has been defined, or by $U - U_0 =$ constant, if at least one surface (for example, a conductor) is known to be an equipotential with an arbitrarily assigned value U_0.

An equivalent definition of an equipotential surface is a surface such that no work is done in moving a test charge about on that surface. This definition leads immediately to the deduction that equipotential surfaces must be everywhere perpendicular to the electric field, since work would be done in moving a charge about on a surface that is not perpendicular to $\mathbf{E}$.

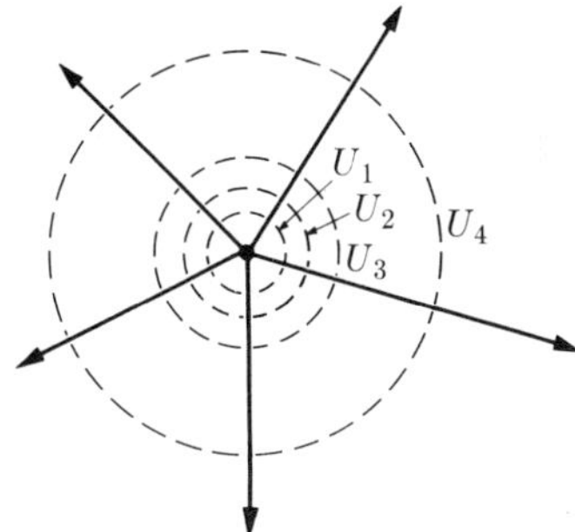

FIG. 21–4. The field (solid lines) and the equipotentials (dashed lines) due to a point charge.

The field produced by stationary electric charges can then be mapped graphically either by drawing the lines of force or by drawing the equipotential surfaces. For example, a point charge gives rise to radial lines of force and therefore to equipotentials, $r =$ constant $= q/(4\pi\epsilon_0 U)$, as in Fig. 21–4.

The functional relationship between potential and field has been given in integral form in Eq. (21–3). We therein assume that the field has first been found from the charge distribution and the potential is to be deduced from the field.

Now suppose that the potential is first found directly from the charge distribution by using the integrals of Eqs. (21–11) or (21–12). The field can then be found from the potential as follows.

The definition of work in differential form is $dW = \mathbf{F} \cdot d\mathbf{s}$. By using the definition of potential energy in differential form, namely, $dV = -dW$, and the definitions of potential $dU = dV/q$ and field $\mathbf{E} = \mathbf{F}/q$, we have

$$-dU = \mathbf{E} \cdot d\mathbf{s} = |\mathbf{E}|\,|d\mathbf{s}| \cos\theta = E_s\,ds, \tag{21–13}$$

where E_S is the projection of the field in the direction of the displacement ds (Fig. 21–5). Equation (21–13) can be rewritten

$$E_s = -\frac{dU}{ds} \tag{21–14}$$

or in components

$$E_x = -\frac{\partial U}{\partial x}, \qquad E_y = -\frac{\partial U}{\partial y}, \tag{21–15}$$

where $\partial U/\partial x$ means y is held constant and $\partial U/\partial y$ means x is held constant during the differentiation.

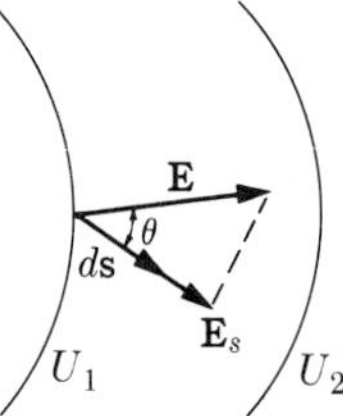

FIG. 21–5. Illustration of the relationship between the field **E**, which is perpendicular to the equipotential lines, and the projection of **E** in the direction of $d\mathbf{s}$.

The maximum value of dU/ds is obviously in the direction of E itself. Therefore, we can write

$$|\mathbf{E}| = -\left(\frac{dU}{ds}\right)\text{max}, \tag{21–16}$$

which is in the direction normal to the equipotential surface. The vector properties are not well displayed by our treatment. You will later learn to express the relationship in the vector notation,

$$\mathbf{E} = -\nabla U.$$

Example 1. Find the potential distribution due to a sphere of radius R with uniform volume charge density ρ.

Solution: The electric field was found in the last chapter for this special case: $E = q/(4\pi\epsilon_0 r^2)$ when $r > R$ and $E = qr/(4\pi\epsilon_0 R^3)$ when $r < R$. Since the external field is the same as that of a point charge, we can choose $U = 0$ at $r = \infty$ and write immediately the same expression as for a point charge as long as $r > R$, namely,

$$U = \frac{q}{4\pi\epsilon_0 r} \qquad \text{for } r > R.$$

We also have $U_R = q/4\pi\epsilon_0 R$ at $r = R$.

For a point inside the sphere, we can find the potential difference by integrating (Eq. 21–3),

$$U_r - U_R = -\int_R^r E\,dr = -\int_R^r \frac{qr\,dr}{4\pi\epsilon_0 R^3}$$
$$= -\frac{q}{8\pi\epsilon_0 R^3}(r^2 - R^2).$$

Then

$$U_r = U_R - \frac{q}{8\pi\epsilon_0 R^3}(r^2 - R^2)$$
$$= \frac{q}{4\pi\epsilon_0 R} - \frac{qr^2}{8\pi\epsilon_0 R^3} + \frac{q}{8\pi\epsilon_0 R},$$

or simply

$$U = \frac{q}{4\pi\epsilon_0}\left(\frac{3}{2R} - \frac{r^2}{2R^3}\right) \qquad \text{for } r < R.$$

A graph of U versus r is shown in Fig. 21–6.

Example 2. Find the potential distribution due to an infinite sheet of uniform charge density σ.

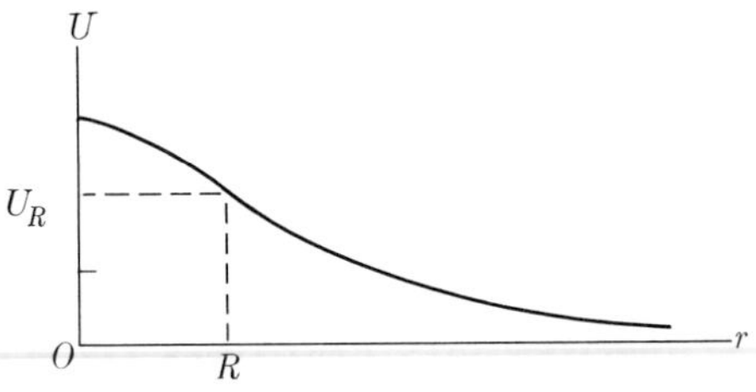

FIG. 21–6. A graph of the potential as a function of r for the case of a uniform spherical charge.

Solution: From Chapter 20 the field is known to be $E = \sigma/2\epsilon_0$. Choosing a coordinate X measured from the sheet along a normal,

$$\Delta U = -\int_{x_1}^{x_2} E\,dx = -\int_{x_1}^{x_2} (\sigma/2\epsilon_0)\,dx$$
$$= -\frac{\sigma}{2\epsilon_0}(X_2 - X_1).$$

In this case, it is possible to choose

$$U_2 = -\frac{\sigma}{2\epsilon_0} X_2,$$

etc., or in general,

$$U = -\frac{\sigma x}{2\epsilon_0}, \qquad (21\text{–}17)$$

which means that we have implicitly chosen to let $U = 0$ at $x = 0$. Note that $U_\infty = \infty$ with this choice!

Example 3. Find the potential due to equal + and − charges separated by distance d.

Solution: The potential can be written

$$U = \frac{q}{4\pi\epsilon_0}\left(\frac{1}{r_1} - \frac{1}{r_2}\right),$$

or if cartesian coordinates are chosen, as shown,

$$U = \frac{q}{4\pi\epsilon_0}\left(\frac{1}{\sqrt{y^2 + x^2}} - \frac{1}{\sqrt{y^2 + (d - x)^2}}\right).$$

Curves of constant U, that is equipotential lines, are shown in Fig. 21–7. The field E could be found from the above by differentiation (Eq. 21–5).

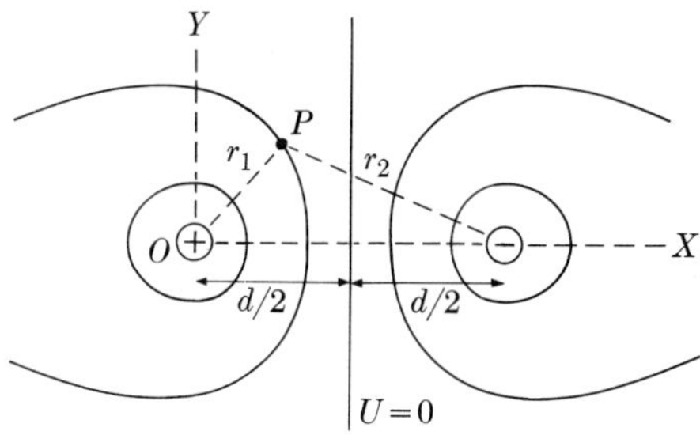

FIG. 21–7. Equal positive and negative charges separated by distance d give rise to equipotentials, as shown.

In the above examples, two methods of analysis have been illustrated, one in which the field is first obtained from the charge distribution, and the potential found from the field; and the other in which the potential is found directly from the charge distribution.

21–6 CONDUCTORS AND POTENTIAL

In Chapter 20, it was proved that, for charges at rest:

1. The excess or locally unbalanced charge on a conductor, positive or negative, resides on the surface of the conductor, i.e., the interior of a conductor is electrically neutral.

2. Since there exist free electrons in a metallic conductor, and since these electrons are stationary in a static situation, the interior electric field must be zero.

A conclusion about the electric potential within conductors in a static situation can be made immediately. The electric potential at all points within a conductor, including all points on the surface, is constant. As a proof, consider two points in the conductor. The potential difference between the two points is the integral of $-\mathbf{E}\cdot d\mathbf{s}$ along a path joining the points (Eq. 21–3). The integral is

$$U_2 - U_1 = -\int_1^2 \mathbf{E}\cdot d\mathbf{s} = -\int_1^2 \mathbf{0}\cdot d\mathbf{s} = 0.$$

Therefore, $U_2 = U_1$ for any points, and the conductor is an equipotential. If the conductor is finite in extent, it is possible to have a finite potential for the conductor with the choice of $U = 0$ at infinity. When we speak of *the potential* of a conductor, the above choice is implied.

In case the conductor is placed in fields due to other charges, these fields induce a redistribution of charge on the surface of the conductor so that the entire conductor remains an equipotential. This condition is, of course, equivalent to the statement in an earlier section that the charge distribution must result in a field at the surface

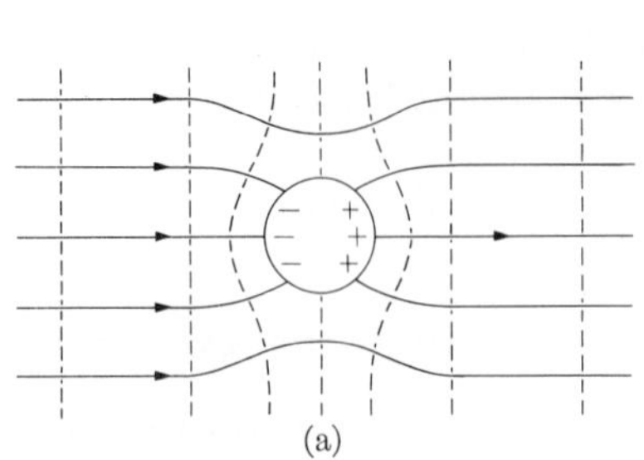

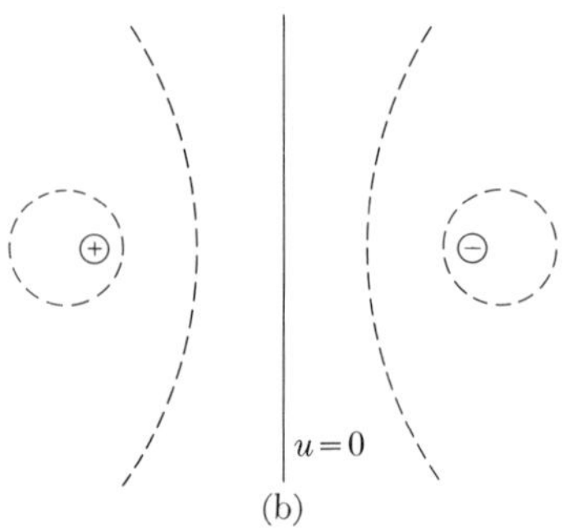

FIG. 21–8. (a) The field (solid lines) and equipotentials (dashed lines) when an initially uncharged conducting sphere is introduced into a uniform field. (b) Equipotentials due to equal and opposite point charges.

that is normal to the surface and an interior field that is zero. Figure 21–8(a) illustrates qualitatively the field and equipotentials for a conducting sphere introduced into an initially uniform field. At large distances the field must still be uniform, and near the sphere the field must be nearly radial. The equipotentials (dashed lines) must be planes at large distances. As the sphere is approached the equipotential planes acquire bumps. The central equipotential surface is a plane with a hemispherical boss on each face coincident with the conducting sphere. The surface charge will be distributed as shown.

Consider again the example of induction produced in an infinite conducting sheet by a point charge. We can now justify the image method in terms of potentials by noting that the plane midway between unlike equal charges (Fig. 21–8b) is an equipotential. Therefore, a conductor could be placed in this plane without altering the potential distribution. Thus the potentials (and field) will be the same in the left half of the region of Fig. 21–8(b), whether there is an equal negative charge, as shown, or whether there is a conducting metal plane coincident with the $U = 0$ equipotential. In the case of the metal plane, there will, of course, be induced charges on the surface. This charge distribution is most easily found from the electric field in the manner discussed in Chapter 20.

The above example is illustrative of a general technique that a conducting surface can be substituted for any equipotential surface without altering the field external to the conductor.

21–7 ELECTRIC CAPACITORS

We have seen that a single value of potential relative to some arbitrary reference can be associated with any metallic conductor in the static case. We shall utilize this fact in a definition of *electrical capacitance.* Capacitance is related to the ability of a metallic system to store electric charge. Imagine that a certain amount of charge is placed upon a metallic object. This object is thus raised to a potential level above its potential in the uncharged state. The resultant potential as usual, is a measure of the work per unit positive charge required to bring an additional charge from infinity to the conductor. We note that the conductor in question will be finite in size if its capacitance is finite and hence the reference potential can be meaningfully chosen to be zero at infinity. If a large amount of charge can be placed on an object with only a small consequent increase in potential, the object is said to have a large electrical capacitance. Conversely, if a small amount of charge placed on an object greatly increases the potential of the object, then the capacitance of the object for electric charge storage is said to be small. Quantitatively, self-capacitance of a metallic conductor is defined to be the ratio of the charge on the conductor divided by the potential of the conductor, or

$$C \equiv \frac{q}{U}\,\frac{\text{coulomb of charge}}{\text{volt of potential}} \quad \text{or} \quad \frac{q}{U}\ \text{farad.} \tag{21-18}$$

The farad measure of capacitance is 1 coul of charge per 1 v of potential. In practice a farad of capacitance is an inconveniently large unit. The microfarad (μf) and the micro-micro-farad ($\mu\mu$f) units of capacitance are in common use.

Example 4. *The Capacitance of a Metallic Sphere.* Let a charge q be placed on a conducting sphere of radius R. The potential of the sphere is $U(R) = q/(4\pi\epsilon_0 R)$, where we have chosen $U = 0$ at infinity as usual. The capacitance of the sphere is then found to be [Eq. (21–18)],

$$C = 4\pi\epsilon_0 R\ \text{farad.} \tag{21-19}$$

Capacitance is a purely geometric property of the object. The capacitance is independent of charge. In the case of the sphere, the capacitance depends linearly on the radius of the sphere, with a constant of proportionality approximately equal to $1/(9\times 10^9)$. A "small" sphere of 1 cm radius ($R = 10^{-2}$ m) has a capacitance equal to approximately 1 $\mu\mu$f, according to the above. The capacitance of the earth, going to the other extreme in size, is still considerably less than a farad. Since $R = 6.4 \times 10^6$ m for the earth's radius, its capacitance is

$$C_{\text{earth}} = \frac{6.4\times 10^6}{9\times 10^9}\ \text{farad} = 0.007\ \text{farad.}$$

Thus we see that an isolated conductor with even a millifarad of capacitance is not likely to be encountered in the laboratory.

The calculation of the capacitance of objects of other than spherical shapes, for example an ellipsoid, can be performed by advanced techniques of computation. In general, the capacitance of an irregular object depends on an "effective" radius of the object. For an object 200 cm long and 60 cm in diameter the capacitance is somewhere between 100 $\mu\mu$f and 30 $\mu\mu$f. Thus an isolated person has a capacitance of about 50 $\mu\mu$f.

Capacitive systems, called *capacitors* or condensors, constructed deliberately for practical charge storage, usually consist of two or more metallic elements in near proximity that are oppositely charged. The advantage of such a system is immediately apparent. Since the objects are oppositely charged, the electric (and potential) fields of each tend to cancel in surrounding space. Thus it is much easier to place additional charge on a positively charged body if a negatively charged body is in the neighborhood. Likewise, the negative element is more easily charged if a positive element is nearby. By the same token, a great gain in capacity is made if the plus and minus charges are held equal, thus keeping the external fields at a minimum. In practice, this is usually accomplished automatically by simply removing charge from one element and transporting it to the other. The capacity of the two-element system then depends only on the charge and the *difference* in potential between the two elements. In particular,

$$C = \frac{q}{\Delta U}, \tag{21-20}$$

or if the potential of one element is chosen as zero,

$$C = \frac{q}{U}. \tag{21-21}$$

Example 5. *Parallel-plate Capacitor.* We choose plates whose separation d is small compared with their dimensions l. Then the field between the plates is essentially that due to infinite plane sheets. So-called edge effects will therefore be neglected. In Chapter 20, the field between infinite sheets of equal uniform charge density was found to be $E = \sigma/\epsilon_0$, where σ, the surface charge density, can be expressed as the total charge q on a plate divided by its area, A. The capacitance is defined by Eq. (21–20). Since the field is known, the potential difference is calculable from Eq. (21–3), that is, $\Delta U = -\int_1^2 \mathbf{E}\cdot d\mathbf{s} = \int_0^d \sigma\, dx/\epsilon_0$, where the x-axis is chosen as shown in Fig. 21–9. The integral gives $\Delta U = \sigma(x_2 - x_1)/\epsilon_0 = \sigma\, d/\epsilon_0$. The capacitance is $C = q/\Delta U = q\epsilon_0/\sigma\, d$.

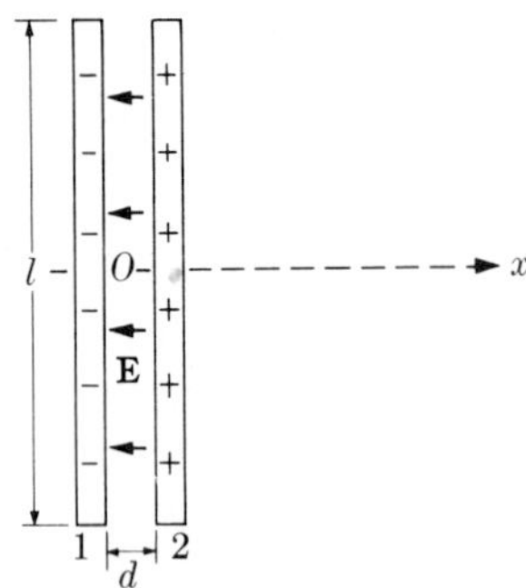

FIG. 21-9. A parallel-plate capacitor consisting of plane parallel conductors separated by a distance d that is small compared with the lateral dimensions l of the plates. The plates are given equal but opposite charge. The origin of the x-coordinate is chosen at plate 1.

But since $\sigma = q/A$, we have

$$C = \epsilon_0 \frac{A}{d}. \tag{21-22}$$

In practice the plates may be strips of aluminum foil separated by a thin insulator and rolled into a cylindrical spiral for compactness. The result is essentially the same as Eq. (21-22), since d is small compared with the radius of the cylinder.

The electric field between the parallel plates has been expressed in terms of the charge as $E = \sigma/\epsilon_0$. It can also be expressed in terms of the potential difference, for example, by direct integration of $\Delta U = -\int_1^2 \mathbf{E} \cdot d\mathbf{s}$, giving

$$E = -\frac{\Delta U}{d}$$

for closely spaced parallel plates.

21-8 ENERGY IN SYSTEMS OF CHARGED CONDUCTORS

Let us assume that a system of metallic conductors is charged and static. To each conductor we can ascribe a definite potential, which can be measured, or computed, if the charges and geometry are known. From the proofs which have been given, all based on the Coulomb law, a general statement about energy in the system can be made.

Let a very small charge Δq (small with respect to the net charges in the system) be transported from one conductor to another (Fig. 21-10). The potential difference is $U_2 - U_1$, which denotes the work per unit charge required to transport unit charge from one conductor to the other. Thus the work required to transport the charge Δq from U_1 to U_2 is

$$W = \Delta q(U_2 - U_1), \tag{21-23}$$

regardless of what path is used between the two conductors. The specification that Δq be small is made so that its transfer does not sensibly affect the potentials we ascribe to the system.

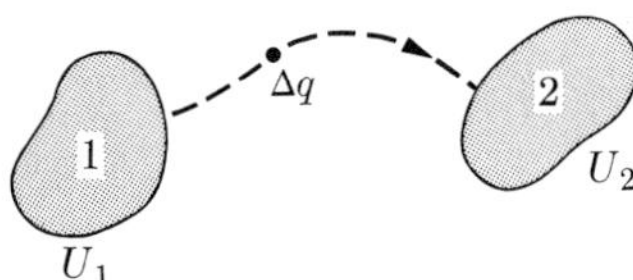

FIG. 21-10. A charge Δq is transported from conductor 1 to conductor 2, which are at potentials U_1 and U_2, respectively.

The *energy of a charged isolated conductor* can be found as follows: Work is required in the process of charging a capacitor. Consider the case in which the capacitor is a single element of conductor. If the conductor is initially uncharged, we may place a small amount of charge on it without performing any work at all; there is no repulsive force acting upon this initial increment of charge. However, in a second step of adding more charge, there is a force of repulsion between the initial charge and the charge to be added. At every successive step of charging, more work is expended in adding each new increment of charge.

In the analysis of the problem, we consider that a capacitor is charged in very small steps by in-

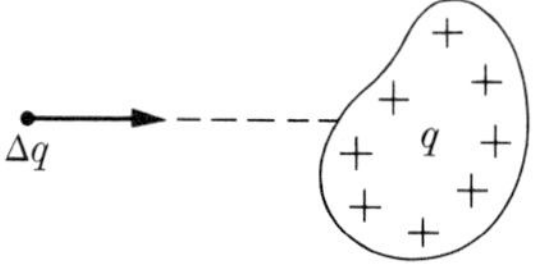

FIG. 21-11. A charge Δq is placed on an isolated conductor that already possesses a charge q.

crements of dq coul (Fig. 21-11). These increments are carried from a reservoir of charge at infinity and placed upon the conductor. At any stage in the charging process the instantaneous charge already on the conductor is q coul and the instantaneous potential of the conductor is U joules/coul. The process of bringing more charge dq from infinity to the conductor involves an amount of work dW' by the electric field, given by the equation defining U, that is, Eq. (21-2′), as

$$dW' = U\,dq, \tag{21-24}$$

where U is a function of q and the geometry of the conductor. (Note that in this case, U_1 is zero by choice.) With this equation, we can compute the energy required to charge the capacitor from 0 to q_1 by use of the definite integral. Note that the charging can be performed according to any arbitrary schedule (not necessarily linear, for example) provided that the increments are infinitesimal. Then the work performed is given by the following integral:

$$W' = \int_0^{W_1} dW = -\int_0^{q_1} U\,dq. \tag{21-25}$$

The potential of the conductor is related to the instantaneous charge by the definition of capacitance, $C = q/U$, where we remember that C is a constant dependent on the geometry. Substituting this expression for U in the integral, we have

$$W' = -\frac{1}{C}\int_0^{q_1} q\,dq = -\frac{q_1^2}{2C}. \tag{21-26}$$

But the energy stored in the capacitor is the work W done by the *external* force that brought up the charges. Since this force is equal and opposite to the electric force,

$$W = -W' = \int_0^{q_1} U\,dq \tag{21-27}$$

we have

$$W = \frac{q^2}{2C}. \tag{21-26′}$$

By using the definition of capacitance, the energy can be written in other forms

$$W = \frac{q^2}{2C} = \frac{qU}{2} = \frac{CU^2}{2}. \tag{21-28}$$

Example 6. If the conductor is a sphere, we have derived the expression for the potential of the sphere as $U = q/(4\pi\epsilon_0 R)$. Then from the energy equation $W = \frac{1}{2}qU$ we have the expression $W = q^2/(8\pi\epsilon_0 R)$ for the energy required to place total charge q on the sphere in terms of the charge and the radius of the sphere.

If a *mutual capacitance* is to be charged, the fundamental process of charging is as follows: The instantaneous charge on one element is $+q$ and on the other $-q$. In the charging process, negative charge is removed from the positive element and placed on the negative element (Fig. 21-12). The net charge on each is changed by a like amount, and the energy dW required from an external agent is the potential difference ΔU

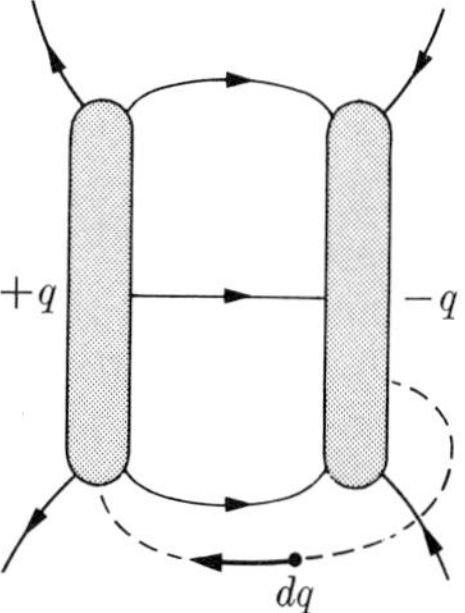

FIG. 21-12. Illustration of the transport of a charge dq from one plate to the other plate of a mutual capacitance (capacitor).

between the elements times the transferred charge dq, that is,

$$dW = \Delta U\, dq.$$

By the definition of mutual capacitance we have $\Delta U = q/C$, so that the energy expression becomes identical in form with that for the self-capacitance of an isolated conductor, viz.,

$$dW = \frac{q\, dq}{C}.$$

From this we arrive at the same set of expressions for the energy of a charged mutual capacitance as for an isolated conductor; that is, Eqs. (21–27), and (21–28) with potential difference ΔU replacing potential U.

21–9 THE ENERGY OF AN ARBITRARY DISTRIBUTION OF ELECTRIC CHARGE

All the charge on a conductor, whatever its position, is at the same potential level U in electrostatics problems. If an arbitrary configuration of charges is to be constructed in free space, then this simplifying assumption is no longer generally true. For example, in the configuration of Fig. 21–13, the potential at the position of each of the three charges is easily computed, but U_1, U_2, and U_3 may all have different values. Therefore, a new analysis of the energy problem must be done for this more general case.

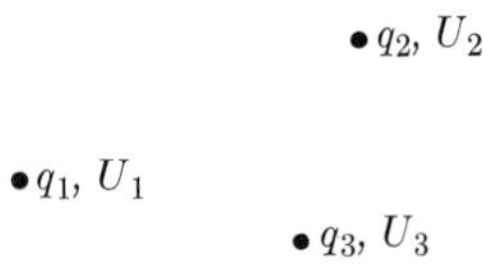

• q_2, U_2

• q_1, U_1

• q_3, U_3

FIG. 21–13. An arrangement of three point charges q_1, q_2, and q_3. The absolute potentials at the positions of the charges are U_1, U_2, and U_3, respectively.

This is the problem: A set of point charges, q_1, q_2, q_3, q_4, · · ·, is found to occupy a definite configuration in space. How much work is required to assemble this physical system? To answer this question, we remove all the charges to infinity and then, step by step, rebuild the system. As

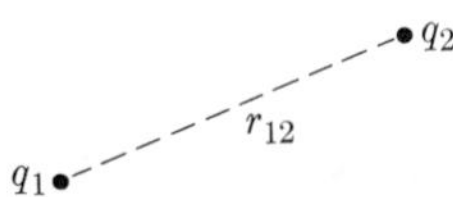

FIG. 21–14. First step in the assembly of the arrangement of charges of Fig. 21–13.

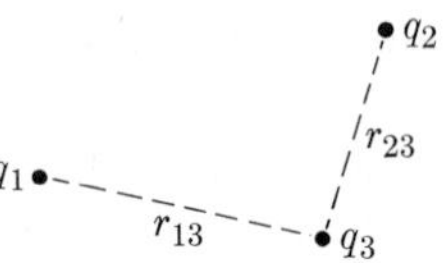

FIG. 21–15. Second step in the assembly of charges into the arrangement of Fig. 21–13.

step 1, the charge q_1 is brought back into the picture. Clearly no work is required in the first step, since there is no electric field other than that due to q_1 itself. In step 2 the charge q_2 is brought into place (Fig. 21–14). This step requires work in the amount W_2, which is simply computed from the interaction of a pair of point charges, giving

$$W_2 = \frac{1}{4\pi\epsilon_0}\frac{q_1q_2}{r_{12}}. \tag{21–29}$$

In the third step, the charge q_3 is brought into place (Fig. 21–15). This charge is brought against the action of both charges, q_1 and q_2, already in place. From the principle of addition, which holds for electrostatic fields, the energy for step 3 is the sum of the energy of the two systems, q_1q_3 and q_2q_3,

$$W_3 = \frac{1}{4\pi\epsilon_0}\left(\frac{q_1q_3}{r_{13}} + \frac{q_2q_3}{r_{23}}\right). \tag{21–30}$$

In a simple repetition of method, we bring the charge q_4 into place. The energy required is

$$W_4 = \frac{1}{4\pi\epsilon_0}\left(\frac{q_1q_4}{r_{14}} + \frac{q_2q_4}{r_{24}} + \frac{q_3q_4}{r_{34}}\right), \tag{21–31}$$

and by an extension of the process we see that the addition of the nth particle requires an amount of work equal to

$$W_n = \frac{1}{4\pi\epsilon_0}\left(\frac{q_1q_n}{r_{1n}} + \frac{q_2q_n}{r_{2n}} + \cdots \frac{q_{n-1}q_n}{r_{n-1,n}}\right). \tag{21–32}$$

The energy of the system must be the same regardless of the order of construction. We have chosen a specific order which is as well justified as any other. Thus when the total energy is found, there should be no memory of the method of construction, and it should not be said that the particle q_3 itself possesses the energy W_3. All that is known is the total energy which is the sum of all terms written above,

$$W_{\text{Total}} = W_1 + W_2 + W_3 + W_4 \cdots + W_n. \tag{21–33}$$

For the purpose of summing this series, a rearrangement of terms is advantageous. First, we summarize the expressions as written:

$$\begin{aligned} W_1 &= 0, \\ W_2 &= \frac{1}{4\pi\epsilon_0}\left(\frac{q_1q_2}{r_{12}}\right), \\ W_3 &= \frac{1}{4\pi\epsilon_0}\left(\frac{q_1q_3}{r_{13}} + \frac{q_2q_3}{r_{23}}\right), \\ W_4 &= \frac{1}{4\pi\epsilon_0}\left(\frac{q_1q_4}{r_{14}} + \frac{q_2q_4}{r_{24}} + \frac{q_3q_4}{r_{34}}\right), \\ W_n &= \frac{1}{4\pi\epsilon_0}\left(\frac{q_1q_n}{r_{1n}}\ \frac{q_2q_n}{r_{2n}} + \cdots \frac{q_{n-1}q_n}{r_{n-1,\,n}}\right). \end{aligned} \tag{21–34}$$

In a rearrangement of terms, we write a series of terms, each of which contains the same charge as a factor. Each series is divided by 2 since each term given above must be used twice (each term contains a pair of charges). Then with a mild exercise of ingenuity, the reader may assure himself that the following expressions are exactly equivalent to the ones given above,

$$\begin{aligned} W_{q1} &= \frac{1}{2}\frac{q_1}{4\pi\epsilon_0}\left(\frac{q_2}{r_{12}} + \frac{q_3}{r_{13}} + \frac{q_4}{r_{14}} + \cdots \frac{q_n}{r_{1n}}\right), \\ W_{q2} &= \frac{1}{2}\frac{q_2}{4\pi\epsilon_0}\left(\frac{q_1}{r_{21}} + \frac{q_3}{r_{23}} + \frac{q_4}{r_{24}} + \cdots \frac{q}{r_{2n}}\right), \\ W_{q3} &= \frac{1}{2}\frac{q_3}{4\pi\epsilon_0}\left(\frac{q_1}{r_{31}} + \frac{q_2}{r_{32}} + \frac{q_4}{r_{34}} + \cdots \frac{q}{r_{3n}}\right), \\ W_{q4} &= \frac{1}{2}\frac{q_4}{4\pi\epsilon_0}\left(\frac{q_1}{r_{41}} + \frac{q_2}{r_{42}} + \frac{q_3}{r_{43}} + \cdots \frac{q}{r_{4n}}\right), \\ W_{qn} &= \cdots \end{aligned} \tag{21–35}$$

By identification it can be seen that each series in parentheses is just the sum of the potentials due to all the other point charges at the position of the charge for which the series is written. From this we may write the terms as follows:

$$\begin{aligned} W_{q1} &= \tfrac{1}{2}q_1U_1, \\ W_{q2} &= \tfrac{1}{2}q_2U_2, \\ W_{q3} &= \tfrac{1}{2}q_3U_3, \end{aligned} \tag{21–36}$$

where U_1 is, for example, the value of the electric potential at the position of q_1. Labeling each charge with the running index i, we can set down a formal expression for the total energy as the sum

$$W = \tfrac{1}{2}\sum_i q_iU_i. \tag{21–37}$$

In the case of a continuous charge distribution —for example, a volume distribution—the sum appearing in the last equation can be replaced by an integral. Let the volume of the charge distribution be divided into cells of volume dV, each cell containing a charge dq. If the distribution is known, it will be characterized by a charge-density distribution $\rho(x, y, z)$, and the potential at every point is known to be $U(x, y, z)$. Then for the sum in Eq. 21–37, we write the integral

$$W = \tfrac{1}{2}\int U\,dq, \tag{21–38}$$

where U is the potential which pertains to the coordinates of dq. In turn, dq can be expressed as the local charge density ρ times the volume element dV; that is, $dq = \rho\,dV$. The integral then becomes

$$W = \tfrac{1}{2}\int \rho U\,dV; \tag{21–39}$$

that is, the energy of a charge distribution in space is computed by performing the volume integral of the product of charge density times the potential.

Example 7. *The Energy of a Uniformly Charged Sphere.* Let a ball of charge of radius R be uniformly

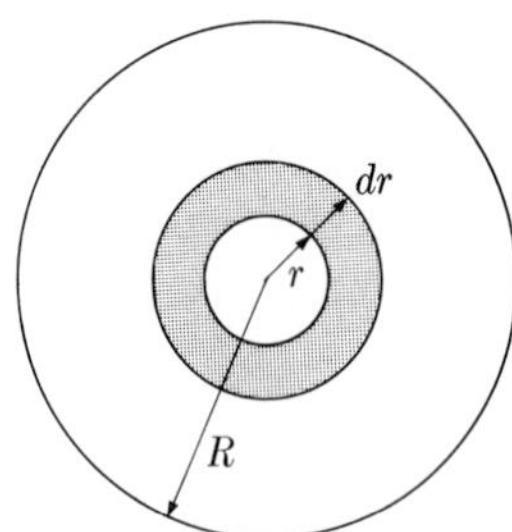

FIG. 21-16. Volume element in the form of a spherical shell of thickness dr to be used in the calculation of the energy of a uniform spherical charge of radius R.

charged with a constant density ρ. The charge density ρ outside R is zero. The integral

$$W = \tfrac{1}{2}\int_0^R \rho U\,dV$$

is performed between the limits $r = 0$ and $r = R$, since for $r > R$ the integral is zero because $\rho = 0$. Since ρ is constant, it may be taken outside the integral sign,

$$W = \frac{\rho}{2}\int_0^R U\,dV.$$

The potential function for a point within a sphere of uniform charge was derived in Example 1 as

$$U(r) = \frac{q}{8\pi\epsilon_0 R}\left(3 - \frac{r^2}{R^2}\right) \quad \text{for } (r < R).$$

The potential is a function only of r, and therefore the potential is constant over a spherical shell of radius r. Therefore, divide the volume into spherical shells of radius r and thickness dr (Fig. 21-16). For each shell the volume element is written

$$dV = 4\pi r^2\,dr.$$

The final expression for the integral is formed by using the expressions given above for $U(r)$ and dV in the integral, yielding

$$W = \frac{\rho}{2}\frac{q\,4\pi}{8\pi\epsilon_0 R}\int_0^R \left(3r^2 - \frac{r^4}{R^2}\right) dr.$$

It is left to the reader to perform the integration indicated and to reduce it to the following form:

$$W = \frac{3}{5}\frac{1}{4\pi\epsilon_0}\frac{q^2}{R}. \tag{21-40}$$

Example 8. *The Classical Radius of the Electron.* One can inquire of classical theory what the radius of the electron should be, regarding it as a ball of electric charge. The rest energy of the electron is given by the theory of relativity to be equal to the mass of the electron times the square of the velocity of light, $W = m_0c^2$. If this energy is contained in the electron, we can equate it to the energy expended electrically in order to construct the electron. From Eq. (21-40), then,

$$m_0c^2 = 3q^2/(20\pi\epsilon_0 R_e),$$

which we can solve for the classical radius of the electron in terms of its known properties, charge, and mass. The result is

$$R_e = \frac{3}{20\pi\epsilon_0}\frac{q^2}{m_0c^2}.$$

The constants for an electron are

$$m_0 = 0.91 \times 10^{-30}\ \text{kg}$$
$$q = 1.6 \times 10^{-19}\ \text{coul}$$
$$c = 3 \times 10^8\ \frac{\text{m}}{\text{sec}}$$
$$\frac{1}{4\pi\epsilon_0} \simeq 9 \times 10^9\ \frac{\text{n}\cdot\text{m}^2}{\text{coul}^2}.$$

Based on these data, the radius is found to be $R_e = 1.7 \times 10^{-15}$ m. Note the inadmissibility, in classical theory, of a point electron, since for a point electron ($R = 0$) the electric energy is infinite. Thus in the formation of the universe, the theory requires an infinite amount of energy for the construction of each point particle of which the universe is made.

As a final comment on calculating the energy, consider the distinction between Eq. (21-38) and Eq. (21-27) (aside from the minus sign). They appear to be contradictory, since they seem to differ only in the factor $\frac{1}{2}$. The answer is that they apply to different methods for calculating the energy. Equation (21–27) describes the process in which the conductor starts with no charge at all and the integral traces the process of assembling the charge on the conductor or transporting it from one conductor to another of a two-element capacitor. Therefore, U is the potential at any stage of the charging process and increases from zero to the final value, that is, U is a function of time, in principle.

On the other hand, Eq. (21–38) describes an integration over a *completed* assembly of charge. Therefore, U is the value of potential of a particular charge, with all the charges in place, and is not a function of time. But in assembling the charges, only the last charge must do work against the full final potential. Thus the factor $\frac{1}{2}$ occurs.

The first method was specifically restricted to assembling charge on a *conductor*, since it is only in this case, in general, that the potential of all charges in the assembly is the same at each stage. The second method can also be used for the case of the conductor but is also valid for any other assembly of charge.

The question of where the electrical potential energy is stored has not been answered in our discussion. The effect of the presence of net electric charge has been described by saying that an electric field is set up in the region surrounding the charge. The potential energy associated with a charge or an assembly of charges is considered to reside in the electric field. Since the field varies from point to point, in general, it is necessary to introduce the idea of energy density in the field. The equation for energy density, $\Delta W/\Delta V$ (where ΔV is a volume element), derived in a problem, is

$$\frac{\Delta W}{\Delta V} = \left(\frac{\epsilon_0}{2}\right) E^2 \, \frac{\text{joules}}{\text{m}^3}, \tag{21–41}$$

which becomes

$$\frac{dW}{dV} = \left(\frac{\epsilon_0}{2}\right) E^2, \tag{21–42}$$

when written in differential form.

21–10 PRODUCTION OF ELECTROSTATIC POTENTIAL DIFFERENCES DIRECTLY BY MECHANICAL WORK

In Chapter 19, it was mentioned that initial contact followed by mechanical separation of two different nonconductors produces a separation of charges. The effects are very marked in the case of synthetic shoe soles or synthetic fiber clothing. The energy required to produce the system of separated charges comes from the mechanical work of pulling apart the oppositely charged members of the system; that is,

$$\tfrac{1}{2}\int \rho U \, dV = \int \mathbf{F} \cdot d\mathbf{s}, \tag{21–43}$$

where the left side is the final electrostatic energy of the system (Eq. 21–39) and the right side is the mechanical work that was required to separate the charged members.

If an object has already been charged by some means, additional objects can be charged by *induction*. Consider the sequence shown in Fig. 21–17. We shall choose $U = 0$ for the large distant conductor C, which is equivalent to letting $U = 0$ at infinity. In part (a), an initially

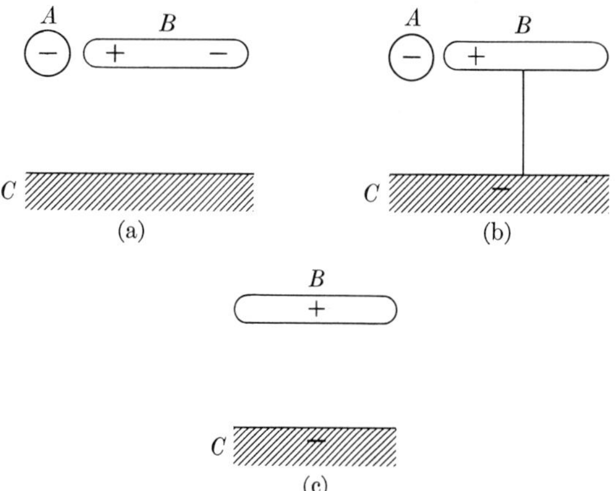

FIG. 21–17. Sequence of operations in charging a conductor B by utilizing the induction effect of a charged object A. More work is required to remove A at the end of the process than was done by A when it was first brought to the vicinity of B.

charged object A has been brought up to a conductor B. The charges on B redistribute themselves in order to maintain B as an equipotential. In addition, the potential of B is lowered by the presence of excess negative charge in its vicinity (on A). If A is removed, the potential of B will return to zero. But now suppose that B is connected to C while A is near B (Fig. 3-17b). The potentials now are $U_B = U_C = 0$. But the potential of B can be zero only if it acquires sufficient plus charge (from C) to offset the effect of the presence of A [see (Fig. 3-17b)]. (The excess minus charge on C does not detectably affect the potential of C, because C is very large.)

Next, the connection between B and C is removed, and, finally, A is removed. Thus, we end up with conductor B charged to a positive potential (Fig. 3-17c).

The electrical energy of the system has been increased. The increase has been at the expense of mechanical work done on A. There was a small electrical force of attraction on A as it was brought up to B in the first place. This force varied at least as fast as $1/(\text{distance})^3$, except in the vicinity of B, but the force was more nearly an inverse-square force as A was removed. Thus the work to remove A was greater than the work done by the electrical system as A was brought up, and this difference in mechanical work accounts for the increase in electrical energy of the system.

Some types of lecture demonstration "electrostatic generators" utilize the induction principle outlined above.

Another type of generator, *the Van de Graaff generator*, utilizes the fact that charge of one sign tends to reside on the exterior of a conductor. Thus, if a charged conductor is touched to the inside of a closed conducting shell, the inner conductor will immediately be discharged, since the two conductors now constitute a single conducting system, which can have no free charge in its interior.

In principle, then, a hollow conductor A, with a small hole that will admit a conductor B (Fig. 21-18) can be charged without apparent limit by simple repetition of the acts of charging B, inserting it into A, and touching it to the inner surface. Practical difficulties of electrical discharges actually limit the potential of A, but it can be millions of volts with proper design, if A approaches a meter in diameter. One difficulty with the above system is the need for an insulating handle H that will support large potential differences. In practice, this and other practical problems are met by "spraying" charges onto a nonconducting belt B that extends from the region at ground potential O into the sphere S at potential U. The sphere is on an insulating column C (Fig. 21-19). The electrical energy in this case is provided by a portion of the mechanical work required to drive the belt, that portion

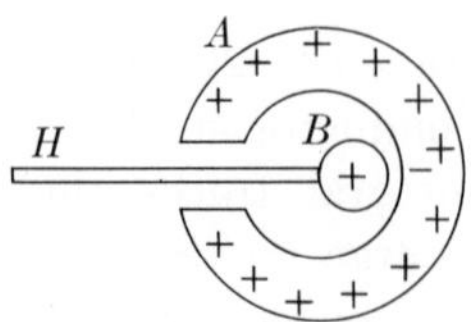

FIG. 21-18. Illustration of the process of charging a hollow conductor A by means of a charged conductor B. Conductor B can have a lower potential than A when outside B, but when it is carried inside A, its potential rises to a value higher than that of A. Consequently, the charge on B flows to A when B is touched to A on the inside of A.

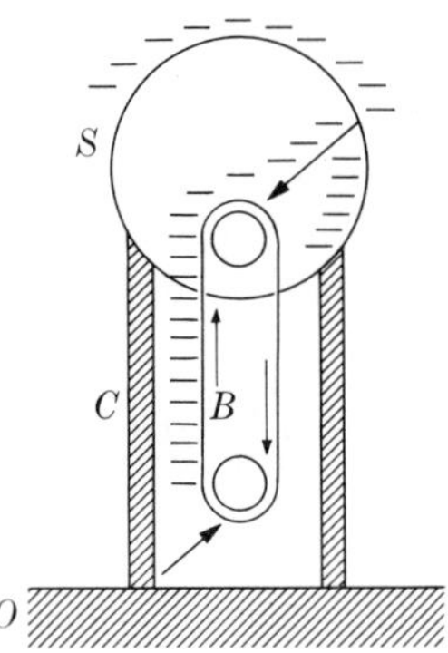

FIG. 21-19. Schematic diagram of a Van de Graaff generator. The belt B carries charge inside the hollow conducting sphere S, where it is transferred to the sphere. The sphere rests on an insulating column C.

corresponding to carrying the charge up to the sphere against the force of electrical repulsion.

21–11 SUMMARY

The electric potential difference ΔU between points 1 and 2 in an electrostatic field is

$$\Delta U \equiv -\frac{W_{12}}{q} = -\int_1^2 \frac{\mathbf{F}\cdot d\mathbf{s}}{q} = -\int_1^2 \mathbf{E}\cdot d\mathbf{s},$$

where W_{12} is the work by the electrical force per unit positive charge. In the case of the field of a point charge,

$$\Delta U = \frac{q}{4\pi\epsilon_0}\left(\frac{1}{r_2} - \frac{1}{r_1}\right),$$

where r is the distance from the charge. The potential at $r = \infty$ can be chosen zero, resulting in the expression for the potential at r

$$U = \frac{q}{4\pi\epsilon_0}\frac{1}{r}.$$

If there is more than one point charge or a continuous charge distribution, the potential difference can be expressed by summations or by integrations

$$\Delta U = \frac{1}{4\pi\epsilon_0}\left(\sum_i \frac{q_i}{r_{2i}} - \sum_i \frac{q_i}{r_{1i}}\right),$$

or

$$\Delta U = \frac{1}{4\pi\epsilon_0}\left(\int_V \frac{\rho\, dV}{r_2} - \int_V \frac{\rho\, dV}{r_1}\right).$$

If the distribution is finite, the potential at infinity can conveniently be chosen zero at infinity and the potential U at any point becomes

$$\Delta U = \frac{1}{4\pi\epsilon_0}\sum_i \frac{q_i}{r_i}$$

or

$$\Delta U = \frac{1}{4\pi\epsilon_0}\int_V \frac{\rho\, dV}{r}.$$

The potential is derivable from the field by means of the integral

$$\Delta U = -\int_1^2 \mathbf{E}\cdot d\mathbf{s},$$

and the field is derivable from the potential by means of the differentiations

$$E_s = -\frac{\partial U}{\partial s},$$

or in cartesian components,

$$E_x = -\frac{\partial U}{\partial x},$$

$$E_y = -\frac{\partial U}{\partial y},$$

or for the radial component in polar coordinates

$$E_r = -\frac{\partial U}{\partial r}.$$

Conductors are equipotentials in electrostatics. When a conductor is placed in an electric field, the free charges in the conductor will be redistributed until the resultant field within the conducting material itself is zero.

The capacitance of an isolated conductor is

$$C \equiv \frac{q}{U}.$$

The mutual capacitance of two conductors is

$$C \equiv \frac{q}{\Delta U}.$$

The electric energy of a charged conductor or of a mutual capacitance is

$$W = \tfrac{1}{2}qU = \tfrac{1}{2}\frac{q^2}{C} = \tfrac{1}{2}CV^2,$$

where U represents potential or potential difference, respectively. The electric energy of any charge distribution is given by

$$W = \tfrac{1}{2}\int_V U\rho\, dV,$$

where U is the potential at the position of a charge element $\rho\, dV$.

The production of potential differences by direct conversion of mechanical energy to electric energy is described.

Problems

1. Charges of + and $-q$ are separated by a distance $2d$, as shown in Fig. 21–20. Choosing cartesian coordinates as shown, find the potential at the origin O; by

(a) direct calculation of the potential,

(b) by the line integral of the field with the path along the OY-axis from ∞ to 0.

(c) Why not choose the OX-axis for the path?

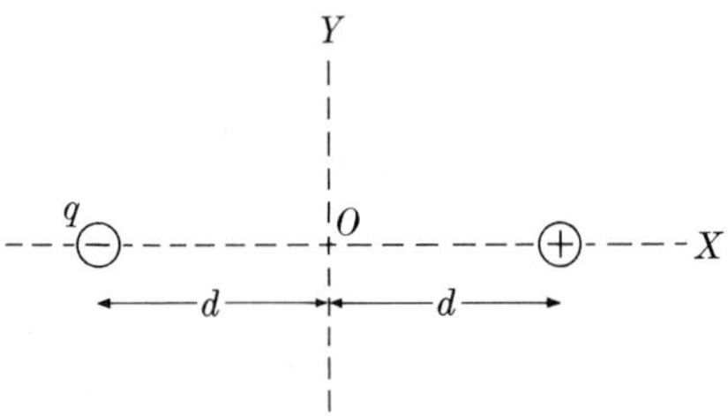

FIGURE 21–20

2. Equal charges of $-q$ are separated by $2d$. Using the same choice of axes as in Problem 1, repeat the calculations of Problem 1 for the present case.

3. Four charges of equal magnitudes q are located at the corners of a square of side d (Fig. 21–21).

(a) Calculate the potential difference between the center of the square C and the center of one side A.

(b) Repeat for the case in which all charges are positive.

(c) What is *the* potential at C in each case?

(d) Comment on the ease of using the line integral of the field to make the above calculations.

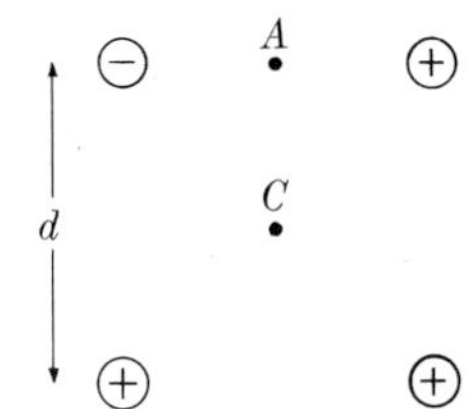

FIGURE 21–21

4. Find *the* potential at the center of a spherical shell of charge of radius R and uniform surface charge density σ

(a) by the method of direct calculation of the potential,

(b) by the method of the line integral of the field.

(c) Find the potential difference between any two points inside the shell.

5. Find the electric field intensity and the potential at the center of a thin ring of charge of radius R (Fig. 21–22). Write the results in terms of

(a) linear charge density, λ coul/m, along the ring,

(b) total charge q on the ring.

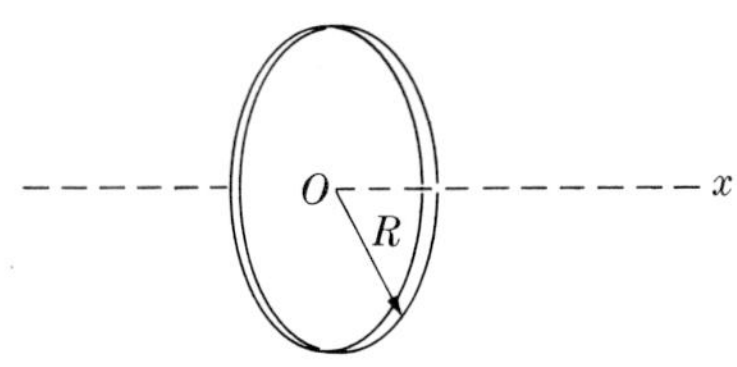

FIGURE 21–22

6. Find the field and potential as a function of x measured along the axis of the ring in Problem 5. Verify that $E = -dU/dx$ in case you found U and E independently.

7. Point charges $+5\,\mu$coul and $-10\,\mu$coul are separated by 10 cm. Find the surface on which $U = 0$.

8. Equal and opposite point charges $+q$ and $-q$ are separated by a distance $2d$, as shown in Fig. 21–23. Find the difference in potential between

(a) two points, y_2 and y_1, on the OY-axis.

(b) two points, x_2 and x_1, on the OX-axis, where x_1 is between the charges and x_2 is to the right of $-q$.

(c) Can part (a) be done using the line integral $\Delta U = -\int \mathbf{E} \cdot d\mathbf{s}$ with the path along the OY-axis?

(d) Can part (b) be done using $\Delta U = -\int \mathbf{E} \cdot d\mathbf{s}$ with the path along OX?

(e) Can it be done with other paths?

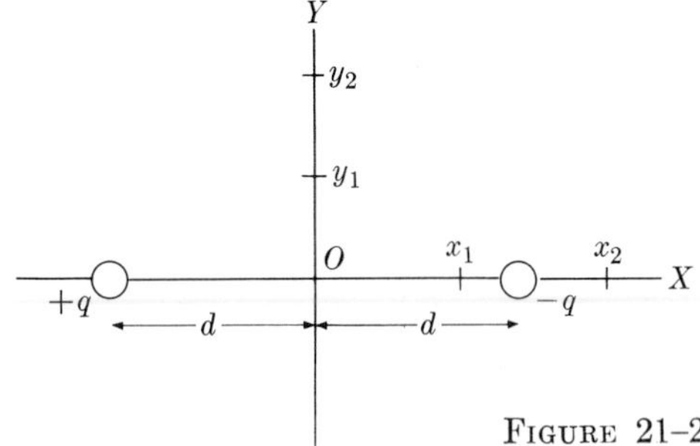

FIGURE 21–23

9. An electron starts from rest at the negative plate of a parallel plate "capacitor" and travels to the positive plate in vacuum between the plates.

(a) With what velocity will it strike the positive plate if the potential difference is 1 v, 500 v, and 500,000 v?

(b) In which cases must relativistic expressions be used?

10. An alpha-particle with kinetic energy 4 Mev $= 4 \times 10^6$ ev is directed straight toward a mercury nucleus (80 times electronic charge).

(a) Find the distance of closest approach to the nucleus.

(b) Compare with the nuclear radius $\simeq 10^{-14}$ m.

11. How much kinetic energy in joules does a 6-times ionized carbon atom have after being accelerated by a potential difference of 10^7 v?

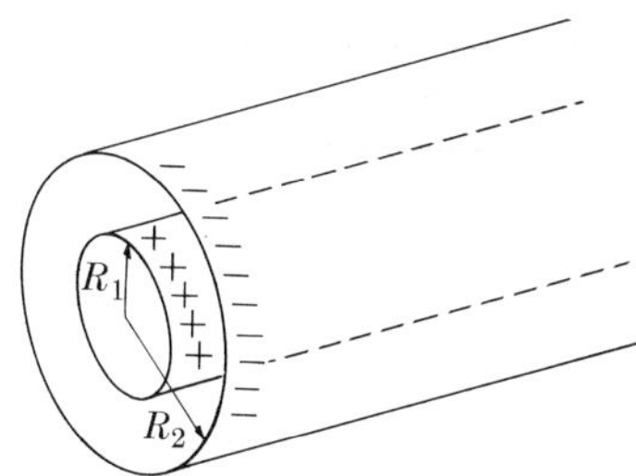

FIGURE 21–24

12. Concentric cylindrical surfaces are given equal and opposite charges. That is, in magnitude the charge per unit length λ of each surface is the same. The surface charge density on each surface is uniform (Fig. 21–24).

(a) Prove that the potential difference between the two surfaces is

$$\Delta U = \frac{\lambda}{2\pi\epsilon_0} \log_e \frac{R_2}{R_1}.$$

[*Hint:* Integrate $E_r\, dr$ from one surface to the other.]

(b) Can the "potential" of a charged, isolated, infinitely long cylinder be found by letting $R_2 = \infty$ in the expression for ΔU in part (a)?

(c) Can the "potential" of an infinitely long line charge be found by letting $R_1 = 0$ in the expression for ΔU in part (a)? What is the result?

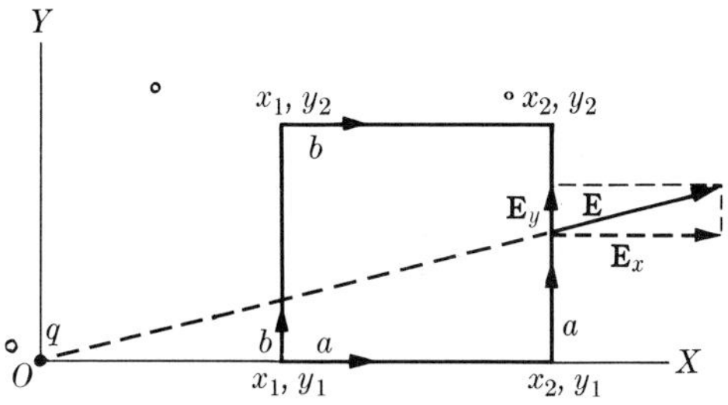

FIGURE 21–25

13. We wish to perform a line integral $\mathbf{E} \cdot d\mathbf{s}$ along two alternative paths in the inverse-square field of a point charge q_1 to show that the result is path-independent (Fig. 21–25). We start at $x_1 = 3$ m, $y_1 = 0$, and end at $x_2 = 9$, $y_2 = 2$.

(a) First, integrate along path a. In the first section of this path, we integrate $E_x\, dx (y = 0, E_y = 0)$ between the limits x_1 to x_2. Then we integrate $E_y\, dy$ from y_1 to y_2 along the line $x = x_2$. (Note that

$$E_y = \frac{q}{4\pi\epsilon_0} \frac{y}{(x_2^2 + y^2)^{3/2}}$$

along this line.)

(b) Second, integrate along the line $x = x_1$, then along the line $y = y_2$.

(c) Show that both results correspond to the expectation that

$$\int_1^2 \mathbf{E} \cdot d\mathbf{s} = \frac{q}{4\pi\epsilon_0}\left(\frac{1}{r_2} - \frac{1}{r_1}\right).$$

14. Concentric metallic cylinders have radii $R_1 = 100$ cm and $R_2 = 150$ cm, as shown in Fig. 21–26. The potential difference between them is 90 v. What is the electric field in n/coul near R_1? near R_2? at any R between R_1 and R_2? at any $R < R_1$ or $> R_2$?

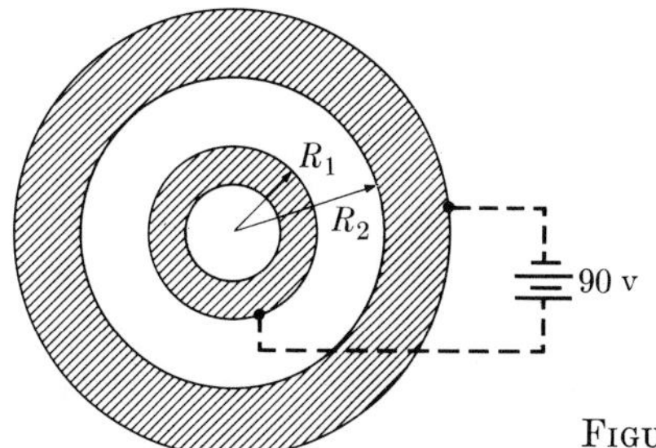

FIGURE 21–26

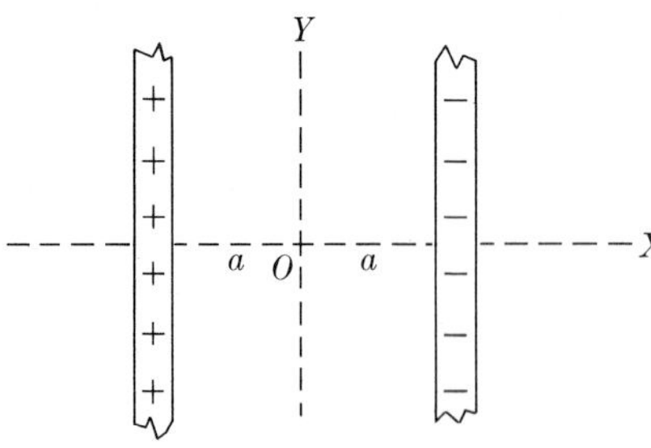

FIGURE 21–27

15. Two parallel infinite planes with equal and opposite surface charge densities σ are spaced $2a$ m apart. We choose axes as in Fig. 21–27.

(a) Letting $U = 0$ at $x = 0$, find an expression for U as a function of x, y, and z.

(b) Repeat for the choice $U = 0$ at $x = -a$.

(c) U can be chosen $= 0$ at $x = \infty$. Is this choice useful in the present example? Explain.

16. A line charge is placed parallel to an initially uncharged plane conductor. Using the method of images, find the field and potential.

17. The method of images for finding the effect of the introduction of a plane conductor is easier if the original charge distribution remains fixed in space than if it is on a finite conductor and therefore free to move. Explain. Draw the image charge distribution for an arbitrary fixed initial charge distribution near a very large plane conductor.

18. A small copper sphere of radius 0.1 mm is "charged" by placing a single electron on it. To what potential will the sphere be charged? What assumption have you made?

19. Can you find the capacitance per unit length of an infinitely long isolated cylindrical conductor of radius R? If the length is finite, could the capacitance be found?

20. Can you find the capacitance per unit area of an isolated infinite plane? If the area is finite, can the capacitance be found?

21. Find the mutual capacitance per unit length of a system of concentric cylinders of radii R_1 and R_2.

22. A spherical metal shell of radius R_2 is concentric with a smaller metallic sphere of radius R_1. A charge q is placed on the inner sphere and $-q$ on the inner surface of the shell. (As we have shown, the charge on the shell will reside on the inner surface.) This is a spherical capacitor.

(a) Show that the mutual capacitance of the system is

$$C = 4\pi\epsilon_0 \frac{R_1 R_2}{R_2 - R_1}.$$

(b) Using this expression, show that in the limit as $R_1 \to R_2$, the expression is the same as that for parallel plates,

$$C = \frac{\epsilon_0 A}{d}.$$

23. A charge distribution is placed on the surface of a *nonconductor*. Under what conditions will the surface be an equipotential?

24. Would it be useful to define capacitance of an isolated spherical nonconductor? Of any system of nonconductors? Explain how you would do it.

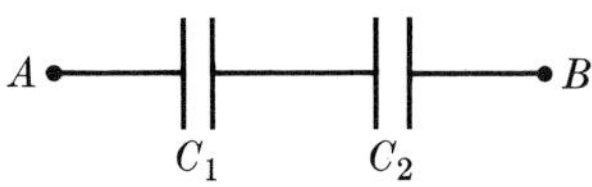

FIGURE 21–28

25. Two capacitors C_1 and C_2 are connected, as shown (series connection). The capacitances are not necessarily equal. They are initially uncharged. The terminals A and B are then connected to some device such as an electrostatic generator, which transfers charge from A to B until the potential difference between A and B becomes ΔU. Give an argument showing that the charge q stored on C_1 is the same as the charge stored on C_2 (Fig. 21–28). If the capacitance of the system is defined by $C = q/\Delta U$, prove that

$$\frac{1}{C} = \frac{1}{C_1} + \frac{1}{C_2}.$$

26. In Fig. 21–29 two capacitors C_1 and C_2 are connected (parallel connection). The capacitances

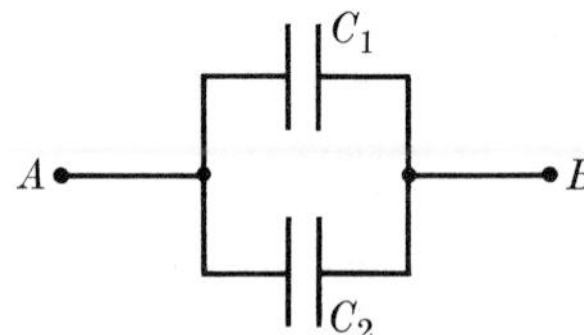

FIGURE 21–29

are not necessarily equal. They are initially uncharged. The terminals A and B are then connected to some device such as an electrostatic generator that transfers total charge q from A to B until the potential difference between A and B becomes ΔU. Give an argument that the total charge transferred is $q = q_1 + q_2$, where q_1 and q_2 are the charge transfers on the individual capacitors. If the capacitance of the combination is defined by $C = q/\Delta U$, prove that

$$C = C_1 + C_2.$$

27. How much energy is required to charge the 2-m radius sphere of a large Van de Graaff generator to 5 Mv?

28. The plates of a parallel plate capacitor of area A and separation d are charged $+$ and $-q$. Assume that d is much less than the plate's dimensions. Why is this assumption helpful?

(a) What is the ΔU between the plates?

(b) The plates are pulled apart until their separation is $3d$, the charge remaining unchanged. What is the new ΔU?

(c) Calculate the change in electrical energy from part (a) to part (b).

(d) Where does the increase in energy come from? Verify by direct calculation of the mechanical work.

29. A metal sphere of radius 1 m has an excess electric charge of 10^{-9} coul. It is connected by a conducting wire to an initially uncharged sphere of radius 30 cm, far away from the larger sphere. (The spheres and wire come to the same potential. Solve this problem by following the wrong but customary procedure of ignoring the capacitance of the wire.)

(a) What will be the equilibrium charge contained on each sphere after the connection is made?

(b) What is the energy of the single charged sphere? What is the energy of the system after the spheres are joined? If there is any loss, where has the energy gone?

(c) Show that charge is distributed on the electrically joined spheres of radius R_1 and R_2 such that

$$\frac{\sigma_1}{\sigma_2} = \frac{R_2}{R_1},$$

where σ is the surface density of electric charge.

(d) Show, therefore, that the surface value of the electric field at each sphere is such that

$$\frac{(E_1)\text{ surface}}{(E_2)\text{ surface}} = \frac{R_2}{R_1}.$$

(e) What is implied by the result in (*d*) for the case in which one of the spheres is a point (lightning rod principle)? What is the charge on the point sphere? What is the electric field immediately about the point sphere?

(f) Why was it specified that the spheres are far apart?

30. Three equal point charges, q coulombs each, are placed at the vertices of an equilateral triangle of sides d. Show that the electrostatic energy of the system is

$$W = \frac{3q^2}{4\pi\epsilon_0 d}.$$

Four equal charges d are placed at the corners of a square of sides d. What is the energy? Can you do this problem using the method of Section 21–8 and Eq. (21–27)? Explain.

31. Two capacitors are identical. One initially contains a charge q, the other is initially uncharged. The capacitors are now joined by conducting wires (Fig. 21–30).

(a) Prove that the stored energy in the joined capacitors is exactly half the energy originally stored in C. (Can you think of a mechanical analogy to this process?)

(b) Let C_1 be originally charged with q and C_2 originally uncharged. What is the energy loss if $C_1 = 2C_2$? If $C_1 = C_2/2$?

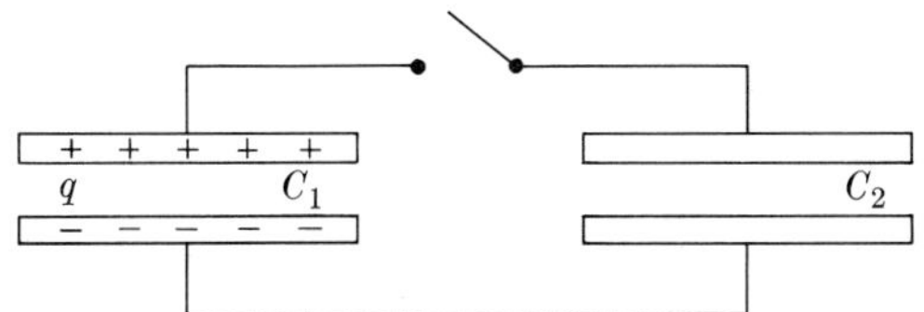

FIGURE 21–30

32. Two capacitors, C_1 and $C_2 = 3C_1$, are both charged to a potential difference ΔU_0. If the $+$ plate of one is connected to the $-$ plate of the other, what will be the final potential difference across each capacitor? What is the charge on each capacitor?

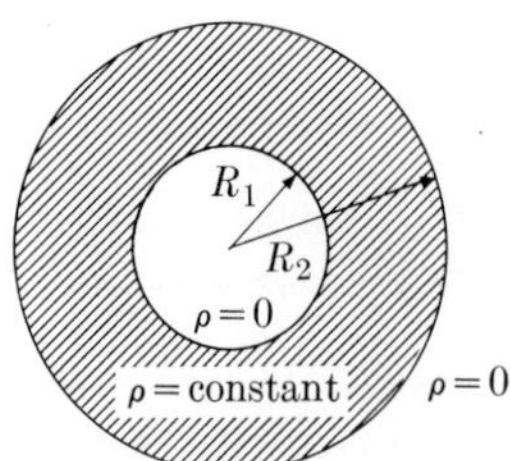

FIGURE 21–31

33. A uniformly charged hollow sphere of radii R_1 and R_2 has a volume charge density ρ (Fig. 21–31).

(a) Find the potential for all regions of space.
(b) What is the electrostatic energy of the system?
(c) Can you use Eq. (21–27) for part (b)?

34. Calculate the energy of an isolated charged spherical conductor by Eq. (21–27), and Eq. (21–38).

35. Derive the energy density expression of Eq. (21–41) by equating the electrostatic energy of a charged parallel plate capacitor to energy density times the volume between the plates. Why is it possible to consider all the energy as residing between the plates?

36. Calculate the energy stored in the field surrounding an isolated, charged spherical conductor. Compare the result with the answer to Problem 34.

37. Calculate the energy per unit length stored in the electric field surrounding an isolated charged wire of radius R_1 and infinite length

(a) out to a distance R_2,
(b) out to infinity.
(c) Compare with the energy per unit length of the charged wire.

38. Consider a parallel plate capacitor as in Fig. 21–32 with plates of area A and separation d. Assume that d is small compared with the dimensions of the plates.

(a) If the plates are given charges $+$ and $-q$, what is the potential difference between them?
(b) Compare the values of $\int \mathbf{E} \cdot d\mathbf{s}$ taken along paths a and b. What is the average value of the tangential component of E along path b if the path length is $8d$?

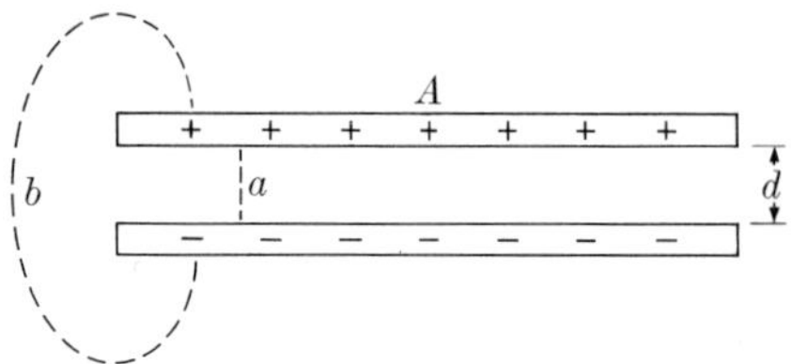

FIGURE 21–32

39. A large number n of electrons is assembled in the form of a uniform, thin spherical shell of charge of radius R. Let e be the electronic charge and m the electronic mass. If the force holding the electrons is suddenly released, the charge distribution will "explode" with spherical symmetry, due to self-repulsion. Find the velocity of the electrons when their separation is very large.

40. Find the cartesian components of the field in Example 3

(a) by differentiating the expression for potential,
(b) directly by using Coulomb's law.

22

Electric Current

22–1 INTRODUCTION

An introduction to dynamic electricity requires a set of definitions which describe the motion of electric charge. Electric charge in motion constitutes an electric current, which is defined as follows:

Establish an imaginary surface S in a region of space where charge is in motion (Fig. 22–1). The current flux through the surface S is defined as the amount of charge transported through the surface per unit of time. Calling the current flux (usually called simply the current) I, we define the concept of average current through the surface boundary as the amount of charge transported through the surface per unit of time. We have

$$I_{\text{av}} \equiv \frac{\Delta q}{\Delta t}\,\frac{\text{coulomb}}{\text{second}} = \frac{\Delta q}{\Delta t}\text{ ampere}, \qquad (22\text{–}1)$$

where the ampere unit of current is fundamental and the coulomb is the derived unit, ampere-second. The instantaneous current is the average current computed in the limit as $\Delta t \rightarrow 0$, or

$$I \equiv \frac{dq}{dt}\text{ amp.} \qquad (22\text{–}2)$$

The current I measures *net* charge transport through a surface. It is a scalar quantity. It is not a velocity. The charge can be obtained from the current by rewriting Eq. (22–2)

$$q = \int I\,dt. \qquad (22\text{–}3)$$

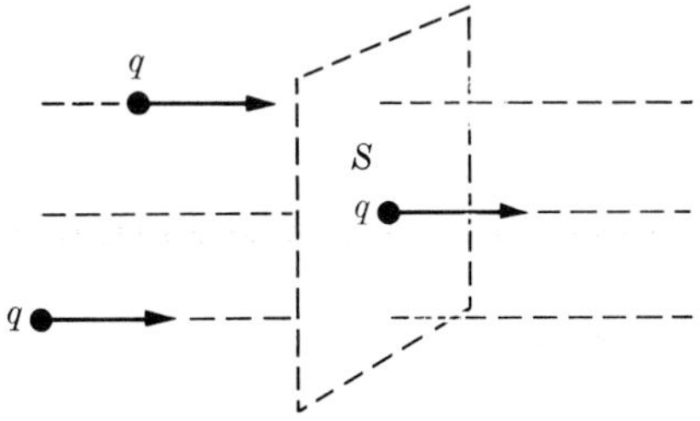

Fig. 22–1. The motion of charges q through an area S outlined by the dashed line.

In contrast with the *concept* of current, which is defined above in terms of the concept of charge, the *unit* of current is basic in the mks system and the charge unit is derived; that is, the ampere is fundamental and the coulomb is an ampere-second. The convention is to choose the direction of flow of positive charge as the direction (positive) of the current. Thus in metals the electron flow is opposite to I.

Volt is then defined as a joule per coulomb or basically as a joule per ampere-second. The definition of ampere must be left until the chapter on magnetic interactions.

Another physical quantity which measures charge transport is current density $\mathbf{J}$. This quantity represents the rate of charge transport through a *unit* surface area, placed *normal* to the direction of flow. It *is* a vector quantity. The unit of current density is the ampere per square meter. The direction of $\mathbf{J}$ is the local direction of the flow of electric charge. A relationship between I and $\mathbf{J}$ will be defined during an inspection of the detailed mechanism of charge transport, which follows.

We consider a region in space that contains charges in motion. Generally, the free charges contained in a metallic conductor are in rapid thermal, chaotic motion. This thermal motion does not constitute a current, since, in random motion, there will be as many charges in motion in any one direction as there are in the opposite direction. Therefore, this random motion is ignored for present purposes. A *drift* motion of a

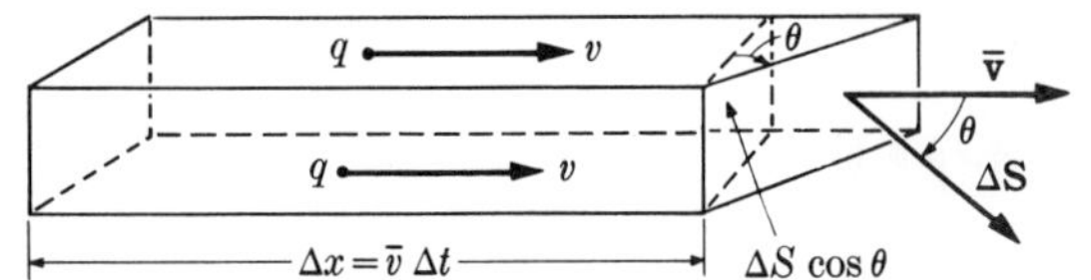

FIG. 22-2. Illustration of the quantities involved in specifying the current in terms of the motion of charges. The average velocity is $\bar{v}$. The parallelepiped has length $\Delta x = \bar{v}\,\Delta t$ and an end face of area ΔS, which is at an angle θ with $\bar{v}$.

charge cloud does, however, constitute a current. Not all charges in a local region of space will have the same velocity; that is, there is a velocity distribution. We may ascribe to the charges in a given region an *average drift velocity* $\mathbf{v}$. Now let us construct a small element of area ΔS in the region of the charge cloud and compute the current through ΔS. In general, the area ΔS can be oriented in any direction relative to the average charge velocity. The number of charges per unit volume, will be called n. The amount of charge which passes through ΔS in the time Δt is contained in a volume ΔV, a parallelepiped whose base is ΔS and whose length, parallel to the charge velocity, is now to be found (Fig. 22-2). If we consider that the passage of charge takes place in a time Δt, all the charges as far behind ΔS as a distance Δx will have time to advance to ΔS and penetrate the area, if $\Delta x = \bar{v}\,\Delta t$. Therefore, $\bar{v}\,\Delta t$ is the length of the volume element ΔV. Then, the volume element equals the projected base area $\Delta S \cos\theta$ times Δx, that is,

$$\Delta V = \Delta x\,\Delta S \cos\theta = \bar{v}\,\Delta t\,\Delta S \cos\theta. \qquad (22\text{-}4)$$

Since expression (22-4) is of the form of the scalar product of $\mathbf{v}$ and $\Delta\mathbf{S}$, we write

$$\Delta V = \Delta t\,\mathbf{v}\cdot\Delta\mathbf{S}. \qquad (22\text{-}5)$$

Since the amount of charge contained in ΔV is the number of charged particles per unit volume n times the charge on each particle e times the size of the volume, we have

$$\Delta q = \rho\,\Delta V = ne\,\Delta V, \qquad (22\text{-}6)$$

and using our expression (22-4) for ΔV we have

$$\Delta q = ne\,\Delta t\,\mathbf{v}\cdot\Delta\mathbf{S}. \qquad (22\text{-}7)$$

We designate the current through ΔS as ΔI, and obtain

$$\Delta I = \frac{\Delta q}{\Delta t} = ne\,\mathbf{v}\cdot\Delta\mathbf{S}, \qquad (22\text{-}8)$$

or for an infinitesimal area $d\mathbf{S}$, we have

$$dI = ne\,\mathbf{v}\cdot d\mathbf{S}. \qquad (22\text{-}9)$$

The product $ne\,\mathbf{v}$ appearing in Eq. (22-9) is the current density, i.e.,

$$\mathbf{J} = ne\,\mathbf{v}\,\frac{\text{amp}}{\text{m}^2}, \qquad (22\text{-}10)$$

if current density is defined by

$$dI = \mathbf{J}\cdot d\mathbf{S}. \qquad (22\text{-}11)$$

If we wish to compute the current through a finite surface, then dI must be integrated over the whole surface, according to

$$I = \iint \mathbf{J}\cdot d\mathbf{S}. \qquad (22\text{-}12)$$

If charges of both signs are in motion, as in a neutral plasma, Eq. (22-10) becomes

$$\mathbf{J} = n_+e_+\mathbf{v}_+ - n_-e_-\mathbf{v}_-. \qquad (22\text{-}13)$$

We have let e be the magnitude of the electronic charge and have followed the usual convention that positive current is in the direction of motion of plus charge.

22-2 MEASUREMENT OF ELECTRIC CURRENT

In the preceding section, the concept and definition of current have been developed. We now turn to some general ideas on the methods for measuring current. When a current flows through a conductor, an ionized gas, or a chemical cell, we observe physical effects that can be used as a means for measuring current. For example, a current in a wire generates heat, which may result in a temperature rise and a consequent expansion of the conductor. This expansion can be used as a measure of the current. Another example, the force between conductors that are carrying currents, will be treated in detail in a later chapter. It will be discussed only in general terms here.

Originally, the standard unit of current in the practical system of units (the international ampere) was defined in terms of the rate of deposition of material on a plate in a chemical cell, in particular, the rate of deposition of silver from silver nitrate solution. Since the mass of silver deposited in a given time is a measure of the charge transport within the same time interval, the international ampere is closely related to the concept of current as the rate of flow of charge. However, it has the disadvantage of not being fundamentally related to the mks system. Therefore, we turn to the usual present-day choice for the standard of current.

The standard for definition of the ampere to be associated with the mks system is based on the results of a measurement of the force by one conductor carrying a current on a second conductor also carrying a current. Consequently, the basic determination of current in this system requires the measurement of a force between current-carrying conductors and the calculation of a constant that depends on the geometry of the conductors and their relative positions. The instrument operating on the above principle is called a *current balance.*

Most laboratory and commercial instruments (ammeters) for measuring current in fact measure the force between elements that carry current. In some cases both of the elements are wires, but in most cases one of the elements is a magnetic material such as iron. The "current" in the latter case is due to the additive currents on the atomic scale that occur in iron and other materials of a similar nature used for permanent magnets. The current to be measured passes through a coil of wire (that is usually pivoted) near the magnet. Since the coil is pivoted, the quantity used as a measure of the current is torque rather than force. In some ammeters the magnet is the moving element. In fact, one of the first methods of detecting currents was the torque on a magnet (compass needle) placed near a conductor. Since the calculation of the geometrical factor would be very laborious for most ammeters, the calibration is done by comparison with standard meters that are in turn calibrated by comparison with a current balance.

22–3 AN ELEMENTARY ELECTRIC CIRCUIT

With this set of definitions for the description of electric current, we proceed to a discussion of the way electric currents are obtained. For the purpose of explanation, consider the transport of charge in metallic conductors. First, it must be said that the rules of electrostatics for metallic conductors are to be abandoned for any conductor in which appreciable current is flowing. Since we are familiar with the capacitor (from our study of electrostatics), it will be used as the energy source in the first part of the discussion.

Consider the case in which the plates of a charged mutual capacitor are joined by a conducting wire (Fig. 22–3):

(a) The potentials at the opposite ends of the wire have the different values, U_- and U_+, of the

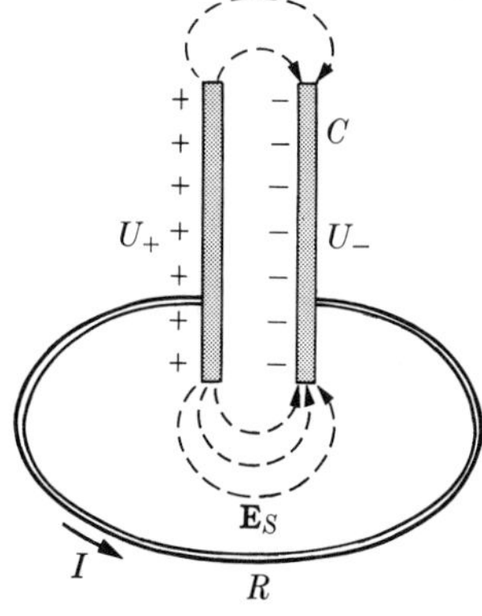

FIG. 22–3. Charge is caused to flow through a conductor R by connecting it to the plates of a charged capacitor C. Some of the lines of the electrostatic field E_S are shown.

two plates. The potential within the wire is therefore not constant, although each plate can itself be approximately an equipotential.

(b) Charge flows through the wire from one plate to the other. Since charge is in motion, the electric field within the wire is not zero, in fact, it cannot be zero if there is any resistance to the flow of charge. Having relaxed the special condition of electrostatics that all conductors are equipotentials, we proceed to an observation of new rules which pertain to the dynamic, rather than the static, electrical system.

It can be found at once that the *rate of discharge* of the condenser and the resultant rate of reduction of the potential difference between the plates depend markedly on the choice of wire. For some choices the discharge may assume explosive proportions. Other choices of wire lead to a discharge which may require minutes or hours, and leisurely experiments may be conducted. In every case, heat is developed in the connecting wire. Therefore some of the physical factors that are related to the rate of discharge are the properties of the wire, the generation of heat, and the potential difference of the plates.

22-4 OHM'S LAW

We now turn to the question of finding the electrical properties of a given wire. For the purpose of quantitative study, the capacitor of Fig. 22-3 is to be charged with a measured amount of charge q. For example, the plates are first discharged and the wire is disconnected. The plates can then be connected to some charging device B in series with a calibrated ammeter A, as in Fig. 22-4. The ammeter reads the instantaneous charging current I_c. The total charge on the plates q_0 can then be obtained from

$$q_0 = \int I_c \, dt \text{ (coulombs).} \qquad (22\text{-}14)$$

The charged capacitor is next connected to the wire whose electrical properties are in question. The ammeter A is again part of the circuit (Fig. 22-5). When the switch is closed, the experimental observation for most conductors is that the initial value of the current I is directly proportional to the initial charge q_0 on the capacitor. Furthermore, the current at any instant of time is found to be directly proportional to the charge on the capacitor at that instant of time; that is,

$$I = k\,(q_0 - \int_0^t I\,dt) = kq. \qquad (22\text{-}15)$$

The general conclusion is that the current for a particular wire is directly proportional to the charge on the capacitor. Since the capacitance is constant, the potential difference ΔU between plates of the capacitor is proportional to the charge

$$\Delta U = \frac{q}{C}, \qquad (22\text{-}16)$$

and therefore the experimental result can be written

$$I = k'\,\Delta U. \qquad (22\text{-}17)$$

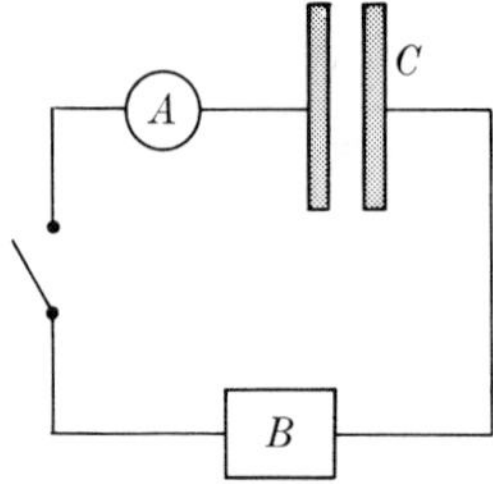

Fig. 22-4. A capacitor C is charged by connecting it to a battery B. The instantaneous value of the current is read with the meter A. The charge on the capacitor is obtained by integrating the current readings.

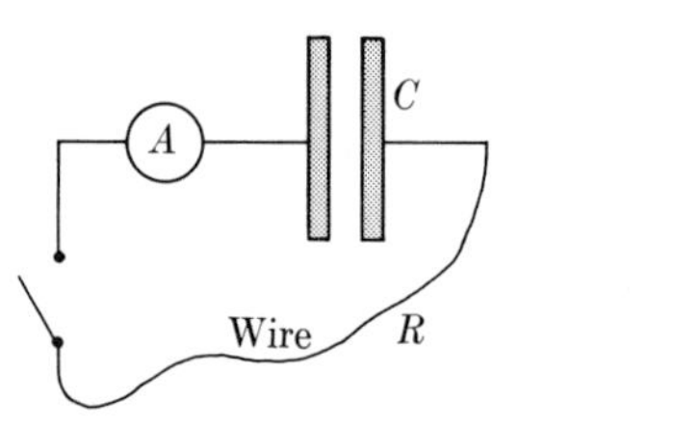

Fig. 22-5. The capacitor of Fig. 22-4 is discharged through the wire R by closing the switch. The instantaneous value of the current is read by the ammeter A.

The constant of proportionality in Eq. (22–17) is the conductance of the wire, or the reciprocal of the constant is the resistance R of the wire. In terms of R, we can rewrite Eq. (22–17) in the form (omitting the Δ)

$$U = IR, \tag{22–18}$$

which is called *Ohm's law.* The resistance R is defined from Ohm's law as

$$R \equiv \frac{U}{I}\cdot \tag{22–19}$$

It is evident from the above that Ohm's law is the result of an experimental observation of the relationship between the current through a conductor and the potential difference between the ends of the conductor. It is a good approximation if the temperature of the conductor is kept constant and other conditions are met.

The potential difference U in Eq. (22–18) can be due to causes other than a charged capacitor. For example, the potential difference can be produced by electrochemical or electromechanical effects, among others. These will be discussed later.

In the present case, we now inquire a little further into the meaning of potential difference. The definition of potential difference ΔU is

$$\Delta U = -\int \mathbf{E}_S \cdot d\mathbf{s}, \tag{22–20}$$

where E_S is the electric field intensity. We are still letting E_S represent the field due to the charge distribution. For example, the charge on the capacitor plates in Fig. 22–3 gives rise to an external field, part of which is shown. Thus, we can take the integral $-\int \mathbf{E}_S \cdot d\mathbf{s}$ along an external path, and the result will be

$$\Delta U = U_- - U_+ = -\int \mathbf{E}_S \cdot d\mathbf{s} \tag{22–21}$$

when we go from the positive to the negative plate. Since E_S is in general, in the direction of ds, the integral $\int \mathbf{E}_S \cdot d\mathbf{s}$ is positive, with the result that $U_+ - U_-$ is a positive quantity, as expected. Strictly speaking, the U in Ohm's law, therefore, is $U_+ - U_-$; that is, U is the potential drop in the direction of the current,

$$U_+ - U_- = IR. \tag{22–22}$$

We now ask about other forces acting on the charges that constitute the current in the wire. As we shall see later in a discussion of energy, it is observed that the rate of loss of energy by the capacitor is just equal to the rate of production of heat by the flow of current in the wire. Since all the energy is thereby accounted for, the charges do *not* have a net gain in kinetic energy during their passage through the wire. Therefore, we must conclude that the average velocity of the charges constituting the current is constant. The average resultant force on a charge must, therefore, be zero. The force that opposes the force due to the electric field is the average force due to collisions with the atoms of the wire. If we designate the latter by E_R, for the average force per unit of charge, we have $E_R = -E_S$ within the wire. Consequently, we can write

$$U_+ - U_- = \int \mathbf{E}_S \cdot d\mathbf{s} = -\int \mathbf{E}_R \cdot d\mathbf{s} = IR, \tag{22–23}$$

where the integrals are taken from the positive to the negative plate.

The unit of R is the *ohm*, which is derived from the ampere as follows. From Eq. (22–19), we see that ohm = volt/ampere. But the volt is defined from $U = W/q$, giving volt = joule/coulomb. Finally, the coulomb is basically the ampere-second, and therefore

$$\text{ohm} = \frac{\text{joule}}{(\text{ampere})^2\ \text{second}} = \frac{\text{kg m}}{(\text{amp})^2\ (\text{sec})^3}\cdot$$

The above discussion of units illustrates the fact that a complete set of basic units for electrical quantities is the meter-kilogram-second-ampere (mksa) system.

The *resistance* is found to depend on the material, shape, and temperature of the wire. In particular, the geometric dependence is that R is directly proportional to the length and inversely proportional to the cross-sectional area of a uniform wire. A summary of the geometric and material dependences is written

$$R = \rho \frac{l}{S} \text{ ohms}, \tag{22-24}$$

where the coefficient of proportionality ρ is called the *resistivity* of the wire. It is a specific property of the material of which the wire is made. The reciprocal of resistivity is called the conductivity of the material,

$$\sigma = \frac{1}{\rho}. \tag{22-25}$$

In terms of the specific electrical properties of the conducting wire, Ohm's law for the wire can be written (Eq. 22-24)

$$U = I\rho \frac{l}{S}. \tag{22-26}$$

The above formulation of Ohm's law is applicable to wires or other elements that have uniform cross section and uniform resistivity. In cases of conductors with properties that vary from place to place within the conductor, a point formulation of Ohm's law is useful. We consider a small volume of length ds in the direction of the local current and base of area dS normal to the flow. Then the resistance of this element is $\rho\, ds/dS$. Furthermore the potential difference between its ends is $dU = E\, ds$ and the current flow is $dI = J\, dS$. Thus, Ohm's law for this small volume, $dU = R\, dI$, becomes

$$E\, ds = \left(\frac{\rho\, ds}{dS}\right) J\, dS,$$

or simply

$$\mathbf{E} = \rho \mathbf{J}. \tag{22-27}$$

This form of Ohm's law is necessary in those problems in which the values of E and ρ (and therefore J) vary from point to point.

22-5 PRODUCTION OF POTENTIAL DIFFERENCES

We have already considered a simple circuit in which the potential difference was attributable to separated charges on a capacitor. This enabled us to extend our knowledge from electrostatics directly to the dynamics of charge flow. The question of how we obtained the charged capacitor, that is, where the energy came from, was ignored. The energy could have come directly from mechanical work, as in the simple electrostatic generators mentioned in the previous chapter, but such devices are neither economical nor convenient except in special cases such as the use of the Van de Graaff machine to produce high voltage at low power.

The most frequently employed devices for producing potential differences depend on magnetic forces (generators) or on chemical effects (batteries). The discussion of the former will be left for a later chapter. The latter will be discussed in general terminology at this time.

It is presumed here that the reader is acquainted with the systematics of electrochemistry. The purpose of this brief review is to connect electrochemical action with the physical laws of electricity.

Let a metallic object, called an electrode, be immersed in an acid or salt solution. The solution may have the power of dissolving neutral atoms of the metal and forcing them into solution in ionic form. For every positive ionic particle dissolved, a number of electrons equal to the valence of the ions is left on the pole. The solution is positively charged, the electrode negatively charged. The electrostatic forces prevent a continuation of the process. The electrode develops an electrostatic attraction for the positive ions, and the solution develops a repulsion for them. Equilibrium is achieved when the chemical force and the electrostatic force are balanced. Actually, dissolution continues, but as many particles are deposited back onto the electrode as leave the electrode in the steady state. If different metals are used, it is found that the chemical affinity of the solution for the metallic ions depends on the metallic element. Thus two different metals immersed in the same solution come to equilibrium at different electric potentials relative to the solution. One electrode is more positively (or negatively) charged than the other. We speak of the electrodes as poles. The terms positive pole and negative pole are used in reference to the potential difference between the poles and not to an absolute potential of any element, which is actually undefined in the process. For the sake of easy symbolism we label one pole + and the other −.

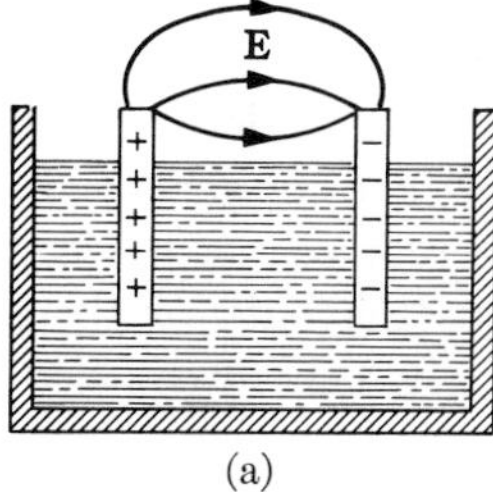

(a)

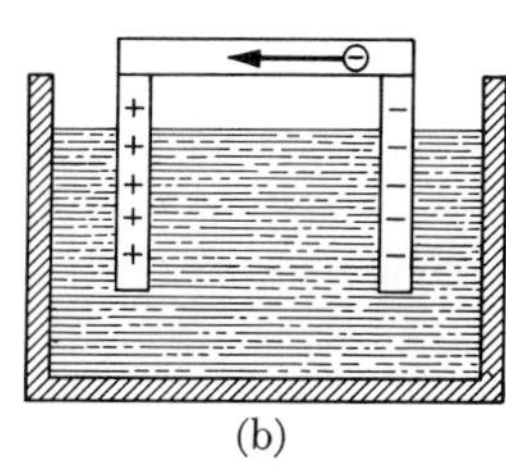

(b)

FIG. 22–6. (a) A portion of the external field between the plates of a battery cell. (b) Flow of electrons when the plates of the battery cell are joined by a conductor.

Because of the difference in potential of the poles, there will certainly be an electrostatic field in the space between the poles outside the liquid (Fig. 22–6a). When the poles are joined by a conductor, as in Fig. 22–6(b), free charges (electrons) will move through the conductor. This situation is identical with the transient stage discussed in Section 22–3 in which the charged plates of the capacitor provided the difference in potential. There is, however, an important difference: In our present example, the electrons that leave the negative pole can be completely replaced by more electrons, if positive ions from the negative pole go into solution at the same rate as the electrons flow in the conductor. Also as electrons arrive at the positive terminal via the external conductor, this terminal may attract more positive ions for deposit, thereby keeping the charge constant at that pole. The net action within the cell can be the "plating" of the element which makes up the −pole onto the +pole, and this process must ultimately end in the destruction of the cell. However, the destruction may require hours and the current level may be several amperes. Thus we are at leisure to conduct experiments with sustained electric currents in metals—a leisure which does not pertain to the discharge currents from capacitors. The conventional symbol for a battery in a circuit will be illustrated in the next figure.

22–6 POTENTIAL DIFFERENCE IN ELECTRIC CIRCUITS

It is the purpose of this section to explore the relationships between electrostatic theory and dynamic electrical systems. We have already noted that the electrostatic conditions for metals —uniform potential and zero electric field within the metal—must be abandoned for current-carrying conductors in dynamic systems. We assert at the outset that two basic definitions are preserved:

1. The electric field intensity is still defined as the force per unit of positive test charge,

$$\mathbf{F} = \mathbf{E}q. \tag{22–28}$$

2. The electric potential difference is still defined as the negative of the work done by the electric field per unit of positive test charge when the test charge is transported from one point in the field to another. In differential form, we have

$$dU = \frac{-dW}{q}. \tag{22–29}$$

Since $dW = \mathbf{F} \cdot d\mathbf{s}$ or $dW = +q\mathbf{E} \cdot d\mathbf{s}$, we have the same differential relationship between potential and field as in electrostatics, namely,

$$\text{đ}U = -\mathbf{E} \cdot d\mathbf{s}. \tag{22–30}$$

One reservation is made, and it is displayed by the line drawn through the d, which denotes the differential of potential. In electrostatics $\text{đ}U$ is an "exact differential": Its integral is independent of path in the electrostatic field. Thus it was proved that the line integral of $\mathbf{E} \cdot d\mathbf{s}$ about a closed path in the electrostatic field is zero, i.e.,

$$\oint \mathbf{E} \cdot d\mathbf{s} = 0.$$

Therefore, no energy is acquired or lost by a test particle, due to electrostatic forces, when it is carried about a closed path in an electrostatic field.

In the case of a continuous flow of charge in circuits, the situation can be the same as in electrostatic fields only if the circuit element is a superconductor. With superconducting materials, there is no transfer of energy to the conductor (that is, no heating effect), and therefore no energy need be supplied to the charges in order to maintain the current flow. But in the case of other types of circuit elements, there are sinks for electrical energy such as the heating of a wire, chemical changes, or mechanical work. In such circuits there must therefore be sources of electrical energy, sources that do work on the charges as the charges move in a closed path around the circuit. As an example, in the electrostatic generator this work is done mechanically in transporting the charge from one terminal of the machine to the other. We now turn to the case of the voltaic cell, in which chemical energy is transformed into electrical energy. The discussion will first be made in the terminology of forces.

For the purpose of distinction, we separate the total electric field into two kinds. Both are defined as force per unit charge. One kind will be called E_s to denote its electrostatic character. The source of the electrostatic field is an electric charge distribution $\rho(x, y, z)$ in space, from which the field is found in principle by the integral

$$\mathbf{E}_s = \frac{1}{4\pi\epsilon_0} \int \frac{\mathbf{r}}{r^3} \rho \, dV,$$

as described in Chapter 20. We have already shown that for this type of field, the integral of $\mathbf{E} \cdot d\mathbf{s}$ about a closed path is zero, or, the equivalent, that the integral between two points is independent of path. Next, all electric fields other than E_s are denoted E_m. The sources of these fields may be, to choose important examples, chemical or magnetic sources. The total electric field is the sum of the two kinds,

$$\mathbf{E} = \mathbf{E}_s + \mathbf{E}_m. \tag{22–31}$$

The electric field component $\mathbf{E}_m$ within a battery is, in fact, confined quite locally to the regions between the poles and solution. Rather than treat the exact case, we propose to consider a battery of many poles so smoothly distributed that the chemical field may be considered to be smooth, distributed, and, in fact, uniform. In this idealized description we represent a battery as in Fig. 22–7. Internal to the battery there must be a chemical field $\mathbf{E}_m$ which forces electrons to the negative pole, causing separation of plus and minus charges. As the electric charge is built up on the end poles, an electrostatic field $\mathbf{E}_s$ is created in the opposite direction, directed from plus to minus.

Fig. 22–7. An idealized cell pictured as being composed of an infinite series of infinitely thin cells, each contributing an infinitesimal amount to the electrochemical effect.

Open circuit. There can be no current before an external connection is made between the poles. At the instant the uncharged electrodes are immersed in the solution, only the field $\mathbf{E}_m$ will exist. Charges will move through the conducting solution because of the presence of $\mathbf{E}_m$. As the charge accumulates on the plates, the field $\mathbf{E}_s$ increases until, at equilibrium, these two fields must be exactly equal and opposite at every point within the battery. If the fields were not balanced, charge would continue to drift. Therefore, when drift has ceased

$$\mathbf{E}_m + \mathbf{E}_s = 0 \tag{22–32}$$

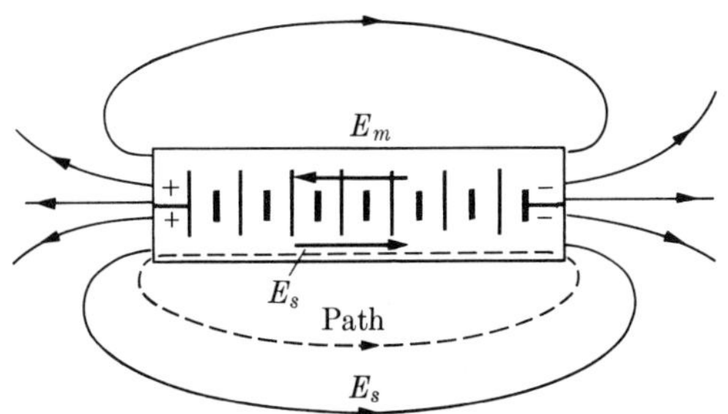

FIG. 22–8. Fields internal and external to the idealized battery cell. A path of integration is shown by the dashed line.

inside the battery. Consequently, no work is required to transport a test charge from one pole to another along a path within the battery.

Outside the battery there is no field component $\mathbf{E}_m$ since there are no chemicals. Thus the electric field outside is just the field $\mathbf{E}_s$ generated by the electrostatic charge distribution on the poles (Fig. 22–8). The lines of force originate on the plus charges and terminate on the minus charges, as shown. Outside the battery, the line integral of $\mathbf{E}_s \cdot d\mathbf{s}$ between any two points will be independent of path, as we have seen in the chapter on electrostatics. Therefore, it is useful to define the quantity, potential difference, as before. Thus, we shall define ΔU_T, the potential difference between the terminals, as the line integral of $\mathbf{E} \cdot d\mathbf{s}$ from the positive to the negative pole. Since this integral is the negative of the potential difference, we have

$$\int_+^- \mathbf{E}_{\text{ext}} \cdot d\mathbf{s} = -(U_- - U_+) = U_+ - U_- = \Delta U_T, \qquad (22\text{–}33)$$

where the path is from the positive to the negative pole. The terminal potential difference ΔU_T is defined in such a way that it is positive in the case of an open circuit condition of a battery.

Now we consider a closed path of integration that passes through the poles, but with one portion outside the battery and the other portion inside the battery. The direction of the path of integration will be such that $d\mathbf{s}$ is in the general direction of $\mathbf{E}$ outside the battery and opposite to $\mathbf{E}_s$ inside the battery. We now consider the line integral of the *total* field along the closed path,

$$\oint \mathbf{E} \cdot d\mathbf{s} = \oint (\mathbf{E}_s + \mathbf{E}_m) \cdot d\mathbf{s} = \int_{\text{ext}} \mathbf{E}_s \cdot d\mathbf{s} - \int_{\text{int}} \mathbf{E}_s \cdot d\mathbf{s} + \int_{\text{int}} \mathbf{E}_m \cdot d\mathbf{s}. \qquad (22\text{–}34)$$

In electrostatics it was shown that the integral $\mathbf{E} \cdot d\mathbf{s}$ around a closed path in an electrostatic field is zero. Therefore two terms in (22–34) cancel, that is

$$\int_{\text{ext}} \mathbf{E}_s \cdot d\mathbf{s} - \int_{\text{int}} \mathbf{E}_s \cdot d\mathbf{s} = 0, \qquad (22\text{–}35)$$

and consequently the entire integral of Eq. (22–34) reduces to the contribution of $\mathbf{E}_m \cdot d\mathbf{s}$ inside the battery. We have

$$\oint \mathbf{E} \cdot d\mathbf{s} = \int_{\text{int}} \mathbf{E}_m \cdot d\mathbf{s} \equiv \mathcal{E}, \qquad (22\text{–}36)$$

where $\mathcal{E}$ is the electromotive force (emf) of the battery. The emf represents work per unit of charge and is therefore measured in volts, the unit of potential difference.

The potential difference has been defined as the negative of the work on a positive test charge (per unit of charge) done by the electric field when the charge moves from one point to another; that is

$$\Delta U = U_2 - U_1 = -\int_1^2 \mathbf{E} \cdot d\mathbf{s}. \qquad (22\text{–}37)$$

It should be pointed out that this is equivalent to the work done by an external agent per unit of charge on a positive test charge as the test charge is moved from one point to the other *with no net change in velocity*. Using the latter way for describing potential difference, we could define the potential difference between the poles of a battery in terms of the work by an "external" agent on a positive test charge as the test charge moves from the negative to the positive pole within the battery, keeping the velocity constant. The "external" agent in this case would be the electrochemical effect. With open-circuit conditions, the test charge experiences no net force while moving through the battery because E_m and E_s are balanced, as we have seen. Therefore, the test charge will move at constant velocity and the work done by the electrochemical agent is just the increase in potential between the negative and positive poles.

If we now consider an external path from the positive pole returning to the negative pole, we find that the test charge would accelerate and therefore gain kinetic energy unless some agent holds back on the charge. Work is done *on* the agent that holds back on the charge to maintain constant velocity. Consequently, there is a drop in potential along the external path from the positive to the negative pole. Graphs are given in Section 22-8 that show the potential as a function of position in various circuits. If the test charge were permitted to follow the above external path with no force of constraint by an external agent, it would gain kinetic energy continuously until reaching the negative pole. It would then strike the negative pole and come to rest, dissipating its kinetic energy in heat and other forms of energy.

Closed circuit. When current is drawn from the battery, for example, by connecting a wire between the terminals, charge must flow inside the battery as well as in the wire (continuity of current). When charges flow through the battery, they collide with molecules of the solution and therefore transfer energy to the solution, that is, raise the temperature of the solution. The effect on the charges that constitute the current can be described by saying that the molecules of the solution exert an average force on the moving charges opposite in direction to their motion. The average force per unit of charge due to collisions can be expressed as an equivalent field E_R. Since the average velocity of the charges does not change during their passage through the battery, the resultant force per unit of charge is zero within the battery, and we have $-E_m = E_s + E_R$ or $|E_m| > |E_s|$ inside the battery. It is unlikely that there is a chemical process in which E_m increases when current flows and therefore we assume that E_s decreases. The decrease in E_s can come only from a decrease in the net charge on the terminals. Since E_s both inside and outside the battery is directly proportional to the charge on the terminals, Eq. (22-35) still holds. The emf remains unchanged (if we assume that the chemical emf is independent of current).

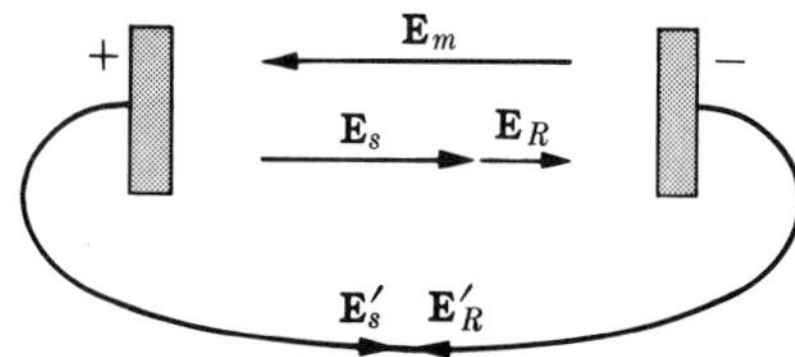

FIG. 22-9. Fields in an idealized battery cell and its external connecting wire.

We now consider the line integrals of E when current is flowing. If we again take the integral around a closed path, with one branch inside and the other outside the battery, we see that inside the battery there are three contributions to the force per unit charge, and in Section 22-4 we saw that there are two forces on the charges moving through the external wire. The relationships among the forces are shown schematically in Fig. 22-9. The value of the line integral around the complete path, when the path is taken through the circuit elements, will be zero in the case of the closed circuit, since the resultant force on a charge is zero everywhere. The integral is

$$\int_{-}^{+} (E_m - E_s - E_R)\, ds + \int_{+}^{-} (E'_s - E'_R)\, ds = 0, \qquad (22\text{-}38)$$

where the primes refer to points in the external circuit. When the terms are rearranged, we have

$$\int_{-}^{+} E_m\,ds - \int_{-}^{+} E_R\,ds - \int_{+}^{-} E'_R\,ds - \int_{-}^{+} E_s\,ds + \int_{+}^{-} E'_s\,ds = 0. \tag{22–39}$$

The last two terms combined are zero (Eq. 22–35). The second and third terms can be expressed as resistances of the solution R_i and of the wire R_e (Eq. 22–23), and the first term is $\mathcal{E}$, the emf (Eq. 22–36). The final result is, therefore,

$$\mathcal{E} = IR_i + IR_e = I(R_i - R_e), \tag{22–40}$$

which is a basic equation for a closed circuit.

The term IR_e is equal to the terminal potential difference ΔU_T, as we see from Eq. (22–23). Consequently, Eq. (22–40) can be written

$$\mathcal{E} = \Delta U_T + IR_i, \tag{22–41}$$

or

$$\Delta U_T = \mathcal{E} - IR_i. \tag{22–42}$$

It should be noted that the signs correspond to the case in which the battery is "supplying" current to the external circuit; that is, the current inside the battery is from the negative to the positive pole.

If we now think of the changes in potential in terms of work done by an "external" agent per unit of positive test charge as the test charge is moved around the circuit, we have the following result: As the test charge moves from the negative to the positive pole inside the battery, work is done by the electrochemical agents in amount $\mathcal{E}$, just as in the open-circuit case. However, as mentioned earlier, E_s is now less than E_m, since current is flowing. Consequently, we might expect the test charge to be accelerated. In fact, it *is* accelerated, but it has only a very short mean free path before it collides with an atom of the solution, thus losing energy. Due to collisions, the test charge drifts from the negative to the positive pole without an overall gain in kinetic energy. The charge does work on the solution, the work manifesting itself as heating of the solution in amount I_iR_i per unit charge. Thus, the *net* work per unit of charge done by external agents on the test charge is $\mathcal{E} - I_iR_i$, which is, therefore, the potential difference ΔU_T between the poles (Eq. 22–42).

Now consider an external path from the positive to the negative pole. If the circuit contains only electrical resistance, the test charge collides with atoms in the resisting medium and drifts with no overall increase in velocity. The charge transfers energy IR to the medium, and hence the potential difference (decrease) is just IR. If the external circuit contains batteries that are being charged, electroplating cells, electric motors, or other devices, part of the work done by the passage of the test charge will result in increases of chemical energy, mechanical energy, etc.

22–7 KIRCHHOFF'S LAWS

In case there is more than one source of emf in series in the circuit, Eq. (22–36) would lead to a simple algebraic sum of the individual emf's, and Eq. (22–40) is then replaced by

$$\sum \text{emf} = I \sum R, \tag{22–43}$$

which is called Kirchhoff's first law.

Example 1. A battery of emf 12 volts and internal resistance 0.05 ohm is connected to a self-starter of resistance 0.07 ohm. What is the current, if the only effect of the starter is a resistance?

Solution: From Eq. (22–43), emf $= IR$ or $I =$ emf$/R = 12/(0.05 + 0.07) = 100$ amp.

Example 2. When the starter of Example 1 is rotating, it exerts a "back emf" of 9.6 v. This emf is opposite to the applied emf (its origin will be treated in a later chapter). Find the current.

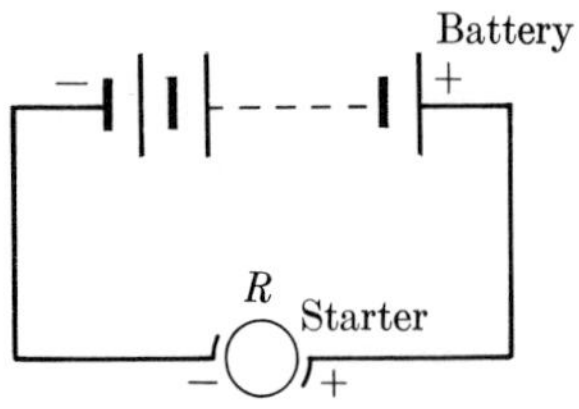

Battery

R Starter

Fig. 22–10. A circuit consisting of a battery in series with a starter that is assumed to be a pure resistance R.

Solution: The equivalent circuit is drawn in Fig. 22–10. We now use Eq. (22–43), which gives

$$I = \frac{\sum \text{emf}}{R} = \frac{12 - 9.6}{0.05 + 0.07} = 20 \text{ amp.}$$

The derivation of Eq. (22–43) was based on an integral around a "closed path" through conductors and sources of emf. This path might be around a simple *series circuit*, as in the above examples, but the derivation does not restrict us to this case. Any closed path is suitable. Thus the law can be applied to any portion of a more complex circuit or network. In such a case, the current I is different in different parts of the circuit, and Eq. (22–39) leads to the more general form of Eq. (22–43), namely,

$$\sum \text{emf} = \sum IR \tag{22–44}$$

around any closed loop. The signs of the IR terms are positive when I is in the direction of the path that we have chosen for the integration around the circuit [Eqs. (22–39), (22–40)]. The emf terms are positive [from the definition, Eq. (22–36)] when the path of integration is in the direction of E_m within the battery, that is, in the direction from the negative to the positive terminal within the battery.

In this derivation of Kirchhoff's circuit law, we have assumed that the current I in a single closed circuit is the same at all points in the circuit. This assumption is a statement of *Kirchhoff's second law.* It can be proven by assuming that it is not true. Let us say that we have a case where current I_1 enters a region P of the circuit and that I_2, a different current, leaves the region P. Then the net charge q in the region is time-dependent, i.e.,

$$\frac{dq}{dt} = I_1 - I_2. \tag{22–45}$$

Consequently, the potential of the region P changes, since the net charge changes. However, if we have a stationary system, in which all field quantities are constant, the potential, and hence the net charge, cannot change in time. Therefore, $dq/dt = 0$ and $I_1 = I_2$.

The actual mechanism which causes equilibrium is found in the electrostatic self-repulsion of a charge q which is built up at any point. If, momentarily in some region, $I_1 \neq I_2$, then charge begins to "pile up" in this region. Such a pile-up will cause an electrostatic force against any further accumulation of charge in that region.

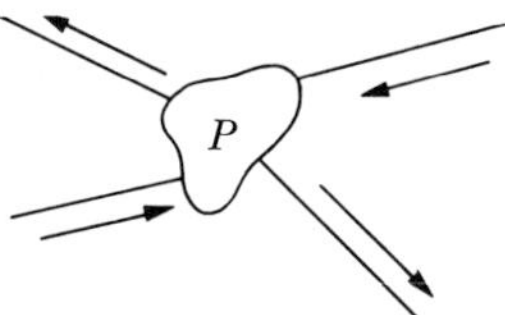

Fig. 22–11. A junction P with currents, indicated by the arrows, flowing into and out of the junction.

In the more general case of junctions of several circuit elements at P, as in Fig. 22–11, Eq. (22–45) becomes $dq/dt = \sum I$. Since dq/dt at P must be zero in the steady state,

$$\sum I = 0, \tag{22–46}$$

or

$$\sum I(\text{in}) = \sum I(\text{out}) \tag{22–47}$$

at any junction. This is a more general statement of Kirchhoff's current law. Algebraic signs of the currents must, of course, be carefully considered.

If we now consider parts of circuits (in place of closed paths), it is convenient to know how to find the *potential difference* between points in the circuits. Ohm's law is a special case in which the part of the circuit in question is a pure resistance and the potential difference ΔU is simply (Eq. 22–18)

$$\Delta U = IR. \tag{22–48}$$

The only subtlety is that $\Delta U \equiv U_2 - U_1$ is positive when I is in the direction from 2 to 1, as in Fig. 22–12; that is, if ΔU is positive, 2 is at higher potential than 1 and current flows toward 1. Thus ΔU in Eq. (22–48) is the *potential drop* in the direction of the current, or *potential rise* when we move against the current. The potential difference between the terminals of a source of emf is given by Eq. (22–42).

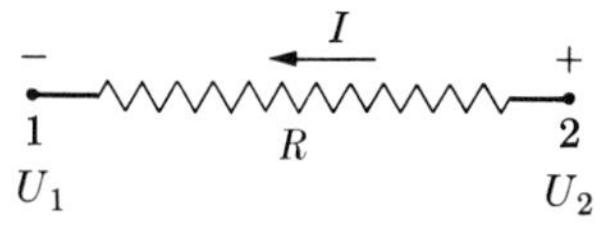

FIG. 22–12. The current I and the potentials of the terminals of a resistor R.

We now return to the application of Kirchhoff's laws. The signs of the terms in the loop law, Eq. (22–44), are determined by the fact that the left side corresponds to potential rises and the right side to potential drops. Thus, we arbitrarily choose a direction around a loop and write positive signs for the emf's of sources that are traversed from the negative to positive terminals (potential rises) and negative signs for the converse. For the IR terms, we write positive signs for resistances that are traversed in the direction of the assumed current direction (potential drop); otherwise, we write negative signs. If the magnitude of an unknown emf or current then proves to be negative, the actual direction is opposite to the assumed direction.

A useful alternative statement of the loop law is that the potential difference between two points must be independent of the path followed through the circuit.

Example 3. Suppose that the starter in Example 2 has a headlight bulb of resistance 0.5 ohm in parallel with it, as in Fig. 22–13. Find the currents. ($\mathcal{E}$ represents emf.)

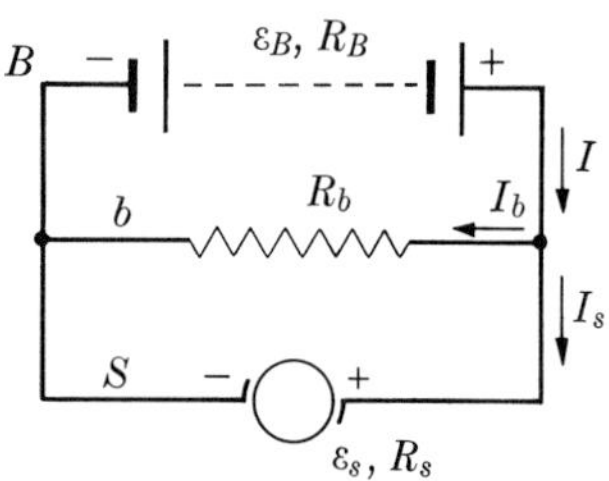

FIG. 22–13. A two-loop circuit consisting of a battery B, a headlight bulb b, and a starter S.

Solution: Assume currents in the directions shown. Then the current law gives: $I = I_b + I_s$. The loop law clockwise around the outer periphery is (Eq. 22–44) $\mathcal{E}_B - \mathcal{E}_S = IR_B + I_SR_S$. The loop law around the lower loop (clockwise) is $-\mathcal{E}_S = I_SR_S - I_bR_b$. The three equations can be solved for the three unknowns, I, I_b, and I_S. Note that a fourth equation, from the loop law for the upper loop, is *not* an independent equation.

Another technique for specifying currents in the case of intermeshing circuit loops is the loop-current method. For example, in the circuit of Fig. 22–13, we might choose to specify I_1 and I_2 as the currents flowing clockwise around the upper and the lower loops, respectively. Then the actual currents in the three parallel branches would be I_1, $I_1 - I_2$, and I_2, in the battery, the resistor, and the starter, respectively. We used Kirchhoff's current law when we added loop currents that are common to a given circuit element (in this case, the resistor) in order to obtain the actual current through that element.

22–8 GRAPHICAL REPRESENTATION

In describing the macroscopic characteristics of a simple circuit, we have used three quantities, electromotive force (including back emf's), current, and resistance. The electromotive force is assumed to be a constant that depends solely on the chemical properties of the battery constituents in the case of a chemical source of emf. In our simplified model, the emf does not depend on the current. The total resistance of the circuit is the resistance internal to the battery plus the resistance of the external load, $R = R_{\text{int}} + R_{\text{ext}}$. The current in the circuit is the electromotive force divided by the total resistance, $\mathcal{E} = I/(\sum R)$. The interrelationships among these quantities can be displayed in a potential diagram of a simple circuit, a graph of the potential as a function of position along a path traced through the circuit. The zero of potential can be chosen anywhere we wish.

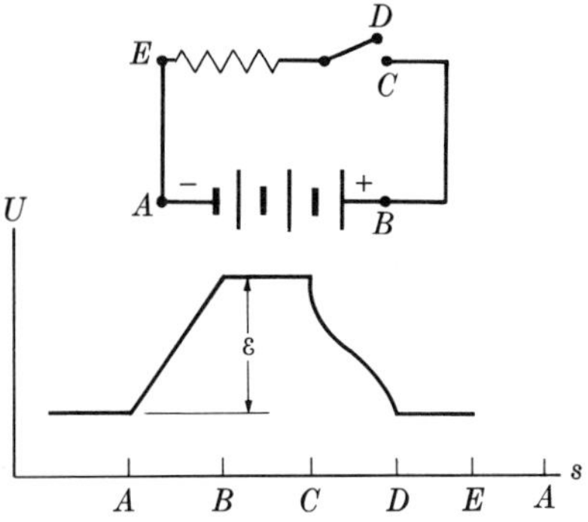

Fig. 22–14. The potential as a function of the distance s measured along the circuit path of the circuit shown in the insert, before the switch is closed.

For an open circuit, we have the potential versus position graph of Fig. 22–14. The positive pole is at a potential $U_+ - U_- = \Delta U_T$ relative to the negative pole. In the case of our idealized uniform battery, the rise in potential is constant inside the battery, with the rate of rise given by $E_m = dU/ds$ or $E_S = -dU/ds$ for a rectilinear path between terminals. The potential difference between the terminals is equal to the emf, that is, $\Delta U_T = \mathcal{E}$, since there is no current. The full terminal potential difference is impressed across the open switch, $\Delta U_{CD} = \Delta U_T$. The changing slope of the potential curve between C and D results from the fact that

$$-dU/ds = E_S$$

is a maximum near the switch terminals and a minimum at the midpoint. There is no potential drop across the external resistor since the current is zero; that is, $\Delta U_{DE} = IR_{\text{ext}} = 0$.

When the switch is closed, the potential graph changes to that shown in Fig. 22–15. The full emf does not appear as potential difference between the battery terminals, since the current inside the battery results in a potential drop in the direction of current flow equal to IR_{int}. Thus, the potential difference between poles is $\Delta U_T = \mathcal{E} - IR_{\text{int}}$. In the terminology of fields, the field E_S and consequently the slope of the potential rise have decreased from the open-circuit case. Since the battery terminals are connected directly to the terminals of the external resistance, the impressed voltage ΔU_T equals the potential drop in the external resistance; that is, $\Delta U_T = IR_{\text{ext}}$. In the above discussion, we have simply repeated the results of the derivation in Section 22–6 that showed $\mathcal{E} - IR_{\text{int}} = IR_{\text{ext}}$, which we have asserted above by stating the terminal potential difference ΔU_T in two ways. In the figure, it was assumed that the wire of the external resistor is uniform and hence the rate of potential drop is uniform.

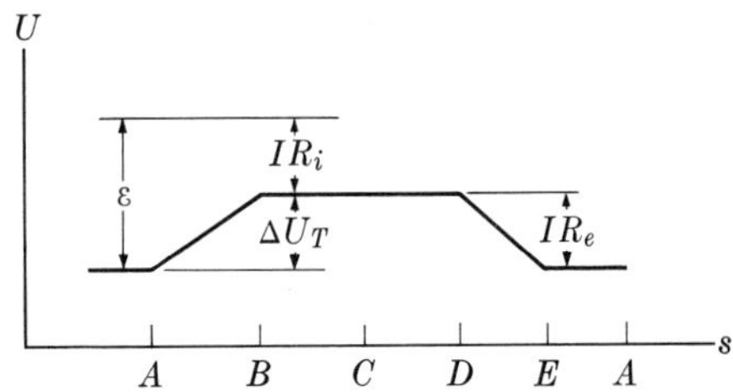

Fig. 22–15. The potential distribution in the circuit of Fig. 22–14, after the switch has been closed.

If a positive charge that is part of the conventional current flow is followed during its passage around the circuit, it is seen to go in the direction of the potential drop in the purely resistive elements. It moves at constant velocity, on the average. The electrostatic field accelerates the charge in the direction of the potential drop, but frequent interactions with the wire reduce the velocity of the charge. The energy transfer to the wire results in the heating of the wire. The electrical potential of the charge decreases in its passage along the wire. Within the battery, the charge is given an increase in electrical potential, since it is moved from the pole that has an excess of negative charge to a pole that has an excess of positive charge. The chemical forces make possible this motion of the charge against the electrostatic field. The chemical force is actually larger than the electrostatic force, but the average retarding force by the solution, due to its electrical resistance, results in equilibrium within the battery.

If the battery is short-circuited, that is $R_{\text{ext}} = 0$, the potential difference between the battery poles becomes zero. If the emf of the battery is assumed to be unchanged, we have

$$\mathcal{E} - IR_{\text{int}} = 0. \tag{22–49}$$

Therefore, for our idealized uniform battery, there are no potential differences anywhere in the circuit.

Real batteries. The next better approximation to a model of a real battery is obtained by recognizing that most of the electrochemical effect takes place in thin layers near the electrodes. The various integrals that we have taken along paths between poles of the battery will give the same overall results as before, *but* the contributions by particular segments of the paths will be quite different, as we shall now see.

In the open-circuit equilibrium condition, the electrostatic field inside the battery must be confined to the boundary layers near the poles, since the equivalent chemical field in our present model is thus confined and $E_{\text{total}} = 0$ everywhere inside the battery, including the boundary layers. The charge and field distributions would be somewhat as shown in Fig. 22–16. The graph of potential versus position will now be quite different from our first model for points inside the battery (Fig. 22–17).

When the external circuit is closed, the charges will move through the solution and collide with molecules of the solution. If we call the average force on the moving charges due to the collisions E_R per unit of charge, we must have (for equilibrium in both the boundary layer and the main body of the solution) $E_m = E_S + E_R$ in the boundary layers and $E'_S = E_R$ in the main body. The total charge on a plate must be less than the total charge in the adjacent boundary layer in order that $E_S \neq 0$ in the main body of the solution. The above conditions and the potential distribution are shown in Figs. 22–18 and 22–19. It is to be noted that the distribution of charge on the battery plates must be nonuniform in order that the external field at the point of con-

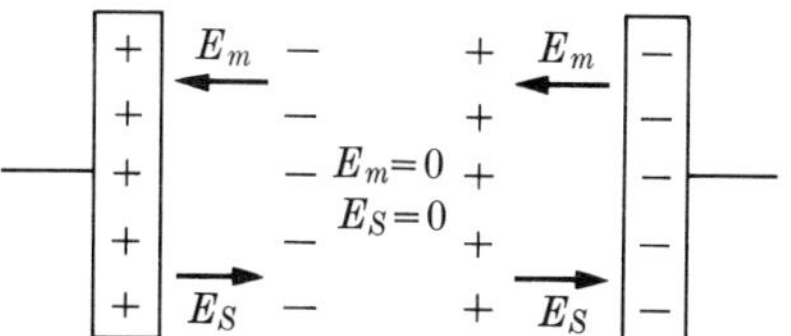

FIG. 22–16. Schematic diagram of the charge distribution and the fields in the case of an electrochemical cell model in which the electrochemical effects are confined to boundary regions near the plates.

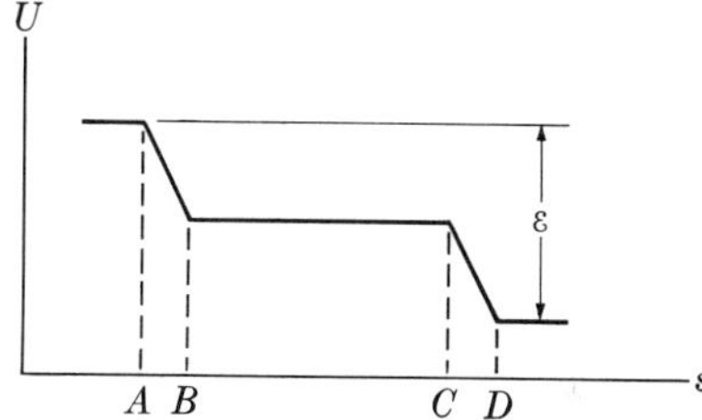

FIG. 22–17. The potential distribution along a line between the plates of the cell of Fig. 22–16.

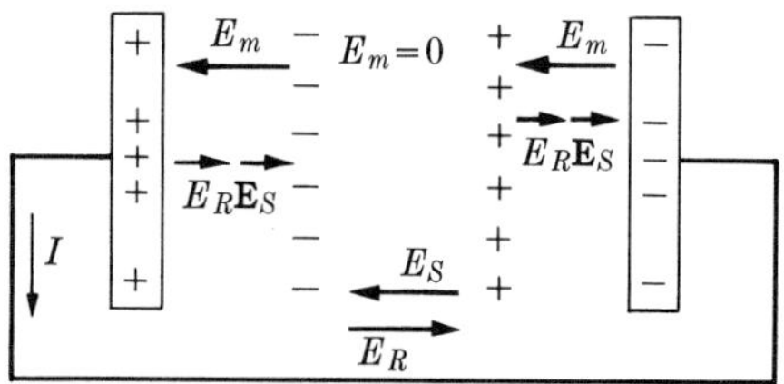

FIG. 22–18. Schematic diagram of the charge distribution and the field distribution within the cell of Fig. 22–16 *but* with current flowing.

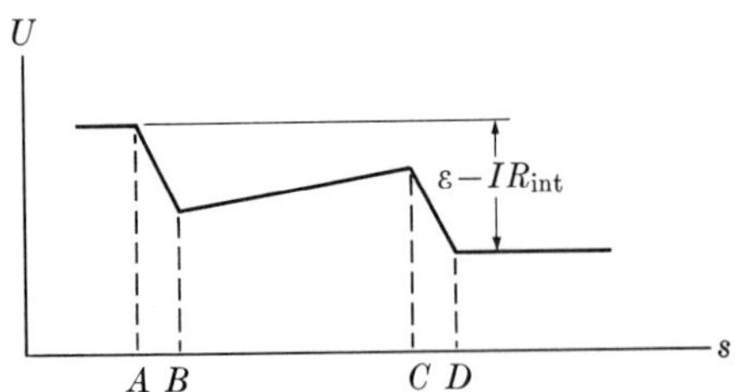

FIG. 22-19. The potential distribution along a line between the plates of the cell of Fig. 22-18.

tact between the wire and plate be in the direction of current flow. The origin of this nonuniformity can be pictured if we think of the charge distribution that will result just before the wire is touched to the plate.

22-9 ENERGY AND POWER IN ELECTRICAL CIRCUITS

Electrical devices are used to transform energy among the widest variety of forms, for example, electrical, chemical, heat and light, mechanical and sound, and even nuclear energy. We now consider some of the general aspects of energy interchanges, leaving until later the details of mechanical-electrical interchange by means of magnetic effects.

From the definition of electric potential difference ΔU the work in transporting charge dq is

$$dW = \Delta U \, dq, \qquad (22\text{–}50)$$

where ΔU is the potential difference in any circuit element. If both sides of (22-50) are divided by dt, we have

$$\frac{dW}{dt} = \Delta U \frac{dq}{dt}, \qquad (22\text{–}51)$$

but, since power is defined by $P \equiv dW/dt$ and current $I = dq/dt$, Eq. (22-51) becomes simply

$$P = I \, \Delta U \qquad (22\text{–}52)$$

for any circuit element. The units are volt-amperes, or joules/sec or, simply, watts.

The potentials in a complete circuit consisting of a single loop are described by Eq. (22-49) ($\sum \text{emf} = I \sum R$). If each term is multiplied by dq and divided by dt, the equation of *conservation of energy* (actually, power in this case) is obtained,

$$\sum (\text{emf}) I = I^2 \sum R. \qquad (22\text{–}53)$$

The terms on the left may be positive or negative, that is, they may correspond to either sources or sinks for electrical energy, depending on the sign of the emf. The terms on the right can only be sinks for electrical energy.

Let us now consider particular types of circuit elements, that is, the various kinds of terms that might appear in Eq. (22-53). A battery that delivers energy or power to the circuit has a positive emf in Eq. (22-53). The electrical energy comes from the transformation of chemical to electrical energy or power. Thus we write

$$P_{\text{chem}} = (\text{emf}) I. \qquad (22\text{–}54)$$

If a battery (or an electrical plating cell) is "opposing" the current, the sign of the emf is negative; electrical energy is transformed to chemical energy or power. Then we write

$$P_{\text{chem}} = -(\text{emf}) I. \qquad (22\text{–}55)$$

Another common source of emf is electromagnetic induction, which can be exploited in order to convert mechanical to electrical power and vice versa. Thus we have

$$P_{\text{mech}} = \pm (\text{emf}) I, \qquad (22\text{–}56)$$

where the sign depends on the direction of the emf and hence the direction of energy conversion.

There are other sources, such as thermoelectric, in which the interchange is between heat and electrical energy, and photoelectric, in which the interchange is from light energy to electrical energy. In each case, the power would be written in the forms above.

The right side of Eq. (22-53) contains only positive terms corresponding to the irreversible transfer of electrical to heat energy by electrical resistance. Qualitatively, if the flow of charge were unimpeded, the charges would simply gain kinetic energy. However, the moving charges interact with the conducting medium (essentially by collisions). The result is the transformation of what might have been a completely ordered flow of charge into the disordered motion that we associate with thermal energy. The term joule-heating is commonly used for this type of energy interchange.

All terms on the right of Eq. (22–53) are, therefore, of the form

$$P_{\text{heat}} = I^2R, \qquad (22\text{–}57)$$

where R is the resistance of the element in question. The element may be a resistor, deliberately introduced to reduce the current or to generate heat, or it may be the internal resistance of one of the energy-transforming devices considered above.

One of the best ways to find the mechanical equivalent of heat J is as follows: The definitions of the units of electrical quantities are based on mechanical units. Consequently, the joule heat, $I^2Rt = W$, dissipated in a resistor, is known in the mechanical unit, joule, when I and R are measured in amperes and ohms. It is very easy to immerse the resistor in water in a calorimeter and thereby measure the heat Q in calories generated by the current. We then have

$$J = \frac{I^2Rt}{Q} \text{ joules/calorie.} \qquad (22\text{–}58)$$

In the case of a source of emf that delivers electrical power to a circuit, we can bring together the energy terms that apply specifically to the source and replace them by P_{net}, where

$$P_{\text{net}} = P_{\text{chem}} - P_{\text{heat}}, \qquad (22\text{–}59)$$

or

$$\Delta U_T I = (\text{emf})I - I^2R_{\text{int}}, \qquad (22\text{–}60)$$

where ΔU_T is the potential difference at the terminals. The term P_{chem} would become P_{mech}, etc., for other cases. Division by I gives the usual expression for terminal potential of a source of emf that is delivering power,

$$\Delta U_T = \text{emf} - IR_{\text{int}}. \qquad (22\text{–}61)$$

If the "source" of emf is absorbing electrical energy, that is, transforming it to chemical or mechanical energy, we have

$$P_{\text{net}} = -P_{\text{chem}} - P_{\text{heat}}, \qquad (22\text{–}62)$$

or

$$\Delta U_T I = -(\text{emf})I - I^2R_{\text{int}}, \qquad (22\text{–}63)$$

or

$$\Delta U_T = -\text{emf} - IR_{\text{int}}. \qquad (22\text{–}64)$$

The graphical representations of (22–61) and (22–64) are given in Fig. 22–20, where it is assumed that the electrochemical effects are confined to very thin layers at the plates of the battery.

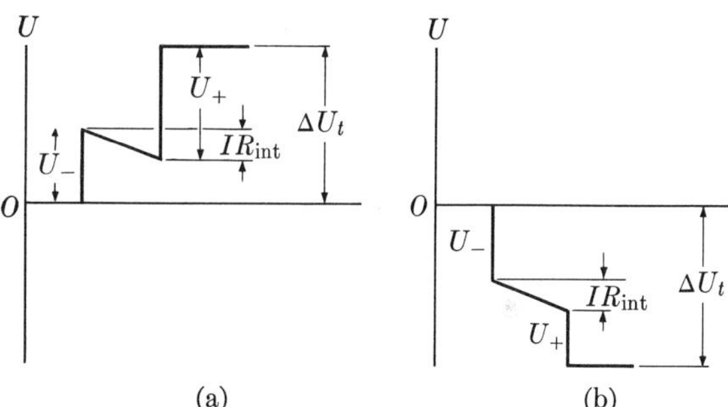

FIG. 22–20. The potential distributions within a cell (a) that is delivering current; (b) that is being charged or is acting as an electroplating cell.

22–10 SUMMARY

The motion of electric charge is described in terms of electric current I, where

$$I \equiv \frac{dq}{dt}.$$

If the current varies from point to point, the description is conveniently made in terms of local current density J, where

$$J = \frac{dI}{dS}.$$

In terms of motion of individual charges of density n of charge e at average velocity v, the current density is

$$J = nev.$$

When current flows in conductors, we do *not* have electrostatic conditions and hence the electric field is no longer zero within the conductor. Also, the conductor is no longer an equipotential. If the temperature and other conditions are kept constant, it is found that the potential difference ΔU between the ends of a conducting wire and the current in the wire are related by

$$\Delta U = IR,$$

where R is a constant characteristic of the wire. This relationship is Ohm's law. The resistance R is found to depend on the length l and the cross-sectional area S of a wire by

$$R = \frac{\rho l}{S},$$

where ρ is a constant characteristic of the material and temperature of the wire.

The production of potential differences by electrochemical effects in a battery is treated according to a simplified model. The nonelectrostatic contribution to the work on charges is termed the electromotive force or the emf or $\mathcal{E}$. In terms of forces, emf can be described in terms of an equivalent "field," force per unit charge, E_m. When no current flows in a battery, the potential difference ΔU_T between the terminals equals $\mathcal{E}$,

$$\Delta U_T = \mathcal{E}.$$

When the terminals of a battery are connected by a wire of resistance R_e, the current in the circuit is given by

$$\mathcal{E} = I(R_e + R_i),$$

where R_i is the resistance of the battery itself. The terminal potential difference is given by

$$\Delta U_T = \mathcal{E} - IR_i.$$

Kirchhoff's laws are the generalization of the above for a circuit or loop in a complex circuit that may have more than one source of emf,

$$\sum \mathcal{E} = \sum IR,$$

plus a statement of current continuity at a junction in a complex circuit,

$$\sum I_{\text{in}} = \sum I_{\text{out}}.$$

Graphical illustrations of the rises and falls in potential in circuit elements as a charge moves around a circuit are presented.

The rates of energy transfer to and from electrical energy, that is, power (P), for various types of circuit elements are

Resistance (electrical to heat)

$$P = I^2R$$

Battery (chemical to electrical)

$$P = I\mathcal{E}$$

Battery (to external circuit)

$$P = I\mathcal{E} - I^2R_i.$$

Problems

($e = 1.6 \times 10^{-19}$ coul)

1. A ring of copper is made whose cross-sectional radius is 1 cm. The radius of the ring is 1 m. If a total charge of 10^{-9} coul is placed on the ring, the field at the surface is nearly equal to the breakdown limit for air. This is a "large" electrostatic charge. The ring is set into a spinning motion about a central axis perpendicular to the plane of the ring. We consider 1000 rps to be a spinning rate corresponding to ultracentrifuge velocities. Thus the spin and the charge are both great from a practical viewpoint. What is the current in amperes created in this extreme situation?

2. A copper wire of cross-sectional area 0.005 cm^2 can carry a current of 10 amp.
(a) What is the current density in this case?
(b) What is the drift velocity of the conduction electrons? The density of copper is about 8 gm/cm^3, its gram-molecular weight is 64, and there is one conduction electron per atom. Electronic charge is 1.6×10^{-19} coul.

3. In the Bohr model of the hydrogen atom, the electron is pictured in a circular orbit, rotating around the nucleus about 10^{15} times per second. What is the equivalent current in amperes? Compare with the result of Problem 1.

4. A wire of 1^2 mm cross-sectional area is strung around the earth at the equator. A current of 1 μa flows through the wire. What is the average time required for one particular electron to travel around the earth in the wire, if the wire is of copper? Copper has one conduction electron per atom. The density of copper is about 8 gm/cc and the at. wt. is 63.5.

5. It is desired to measure the potential difference ΔU between the plates of a parallel-plate capacitor in terms of fundamental quantities. Therefore, the force F of one plate on the other is measured. Derive an expression for ΔU in terms of the measured quantities F, plate area A, and the plate separation d. Assume that d is much less than the dimensions of the plates.

6. In the discussion of the discharge of a capacitor (Fig. 22-21), we had $\Delta U = IR$, where ΔU is the potential difference impressed between the ends of the wire. If q is the instantaneous charge on the plates and C is the capacitance, we have $\Delta U = q/C = IR$. Also $I = -(dq/dt)$ by definition, where the minus sign denotes that the capacitor is being discharged. Then the differential equation for the discharge is

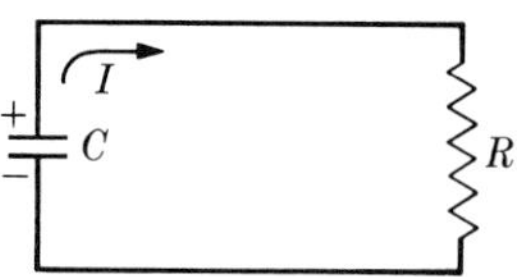

FIGURE 22–21

$$\frac{q}{C} = -\frac{dq}{dt} R.$$

It is "separable" and can be written

$$\frac{dq}{q} = \frac{dt}{RC}.$$

(a) Show by direct integration that the solution to this equation is of the exponential form,

$$q = q_0 e^{-t/RC}, \qquad (22\text{–}65)$$

where RC is the time constant, the time for the charge to decay to a fraction $1/e$th of its initial value.
(b) Show by dimensional analysis that the product (ohm-farad) is a second of time, i.e., that RC is in seconds.
(c) Show that the expression for the current in the wire is

$$I = \frac{\Delta U_0}{R} e^{-t/RC}.$$

7. A capacitor of capacitance C_1 is given an initial charge q_0. It is then connected via a resistance R to a second capacitor of capacitance C_2 that is initially uncharged (Fig. 22–22).

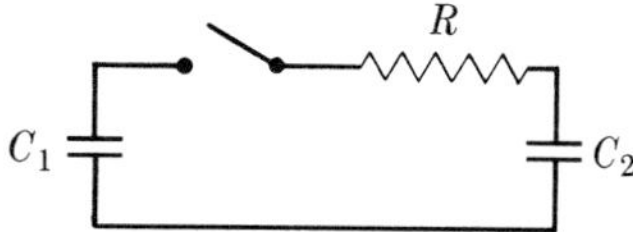

FIGURE 22–22

(a) Since the sum of the potentials around the closed circuit must be zero, show that

$$\frac{q}{C_1} - \frac{q_0 - q}{C_2} - IR = 0,$$

where q is the charge remaining on C_1 at time t after the switch is closed.

(b) Find q and I as functions of time.

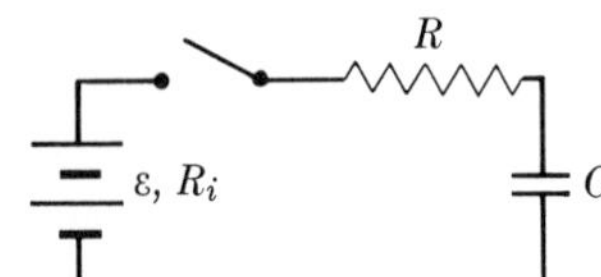

FIGURE 22–23

8. An uncharged capacitor of capacitance C is suddenly connected to a battery of emf $= \mathcal{E}$ and internal resistance R_i. An external resistance R is in series (Fig. 22–23).

(a) Show that

$$\mathcal{E} - \frac{q}{C} = I(R + R_i),$$

where q is the instantaneous charge on the capacitor.

(b) Find q and I as functions of the time t after the switch is closed.

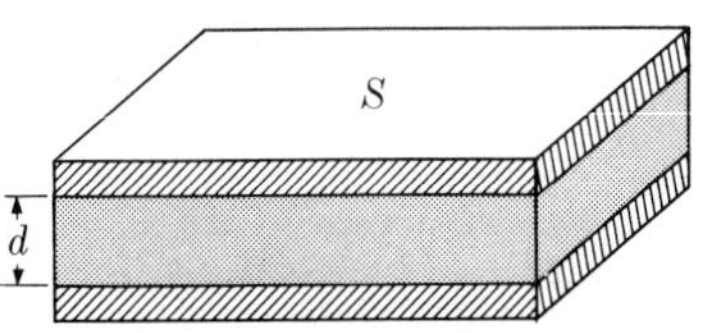

FIGURE 22–24

9. The space between the plates of a parallel plate capacitor is filled with a material of resistivity 2 ohms cm (Fig. 22–24). The plate area is 100 cm^2 and the separation is 1 cm. If the plates are initially charged to 100 v potential difference,

(a) what is the initial current between the plates?

(b) Derive an equation for the charge on the plates as a function of time and for the current as a function of time.

(c) Verify the form of Ohm's law in Eq. (22–27) in this case.

10. An electrical conducting layer can be deposited on glass with only a small effect on the transparency. For a given layer of uniform thickness, the resistance is given in specification sheets as so many ohms per square. Show how these units come about.

11. Concentric conducting spherical shells of radii 1 cm and 10 cm are separated by material of uniform resistivity 2 ohms cm (Fig. 22–25). If the shells are initially charged to a potential difference of 100 v.

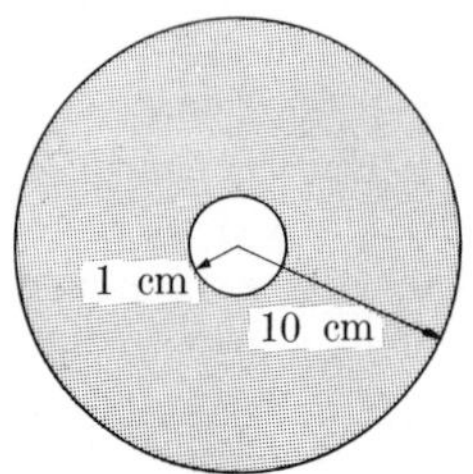

FIGURE 22–25

(a) find the initial current density as a function of r [*Hint:* Use the Eq. (22–24) form of Ohm's law.]

(b) Find the initial current from your result of (a).

(c) What is the resistance of the conducting material between the shells? Could you find the resistance by direct integration?

12. An idealized battery cell consisting of plane parallel plates of area 10 cm^2 and separation 1.0 cm is to be pictured as having all the "chemical" field E_m appearing within layers 1 mm thick at each plate. If the emf of the cell is 2 v and we assume that half the emf appears between each pole and the solution, find the field components E_s and E_m as a function of position within the *open-circuit* cell. Make a graph of *potential* versus position between the plates.

13. A battery of emf 6 v is connected to an external resistor of 12 ohms, and a current of 0.4 amp results. Find the internal resistance of the battery.

14. An automobile generator of emf 7 v and internal resistance 0.2 ohm is charging a battery of emf 6.3 v and internal resistance 0.05 ohm. Find the current and the terminal voltage.

15. In Problem 14, the headlights with resistance of 0.3 ohm are connected in parallel with the battery (Fig. 22–26). Find the currents and terminal potentials.

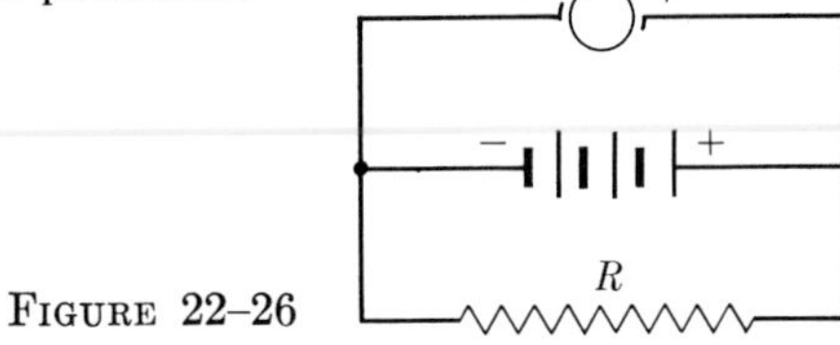

FIGURE 22–26

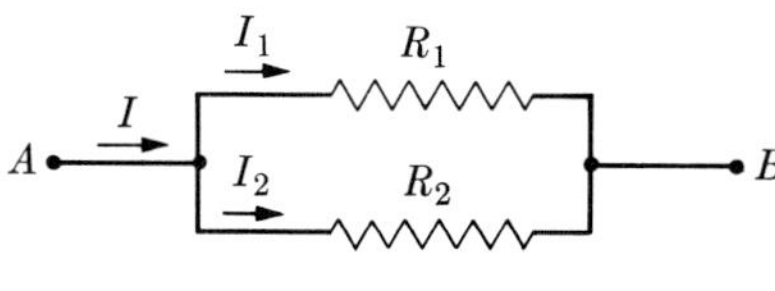

FIGURE 22–27

16. Two resistors R_1 and R_2 are joined in parallel, as schematized in Fig. 22–27. A potential difference ΔU is impressed across the terminals AB, and the current passing from A to B is $I = I_1 + I_2$. Defining the "total" resistance between the terminals as $R = \Delta U/I$, prove that R is given in terms of R_1 and R_2 by the relationship

$$\frac{1}{R} = \frac{1}{R_1} + \frac{1}{R_2}. \tag{22–66}$$

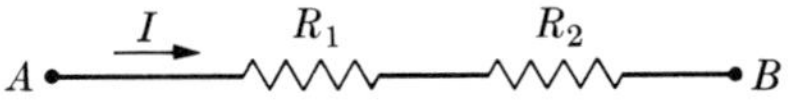

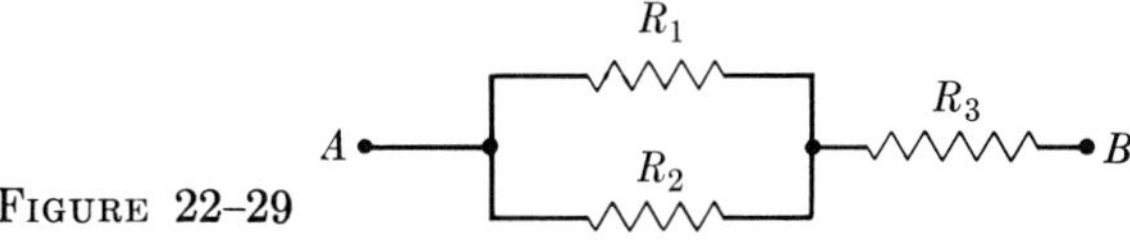

FIGURE 22–28

17. Two resistors R_1 and R_2 are joined in series, as shown in Fig. 22–28. A potential difference ΔU is impressed across the terminals AB. The total resistance between the points AB is defined as $R = \Delta U/I$. Prove that R is given in terms of R_1 and R_2 by the relationship,

$$R = R_1 + R_2. \tag{22–67}$$

18. Find the resistance (total) between A and B in each of the resistor combinations of Fig. 22–29 to Fig. 22–31, using the results of Eq. (22–66) and (22–67) for series and for parallel series combinations.

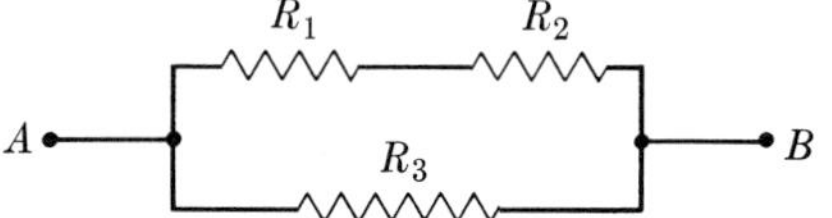

FIGURE 22–29

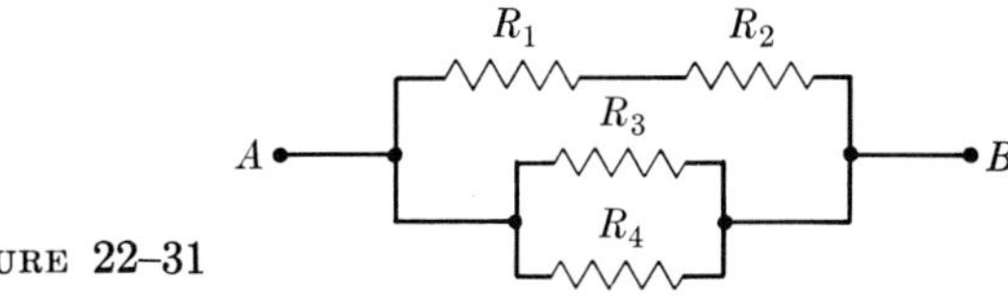

FIGURE 22–30

FIGURE 22–31

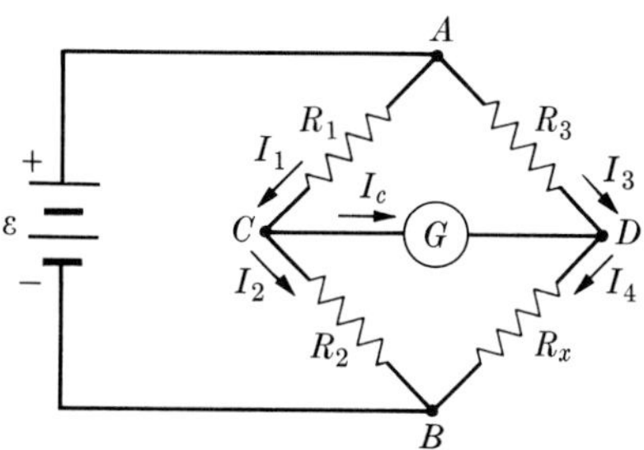

FIGURE 22–32

19. A *Wheatstone bridge* is a device for measuring an unknown resistance R_x in terms of three known resistances R_1, R_2, and R_3. The method is a "null" method and is therefore independent of the calibration of meters. Figure 22–32 is the basic circuit of the Wheatstone bridge. The operator adjusts R_1/R_3 and R_2 until the current through the galvanometer G is zero (within the sensitivity of the galvanometer). The bridge is then said to be balanced. With the bridge balanced, prove that

(a) $\Delta U_{CD} = 0$,
(b) $I_1 = I_2$, and $I_3 = I_4$,
(c) $\Delta U_{AC} = \Delta U_{AD}$, and $\Delta U_{CB} = \Delta U_{DB}$,
(d) $I_1 R_1 = I_3 R_3$, and $I_2 R_2 = I_4 R_x$,
(e) finally,

$$R_x = \frac{R_3}{R_1} R_2. \tag{22–68}$$

20. A *potentiometer* is a device for measuring an unknown potential difference in terms of the emf of a "standard cell." The method is a null method and is therefore independent of internal resistances. Figure 22–33 is the basic circuit of a potentiometer. A

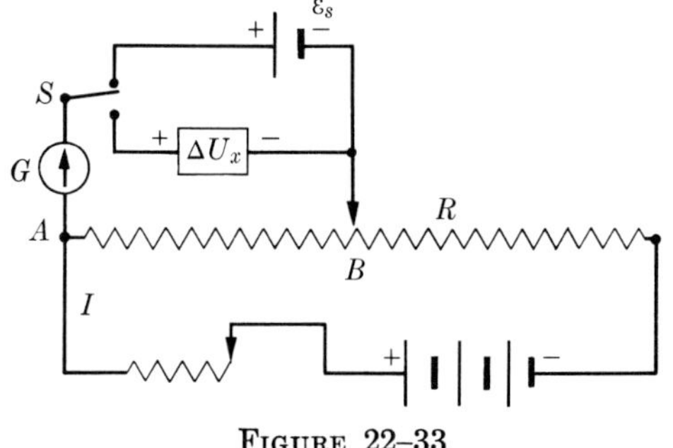

FIGURE 22–33

battery passes an adjustable current I through a long wire of total resistance R. The switch S permits the connection of either the standard cell $\mathcal{E}_s$ or the unknown potential difference ΔU_x into the upper branch circuit. The sliding contact B is adjusted until there is *no* current through the galvanometer. In general, there is a position for balance B_s with the standard cell, and a different position of balance B_x with the unknown ΔU_x in the upper branch. Let R_s and R_x be the corresponding resistances of the wire segments between A and B_s or A and B_x, respectively. Show that

(a) $IR_s = \mathcal{E}_s$ and $IR_x = \Delta U_x$,
(b) $\Delta U_x = \mathcal{E}_s R_x / R_s$;
(c) finally,

$$\Delta U_x = \mathcal{E}_s \frac{l_x}{l_s}, \quad (22\text{–}69)$$

where l is the length of wire between A and B.

21. An ammeter and a voltmeter are to be used to measure the resistance R of a certain resistor. The voltmeter reads correctly the potential difference V at its terminals, and the ammeter reads correctly the current I passing through the ammeter. The voltmeter resistance is R_V and the ammeter resistance is R_A.

(a) Find R in terms of I, R_V, and V if the connections are made as in Fig. 22–34.

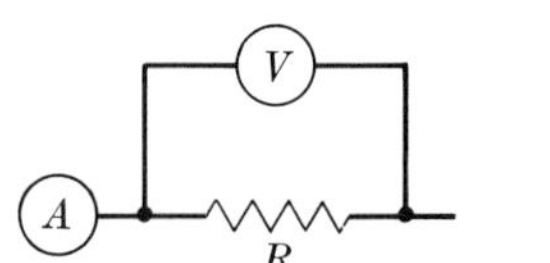

FIGURE 22–34

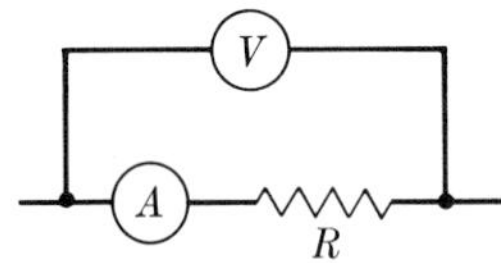

FIGURE 22–35

(b) Find the true value of the resistor R in terms of V, R_A, and I if the connections are made as in Fig. 22–35.

(c) Ordinarily, R_V is large and R_A is small. Which of the two circuits involves the smaller correction of the meter readings if R is small? if R is large?

22. Use the result of Problem 6(c) to find the heat dissipated in R by the direct integration $\int I^2 R\, dt$. Show that the result equals the initial electrostatic energy of the capacitor, as expected. Write the equation for the instantaneous power.

23. Find the power delivered or dissipated by each element of the circuit and check your result for conservation of energy
(a) for Problem 13,
(b) for Problem 14,
(c) for Problem 15.

24. A resistance R_e is connected to a battery whose internal resistance is R_i.

(a) Show that the potential difference impressed across R_e is

$$\Delta U = \frac{R_e}{R_e + R_i} \text{(emf)},$$

where emf is the electromotive force of the battery.

(b) The power delivered to R_e is $I^2 R_e$. If $R_e = 0$, the power is zero, since the current is finite. If $R_e = \infty$, the power is zero since the current is zero. (Prove that this is a correct statement.) Since the power is zero for these extreme values of R_e, we expect maximum power at some intermediate value of R_e. Prove that $I^2 R_e$ is maximum when $R_e = R_i$.

25. A battery has an emf of 10 v and an internal resistance of 1 ohm.

(a) What is the terminal potential difference when the battery delivers 3 amp? At what rate is energy being abstracted from the chemicals of the cell? At what rate is energy being delivered to the external load? At what rate is energy being transformed into heat within the cell?

(b) An external source of electric potential is used to charge the cell, that is, to drive current through the cell in the reverse direction, from + to −. If the charging current is 3 amp, what is the terminal potential difference of the cell. How much energy is stored in the cell per second? At what rate is energy being lost in heating the cell?

26. Electric current I flows in a copper wire of cross section 1 cm^2. In a certain region the wire is constricted to a cross-sectional area of 1 mm^2. What is the ratio of electric field strengths in the two regions?

27. The stream of electrons in a TV tube is about 1 mm^2 in cross section and constitutes a current of about 0.1 ma. If the electrons have a constant energy of 15,000 ev during the last part of their path to the screen,

(a) find the velocity of the electrons,

(b) find the density of electrons in the beam (assume it is uniform),

(c) find the charge density ρ, in the beam.

28. Make graphs of q versus t, i versus t, and ΔU versus t for Problem 7. Give scales of both ordinates and abscissas. Make the initial slopes of your graphs correct.

29. Electrons are emitted from the negative plate of a certain parallel plate capacitor at a constant rate of N per second. The electrons then travel through vacuum to the positive plate. Assume that the electrons in the beam do not appreciably alter the electric field. The plate area is A, the separation is d, and the potential difference is maintained at ΔU volts.

(a) Find the current density and electron density as functions of x (Fig. 22–36).

(b) Find the total number of electrons in flight at one instant of time.

(c) How much electrical power is required to maintain the potential?

(d) What happens to the electrical power that is put into the system?

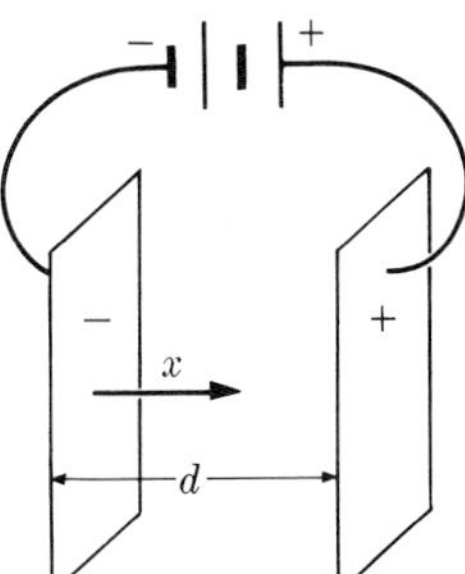

FIGURE 22–36

30. Suppose the potential difference in Problem 29 is initially ΔU, but the plates are disconnected from the source of potential difference at $t = 0$. Repeat the calculations of Problem 29, including the time dependence.

23

The Magnetic Field

23–1 INTRODUCTION

Electric charges in motion experience forces of interaction in addition to those forces which are described by the electrostatic field. These forces are called magnetic forces, and the interaction is described by means of a magnetic field.

The basic fact of magnetism, that there exists a velocity-dependent force between electric charges, was obscured by the historical evolution of the subject. The magnetic field was defined and an attempt was made to describe specifically the interaction between "permanent" magnets long before electric charges or electric currents were associated with the structure of matter.

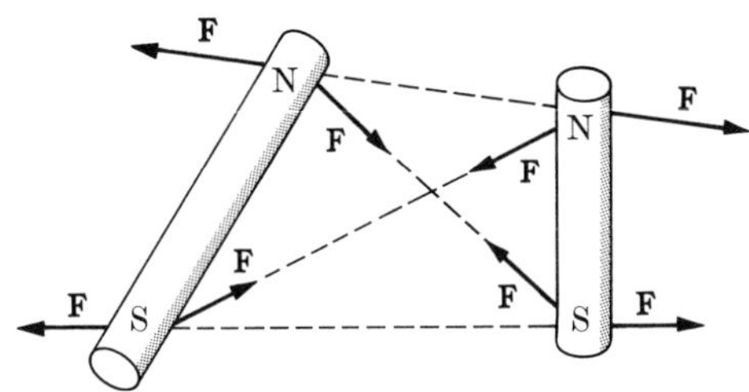

FIG. 23–1. Two permanent magnets with north (N) and south (S) poles near the ends. The various forces of attraction and of repulsion between the poles are shown.

Permanent magnets were observed to have the power of attraction or repulsion for one another. The seat of the interaction was traced to the ends of the magnets, which were said to contain magnetic poles, with a different kind of pole (called north N and south S, see below) at either end. As in the electrostatic system, like poles repel and unlike attract (Fig. 23–1). It was found that the earth itself exerts magnetic forces, as though it had magnetic poles itself. The effect is to produce a roughly north-south orientation of a magnet. From this observation, there arose the designation north-seeking and south-seeking poles (or simply north and south poles) for the poles on the magnet in question. Thus, the effect of the earth could be described by saying that the earth has a south-seeking or south magnetic pole in the direction of the north geographic pole, and similarly for the other pole. North and south poles are always to be found in equal and opposite pairs on a single magnet; they cannot be separated from each other. Thus the simplest system involving a pair of permanent magnets is described by four separate interactions in the language of magnetic poles. Experiment showed that a Coulomb law of force operates between each pair of poles, i.e.,

$$|\mathbf{F}| = k\,\frac{m_1 m_2}{r^2}, \qquad (23\text{–}1)$$

where k is a magnetic constant of proportionality and m_1 and m_2 are the pole strengths. As in the electrical case, this law can be translated into a field form. The magnetic field **H** is defined as the force per unit north pole,

$$\mathbf{H} = \frac{\mathbf{F}}{m}\,\frac{\mathrm{n}}{\text{unit pole}}, \qquad (23\text{–}2)$$

and the field due to a point pole is therefore

$$|\mathbf{H}| = k\,\frac{m}{r^2}\,\frac{\mathrm{n}}{\text{unit pole}} \qquad (23\text{–}3)$$

directed away from a north pole. From this point of departure, it can be seen then that the whole of electrostatic theory can be recapitulated, with magnetic symbols replacing the electric.

It seemed, then, that a new field, not associated with the electric field at all, was present in nature.

Moreover, the magnetic field so conceived was static, arising from static poles in inert matter. As long as the experiments were conducted in the static domain, electricity and magnetism appeared to be quite independent. A charged pith ball suspended in the strongest magnetic field senses no force at all. Charges and poles at rest are observed not to interact.

It was not until the invention of the voltaic cell that this static picture of magnetism was found to be restricted and incomplete. The cell provided physicists for the first time with continuous currents of the order amperes, rather than the microamperes which could be derived from electrostatic machines. With the advent of such currents in the laboratory, the discovery of new processes followed one another in quick succession. For example:

1. A bar of magnetized iron experiences a torque in the vicinity of a wire carrying electric current (Fig. 23–2). Therefore, magnetism must not be wholly associated with poles but with electric currents as well.

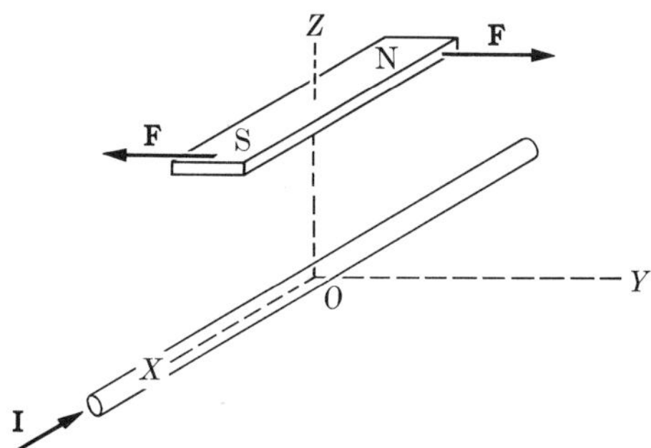

FIG. 23–2. The forces **F** on the poles of a permanent magnet placed above a wire that is carrying a current **I**, as shown.

2. Wires carrying currents exert forces upon one another (Fig. 23–3). Since the field of a current can also affect magnets, the action of current upon current is also called magnetic, although no magnetized material is required.

Subsequently, it was also proved that the atomic currents in iron can explain the action of one magnet upon another. Thus, the whole study was oriented away from the historic pole concept and toward the basic interaction of currents. Since currents are nothing more than electric charges in motion, electric and magnetic interactions are connected and not independent. The electric charge is the source of both fields, in fact, there is found to be no physical distinction between the two fields when the relativistic effects due to motion of the observer are taken into account. An electric field according to one observer can become partly electric and partly magnetic according to a second ("moving") observer, etc.

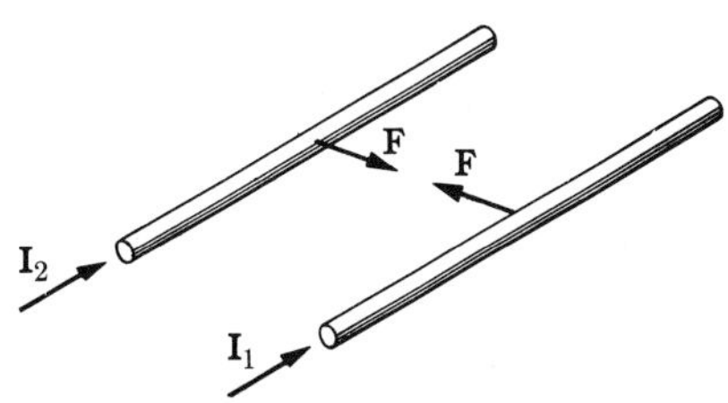

FIG. 23–3. The magnetic force **F** of attraction between two wires carrying currents in the same direction.

23–2 THE MAGNETIC FIELD DEFINED

The magnetic interaction of electric charges can be stated in an action-at-a-distance form. In this form, the force of interaction depends on the relative velocities of the charged particles, the charge of each, the relative direction of motion, and the distance between the charges. The action-at-a-distance formulation is extraordinarily com-

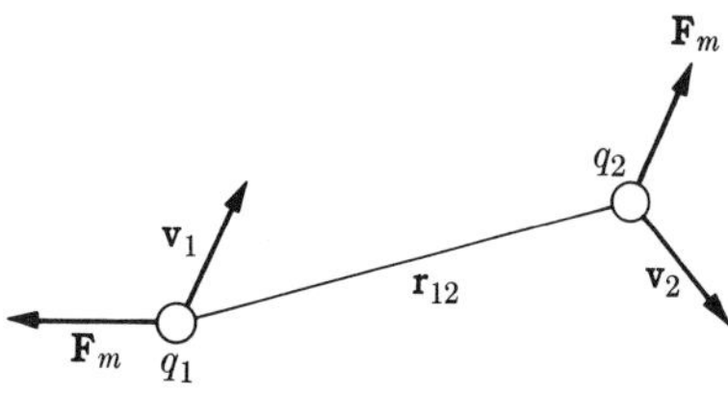

FIG. 23–4. Two charges q_1 and q_2 moving at velocities $\mathbf{v}_1$ and $\mathbf{v}_2$, respectively, experience magnetic forces $\mathbf{F}_m$ that depend on the charges, their velocities, and their relative position $\mathbf{r}_{12}$.

plex in comparison with the Coulomb law of electrostatics (see Fig. 23-4 for a qualitative idea of the degree of complexity). Consequently, we proceed directly to a field formulation of the problem. One moving charge is said to generate a magnetic field. The other moving charge experiences a force due to the influence of the field upon it. The study is then in two parts: (1) a description of the generation of magnetic fields by moving charge, and (2) a description of the influence of magnetic fields upon moving charges. The field is defined through its effects on a moving charge. We shall first discuss the effects of a magnetic field, leaving the question of origin until later.

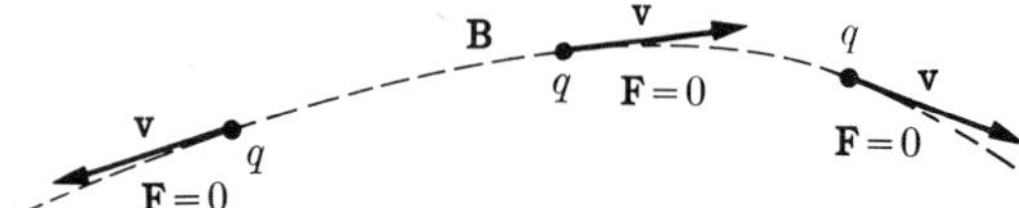

Fig. 23-5. Definition of the direction of a magnetic field line **B** (dashed) in terms of the direction of the velocity for which test charges q experience no magnetic force.

Let a region of space which exhibits a magnetic influence be explored by a point test charge. We find first that a test charge experiences a force, in addition to the electrostatic and gravitational force upon it, which is proportional to the speed of the particle, all other things remaining the same, i.e., $F \sim v$. In a second experiment, the magnitude of the test charge is varied, and it is found that the force is directly proportional to the electric charge, all other things remaining the same, that is, $F \sim q$. In a third test, the directional properties of the force are explored. At any point in space a direction can be found such that the test charge moving along this direction, in either sense, experiences *zero force* (Fig. 23-5). This direction determines the direction of the magnetic field **B**. By definition, **B** is in the direction defined above. This discovery does not provide us with the sense of **B**, and here is another point of contrast between the electric and magnetic fields. The electric field E is given the sense of the force on a positive charge. The magnetic field is given a sense agreeing with the convention of permanent magnets, the force on a north-seeking pole. Magnetic field lines can be mapped by drawing lines such that **B** is tangent to a given line at each point along the line (Fig. 23-6). The magnetic field can thus be mapped as one would electric fields. One important difference will be noted later, i.e., electric field lines begin and end on charges, whereas magnetic field lines close on themselves. No isolated magnetic poles have yet been observed.

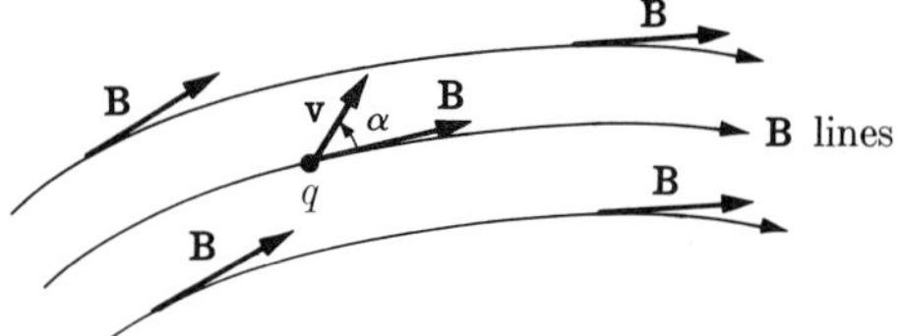

Fig. 23-6. Direction of the field vectors **B** relative to the field lines.

If the angle α between the velocity vector of the test charge and the field is varied, it is found that the force experienced by the charge is proportional to $\sin \alpha$; all other things remaining the same, $F \sim \sin \alpha$ (see Fig. 23-6). The results that have been given so far show the dependence of the magnitude of the force on the test charge upon the physical variables q, v, and α. The rules are summarized in an equation for the magnitude of the force. Since F is proportional to q, v, and $\sin \alpha$, we have the proportionality,

$$|\mathbf{F}| \sim q|\mathbf{v}| \sin \alpha.$$

The coefficient of proportionality that is introduced here is the field strength itself. The definition of field strength B is given implicitly by

$$|\mathbf{F}| = q|\mathbf{v}|\,|\mathbf{B}| \sin \alpha. \tag{23-4}$$

In the mks system of units, $|\mathbf{F}|$ is given in newtons of force, $|\mathbf{v}|$ in meters per second, and q in coulombs of charge. Then the unit of $|\mathbf{B}|$ is a consequence of Eq. (23-4) and the choice of units.

The name given to the unit is the weber per square meter. Solving for B in Eq. (23–4), we have

$$|\mathbf{B}| \equiv \frac{|\mathbf{F}|}{q} \frac{1}{|\mathbf{v}|} \frac{1}{\sin \alpha} \frac{\text{newton sec}}{\text{coul·m}} \tag{23–5}$$

and, therefore, the weber per square meter can be expressed explicitly in terms of previously defined mechanical and electrical units, as

$$1 \frac{\text{weber}}{\text{m}^2} = 1 \frac{\text{newton sec}}{\text{coul·m}}.$$

Physically, the unit of field strength can be expressed in this way: a coulomb of charge traveling at a rate of one meter per second in a direction perpendicular to a field of one weber per square meter experiences a force of one newton.

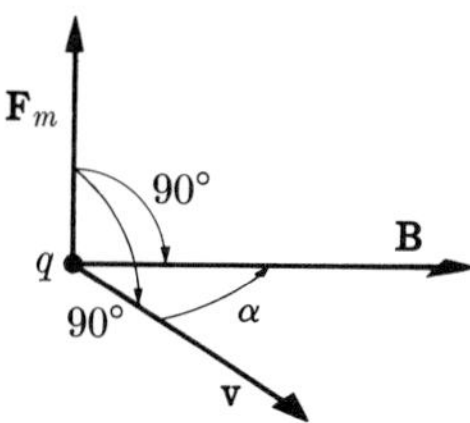

FIG. 23–7. Relative directions of the vectors **B**, **v**, and the magnetic force $\mathbf{F}_m$.

The directional properties of the magnetic force remain to be described. It is found that the magnetic force is always perpendicular to the velocity vector of the test charge and is always perpendicular to the direction of the field (Fig. 23–7). These two rules can be summarized by saying that the two directions, **v** and **B**, determine a plane and that **F** is normal to this plane. The definition in vector analysis of the vector product of two vectors lends itself perfectly to the description of **F** in terms of **B** and **v**. In a formal definition, the vector product of two vectors **a** and **b** is the vector **c**, where the magnitude of **c** is the area of the parallelogram defined by **a** and **b** (that is, $|\mathbf{c}| = |\mathbf{a}|\,|\mathbf{b}| \sin \alpha$) and the direction of **c** is normal to the parallelogram. The sense of **c** can be found by the right-hand screw rule. If $\mathbf{c} = \mathbf{a} \times \mathbf{b}$, the sense is found by the direction of advance of a right-threaded screw when twisted in the direction of rotation that would turn **a** into **b** (through the angle $< 180°$).

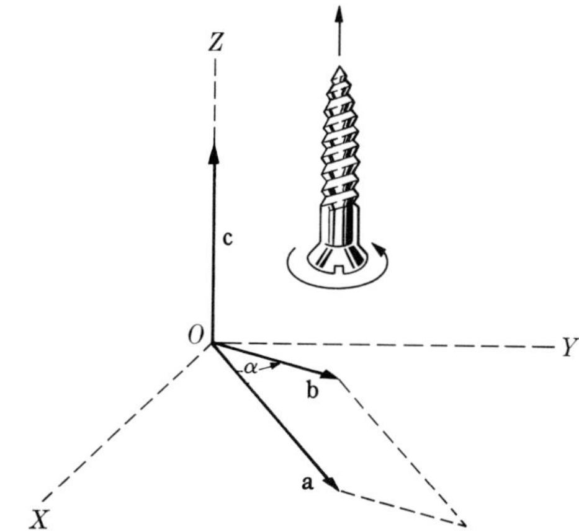

FIG. 23–8. The direction of vector **c** that is the vector product of **a** and **b** ($\mathbf{c} = \mathbf{a} \times \mathbf{b}$) described in terms of the direction of advance of a right-handed screw when rotated from the direction of **a** into the direction of **b**.

The direction of **B** is therefore correctly given if the force on a moving charge is written

$$\mathbf{F} = q\mathbf{v} \times \mathbf{B}. \tag{23–6}$$

As we shall see later, the sense is consistent with our earlier arbitrary choice that the sense of the magnetic field due to the north pole of a permanent magnet is outward from the pole. If there is no other force, the kinetic energy of q must remain constant since $|\mathbf{v}| =$ constant.

We noted in the introduction that the magnetic force on a charged particle is in addition to the electric force. With the formulation of a magnetic force, it is now possible to write an expression for the *total* force experienced by a charged particle. The electric force is given by the product of the electric charge and the electric field, $\mathbf{F}_e = q\mathbf{E}$. The magnetic force is given by Eq. (23–6). The net electromagnetic force on a charged particle is the vector sum of the magnetic and electric forces, i.e.,

$$\mathbf{F} = q(\mathbf{E} + \mathbf{v} \times \mathbf{B}). \qquad (23\text{–}7)$$

This formula is called the Lorentz law of force.

23–3 MAGNETIC FLUX

Although the concept will not be used extensively until later, we now introduce the idea of magnetic flux.

As in electric field theory, we relate the field strength B weber/m^2 to a magnetic flux. It is not conventional to call the magnetic field lines "lines of force"; rather, they are called lines of induction, for reasons which will appear when further properties of magnetism are introduced. Let it be noted again that an electric charge traveling along a line of induction experiences zero magnetic force. The lines thus defined and drawn in space constitute a directional map of the magnetic field. The proper connection between the density of lines and the field strength cannot be derived until the detailed structure of the field in relationship to its sources is known. It is asserted here that the same connection is possible in magnetism that was chosen in the electric field case, that is, the field strength corresponds to the normal surface density of field lines. When the field is uniform in intensity, it is represented by straight, uniformly spaced lines. If an area S is constructed normal to the direction of the field, the magnetic flux ϕ is defined by

$$\phi \equiv BS. \qquad (23\text{–}8)$$

If the field is not uniform and if the surface is not perpendicular to the field, we use the more general expression

$$d\phi = \mathbf{B} \cdot d\mathbf{S}, \qquad (23\text{–}9)$$

just as in the case of electric fields. The vector $d\mathbf{S}$ has the direction of the normal to the surface element $d\mathbf{S}$ (outwardly directed for closed surfaces).

The net flux through any surface is then given by an integral over the surface,

$$\phi = \iint \mathbf{B} \cdot d\mathbf{S}. \qquad (23\text{–}10)$$

Further discussion is left until later.

23–4 MOTION OF A PARTICLE IN A CONSTANT MAGNETIC FIELD

We first consider only magnetic fields that do not vary with time. The work done by a force is $dW = \mathbf{F} \cdot d\mathbf{s}$ during a small displacement $d\mathbf{s}$. The direction of the magnetic force was found to be perpendicular to $\mathbf{v}$ or $d\mathbf{s}/dt$. Therefore, $dW = |\mathbf{F}|\,|d\mathbf{s}| \cos\theta$ is zero, because θ is always 90° for the magnetic force.

A direct consequence of the above is that the speed must remain constant in a pure magnetic field. If there is an electric field as well, the particle can change speed, as we have seen in the preceding chapters. The case of time-dependent magnetic fields will be treated in later chapters.

In the special case of *uniform magnetic fields*, the motion of charged particles is relatively simple. If the *initial velocity is perpendicular to* **B**, both the force and the velocity lie in a fixed plane, perpendicular to **B**. Since the force is constant in magnitude and always perpendicular to **v**, the resultant motion is a circle, as we learned in mechanics. If a cylindrical polar coordinate

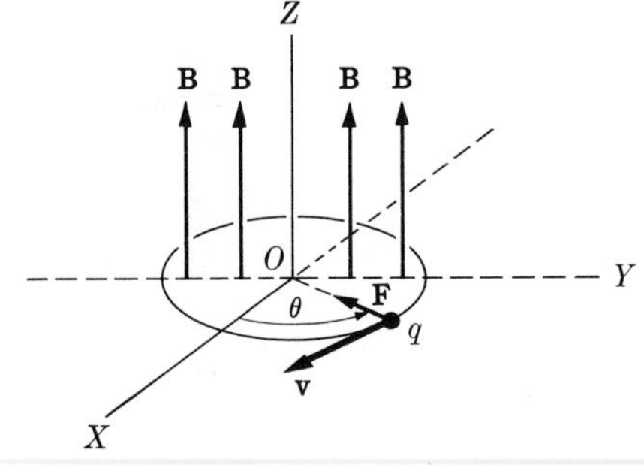

FIG. 23–9. Circular motion of a charge that is given an initial velocity **v** perpendicular to a uniform magnetic field **B**.

system is chosen with the OZ-axis in the direction of $\mathbf{B}$ as in Fig. 23–9, and passing through the center of the circular path, we have, from Newton's second law, $\sum F_r = ma_r$. The result is

$$qvB = \frac{mv^2}{r},$$

or, canceling the v,

$$qB = \frac{mv}{r}. \tag{23–11}$$

When the velocity is expressed in terms of the angular velocity, $\omega \equiv v/r$, the above equation becomes

$$\omega = \frac{qB}{m}, \tag{23–12}$$

which shows that the angular velocity (and hence the period) is independent of velocity. This result will be generalized after Example 1.

Example 1. Most of the accelerators that are used to produce beams of high-energy particles for studies of nuclear physics utilize magnetic fields to constrain the motion of the particles. Find the magnetic field required to constrain a beam of protons of energy 10 Mev in a circular path of radius 200 m.

Solution: The velocity of the protons is obtained from $W = eU = \frac{1}{2}mv^2$, where e is the charge (electronic), U is 10^6 v, etc. Thus $v = \sqrt{2eU/m}$.

The motion of the proton is given by Eq. (23–9). Therefore,

$$B = \frac{mv}{er} = \frac{\sqrt{2Um/e}}{r}$$

$$= \frac{\sqrt{2 \times 10^7 \times 1.8 \times 10^{-27}/1.6 \times 10^{-19}}}{200}$$

or

$$B = 2.3 \times 10^{-4} \text{ weber/m}^2.$$

We now consider the motion in a uniform field if the initial velocity is not perpendicular to $\mathbf{B}$. We again choose polar coordinates with OZ in the *direction* of B (Fig. 23–10), leaving the question of the *position* of OZ until later. The velocity can be resolved into components v_z and v_θ, parallel and perpendicular, respectively, to OZ. Since the force, $q\mathbf{v} \times \mathbf{B}$ has no z-component, $v_z = \text{constant} = v_0 \cos \beta$.

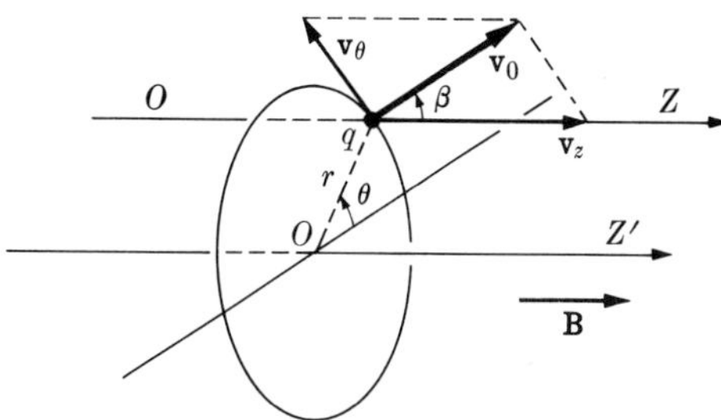

FIG. 23–10. A charge q is given an initial velocity $\mathbf{v}_0$ at an angle β with a uniform magnetic field $\mathbf{B}$. The velocity $\mathbf{v}_0$ is shown resolved into components parallel (v_z) and perpendicular (v_θ) to the field. The component v_z remains constant, but the θ-component rotates, and the projection of the path on the plane perpendicular to $\mathbf{B}$ is circular.

The force is always perpendicular to $\mathbf{v}$ and hence perpendicular to the component $\mathbf{v}_\theta$. Thus, the projection of the motion in the polar plane will be circular. In particular, if the polar axis OZ' passes through the center of the circle,

$$F = F_r = qBv \sin \beta = qBv_\theta,$$

and applying Newton's second law,

$$qBv_\theta = ma_r = \frac{mv_\theta^2}{r}.$$

It is instructive to express this result in terms of angular velocity ω,

$$qB = m\omega,$$

showing that the angular velocity and hence the frequency and period are again independent of the magnitude and direction of the initial velocity. The frequency,

$$f = \frac{qB}{2\pi m}, \tag{23–13}$$

is called the cyclotron frequency (see Problems). Since v_z remains constant, the path of the charged

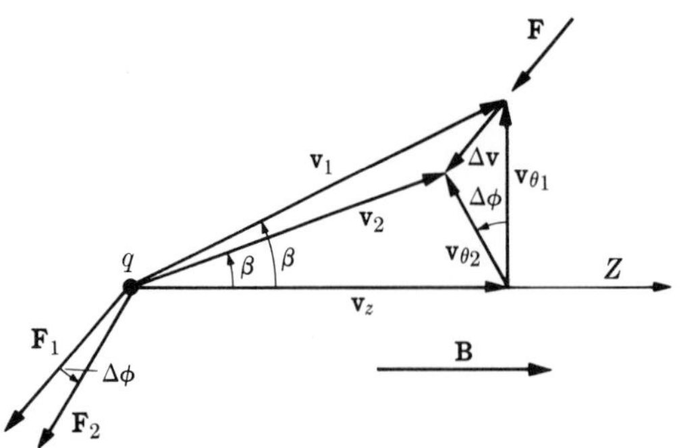

FIG. 23–11. A charged particle with velocity $\mathbf{v}_1$ at an angle β with a uniform magnetic field $\mathbf{B}$ experiences a force $\mathbf{F}$ that changes the direction of $\mathbf{v}_1$ to the new direction $\mathbf{v}_2$, such that β is unchanged. The component $\mathbf{v}_z$ is unchanged while the component $\mathbf{v}_\theta$ changes direction without change in magnitude.

particle is a helix of constant pitch. The period τ is then

$$\tau = \frac{2\pi m}{qB}. \tag{23–14}$$

A more general picture of the motion is obtained by examining the change in velocity *before* resolving it into components. The change in velocity $\Delta\mathbf{v}$ is in the direction perpendicular to $\mathbf{B}$ and to the instantaneous velocity $\mathbf{v}$ (Fig. 23–11). Since $\mathbf{F}$ is always perpendicular to $\mathbf{v}$, it does not change the magnitude of $\mathbf{v}$. Since $\mathbf{F}$ is also always perpendicular to $\mathbf{B}$, it does not change the direction of $\mathbf{v}_z$. It changes only the direction of $\mathbf{v}_\theta$, as shown. Strictly, $\Delta\mathbf{v}$ is in the direction of $\mathbf{F} = (\mathbf{F}_1 + \mathbf{F}_2)/2$, but in the limit as $\Delta\mathbf{v} \to 0$ this subtlety is unimportant. Therefore, we see that $\Delta\mathbf{v}_{12} = \Delta\mathbf{v}_{12\theta}$, which justifies the earlier, intuitive, argument.

Example 2. Show that a narrow conical beam of charged particles, all leaving a point source at the same speed, can be approximately focused by a uniform longitudinal magnetic field.

Solution: Choose the OZ-axis parallel to B and through the point source. Then a particle of velocity $\mathbf{v}$ will move in a helix whose projection is a circle (Fig. 23–12a). The particle will complete one revolution and therefore *return to the OZ-axis* in $2\pi m/qB$ seconds (Eq. 23–14) independent of velocity.* The end view shows that a particle 2 of higher velocity simply moves in a proportionally larger helix. The point z_1 (Fig. 23–12b) at which any particle crosses the Z-axis is given by

$$z_1 = v_z t_1 = \frac{v_z 2\pi m}{qB} = \frac{v_o(\cos\beta)2\pi m}{qB}.$$

For small angles of emission β,

$$z_1 \simeq \frac{v_o 2\pi m}{qB},$$

showing that z_1 is about the same for all the particles of the same initial speed $|\mathbf{v}_0|$ (Fig. 23–12b).

* The radius of the helix, $r = mv_\theta/(qB)$, is directly proportional to v_θ and, therefore, the period is independent of v_θ.

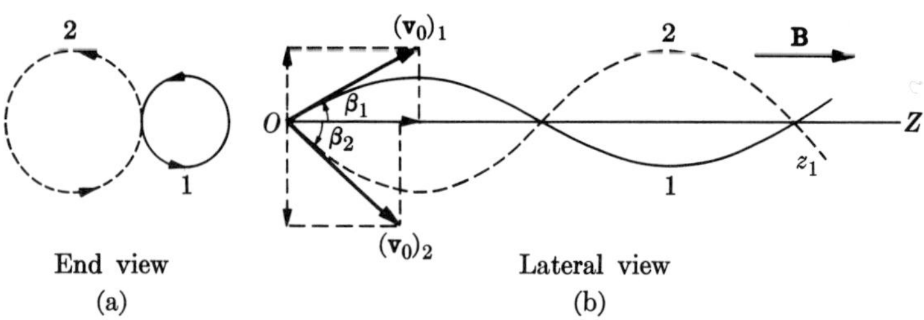

FIG. 23–12. End view (a) and lateral view (b) of the trajectories of two charged particles in a uniform magnetic field $\mathbf{B}$. The particles leave the origin O with velocities that differ in direction but not in magnitude. They return to approximately the same point, z_1, on the OZ-axis.

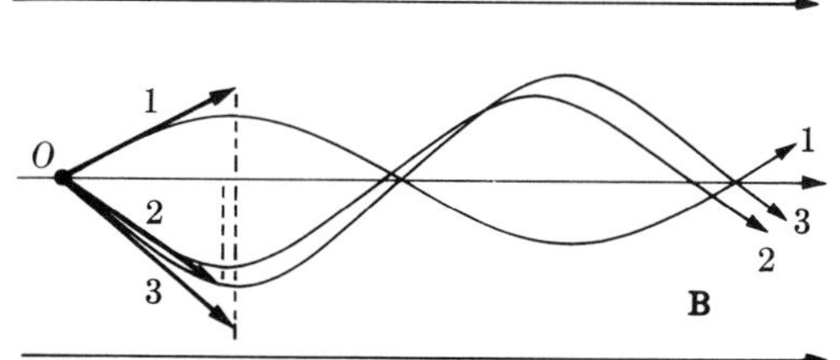

FIG. 23-13. Three particles leave point O with velocities at different angles relative to a uniform magnetic field B. Particles 1 and 2 have the same speed but they do not cross the axis at nearly the same point because the angles with **B** are *not* small. Particles 1 and 3 return to the same point because their components along B are the same.

The result of Example 2 is the basis for the "magnetic" focusing used to obtain images with the electron microscope. The combination of a constant drift velocity parallel to the field and circular motion perpendicular to the field is a helical trajectory. In the helical motion we have noted that after every completed period of revolution, the particle returns to the field line upon which it started. This is a "trapping" effect of a magnetic field which can be summarized as follows: A charged particle in motion in a uniform magnetic field is constrained to move in a region *along* the magnetic field lines; it will never permanently leave any field line which it has once crossed if there are no other forces acting on it. In general, particles starting with the same speed from a common point O in space will not return to a common second point (Fig. 23-13, particles 1 and 2) even though they must return to the same line of the uniform B field. We have seen above that the trajectories will have approximately common points of crossing if the speeds are the same and the angles of the velocity with B are small. Obviously, the condition for an exactly common point of crossing is that the longitudinal components of velocity must be equal (Fig. 23-13, particles 1 and 3).

In *nonuniform* magnetic fields the motion of charged particles is more complex. The force and hence the acceleration at any point can be found from Eq. (23-4). We have proved that the energy and speed remain constant. But the paths may be complex, and numerical methods of computation must be employed in most cases. Certain qualitative features are apparent. In two examples we will consider particular configurations of magnetic fields. (The main discussion of the origin of magnetic fields will be left until the next chapter.)

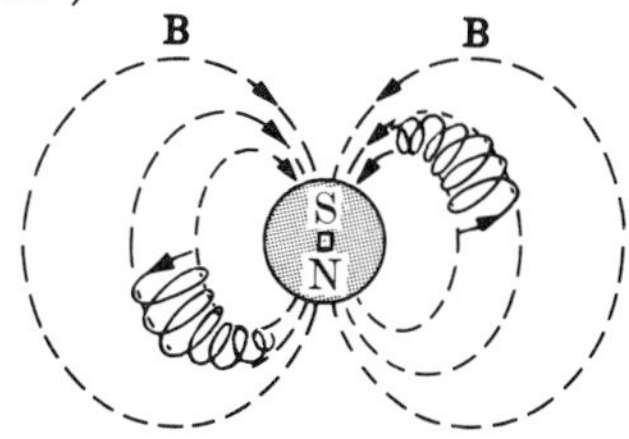

FIG. 23-14. Some of the magnetic field lines of the earth (dashed lines) and resulting trajectories (solid lines) of particles trapped in Van Allen belts.

The magnetic field of the earth is not at all uniform over distances comparable with the dimensions of the earth. However, the field out to several earth radii is quite regular, as shown in Fig. 23-14 by the dashed lines.

Charged particles above the atmosphere of the earth move in helices about the magnetic field lines (Fig. 23-14). As the particles approach the polar regions, the field lines converge, with two results. The radius of the spiral diminishes because the field intensity increases. In addition the force has a component back toward the equatorial region. If the particle energy is not too high, its component of velocity along the field lines is reversed. Thus, particles with energies up to a few Mev spiral back and forth from one polar region to the other. These particles constitute the Van Allen belts of radiation. They ultimately leave these regions because of scattering by collisions, because of energy loss when the point of reversal of the helix is in the upper atmosphere, or because of perturbing effects on the magnetic field or on the particle motion caused by the magnetic effects of streams of particles from the sun.

Effects of a similar sort can be used to produce magnetic "bottles" that prevent charged particles from reaching the walls of the container if they are not deflected by collisions with other particles. Such methods are being employed to contain "plasmas" (i.e., gases of ionized atoms) in studies of controlled fusion.

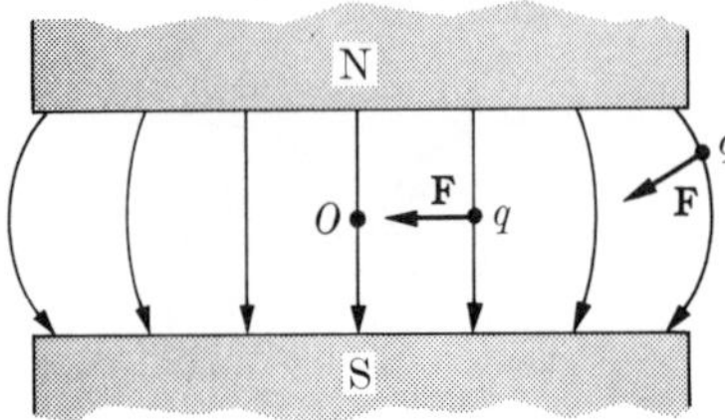

FIG. 23-15. Forces on charges at two different points in the field of a typical electromagnet with cylindrical steel pole pieces. The charges (positive) are moving into the page. The force on the charge near the periphery of the magnet poles is seen to have a component that restores the charge toward the central plane.

A second example is the focusing effect in the fringing field of a cyclotron (Fig. 23-15). The useful part of the magnetic field of a cyclotron is located between two cylindrical iron poles, N and S, of a large electromagnet. The field is essentially uniform in the central region if the poles are flat, but the field becomes nonuniform at the edges of the poles, as shown. Particles move in nearly circular paths in the central plane CC', seen edge-on between the poles N and S. The particles spiral outward as their energy is increased by suitable application of alternating electric fields. If particles in orbits of radii comparable with the pole radii wander from the central plane, they experience restoring forces, as shown in Fig. 23-15. (In recently built cyclotrons, nonuniform fields are deliberately created throughout the space between the poles by means of ridges and valleys on the pole faces. Net focusing is thereby produced for particles at any radius. The mechanism of this focusing is a bit complex and will be left for classroom discussion.)

23-5 MOTION IN MAGNETIC AND ELECTRIC FIELDS (MEASUREMENT OF q/m)

In a uniform magnetic field, the momentum-to-charge ratio for a particle can be determined from measured values of B and r. Equation (23-11) leads to

$$\frac{mv}{q} = \frac{p}{q} = Br. \tag{23-15}$$

If the charge is known, the momentum is known,

$$p = qBr. \tag{23-16}$$

Equation (23-16) is also relativistic, since the magnitude of v and hence of m is constant.

In the first studies of a new atomic particle, neither the mass nor the charge is known and hence the most that can be learned from the motion in a magnetic field is p/q.

When an electric field is added, a different combination of q, m, and v can be measured. For example, we have already seen that an electric field in the direction of motion gives a particle starting from rest the kinetic energy (nonrelativistic) given by

$$\tfrac{1}{2}mv^2 = q\,\Delta U, \tag{23-17}$$

where ΔU is the difference in potential through which the particle is accelerated. Thus, by combining the results of (23-15) and (23-17), q/m can be found in terms of measurable quantities. The experimental result for electrons is

$$q/m = 1.76 \times 10^{11}\ \text{coul/kg}.$$

The motion of charged particles in uniform *lateral* electric fields produces a parabolic trajectory. From the observed trajectory, mv^2/q can be determined. Again, if the particle trajectory is also observed in a magnetic field, the ratio q/m can be found.

The combined effects of electric and magnetic fields in the *same region* can also be utilized. If the fields and the velocity are mutually perpendicular, as in Fig. 23-16, the forces are along the

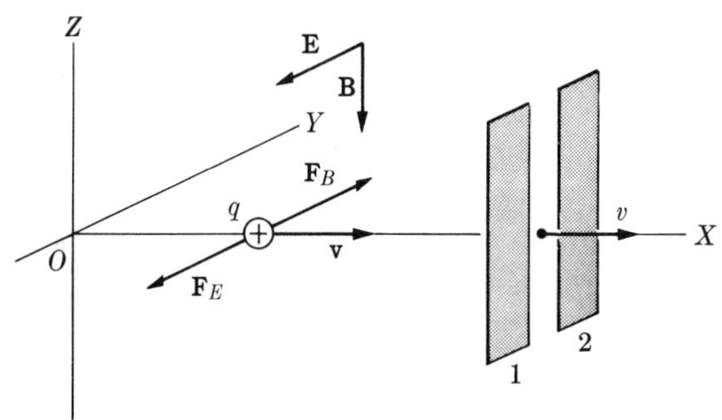

FIG. 23–16. A positively charged particle q moving at right angles to a uniform electric field and a uniform magnetic field. The two fields are perpendicular, as shown. The magnitudes and directions of the fields are such that the forces are equal and opposite. The path of the particle is therefore rectilinear.

same line. If, in addition, the fields are adjusted in magnitude so that $qvB = qE$, we have

$$v = \frac{E}{B}. \tag{23–18}$$

In this way, the velocity can be measured directly. This measurement can then be combined with any of the others treated previously, in order to obtain q/m.

In the above discussion, we have assumed that all the particles had the *same velocity*. If the beam is not homogeneous in velocity, the "crossed field" method of Fig. 23–16 can be used with a slit to select a beam of velocity given by Eq. (23–18). Slower particles will strike screen 1 and faster particles screen 2.

Another method, which was used historically to study beams of charged atoms that were inhomogeneous both in velocity and in q/m ratio, utilizes parallel (transverse) fields (Fig. 23–17). Since one force depends on velocity and the other does not, the beam fans out and leaves a parabolic trace on a screen as shown.

Each point on a parabola corresponds to a different velocity.

Each parabola corresponds to atoms of a particular q/m ratio.

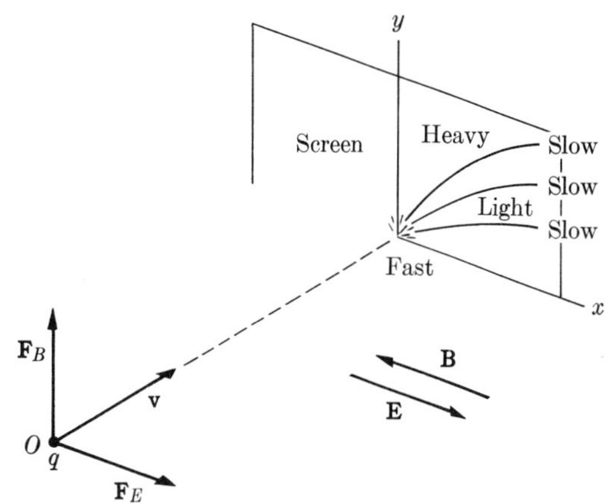

FIG. 23–17. Positive particles start from O all in the same direction and move in a region of uniform E and B fields, as shown. The velocities of the particles have a continuous range of values within certain limits. Three different charge-to-mass ratios are assumed. The particles are spread out into sheet-like beams whose parabolic traces on a screen are shown. Each parabola corresponds to a different charge to mass ratio.

The experimental result for the proton is $q/m = 0.96 \times 10^8$ coul/kg.

Since all electric or magnetic forces are directly proportional to q, all accelerations are proportional to q/m and no combination of observed motions will permit a determination of q or m separately. This difficulty was overcome by Millikan in his famous *oil-drop experiment* (see Problems). In this experiment, the charge-to-mass ratio of tiny oil drops was measured by the observed effect of the force by an electric field on charged drops. But the oil drops were large enough so that the effect of air resistance was observable and permitted the measurement of the size and, hence, the mass of a particular drop. On the other hand, the drops were small enough so that a net charge of a few electrons sufficed to permit electric forces comparable with the weight of the drop. Millikan made the remarkable discovery that changes of charge on a drop occurred but the total charge was always a multiple of 1.6×10^{-19} coul. Thus the electron charge was determined. The charge of other atomic particles can be determined by comparison of a property, such as ionizing power, which depends only on velocity and charge, or, in the case of the proton, by the observed electrical neutrality of non-ionized hydrogen.

Once the charge of an atomic particle is known, the *mass* is found from the measurement of q/m. The results are $m_e = 9.1 \times 10^{-31}$ kg; $m_{\text{proton}} = 1.67 \times 10^{-27}$ kg.

23–6 FORCE ON A CURRENT-CARRYING WIRE

When electric charges move in a wire that is immersed in a magnetic field, the moving electric charge experiences the usual magnetic force of free charges. If the wire has finite cross section (that is, if it is not a line) the charges will be deflected from their paths, as in Fig. 23–18. If the current is in the OX-direction and B in the OY-direction, as shown in Fig. 23–18, either positive or negative carriers would be deflected upward as shown. The result would be a transverse electric field, downward if the current is due primarily to positive carriers, and upward if the current is due primarily to negative carriers. This Hall effect is used to determine the nature of the carriers and their interactions with the medium. In the case of metals, electrons are the carriers.

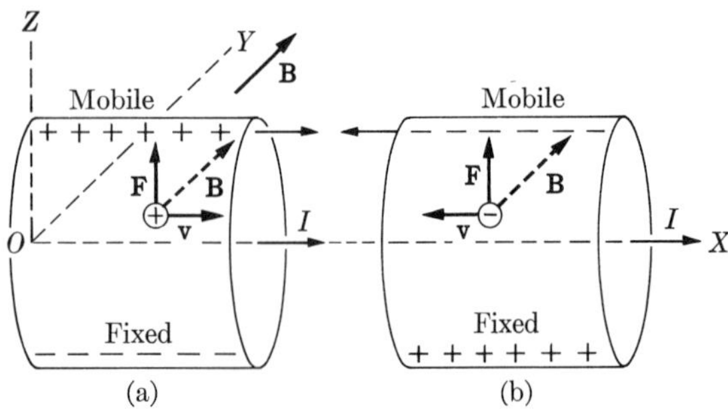

FIG. 23–18. Effect of a transverse magnetic field on the charges moving through (a) a conductor with mobile positive current carriers and (b) mobile negative current carriers. The conventional current is to the right in both cases. The result is a transverse separation of charge in both cases (in a plane perpendicular to the transverse magnetic field). However, the polarity of the charge separation is different in the two cases.

The transverse deflection concentrates the current toward one face of a conductor. The resulting transverse separation of charge reaches a steady state when the resulting transverse electric field produces an electrostatic attraction on the moving charge that balances the magnetic force on the moving charge. However, the only *external force* due to electrical effects is the force by the magnetic field on the moving stream of charge. The charges cannot escape from the wire and hence the lateral force on the moving charges must be sustained by the wire as a whole. The mechanism in the case of conductors is that the external force acts on the moving electrons. The electrons in turn transmit the lateral force to the wire partly by their electrostatic attraction for the excess positive charge on the other side of the wire but mostly by collisions with the atoms of the crystal lattice of the wire. Finally, the positive charges in turn exert the force on the wire as a whole, since they are bound in the crystal lattice of the wire.

For most purposes, we need not be concerned with the above details. We simply use the result that the wire must experience the sum of the external forces on the individual carriers.

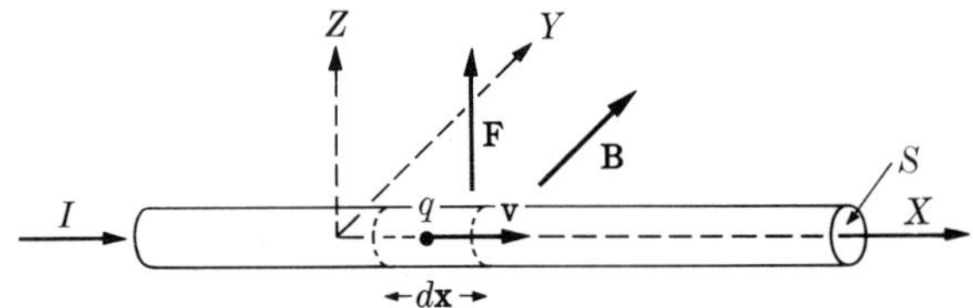

FIG. 23–19. The force **F** on a wire carrying a current I in a direction perpendicular to a magnetic field B.

We shall now calculate the force on a current-carrying conductor. Cartesian coordinates are chosen, as shown in Fig. 23–19. Consider an element of wire of cross-sectional area S and length dx containing (dn) carriers of charge e

moving with average velocity component v in the direction of the wire axis. A magnetic field B is perpendicular to the wire axis. The force on element $d\mathbf{x}$ is then

$$d\mathbf{F} = (dn)e\mathbf{v} \times \mathbf{B} \tag{23–19}$$

or

$$d\mathbf{F} = (dn)e\frac{d\mathbf{x}}{dt} \times \mathbf{B} = \frac{dq}{dt}\, d\mathbf{x} \times \mathbf{B}. \tag{23–20}$$

But since $dq/dt = I$, we have

$$d\mathbf{F} = I\, d\mathbf{l} \times \mathbf{B} \tag{23–21}$$

for the force on any element of wire of length $d\mathbf{l}$ carrying current I in a magnetic field. The force on a wire of finite length is found by the integration

$$\mathbf{F} = \int I\, d\mathbf{l} \times \mathbf{B}. \tag{23–22}$$

In the special case of a straight wire segment of length L in a uniform magnetic field at angle α relative to the field,

$$|\mathbf{F}| = IL|\mathbf{B}| \sin \alpha. \tag{23–23}$$

Example 3. Find the current necessary to support a horizontal wire in a horizontal magnetic field of intensity B if B is perpendicular to the wire.

Solution: The force due to the magnetic field must be equal and opposite to the pull by the earth, thus $I\,L\,B = mg$. If ρ is the density and S is the cross-sectional area of the wire, we find

$$I = \frac{mg}{LB} = \rho S g/B.$$

23–7 ENERGY INTERCHANGES

Consider a simple circuit made up of a battery joined to an open U-shaped wire and closed by a length L of wire that is free to move along the arms of the U, as in Fig. 23–20. If the circuit is immersed in a uniform magnetic field normal to the circuit, the cross wire L experiences a magnetic force $F_B = IBL$. During a displacement ds in the direction of F_B, work will be done by the magnetic force in amount

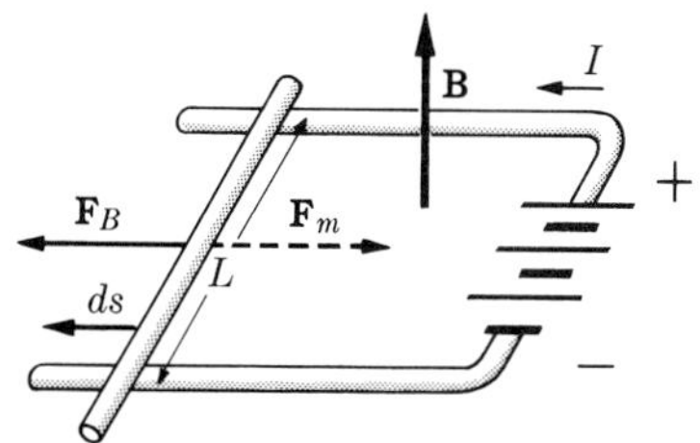

Fig. 23–20. A straight wire of length L and carrying a current I experiences a force $\mathbf{F}_B$ due to a magnetic field $\mathbf{B}$. An additional force $\mathbf{F}_m$ by an outside agent is required for equilibrium.

$$dW = F_B\, ds = IBL\, ds. \tag{23–24}$$

If there is no other horizontal force, this work will increase the kinetic energy of the wire L. If an outside force, $F_m = -F_B$, is also applied to the wire, its velocity will remain constant and the work by the magnetic force will be done *on* an outside agent, the agent that exerts the force F_m.

Now consider the general case in which B makes an angle α with an element dL of the sliding wire and the displacement ds of this element makes an angle θ with the normal to the B, dL-plane (Fig. 23–21). Axes are chosen, with OY along B, and dL lying in the OXY-plane.

The work done by the magnetic force in a displacement ds is $dW = \mathbf{F}_B \cdot d\mathbf{s}$, or

$$dW = I\, d\mathbf{L} \times \mathbf{B} \cdot d\mathbf{s} = I\, dLB \sin \alpha\, ds \cos \theta, \tag{23–25}$$

where α is the angle between $d\mathbf{L}$ and $\mathbf{B}$, and θ is the angle between $d\mathbf{s}$ and $\mathbf{F}_B$.

The vectors $d\mathbf{L}$, $\mathbf{B}$, and $d\mathbf{s}$ form the edges of a parallelepipedon (Fig. 23–21). The product $B\, dL \sin \alpha$ is the area of the BL face and $ds \cos \theta$ is the projected height. Therefore, $d\mathbf{L} \times \mathbf{B} \cdot d\mathbf{s}$ is the volume. Clearly, the product is unchanged if the order of the terms is changed in the above product. Some orders of multiplication will, however, give negative answers. The positive

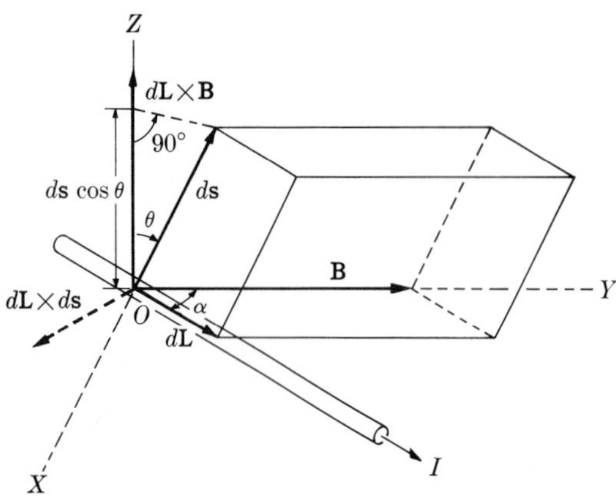

FIG. 23–21. Illustration of the three vectors $d\mathbf{L}$ (along the current-carrying wire), $\mathbf{B}$ (the magnetic field), and $d\mathbf{s}$ (the displacement of the wire) that are involved in calculating the work done by the magnetic force. The triple scalar products of Eqs. (23–25) and (23–26) are represented by the volume of the parallelepipedon. The cross-product factors in the triple scalar products are shown.

answers correspond to the ordering of the cross-product terms such that the cross-product vector points into the same hemisphere as the third edge. Hence, $d\mathbf{L} \times \mathbf{B} \cdot d\mathbf{s} = -\mathbf{B} \cdot d\mathbf{L} \times d\mathbf{s}$, where the cross product must always be taken first so that the triple product has meaning.

We can now rewrite (23–25) as

$$dW = -I\mathbf{B} \cdot d\mathbf{L} \times d\mathbf{s}, \qquad (23\text{–}26)$$

but $d\mathbf{L} \times d\mathbf{s}$ is just the area $d\mathbf{S}$ swept out by the wire in moving a distance $d\mathbf{s}$. Therefore,

$$dW = -I\mathbf{B} \cdot d\mathbf{S} = -I\, d\phi, \qquad (23\text{–}27)$$

according to our earlier definition of flux, $d\phi = \mathbf{B} \cdot d\mathbf{S}$. Note that it was not necessary for $\mathbf{B}$ to be independent of position in the above analysis. The flux $d\phi$ is simply the change in flux enclosed by the closed circuit or the flux "cut" by the wire element $d\mathbf{L}$ in moving the distance $d\mathbf{s}$.

Thus mechanical work is obtained in amount calculable from the preceding equations of this section. Clearly, this energy must originate as electrical energy delivered by the battery, but at this point we are at a loss as to how to calculate this energy from electrical properties. The electrical energy transformations that do not result in joule heating (I^2Rt) have previously been described in terms of an emf by $I\mathcal{E}t$. We have seen that such an emf, one that involves conversion of electrical to chemical or mechanical energy, opposes the current flow. We now hypothesize such an emf to account for the energy conversion discussed above. Then we have

$$dW = -I\, d\phi = I\mathcal{E}\, dt, \qquad (23\text{–}28)$$

where the minus sign indicates that the emf opposes the current. We can immediately rewrite Eq. (23–28) to obtain

$$\mathcal{E} = -\frac{d\phi}{dt} \qquad (23\text{–}29)$$

for the back emf that accounts for the energy transformation. The battery thus delivers an amount of power $\mathcal{E}I$ to the external circuit, which is transformed to mechanical power. *The magnetic field simply acts as an agent that enables this transformation to take place.* The "energy of the magnetic field" has not entered into the discussion. In fact it remained unaltered in the case we considered, since B was assumed constant with time. When $\mathbf{B}$ is constant with time, Eq. (23–27) can be written in terms of velocity as follows: Since $d\phi/dt = \mathbf{B} \cdot \mathbf{L} \times d\mathbf{s}/dt = \mathbf{B} \cdot \mathbf{L} \times \mathbf{v}$, we have

$$\mathcal{E} = -\mathbf{B} \cdot \mathbf{L} \times \mathbf{v}. \qquad (23\text{–}30)$$

The emf introduced in an *ad hoc* manner in this section will be justified in detail in a later chapter.

23–8 FORCE AND TORQUE ON A CURRENT LOOP

For simplicity, we select a loop of the form of a rectangular frame of sides a and b in a uniform field B (Fig. 23–22). The net forces on the *horizontal* members a of the loop are equal, in the same line, and opposite. There is neither a net

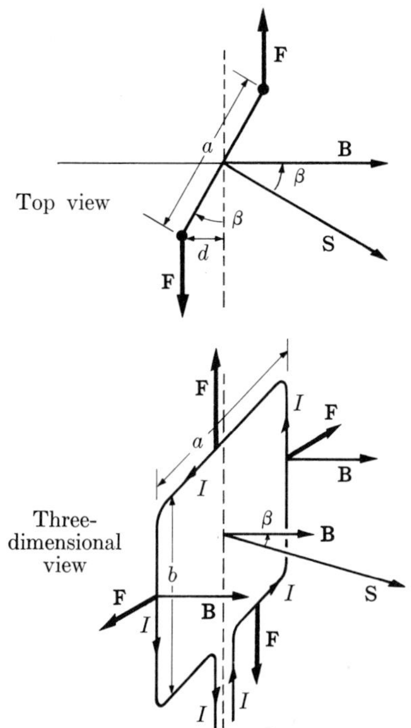

FIG. 23–22. The forces on the sides of a rectangular loop of current-carrying wire placed in a uniform magnetic field.

force nor a net torque due to those forces. In the case shown, these forces tend to expand the loop, and if the current is reversed, these forces tend to compress the loop. Since the loop is presumed to be rigid, these forces produce no changes.

On the vertical members of the loop, the forces are also equal and opposite, but the lines of action of the forces are generally not along the same line. There is no net force on the loop but there may be a torque. We can say generally at this point that a *closed circuit experiences no net force in a uniform magnetic field.*

The torque on the loop is caused by forces

$$F = BIb, \qquad (23\text{–}31)$$

whose moment arms are (Fig. 23–22)

$$d = \frac{(a \sin \beta)}{2} \cdot \qquad (23\text{–}32)$$

The torque is given by the product of force times moment arm (times two, since there are two forces),

$$\tau = 2F\,d = BIab \sin \beta = BIS \sin \beta, \qquad (23\text{–}33)$$

where S is the area.

A property of the loop, independent of magnetic field or the orientation of the loop, is the product Iab. This is the current in the loop times the loop area. It is called the *magnetic moment* M of the loop and it is defined by

$$M \equiv IS \text{ amp–m}^2. \qquad (23\text{–}34)$$

Then the torque can be written (uniform B),

$$\tau = MB \sin \beta. \qquad (23\text{–}35)$$

It is conventional to represent the magnetic moment as a vector quantity. It is a vector whose magnitude is given by the definition above and whose direction is given by the direction of **S**, namely, normal to the plane of the loop. The sense of **S** is undefined so far as the area itself is concerned. Therefore, the sense is defined in terms of Eq. (23–35), to be seen later. It will turn out that the sense can be given by a "right-hand rule" in terms of the current around the loop. If the fingers of the right hand are curled in the direction of the current loop, the thumb points in the direction of **S** and hence of **M** (Fig. 23–23). When Eq. (23–35) is rewritten in

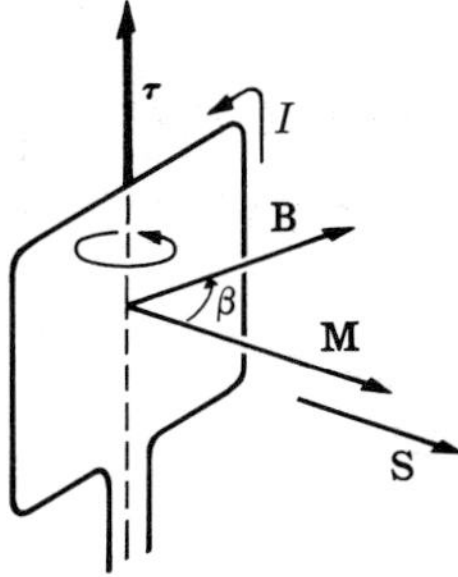

FIG. 23–23. The magnetic moment **M** of a current-carrying loop and the torque τ on the loop when it is placed in a magnetic field **B**.

vector notation, there results

$$\tau = \mathbf{M} \times \mathbf{B}. \tag{23–36}$$

The torque tends to rotate **M** into the direction of **B**. Although the torque is zero when **M** is antiparallel to **B**, this position is unstable in that the slightest displacement will result in a torque turning **M** parallel to **B**.

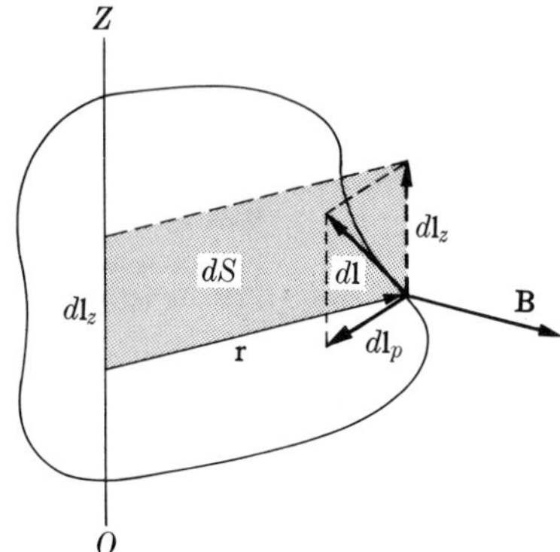

FIG. 23–24. Illustration of the vectors involved in the calculation of the torque on an irregularly-shaped current loop pivoted about an axis that is perpendicular to the magnetic field **B**.

The above derivation has been made for the case of a rectangular coil with the axis of rotation parallel to two sides. We now show that Eqs. (23–35) and (23–36) hold regardless of the shape for a coil pivoted on an axis that is perpendicular to a uniform magnetic field (Fig. 23–24). The OZ-axis is chosen along the axis of rotation of the coil, and cylindrical polar coordinates are used. An element of the loop dl is resolved into components dl_z and dl_p, that are, respectively, parallel and perpendicular to the OZ-axis. Since B also lies in the plane perpendicular to OZ, the force component $I\,d\mathbf{l}_p \times \mathbf{B}$ is parallel to OZ and exerts no torque about the OZ-axis. Note that dl need not lie in the OZr-plane. The torque by $d\tau$ about OZ is, therefore,

$$d\tau = \mathbf{r} \times d\mathbf{F} = \mathbf{r} \times (I\,d\mathbf{l}_z \times \mathbf{B}).$$

In *this special case* in which **r** and **B** are both perpendicular to dl_z, the student can show with a diagram that the order of the vector multiplication can be changed. The result is

$$d\tau = (\mathbf{r} \times I\,d\mathbf{l}_z) \times \mathbf{B} = I\,d\mathbf{S} \times \mathbf{B} = d\mathbf{M} \times \mathbf{B},$$

which, upon integration, gives

$$\tau = \mathbf{M} \times \mathbf{B} \tag{23–36}$$

for a loop of any shape in a uniform field perpendicular to the axis of rotation.

23–9 MOTION OF A CURRENT LOOP (METERS AND MOTORS)

If a current loop is free to rotate in a uniform magnetic field, we have

$$\sum \tau = -MB \sin\theta, \tag{23–37}$$

where the minus sign is introduced to show that the torque is a restoring torque that tends to return M to the direction of B. For small angles, $\sin\theta \approx \theta$. Newton's second law for rotation of rigid bodies, $\sum\tau = \mathfrak{M}\alpha$, where $\mathfrak{M}$ is the moment of inertia and α is the angular acceleration, becomes

$$-MB\theta = \mathfrak{M}\alpha, \tag{23–38}$$

which indicates that the motion is simple harmonic since the acceleration is directly proportional to the displacement. The period of the motion is

$$T = 2\pi\sqrt{\mathfrak{M}/k} \qquad \text{or} \qquad T = 2\pi\sqrt{\mathfrak{M}/(MB)}. \tag{23–39}$$

Thus, the strength of a magnetic field B can be measured by measuring the period of oscillation of a coil that carries current while in the field.

In many cases, a moving coil is mounted in a field that is radial over a wide range of angles. Since the field is radial, we have $\sin\theta = 1$ in Eq. (23–37). An iron core and iron pole pieces shaped as in Fig. 23–25 provide such a device in the standard movement of most electric meters. A spring is connected to the coil to provide a

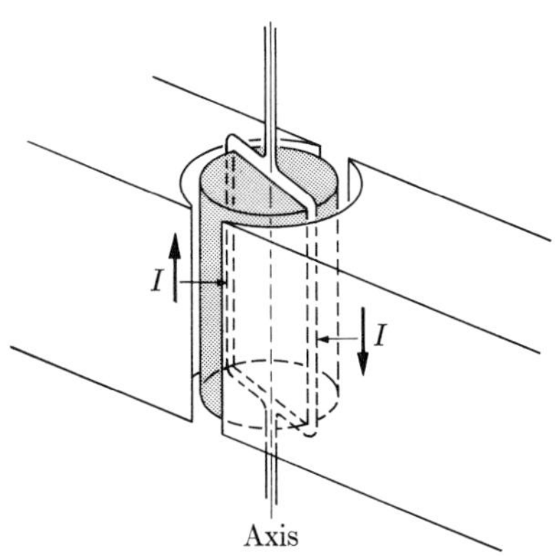

FIG. 23–25. A rectangular current-carrying loop that can rotate in a field that is directed radially. The result is that the torque due to the magnetic field is independent of angle.

restoring torque proportional to the displacement, $\tau_S = -K\theta$. Then when a current is passed through the coil, rotation occurs until $\sum \tau = 0$, that is,

$$ISB - K\theta = 0 \quad \text{or} \quad \theta = \left(\frac{SB}{K}\right) I. \tag{23–40}$$

Thus, we have a *meter* whose deflection is directly proportional to the current.

The typical basic meter, called a *galvanometer*, may deflect full scale for a current of a small fraction of an ampere and it may have a resistance of a few ohms. In order to extend its range to larger currents when it is used as an *ammeter*, low resistance "shunts" are put in parallel with the meter. Thus most of the current passes through the shunt with two results: The instrument can be used to measure larger currents, and the overall meter resistance can be made small enough so that it does not appreciably increase the resistance of the circuit into which it is introduced.

In order to measure potential differences, resistances are put in *series* with the basic meter, thus limiting the current to the rated value when the potential difference is applied. This also means that the current used in measuring the potential is as little as possible, thus minimizing changes produced in the circuit while making a measurement. The meter is therefore called a *voltmeter*.

Finally, if the coil is wound on the iron core (Fig. 23–25), and the coil and core are free to rotate, it is possible to have a torque that is always in the same direction. This is accomplished by carrying the current to the coil on a rotary switching device (commutator and brushes) that reverses the current at just the point where the torque would otherwise reverse. Such a device is called a *motor*. It is the same, in principle, as the linear motion device discussed at length in Section 23–7. It converts electrical energy into mechanical energy. The analysis of Section 23–7 applies equally to this case. The rotational motion is preferred because of mechanical convenience.

23–10 SUMMARY

Historically, the ideas of magnetic forces came from the discovery and study of the forces between permanent magnets. Later, it was found that electric currents in wires also give rise to magnetic forces. Today, all the magnetic effects that have been observed can be interpreted in terms of moving charges.

The magnetic field is defined as a property of a region that gives rise to a force on moving charges by virtue of their motion. The direction of the field is specified by the direction of motion of a charge that experiences no force due to its motion. For motion in a direction making an angle α with the field,

$$F = qvB \sin \alpha.$$

When the above equation is solved explicitly for B, it becomes the defining equation for the magnitude of the field. The mks unit for B is the weber per square meter. In vector notation, we have

$$\mathbf{F} = q\mathbf{v} \times \mathbf{B},$$

or, including the electric field,

$$\mathbf{F} = q(\mathbf{E} + \mathbf{v} \times \mathbf{B}).$$

The magnetic flux is defined by

$$\phi = \iint \mathbf{B} \cdot d\mathbf{S}.$$

A charged particle moving under the influence of a uniform magnetic field alone follows a circular path if its initial velocity is at right angles to the field. The angular velocity of the motion is independent of velocity and hence of the energy

$$\omega = \frac{qB}{m}.$$

If the initial velocity is not at right angles to the uniform field, the velocity component parallel with the field remains constant, while the projection of the path on the plane perpendicular to the field is a circle with motion at the above angular velocity. The path in space is a uniform helix. An application of these results for the case of particles originating from a common point with velocities of the same magnitude and angles with the field that are not too large leads to the idea of magnetic focusing; that is, all the particles return to nearly a common point.

The effects of "mirror" reflections and of focusing in nonuniform magnetic fields are described qualitatively in special cases.

The motion of charged particles in various combinations of uniform electric and magnetic fields is discussed. Applications that are used in the measurement of charge to mass ratios of atomic particles are treated. The results are q/m of 1.76×10^{11} coul/kg for the electron and q/m of 0.96×10^8 coul/kg for the proton.

The mechanism for the transfer of the force on charges moving within a conductor to the conductor itself is described. The force itself is

$$F = ILB \sin \alpha$$

on a straight wire of length L at angle α with the field. When the conductor is permitted to move under the influence of the magnetic force, work is done by the force in amount

$$dW = -I\, d\phi,$$

where $d\phi$ is the flux cut by the conductor. The work can be described in terms of a back emf

$$\mathcal{E} = -\frac{d\phi}{dt}.$$

The forces on a complete circuit loop located in a magnetic field result, in general, in a torque τ on the loop. In a uniform field

$$\tau = BIS \sin \beta,$$

where S is the area of the loop and β is the angle between the field and the normal to the plane of the loop. It is customary to define magnetic moment

$$\mathbf{M} = I\mathbf{S}$$

in terms of which

$$\tau = \mathbf{M} \times \mathbf{B}.$$

For small angular displacements from the position of zero torque, a current loop pivoted in a uniform magnetic field will execute simple harmonic angular motion. Electric motors are devices consisting of coils that experience torques in suitable magnetic field configurations, with continuous rotation made possible by either a rotating field or by a suitable switching device. Electric meters can be constructed by providing an elastic torque that opposes the magnetic torque, the deflection then becoming proportional to the current.

Problems

Constants: $m_e = 9 \times 10^{-31}$ kg;
$m_p = 1.66 \times 10^{-27}$ kg;
$q_e = -q_p = -1.6 \times 10^{-19}$ coul.

1. A uniform magnetic field B lies in the OY-direction, as shown in Fig. 23–26. Find the magnitude and direction of the force on a charge q whose instantaneous velocity is v for each of the directions shown in Fig. 23–26. The figure is a cube.

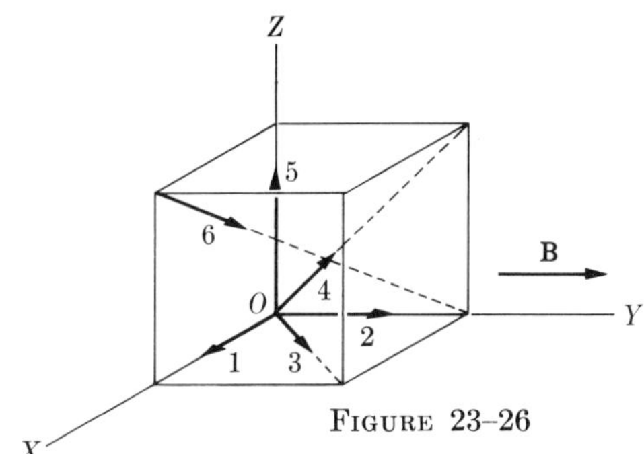

FIGURE 23–26

2. The strongest magnetic field that is reasonably obtainable over large volumes is about 1.5 webers/m^2.
(a) Find the radius of the path of a 30-Mev proton (nonrelativistic) in a field of this magnitude.
(b) The Brookhaven accelerator gives protons an energy of about 30 Bev (30×10^9 ev). Find the radius of the path of these particles in a field of 1.5 webers/m^2. [*Note:* The particles in (b) are relativistic and it is therefore necessary to use the expressions, total energy, $W = m_0c^2/\sqrt{1 - v^2/c^2}$, and momentum, $p = m_0v/\sqrt{1 - v^2/c^2}$.]

3. Protons of 3×10^6 ev kinetic energy are shot through a hole in a direction nearly parallel with a uniform magnetic field of strength 2 webers/m^2. In what distance will the particles return to a common point of intersection, that is, be refocused? What is the period of circulation in the magnetic field?

4. A proton circulates in a region of uniform magnetic field $B = 1.5$ webers/m^2. The field is restricted to a circular region of radius 0.05 m. Outside this region the field is zero. What is the maximum velocity that the proton can have such that it can be confined to a circular orbit in the field? What is the frequency of rotation? Through what potential difference must the proton be accelerated to have this maximum velocity?

5. A proton is in motion in a magnetic field at an angle of 30° with respect to the field lines. The velocity is 10^7 m/sec and the field strength is 1.5 webers/m^2. Compute:
(a) The radius of the helix of motion,
(b) the distance of advance per revolution,
(c) the frequency of rotation in the field.

6. Charged particles are shot into a region of crossed electric and magnetic fields. The incident particle velocity is normal to the plane of the two fields, and the fields are normal to each other. The magnetic field strength is 0.1 weber/m^2. The electric field is generated between a pair of equal and oppositely charged parallel plates, placed 2 cm apart. When the potential difference between the plates is 300 v, there is no deflection of the particles. What is the particle velocity?

7. Protons ($m = 1.66 \times 10^{-27}$ kg, $q = 1.6 \times 10^{-19}$ coul) are accelerated, from rest, through a potential difference of 10^6 v. These are then shot into a region of uniform magnetic field, with the trajectory perpendicular to the field. We use the greatest magnetic field strength which can be obtained in ordinary practice, which is about 2 mks units (2 webers/m^2). What will be the trajectory radius for the 10^6 v protons in a field of 2 webers/m^2?

8. One of the processes for separating U_{235} and U_{238} was based on the difference of radii of the paths in a magnetic field. Assume that singly ionized atoms of U start from a common source and move perpendicular to a uniform field. Find the maximum spatial separation of the beams when the radius of curvature of the U_{235} beam is 0.5 m in a field of 1.5 webers/m^2 (a) if the energies are the same, (b) if the velocities are the same.

9. Find the current density (assumed uniform) required in a horizontal aluminum wire to make it "float" in the earth's magnetic field. The density of Al is 2.7 gm/cm^3. Assume that the field is about 7×10^{-5} weber/m^2 and at an angle 75° below the horizontal. What should be the direction of the wire?

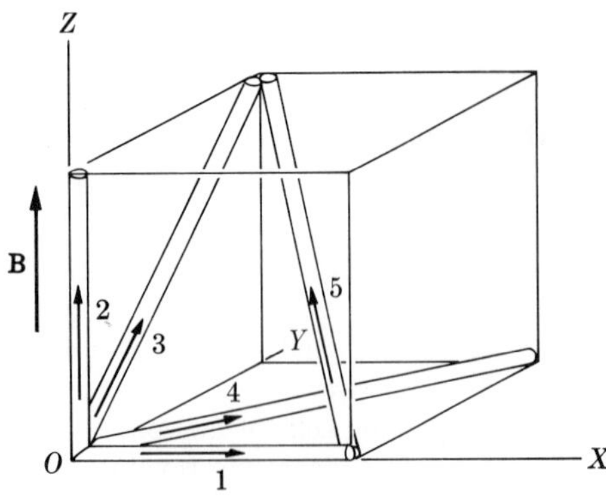

FIGURE 23–27

10. Find the force on each of the wire segments, Fig. 23–27, if the field, $B = 1.5$ webers/m^2, is parallel to OZ and $I = 2$ amp. An edge of the cube is 10 cm.

11. In Problem 4, what is the total flux in the magnetic field in the circular region? Is it necessary to have flux throughout the region in order to maintain the maximum energy proton in its circular path?

12. Suppose the sliding wire in Fig. 23–20 is perpendicular to the side rails, which are separated by a distance d.

(a) Assuming that the current remains constant, find the velocity of the wire segment as a function of time, starting from rest. Let the mass of the sliding wire be m and assume that friction is negligible.

(b) Write the equation that could be solved for the current if the wires have a resistance of r ohms per meter of length, the battery emf is E_0, and its $R = 0$.

13. Calculate the back emf in the wire in Problem 12(a) as a function of time.

14. Find the work done on the wire in Problem 12(a) as the wire moves a distance D. Account for the effect of the work (a) if the rod is free to slide, (b) if the rod is constrained to move at uniform velocity.

15. A wire loop, in the form of a square of side 10 cm, lies in the OX-plane, as shown in Fig. 23–28(a). A current of 10 amp flows in the loop, as shown. If the field B is given by $B_x = B_y = 0$ and $B_z = 0.1x$ weber/m^2, where x is in meters, find the force on each side of the square and the resultant force on the loop.

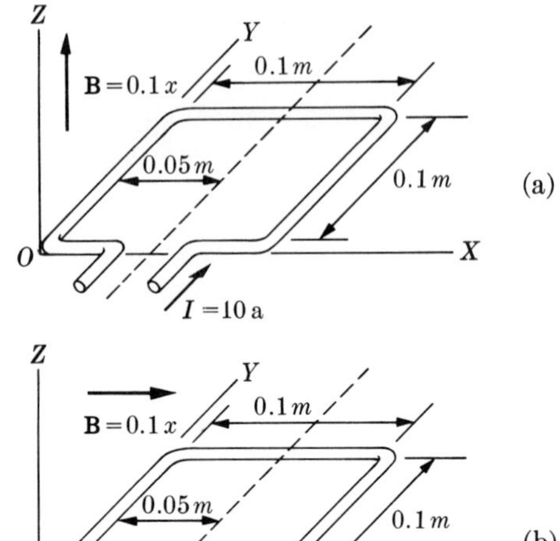

FIGURE 23–28

16. Repeat Problem 15, if $B_y = B_z = 0$ and $B_x = 0.1x$ weber/m^2 with x in meters (Fig. 23–28b).

17. Find the work to move the loop of Problem 15 a distance D (Fig. 23–28a) (a) in the OX-direction, (b) in the OY-direction, (c) in the OZ-direction.

18. Find the torque on a square coil of 200 turns of wire 5 cm on a side pivoted about one edge in a uniform magnetic field of 2 webers/m^2, when the plane of the coil is at an angle of 60° with B as shown in Fig. 23–29 and $I = 2a$.

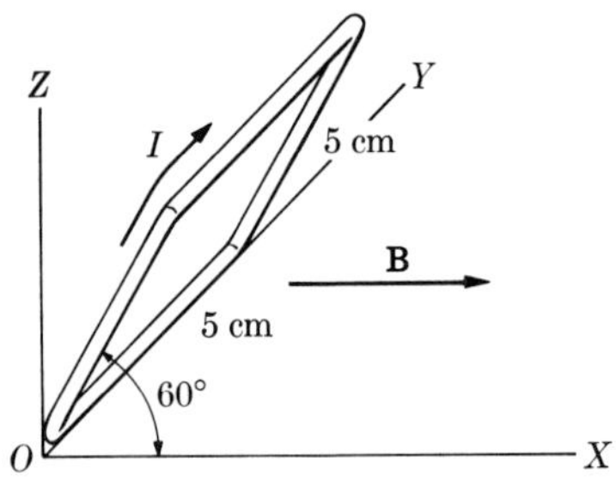

FIGURE 23–29

19. Find the torque on the loop in Fig. 23–28(b) if it is pivoted about an axis parallel to OY at $z = 0$, $x = 5$ cm.

20. A triangular loop of wire carrying a current of 5 amp lies in the XY-plane, as shown in Fig. 23–30. There is a magnetic field given by $B_y = B_z = 0$ and $B_x = 100x^2$ webers/m^2, where x is in meters.

(a) Find the forces on each of the three sides.

(b) Find the torque if the coil is pivoted about the OY-axis.

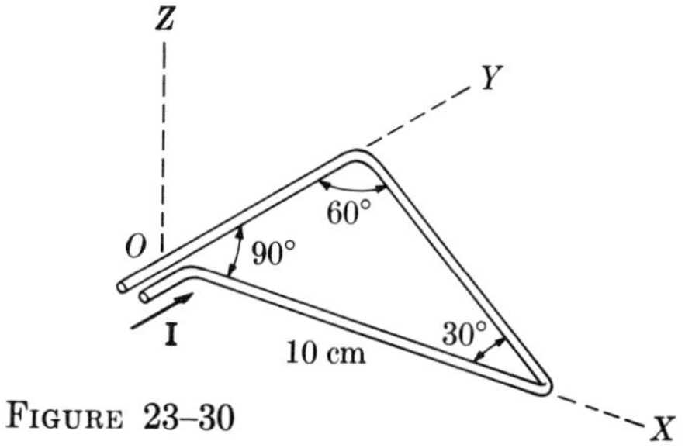

FIGURE 23–30

21. What would be the equilibrium angle of the loop in Fig. 23–28(b), i.e., at what angle is the torque zero? Will the loop execute simple harmonic motion (SHM) about the equilibrium angle? Write an equation for torque as a function of angular displacement from the equilibrium position.

22. Will the loop in Fig. 23–28(b) execute angular SHM about its equilibrium position if $B = 0.1x^2$?

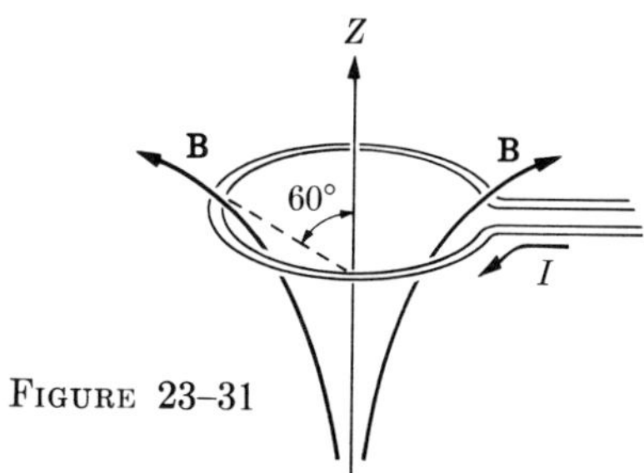

FIGURE 23–31

23. A circular loop of radius 30 cm centered on OZ is located in a divergent field, as shown in Fig. 23–31. The field is symmetrical about the Z-axis and makes an angle of 60° with OZ at the position of the wire. Find the force on the wire.

24. Prove that the effects are small of the closely spaced parallel wires leading to loops such as depicted in all the problems. Why is it desirable to twist the leads together if electrical torques due to the leads are to be minimized?

25. The work done by a torque τ is $W = \int_{\theta_1}^{\theta_2} \tau \, d\theta$.

(a) Find the work done by the magnetic forces when the coil in Problem 18 rotates from its position in Fig. 23–29 to the position of zero torque. What is the result of the work done by the magnetic forces?

(b) Find the work done when the coil of Fig. 23–28(b) rotates to the position of zero torque.

26. The electron in a hydrogen atom in its lowest energy state revolves about the proton in a circular orbit of radius $r_0 = 0.5 \times 10^{-10}$ m according to the Bohr model. The centripetal force is the electrostatic force of attraction.

(a) Find the frequency of revolution in terms of r_0, etc.

(b) If a magnetic field is applied perpendicular to the plane of the orbit, the centripetal force is the resultant of the electric and magnetic forces. Show that the *change* in angular frequency of revolution when a field B is applied, assuming that r_0 stays constant, is

$$\Delta\omega = \pm \frac{q}{m} B \frac{\omega}{\omega + \omega_0}$$

or, simply,

$$\pm \frac{q}{m}\frac{B}{2} \qquad \text{when} \qquad \omega \simeq \omega_0.$$

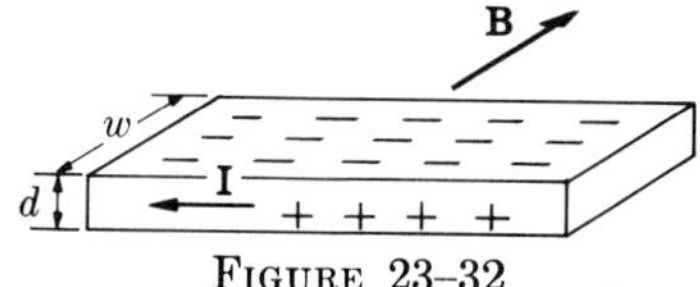

FIGURE 23–32

27. If a flat strip of conductor is placed in a transverse magnetic field, as in Fig. 23–32, the current density will become *nonuniform* with a concentration of electrons flowing along the top surface, leaving plus charges in excess along the bottom surface.

(a) Find the resulting transverse electric field for a current I in a magnetic field B. Let σ be the surface density of conducting charges. Assume (unrealistically) that the only forces on an electron are due to the field B and the electric field that you are calculating.

(b) Find the surface density of electrons on the upper face that would produce the field in (a).

28. Show that the traces on the screen in Fig. 23–17 are parabolas (that is, find y as a function of x) for the case of small deflections in x and y. For small deflections it can be assumed that v_z, F_E, and F_B are constant.

24

Production of Magnetic Fields

24–1 INTRODUCTION

In Chapter 23, the magnetic field was defined in terms of forces on charges moving in the field. The question of the origin of the field was left unanswered, at least, quantitatively. It is found that moving charges give rise to magnetic fields, that is, when the region surrounding a moving charge is explored by means of a second moving charge (used as a test charge), magnetic forces (described in the previous chapter) are experienced by the test charge. Fields of easily observed magnitude are most readily produced and studied in the case of a group of moving charges that constitute a current in a conductor. The current is said to be the "source" of the magnetic field. The field can, in principle, be explored and measured by the force on a moving charge or the torque on a small current-carrying coil (or even by the effect on a permanent magnet).

We start by exploring the field produced by a long, straight wire carrying a current I. The following results are derived from the observations:

(1) The magnetic field lines are everywhere circles concentric with the wire. The field vector B is tangent to these circles at all points, i.e., B has only the tangential component B_θ in polar coordinates (Fig. 24–1).

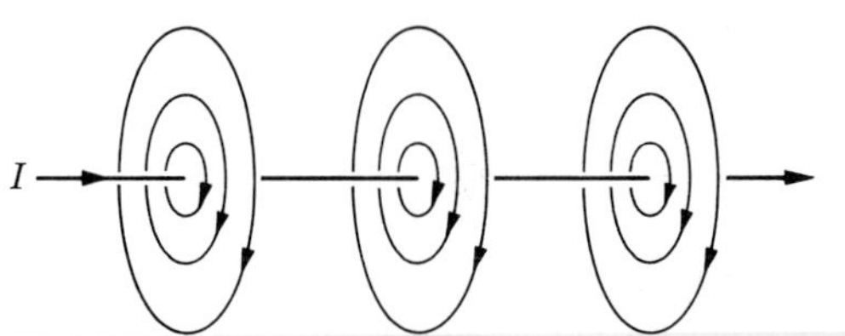

FIG. 24–1. Magnetic field lines representing part of the field due to a long, straight wire that is carrying current.

(2) The sense of the magnetic field lines is given by a right-handed screw rule (Fig. 24–2), in which B is the direction of rotation of a right-handed screw when advancing in the direction of I.

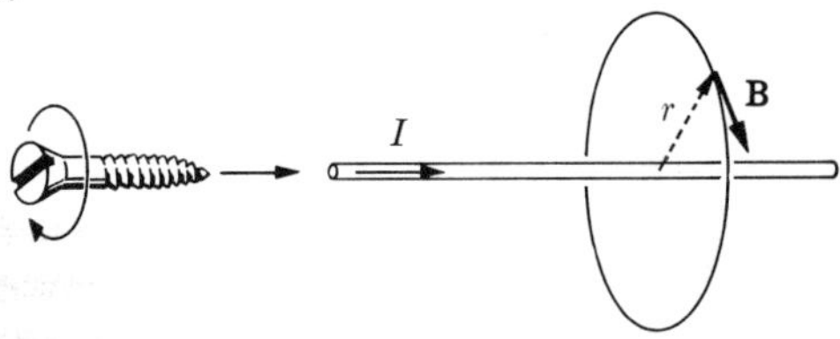

FIG. 24–2. Right-hand screw rule for finding the configuration of the magnetic field due to a straight current. The screw advances in the direction of the current when twisted in the direction of the field lines.

(3) The field strength at any point is inversely proportional to the radial distance of the point from the center of the wire.

(4) The field is directly proportional to the current in the wire.

In summary, B is proportional to the ratio I divided by r, that is,

$$B \propto \frac{I}{r} \quad \text{or} \quad B = K\frac{I}{r}.$$

It is customary to express K as

$$K = \frac{\mu_0}{4\pi}, \tag{24–1}$$

where μ_0 is called the magnetic permeability of

vacuum. The constant μ_0 is assigned an arbitrary value

$$\mu_0 = 4\pi\ 10^{-7}\ \text{n/amp}^2, \tag{24–2}$$

and the resulting equations for interactions between currents are used as the *definition* of the ampere (see Section 24–3).

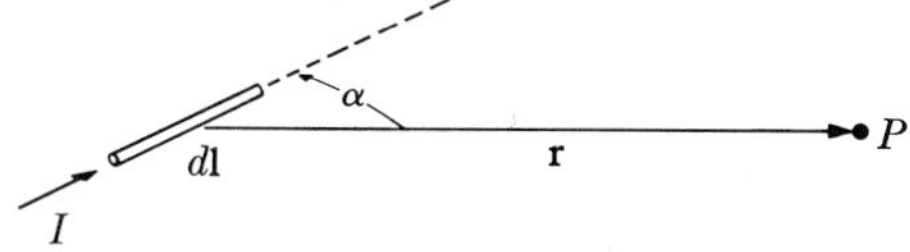

FIG. 24–3. The quantities to be used in specifying the contribution of the element of wire $d\mathbf{l}$ to the magnetic field at P.

24–2 THE LAW OF BIOT AND SAVART

From an analytical viewpoint, it would be desirable to know first of all the field produced by an infinitesimal current element in place of the field due to an extended wire. An infinitesimal element can be imagined as a segment of wire of infinitesimal length dl carrying the current I (Fig. 24–3). Furthermore, the diameter of the element is to be small compared with the distance r to the point where the field is to be determined. Then the magnetic field for any point P in space about the element could be explored and a suitable law thereby formulated. Finally, we would then be able, by integration, to predict the field due to any current configuration. This approach would follow our procedure in electrostatics of building up an extended electrostatic source out of point elements. In the magnetic case, however, the laws of nature rule out this simple, logical procedure. Currents must flow in closed circuits, and they cannot be broken into segments: to cut a circuit into segments is to destroy it. With the direct approach barred, the next possibility is indirect and inductive. One can search for a probable expression for the field due to a current element and then submit it to a trial. If integrals of the expression give the correct result for the magnetic field due to any realizable current distribution, then we assume that the differential expression is a "correct" law of nature. The solution of this inductive problem was given by Biot and Savart, and the differential expression bears the name, the Biot-Savart law. It is

$$dB = \frac{\mu_0}{4\pi}\frac{I\,dl\sin\alpha}{r^2}, \tag{24–3}$$

where dB is the magnetic field at a point due to a current element dI at a distance r from the point. The angle α is formed by dl and r (Fig. 24–3).

The vector properties have not yet been described. The experimental results described in Section 24–1 indicate that $d\mathbf{B}$ is perpendicular to $d\mathbf{l}$ and to $\mathbf{r}$. The $\sin\alpha$ in Eq. (24–3) indicates a vector product, thus

$$d\mathbf{B} = \frac{\mu_0}{4\pi}\frac{I\,d\mathbf{l}\times\mathbf{r}}{r^3}, \tag{24–4}$$

where the inverse square form has been preserved by making the denominator r^3. Figure 24–4 shows the spatial relationships among the vector quantities in Eq. (24–4). In the figure, $d\mathbf{l}$ lies along OY. The field at P is perpendicular to OY and to $\mathbf{r}$. It therefore lies in a plane parallel to OXZ.

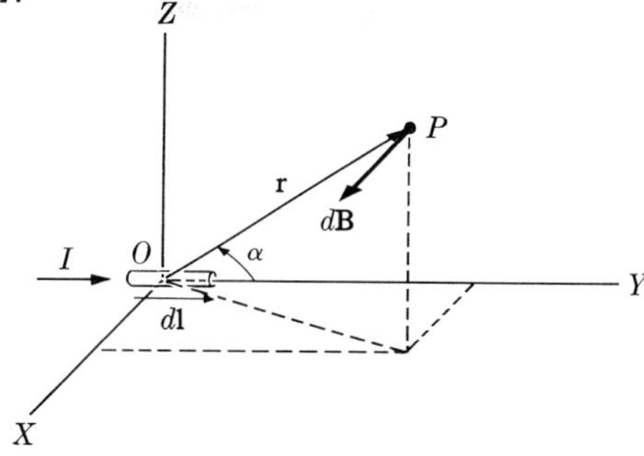

FIG. 24–4. The wire element $d\mathbf{l}$ contributes the amount $d\mathbf{B}$ to the magnetic field at point P. The vector $d\mathbf{B}$ is parallel to the OXZ-plane.

The test of the usefulness of the Biot-Savart law must be made by using it to predict the field produced by current configurations that are physically possible. It is found that the predictions agree with the observed fields. We now consider some examples.

Example 1. Find the field at small distances from a long, straight wire (assuming large distances from the remaining portions of the circuit).

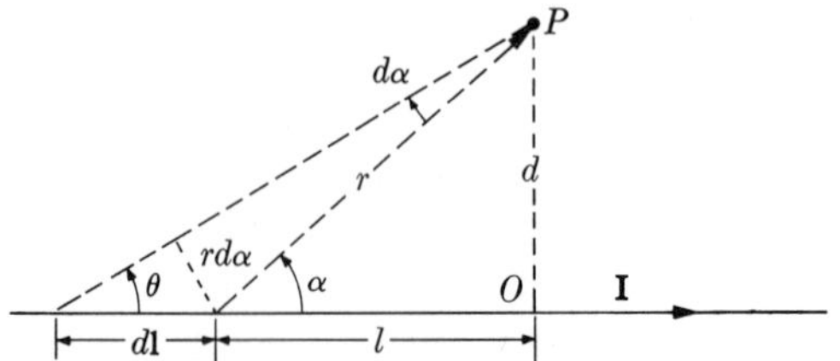

FIG. 24-5. Quantities to be used in the calculation of the magnetic field due to a long, straight wire that carries current I.

Solution: Let the point P be at a radial distance d from the wire. An element of the wire dl is chosen at a distance l from the origin of a coordinate system (Fig. 24-5). It is advantageous to formulate the integral in terms of the angular variable α of Eq. (24-3). From the diagram it can be seen that the variable r is given by $r = d/\sin\alpha$. From the small triangle with hypotenuse dl, we also have $dl \sin\theta = r\, d\alpha$. But as $d\alpha \to 0$, the angles θ and α become equal, and $dl \sin\theta = dl \sin\alpha = r\, d\alpha$. When these expressions are used to transform variables in Eq. (24-3), there results

$$dB = \frac{\mu_0}{4\pi}\frac{I}{d}\sin\alpha\, d\alpha.$$

We note that the vector contributions due to all elements dl of the wire are in the same direction. Therefore, the field is given by

$$B = \frac{\mu_0 I}{4\pi d}\int_0^{\pi} \sin\alpha\, d\alpha = -\frac{\mu_0 I}{4\pi d}\cos\alpha\Big|_0^{\pi}.$$

The result is

$$B = \frac{\mu_0 I}{2\pi d} \tag{24-5}$$

for the field strength at a distance d from a straight wire. Figure 24-1 shows the direction of B more clearly. It is out of the page in Fig. 24-5 at point P.

24-3 DEFINITION OF THE AMPERE OF CURRENT

In the preceding section, the magnetic field of a straight wire was found to depend only on distance from the wire. Thus if a second straight wire is placed parallel to the first, the field will be the same everywhere along the second wire. The force on the second wire is

$$\mathbf{F}_2 = I_2 \mathbf{l}_2 \times \mathbf{B},$$

or

$$F_2 = I_2 l_2 B, \tag{24-6}$$

since B is perpendicular to the current in the second wire. The value of B due to the first wire is given by Eq. (24-5). Thus the force is

$$F_2 = 2\frac{\mu_0}{4\pi}\frac{I_1 I_2 l_2}{d}, \tag{24-7}$$

where d is the wire separation. The direction of the force is shown in Fig. 24-6. The figure also illustrates the fact that wire 1 experiences a force due to the field B_2 produced by I_2. The equation for the magnitude of the force F_1 is

$$F_1 = I_1 l_1 B_2 = 2\frac{\mu_0}{4\pi}\frac{I_1 I_2 l_1}{d},$$

which indicates that the forces per unit length are equal (and opposite), as expected from Newton's third law. When electric and magnetic forces are involved, we cannot assert in general that the forces on "interacting" pairs of charges or currents are equal and opposite. The fields are the actual mechanism for the interaction and the fields themselves can possess momentum.

Equation (24-7) is the basis of the *definition of the ampere.* A current of one ampere in a long, straight wire exerts a force of $\mu_0/2\pi(= 2 \times 10^{-7}/\text{n/m})$ on a long, parallel wire at a distance of 1 m carrying an equal current.

In practice, the effect of long, straight wires is approximated by parallel circular coils separated by a distance that is small compared with their radii, as in Fig. 24-6 (insert), where $d \ll R$. The force on one coil is then used to determine the current. In the accurate work of establishing the primary current standard, the exact theory for circular coils is, of course, used.

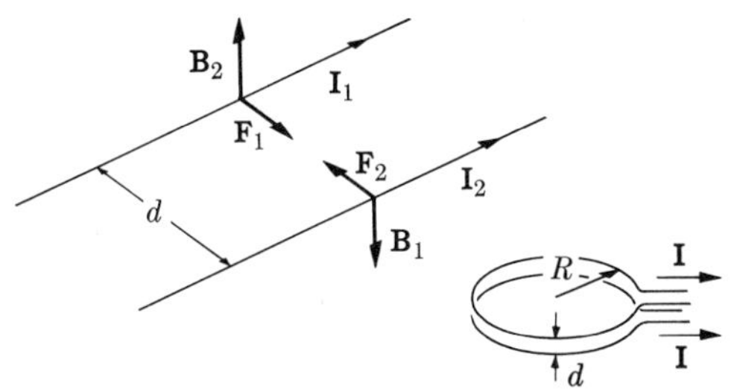

FIG. 24–6. The forces of attraction between parallel currents due to the magnetic fields set up by the wires. The insert shows a practicable method of approximating forces due to long, straight wires. The separation d is made small compared with the radius R.

The system of parallel currents contains in it a trivial apparent paradox whose answer lies in a closer inspection of the problem. Charges in motion generate a magnetic field. One should always ask, In motion relative to what? The answer must, of course, be that motion is measured relative to an observer. Now if an electric charge travels past us with velocity v, we detect, with instruments in our hand, both an electric field and a magnetic field generated by the charge. What should be the result if we move along with the charge at the same velocity v, carrying our instruments with us? The answer might seem to be that we shall detect an electric field due to the charge *but* a zero magnetic field, since the velocity contained in the magnetic field laws is *relative velocity.*

Next we note that equal currents traveling in parallel paths exert an attractive magnetic force upon one another, per unit length, given by

$$\frac{F}{l} = \frac{\mu_0}{2\pi}\frac{I^2}{d}.$$

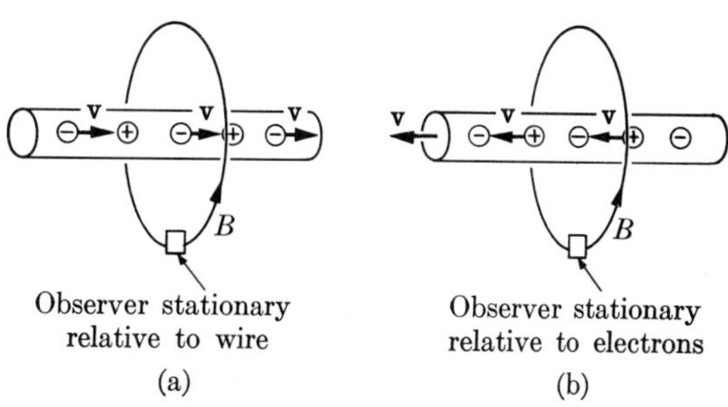

FIG. 24–7. Illustrating the measurement of magnetic field intensity (a) according to an observer at rest relative to the wire, and (b) according to an observer at rest relative to the electrons that constitute the current and therefore in motion relative to the wire. Observer (b) would move with the drift velocity of the conduction electrons.

Yet the currents (the moving charges) are in fact stationary relative to one another. This is the promised paradox. The resolution of this paradox is to be found in asking, If we travel beside a wire, at the drift velocity of the charges in the wire, carrying with us magnetic-field measuring instruments, do we sense the same magnetic field just as if we were stationary? The answer is yes. When moving parallel to the wire at the drift velocity of the electrons, the conducting electrons are stationary relative to the observer. Then, however, the wire containing bound positive charges must be regarded as moving in the negative direction with the original drift velocity (Fig. 24–7b). The current due to the positive charges fixed in the wire traveling toward the left is the same as that due to negative charges traveling toward the right. By extending the argument, it is seen that the observed current and the observed magnetic field due to a current-carrying wire are independent of the observer's velocity.

In the case of free charges moving through a "vacuum" (for example, beams of electrons in a cathode ray tube), the above discussion is not valid. We leave this relativity question until a later section.

24-4 FORCE BETWEEN CURRENTS IN GENERAL

The field approach is usually the most straightforward. Using the field method, Eq. (24-3) is expressed in integral form and evaluated for the particular current configuration of one of the conductors in question. Thus the field is found as a function of space coordinates (and time, if the current is not constant). Then the force on the second current is found by integrating $d\mathbf{F} = I_2\, d\mathbf{l} \times \mathbf{B}$ over the length of the second wire. In many cases, the integrals are simple to evaluate because of special symmetry of the particular configuration (Example 1 was such a case).

In formal notation, the intermediate step of finding the field can be omitted in the calculation of the force of interaction between currents. Thus we might write

$$d\mathbf{F}_1 = I_1\, d\mathbf{l}_1 \times d\mathbf{B}_2 = \frac{\mu_0}{4\pi} I_1 I_2\, d\mathbf{l}_1 \times \left(\frac{d\mathbf{l}_2 \times \mathbf{r}}{r^3}\right). \tag{24-8}$$

However, no simplification has really been gained since the process of calculation will be exactly the same as before, namely, an integration over l_2 followed by an integration over l_1.

In Chapter 23, it was seen that current-carrying wires may experience torques as well as forces when placed in magnetic fields. Therefore, in the interaction between two current-carrying wires, there may be torques of interaction as well as forces.

24-5 WIRES OF FINITE CROSS SECTION

We have been concerned thus far with current filaments of negligible cross-sectional area as sources of magnetic field. If we wish to deal with a wire of finite cross section, then it is necessary to recognize that points within an element of length dl are at different distances r and at different polar angles from the field point. Let the cross section of the wire be divided into elements of area dS (Fig. 24-8). The current through each element is

$$dI = J\, dS,$$

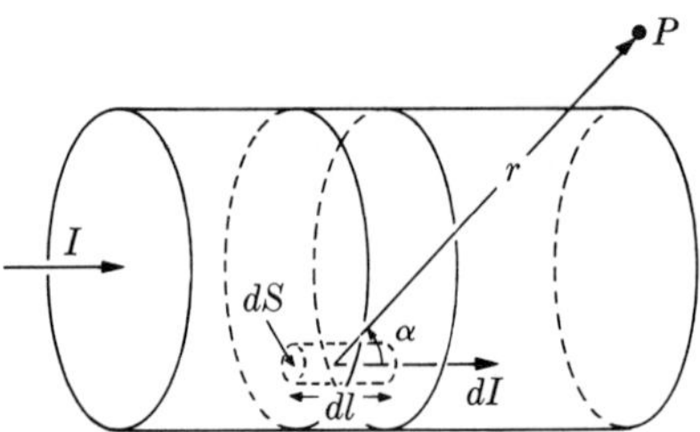

FIG. 24-8. Illustration of an element of current dI, in a volume element dS, dl of a conductor, used in the calculation of the magnetic field at P due to an extended current.

and the source strength of the element is

$$dI\, dl = J\, dS\, dl \qquad \text{or} \qquad dI\, dl = J\, dV.$$

Then the contribution to the magnetic field at the point P can be written

$$dB = \frac{\mu_0}{4\pi} \frac{J\, dV \sin \alpha}{r^2}. \tag{24-9}$$

For a finite wire, the total magnetic field is found by an integration over the volume of the wire, rather than simply an integration over the length of the wire. In vector form the expression for $d\mathbf{B}$ becomes

$$d\mathbf{B} = \frac{\mu_0}{4\pi} \frac{\mathbf{J} \times \mathbf{r}\, dV}{r^3}. \tag{24-10}$$

24-6 FIELDS AND FORCES FOR INDIVIDUAL MOVING CHARGES

In Chapter 23, the force on a charge moving in a magnetic field was found to be $\mathbf{F} = q\mathbf{v} \times \mathbf{B}$. In fact, this expression was used to define the magnetic field intensity. The force between a moving charge and a current can be found by first calculating the field due to the current.

Example 2. Find the force on a charge q moving with velocity v in the vicinity of a straight wire carrying a current I.

Solution: The magnetic field due to the wire is $B = 2(\mu_0/4\pi)\, I/d$. The force on the charge is therefore $F = 2(\mu_0/4\pi)\, qvI \sin\theta/d$ (see Fig. 24-9). In

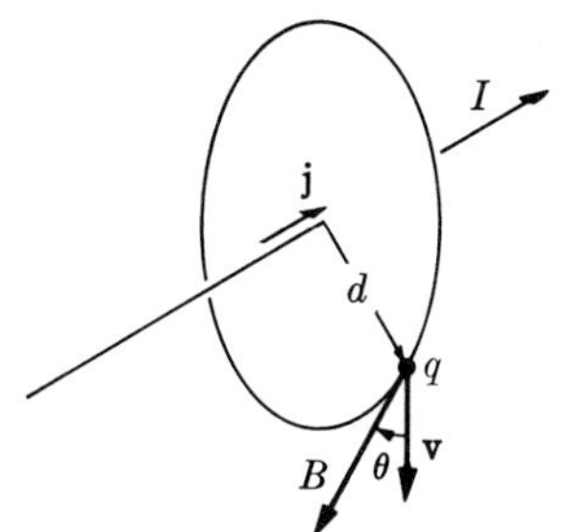

FIG. 24–9. A charge q moving at velocity $\mathbf{v}$ at a distance d from a long, straight current I. The direction of I is specified by a unit vector, $\mathbf{j}$ as shown.

vector notation, $\mathbf{F} = 2(\mu_0/4\pi)q(I/d^2)\mathbf{v} \times (\mathbf{j} \times \mathbf{d})$, where $\mathbf{j}$ is a unit vector in the direction of the current.

The force between two moving charges can be treated in a similar manner, i.e., by first finding an expression for the magnetic field due to a moving charge. If the current density expression $J = nev$ is substituted in Eq. (24–9), there results

$$dB = \frac{\mu_0}{4\pi}\frac{nev\,dV\sin\theta}{r^2}, \qquad (24\text{–}11)$$

where n is the number of particles of charge e per unit volume.

For a finite-sized charge we would let $ne = \rho$, the charge density, and have

$$dB = \frac{\mu_0}{4\pi}\frac{\rho v\,dV\sin\alpha}{r^2}. \qquad (24\text{–}12)$$

For a single point charge in the region, $q = \rho\,dV$, integration is unnecessary, and we have simply,

$$B = \frac{\mu_0}{4\pi}\frac{qv\sin\alpha}{r^2}, \qquad (24\text{–}13)$$

or, in vector notation,

$$\mathbf{B} = \frac{\mu_0}{4\pi}\frac{q\,\mathbf{v}\times\mathbf{r}}{r^3}. \qquad (24\text{–}14)$$

Portions of the field are shown in Fig. 24–10. Note that the field goes to zero along the line of motion ($\sin\alpha = 0$) or at large distances.

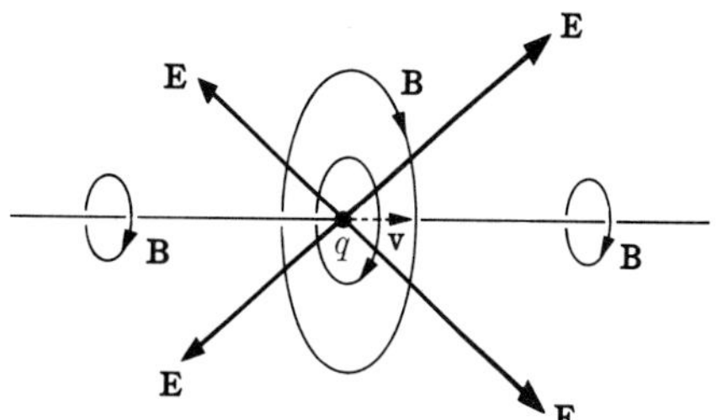

FIG. 24–10. Representative lines of the electric and magnetic fields due to a charge q moving at velocity $\mathbf{v}$.

It is of interest now to compare the basic expressions for the electric and magnetic fields generated by a point charge. The electric field is

$$\mathbf{E} = \frac{1}{4\pi\epsilon_0}\,q\,\frac{\mathbf{r}}{r^3}, \qquad (24\text{–}15)$$

and the magnetic field is given by Eq. (24–14). Therefore, the magnetic field can be written as the vector product: the particle velocity times the electric field, with the electromagnetic coefficients correctly arranged, i.e.,

$$\mathbf{B} = \mu_0\epsilon_0\mathbf{v} \times \mathbf{E}. \qquad (24\text{–}16)$$

This is the single and compact relationship between the electric and magnetic field generated by the ultimate source of both fields, the individual electric charge.

It is interesting to note that the product $\mu_0\epsilon_0 = 1/c^2$ where c is the velocity of light. This suggests a connection between electromagnetism and light. We shall see later that light is in fact an electromagnetic wave phenomenon.

The magnetic field is used to describe the dynamic interaction of electric charges, or electric currents. If an electric charge is in motion, it creates a magnetic field equal to

$$\mathbf{B}_1 = \frac{\mu_0}{4\pi}\frac{q_1\mathbf{v}_1\times\mathbf{r}_{12}}{r_{12}^3}. \qquad (24\text{–}17)$$

The subscripts have been added for clarity. A

second electric charge in motion in the field of the first experiences a force given by the equation,

$$\mathbf{F}_2 = q_2\mathbf{v}_2 \times \mathbf{B}_1. \tag{24-18}$$

The action-at-a-distance expression for the interaction is found from Eqs. (24-17) and (24-18),

$$\mathbf{F}_2 = \frac{\mu_0 q_1 q_2}{4\pi r_{12}^3}\mathbf{v}_2 \times (\mathbf{v}_1 \times \mathbf{r}_{12}). \tag{24-19}$$

(Since action at a distance is not instantaneous, $\mathbf{v}_1$ and $\mathbf{r}_{12}$ must be evaluated earlier than $\mathbf{v}_2$.)

The above equations hold for cases in which both $\mathbf{v}_1$ and $\mathbf{v}_2$ are small compared with the velocity of light. The velocities are to be measured relative to an observer at rest in the laboratory. Relativistic effects will be described after an example.

Example 3. Find the magnetic force between an electron and a proton moving as shown in Fig. 24-11 at the instant that they are in the positions indicated. The proton is moving along OZ and the electron is moving parallel with OY.

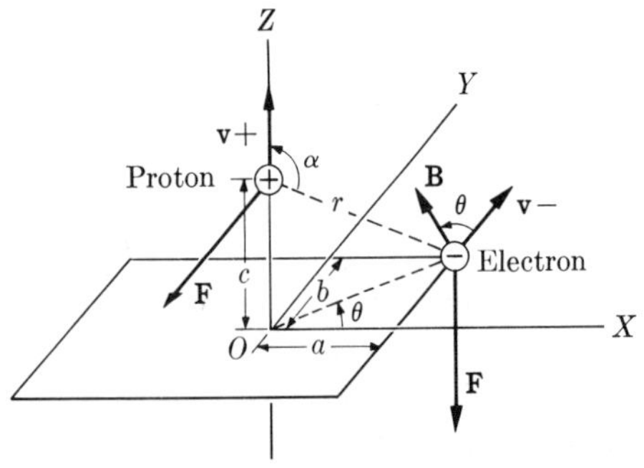

FIG. 24-11. A proton is moving with velocity v_+ along the OZ-axis, and an electron is moving with velocity v_- parallel to the OY-axis in the OXY-plane. The resulting magnetic force on the electron is downward ($-OZ$ direction), as shown.

Solution: The magnetic field at the electron due to the proton lies in the xy-plane, as shown. Its magnitude is obtained from Eq. (24-13) as $B = 10^{-7}ev_+ \sin\alpha/r^2$, where $r = \sqrt{a^2+b^2+c^2}$ and $\sin\alpha = (a^2+b^2)^{1/2}/r$. The magnetic force is then found from Eq. (24-18) as $F = ev_-B\sin\theta$, where B is given above and $\sin\theta = b/(b^2+a^2)^{1/2}$. Therefore the force has magnitude $F = -10^{-7}e^2v_-v_+b/(a^2+b^2+c^2)^{3/2}$ and direction parallel to $-OZ$. The minus sign comes from our use of e as $+1.6 \times 10^{-17}$ coul. There would also be an electrostatic force, $F = -4\pi\epsilon_0(e^2/r^2)$. The magnetic force on the proton in this example will have the same magnitude as the magnetic force on the electron (Eq. 24-19) *but* the forces are not opposite in direction! The force on the proton is in the $-OY$ direction! We must conclude that the fields carry momentum and participate in the interaction in a very real way.

We consider now the simplest case, two like charges q moving at the same velocity v in parallel paths separated by d. According to a laboratory observer, the force of interaction between the charges is

$$F = \frac{1}{4\pi\epsilon_0}\frac{q^2}{d^2} - \frac{\mu_0}{4\pi}\frac{q^2}{d^2}v^2, \tag{24-20}$$

where the first term is the electrostatic and the second term the magnetic force. This equation is for $v \ll$ velocity of light. The electrostatic force is repulsive but the magnetic force is attractive (Fig. 24-12). The positive direction has been chosen outward along the line between charges.

According to an observer moving with velocity v beside the charges, there is no magnetic field

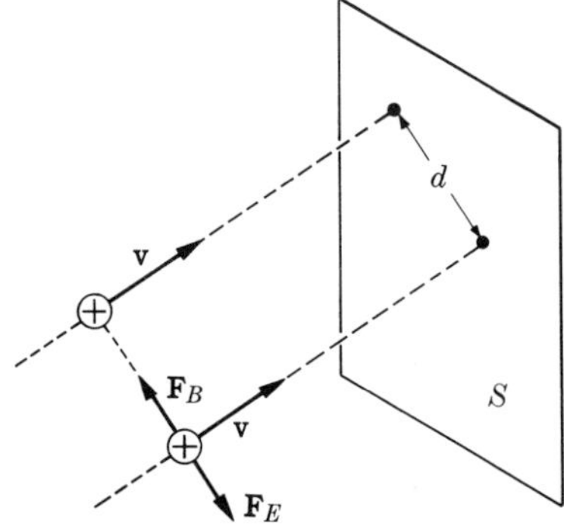

FIG. 24-12. The forces on a positive charge due to another positive charge moving at the same velocity beside the first charge, as evaluated by a laboratory observer.

since there is no motion of the charges. Therefore, the force is purely electrostatic for such an observer. Note the distinction between this example and that of parallel currents in wires.

If Eq. (24-20) is assumed to hold for all velocities, there would exist a velocity v_0 for which the resultant force between the charges is zero. In particular, $v_0 = 1/\mu_0\epsilon_0 = c$, where c is the velocity of light. This velocity is impossible for reasons of mechanical energy, since we have seen that the kinetic energy of a particle becomes infinite as $v \rightarrow c$. Therefore, the problem must be treated relativistically.

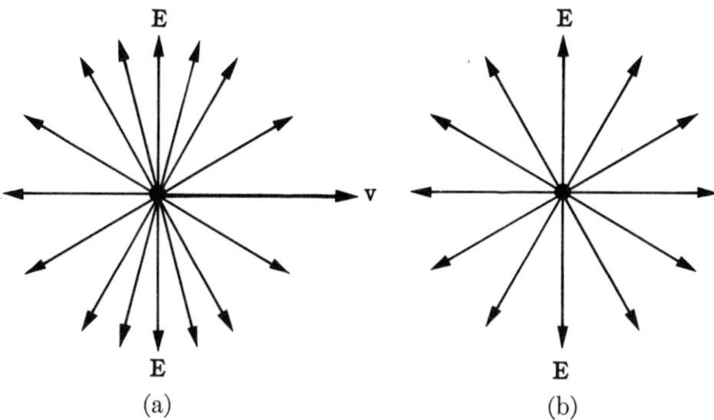

FIG. 24-13. Relativistic contraction of the electric field toward the plane through the charge and perpendicular to the direction of motion. (a) Side or top view. (b) Front or back view.

The restrictions of relativity result in a compression of both the electric and the magnetic fields toward the plane that is perpendicular to the velocity of the moving charge, as shown in Fig. 24-13 for the electric field. According to a laboratory observer, the fields in the plane perpendicular to the motion and passing through the charge are given by

$$E = \gamma\left(\frac{q}{4\pi\epsilon_0 r^2}\right) \quad \text{and} \quad B = \gamma\,\frac{\mu_0}{4\pi}\,\frac{qv}{r^2}, \tag{24-21}$$

where γ is the relativistic factor, $\gamma = 1/\sqrt{1 - v^2/c^2}$. The expression for the total force (Eq. 24-20) can then be written

$$F = \gamma\,\frac{q^2}{4\pi\epsilon_0 r^2}\,(1 - \mu_0\epsilon_0 v^2)$$

$$= \gamma\,\frac{q^2}{4\pi\epsilon_0 r^2}\left(1 - \frac{v^2}{c^2}\right)$$

or

$$F = \frac{F_0}{\gamma}, \tag{24-22}$$

where F_0 is the total force at zero velocity, i.e., the low-velocity electrostatic force. Equation (24-22) shows that the force between like charges moving in parallel paths at the same velocity is always repulsive and approaches zero only as $v \rightarrow c$. The observer moving with the charges still finds only the electrostatic force, F_0.

It may occur to the reader that both observers should agree on the lateral separation d of the charges, for example, when they hit the screen S in Fig. 6-12. The answer is that the observers not only disagree on the lateral forces, but they also disagree on the lateral acceleration, on the mass, and on the time and distance of flight.

24-7 AMPERE'S LAW FOR THE MAGNETIC FIELD

There exists an integral theorem on the structure of the magnetic field which is an aid in computation as well as a guide to understanding the general character of the field. It occupies a position in magnetic field theory which is comparable to the Gauss theorem for the electrostatic field. It will be recalled that in electric theory, the field is related to its sources by the equation,

$$\mathbf{E} = \frac{1}{4\pi\epsilon_0}\int\frac{\rho\mathbf{r}\,dV}{r^3}.$$

Given any charge distribution ρ, the field can in principle be found by this integral. It was also shown that the integral of the normal component of $\mathbf{E}$ over any closed surface is given quite simply by the net charge q contained within the surface divided by ϵ_0, that is,

$$\int E\,dS\cos\theta = \frac{1}{\epsilon_0}\int \rho\,dV.$$

This theorem enabled us to find the field with only simple integrations in many cases.

Similarly, the magnetic field can be found by integrating over all current elements,

$$\mathbf{B} = \frac{\mu_0}{4\pi}\int \frac{\mathbf{J}\times\mathbf{r}\,dV}{r^2}.$$

Thus, if any arbitrary current distribution is given, we have, in principle, the means to compute the magnetic field for all points in space. There is a further similarity to electrostatics, an analogy to Gauss' law. From the magnetic field equation, we can derive a theorem concerning the line integral of the magnetic field about any closed path in space. This theorem is

$$\oint |\mathbf{B}|\,|d\mathbf{s}|\cos\alpha = \oint \mathbf{B}\cdot d\mathbf{s} = \mu_0 I, \qquad (24\text{–}23)$$

where $\oint$ signifies a line integral around a closed path (Fig. 24–14), and I is the net current threading through the closed path. That is, the closed line integral of B equals the net current flux through the surface S bounded by the path (times the constant μ_0). Just as in Gauss' law, this theorem is particularly valuable in cases of symmetry. The validity of the theorem will be demonstrated for a particular case, that of the long, straight wire. Since the magnetic field is in

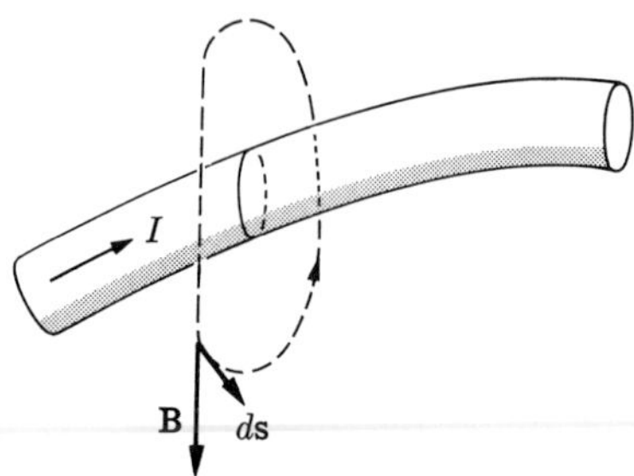

FIG. 24–14. Path of a line integral (dashed) encircling a current I.

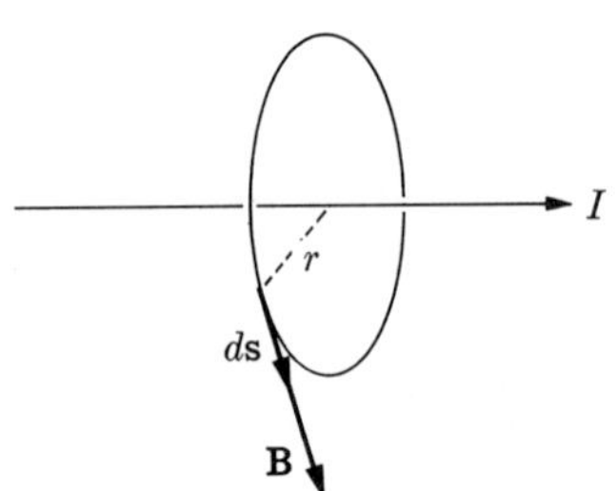

FIG. 24–15. Circular line integral path around a long, straight current. The path is centered on the current.

the tangential direction about the wire, it is simplest to establish a circular path as in Fig. 24–15. Then the angle between the field B and the path element ds is always zero and $\cos\alpha = 1$. Also, on a circle the magnetic field is constant at all points (Eq. 24–5) because

$$B = \frac{\mu_0 I}{2\pi r}.$$

The integral is evaluated directly as follows:

$$\int \mathbf{B}\cdot d\mathbf{s} = \frac{\mu_0 I}{2\pi r}\times 2\pi r = \mu_0 I.$$

It is next proved that the integral is path-independent for any path lying in a plane perpendicular to the current. We choose polar coordinates, with the current as origin. For an arbitrary path, the field is inclined at an angle α relative to the path element $d\mathbf{s}$ (Fig. 24–16).

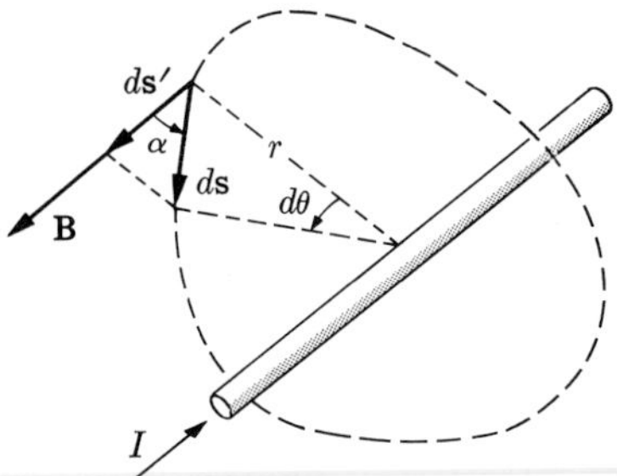

FIG. 24–16. A noncircular line integral path in a plane perpendicular to a long, straight current I and encircling the current.

But, since $ds \cos\alpha$ is the projection ds' of ds in the direction of B and since B is tangent to a circle of radius r, we have

$$ds \cos\alpha = ds' = r\,d\theta$$

where ds is equivalent to the arc of the circle when $d\theta \to 0$. The integrand becomes

$$\mathbf{B}\cdot d\mathbf{s} = Br\,d\theta = \left(2\,\frac{\mu_0}{4\pi}\,\frac{I}{r}\right) r\,d\theta = 2\,\frac{\mu_0}{4\pi}\,I\,d\theta. \tag{24–24}$$

Since $d\theta$ is the only variable, the line integral is easily evaluated; in fact $\oint d\theta = 2\pi$, and we see immediately that the integral gives $\mu_0 I$ independent of path. This is the result if the arbitrary path is chosen to encircle the wire. The case of a path that is not confined to a plane is left as an exercise for the student.

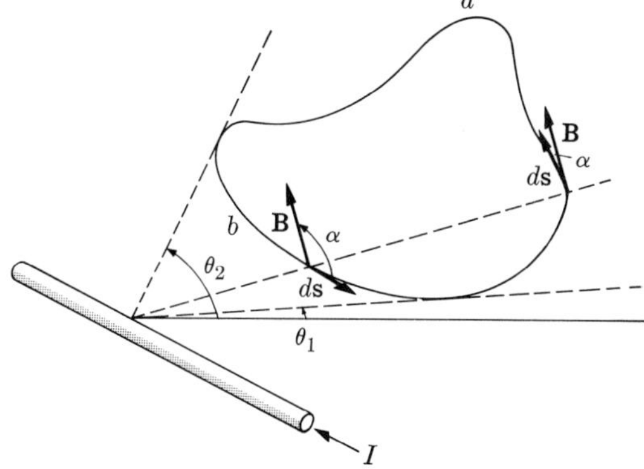

Fig. 24–17. A noncircular line integral path in a plane perpendicular to a long, straight current I. The path does *not* encircle the current.

Next consider a path that does not encircle the wire. Lines are drawn outward from the wire tangent to the path at the largest angles (Fig. 24–17). The points of intersection of the tangent lines with the path divide the path into two sections, a and b. We integrate counterclockwise about the path for the two sections separately. For section a we have [using Eq. (24–24)],

$$\int_a |\mathbf{B}|\,|d\mathbf{s}| \cos\alpha = \frac{\mu_0 I}{2\pi}\,(\theta_2 - \theta_1).$$

For section b we have

$$\int_b |\mathbf{B}|\,|d\mathbf{s}| \cos\alpha = \frac{\mu_0 I}{2\pi}\,(\theta_1 - \theta_2).$$

The two integrals are equal and opposite. From an inspection of the integral, it can be seen that $\cos\alpha$ along path a is $+$, along path b is $-$. Since the integrations along the two sections just cancel, the total line integral is zero, i.e.,

$$\int \mathbf{B}\cdot d\mathbf{s} = 0. \tag{24–25}$$

Finally, we can utilize the principle of superposition (the resultant $\mathbf{B}$ is the vector sum of individual contributions) to assert that Ampere's law holds for any distribution of straight currents through the loop, i.e.,

$$\oint \mathbf{B}\cdot d\mathbf{s} = \mu_0 \int_S \mathbf{J}\cdot d\mathbf{S}, \tag{24–26}$$

where the line integral is to be taken around the periphery of the surface over which the integral on the right is taken.

In case several individual wires are involved, we would write

$$\oint \mathbf{B}\cdot d\mathbf{s} = \mu_0 \Sigma I. \tag{24–27}$$

It can be shown that Ampere's law is not restricted to straight line currents; the current elements can have any form, as in Fig. 24–18.

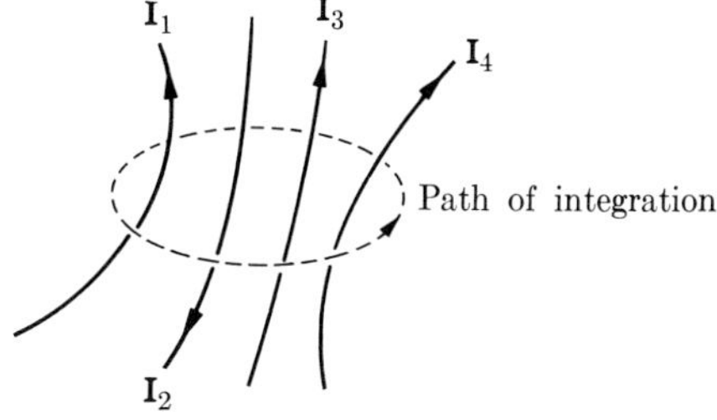

Fig. 24–18. A line integral path that encircles several currents.

Example 4. Using Ampere's law, compute the magnetic field due to a long, straight wire of radius R carrying a uniform current density J.

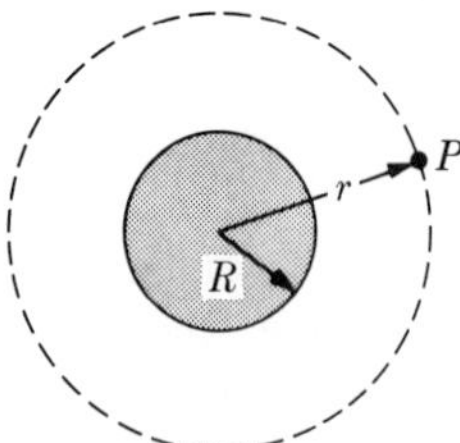

FIG. 24-19. A circular line integral path of radius r concentric with a wire of radius R.

Solution: Choose a point P outside the wire (Fig. 24-19). From the cylindrical symmetry of the source, we note that B is only a function of r, and cannot depend on θ. Therefore, we construct a circular path through P concentric with the wire. Equation (24-26) then gives

$$\oint \mathbf{B} \cdot d\mathbf{s} = B2\pi r = \mu_0 I,$$

or $B = \mu_0 I/(2\pi r)$, just as if all the current were concentrated at the center of the wire.

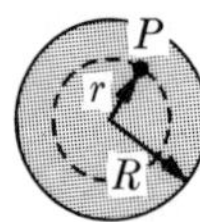

FIG. 24-20. A circular line integral path of radius r concentric with and lying inside a wire of radius R.

For a point P inside the wire, we again note the cylindrical symmetry and construct a circular path through the point P (Fig. 24-20). Ampere's law gives

$$\oint \mathbf{B} \cdot ds = B2\pi r = \mu_0 I = \mu_0 \pi r^2 J$$

or

$$B = \frac{\mu_0 J r}{2}.$$

We see that B increases linearly with r from the center of the wire out to its surface and then decreases as $1/r$.

24-8 MAGNETISM DUE TO ATOMS

The details of this topic must be left for a study of atomic structure. A few general ideas will be presented here in order to make the discussion of magnetic effects more complete.

In the introduction to Chapter 23, permanent magnets were said to give rise to magnetic interactions. Since there are no electric currents or other obvious motions of charges on the macroscopic scale in permanent magnets, it is reasonable to assume that the magnetic effects are attributable to motion of charge on the atomic scale. This supposition is verified by experiment. The experiments are usually indirect in the customary sense, but the results are incontrovertible. Atoms do possess magnetic properties for two reasons: they contain charged particles that are in motion, and the constituent particles themselves (even those that are uncharged) exhibit an inherent magnetic property. The latter is presumably due to circulation of charge "within" the particle in question. The term "spin" is used for the property of a particle that gives rise to magnetic (and mechanical) effects independent of any general translational motion of the particle.

Therefore, an atom produces a magnetic field that is the sum of the fields contributed by the spins and by the motions of the individual constituent particles. There is a basic reason (minimum energy) for the spins and motions to orient themselves so that the magnetic field is a minimum. Thus most atoms exhibit only very weak magnetic effects externally even though magnetic effects may be quite strong internally.

In a few metals, alloys, and compounds, the above-described tendency for a minimizing of magnetic effects does not occur. The net effect is that of several unbalanced parallel spins within each atom and a further alignment of the effects of groups of atoms within macroscopic domains. The additive effects can be very strong, as evidenced by the strengths of magnetic fields produced by permanent magnets, fields of strength comparable with those produced by cur-

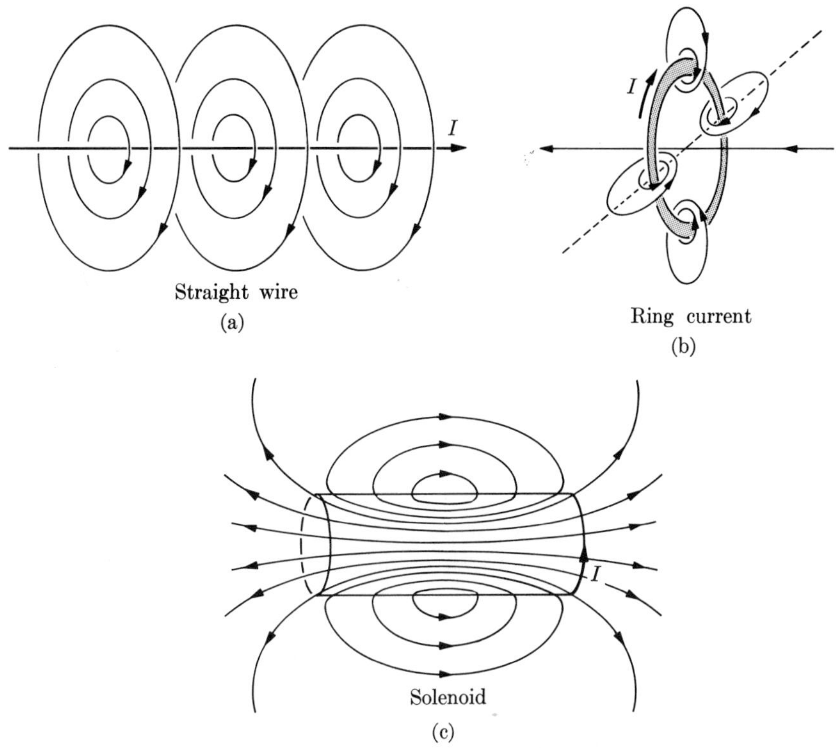

Fig. 24–21. Magnetic field configurations for three simple current geometries.

rents in wires. This phenomenon is called ferromagnetism because the commonest materials displaying the effect are iron, its alloys, and one of its oxides.

24–9 MAGNETIC FIELD MAPS

It is useful to have a pictorial representation of physical quantities for typical situations of frequent application or of particular symmetry. In the present case of magnetic fields, the direction of the field was defined in Section 23–2. The idea of lines of force that give a sort of continuous representation of direction was also developed. Finally, in Section 23–3, the flux density of lines was defined as a representation of the *magnitude* of the field. Thus, just as in the case of the electric field, a graphical representation can be made in which the direction and flux density of lines demonstrate the nature of the field. A two-dimensional drawing will usually be a cross section of the field through a plane of symmetry. Unless the plane is perpendicular to the field, it may be difficult to preserve the quantitative relationship between density of lines and field intensity.

In this chapter, lines of force have been drawn to represent the direction of the fields for cases of a current in a long, straight wire (Fig. 24–1) and of a single moving charge (Fig. 24–10). These drawings could also have been made in a manner that displays quantitatively the variation in magnitude of the field. The result for a current in a long, straight wire is shown in Fig. 24–21. The spacing of the lines is uniform in the direction of the wire, but it increases linearly with radial distance from the wire. Consequently, the flux density falls off inversely as $1/r$, in the manner of the field strength.

Most of the other simple current configurations are the subjects of the Problems. Field maps of some of the simple configurations are given in Fig. 24–21 (a), (b), and (c). For the solenoid, the condition that the field at the longitudinal center is twice the field at the ends is shown schematically.

The field due to the aligned atomic spins in a uniformly magnetized permanent magnet is the same as that of a coil whose turns coincide with the lateral sides of the magnet. For example, a cylindrical bar magnet that is uniformly magnetized longitudinally gives rise to the same magnetic field externally as a solenoid such as the one in Fig. 24–21(c) of the same length and diameter as the bar magnet.

The source of the earth's field is not known. The configuration of the field out to several earth radii is the same as that of a permanent magnet, or of a solenoid, or of a ring current located near the center of the earth and with dimensions small compared with the radius of the earth. Such a field is called a dipole field. The field of the earth probably originates in circulating currents in the earth's core. The field is shown qualitatively in the preceding chapter (Fig. 23–14). There is increasing evidence that the field is greatly modified at large distances by streams of charged particles.

24–10 SUMMARY

The nature of the magnetic field produced by a given current configuration is correctly predicted by integration of the differential law of Biot-Savart over the current distribution that produces the field. The law of Biot-Savart is

$$dB = \frac{\mu_0}{4\pi} I \frac{dl \sin \alpha}{r^2},$$

where r is the distance from the wire element dl to the point P for which the field is being calculated and α is the angle between dl and r. The vector form is

$$dB = \frac{\mu_0}{4\pi} I \frac{d\mathbf{l} \times \mathbf{r}}{r^3}.$$

For a point distant d from a long, straight wire, the law gives

$$B = \frac{\mu_0}{2\pi} I \frac{1}{d}.$$

The *ampere* is the basic electrical quantity in the mksa system of units. It is defined as the current in a long, straight wire that produces a force of 2×10^{-7} n/m on a long, straight wire carrying the same current when the wires are parallel and separated by one meter.

The law of Biot-Savart can also be expressed in terms of the current density $\mathbf{J}$ in an elementary volume dV,

$$d\mathbf{B} = \frac{\mu_0}{4\pi} \frac{\mathbf{J} \times \mathbf{r}}{r^3} dV.$$

The above expression can lead to the law for the magnetic field produced by a single charge moving at velocity v,

$$d\mathbf{B} = \frac{\mu_0}{4\pi} q \frac{\mathbf{v} \times \mathbf{r}}{r^3}.$$

The relationship between the electric and magnetic fields of a single charge is

$$\mathbf{B} = \mu_0 \mathcal{E}_0 \mathbf{v} \times \mathbf{E}.$$

The force of interaction between moving charged particles is treated and the relativistic expression in the special case of charges moving side by side is given.

Ampere's law states the relationship between the line integral of B around a closed path and the total current encircled by the path

$$\oint \mathbf{B} \cdot d\mathbf{s} = \mu_0 \int_S \mathbf{J} \cdot d\mathbf{S} = \mu_0 I.$$

Its usefulness is analogous to the usefulness of Gauss' law for electric fields, namely, it enables us to calculate the field easily in certain important special cases.

A brief description is given of the magnetic effect of atoms, that is, "currents," on the atomic and subatomic scale.

Examples are given of the maps of magnetic field lines for several important configurations.

Problems

1. A circuit in the form of a circular loop of wire of radius R carries electric current I (Fig. 24–22).

(a) Prove, by direct integration of the Biot-Savart law that the field at the center of the loop is

$$B = \frac{\mu_0 I}{2R}. \qquad (24\text{–}28)$$

Note that the term $\sin\alpha$ is constant and equal to unity.

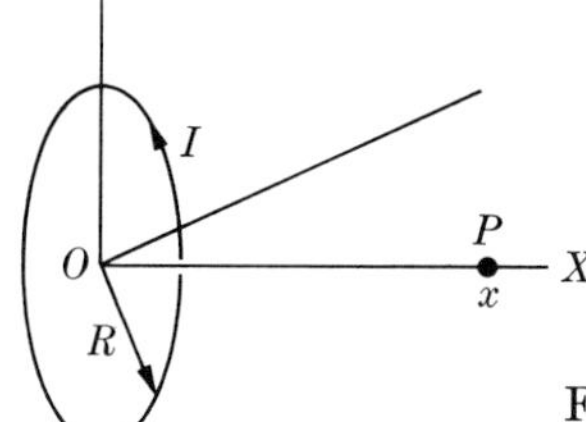

FIGURE 24–22

(b) Find the strength of the magnetic field at a point P on the axis of the loop at a distance x from the center of the loop (Fig. 24–22). (Note that $\sin\alpha$ still equals 1. Also, the components of the field perpendicular to the x-axis cancel. The net field is along the x-axis.)

(c) Using the definition of the magnetic moment of the loop, $M = \pi R^2 I$, show that the field can be expressed as

$$B = \frac{\mu_0}{2\pi} \frac{M}{(x^2 + R^2)^{3/2}},$$

where M assumes the role of the "source strength" of the loop. Show that for $x \gg R$, the field assumes the form of an inverse cube law:

$$B = \frac{\mu_0}{2\pi} \frac{M}{x^3}.$$

(Note that the form of the last expression is similar to that for the electric dipole.)

(d) In what way does a closed current loop exhibit the form of a "dipole source" of magnetic field? (Recall that an electric dipole is formed by equal and opposite charges, closely spaced.)

2. Parallel wires each carry the same current I in opposite directions. They are spaced a distance d apart. Find expressions for the magnetic field for points on the x-axis and points on the y-axis as chosen in Fig. 24–23. What are the approximate expressions when the distance to the field point is much greater than d? Sketch the field lines in the xy plane.

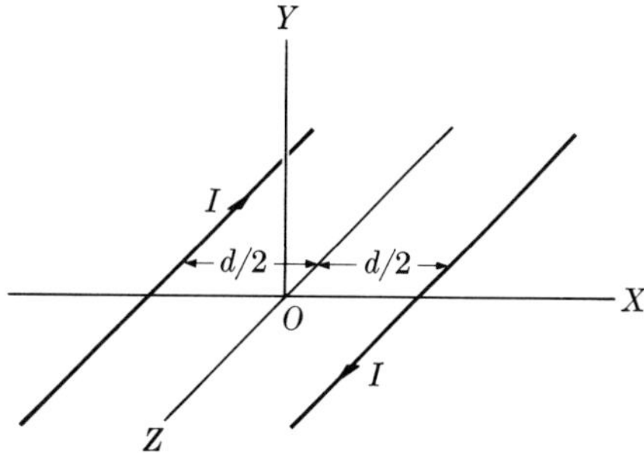

FIGURE 24–23

3. A long, straight wire and a rectangular wire frame lie on a table top (Fig. 24–24). The side of the frame parallel to the wire is 30 cm long, the side perpendicular to the wire is 50 cm long. The current $I_1 = 10$ amp and current $I_2 = 20$ amp.

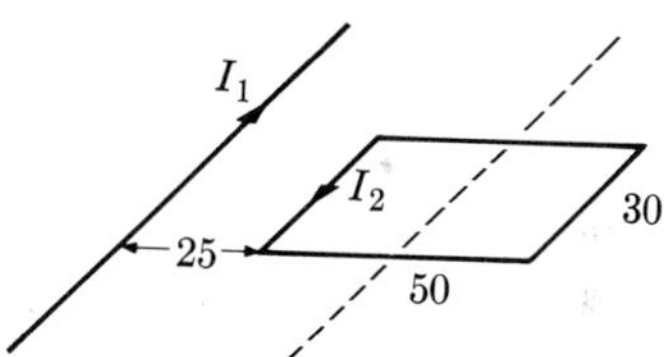

FIGURE 24–24

(a) What is the force on the loop?

(b) How much energy is required to move the frame to infinity, assuming that I_2 is kept constant?

(c) What is the torque on the loop about the straight wire as an axis? about the dashed line as an axis?

(d) Find the torque after the coil has been rotated 45° about the dotted axis.

(e) What is the total magnetic flux through the frame when it is lying flat?

4. Two identical circular coils carry equal currents in the same direction (Fig. 24–25). The loops are parallel and coaxial. The spacing of the coils d

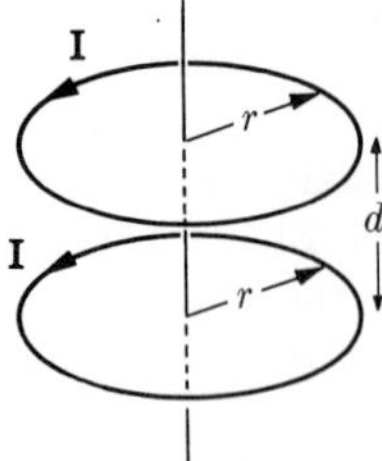

FIGURE 24–25

equals the coil radius r. Using the results of Problem 1(b), compute the magnetic field strength on the axis of the coils

(a) at the center,

(b) in the plane of one coil.

(c) What is the percent change in field strength between the above points?

5. Two circular coils of radius 20 cm are placed parallel, with a separation of 1 cm between their planes. If each coil has 10 turns and carries a current of 5 amp, what is the force between the coils? (Approximate the field by that of a long, straight wire.)

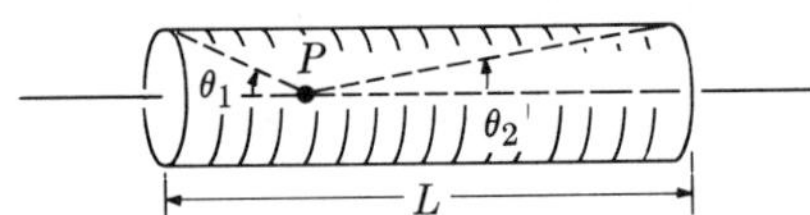

FIGURE 24–26

6. (a) Using the result of Problem 1(b), show that the field at a point P on the axis of a solenoid of length L with N turns (Fig. 24–26) is

$$B = \mu_0 \frac{NI}{2L} (\cos\theta_2 + \cos\theta_1), \qquad (24\text{–}29)$$

where θ_1 and θ_2 are angles subtended by the solenoid ends at point P, as shown.

(b) Show that the field at the center of an infinitely long solenoid is

$$B = \mu_0 NI/L. \qquad (24\text{–}30)$$

(c) Show that the field at the end of a very long solenoid is

$$B = \mu_0 NI/(2L). \qquad (24\text{–}31)$$

7. A thin flat conductor of great length has a uniform current density i per unit width, that is $I_{\text{Total}} = iw$, where w is the width (Fig. 24–27).

(a) Find the magnetic field strength at a point P, at a perpendicular distance d above the center of the strip, as shown. [*Hint:* The expression for the field due to a long, straight strip of width dw is the same as for a long, straight wire.]

(b) What is the field if $d \gg w$?

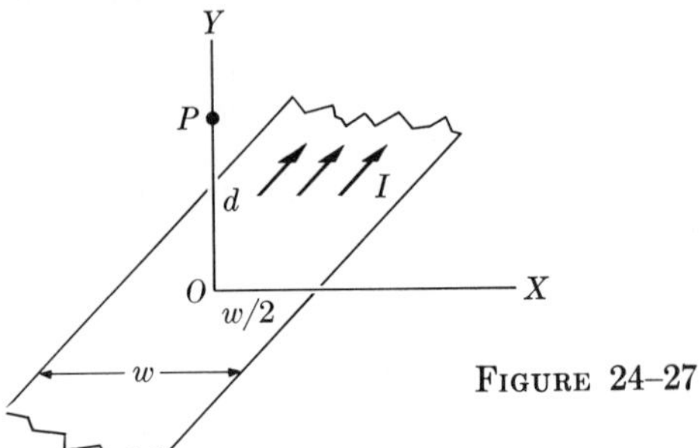

FIGURE 24–27

8. A cylindrical shell of great length carries current I with uniform current density J (Fig. 24–28). Show that the magnetic field is

$$B = \frac{\mu_0}{2\pi}\frac{I}{r}; \qquad (r > R_2)$$

$$B = \frac{\mu_0 I}{2\pi}\frac{1}{R_2^2 - R_1^2}\left(r - \frac{R_1^2}{r}\right); \qquad (R_1 < r < R_2)$$

$$B = 0; \qquad r < R_1. \qquad (24\text{–}32)$$

[*Hint:* Use Ampere's law.]

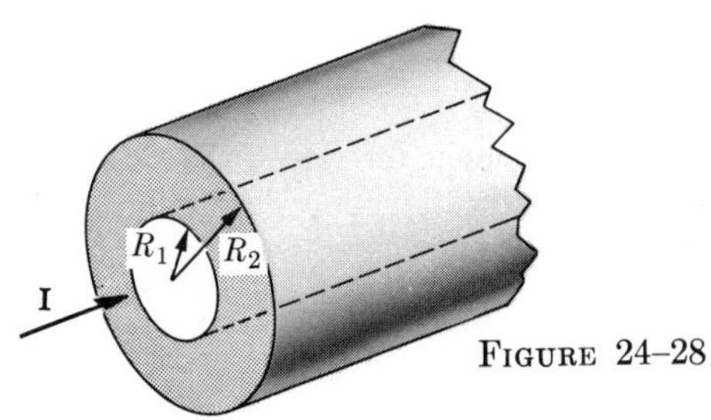

FIGURE 24–28

9. A coaxial cable is formed by surrounding a solid cylindrical conductor of radius R_1 with a concentric conducting shell of inner radius R_2 and outer radius R_3 (Fig. 24–29). In usual practice a current I is sent down the inner wire and is returned via the outer shell. Find the magnetic field for all points about and within the conductor, using Ampere's law. Plot B as a function of r. Assume uniform current density.

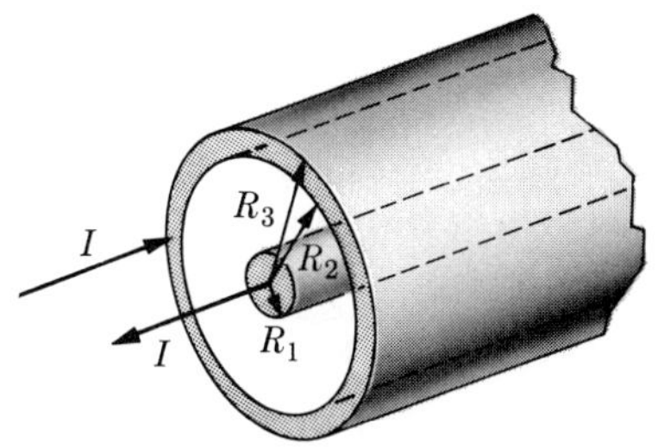

FIGURE 24–29

10. (a) Repeat Problem 7 in case $w \to \infty$, showing that $B = \mu_0 i/2$. Compare this result with the electric field of a uniform, infinite sheet of charge.

(b) Use Ampere's law to find the result of part (a). Choose a path for the integral, as shown by the dashed rectangle in Fig. 24–30. The current sheet is seen edge-on and the current is flowing into the page.

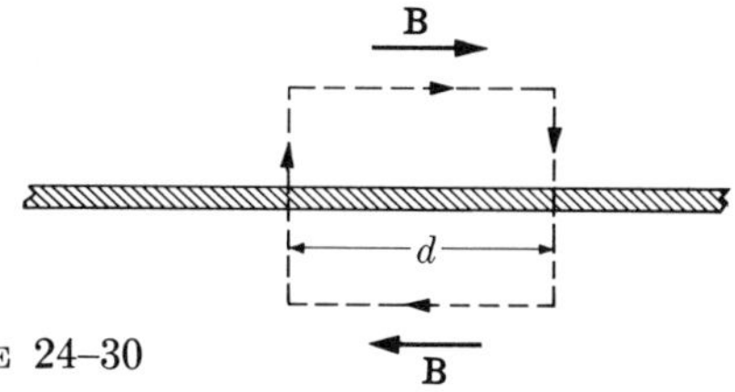

FIGURE 24–30

(c) What is the symmetry argument that leads to the conclusion that B must be parallel to the sheet (but perpendicular to the current), as shown?

11. Prove that a closed current-carrying loop of arbitrary orientation experiences zero resultant force in a uniform magnetic field.

12. Consider a single charge q moving in a circular path of radius r at speed v.

(a) Show that the equivalent current is $qv/(2\pi r)$.

(b) Show that the magnetic moment of this "current" is $qvr/2$.

(c) Show that the gyromagnetic ratio, defined as magnetic moment divided by angular momentum (mvr), is $q/(2m)$.

13. Consider a very long solenoid with turns that are very closely spaced and that therefore approximate a continuous cylindrical sheath of current, as in Fig. 24–31.

(a) Use a symmetry argument to show that the field at any interior point P can have only a component parallel to the solenoid axis. [*Hint:* Consider

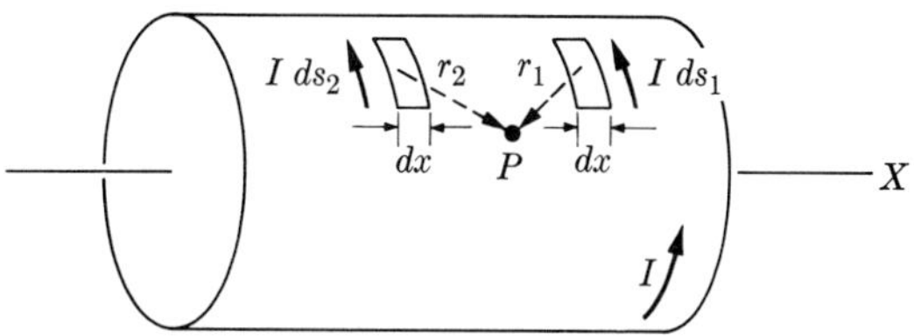

FIGURE 24–31

current elements $i\ ds\ dx$ symmetrically located relative to P, as shown.]

(b) Where, specifically, does the effect of finite solenoid length destroy the argument that the field is purely longitudinal? Does it affect the argument for a point on the solenoid axis?

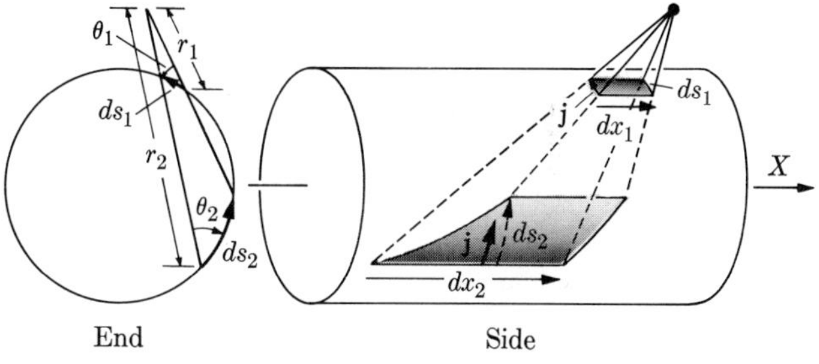

FIGURE 24–32

14. Consider a point P exterior to a long solenoid with closely spaced turns of fine wire.

(a) Prove that the field is zero at any point P by considering paired elements of current, as in Fig. 24–32. In this case the current density formulation must be used, $dB \sim i\ ds\ dx \sin\theta/r^2$ where i is the current per unit width dx of current element.

(b) What is the effect on the above argument if the solenoid is of finite length? if the length is large compared with the solenoid radius and the distance to P?

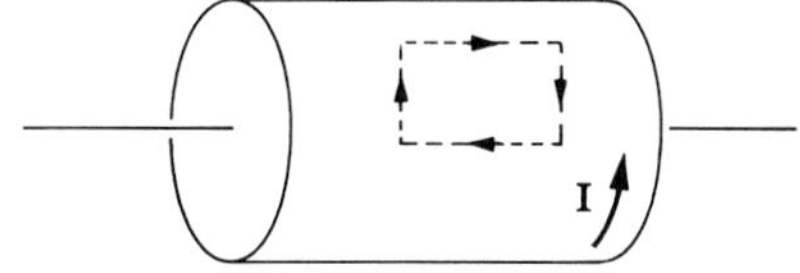

FIGURE 24–33

15. Assuming the result of Problem 13, that B is everywhere parallel to the axis inside a long solenoid, use Ampere's law to prove that the *magnitude* of B is independent of distance from the axis. Choose a

closed path such as shown in Fig. 24–33, with sides parallel and perpendicular to the solenoid axis.

16. Assuming the results of Problems 13 and 14, prove that the field intensity inside a long solenoid is $B = \mu_0 IN/L$, where N/L is the number of turns per unit length. [*Hint:* Use Ampere's law for a rectangular loop with sides parallel and perpendicular to the solenoid axis, as shown in Fig. 24–34.]

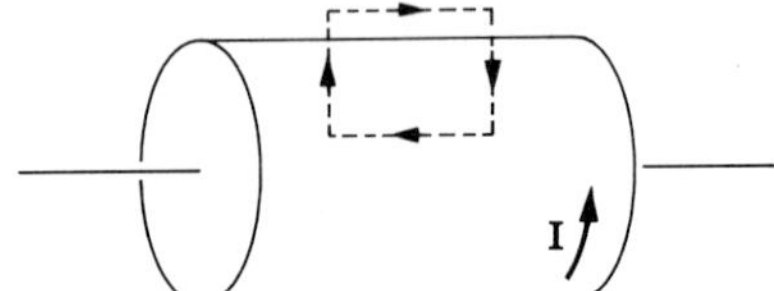

FIGURE 24–34

17. Apply Ampere's law to a circular path in a plane perpendicular to the axis of a long solenoid, as in Fig. 24–35. What is the result

(a) if the solenoid is approximated by a uniform sheet of current?

(b) if the solenoid is a real solenoid with a wire wound in a helix?

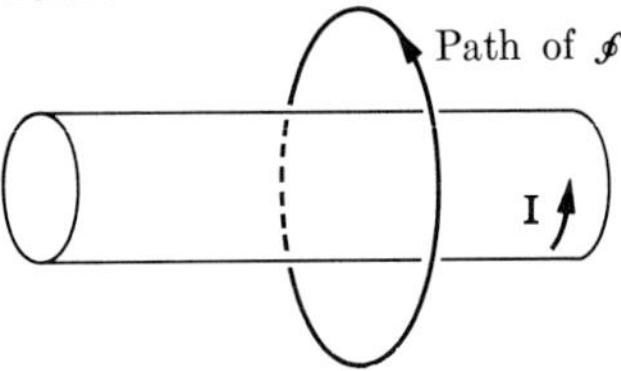

FIGURE 24–35

18. Consider a solenoid wound on a toroidal form, as in Fig. 24–36.

(a) Show that the arguments of Problems 13 and 14 apply, i.e., the field is longitudinal inside and zero outside.

(b) Use the technique of Problem 16 to find B as a function of r. [*Hint:* Choose a path consisting of two lines with constant r and two lines that are radial.]

(c) Check your result for (b) by choosing an Ampere's law path on a circle inside the torus, as shown by the dashed line in Fig. 24–36.

(d) Repeat Problem 17 for the toroidal coil.

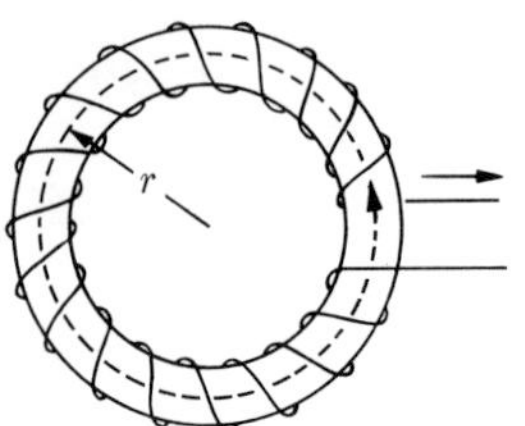

FIGURE 24–36

19. Consider two electrons moving in straight, parallel paths separated by 0.1 mm.

(a) If they are moving side by side at the same velocity of 10^7 m/sec, find the electric and the magnetic forces between them, as seen by a laboratory observer (assuming that 10^7 m/sec can be considered a nonrelativistic velocity).

(b) What is the force in (a) according to an observer moving with the electrons?

(c) Repeat the above for the case of velocity 2.4×10^8 m/sec, which is relativistic.

20. Equal negative charges q separated a distance d are moving side by side with the same velocity v. One of the charges passes very close to a stationary positive charge Q at time t_0.

(a) Find the classical force on the second charge q at t_0 neglecting the time for propagation of the field.

(b) Show that this force is zero if $Q/q = 1 - (v^2/c^2)$.

(c) Show that an observer moving with the charge q disagrees with (b).

(d) Show that relativity resolves the above paradox, that is, the force is zero for each observer if $Q/q = 1/\gamma$.

(e) Why does it seem plausible that we are actually discussing the force at time $t_0 + (d/c)$?

25

Electromagnetic Induction

25–1 INTRODUCTION

In the historical evolution of the subjects of electricity and magnetism, the electric and magnetic fields were conceived as separate, unrelated entities. The forces between stationary charged objects seemed to be completely unrelated to the forces between magnetized objects. Thus for a limited set of circumstances, the fields may indeed be thought to be quite independent of one another. However, as the observational evidence unfolds, this independence is revealed to be artificial and finally is revealed to be false. From the foregoing chapters we know that the concepts of the two fields form parts of a unified topic, the interaction of electric charges. In general, the interaction is both electric and magnetic, i.e., electromagnetic. One case of relationship between the fields was briefly discussed in the last chapter in terms of energy interchanges. After a discussion of simple experiments, we shall complete the discussion of the deduction of the relationship between fields, started in the last chapter, and then generalize the relationship inductively in terms of further experiments.

25–2 THE INDUCTIVE APPROACH

The laws of electromagnetic induction will be deduced (Section 25–3) from the Lorentz force law of Chapter 23. In the present section, we shall see how the laws might be induced from experimental results. The purpose is to give the reader an intuitive feeling for the phenomenon before the formalism of the deductive method is presented.

It can be observed at once that the existence of a *steady* magnetic field in the region of an electric circuit has no influence upon the flow of current in the circuit except for such small effects as the deflection of the charge to one side of the conductor discussed in Chapter 23. However, if the magnetic field in the vicinity of a fixed loop of wire is varied, current is caused to flow as if a battery were contained in the circuit. Let a circuit be constructed to test the relationship between *variation* in magnetic field and the flow of charge. A test loop A is made with tightly twisted leads connecting the loop with poles of an electrolytic cell C, as in Fig. 25–1. The cell is used to measure the amount of charge Δq that flows in the circuit, by measuring the deposition of metal on a plate of the cell. (An equivalent indirect procedure would be to calculate $\int I\,dt$ from a measurement of I vs. t.) A second electric circuit D may be used to generate a magnetic field B in the region of the test loop. The following results are found by experiment:

(a) Let the position and shape of both loops be held fixed, while the current I_1 in D is varied.

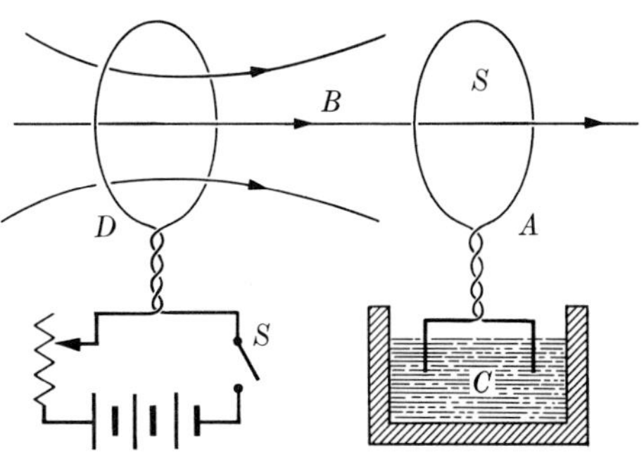

FIG. 25–1. A test loop A is connected to an electrolytic cell C which measures the total charge transported through A by the deposition of metal on the positive plate of the cell. The current through an adjacent loop D can be altered by opening or closing the switch S.

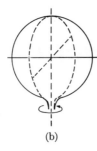

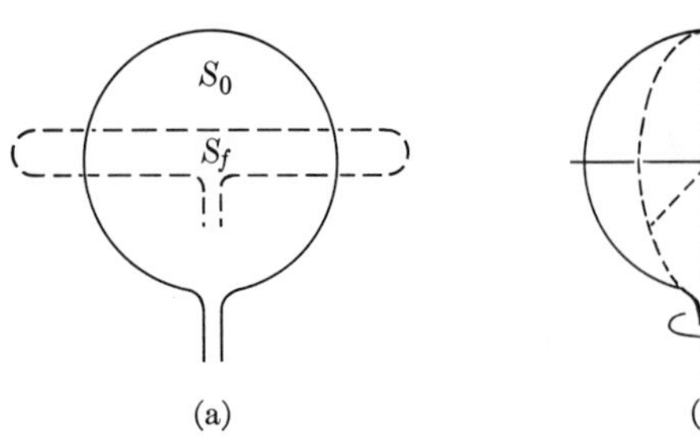

FIG. 25-2. (a) Showing a possible change in the area of the test loop S of Fig. 25-1. (b) Showing a possible change in orientation of the test loop of Fig. 25-1.

Thus the only variation is in local field strength. It is found that the amount of charge transported through the cell, and therefore through the test circuit, is directly proportional to the change in the field strength at the test loop, i.e.,

$$\Delta q \propto \Delta B.$$

(b) In a second test, the source of magnetic field is held constant in strength and structure. The area of the test loop is changed, either by a distortion of the loop so that greater or less area is encompassed by the wire in Fig. 25-2(a), or by a rotation of the direction of the loop area in Fig. 25-2(b). We find that the amount of charge transported is directly proportional to the change in the area S_n of the loop normal to the field lines, i.e.,

$$\Delta q \propto \Delta S_n.$$

No other factors connected with the structure of the loop or of the field affect these results. There is, for example, no path dependence of the manner of change of B or ΔS_n. The change in B may be slow, fast, or interrupted. The area may be first expanded and then contracted, or rotated several times. The observed Δq depends only on differences between the initial and final values of B and S_n. Variations of B and S_n have been made independently in the above. Variations of both at once show that the transport of charge depends linearly on the change in the product of BS_n, i.e.,

$$\Delta q \propto \Delta(BS_n).$$

This product of field strength times normal area is in fact the definition of the net magnetic flux, ϕ, penetrating the test loop, provided that B is uniform in the region of the loop. Thus

$$\Delta q \propto \Delta\phi$$

where

$$\phi = BS_n.$$

If the loop is so large that a variation of field over the loop is appreciable, then ϕ is defined in integral form, as in Chapter 24, thus

$$\phi = \int B\, dS_n = \int \mathbf{B} \cdot d\mathbf{S}.$$

(c) There is a third variable pertaining to the electrical property of the test circuit itself. The amount of charge transport due to any cause is inversely proportional to the total electrical resistance of the test circuit, i.e.,

$$\Delta q \propto \frac{1}{R}\cdot$$

These three experimental findings are summarized in a complete expression of the proportionality,

$$\Delta q \propto \frac{\Delta\phi}{R}\cdot$$

Since the coefficient of proportionality is unity in the mks system of units, as we shall see later, we have

$$\Delta q = \frac{\Delta\phi}{R} \text{ coul.} \tag{25-1}$$

This is the basic experimental form of the *Faraday law of induction*. It can be easily interpreted in terms of current flow in the circuit and an equivalent electromotive force in the circuit. These, however, must be expressed in terms of instantaneous values. We write Eq. (25-1) in the differential form,

$$R\, dq = d\phi,$$

and, since $dq = I\, dt$, we have

$$I\, dtR = d\phi.$$

Dividing through by dt, we obtain

$$IR = \frac{d\phi}{dt},$$

an expression involving the time rate of change of magnetic flux through the loop. This change in flux has had the effect of forcing charge to flow through the circuit, and such an effect is interpreted in terms of an equivalent electromotive force in the circuit. From Kirchhoff's law, electromotive force equals the product IR. Thus the derivative $d\phi/dt$ is identified as the source of electric potential difference in the circuit: It occupies the role of a battery, such that

$$\mathcal{E} = -\frac{d\phi}{dT}. \tag{25–2}$$

A word must be said about the introduction of the minus sign into Eq. (25–2). In the foregoing laws of proportionality, no mention was made of the direction of the flow of charge relative to the manner in which B or S_n is changed (i.e., an increase or a decrease in B or S_n). The directional relationships are summarized in a statement of Lenz's law: The change of current in the test circuit is always such that it *opposes* the cause of this change. To illustrate this law, suppose that we increase the external magnetic field through the test loop. Then the net flux through the loop is increased by external means (Fig. 25–3). At the same time, a flow of charge in the circuit will cause a magnetic field to be generated by the test circuit itself. This magnetic field must, by Lenz's law, be toward the left if the increase in external field is toward the right. The induced current and induced field will thus oppose the increase that we are impressing externally. The induced emf and hence the induced current will be as shown in Fig. 25–3.

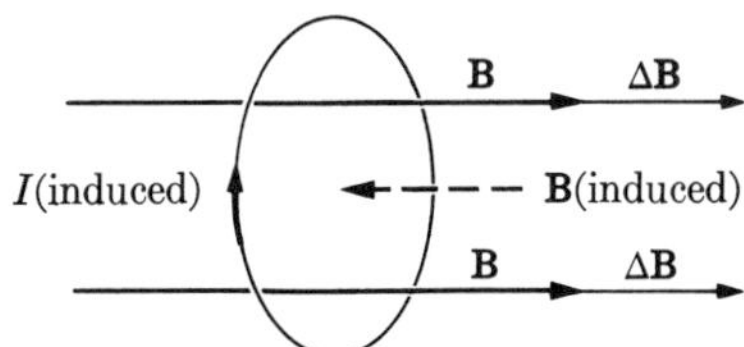

Fig. 25–3. Illustration of one example of Lenz's law. The field **B** from some source not shown is increased by Δ**B**. The induced **B** is opposite to Δ**B** and therefore the induced current that gives rise to the induced field is in the direction shown.

Lenz's law becomes a necessity when the system is submitted to a logical scrutiny. Assume that the opposite of Lenz's law holds for such systems. Then an attempt to increase the flux through the loop would be accompanied by the production of still more flux through the loop due to the induced current. This further increase in flux induces more current which induces more flux, and so on. We have a runaway system. Thus, if we place a closed loop of wire on the table, in the earth's magnetic field, and if there should be the slightest fluctuation in this field due to any cause, then the fluctuation would be reinforced. We would discover an infinite field about all the stationary loops in the world and thus an inexhaustible source of energy.

In this section, we have explored and formalized the experimental evidence that emf's are induced not only when conductors move in magnetic fields but also when the fields change with time.

25–3 THE DEDUCTIVE APPROACH TO ELECTROMAGNETIC INDUCTION

In Chapter 23, reference was made to the fact that motion of a conductor in a magnetic field

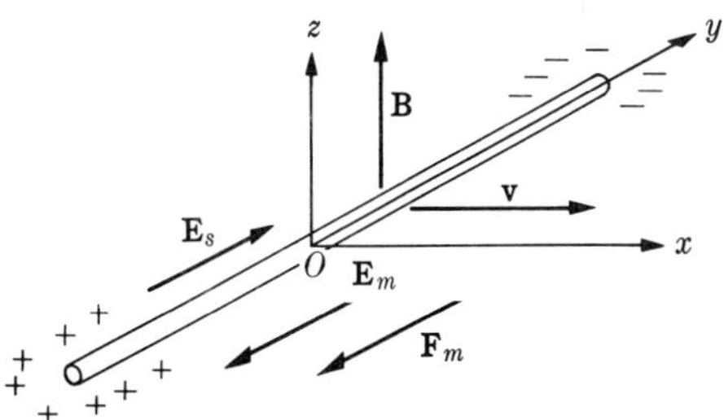

Fig. 25–4. The charge separation resulting from the motion of a conductor through a magnetic field. Equilibrium is reached when the magnetic force is balanced by the electric force that results from the charge separation.

results in an induced emf. We shall now derive the law for the induced emf from the Lorentz law of force on charges moving in a magnetic field.

First, consider this special case: Let a conducting wire be moved with velocity v, perpendicular to the wire and perpendicular to a uniform magnetic field, as in Fig. 25–4. A magnetic force is exerted on the conduction electrons in the wire, forcing them to move toward the far end of the wire. Due to the removal of electrons, the near end of the wire becomes positively charged. The result of this charge distribution is an electrostatic field, directed along the wire, from positive to negative charge. When the electrostatic and magnetic forces are balanced, equilibrium is achieved. We can interpret the result in terms of an *effective* electromotive force which has been created in the wire. It is as if a battery had been placed in the wire, generating an electric field E_m which is able to sustain an electrostatic imbalance of charge from end to end of the wire. The *equivalent* electric field E_m is by definition the magnetic force per unit charge, $F_m = qvB$ (not the electrostatic force). Therefore the expression for the equivalent electric field E_m in the wire due to the magnetic force is

$$E_m = \frac{F}{q} = \frac{qvB}{q} = vB. \qquad (25\text{–}3)$$

The electromotive force $\mathcal{E}$ in the wire is the integral of $\mathbf{E}_m \cdot d\mathbf{l}$ along the wire, and since E_m is uniform, we have

$$\mathcal{E} = \int \mathbf{E}_m \cdot d\mathbf{l} = E_m l, \qquad (25\text{–}4)$$

where l is the length of the wire. The emf is, therefore,

$$\mathcal{E} = vBl. \qquad (25\text{–}5)$$

Now consider the more general case, in which the vectors $\mathbf{B}$, $\mathbf{v}$, and $d\mathbf{l}$ are not necessarily mutually perpendicular. We use vector notation and have

$$\mathbf{E}_m = \frac{\mathbf{F}_m}{q} = \frac{(q\mathbf{v} \times \mathbf{B})}{q} = \mathbf{v} \times \mathbf{B}. \qquad (25\text{–}6)$$

We can also permit $\mathbf{B}$ and $\mathbf{v}$ to be functions of position. The emf is then, more generally,

$$\mathcal{E} = \int \mathbf{E}_m \cdot d\mathbf{l} = \int \mathbf{v} \times \mathbf{B} \cdot d\mathbf{l}, \qquad (25\text{–}7)$$

which becomes

$$\mathcal{E} = \mathbf{v} \times \mathbf{B} \cdot \mathbf{l} \qquad (25\text{–}8)$$

in the *special case of a straight wire in translational motion in a uniform field.*

We can rewrite Eq. (25–7) in more general terms, as follows. Letting the velocity $\mathbf{v}$ of the segment $d\mathbf{l}$ of the conductor be $d\mathbf{s}/dt$, we have

$$\mathcal{E} = \int \frac{d\mathbf{s}}{dt} \times \mathbf{B} \cdot d\mathbf{l}. \qquad (25\text{–}9)$$

Geometrically, the product on the right is the volume of a parallelepipedon. Therefore exchanges among the three factors can at most change the sign. A simple diagram can show that the following reordering does *not* affect the sign,

$$\mathcal{E} = \int \mathbf{B} \cdot d\mathbf{l} \times \frac{d\mathbf{s}}{dt}. \qquad (25\text{–}10)$$

Finally, we note that $d\mathbf{l} \times d\mathbf{s}$ is simply the area $d\mathbf{S}$ swept out by the conductor element $d\mathbf{l}$ in time dt. Therefore,

$$\mathcal{E} = -\int \mathbf{B} \cdot \frac{d\mathbf{S}}{dt}. \qquad (25\text{–}11)$$

The reason for the minus sign will be shown by the example below. The sign of the integrand may not be the same for all elements of a conductor; therefore, it may be necessary to refer to Eq. (25–10) in order to be sure of the signs.

Example 1. Find the emf induced in a two-bladed airplane propeller of length 2 m if the propeller is rotating at 300 rpm. Consider the case of the airplane at rest on the ground at the equator, with the propeller axis pointed north ($B = 6 \times 10^{-5}$ weber/m^2).

Solution: From Fig. 25–5, we see that $d\mathbf{l} \times d\mathbf{s}$ is parallel with $\mathbf{B}$ for the right blade but antiparallel for the left blade. Thus $\mathbf{B} \cdot d\mathbf{l} \times d\mathbf{s}/dt$ changes sign in

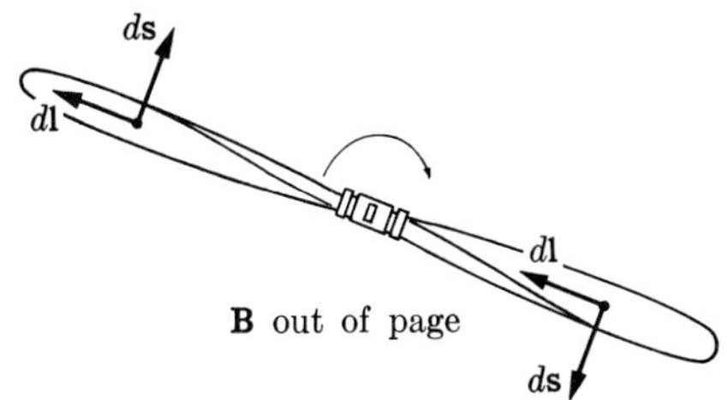

FIG. 25–5. An airplane propeller rotating with its axis of rotation in the direction of a uniform magnetic field **B**.

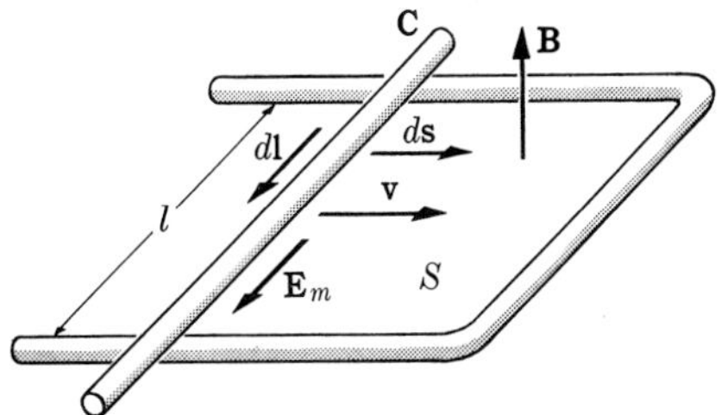

FIG. 25–6. A straight conductor C sliding on the sides of U-shaped conductor, as shown. A magnetic field is at right angles to the plane of the conductors.

integrating from one tip to the other, and $\mathcal{E}$ (tip to tip) $= 0$.

If we consider $\mathcal{E}$ (hub to tip), we have

$$\mathcal{E} = \int \frac{\mathbf{B} \cdot d\mathbf{S}}{dt} = \frac{Br^2\omega}{2},$$

where ω is the angular velocity. Thus $\mathcal{E} = 3\pi\, 10^{-4}$v.

If B is a function of position alone, we can rewrite Eq. (25–11) as

$$\mathcal{E} = \frac{d}{dt} \int - \mathbf{B} \cdot d\mathbf{S} \qquad (25\text{–}12)$$

or, in terms of the magnetic flux, $\phi \equiv \int \mathbf{B} \cdot d\mathbf{S}$, we have,

$$\mathcal{E} = -\frac{d\phi}{dt} \qquad (25\text{–}13)$$

where $d\phi$ is the net effect of flux cut by all elements of the conductor in its motion relative to the magnetic field.

Once again you are cautioned to use these equations with care because cancellation effects, due to possible variation in signs of the integrands, do not appear explicitly in some of the equations. For instance, in Example 1 we might have used Eq. (25–13) blindly for the entire propeller and wrongly concluded that there is an emf between the tips.

We now turn to the cases of more frequent concern—closed conducting loops or loops whose external leads constitute a closely spaced pair. The emf of most interest is then the emf for the entire loop, although it may actually be localized. The emf is found by carrying out the line integral (25–7) around the entire loop. In Eq. (25–13), the change in flux $d\phi$ is then the net flux cut by the entire loop of conductor. But, for the closed loop, the net flux cut by the conductors must be the same as the *change* in net flux through the area surrounded by the loop. A simple example is shown in Fig. 25–6 in which we have a conducting element c moving to the right at velocity v through a field B. Flux is cut by c at the rate vBl webers/sec, which is obviously the rate of decrease of total flux through the area S enclosed by the loop. If the other parts of the loop are also moving, we would write

$$\mathcal{E} = \oint \mathbf{E}_m \cdot d\mathbf{l} = -\frac{d\phi}{dt}, \qquad (25\text{–}14)$$

where the line integral is taken around the loop through which ϕ is measured. We are now ready to account for the minus sign. The area S must be upward in the figure, if the flux $\phi = \mathbf{B}_{\text{av}} \cdot \mathbf{S}$ is to be a positive number. But the area is decreasing and therefore $d\mathbf{S}$ must be downward. On the other hand, $d\mathbf{l} \times d\mathbf{s}$ in Eq. (25–10) and Fig. 25–6 is upward. Consequently, we have $d\mathbf{l} \times d\mathbf{s} = -d\mathbf{S}$, as promised.

We now consider a few examples. If a closed loop has motion of pure translation in a *uniform* field (Fig. 25–7), there are induced emf's in parts of the loop such as b and c, but these emf's cancel when the complete loop is considered. If Eq. (25–7) or Eq. (25–9) is used, the cancellation would be obvious, whereas the cancellation is not

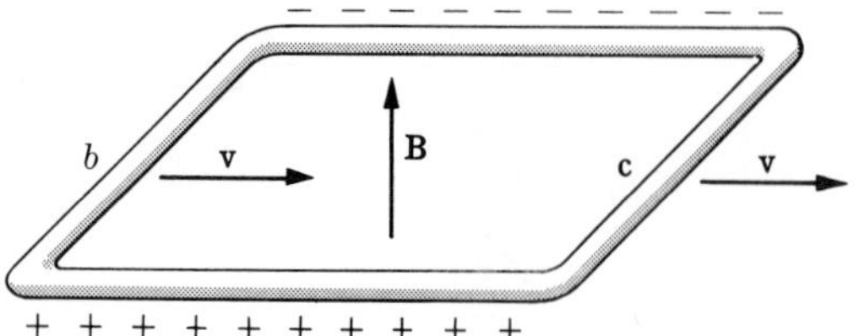

FIG. 25–7. A rectangular loop moves in such a way that two sides move perpendicularly to a magnetic field **B**.

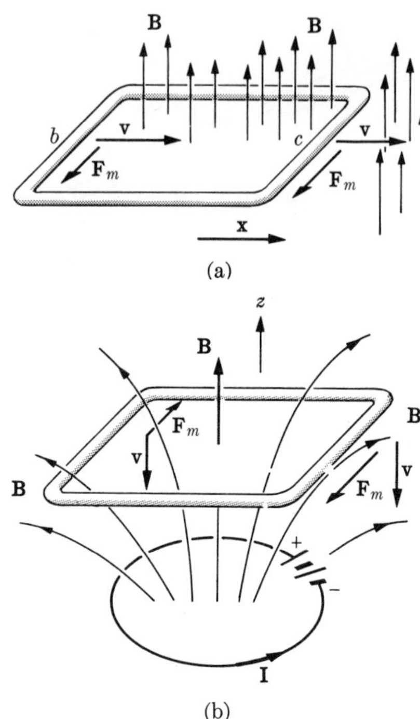

FIG. 25–8. Two simple types of motion of conducting loops relative to nonuniform magnetic fields. In (a) the field is rectilinear but varies in intensity. In (b) the field has axial symmetry but is strongly divergent in the region of the test loop. The field could be due to a coil, as shown.

so obvious if Eq. (25–11) or (25–13) is used. But when we use the formulation of the preceding paragraph, in which the change in total flux *through the loop* is considered, it is obvious that $d\phi$ through the loop is zero and the total emf is therefore zero. There will be an initial flow of electrons toward the far side (Fig. 25–7) when the loop is set in motion, but there will be no net circulation of charge around the loop.

On the other hand, if a loop such as in Fig. 25–7 is in a region of nonuniform magnetic field, a motion of pure translation will result in a change of flux through the loop and a consequent emf. The emf is most readily found by Eq. (25–14) but, of course, other forms, such as Eq. (25–7), could be used.

In Fig. 25–8(a), the change in net flux ϕ through the loop occurs because side c passes through more lines of induction in a given time than side b. The total flux through the loop can be found as a function of the position of the coil and hence as a function of x from the definition of flux,

$$\phi(x) = \int \mathbf{B} \cdot d\mathbf{S} = \int B(x)\, dy\, dx. \qquad (25\text{–}15)$$

The emf can then be found from

$$\mathcal{E} = -\frac{d\phi(x)}{dt}, \qquad (25\text{–}16)$$

when the motion of the loop $x(t)$ is specified. An alternative approach is to go back to the earlier stage in the derivation (Eq. 25–7), where the emf was formulated directly in terms of the force on a charge moving in the field. We then find that the magnetic forces are in the same direction in sides b and c but the force is greater in c. Consequently, there is a net emf in the loop. The two approaches are, of course, completely equivalent.

In Fig. 25–8(b), the change in net flux occurs because field lines enter the loop from all sides during the motion. Again, the emf can be calculated from the change in flux. We first find

$$\phi(z) = \int \mathbf{B} \cdot d\mathbf{S}, \qquad (25\text{–}17)$$

and then find the emf from

$$\mathcal{E} = -\frac{d\phi(z)}{dt} \qquad (25\text{–}18)$$

and knowledge of the motion. An alternative approach in this case is, again, to find the local value of

$$\mathbf{E}_m = \frac{\mathbf{F}_m}{q} = \mathbf{v} \times \mathbf{B} \qquad (25\text{–}19)$$

at the wire, and then take the line integral along the wire in order to find the emf. We see from the figure that $\mathbf{F}_m$ is directed approximately clockwise in all parts of the loop.

In all the above, the conductors could just as well have been stationary, with the source of the field in motion; that is, from the point of view of an observer on the conductor, there would be no distinction between moving conductor and moving field source. For example, in Fig. 25–8(b), the field might be due to a current-carrying coil placed below the test loop, as shown. Then, the induction effects would be the same regardless of whether the coil is moving upward or the test coil is moving downward relative to the laboratory.

The effect of change in flux due to a *time* variation in strength of the source of the field will be treated in a later section.

25–4 MECHANICAL-ELECTRICAL ENERGY INTERCHANGE

Electrical to mechanical. The role of the magnetic field in the conversion of electrical energy to mechanical energy was considered in Chapter 23. It was pointed out that the electrical effect could be attributed to a "back emf." We are now in a position to understand the origin of the back emf; it is nothing more than the induced emf that we have been discussing. When a current is sent through a wire that is in a magnetic field (not parallel with the wire), the wire experiences a force. If it is free to move, the wire will either increase its own kinetic or potential energy or it will do work on an outside system.

The magnetic force on a wire element $d\mathbf{l}$ is

$$d\mathbf{F}_B = I\, d\mathbf{l} \times \mathbf{B} \qquad (25\text{–}20)$$

as we have seen in Chapter 23 (see Fig. 25–4). The work done by this force in a displacement $d\mathbf{s}$ is

$$dW = d\mathbf{F}_B \cdot d\mathbf{s} = I\, d\mathbf{l} \times \mathbf{B} \cdot d\mathbf{s}. \qquad (25\text{–}21)$$

In our discussion of circuits, we have been using the concept of power, $P = dW/dt$, in place of work. Thus Eq. (25–21) becomes

$$dP = I\, d\mathbf{l} \times \mathbf{B} \cdot \frac{d\mathbf{s}}{dt} \qquad (25\text{–}22)$$

where the differential form is used because the total power is obtained by integration along the conductor (with respect to $d\mathbf{l}$).

However, when the conductor moves through the magnetic field, there is an induced emf as usual. This is the electrical result of the motion. The induced emf can be calculated by any of the expressions of Section 25–3, but it is more convenient for our present purposes to use the differential form for the emf in an element of conductor dl. The differential form is simply

$$d\mathcal{E} = \frac{d\mathbf{s}}{dt} \times \mathbf{B} \cdot d\mathbf{l}, \qquad (25\text{–}23)$$

if we utilize Eq. (25–9), for example.

By referring to Fig. 25–9, we note immediately that the emf is opposite in direction to the current that gave rise to the motion; that is, since $d\mathbf{s} \times \mathbf{B}$ is opposite to $d\mathbf{l}$, the cosine of the angle is negative and $d\mathcal{E}$ is therefore negative. This is an example of *Lenz's law, which states that electromagnetic induction effects must always oppose the agent causing them or must oppose changes in position, field, flux, etc.*

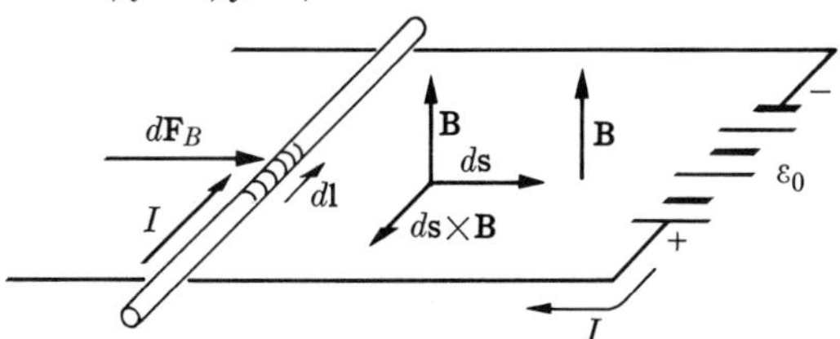

Fig. 25–9. A current I is caused by the battery emf. Since the circuit is located in a magnetic field $\mathbf{B}$ arising from an external source, there is a magnetic force dF_B on the element dl. As the element moves a distance $d\mathbf{s}$, there is an induced emf in the direction $d\mathbf{s} \times \mathbf{B}$.

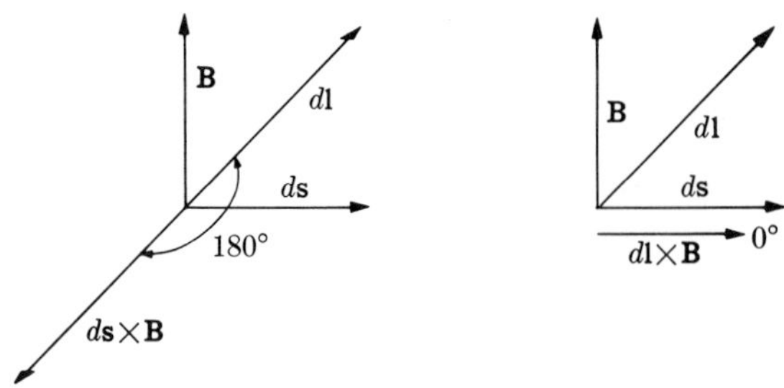

FIG. 25–10. Geometrical demonstration that $d\mathbf{s} \times \mathbf{B} \cdot d\mathbf{l} = -d\mathbf{l} \times \mathbf{B} \cdot d\mathbf{s}$.

Thus the *induced* emf opposes the flow of current and is, therefore, opposite to the emf, $\mathcal{E}_0$, that gave rise to the current in the first place. It is for this reason that the induced emf is called a back emf. Kirchhoff's law for a circuit, such as Fig. 25–9, is then

$$\mathcal{E}_0 - \mathcal{E}_i = I\sum R, \tag{25–24}$$

where $\mathcal{E}_i$ is the induced emf.

We return to the main train of argument and note that the work or power (Eq. 25–22) can be expressed in terms of the induced emf (Eq. 25–23). The order of multiplication must be altered in Eq. (25–23), [with a resulting change in sign (Fig. 25–10)] before substitution can be made into Eq. (25–22). Thus, we have

$$dP = -I\,d\mathcal{E}_i \tag{25–25}$$

or

$$P = -I\mathcal{E}_i \tag{25–26}$$

is the mechanical power delivered to the movable wire due to the interaction of current and magnetic field. The minus sign simply signifies that the emf and current are opposite in direction in this case and, therefore, P will in fact be positive. In the next section, we shall see that the transformation from mechanical to electrical power will result in different signs, as expected.

The power equation for the circuit of Fig. 25–9 is found by multiplying Eq. (25–24) by I, giving

$$\mathcal{E}_0 I = \mathcal{E}_i I + I^2\sum R, \tag{25–27}$$

or, in general terms, the power supplied by the prime source of emf equals the mechanical power output plus the joule heating.

In the above, we have neglected the effect of the current in the loop on the magnetic field. We have, in effect, assumed that the external field B is large compared with fields produced by the circuit current, or, at least, with variations in B due to the contributions by a possibly varying current.

The above discussion constitutes the basic theory for loudspeakers, motors, etc. In the case of loudspeakers, a movable coil is situated in a magnetic field. A varying current is sent through the coil, producing a varying motion of the coil in the magnetic field. The coil is coupled to the air by means of a paper diaphragm and therefore delivers mechanical energy to the air in the form of sound waves. The induced back emf in the moving coil is related to the power going into sound, as specified by Eq. (25–26).

In the case of motors, coils are free to rotate in a magnetic field. When a current is sent through the coils, forces produce rotation and deliver mechanical power. The induced emf again is related to the electrical power transformed to mechanical power, as in our equations above. In order to produce unidirectional rotation with unidirectional (dc) sources of electric power, a reversing "switch" or commutator is fixed to the rotating shaft.

It is important to note that the magnetic field B has *not* supplied the energy that produces the mechanical work in the process that we are discussing. The magnetic field simply acts as an agent that makes possible the transformation of electrical energy to mechanical energy. The energy itself comes from the *external* source of emf, the battery in the present example.

Mechanical to electrical. Our discussion now returns to the subject of the motion in magnetic fields of conductors that are not connected to external sources of emf (e.g., Figs. (25–4, –5, or –6). In the derivations of the equations for the induced emf, the question of forces, work, and power required to move the conductor through the magnetic field was not considered. We now turn to this question. If no current flows in the conductor, there is no force due to motion in the magnetic field. Hence, no mechanical force is required (in the absence of friction) to maintain the motion. But if the net emf around a closed conducting path due to induction is not zero, current will flow (Fig. 25–6). There will be a magnetic force on any current-carrying elements located in the magnetic field. In order to maintain the motion of a moving element, an external mechanical force must be applied and energy must be delivered to the system.

If there is a current I in the moving conductor, the magnetic force is given by Eq. (25–20). The mechanical (external) force that is required to maintain the motion must be

$$d\mathbf{F}_e = -I\, d\mathbf{l} \times \mathbf{B}. \qquad (25\text{–}28)$$

The work done by the mechanical force on the element $d\mathbf{l}$ in a displacement $d\mathbf{s}$ must be

$$dW = -I\, d\mathbf{l} \times \mathbf{B} \cdot d\mathbf{s}, \qquad (25\text{–}29)$$

and the power

$$dP = -I\, d\mathbf{l} \times \mathbf{B} \cdot \frac{d\mathbf{s}}{dt}. \qquad (25\text{–}30)$$

When we examine the expression for the induced emf, $d\mathcal{E} = d\mathbf{s}/dt \times \mathbf{B} \cdot d\mathbf{l}$, and note the change in sign when changing the order of multiplication, we find that the power can be expressed as

$$dP = I\, d\mathcal{E}, \qquad (25\text{–}31)$$

or

$$P = I\mathcal{E}. \qquad (25\text{–}32)$$

That is, the mechanical work required equals the electrical energy delivered by the induced emf. Note that I and $\mathcal{E}$ are in the same direction when mechanical power is being transformed into electrical power.

The *electric generator* is a device in which coils are rotated in magnetic fields, thus developing induced emf's in the moving conductors. The generator is usually connected to an external circuit. When current flows, the mechanical power required to maintain the flow of current is given by Eq. (25–32). The current can be unidirectional (dc) in the case of a homopolar generator (see Problems) or a generator with a switching mechanism (commutator).

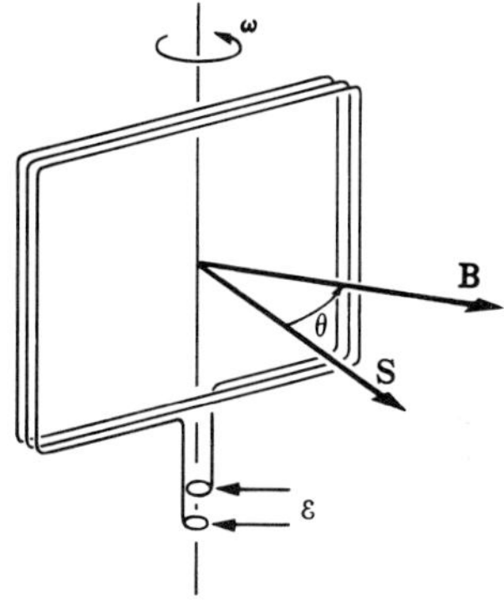

Fig. 25–11. A rectangular coil that is forced to rotate in a magnetic field **B**. An induced emf, indicated by $\mathcal{E}$, appears at the terminals.

Most generators are of the alternating-current type in which the direction of the induced emf reverses periodically. A simplified example is shown in Fig. 25–11. A flat coil of N turns, and area S rotates in a uniform field about an axis perpendicular to the field. The emf is given by

$$\mathcal{E} = -\frac{N\, d\phi}{dt}, \qquad (25\text{–}33)$$

where $\phi = \mathbf{B} \cdot \mathbf{S} = BS \cos\theta$. Since B and S are constants, we have

$$\mathcal{E} = NBS\omega \sin \omega t, \qquad (25\text{–}34)$$

where $\omega = d\theta/dt$, the angular velocity of rotation of the coil.

25–5 TIME-VARYING SOURCE OF FIELD

A model of the effect of time-dependent magnetic fields, in which the time dependence originates in a time variation in the magnitude of the currents giving rise to the field, can be constructed in terms of the lines of magnetic induction B. The number of lines of induction changes as the current giving rise to the lines changes. The lines due to an element of current form closed loops, with the greatest concentration in the region of that particular current element. In Fig. 25–12, for the sake of clarity, only the field lines in a single plane are shown.

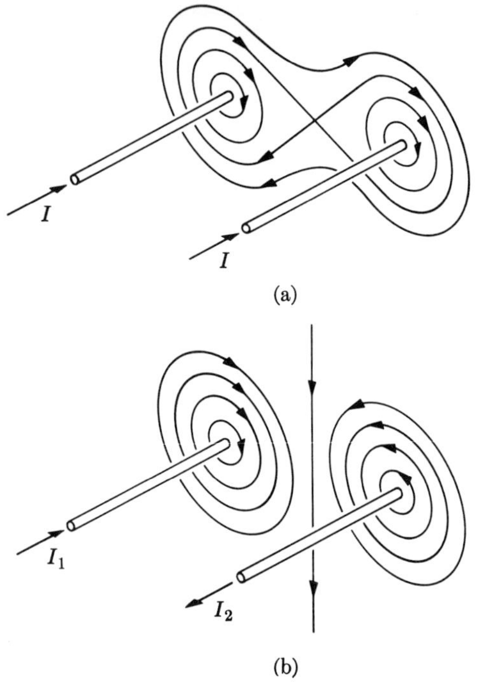

FIG. 25–12. Field lines due to (a) two parallel currents and (b) two antiparallel currents.

When the current increases, more field loops must be formed. We picture the new field loops as originating at the current element and propagating outward. The lines that already existed will move outward in a manner that makes the *line density* represent the magnitude of B at all points. When the current decreases, the loops move inward toward the current element and disappear at the current element itself. Two cases are shown in (Fig. 25–12) of the combined effect of current elements. In (a) the current elements are in the same sense and are equal in strength. If the currents increase together, field lines will move outward from the currents; they will coalesce at the midpoint and then move outward as a single loop enclosing both currents. In (b) the currents are equal but opposite. When the currents are increasing, loops move outward. But, in contrast with (a), the loops do not coalesce. They become more and more crowded in the space between the currents.

The motion of the loops must diminish with distance in a manner that will provide the same fractional increase in flux density at each point in space. The increases will not occur simultaneously at all distances, but will propagate outward in a wave-like manner at the speed of light.

By using the above model, we can predict the effects of induction that result when the field changes with time while the geometry remains fixed. The direction of motion of the lines resulting from changing currents can be deduced from the configuration of the steady-state field. The direction of the Lorentz force on a charge at a given point can then be determined. The magnitude of the force is easily calculated from the above model in cases of special symmetry.

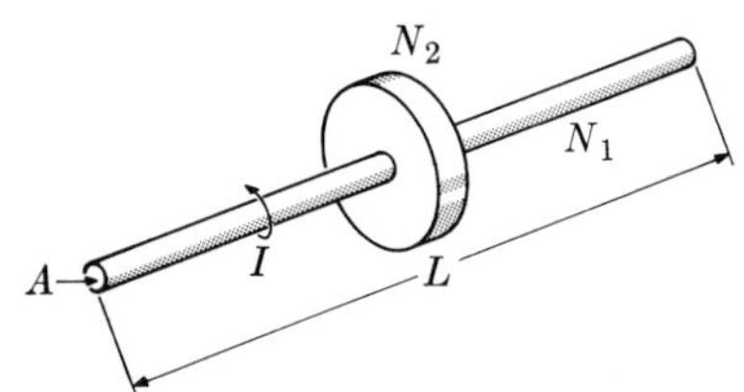

FIG. 25–13. A long solenoid N_1 encircled by a short solenoid N_2.

Example 2. A long solenoid of length L and area A with N_1 turns has a variable current that is given by $I = I_0 \sin \omega t$. Find the emf in a secondary coil of N_2 turns that encircles the solenoid, as shown in Fig. 25–13.

Solution: The induced emf *per turn* in the secondary is $\mathcal{E} = -d\phi/dt$ where $\phi = \int \mathbf{B} \cdot d\mathbf{S}$. We have seen in the Problems of Chapter 24 that the

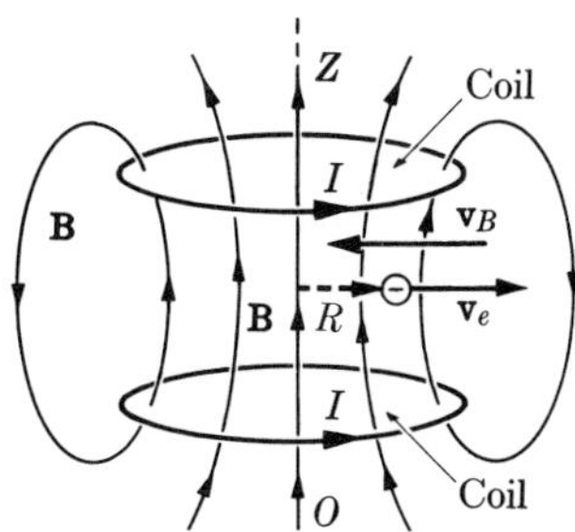

FIG. 25–14. The magnetic field due to two ring-shaped coils. When the currents I increase, the field lines within the coils move inward. The result is an electric field, which at the radius R, as shown, is directed into the page.

field of a long solenoid is confined to its interior and is uniform. Furthermore, the magnitude at the longitudinal center is $B = \mu_0 I N_1/L$. Thus $\phi = \mu_0 I N_1 A/L$. Therefore, the emf induced in coil 2 will be $\mathcal{E} = -(\mu_0 N_1 N_2 A I_0 \omega/L) \cos \omega t$.

Example 3. In the simplest model of the particle accelerator, called the betatron, electrons are accelerated in a region of increasing magnetic field that is produced by an increasing current in the magnetizing coils. For simplicity, we consider the field to be produced by the coils alone (Fig. 25–14). The field has axial symmetry about the Z-axis. Show that the force on an electron placed in the field is tangent to a circle centered on OZ.

Solution: From symmetry, the B lines must move radially inward (v_B) as I increases. The force on the electron is therefore equivalent to the case of the electron moving radially outward (v_e). The equivalent Lorentz force $e\mathbf{v} \times \mathbf{B}$ is therefore tangential and counterclockwise (the charge is negative). If the electron is injected into the field with an initial tangential velocity, the Lorentz force due to the effect of the field itself (*not* the effect of the change in field) will be radial. The electron will follow a path with instantaneous radius R given by $\sum F = ma$ or $evB = mv^2/R$. If the moment of injection is chosen so that B has the right value, R will be exactly the distance to the axis OZ and the electron will start to move on a circular arc centered on the axis. If B now increases with time, there is a tangential force and v increases. If the spatial distribution of the field is appropriately chosen, B at the electron (that is, at distance R from the axis) will increase at just the right rate to always satisfy $evB = mv^2/R$, with *R constant*.

If the above conditions are met, the electron moves in a circular path of radius R. We can easily calculate the conditions on B. One condition is given above, namely,

$$B_R = \frac{mv}{eR} = \frac{p}{eR},$$

where p is the momentum of the electron.

The effect of the time variation in B can be evaluated by considering the variation in flux ϕ within the circle of radius R. The law of induction is

$$\oint \mathbf{E}_m \cdot d\mathbf{s} = -\frac{d\phi}{dt} = -\frac{d}{dt}\iint \mathbf{B} \cdot d\mathbf{S},$$

where we remember that E_m is the tangential force F_θ per unit charge, $E_m = F_\theta/e$. But, from Newton's second law, we have

$$F_\theta = \frac{dp_\theta}{dt}.$$

From the condition on B_R, we obtain $p_\theta = eRB_R$. Bringing all the above together, we have

$$\oint \frac{1}{e}\frac{d(eRB_R)}{dt}\,ds = -\frac{d}{dt}\iint \mathbf{B} \cdot d\mathbf{S},$$

which becomes

$$\frac{d}{dt}\oint RB_R\,ds = -\frac{d}{dt}\iint \mathbf{B} \cdot d\mathbf{S},$$

or simply

$$\oint RB_R\,ds = -\iint \mathbf{B} \cdot d\mathbf{S}.$$

But since RB_R is constant, the integral on the left is simple to evaluate

$$\oint RB_R\,ds = 2\pi R^2 B_R,$$

and we have finally

$$2B_R = \frac{1}{\pi R^2}\iint \mathbf{B} \cdot d\mathbf{S}.$$

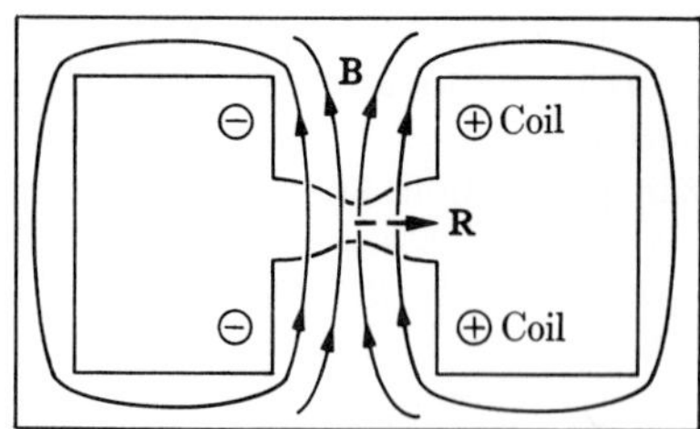

FIG. 25–15. Cross section of a possible betatron magnet that satisfies the condition of stronger average field within the radius R than at the radius R itself.

The expression on the right is the definition of the value of B averaged over the surface πR^2. Consequently,

$$2B_R = B_{av}$$

for all values of time. Thus, the field at the radius R of the circular path of the electron is to be half the average field within the circle, a condition that is easily met, for example, by having a second field-producing coil of radius smaller than R. In practice, the field is usually produced by the effect of coils that are wound on an iron magnet. The field condition above is then met by appropriate disposition of the iron (Fig. 25–15).

25–6 SELF-INDUCTANCE

In the argument pertaining to Lenz's law, it was at least implied that an emf is induced in a circuit where the magnetic flux through the circuit is changed by any cause whatever. The flux can be changed by external or internal causes, the latter a change in the current of the circuit itself.

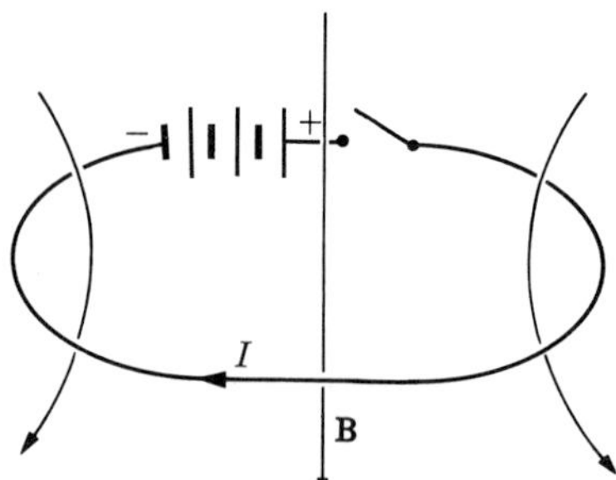

FIG. 25–16. The field **B** due to a current loop.

Consider for the moment an experiment to be performed on an elementary circuit consisting of a wire, a switch, and a battery, as in Fig. 25–16. The switch is closed and charge flows in the circuit. From Ohm's law, the equilibrium magnitude of the electric current is the emf of the battery divided by the total resistance of the circuit, i.e.,

$$I = \frac{\text{emf}}{R}.$$

By experiment it is found that this equilibrium value of the current is not suddenly achieved when the switch is closed. Rather, the current increases *toward* this equilibrium value in a definite way which depends, among other things, on the geometric form of the circuit path (Fig. 25–17). There is a property of the circuit, called self-inductance, which determines the *rate* at which the equilibrium current is approached. The explanation follows.

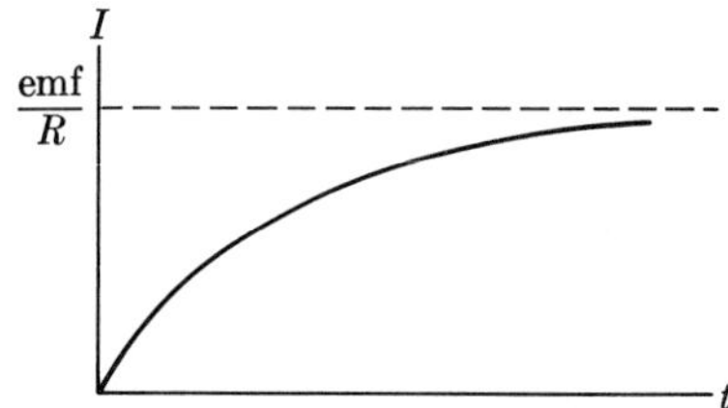

FIG. 25–17. The current I versus the time t after the switch is closed in the circuit of Fig. 25–16.

As the current is built up in the wire, a magnetic field is created about the wire, as in Fig. 25–16. Since the current must change with time from zero to its final value, so must the magnetic field, and therefore the flux through the loop change with time. An electromotive force opposing any change in the current—in this case opposing the increase in current—is induced in the circuit. As usual this emf is given by

$$\mathcal{E} = -\frac{d\phi}{dt}, \qquad (25\text{–}35)$$

where ϕ is the flux penetrating the area bounded

by the loop. Since the magnetic field is not necessarily uniform over this area, we have

$$\phi = \int \mathbf{B}(x, y, z) \cdot d\mathbf{S}. \qquad (25\text{–}36)$$

However, the magnetic field at any point is proportional to the current in the wire, since from Chapter 24 we have

$$B = I \frac{\mu_0}{4\pi} \int \frac{d\mathbf{l} \times \mathbf{r}}{r^3} = I\,\mathbf{K}(x, y, z), \qquad (25\text{–}37)$$

where the integral is taken over all elements $d\mathbf{l}$ of the wire. The integral depends *only* on the geometry of the circuit since it contains only geometrical factors. We see that the origin of the self-induced emf derives from the fact that each element of conductor experiences the effect of the magnetic field due to all the other elements of the wire.

The self-induced emf can now be written by substituting (25–37) into (25–36) then into (25–35), giving

$$\mathcal{E} = -\frac{d}{dt} \int I\,\mathbf{K}(x, y, z) \cdot d\mathbf{S}.$$

But I is not a function of (x, y, z) and the integral is not a function of time (for an undeformable coil); therefore

$$\mathcal{E} = -\frac{dI}{dt} \int \mathbf{K}(x, y, z) \cdot d\mathbf{S}. \qquad (25\text{–}38)$$

The integral, which is the purely geometric factor, is represented by L, called the *coefficient of self-inductance*. Thus

$$\mathcal{E} = -L \frac{dI}{dt}, \qquad (25\text{–}39)$$

where L is the purely geometrical factor defined above; that is,

$$L \equiv \int \mathbf{K}(x, y, z) \cdot d\mathbf{S} \qquad (25\text{–}40)$$

with

$$\mathbf{K}(x, y, z) \equiv \frac{\mu_0}{4\pi} \int \frac{d\mathbf{l} \times \mathbf{r}}{r^3}. \qquad (25\text{–}41)$$

The reader will readily understand from the appearance of the above expressions that the calculation of L is usually tedious. In a few cases, the geometrical complications are avoidable due to symmetry or other simplifying conditions. In order to treat some of the simple cases, it is convenient to combine Eqs. (25–35) and (25–39), with the result

$$\frac{d\phi}{dt} = L \frac{dI}{dt}$$

or

$$L = \frac{d\phi}{dI}. \qquad (25\text{–}42)$$

In the usual situations, the geometrical configuration remains fixed and consequently, we usually have

$$L = \frac{\phi}{I}, \qquad (25\text{–}43)$$

where ϕ is the flux through the circuit loop of self-inductance L.

The unit of L, the *henry*, is a joule/amp^2 in the mksa system. In a circuit of inductance one henry, a rate of change of current of one ampere per second, causes an induced emf of one volt. The emf in this case is often called the back emf in the circuit to denote that it acts to oppose changes in the current.

Example 4. Find the self-inductance of a toroidal coil of N turns, if the turn radius r is small compared with the toroid radius R.

Solution: The field inside the toroid is $B = nI\mu_0$ (Chapter 24), where n is the number of turns per unit length, $n = N/2\pi R$. The field will be approximately uniform within the coil, since $r \ll R$. Consequently,

$$\phi = B_{\text{av}}S = (NI\mu_0/2\pi R)\pi r^2.$$

We can now apply Eq. (25–43) and write

$$L = \frac{\phi}{I} = N\mu_0 r^2/(2R),$$

but we have overlooked the fact that we have N

turns, in each of which there is an induced emf. That is, Eq. (25–35) becomes

$$\mathcal{E} = -N \frac{d\phi}{dt}, \qquad (25\text{–}44)$$

when $d\phi/dt$ is the same for each of the N turns as in the present case. Consequently, $L = N\phi/I$ in the present case, which becomes

$$L = \mu_0 N^2 r^2/(2R)$$

for the self-inductance of a toroid when $r \ll R$.

25–7 CIRCUITS WITH SELF-INDUCTANCE

When Kirchhoff's law is applied to a circuit in which the current is changing, one of the emf terms will be the self-inductance term, $\mathcal{E} = -L\, dI/dt$, if there is a coil in the circuit.

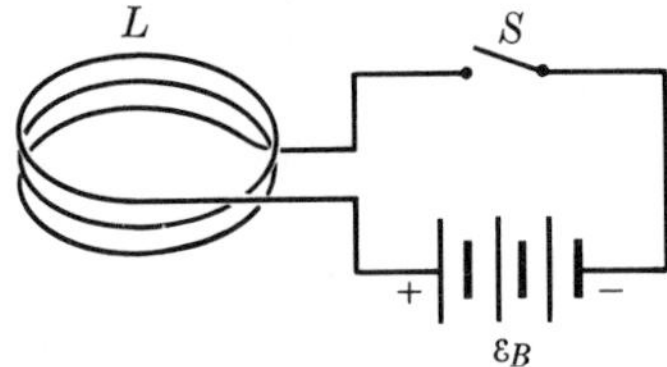

FIG. 25–18. A circuit consisting of a self-inductance L in series with a battery.

Example 5. Consider the circuit of Fig. 25–18 in which a coil, battery, and switch are in series. When the switch is closed, Kirchhoff's law gives

$$\mathcal{E}_B + \mathcal{E}_L = IR,$$

where $\mathcal{E}_B$ is due to the battery and $\mathcal{E}_L$ to the coil. Then

$$\mathcal{E}_B - L\frac{dI}{dt} = IR,$$

which is a simple differential equation that can be solved by separating the variables I and t. The solution is

$$I = \frac{\mathcal{E}_B}{R}\left(1 - e^{-(R/L)t}\right),$$

which you can verify by substitution in the differential equation and by verifying the results for $t = 0$ and $t = \infty$.

25–8 ENERGY IN THE MAGNETIC FIELD

In Chapter 21, it was shown that the energy in charged capacitors, $W = \frac{1}{2}CV^2$, could be interpreted as energy stored in the electric field with energy density $\epsilon_0 E^2/2$ joules/m^3. The energy in any electrostatic system can be so assigned to a distribution of energy throughout the electric field.

We can now establish the equivalent expressions for currents. Energy resides in the magnetic field. The instantaneous power delivered to a self-inductance due to its self-inductance alone is

$$P = -\mathcal{E}I = L\frac{dI}{dt}I. \qquad (25\text{–}45)$$

The energy is equal to the work, which is related to power by $P = dW/dt$. We thus have

$$P = \frac{dW}{dt} = L\frac{dI}{dt}I$$

or simply

$$dW = LI\,dI,$$

which upon integration gives

$$W = \tfrac{1}{2}LI^2. \qquad (25\text{–}46)$$

We see that in contrast with a capacitor, the energy in a self-inductance is a maximum when the current is a maximum.

The energy can be considered to be stored in the magnetic field. The energy density can be found by considering a toroidal solenoid of radius much greater than the radius of the coil itself. An expression for the self-inductance can be found from the induced emf,

$$\mathcal{E} = -N\frac{d\phi}{dt},$$

which can also be written

$$\mathcal{E} = -L\frac{dI}{dt}.$$

Thus we have

$$N\phi = LI, \qquad (25\text{–}47)$$

and the energy [from Eq. (25–46)] can be written

$$W = \tfrac{1}{2}N\phi I. \tag{25–48}$$

The field in a toroidal coil is entirely internal and is nearly uniform when the radius is large compared with the cross-sectional radius (see the last problem in Chapter 24). Then $B = \mu_0 NI/l$, where l is the circumference of the toroid. The flux is $\phi = BA$, where A is the cross-sectional area of the toroid. Writing (25–48) in terms of B alone, we have

$$W = \frac{\frac{1}{2}B^2 Al}{\mu_0}.$$

But Al is the volume in which the field is confined and therefore the energy density is

$$\frac{W}{V} = \frac{1}{2}\frac{B^2}{\mu_0}\ \text{joules/m}^2. \tag{25–49}$$

The energy stored in a magnetic field surrounding a current distribution is assumed to have the energy density given by (25–49).

25–9 MUTUAL INDUCTANCE

The effect of induction in coil 2 due to a changing current in coil 1 can be specified by a con-

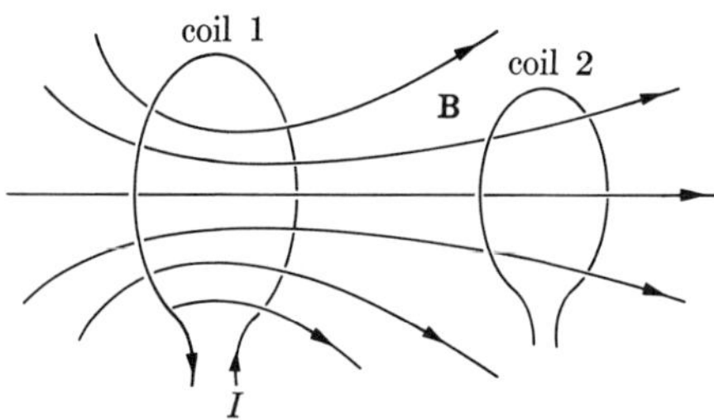

Fig. 25–19. Some of the field lines **B** due to a current I in coil 1 thread through a neighboring coil 2. Induced emf's appear in 2 when the current in 1 is changed.

stant called the mutual inductance between the coils. Just as in the case of self-inductance, the mutual inductance depends only on the geometry of the coils.

The emf induced in coil 2 is

$$\mathcal{E}_2 = -\frac{d\phi}{dt} = -\frac{d}{dt}\iint \mathbf{B}\cdot d\mathbf{S}, \tag{25–50}$$

where the integral is carried out over the area enclosed by coil 2. As we see in Fig. 25–19, not all the flux from coil 1 is necessarily enclosed by coil 2. The field at any point in the plane of coil 2 depends directly on the current in 1 and the geometry G_{12} of coil 1 relative to coil 2. Thus

$$B = I_1 G_{12},$$

and, therefore,

$$\mathcal{E}_2 = -\frac{dI_1}{dt}\iint G_{12}\mathbf{B}\cdot d\mathbf{S}_2, \tag{25–51}$$

since the geometry is time-independent in the present example. The above integral is a constant for a given configuration of the coils. It is the constant called the mutual inductance M_{12}. We thus have

$$\mathcal{E}_2 = -M_{12}\frac{dI_1}{dt}. \tag{25–52}$$

In special cases, such as a long solenoid inside a short solenoid (Example 2), all the flux from coil 1 links with coil 2. Furthermore, in Example 2, the flux is easily calculated. The result is that the mutual inductance in Example 2 is

$$M_{12} = \frac{\mu_0 N_1 N_2 A}{L}, \tag{25–53}$$

which the reader can easily derive.

Circuit devices consisting of two or more coils arranged so that changing currents in one induce currents in the other coils are very common. They are called transformers, since they are sometimes used to "transform" large emf's to low emf's, or vice versa.

25–10 CIRCUITS WITH SELF-INDUCTANCE AND CAPACITANCE

Consider a circuit, as shown in Fig. 25–20, in which a capacitor C can be charged to a potential

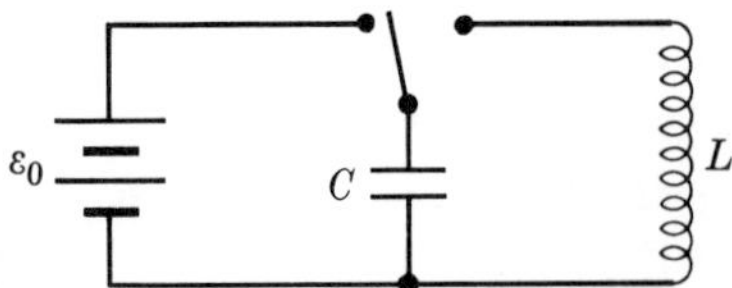

Fig. 25-20. Circuit in which a capacitor C can be charged by a battery and then connected in series with a self-inductance L.

difference $\mathcal{E}_0$ by means of a battery and then switched over to an inductance L. Kirchhoff's law for the second circuit is

$$\mathcal{E}_C + \mathcal{E}_L = 0, \tag{25-54}$$

or

$$\frac{q}{C} = -L\frac{dI}{dt}. \tag{25-55}$$

When the definition of $I = dq/dt$ is introduced into (25-55), we have the familiar form of an equation whose solution is simple harmonic motion,

$$\frac{d^2q}{dt^2} = -\frac{1}{LC}q. \tag{25-56}$$

A possible solution is

$$q = q_0 \cos 2\pi ft, \tag{25-57}$$

where

$$2\pi f = \sqrt{1/(LC)} \tag{25-58}$$

and

$$q_0 = \mathcal{E}_0 C. \tag{25-59}$$

The current is

$$\begin{aligned} I &= -2\pi f \mathcal{E}_0 C \sin 2\pi ft \\ &= -\mathcal{E}_0\sqrt{C/L}\sin\sqrt{1/LC}\,t. \end{aligned} \tag{25-60}$$

The above result has tremendous practical importance. We have previously mentioned that alternating current of the above form can be obtained by rotating a coil in a magnetic field. However, the frequency is determined by the frequency of rotation of the coil and, consequently, mechanical limitations restrict the maximum frequencies obtainable with a rotating coil to something of the order of 10,000 cps. On the other hand, by using an LC circuit of the above sort with small values of L and C, currents oscillating at frequencies of hundreds of millions of cps are quite easily obtained.

The importance of high-frequency oscillating currents lies in the result (to be discussed later) that radio waves (electromagnetic waves) are emitted copiously by currents that are changing rapidly—for example, high-frequency oscillating currents. In practice, energy must be supplied regularly in order to replenish the energy dissipated in the resistance of the circuit and in the radiation of electromagnetic waves by the circuit. The latter will be discussed in subsequent chapters.

25-11 MAXWELL'S EQUATIONS

The analysis of the law of induction is now carried further. The electromotive force in a circuit is defined as the closed line integral of $\mathbf{E} \cdot d\mathbf{s}$ about the circuit, where $d\mathbf{s}$ follows the path of the circuit. Thus we say, by definition, that if a changing magnetic field has caused charge to flow in a circuit, then the changing magnetic field has impressed an electric field in the wire of the circuit. A changing magnetic field has thereby created an electric field. We write the emf in the circuit in terms of the electric field as

$$\text{emf} = \oint \mathbf{E} \cdot d\mathbf{s},$$

where $\mathbf{E}$ is the value of the electric field impressed at the different points along the wire. Then, from the law of induction, we have a relationship between the electric field and the changing magnetic field, namely,

$$\oint \mathbf{E} \cdot d\mathbf{s} = -\frac{d\phi}{dt} = -\frac{d}{dt}\int \mathbf{B} \cdot d\mathbf{A}, \tag{25-61}$$

where the line integral is taken around the periphery of a surface and the surface integral is taken over the same surface. We see from Eq. (25-61) that an electric field is produced in space by a magnetic field that changes with time.

Another relationship between the fields is implicit in Ampere's law,

$$\oint \mathbf{B} \cdot d\mathbf{s} = \mu_0 I = \int \mu_0 \mathbf{J} \cdot d\mathbf{A}, \qquad (25\text{–}62)$$

where I is the total current enclosed by the path of the line integral B, and the integral of J (the current density) is taken over the area enclosed by the path. But suppose that we now consider the elementary entities that constitute a current, namely, individual moving charges. The current in Eq. (25–62) can, of course, be written in the terminology of the moving charges, giving

$$\oint \mathbf{B} \cdot d\mathbf{s} = \mu_0 nev, \qquad (25\text{–}63)$$

where nev refers to the column of moving charges constituting the current that is enclosed by the path of the line integral. The following question now occurs: Since point charges can be in the plane of the path of the line integral *only* at certain instants of time (see Fig. 25–21), exactly what does Faraday's law mean when the particulate nature of charge is considered? The question is more striking if we consider the passage of a single charge through the plane of the path of integration. Does the line integral have a finite value only at the instant that the charge is in the plane of integration? We already know that the answer to this question is no, since the magnetic field of a moving charge is zero only along a line in the directi›n of motion (and at infinity).

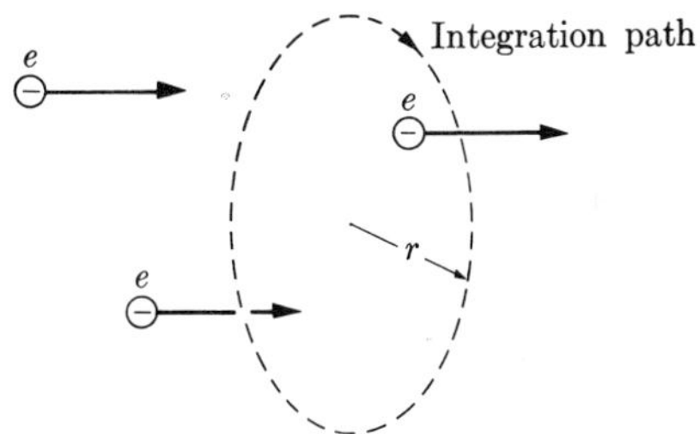

FIG. 25–21. A line integral path for the application of Faraday's law in a region where charges are moving.

From the above, it is seen that there is something missing in Faraday's law. The missing idea is that a changing electric field through the area encircled by the line integral is equivalent to a current through the area. In order to write Ampere's law in terms of change in electric flux, we can consider a single charge moving along the axis of a circular integration path, as shown in Fig. 25–22. At the instant the charge is in the plane of the path, the field anywhere on the path of integration is

$$B = \frac{\mu_0}{4\pi} \frac{qv}{r^2} \qquad (25\text{–}64)$$

where r is the radius of the integration path and v is the velocity of the charge (Section 24–6). The line integral of B around the path can therefore be written as

$$\oint \mathbf{B} \cdot d\mathbf{s} = \int_0^{2\pi r} \frac{\mu_0}{4} \frac{qv}{r^2}\, ds = \frac{\mu_0}{2} \frac{qv}{r}. \qquad (25\text{–}65)$$

In Eq. (25–65), the line integral of B has been expressed in terms of the motion of the charge q.

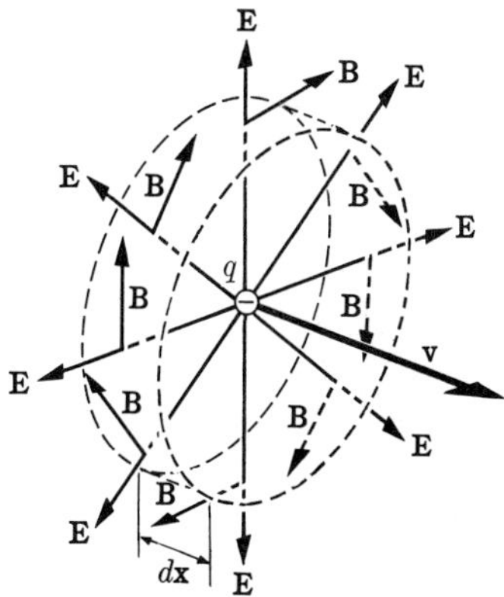

FIG. 25–22. The electric and magnetic fields in the central plane of a charge moving with velocity v.

We shall now show that the change in *electric* flux N threading through the loop can *also* be expressed in terms of motion of the charge that gives rise to the electric flux. For simplicity, we choose the instant when the charge lies in the plane of the path of the line integral. As explained in Chapter 20, the total electric field flux from the charge is

$$N = \frac{q}{\epsilon_0}, \tag{25–66}$$

of which half threads through the integration loop at the instant in question (see Fig. 25–23, in which the loop is viewed nearly edge-on). When the charge moves a distance dx, the E-lines lying in a circular band of radius r and width dx cross the integration loop. Therefore, the decrease dN in the flux through the plane of the loop is

$$dN = E\,2\pi r\,dx = \left(\frac{1}{4\pi\epsilon_0}\frac{q}{r^2}\right)2\pi r\,dx, \tag{25–67}$$

where E is the field strength at distance r, and $2\pi r\,dx$ is the element of area corresponding to the motion of the charge through a distance dx. The time rate of change of flux can be found by dividing by dt in Eq. (25–67), with the result

$$\frac{dN}{dt} = \frac{1}{2\epsilon_0}\frac{q}{r}\frac{dx}{dt} = \frac{1}{2\epsilon_0}\frac{qv}{r}. \tag{25–68}$$

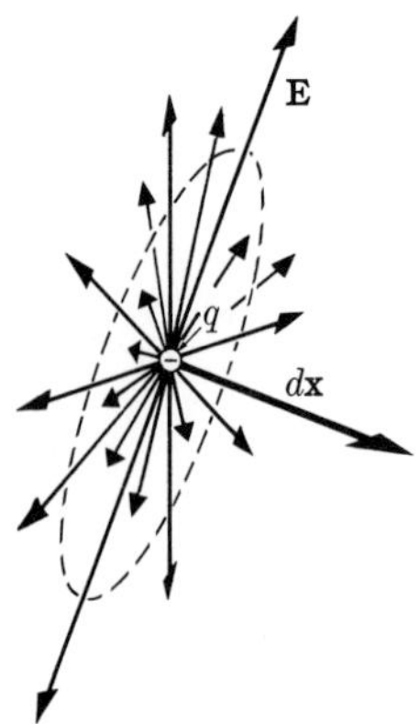

FIG. 25–23. Diagram to illustrate the calculation of the change in electric flux through a line integral path when a charge moves a distance $d\mathbf{x}$ out of the plane of the integration loop.

By comparing (25–65) and (25–68), we see that

$$\oint \mathbf{B}\cdot d\mathbf{s} = \epsilon_0\mu_0\frac{dN}{dt} \tag{25–69}$$

or, in terms of electric field (since $N \equiv \int \mathbf{E}\cdot d\mathbf{A}$)

$$\oint \mathbf{B}\cdot d\mathbf{s} = \epsilon_0\mu_0\frac{d}{dt}\int \mathbf{E}\cdot d\mathbf{A}, \tag{25–70}$$

where the line integral is taken around the periphery and the surface integral is taken over the area outlined by the line integral. Equation (25–70) relates magnetic field strength to a time rate of change of electric field. We have considered a special case in the above derivation, but the result can be shown to be valid in general.

These two relationships, (25–61) and (25–70), are forms of Maxwell's equations of electrodynamics relating electric and magnetic fields. The other general laws are Gauss's law or theorem,

$$\oint \mathbf{E}\cdot d\mathbf{A} = \int\frac{\rho\,dV}{\epsilon_0}, \tag{25–71}$$

and a similar law (which we have not discussed) for magnetic fields,

$$\oint \mathbf{B}\cdot d\mathbf{A} = 0, \tag{25–72}$$

where the surface integral is over a closed surface in each case. Equation (25–72) is simply a statement of the fact that magnetic field lines cannot begin or end anywhere, in contrast with electric field lines, which begin and end on charges.

Equations (25–61), (25–70), (25–71), and (25–72) (repeated below) are the integral forms of Maxwell's equations. They will be rewritten in differential form in a later chapter.

$$\oint \mathbf{E}\cdot d\mathbf{s} = -\frac{d}{dt}\int \mathbf{B}\cdot d\mathbf{A},$$

$$\oint \mathbf{B}\cdot d\mathbf{s} = \epsilon_0\mu_0\frac{d}{dt}\int \mathbf{E}\cdot d\mathbf{A},$$

$$\oint \mathbf{E}\cdot d\mathbf{A} = \int\frac{\rho\,dV}{\epsilon_0}, \qquad \oint \mathbf{B}\cdot d\mathbf{A} = 0.$$

25–12 SUMMARY

Electromagnetic induction is described from the experimental approach, and results of the experiments are summarized in the law for the induced emf in terms of the time rate of change in magnetic flux through a circuit loop,

$$\mathcal{E} = -\frac{d\phi}{dt}\cdot$$

Lenz's law states that the induced emf and the resulting current must be of such a nature as to oppose the change that causes the emf.

The law of induction is then deduced from the law of force on charges that are moving in a magnetic field, with the result

$$\mathcal{E} = \int \mathbf{v} \times \mathbf{B} \cdot d\mathbf{l},$$

where dl is a short segment of conductor and v is its velocity. From the above, it can be shown that

$$\mathcal{E} = -\frac{d\phi}{dt},$$

where $d\phi/dt$ is the net flux cut by the moving conductor, or the change in flux through a circuit loop due to motion of the loop relative to the source of the field.

When the power is analyzed, it is found that, in a series circuit,

$$\mathcal{E}_0 I = \mathcal{E}_i I + I^2 \sum R,$$

where $\mathcal{E}_0$ is the emf of the source that gives rise to a current and $\mathcal{E}_i$ is the emf induced in the circuit if there is motion in an external B field by portions of the conducting circuit. The $\mathcal{E}_i I$ term represents the conversion of electrical power to mechanical power, for example in an electric motor.

On the other hand, if portions of a conducting loop are moved through a magnetic field by an external mechanical force, the $\mathcal{E}_i I$ term represents the conversion of mechanical power to electrical power, as in an electrical generator. The simplest device of this sort is a coil that is forced to rotate in a magnetic field. If simple slip-ring connections are made to the rotating coil, the resulting emf (uniform B field) is

$$\mathcal{E} = NBS \sin \omega t,$$

where N is the number of turns in the coil, S is its area, and ω is the angular velocity of rotation.

Induction in fields that vary with time because the source current is time-dependent is analyzed. The ideas are applied to the analysis of the betatron type of electron accelerator, as an illustrative example.

The emf induced in a conductor due to the change in magnetic field produced by a changing current in the conductor itself results in the phenomenon called self-inductance. The self-inductance is shown to depend only on the geometry of the conductor. It is measured by L and, by definition, L represents the geometric coefficient in

$$\mathcal{E} = -L\frac{dI}{dt}\cdot$$

If the same flux passes through each of the N turns of a coil,

$$L = N\frac{d\phi}{dI},$$

an expression that in simple cases enables a calculation of L to be made.

The total energy in a magnetic field is found in terms of the electrical energy $\int \mathcal{E}_i I\, dt$ required to establish the field. The energy density in the field is found to be

$$\tfrac{1}{2}\mu_0 B^2 \text{ joules/m}^3.$$

The mutual inductance between conductors is the geometric factor that relates the emf induced in one conductor to the change of the current in the other conductor. It is the factor M_{12} in

$$\mathcal{E}_2 = -M_{12}\frac{dI_1}{dt}\cdot$$

An important type of circuit, one that contains inductance and capacitance with a negligible resistance, is found to sustain simple harmonic currents. The frequency can be made high enough so that the circuit can become an effective source of electromagnetic waves.

Maxwell's equations are obtained in integral form by showing that Faraday's law can be written in the form

$$\oint \mathbf{B} \cdot d\mathbf{s} = \epsilon_0 \mu_0 \frac{d}{dt} \int \mathbf{E} \cdot d\mathbf{A},$$

where the line integral is taken around the periphery of the area covered by the surface integral on the right.

Maxwell's equations in the integral form consist of the law of induction, Faraday's law in the above form, Gauss' law, and the equivalent of Gauss' law for magnetism,

$$\oint \mathbf{E} \cdot d\mathbf{s} = -\frac{d}{dt} \int \mathbf{B} \cdot d\mathbf{A},$$

$$\oint \mathbf{B} \cdot d\mathbf{s} = \epsilon_0 \mu_0 \frac{d}{dt} \int \mathbf{E} \cdot d\mathbf{A},$$

$$\oint \mathbf{E} \cdot d\mathbf{A} = \int \frac{\rho \, dV}{\epsilon_0},$$

$$\oint \mathbf{B} \cdot d\mathbf{A} = 0.$$

Problems

1. An airplane with wingspread 30 m is flying at a speed of 300 m/sec north 30° west at a point on the earth where the magnetic field is 6×10^{-5} weber/m^2 and 60° down from the horizontal.
(a) Find the induced emf from tip to tip.
(b) Can this emf be detected by connecting a voltmeter from tip to tip? Explain.

2. (a) An airplane at the equator is at rest on a runway headed north. Find the induced emf in a two-bladed propeller of overall length 4 m when rotating 600 times per minute. See below for B.
(b) Find the emf when the plane is at the North Pole and taxiing at 50 m/sec. (Let $B = 5 \times 10^{-5}$ weber/m^2 in both cases, with B horizontal and vertical at the equator and North Pole, respectively.)

3. A rod of length 2 m falls freely from rest near the equator. If the orientation of the rod is E-W, find the induced emf
(a) as a function of time,
(b) as a function of height.

4. A metal plate is moved at velocity v through a uniform magnetic field of intensity B, as shown in Fig. 25–24. Find the charge density on the front and back faces, assuming that the plate was uncharged initially. Assume that $d \ll l$.

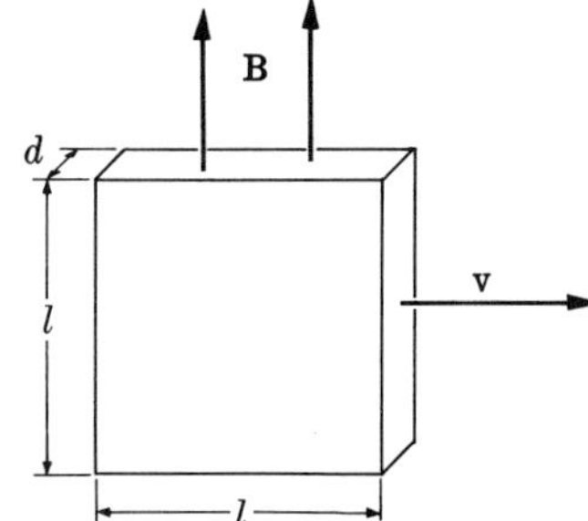

FIGURE 25–24

5. A rectangular loop is moved through a region in which the magnetic field is given by $B_y = B_z = 0$, $B_x = (6 - y)$ webers/m^2 (see Fig. 25–25). Find the emf in the loop as a function of time, with $t = 0$ when the loop is in the position shown in the figure:
(a) if $v = 2$ m/sec,
(b) if the loop starts at rest and has an acceleration of 2 m/sec^2.
(c) Repeat for motion parallel to OZ in place of OY.
(d) Find the currents if R (loop) $= 2$ ohms.

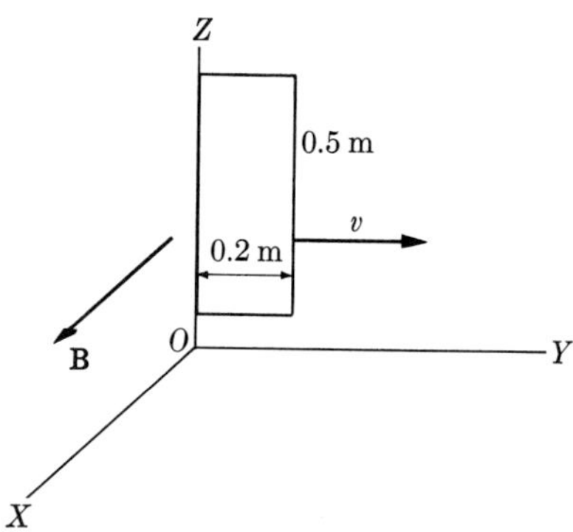

FIGURE 25–25

6. Suppose that the loop in Problem 5 is pivoted about the OZ-axis.

(a) What is the *average* emf during the first 90° of rotation if the period of rotation is 1/5 sec per revolution?

(b) Find the instantaneous emf and current as functions of time.

7. If the resistance of the loop in Problem 5 is 3 ohms,

(a) find the mechanical power required in parts (a) and (b) of that Problem.

(b) Find the work required to move the coil 6 m, starting from $y = 0$.

8. Find the force required to move the coil in Problem 7.

9. A circular loop of radius 30 cm is normal to a uniform field of intensity $B = 0.1 \sin(300t)$ webers/m^2. Find the induced emf.

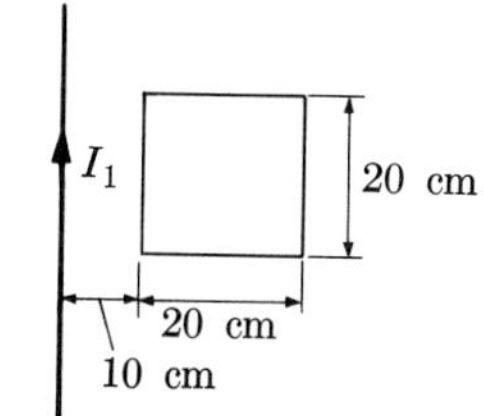

FIGURE 25–26

10. The square loop in Fig. 25–26 is placed in the plane of a long, straight wire. The current in the straight wire increases with time as I_1 (amp) = $5t^2$ where t is in seconds.

(a) Find the emf induced in the square loop if it is held in place.

(b) If the resistance of the loop is 2 ohms, find the induced current in the loop.

(c) Find the force on the loop.

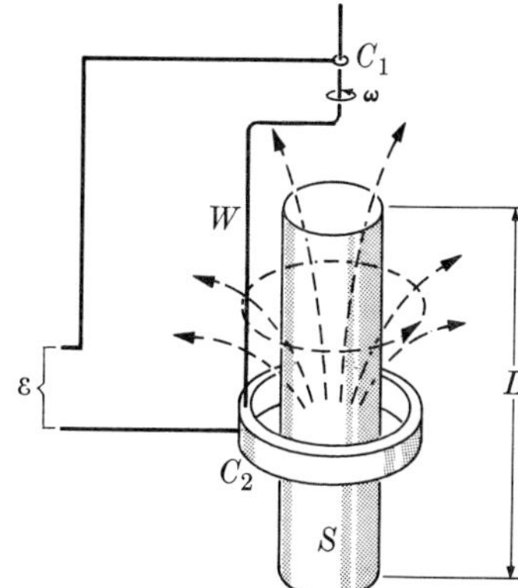

FIGURE 25–27

11. A simple homopolar generator is shown in Fig. 25–27. A solenoid S of length L with N turns has a wire W rotating about it at angular velocity ω. The wire makes sliding contacts on C_1 and C_2 and gives rise to an emf. The cross-sectional area of the solenoid is A, and a current I flows in its wires. Noting that all the flux through the solenoid at its midsection (Fig. 25–27) is cut by the wire W during each revolution, find the induced emf. Assume that L is large compared with the radius, so that $B = \mu_0 IN/L$.

12. A very long rectangular loop of conductor of resistance 0.01 ohm is held in a vertical plane, with its bottom wire just within the edge of a magnetic field of strength 1.5 webers/m^2, as shown in Fig. 25–28. The field is directed into the plane of the paper and extends for a long distance below H. If the mass of the loop is 50 gm,

(a) find the maximum velocity of fall of the loop if it is released from rest, assuming that the the loop is very long.

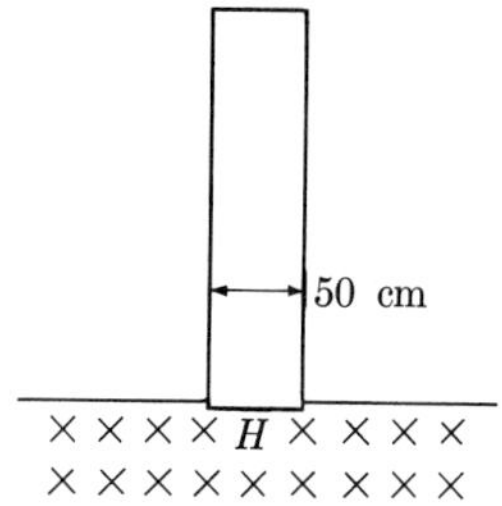

FIGURE 25–28

(b) What is the rate of heating of the coil at the terminal velocity?

(c) Where does the energy that produces the heat come from? Verify by direct calculation.

13. The permanent magnet in Fig. 25–29 gives a total flux of 2×10^{-4} weber. The loop L is just large enough so that the magnet will pass into the loop.

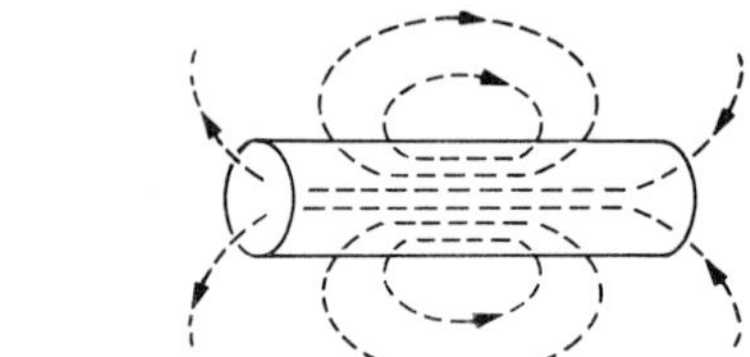

FIGURE 25–29

(a) If the resistance of the loop is 0.2 ohm, how much charge flows through a given point in the loop when the magnet is brought up from a large distance and thrust into the loop up to the midpoint of the magnet?

(b) If the time for the motion in (a) is 0.4 sec and the instantaneous velocity is varied in such a manner that $d\phi/dt$ is constant, how large is the induced current in the loop?

(c) How much *energy* is dissipated in the loop?

(d) How much mechanical *work* was required to move the magnet?

(e) What was the mechanical power required?

(f) Can you find the force required? Explain.

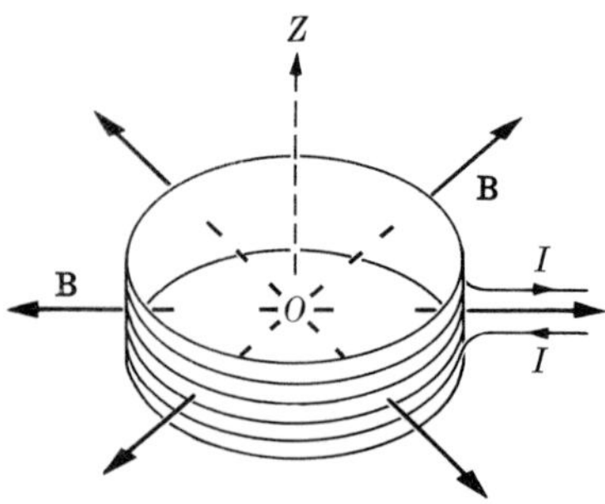

FIGURE 25–30

14. A loudspeaker coil is mounted in a uniform radial field, as shown in Fig. 25–30. It is supported by a paper diaphragm that acts as a Hooke's-law spring for motion in the OZ-direction. If a particular coil of 40 turns and radius 1 cm is in a field of 0.3 weber/m^2:

(a) What must be the spring constant of its support if the coil is to be displaced 2 mm when a current of 0.2 ampere is passed through it?

(b) How much work was done in the displacement?

(c) If the displacement took place in 0.005 sec, how large was the average back emf?

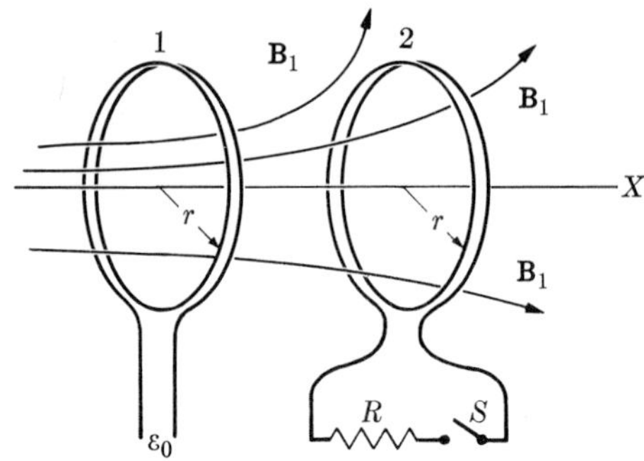

FIGURE 25–31

15. Two coils are placed coaxially, as shown in Fig. 25–31. Coil 1 is connected to an external source of emf labeled $\mathcal{E}_0$. Assume that the geometry is such that one-fifth the magnetic field lines produced by coil 1 passes through coil 2 and vice versa. The resistances of the coils are R_1 and R_2 and coil 2 is connected to an external resistance R, as shown. The number of turns in the coils is N_1 and N_2. The total flux produced by coil 1 is given by $\phi = (L_1/N_1)I_1$, where L_1 is the self-inductance of coil 1.

With switch S open:

(a) Find the emf induced in coil 2 when I_1 increases uniformly from 0 to I_0 in t sec.

(b) Find the induced emf in coil 2 when $I_1 = I_0 \sin \omega t$.

(c) How much energy is required from circuit 1 as a result of the induction in coil 2?

With switch S closed:

(d) Find the induced emf and current in coil 2 with current I_1 as in (a).

(e) Repeat for current I_1 as in (b).

(f) How much energy is required from circuit 1 as a result of the induction in coil 2 in part (d)?

16. The apparatus of Problem 15 is again considered, but we now discuss the emf applied to coil 1 and the power supplied by that source of emf.

Suppose that the current $I_1 = kt$, where t is the time, and that the switch S is open.

(a) Show that the back emf is kL_1 and hence that the applied emf must be $\mathcal{E}_0 = kL_1 + I_1R_1 = k(L_1 + R_1t)$. [*Hint:* Apply Kirchhoff's law.]

(b) Show that the power delivered by $\mathcal{E}_0$ is $k^2(L_1t + R_1t^2)$.

Now with switch S closed, we know from symmetry that the induced current in coil 2 produces flux through coil 1 equal to one-fifth the flux produced by I_2.

(c) Find the direction of the emf "induced" in coil 1 by the current in coil 2. (It should be in the same direction as $\mathcal{E}_0$.)

(d) What is the qualitative effect of I_2 (and hence the effect of the closing of switch S) on the current I_1?

(e) In view of the above, what is the mechanism by which coil 2 obtains power or energy from coil 1?

17. (a) Find the total power P_0 delivered by the battery in Fig. 25–14 (Example 3).

(b) Find the power P_R dissipated as heat.

(c) Compare (a) with (b) and account for the difference, $P_0 - P_R$, by showing that $\int_0^\infty (P_0 - P_R)\, dt = \frac{1}{2}LI_\infty^2$, the energy stored in the magnetic field.

18. A coil of self-inductance L and negligible resistance is connected to a battery of internal resistance R_B and emf $= \mathcal{E}_B$.

(a) Write Kirchhoff's law for the circuit when the coil is switched suddenly from the battery to a resistance R (see Fig. 25–32).

(b) Find the current as a function of time after the switching.

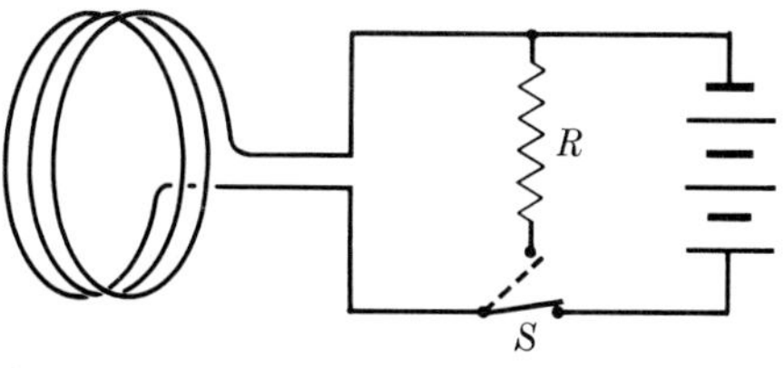

FIGURE 25–32

(c) Calculate the energy dissipated in the resistance R.

(d) Where did the energy dissipated in R come from?

19. A capacitor of capacitance C contains initially a charge Q. It is suddenly connected to a resistanceless self-inductance L.

(a) Show that Kirchhoff's law gives:

$$\frac{q}{C} = -L\frac{d^2q}{dt^2}$$

for the charge q on the capacitor at any time.

(b) Solve for q as a function of time.

(c) Find I as a function of time.

(d) Prove that the total energy

$$\frac{1}{2}\frac{q^2}{C} + \frac{1}{2}LI^2 = \text{constant}.$$

20. (a) Show the way to calculate, in principle, the self-inductance of a single circular loop of radius R.

(b) Can the radius of the wire itself be negligibly small? Explain.

21. Calculate the self-inductance per unit length of coaxial cable with central wire radius R_1 and outer shell radius R_2 (see Problem 24–9 for description).

26

One-Dimensional Wave Propagation

26–1 INTRODUCTION

In the chapters on electricity and magnetism, we have seen that charged objects exert forces on one another. The forces that were discussed are the Coulomb force due to the charge itself and the Lorentz force due to motion of the charge. The concepts of electric and magnetic fields were introduced for the analysis of the above forces. It was found that the two fields are interdependent when the fields vary with time. The nature of the interdependence is given quantitatively by Maxwell's equations, which were derived in their integral form in the earlier chapters.

Maxwell predicted an additional form of electromagnetic interaction between charges, an interaction that occurs when charge is *accelerated*. The phenomenon is known as *electromagnetic radiation*. The accelerated charge actually emits energy in the form of the electromagnetic radiation, energy that flows away from the charge in the form of *waves* (the subject to be introduced in this chapter). The experimental verification of Maxwell's prediction by Hertz was made in the realm of what we now call radio waves.

Since the wave nature of electromagnetic radiation cannot be ascertained directly by our senses, we shall first take up a study of mechanical wave motion of a sort that can be seen directly, for example, a wave in a rope or a string. Not only the process of wave motion itself but also the process of generation of the waves at their source is more easily comprehended for mechanical waves than for electromagnetic waves. An additional simplification will be utilized initially by considering waves that travel along one direction only.

After some familiarity with wave motion has been gained by the study of mechanical waves, we shall turn to the wave motion of greatest interest to us here, electromagnetic waves.

26–2 WAVE VELOCITY IN A STRING

The one universal property of wave motion is the velocity of propagation. In general, the velocity depends on the properties of the medium and on the shape of the wave. However, we shall first treat the simplest case, the case in which the velocity depends only on the properties of the medium. In addition, we choose the case in which the medium is uniform, thus adding the simplification that the velocity is the same at all points.

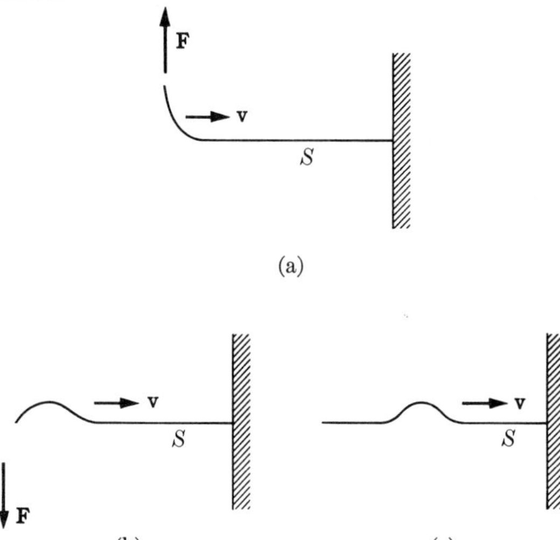

FIG. 26–1. The left end of the taut string S is given an upward and downward jerk, returning it to its initial position. As a result, a pulse travels along the string, as shown.

An analysis of wave motion will be given, using the example of a lateral disturbance in a tightly stretched string. An over-simplified derivation of the velocity of a pulse in a string is given first. A pulse is formed in a string if one end of a string is given a sudden, violent shake (Fig. 26–1). Such a process is easily demonstrated in practice. The disturbance of equilibrium, the pulse form, travels along the string at a definite speed. Assume for the moment the observed fact and the prediction of wave theory for an ideal string—that the pulse remains constant in form as it proceeds along the string. As the pulse advances, different parts of the string are drawn into motion and then are returned to equilibrium. This traveling disturbance, which is called the wave, is not a "closed" mechanical system. It does not embody definite mechanical elements which always remain part of a definite system. Rather, new elements of the string are drawn into the pulse and then discarded. There are two alternative approaches to the analysis of this action. One approach is to say that the disturbance flows through the medium. This is the point of view of an observer who is stationary relative to the string. Another point of view proves fruitful for the present calculation. Let the observer move along the string at the velocity of the wave. Then to him the pulse form itself is a stationary form through which the string is caused to flow. He can stand beside the pulse and watch string enter into and leave the arc of disturbance from right to left (Fig. 26–2). We focus our attention on a portion of the arc Δl.

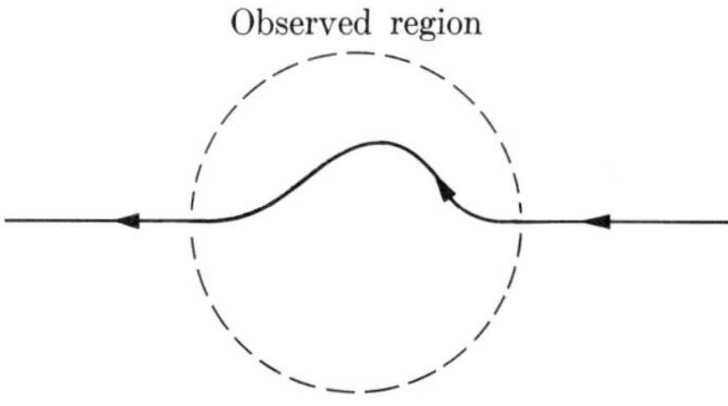

FIG. 26–2. An observer who moves to the right at the speed of the pulse sees the string moving to the left, as shown.

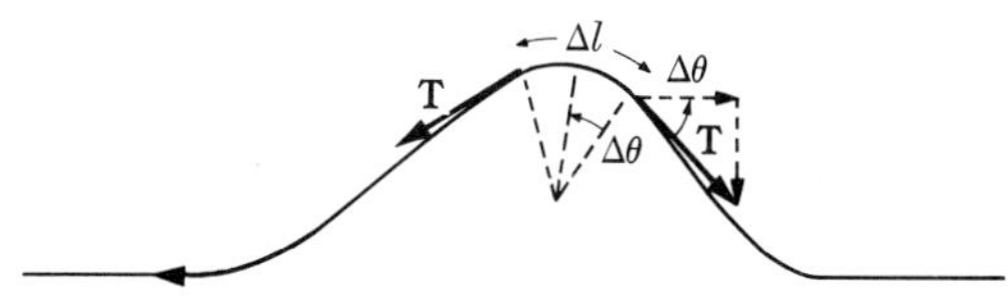

FIG. 26–3. The external forces on a length Δl of the string are the tensions T by the adjoining portions of the string. The tensions are equal in magnitude but differ in direction.

A sufficiently short segment Δl is the arc of a circle of radius R, as in Fig. 26–3. The external forces acting on the element Δl are the tension forces, tangent to the string as shown in Fig. 26–3. (We are assuming that the gravitational force is small compared with T.) The horizontal components of T balance, since the horizontal velocity is constant. The vertical components add, and their sum is the resultant force on the sector Δl. From the diagram, we see that

$$|\sum \mathbf{F}| = 2T \sin \Delta\theta. \qquad (26\text{–}1)$$

This force is perpendicular to the direction of motion of the string. It is the force which causes the radial acceleration toward the center of curvature of the motion. From Newton's second law, $\sum F = ma_R$, we have

$$2T \sin \Delta\theta = \Delta m \, \frac{v^2}{R}, \qquad (26\text{–}2)$$

where Δm is the mass of the element of string and v is the tangential velocity of the string. The velocity v is also the velocity of the pulse in the coordinate system in which the string is at rest.

For small $\Delta\theta$, we have $\sin \Delta\theta \simeq \Delta\theta$. We also note that $2\,\Delta\theta = \Delta l/R$ and Eq. (26–2) can therefore be rewritten

$$v^2 = T \, \frac{\Delta l}{\Delta m} \cdot \qquad (26\text{–}3)$$

But $\Delta m/\Delta l$ is the mass per unit length of the string, which we shall designate by ρ. Therefore,

$$v = \sqrt{T/\rho}, \qquad (26\text{–}4)$$

where T is the tension and ρ the mass per unit length of the string.

Assumptions have been made that restrict the generality of the above derivation. The pulse form has been assumed to be unchanging. If the form varies, the calculation of a definite wave velocity would lose its meaning. A more general derivation follows in the next section.

26-3 WAVE EQUATION FOR TRANSVERSE WAVES IN A STRING

It has been assumed above that a wave form once impressed on a string is transmitted unchanged and at a definite velocity along the string. With this assumption, the wave velocity of Eq. (26-4) was derived. That this is a correct portrayal of a wave disturbance in an ideal string can be shown by a more general approach to the problem. The general solution is obtained through the detailed application of Newton's laws to the string. A general differential equation of motion is obtained which, in turn, yields wave motion solutions.

Consider an element of string of length Δl, as shown in Fig. 26-4. The OX-axis is chosen along the line of the undisturbed string. We consider only pulses or waves in which the displacements are not large and the shape of the wave has no steeply inclined portions. If displacements are small, the length of the string is not altered appreciably by the displacements, and the magnitude of the tension remains approximately constant. If the wave is nowhere very steep, the angles of the disturbed string are never large and simplifications occur.

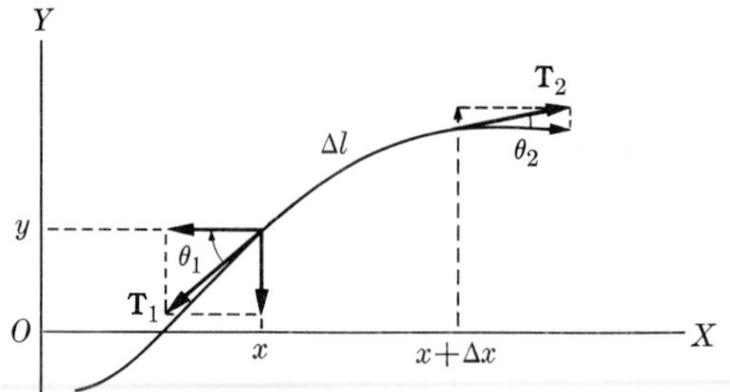

FIG. 26-4. The external forces $\mathbf{T}_1$ and $\mathbf{T}_2$ on a segment Δl of a string that is displaced laterally by a wave.

The external forces acting on Δl are $\mathbf{T}_1$ and $\mathbf{T}_2$, which are the forces exerted by the adjoining portions of the string. The gravitational force mg is usually negligible or, if not negligible, it is a constant force that merely alters the shape of the undisturbed string. The resultant force on Δl is therefore

$$\sum \mathbf{F} = \mathbf{T}_1 + \mathbf{T}_2. \qquad (26\text{-}5)$$

It is convenient to analyze the problem in cartesian components; therefore, we rewrite Eq. (26-5) as

$$\sum F_x = T_2 \cos\theta_2 - T_1 \cos\theta_1,$$
$$\sum F_y = T_2 \sin\theta_2 - T_1 \sin\theta_1. \qquad (26\text{-}6)$$

Since we are treating only the case in which θ_1 and θ_2 are small, we use the Maclaurin series expansions of the cosine functions,

$$\cos\theta = 1 - \frac{\theta^2}{2!} + \frac{\theta^4}{4!} + \cdot \qquad (26\text{-}7)$$

For small angles only the first term need be used. The first expression in Eq. (26-6) becomes

$$\sum F_x \simeq T_2 - T_1 = 0,$$

since the x-component of acceleration is zero for a particle of the string. Therefore, $T_2 = T_1$, and the second expression of Eq. (26-6) becomes (dropping subscripts on T)

$$\sum F_y = T(\sin\theta_2 - \sin\theta_1). \qquad (26\text{-}8)$$

But, for small angles, $\sin\theta \simeq \tan\theta$ and therefore

$$\sum F_y = T(\tan\theta_2 - \tan\theta_1),$$

or, since $\tan\theta = dy/dx$,

$$\sum F_y = T\left[\left(\frac{dy}{dx}\right)_2 - \left(\frac{dy}{dx}\right)_1\right],$$

or

$$\sum F_y = T\Delta\left(\frac{dy}{dx}\right). \qquad (26\text{-}9)$$

It should be noted at this point that, in this approximation, the vertical forces also vanish if dy/dx is constant. The restoring force in the motion depends on the *change in slope* along the string, or the derivative of the slope.

Since the resultant force on the segment equals the mass Δm of the segment times the acceleration in the y-direction,

$$\sum F_y = \Delta m a_y,$$

we have

$$T\Delta\left(\frac{dy}{dx}\right) = \rho\,\Delta x\,\frac{d^2y}{dt^2}. \tag{26–10}$$

Note that the substitution $\rho\,\Delta x = \Delta m$ was also based on the fact that θ is small and therefore $\Delta l \simeq \Delta x$. Appearing on the left side of the equation is the term $\Delta(dy/dx)$, which represents the change in the derivative from one end of the segment Δl to the other. On the other side is Δx, the horizontal length of the segment. These terms may be combined to represent the change in dy/dx per unit length, $\Delta(dy/dx)/\Delta x$, giving us

$$T\,\frac{\Delta}{\Delta x}\left(\frac{dy}{dx}\right) = \rho\,\frac{d^2y}{dt^2}. \tag{26–11}$$

Finally, we obtain a point relationship between the space and time derivatives when $\Delta x \to 0$. Then Eq. (26–11) becomes

$$T\,\frac{d^2y}{dx^2} = \rho\,\frac{d^2y}{dt^2}, \tag{26–12}$$

which is called a wave equation.

In the derivation of this equation it has been possible to identify the expressions which are obtained with the actual point elements of string under discussion. However, the use of the standard symbols of calculus for total differentiation is incorrect. Reconsider the intended meaning of these symbols. The transverse displacement y of a point of the string is a function of both horizontal distance x along the string and of the instant of time t of observation. Consequently, we write $y(x, t)$, indicating that y is a function of two variables, x and t. The second derivative with respect to time, d^2y/dt^2, is the instantaneous acceleration of a point on the string. It varies along the string and is definite only if the point is specified. Therefore, in performing the time differentiation, *x is specified,* and this means that x, one of the independent variables, is held constant. The special symbol adopted for this operation, the differentiation of a function with respect to one independent variable, with others held constant, is called *partial* differentiation. It is written $\partial^2y(x, t)/\partial t^2$. It specifies the actual intent of the physical derivation which has been performed. The coordinate derivative d^2y/dx^2 is the space rate of change of slope at any point on the string, and it is a function which varies in time. It is definite only when the other independent variable t is specified. It has to do with the instantaneous, or frozen, form of the string at any instant. In the process of this differentiation, *t is held constant.* The operation is written $\partial^2y(x, t)/\partial x^2$. With these restrictions, emphasized by the notation as defined, we arrive at the correct form of the differential equation of wave motion in a string,

$$\frac{T}{\rho}\,\frac{\partial^2y}{\partial x^2} = \frac{\partial^2y}{\partial t^2}. \tag{26–13}$$

Equation (26–13) is a second-order partial differential equation. We assert the general solution of the equation and submit it to trial. The general solution is of the form

$$y = F(u), \tag{26–14}$$

where u (the argument of any function F) must be of the form

$$u = (x \pm vt) \tag{26–15}$$

where v is a constant of the motion. To prove that this function is a solution, we perform the derivatives indicated by the wave equation.

The first space derivative is

$$\frac{\partial y}{\partial x} = \frac{\partial F(u)}{\partial u}\,\frac{\partial u}{\partial x},$$

but since $u = x \pm vt$, we have $\partial u/\partial x = 1$ and therefore

$$\frac{\partial y}{\partial x} = \frac{\partial F(u)}{\partial u}.$$

Similarly, the second derivative is

$$\frac{\partial^2 y}{\partial x^2} = \frac{\partial}{\partial x}\left(\frac{\partial F(u)}{\partial u}\right) = \frac{\partial^2 F(u)}{\partial u^2}\frac{\partial u}{\partial x} = \frac{\partial^2 F(u)}{\partial u^2},$$

since $\partial u/\partial x = 1$, as before.

The first time derivative is

$$\frac{\partial y}{\partial t} = \frac{\partial F(u)}{\partial u}\frac{\partial u}{\partial t},$$

but since

$$\frac{\partial u}{\partial t} = \frac{\partial(x \pm vt)}{\partial t} = \pm v,$$

we have

$$\frac{\partial y}{\partial t} = \pm v\frac{\partial F(u)}{\partial u}.$$

Proceeding similarly for the next derivative, we have

$$\frac{\partial^2 y}{\partial t^2} = \frac{\partial}{\partial t}\left[\pm v\frac{\partial F(u)}{\partial u}\right]$$
$$= \pm v\frac{\partial^2 F(u)}{\partial u^2}\frac{\partial u}{\partial t} = v^2\frac{\partial^2 F(u)}{\partial u^2}.$$

Substituting into the wave equation the above expressions for the slope derivative and the acceleration, we find

$$\frac{T}{\rho}\frac{\partial^2 F(u)}{\partial u^2} = v^2\frac{\partial^2 F(u)}{\partial u^2}, \qquad (26\text{–}16)$$

which shows that any function of $u = x \pm vt$ is a solution, provided that it can be differentiated, and

$$\frac{T}{\rho} = v^2, \qquad (26\text{–}17)$$

or

$$v = \sqrt{T/\rho}. \qquad (26\text{–}18)$$

This is the expression for wave velocity derived in the preceding section. The formal identification of v with wave velocity remains to be shown in the following section.

26-4 WAVE VELOCITY

The velocity of a wave is found by observing the motion of some "point" on the wave form. For example, we could watch the motion of the peak of the wave as it progresses along the string. Or any general point can be noted, such as the point P corresponding to some definite displacement y_0, as indicated in Fig. 26-5. Suppose, then, that we follow the point P of displacement y_0 along the x-axis. Note that no material particle is in motion along the string. It is a "form" which is in motion. The velocity v of this form is called the *wave velocity*. Of the alternative solutions, one with $+v$ and the other with $-v$, we first choose

$$y = F(x - vt).$$

When $y = y_0$ is constant, the argument $x - vt$ must be constant, i.e.,

$$x - vt = \text{constant}.$$

Differentiating this expression with respect to time, we have

$$\frac{dx}{dt} - v = 0,$$

or (noting that we have kept y constant),

$$\left(\frac{dx}{dt}\right)_{y=y_0} = v. \qquad (26\text{–}19)$$

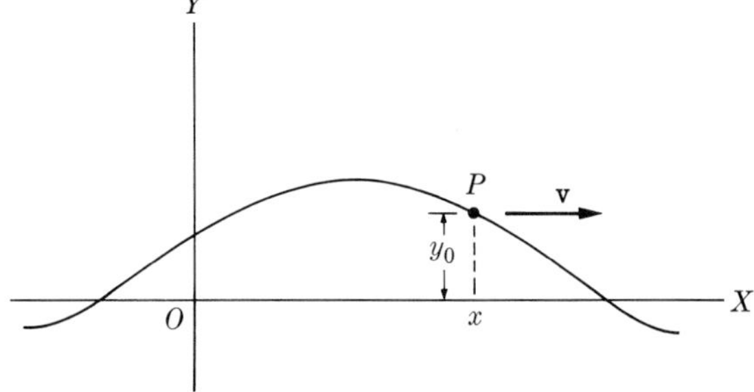

FIG. 26-5. A point P on a wave, where the point is defined by a fixed value y_0 of the lateral displacement y. The point P so defined must travel with the wave.

But the rate of motion of the x-coordinate for a selected displacement y_0 is our definition of wave velocity, and we find that this is equal to the constant v of the trial solution (Eq. 26–14) of the wave equation. Therefore, v is the wave velocity. Since the velocity is positive, the motion is toward the right in Fig. 26–5. The other solution corresponds to the argument, $u = x + vt$. If we again set the argument constant, $x + vt =$ constant, and differentiate with respect to time, there results

$$\frac{dx}{dt} + v = 0,$$

or

$$\left(\frac{dx}{dt}\right)_{y=y_0} = -v. \tag{26–20}$$

This solution represents a wave traveling with the same constant speed as before, but the motion is toward the left. The general solution therefore provides for wave motion, in either sense, along the string.

The wave form, which is given by the function F, does not appear in the expression for velocity. Therefore the wave velocity is independent of wave form for wave forms with small displacements and small slope angles, at least, in this case of transverse waves in strings. We later find that this property is *not* universal for all types of waves.

26–5 OTHER TYPES OF WAVES

In the above example of wave motion, the particles moved perpendicularly to the direction of propagation of the wave (at least in the limit of small displacements). We called the wave a transverse wave, meaning that the particle motion was transverse to the direction of propagation. The question of the origin of the tension T in the string was not raised. The tension might have been produced, for example, by simply stretching an elastic string, as in violins, pianos, and other stringed instruments. However, it is *not* necessary for the "string" to provide the tension by means of its spring-like properties in order to support the motion of transverse waves. The tension might be provided by simply passing one end of a horizontal string over a pulley and hanging a weight from the string or by hanging the string vertically (Fig. 26–6). In these cases the string could be completely inextensible. In fact the string could be replaced by a chain.

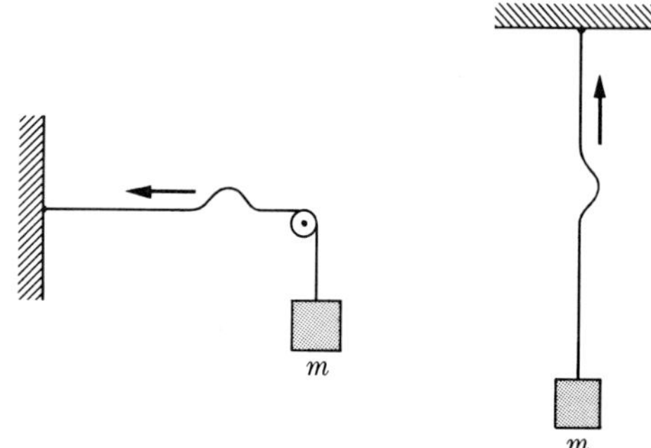

Fig. 26–6. Examples in which the tension is provided by the weights m.

Another example of transverse wave motion is surface ripples on a liquid. For small vertical displacements of the liquid at the surface, the principal contribution to the resultant force on an element of the liquid is from surface tension. Thus, the velocity of propagation depends on the density and the surface tension force of the particular liquid.

Transverse waves can also be produced in two-dimensional sheets or in solid blocks of elastic materials. For example, if a blow is struck on a block of elastic material, as in Fig. 26–7, displacing the material locally, as shown by the

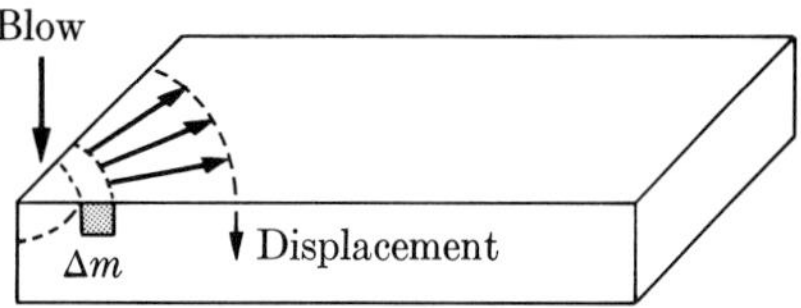

Fig. 26–7. A transverse pulse traveling outward radially from the point where a sudden transverse displacement was produced by a blow.

dashed line, a transverse (shearing) force is exerted on the adjoining material Δm, and Δm is in turn displaced downward, etc. Thus a transverse wave will be propagated radially outward in the horizontal plane. In other directions, the wave will not be purely transverse; for example, it will be longitudinal downward (see below). The velocity will be determined by the density and the elasticity for this type of deformation.

Longitudinal waves also occur frequently. We again choose the example of a string, but in this case the displacement is to be in the direction of the string. If the string is elastic, a resultant *longitudinal* force will then act on elements in the region of the displacements (Fig. 26–8). In the figure, an enlarged segment of string is shown, with equally spaced markers painted on the string. The string is stretched even in its undisturbed state in order that "compression" as well as extension can occur. The velocity of the wave will be determined by the density and the elastic constant of the string.

We now return to Fig. 26–7, and note that a longitudinal wave would be set up in the downward direction as a result of the blow. In other directions, both transverse and longitudinal waves are excited. These waves travel at different velocities, in general, since the elastic constants for longitudinal and for transverse displacements are usually different. In the case of the earth, for example, earthquake shocks generate both transverse and longitudinal waves, with the velocity of the longitudinal waves much greater than that of the transverse waves.

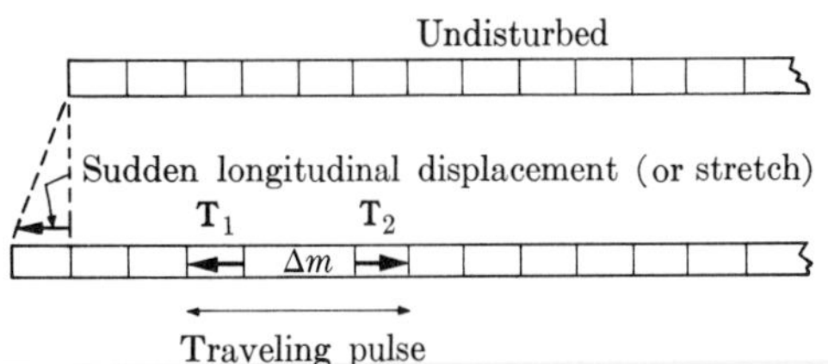

FIG. 26–8. A longitudinal wave pulse resulting from a sudden longitudinal displacement in an elastic string.

In a fluid, only longitudinal waves are possible since no transverse elastic forces are possible. Longitudinal waves in air (or even in fluids and solids) are called sound waves. They can be described in terms of (a) the average longitudinal displacement of the particles from their "rest" position, (b) the departure of the density from its equilibrium value, (c) the departure of pressure from equilibrium, or (d) the departure of temperature from equilibrium. The velocity of propagation depends, as usual, on constants of the medium.

Large-scale water waves involve a complicated motion of the water that is roughly elliptical. The forces are due to nonuniformities in pressure brought about by the differences in surface height. The velocity of these waves depends on the *wave form* as well as on constants of the medium and the gravitational force. On the other hand, it can be shown that the velocity is independent of wave form for some types of mechanical waves of small amplitude, such as transverse waves in a string (as proved in Section 26–4), sound waves (that is, longitudinal waves), etc.

26–6 WAVE FORM; MONOCHROMATIC WAVES

In demonstrating the validity of the wave-motion solution to Eq. (26–13), the only assumption was that T/ρ is constant. Therefore, we can replace the T/ρ factor by any $v^2(=$ constant) and be moderately confident that the resulting equation, called a wave equation,

$$v^2 \frac{\partial^2 y}{\partial x^2} = \frac{\partial^2 y}{\partial t^2}, \tag{26–21}$$

is a differential equation applicable to other physical systems that will support wave motion. The physical constants of the particular system determine the value of v.

It has been seen that *any* wave form $F(u)$, where $u = x \pm vt$, that can be differentiated with respect to time and with respect to position coordinates, is a solution of the wave equation

(26–21). (There are also the implicit limitations of small amplitude and small slope angles that were assumed in the derivation of the wave equation.) Since any wave form satisfies the wave equation, what does determine the wave form? One of the determinants of the wave form is the motion at the source of the disturbance that gives rise to the wave. For simplicity, we assume that there is a single source, at the position $x = 0$, and that the string or other medium extends very far from the source. The latter condition guarantees that there will be no secondary sources due to reflection, an effect that will be discussed later.

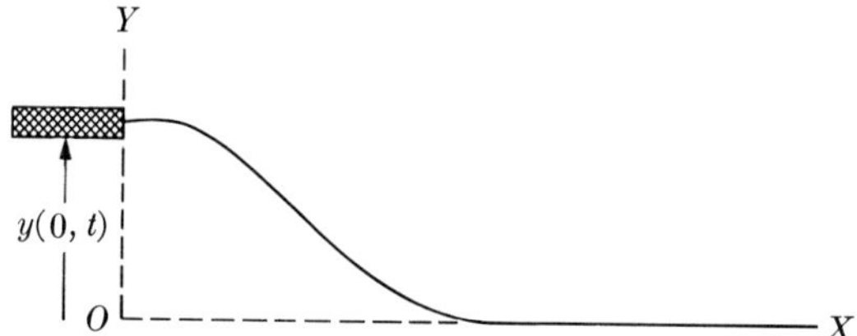

FIG. 26–9. The source of the wave is the lateral motion $y(O, t)$ impressed on the end of the string by the motion of the crosshatched member to which the string is fastened.

Since the disturbing agent acts at the point $x = 0$, as in Fig. 26–9, this point of the string is constrained to follow exactly the motion of the disturbing agent itself. Let this motion be represented by

$$y(0, t) = \mathfrak{F}(t).$$

This is the motion of *one* point on the string. The solution for the motion of *all* points on the string to the right of the source, $y(x, t) = F(x - vt)$, must include the point $x = 0$. Therefore, we write

$$y(0, t) = F(-vt) = \mathfrak{F}(t). \qquad (26\text{–}22)$$

Now consider the specific and important special case in which the source executes *simple harmonic motion.* We choose to describe this motion by

$$\mathfrak{F}(t) = A \sin (2\pi f t). \qquad (26\text{–}23)$$

From Eqs. (26–22) and (26–23), we can write [remembering that $\sin(-\theta) = -(\sin\theta)$]

$$F(-vt) = A \sin\left[\frac{2\pi f}{v}(-vt)\right]. \qquad (26\text{–}24)$$

The motion for *any* point x of the string can now be found by replacing the argument $(-vt)$ at $x = 0$ by the argument $(x - vt)$ for any point. The result is

$$y(x, t) = A \sin\left[2\pi f\left(\frac{x}{v} - t\right)\right]. \qquad (26\text{–}25)$$

It will be instructive to the reader to substitute this function into the general wave equation,

$$\frac{\partial^2 y}{\partial x^2} = \frac{1}{v^2}\frac{\partial^2 y}{\partial t^2},$$

for the assurance that the functional form is a possible solution.

Equation (26–25) is of special importance to wave theory. It represents a monochromatic, or single frequency, wave. At a later point we shall discuss complex waves which may require several frequencies or even an infinite number of frequencies for their description. However, such complex waves can always be built up of a series of monochromatic waves. Therefore, the study of monochromatic waves is fundamental to wave theory.

We now explore in more detail the meaning of the waves that we have been discussing, so-called *running or traveling waves.* The function $y(x, t)$ is a function of two independent variables which specify, respectively, the coordinate and the time. A snapshot of the whole wave requires that t be given a definite value. For example, let $t = 0$. Then the *form* of the wave at this time is frozen and is given by the equation,

$$y(x, 0) = A \sin\left(\frac{2\pi f x}{v}\right) = A \sin\theta, \qquad (26\text{–}26)$$

where $\theta = 2\pi f x/v$. The displacement as a function of position x or phase θ is given at $t = 0$

by $y(x, 0)$, which is plotted in Fig. 26–10. At a somewhat later time, $t = t_1$, the function becomes

$$y = A \sin\left(\frac{2\pi fx}{v} - 2\pi ft_1\right), \quad (26\text{–}27)$$

where the last term in the parentheses is constant and we set it equal to θ_1, that is,

$$y = A \sin\left(\frac{2\pi fx}{v} - \theta_1\right). \quad (26\text{–}28)$$

Equation (26–28) represents a wave form of the same amplitude and frequency in space as Fig. 26–10 but displaced by an angle θ_1 (see Fig. 26–11). For example, if $t_1 = 1/(4f)$, we have $\theta_1 = 2\pi ft_1 = \pi/2$, and the wave form is shifted 90° to the right. Since the angular shift toward the right is linear in time, the space wave form runs toward the right at constant speed.

As the wave progresses, and the wave form shifts toward the right, each particle on the wave is caused to execute linear simple harmonic motion in the vertical direction. At the coordinate x_1, the equation of motion is

$$y(x_1, t) = A \sin\left(\frac{2\pi fx_1}{v} - 2\pi ft\right), \quad (26\text{–}29)$$

where now the first term in the parentheses becomes constant. When we set it equal to ϕ_1, the equation of motion of the particle at x_1 is

$$y(x_1t) = A \sin(\phi_1 - 2\pi ft).$$

The only difference as we shift our observation from point to point along the x-axis is the change in the initial phase angle of the motion ϕ_1. *Each point oscillates with the same frequency and amplitude as every other point*, including the point at the wave source. This is the character of a running wave; the particles which make up the wave oscillate with a progressively shifting phase of oscillation.

There are certain constant features of the motion contained in the equation of motion, features that we now describe.

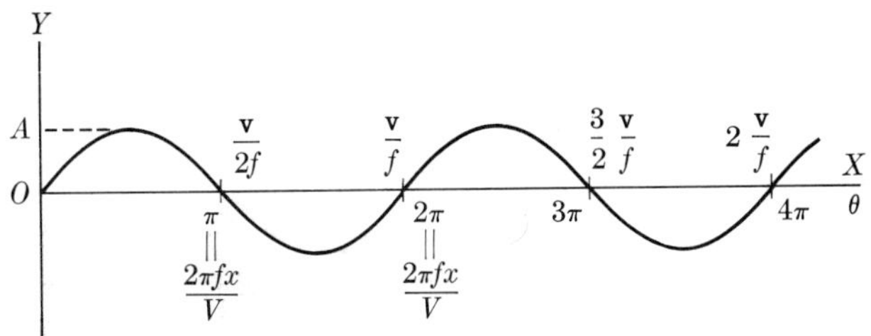

FIG. 26–10. The lateral displacement y plotted as a function of distance x along the string at a fixed value of the time ($t = 0$). The abscissas are also shown in terms of the phase angle θ.

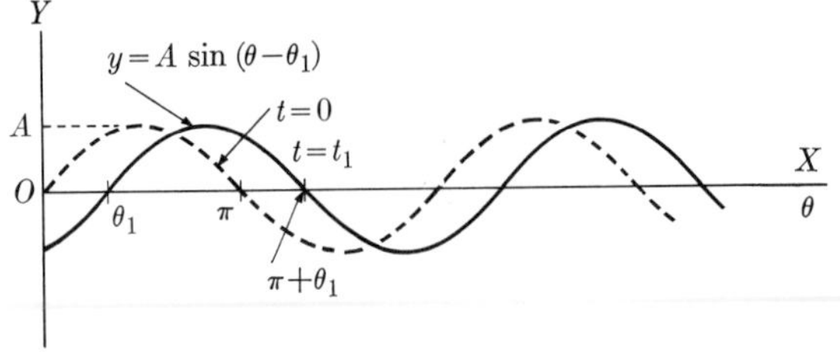

FIG. 26–11. The wave at $t = 0$ is represented by the dashed line and at a later time, t_1, by the solid line.

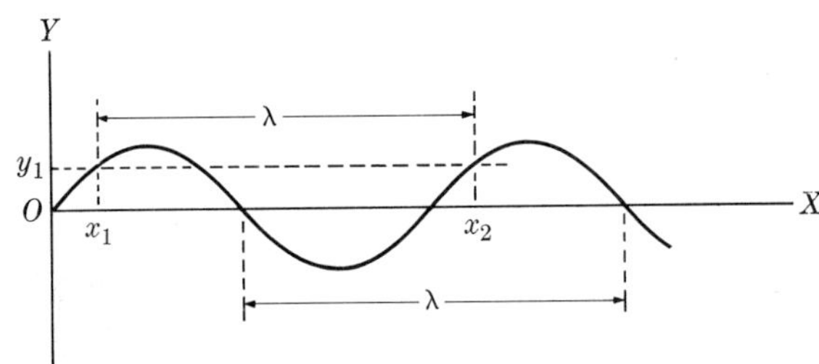

FIG. 26–12. The wavelength λ is the longitudinal distance between adjacent points of the wave that have the same value of y and of the derivatives of y with respect to x.

(a) *Wavelength.* The wavelength λ is the distance $x_2 - x_1$ between nearest points on the wave which oscillate in the same phase. Examples of two such pairs of nearest points are shown in Fig. 26–12. We note immediately that an equivalent definition of wavelength is to say that it is the distance between two points of the wave form that have the same value of y and of

dy/dx. Since the sine function repeats for every change of 2π in its argument, we have

$$\frac{2\pi f x_2}{v} - \frac{2\pi f x_1}{v} = 2\pi$$

or

$$x_2 - x_1 = \lambda = \frac{v}{f}, \qquad (26\text{–}30)$$

which we remember is for a *monochromatic wave.* Equation (26–30) gives us the wavelength of the wave, a constant quantity, in terms of the wave velocity in the medium and the frequency of motion of points on the wave. It will be remembered that the wave velocity is a property of the medium, but that the frequency is determined by the wave source. The quantity λ, which describes the wave form, therefore depends on both the source and the medium.

(b) *Wave period.* The period of motion τ is the time required for a particle on the wave to execute a complete cycle of motion. It is the reciprocal of the frequency of motion, i.e.,

$$\tau = \frac{1}{f}. \qquad (26\text{–}31)$$

As a consequence of the relationships shown in (a) and (b), the equation of motion

$$y = A \sin 2\pi f\left(\frac{x}{v} - t\right),$$

can be written in the symmetric form,

$$y = A \sin 2\pi\left(\frac{x}{\lambda} - \frac{t}{\tau}\right). \qquad (26\text{–}32)$$

The dimensionless ratio x/λ measures distance along the wave in units of wavelength, and the dimensionless ratio t/τ measures time in units of the period of motion.

(c) *Angular frequency.* The recurring factor of 2π is often absorbed into the frequency term by writing

$$\omega = 2\pi f\left(\frac{\text{rad}}{\text{sec}} \text{ or sec}^{-1}\right). \qquad (26\text{–}33)$$

It is seen that ω has the dimensions and form of angular velocity in circular motion. We recall that ω is the angular velocity of a point on the reference circle that can be used to describe SHM.

(d) *Wave number.* This is usually defined as the reciprocal of wavelength. In this form it measures the number of wavelengths per meter of length along the wave. We shall adopt another conventional form for wave number which measures (or counts) the number of waves per 2π meters of length along the wave. Using this form, we define the wave number K as

$$K \equiv \frac{2\pi}{\lambda}\ \text{m}^{-1}. \qquad (26\text{–}34)$$

The definitions of K and ω can be incorporated into the equation for a monochromatic wave, giving

$$y = A \sin (Kx - \omega t). \qquad (26\text{–}35)$$

This is a form which is to be frequently used in the analyses of wave motion which follow. It is important that the reader acquaint himself with all the above different expressions and the correspondences among them. The reader can easily show that the angular velocity, wave number, and wave velocity are related by

$$v = \frac{\omega}{K} \qquad (26\text{–}36)$$

for *this particular case,* that is, monochromatic waves.

(e) *Initial phase.* A more general form of the equation of wave motion is required if we do not make the special assumption that the initial phase at the origin is zero. For more generality, we introduce a phase angle θ_0; thus

$$y(x, t) = A \sin (Kx - \omega t - \theta_0). \qquad (26\text{–}37)$$

The initial phase angle can be determined if y is given for any particular values of x and t. For example, if y is known at $x = 0$ and $t = 0$, we have

$$\sin \theta_0 = -\frac{y_0}{A}, \qquad (26\text{–}38)$$

where y_0 is the value of y at $x = 0$ and $t = 0$.

26–7 THE SUPERPOSITION OF WAVES OF THE SAME FREQUENCY

More than one wave disturbance may simultaneously occur in a medium. Consider, for example, the case of a "collision" of two waves traveling in opposite directions along a string, as in Fig. 26–13. What is the wave motion at a point where the two waves overlap? The answer to this question is contained in the general *principle of additivity* for wave motion. The net displacement at any point is the sum of the displacements which would have been caused separately by the two waves (*when the displacements and slopes are small enough so that the wave equation is satisfied*). For a proof, it can be shown that if two solutions to the wave equations can be found,

$$y_1 = F_1(x \pm vt) \quad \text{and} \quad y_2 = F_2(x \pm vt), \tag{26–39}$$

then the function

$$F = F_1(x \pm vt) + F_2(x \pm vt) \tag{26–40}$$

is also a solution. The proof is easily made by substituting Eq. (26–40) in the wave equation.

It can be seen immediately that any number of wave solutions can similarly be superimposed, and the result is still a solution of the wave equation. For simplicity, we are first considering only two waves. In general, the two components can have different amplitudes, frequencies, velocities, and planes of vibration, For further simplicity, we first choose the special case of vibration in the same plane with the same amplitudes, frequencies, and velocities. Later, the case of different frequencies and, finally, different frequencies *and* velocities will be treated.

As an illustration of the application of the law of wave addition, we select the special case in which two running waves are traveling in opposite directions along a string. Let the waves be simple harmonic in form with identical frequency and amplitude, as in Fig. 26–13. Assume that separate and well-developed running waves have been started from opposite ends of the string. For the wave running to the right, we have

$$y_1(x, t) = A \sin (Kx - \omega t), \tag{26–41}$$

and for the wave running to the left, we have

$$y_2(x, t) = A \sin (Kx + \omega t), \tag{26–42}$$

where we have chosen a case with initial phase zero for both waves. At the place the waves overlap, the displacement equation is

$$y = A \sin (Kx - \omega t) + A \sin (Kx + \omega t). \tag{26–43}$$

The special properties of the total motion can be exposed through the use of the trigonometric identity,

$$\sin \theta_1 + \sin \theta_2 = 2 \sin \tfrac{1}{2}(\theta_1 + \theta_2) \cos \tfrac{1}{2}(\theta_1 - \theta_2).$$

By application of this rule, we have for Eq. (26–43)

$$\begin{aligned} y &= 2A \sin (Kx) \cos (-\omega t) \\ &= 2A \sin (Kx) \cos (\omega t), \end{aligned} \tag{26–44}$$

since $\cos(-\omega t) = \cos \omega t$.

The above equation can be rewritten as

$$y = B \cos \omega t, \tag{26–45}$$

demonstrating that the result of superposition in this case is simple harmonic motion of each segment of the string (just as in the case of a single traveling wave) *but* with an amplitude B that is a function of the position x; namely,

$$B = 2A \sin Kx = 2A \sin \frac{2\pi x}{\lambda}. \tag{26–46}$$

The factor $\sin(2\pi x/\lambda)$ is zero and hence the

FIG. 26–13. Illustration of waves traveling in opposite directions on the same string. The waves lie in the same lateral plane.

amplitude B is zero when

$$x = 0, \frac{\lambda}{2}, \lambda, \ldots n\frac{\lambda}{2}, \qquad (26\text{–}47)$$

where n is zero or any integer. There is no motion at any time at the points defined by Eq. (26–47). Such points are called *nodes.*

The amplitude is a maximum, $2A$, when $\sin(2\pi x/\lambda) = 1$. The amplitude maxima occur at

$$x = \frac{(2n+1)}{4}, \qquad (26\text{–}48)$$

points that are called anti*nodes.*

The individual effects of the two waves at nodes and at antinodes is shown in Fig. 26–14. We speak of the waves as 180° out of phase at the nodes and exactly in phase at the antinodes.

The resulting motion, depicted in space, is called "standing" wave motion since the wave form does not appear to travel. The string is shown at various instants of time in Fig. 26–15. The dashed lines show the string at the limits of its motion, and the solid line shows the string at an intermediate time.

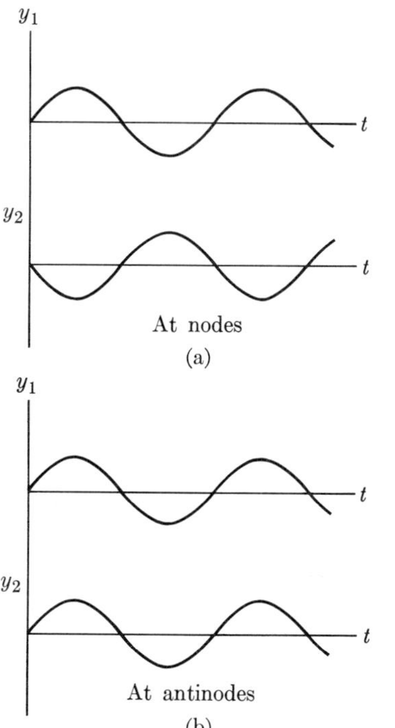

Fig. 26–14. The lateral displacement y versus time t for the traveling waves of Eqs. (26–41) and (26–42) for two different values of x, (a) $n\lambda/2 = x$ at nodes and (b) $(2n+1)/4 = x$ at antinodes.

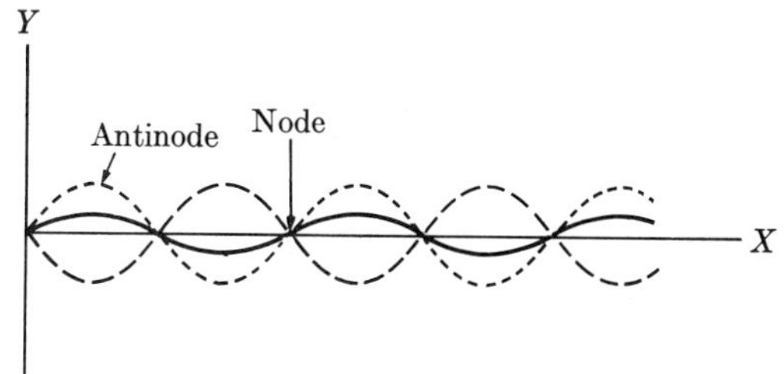

Fig. 26–15. The shape of the string at three different values of the time in the case of a standing simple harmonic wave. The dotted line is at $t = 0$, the dashed line at $t = \tau/2$, and the solid line at $t = 0.8\tau$.

In summary, the effect of two traveling waves of the same amplitude and frequency that travel in opposite directions is a standing wave. In a region between two nodes, all segments oscillate *in phase,* whereas the phase of a traveling wave varies continuously from point to point. On the other hand, the amplitude in a standing wave varies from point to point, but it is the same for all segments in traveling-wave motion. If the amplitudes of the two traveling waves are not the same, the results will obviously be similar to that above, but with the addition of a traveling-wave component to the standing wave. The amplitude of the traveling-wave component would be just the difference in amplitudes of the original component waves.

In common experience, there are not many cases of two separate origins for the traveling waves of the sort discussed above. A frequent occurring example is one in which a string is fixed at both ends and is set into vibration by a driving force F near one end, as shown in Fig. 26–16. The wave traveling to the right is "reflected" from B and travels back to the left. The result is waves of the same frequency traveling in opposite directions, the situation we have just analyzed.

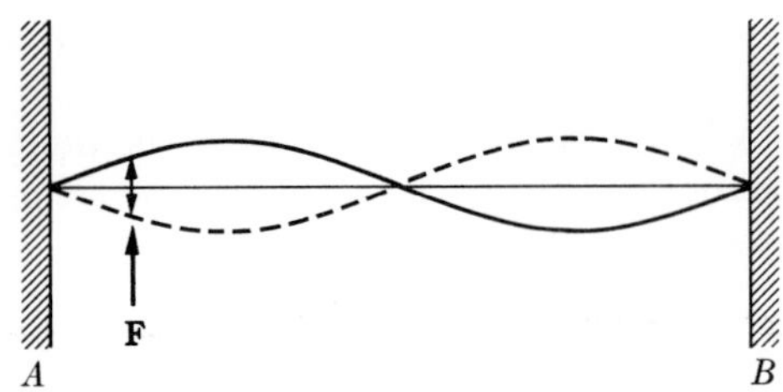

FIG. 26–16. A standing wave established by reflection of traveling waves at fixed points of support of the ends of the string.

A common example of the above is a violin or piano string. The driving force has no particular frequency of its own. The result is that the string selects, from the source, a frequency such that an even number of half wavelengths fits into the distance between supports. This phenomenon is called resonance. In the case of the violin, the driving force, which is the moving bow, "locks in" at the resonant frequencies. The lowest possible frequency usually predominates, with higher resonant frequencies (overtones) contributing various amounts. In the case of a string, it is obvious that the overtones are integral multiples of the lowest frequency [see Eq. (26–47)]. The overtones are called harmonics in such a case.

One effect of resonance is that the amplitude of the driving force can be much smaller than the maximum amplitude of the wave, as illustrated in Fig. 26–16.

A formal feature of the above example is that the motion of the string must satisfy "boundary conditions," namely, the amplitude must be zero at A and at B.

26–8 THE SUPERPOSITION OF WAVES OF DIFFERENT FREQUENCIES

For small amplitudes, the principle of superposition applies regardless of the frequencies that the waves have, since the argument at the beginning of Section 26–7 did not depend on frequency.

If the frequencies are different, the wavelengths (or wave numbers) must be different, even though the velocities are the same (Eq. 26–30). Therefore, Eqs. (26–41) and (26–42) must be generalized to

$$\begin{aligned} y_1(x, t) &= A \sin (K_1 x - \omega_1 t), \\ y_2(x, t) &= A \sin (K_2 x - \omega_2 t), \end{aligned} \quad (26\text{–}49)$$

where the waves are traveling in the same directions. When Eqs. (26–49) are added and the trigonometric identity,

$$\sin \theta_1 + \sin \theta_2 = 2 \sin \tfrac{1}{2}(\theta_1 + \theta_2) \cos \tfrac{1}{2}(\theta_1 - \theta_2),$$

is used, there results,

$$\begin{aligned} y(x, t) = 2A \sin &\left(\frac{K_1 + K_2}{2} x - \frac{\omega_1 + \omega_2}{2} t \right) \\ \times \cos &\left(\frac{K_1 - K_2}{2} x - \frac{\omega_1 - \omega_2}{2} t \right). \end{aligned} \quad (26\text{–}50)$$

In the present problem, the result of superposition is more directly understood if we retain the

$$y = A \sin \left[2\pi f \left(\frac{x}{v} - t \right) \right]$$

formulation of a single wave. Then the result of superposition of the two waves is

$$\begin{aligned} y = 2A \sin &\left[2\pi \frac{f_1 + f_2}{2} \left(\frac{x}{v} - t \right) \right] \\ \times \cos &\left[2\pi \frac{f_1 - f_2}{2} \left(\frac{x}{v} - t \right) \right], \end{aligned} \quad (26\text{–}51)$$

where f_1 and f_2 are the frequencies of the component monochromatic waves. It is immediately evident from Eq. (26–51) that the result is a *product* of two monochromatic waves that travel at the same velocity, one with a frequency

$$f_c = \frac{f_1 + f_2}{2} \quad (26\text{–}52)$$

and the other with a frequency

$$f_m = \frac{f_1 - f_2}{2}. \quad (26\text{–}53)$$

The former is called a *carrier* and the latter a

modulation frequency for reasons that will become apparent during the discussion that follows.

In order to understand the wave form, we now consider the dependence of y on x for fixed t, for example $t = 0$. The result is "sinusoidal" variation of y at frequency f_c [from the sine factor in (26–51)] but with an amplitude that varies at the lower frequency f_m of the cosine factor in (26–51). The result is shown in Fig. 26–17 at $t = 0$ for the case in which $f_c = 10f_m$. The entire pattern simply moves to the right at velocity v as time progresses. Thus the vibration at a particular x takes place at frequency f_c with an amplitude that is modulated at frequency f_m.

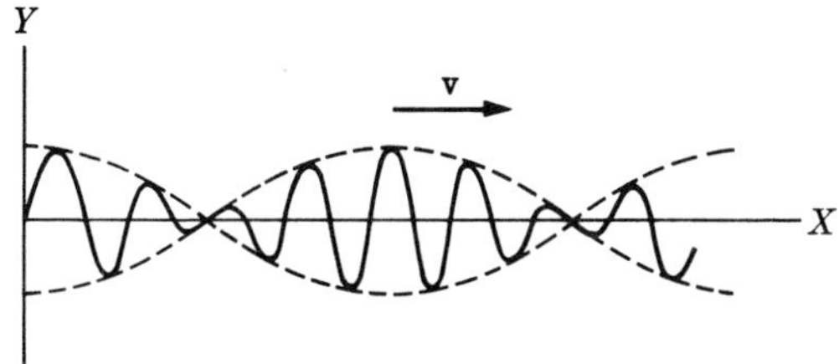

FIG. 26–17. The solid line represents the wave form resulting from the superposition of two waves of the same amplitude but different frequencies traveling in the same direction at the same velocity. The dashed line is the envelope of the wave.

Wave motion in three dimensions will be treated later. However, at this time, we can note that the waves from two sources whose separation is small compared with the distance to the point of observation are traveling along nearly the same direction. The above discussion is therefore directly applicable to such a case. In addition, it can be seen that *longitudinal* waves in air (sound waves), arriving at a point from quite different directions, will add in the above manner, since changes in pressure are not dependent on direction.

The modulation frequency is also called the *beat* frequency. In the case of sound, the beat frequency is heard as a pulsation in the amplitude of the "carrier" frequency. The phenomenon is used as a sensitive method for tuning musical instruments to the same frequency. It is noticed in airplanes when one motor is running at a slightly different frequency from another.

In the case of radio, the order of events is reversed. A single frequency carrier wave is first generated. This carrier is modulated at much lower frequencies, for example, at sound frequencies. The result is similar to Fig. 26–17, but with a ratio of frequencies more nearly a thousand to one. The carrier "wave," when modulated by a single simple harmonic wave, is equivalent to two simple harmonic waves with frequencies that differ by twice the modulation frequency (Eq. 26–53). If the modulation contains many frequencies (see next section), there results a band of carrier frequencies whose width depends on the highest modulation frequency. It is for this reason that radio stations must be assigned a band of frequencies.

26–9 COMPLEX WAVES

The particular solution of the wave equation that we have been using, the simple monochromatic wave (Eq. 26–25),

$$y(x, t) = A \sin\left[2\pi f\left(\frac{x}{v} - t\right)\right],$$

represents an idealization which is never to be found in nature. Complex waves occur which cannot be described by a single frequency, as in Eq. (26–25). However, we have treated monochromatic waves in detail for two reasons: first, many sources and their resultant waves are closely enough monochromatic so that the above is a very good approximation; second, the easiest way of treating nonmonochromatic waves is by constructing the wave (mathematically) as a sum of monochromatic constituents.

For example, the wave shown in Fig. 26–18, while it is repetitive, is certainly not a simple harmonic wave. Such waves, however, can *always* be represented as a composition of a set of simple harmonic waves. The example of Fig. 26–18 is contrived so that it can be reduced to a set of two simple harmonic waves, a and b, of

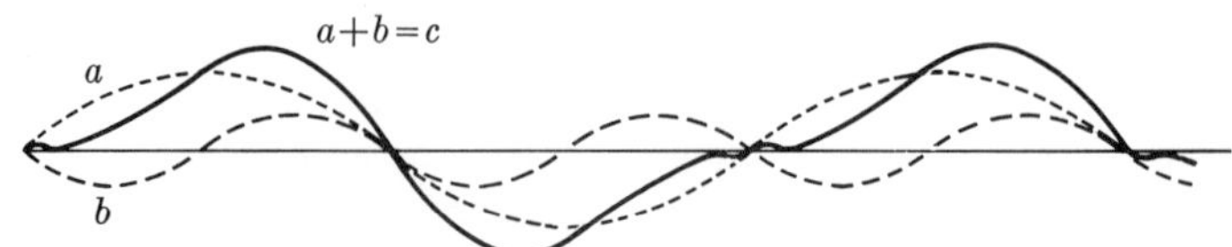

FIG. 26–18. The result of superposition of two simple harmonic waves of different frequency and amplitude.

different frequencies and amplitudes which can be added to give the wave c.

If these two amplitudes and frequencies are resident in the wave, it is because the physical source of the wave had such properties in its motion. Thus we must consider the wave sources in order to see why the waves themselves are not monochromatic.

While we have shown only a selected example, it can be proved that *any* repetitive wave can be analyzed into simple harmonic components. It is possible to choose frequencies and amplitudes of a set of simple harmonic waves such that the sum of the set or series gives the complex wave exactly. Generally, the series will contain an infinite number of terms. Such a series is called a *Fourier series.* In its general form it is written

$$\begin{aligned} f(x) &= \\ &A_0 + A_1 \sin x + A_2 \sin 2x + \cdots A_n \sin nx \\ &\quad + B_1 \cos x + B_2 \cos 2x + \cdots B_n \cos nx \\ &= A_0 + \sum_{n=1}^{\infty} (A_n \sin nx + B_n \cos nx) \\ &\qquad \text{(where } n = 1, 2, 3, 4 \cdots). \end{aligned} \tag{26–54}$$

The frequencies of the components of the wave are integral multiples of a "fundamental" frequency. The Fourier analysis of a complex wave requires the finding of the appropriate set of amplitudes for the terms of different frequency. While it is not our purpose here to set down the rules by which such series are formed, it is important to the discussion which follows to know that in every case a series of simple harmonic waves exists as a representation of complex waves. We shall consider only special cases of the composition of waves.

We return now to the question of why real waves cannot be strictly monochromatic. One reason is that no oscillator serving as the source can run indefinitely and therefore the wave train can never be infinitely long. We return to this point later. Suppose the oscillator, however, runs so long that we can neglect the fact that the length of the wave is finite, at least for the moment. The amplitude of motion of the oscillator must also be constant if the wave is to be monochromatic, since we have already seen that a variation in wave amplitude corresponds to at least two simple harmonic components even in the simplest case.

We consider now the effect of finite length of the wave train. A simple harmonic wave of finite length is not really a simple harmonic wave at all, since additional components must be added to it in order to drop the amplitude to zero at the ends. We have seen that the addition of a second simple harmonic component brings the amplitude to zero Δf times per second, where Δf is the difference in frequency of the two components. In order to bring the amplitude to zero and *keep* it at zero for all times and positions preceding and following the finite wave train, as in Fig. 26–19, more than two simple harmonic components are needed. In fact, the number required is infinite,

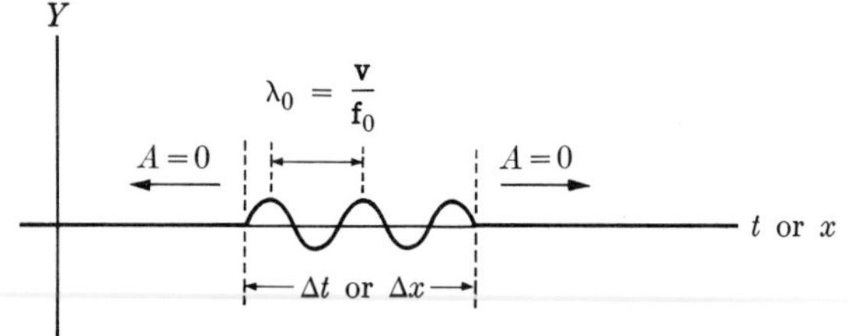

FIG. 26–19. A wave pulse consisting of a sine curve of $2\frac{1}{2}$ wavelengths or periods preceded and followed by zero displacement.

but all the components of appreciable amplitude have frequencies near the basic frequency f_0 of the train. In fact, all frequencies near the basic frequency are required. It is therefore necessary to represent the amplitude of the various components as a continuous function of the frequency of the component (Fig. 26–20). The ensemble of components in this case is called a *Fourier integral representation*, in contrast with the Fourier series representation of *repetitive* complex waves.

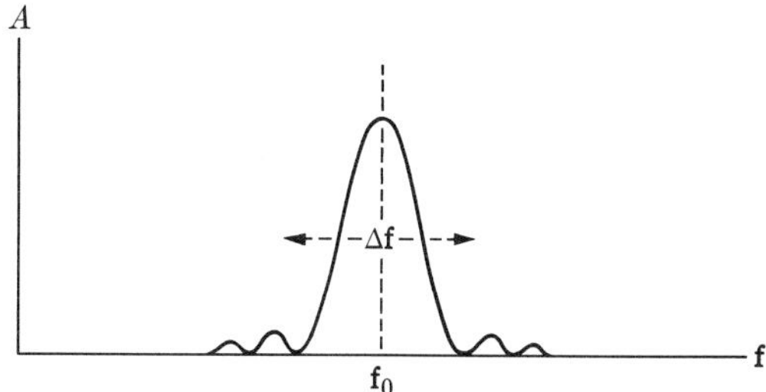

FIG. 26–20. The amplitude A of the simple harmonic components of the pulse of Fig. 26–19 versus frequency, f, of the component. The maximum A is at the "frequency" f_0 of the sine-curve segment.

The range of frequencies Δf (see Fig. 26–20) required to represent a wave train of length Δt (see Fig. 26–19) is given by

$$\Delta f \simeq \frac{1}{\Delta t}, \tag{26–55}$$

which will be demonstrated to you in more advanced texts.

Two relatively extreme examples will be given. In the case of visible light, each wave train is emitted for about 10^{-8} sec. Thus Δf is about 10^8 sec^{-1}, which is to be compared with the basic frequency of the train, $f_0 \simeq 10^{15}$ sec^{-1}. We see that the spread in frequencies is very small compared with the basic frequency. The wave differs from monochromaticity by only 1 part in 10^8. But this small departure is important when the light enters a dispersive medium, as we shall see in the next section.

Now consider a single pulse as the source of a wave—for example, a stick dropped into water. The pulse can be approximated by one-half a complete sine-wave of frequency f_0. We then have

$$\Delta t = \frac{1}{2}\frac{1}{f_0},$$

or

$$\Delta f \simeq 2f_0,$$

which indicates that the pulse is made up of simple harmonic waves whose amplitudes are large over a wide range of frequencies. The "wave" bears no resemblance to a single simple harmonic wave.

The above discussion indicates that it is necessary to be able to analyze *non*simple harmonic waves, since simple harmonic waves never occur in nature.

26–10 DISPERSION AND GROUP VELOCITY

In the preceding section we saw that any wave can be considered as being made up of a mixture of simple harmonic waves. If the velocities of all the simple harmonic components are the same, the complex wave form must move through the medium with the same velocity as its component harmonic waves. The above is the case with most mechanical waves and with light waves (electromagnetic waves) in vacuum.

However, light waves in transparent media and water waves experience dispersion; that is to say, the velocity is a function of the wavelength of the simple harmonic wave component. The result, as we shall see, is that the resultant wave travels at a different velocity from the velocities of the simple harmonic components. The velocity of the resultant wave form is called the *group* velocity, while the velocity of a simple harmonic component is called the phase velocity for that frequency. The difference between phase and group velocities is very large and easily observed in the case of water waves. Individual components can be "seen" to advance more rapidly than the overall wave pattern, dying in amplitude as they overtake a zero point in the general wave pattern and growing again as they advance into regions of crests. When a component wave arrives at the vanguard of the general wave, it dies completely. Thus it is observed that the group velocity is less than the phase velocities for water waves.

We now turn to the analysis. We establish a single wave composed of two simple harmonic waves traveling in the same direction along the same lines, with different but nearly equal frequencies, that is,

$$\frac{\omega_1 - \omega_2}{\omega_1} \ll 1. \tag{26–56}$$

For simplicity the amplitudes corresponding to the different frequencies are chosen equal. Therefore, the expressions for the wave components are

$$\begin{aligned} y_1 &= A \sin (K_1 x - \omega_1 t), \\ y_2 &= A \sin (K_2 x - \omega_2 t), \end{aligned} \tag{26–57}$$

where the two wave velocities (phase velocities) are different. The angular frequency, wave number, and *phase* velocity are related, as usual, in the form,

$$\begin{aligned} v_1 &= \frac{\omega_1}{K_1}, \\ v_2 &= \frac{\omega_2}{K_2}. \end{aligned} \tag{26–58}$$

Graphically, the addition of the two waves can be simply shown. At certain intervals in space the waves constructively interfere to produce amplitude maxima. At intervening points, the waves destructively interfere, and the wave train is successively pinched off into groups, as in Fig. 26–17. However, we now discover something new; the high-frequency pattern will now be found to have a different velocity from its envelope (the low-frequency pattern). Therefore, the high-frequency pattern "threads" its way through the low-frequency pattern while moving to the right or to the left *relative to* the envelope. These envelopes are called "wave groups" or "wave packets." The velocity of the packet is now to be derived.

Let the two waves of Eq. (26–57) be added, using the usual rule for the sum of sine functions. The result is

$$\begin{aligned} y = 2A \sin &\left[\frac{(K_1 + K_2)}{2} x - \frac{(\omega_1 + \omega_2)}{2} t\right] \\ \times \cos &\left[\frac{(K_1 - K_2)}{2} x - \frac{(\omega_1 - \omega_2)}{2} t\right]. \end{aligned} \tag{26–59}$$

Since the frequencies are nearly the same, we write

$$K_2 = K_1 + dK, \tag{26–60}$$

and

$$\omega_2 = \omega_1 + d\omega. \tag{26–61}$$

Then, Eq. (26–59) can be written

$$\begin{aligned} y(x, t) = 2A \sin &\left[\left(K_1 + \frac{dK}{2}\right) x - \left(\omega_1 + \frac{d\omega}{2}\right) t\right] \\ \times \cos &\left(\frac{dK}{2} x - \frac{d\omega}{2} t\right), \end{aligned}$$

or, since $dK \ll K$ and $d\omega \ll \omega$, the result can be written (reordering the sine and cosine factors)

$$y(x, t) = 2A \cos \tfrac{1}{2}(x\, dK - t\, d\omega) \sin (Kx - \omega t). \tag{26–62}$$

The sine term is simply a wave traveling at the phase velocity $v = \omega/K$ but with an "amplitude," given by the cosine term. The cosine factor denotes the modulation of the wave into packets. If we follow, in the progress of the wave, a position of given reinforcement, then the cosine factor is to be held constant, which means that

$$(x\, dK - t\, d\omega) = \text{const},$$

or

$$x = \frac{d\omega}{dK} t + \text{const}.$$

The velocity of the packet, or group velocity, is therefore

$$v_{gr} = \frac{d\omega}{dK}. \tag{26–63}$$

In general, phase velocity is a function of K,

$$\omega = Kv = K\, v(K). \tag{26–64}$$

By substitution of (26–64) into (26–63), we have

$$v_{gr} = v + K\frac{dv}{dK}. \qquad (26\text{–}65)$$

For low-amplitude sound waves, waves in strings, etc., v = constant, and therefore $v_{gr} = v$, showing that the group travels at the same velocity as the simple harmonic components, which we have already demonstrated in Section 26–8.

For visible light waves of most wavelengths in most transparent media, the velocity increases with increasing wavelength. Since this variation is generally described in terms of velocity versus wavelength, it is convenient to rewrite Eq. (26–65) in terms of v and λ. We first use the chain rule to rewrite Eq. (26–65) in the form

$$v_{gr} = v + K\frac{dv}{d\lambda}\frac{d\lambda}{dK},$$

or

$$v_{gr} = v + K\frac{dv}{d\lambda}\Big/\frac{dK}{d\lambda}. \qquad (26\text{–}66)$$

But the definition of K is

$$K = \frac{2\pi}{\lambda}. \qquad (26\text{–}67)$$

Finally, we substitute Eq. (26–67) into Eq. (26–66), and obtain another expression relating the group velocity to the phase velocity

$$v_{gr} = v - \lambda\frac{dv}{d\lambda}, \qquad (26\text{–}68)$$

where v is the phase velocity, i.e., the velocity for a simple harmonic wave of wavelength λ.

In Fig. 26–21 two simple harmonic waves of different wavelengths and velocities and one of the resultant packets are shown.

Experimentally, it is the group velocity that is found when the speed of transmission of energy is measured (for example, light signals), but it is the phase velocity that is found in the case of refraction (next chapter).

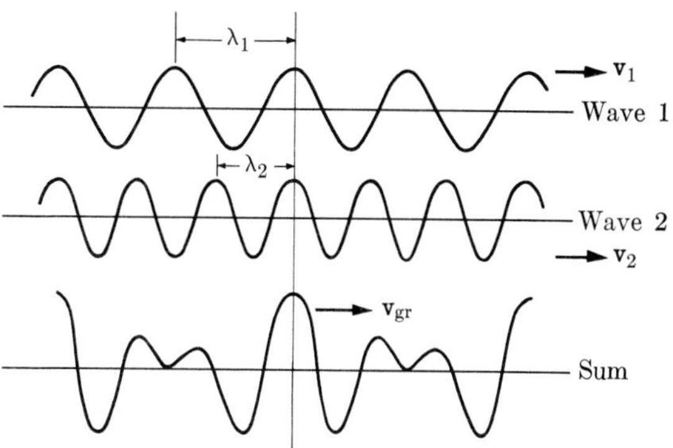

FIG. 26–21. Waves 1 and 2 have different wavelengths *and* different velocities. The amplitudes are the same. The sum is a series of wave packets, one of which is shown, that travel at a velocity v_{gr}, differing from both of the wave velocities.

26–11 POLARIZATION

It has been implicit in the discussion of transverse waves that the vibration was in a plane. In particular, in the treatment of the superposition of transverse waves, it was assumed that the two waves vibrated in the same plane.

Waves of the above nature are said to be *plane polarized.* They are produced either by a source that vibrates in a single plane or by the passage of an unpolarized wave through a *polarizer.* A polarizer for the waves in a string might be a simple slit, as in Fig. 26–22. The incident unpolarized wave, which vibrates in varying directions, is limited to vibration in a vertical plane while in the slit and, hence, thereafter.

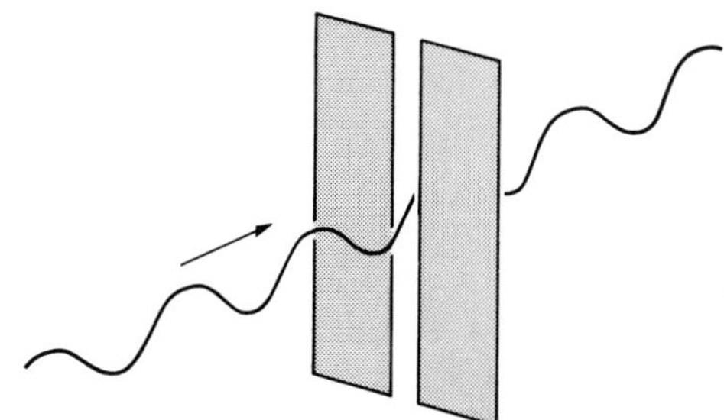

FIG. 26–22. A polarizer for waves in a string. It consists of a simple slit.

Any kind of transverse wave can be polarized, whereas no longitudinal wave can be polarized.

Circular polarization, or more generally, elliptical polarization, is also possible. In these cases, the path of a particle is not simply sinusoidal along a transverse line but it is circular or elliptical in a transverse plane. Circular or elliptical polarization can be the result of the superposition of two plane-polarized waves with displacements at right angles and with phases differing by 90° (Fig. 26–23). If the amplitudes are equal, circular polarization results; otherwise, elliptical polarization results. Conversely, circular or elliptical polarized waves can be "resolved" into plane-polarized components.

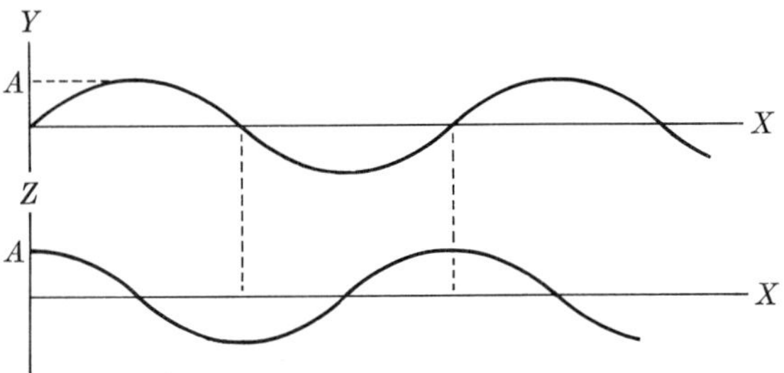

FIG. 26–23. The cartesian components of lateral displacement of a circularly polarized wave traveling along the x-axis.

We note in passing that a plane-polarized wave can be pictured as being composed of two circularly polarized waves that rotate in opposite directions.

26–12 REFLECTION AND TRANSMISSION

When a wave is incident on a boundary where the properties of the medium change abruptly, there is an abrupt change in velocity. However, there *cannot* be a corresponding abrupt change in the displacement or even in the slope of the displacement. These so-called conditions of continuity place limitations on the wave motion on either side of the boundary, including the requirement that there be a reflected component. The frequency must remain unchanged since the wave incident on the boundary acts as the source for the waves leaving the boundary.

First, consider the continuity conditions themselves. If we choose waves on a string as an example, the boundary would consist of a change in the mass per unit length of the string. It is obvious that the displacement must be continuous at the boundary, since, otherwise, there would be a fracturing at the joint. The requirement of continuity in the slope is not so obvious. If there were a sharp change in slope at the point of the boundary, there would be a finite resultant lateral force $\sum F$ on a *point* ($\Delta l = 0$) of the string (the boundary point) as in Fig. 26–24. Since the point has vanishingly small mass ($\Delta m = 0$), this would lead to an infinite acceleration. Therefore, the slope must be continuous.

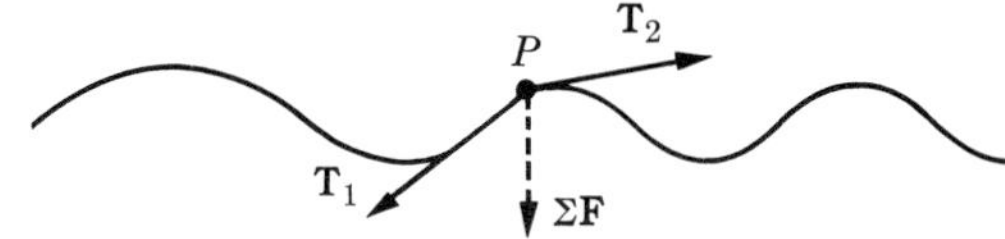

FIG. 26–24. The outside forces T_1 and T_2 acting on a point at which there is a discontinuity in the slope of a fictitious wave. The resultant force $\Sigma\mathbf{F}$ is finite even for zero mass!

The formal statement of the above is that $\sum F/\Delta m \to \infty$, as $\Delta l \to 0$. It is left as an exercise for the reader to show that the same difficulty does *not* occur if the slope is continuous, that is, to show that, for an element of string of length Δl and mass Δm, $\sum F/\Delta m$ remains finite as $\Delta l \to 0$.

The above arguments would apply to any small-amplitude wave. The first condition, continuity in displacement, leads to

$$y_0 + y_R = y_T, \tag{26–69}$$

where y_0 is the incident wave, y_R the reflected wave, and y_T the wave continuing beyond the boundary (the transmitted wave). If the incident wave is traveling to the right, we have

$$y_0 = A_0 \cos(K_1 x - \omega t), \tag{26–70}$$

where the cosine formulation will prove useful in discussing signs. The reflected and transmitted waves are given by

$$y_R = A_R \cos (K_1 x + \omega t),$$
$$y_T = A_T \cos (K_2 x - \omega t). \qquad (26\text{–}71)$$

Choosing the boundary at $x = 0$ for convenience, the displacement continuity condition (Eq. 26–69) leads to

$$A_0 + A_R = A_T, \qquad (26\text{–}72)$$

where the plus sign arises from the fact that $\cos(-\omega t) = \cos \omega t$.

The slope continuity condition is expressed as

$$\frac{dy_0}{dx} + \frac{dy_R}{dx} = \frac{dy_T}{dx}. \qquad (26\text{–}73)$$

Using the expressions for displacements in Eqs. (26–70) and (26–71), we have

$$K_1 A_0 - K_1 A_R = K_2 A_T, \qquad (26\text{–}74)$$

in which we have made use of the fact that $\sin(-\omega t) = -\sin \omega t$. Since the velocities are usually the known quantities, it is convenient to use $K_1 = \omega/v_1$ and $K_2 = \omega/v_2$ to write Eq. (26–74) in the form

$$v_2(A_0 - A_R) = v_1 A_T. \qquad (26\text{–}75)$$

When Eqs. (26–72) and (26–75) are solved for the amplitudes of the transmitted and reflected waves, there results

$$A_T = \frac{2v_2}{v_1 + v_2} A_0, \qquad (26\text{–}76)$$

and

$$A_R = \frac{v_2 - v_1}{v_1 + v_2} A_0. \qquad (26\text{–}77)$$

The above results have been derived for "one-dimensional" transverse waves. They apply equally well to other types of one-dimensional waves, such as longitudinal waves. In addition, infinite plane waves propagate in one direction only and therefore are described by the above analysis, provided that the boundaries between media are infinite planes parallel to the wave fronts. We now consider some examples.

Example 1. Find the transmitted and reflected amplitudes for a wave that is incident on a medium of infinite density, that is, a medium in which $v = 0$.

Solution: Equations (26–76) and (26–77) are solved for A_T and A_R for the case of $v_2 = 0$. The results are $A_T = 0$ and $A_R = -A_0$. The minus sign for the reflected amplitude shows that the reflected wave is 180° out of phase with the incident wave at the boundary. Therefore, the result of superposition is zero amplitude at the boundary for all t, as expected.

Example 2. Find the transmitted and reflected amplitudes for a wave that is incident on a free boundary; that is, a medium with zero density, in which $v = \infty$.

Solution: When we set $v_2 = \infty$ in Eqs. (26–76) and (26–77), we obtain $A_R = A_0$ and $A_T = 2A_0$. The reflected wave is in phase with the incident wave, and the resultant amplitude at the boundary is twice the amplitude of the incident wave. The transmitted wave is fictitious, since there is no medium. Total reflection has occurred just as in Example 1, but with a maximum in the resultant amplitude occurring at the boundary.

The first example is illustrated by a string that is "fixed" at its end by being connected to a massive object, such as a piano or a violin. The result of superposition of the incident with the reflected wave is cancellation at the boundary. The second example is illustrated by a tuning fork. The ends of the tuning fork are free. When transverse waves are set up in the fork—by striking a tip, for example—the incident and reflected waves are in phase at the ends, thus giving large amplitude at these points.

26–13 ENERGY FLOW IN WAVE MOTION

Since the front of an advancing mechanical wave sets matter in motion that was previously at rest, there must be a flow of energy associated with the wave motion. Consider a source that has been sending out a wave for a certain length of time such that the wave has reached point x (Fig. 26–25). In an additional time dt, the wave sets a length dx of mass $\rho\, dx$ into simple harmonic motion. The energy of $\rho\, dx$ becomes

$$dW = \tfrac{1}{2}\rho\, dx\, v_m^2, \tag{26–78}$$

where v_m is the maximum transverse velocity. (Remember that the energy of simple harmonic motion is $W = \frac{1}{2}mv_y^2 + \frac{1}{2}ky^2 = \frac{1}{2}mv_m^2 = \frac{1}{2}kA^2$.)

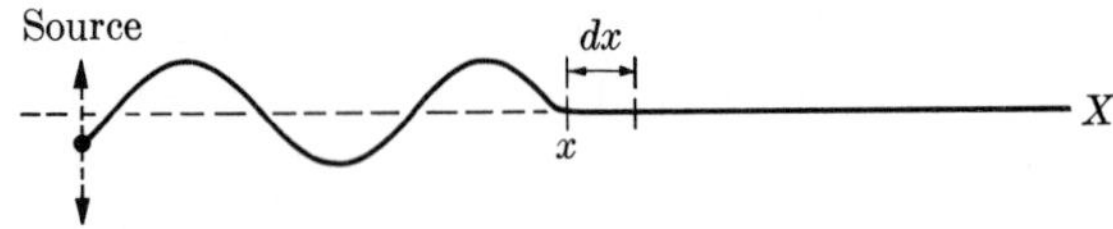

FIG. 26–25. Illustration of the transmission of energy by a wave front to an element of string dx just ahead of the front.

The rate of energy flow is

$$\frac{dW}{dt} = \tfrac{1}{2}\rho\,\frac{dx}{dt}\, v_m^2. \tag{26–79}$$

But dx/dt is just the velocity of propagation v, and since $v_y = dy/dt = -\omega A \cos(Kx - \omega t)$, we have $v_m = -\omega A$.

Thus the rate of energy flow [Eq. (26–79)] becomes

$$\frac{dW}{dt} = \tfrac{1}{2}\rho\omega^2 A^2 v. \tag{26–80}$$

Note that v is the group velocity, since, in the derivation, v was the rate at which the first wave front advances.

In the case of a plane wave, the energy flow per unit area or intensity I is the most useful way of specifying energy effects. Then we would let ρ represent mass per *unit volume* dV and write

$$\begin{aligned} dW &= \tfrac{1}{2}\, dm\, v^2{}_{\max} \\ &= \tfrac{1}{2}\rho\, dV v^2{}_{\max} = \tfrac{1}{2}\rho\, dx\, dS\, v^2{}_{\max}, \end{aligned} \tag{26–81}$$

where dS is the element of area perpendicular to the direction of wave propagation. Then we have

$$I = \frac{dW}{dS\, dt} = \tfrac{1}{2}\rho\omega^2 A^2 v, \tag{26–82}$$

where ρ is the volume density and dx/dt is replaced by group velocity v.

26–14 SUMMARY

The concept of one-dimensional transverse mechanical waves is developed. The velocity of propagation of transverse waves in a string is derived from Newton's second law and found to be

$$v = \sqrt{T/\rho},$$

where T is the tension and ρ is the mass per unit length of the string.

When a more rigorous application of Newton's laws is made, a differential equation, called a wave equation, results,

$$T\,\frac{\partial^2 y}{\partial x^2} = \rho\,\frac{\partial^2 y}{\partial t^2}.$$

Any function $y = F(x \pm vt)$ is a solution of the wave equation if the function itself and its first two derivatives are well behaved. The solutions are described as pulses or waves. Their velocity v is defined as the velocity of a geometrical point on the string with $y =$ constant. We note that the point so defined is *not* fixed to the string. The velocity is

$$v = \sqrt{T/\rho},$$

as obtained with the less rigorous derivation.

Longitudinal waves and waves that combine lateral and longitudinal motion are merely described.

A simple type of wave is a continuous wave of sinusoidal form,

$$y = A \sin 2\pi f\left(\frac{x}{v} - t\right).$$

Such a wave can be generated by moving one segment of the string with lateral simple harmonic motion by means of an external agent. Graphs of the wave form (shape of the string) at certain instants of time are presented. They are sinusoidal in form. Similarly, graphs of the position versus time for chosen segments of the string are sinusoidal in form.

The wavelength λ is the distance between nearest equivalent points in the graph of the wave form. The period τ is the time between nearest equivalent points on the graph of the displacement versus time. Frequency is the reciprocal of the period. These quantities are related by

$$f\lambda = v.$$

The argument of the wave solutions is more symmetrical if expressed in terms of angular frequency ω and wave number K,

$$\omega = 2\pi f \qquad K = \frac{2\pi}{\lambda}.$$

For the sinusoidal solution, we then have

$$y = A \sin (Kx - \omega t).$$

The wave velocity for the *sinusoidal wave* is

$$v = \frac{\omega}{K}$$

in terms of wave number and angular frequency.

The sum of solutions of the wave equation is also a solution. In consequence, it is possible (a) to analyze complex wave forms into simple harmonic components and (b) to predict the existence of various types of complex wave forms resulting from sources that put various combinations of simple harmonic waves onto the same string. We consider some examples.

When simple harmonic waves of the same amplitude and frequency travel in opposite directions on the same string (vibrating in the same lateral plane), the result is a standing wave. Each segment of the string executes simple harmonic motion but (a) all segments oscillate in the same phase (or 180° out of phase) and (b) the amplitude of oscillation is a sinusoidal function of the position of the segment. The equation is

$$y = 2A \sin (Kx) \cos (\omega t).$$

Standing waves or combinations of standing waves like those described above are the mode of response of all stringed musical instruments. Points of large amplitude are called antinodes and points of small amplitude are called nodes.

When waves of the same amplitude but different frequency travel in the same direction on a string, the result is a traveling wave in the form of wave packets. The packets consist of a high-frequency wave (frequency that is the average of the two component frequencies) that is modulated at a low frequency (one-half the difference of the component frequencies).

A brief analysis is given of the method for describing any continuous wave in terms of a sum of sinusoidal components (Fourier series) and of the method for describing a wave pulse in terms of a continuum of sinusoidal components that differ in frequency by infinitesimal amounts (Fourier integrals).

Waves of different frequencies travel at different velocities in water. The result of the superposition of two frequencies, in this case, is wave packets in which the packets travel at a velocity different from that of the components. The velocity of the packets is called the group velocity. It is the velocity at which energy is transmitted by the wave motion. The velocity of a sinusoidal component is called the phase velocity. The group velocity is given by

$$v_{\text{gr}} = \frac{d\omega}{dK} = v - \lambda \frac{dv}{d\lambda}.$$

The phenomenon of variation of velocity with frequency is called dispersion. There is no dispersion for waves in strings, sound waves of ordinary amplitudes, or light waves in vacuum. There is dispersion for water waves and for light waves not in vacuum.

Polarization of waves is briefly discussed.

When there is a change (boundary) in the supporting medium that results in a change in the velocity of waves, then reflection occurs. The requirements of continuity in displacement and slope at the boundary lead to the following two equations for the amplitudes of the transmitted A_T and the reflected A_R wave:

$$A_T = \frac{2v_2}{v_1 + v_2} A_0, \qquad A_R = \frac{v_2 - v_1}{v_1 + v_2} A_0,$$

where the v's are the velocities on the two sides of the boundary.

Wave motion is one of the most important means of transmitting energy. The rate of transmission of energy by a transverse wave on a string is found to be

$$\frac{dW}{dt} = \tfrac{1}{2}\rho\omega^2 A^2 v.$$

In the case of a plane wave, the energy flow depends on the area of the wave front. The *intensity* is defined as the rate of energy flow per unit area. The intensity is found to be

$$I = \frac{dW}{dS\,dt} = \tfrac{1}{2}\rho\omega^2 A^2 v,$$

where the velocity is the group velocity. In the former case ρ is mass per unit length; in the latter case it is mass per unit volume.

Problems

1. A string of length 2 m and mass 4 gm is hung vertically, with a mass of 2 kg supported at the bottom end (Fig. 26–26). Find the velocity of transverse waves in the string.

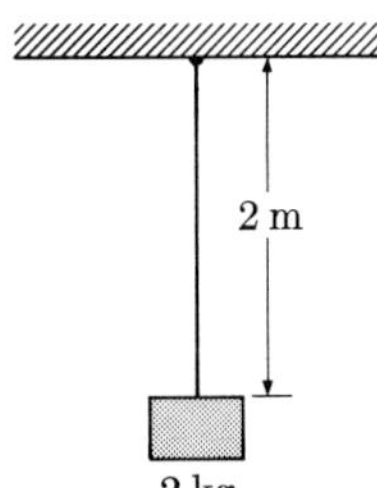

FIGURE 26–26

2. Show that $F(vt - x)$ is a solution of the wave equation.

3. Show that $(x - vt)$ is a solution of the wave equation. What was the motion of a source at $x = 0$ that produced such a wave?

4. For any $y = F(x - vt)$, with v constant, show that dy/dx is proportional to dy/dt. In the case of wave motion, what is the physical property specified by dy/dx? by dy/dt?

5. A rope of length L and mass M hangs freely from a ceiling.

(a) Find an expression for the velocity of a transverse wave as a function of position along the rope.

(b) Show that a transverse pulse will traverse the rope in a time $2\sqrt{L/g}$.

6. A vibrating source at the end of a stretched string has a displacement given by the equation $y = 0.1 \sin 6t$, where y is in meters and t is in seconds. The tension in the string is 4 n and the mass per unit length is 0.010 kg per meter. Assume that the string is so long that no reflected wave occurs.

(a) What is the wave velocity in the string?

(b) What is the frequency of the wave?

(c) What is the wavelength?

(d) What is the equation of motion at a point 1 m from the source? 3 m?

(e) Make a graph for y versus t at $x = 3$ m.

(f) What is the amplitude of motion?

(g) Make a graph of the wave form at $t = \pi/12$ sec.

7. Given the equation for a wave in a string $y = 0.03 \sin (3x - 2t)$, where y and x are in meters and t is in seconds, answer the following:

(a) At $t = 0$, what is the displacement at $x = 0$, at $x = 0.1$ m, 0.2 m, 0.3 m?

(b) At $x = 0.1$ m, what is the displacement at $t = 0$, $t = 0.1$ sec, $t = 0.2$ sec?

(c) What is the equation for the velocity of oscillation? What is the maximum velocity of oscillation?

(d) What is the velocity *of the wave*?

(e) What is the rate of progress of a point $y = 0.02$?

8. Radio waves travel at the velocity of light. What is the wavelength of a radio wave in the broadcast band, say $f = 500$ kc/sec? ($v = 3 \times 10^8$ m/sec.)

9. Show that the standing wave formulation of Eq. (26–44) is a solution of the wave equation by direct substitution in the wave equation.

10. Two waves of equal frequency and amplitude run in *opposite* directions along a string. The frequency is $f = 100$ cps, the wave velocity is 10 m/sec.

(a) What is the distance between nodal points on the string?

(b) Sketch the individual waves and their sum for a *fixed instant of time* and again 1/400 sec later.

(c) Sketch the displacement versus time for a *fixed position* and again for a position 0.025 m from the first position.

11. Two waves of the same amplitude and velocity but of different frequencies, 1000 and 1010 cps, travel in the *same* direction at 10 m/sec. Write equations for the separate waves and for their sum. Make a sketch of the wave form.

12. Starting with Eq. (26–50) in which the waves are described in terms of the parameters, wave number, and angular velocity, show that both the wave corresponding to the cosine factor and the wave corresponding to the sine factor travel at the same speed as the original component waves y_1 and y_2 of Eq. (26–49), when $v_1 = v_2$, that is, $\omega_1 = k_1 v_1$ and $\omega_2 = k_2 v_2$.

13. Rewrite Eq. (26–49) for the case in which the two waves travel in *opposite* directions.

(a) Show that the result of superposition can be expressed in a form similar to Eq. (26–50).

(b) Find the velocities of the sine and cosine factor waves of part (a) when $v_1 = v_2$.

(c) Show that the product of the two velocities in (b) is v^2, where v is the velocity of the original component waves y_1 and y_2.

(d) Under what conditions do the modulation and the carrier waves go right? Left?

14. (a) Derive an equation for the particle velocity (dy/dt) in a standing wave.

(b) Show that the wave velocity for a standing wave is zero. [*Hint:* Apply the operation d/dt, with y held constant, to a standing wave equation, such as Eq. (26–45), and remember that the wave velocity is $(dx/dt)_y = \text{const.}$]

15. Two waves of different amplitudes, A_1 and A_2, but of the same frequency ω run in opposite directions on a string at the same speed, $v = v_1 = -v_2$. Add the two waves and show that the result is a standing wave plus a traveling wave.

16. Two waves of equal amplitudes, velocities, and frequencies but with a phase difference of $\pi/4$ run in the same direction on a string. Add the two and show that the result is a running wave.

17. A certain standing wave is described by $y = 0.6 \sin 6\pi x \cos 10\pi t$.

(a) Graph the wave form at $t = \frac{1}{40}$.

(b) Graph the motion of a point on the string at $x = \frac{1}{36}$.

18. Two waves of slightly different frequency and of the same amplitude travel together in the same medium. If $f_1 = 1000$ cps, $f_2 = 1010$ cps, $v_1 = 100$ mps, and $v_2 = 98$ mps, write the wave equation for the separate waves. What is the length of a wave group? What is the group velocity?

19. A certain wave is excited by a source whose motion can be represented by

$$y = \frac{8}{\pi^2} A \times \left[\sin(\omega t) - \frac{1}{3^2}\sin(3\omega t) + \frac{1}{5^2}\sin(5\omega t) - \cdots\right].$$

(a) Construct the approximate wave form by adding the first three terms graphically, assuming that the velocities are independent of frequency. (Note that $\frac{1}{1} + (\frac{1}{3})^2 + (\frac{1}{5})^2 + \cdots = \pi^2/8$.)

(b) What do you think the infinite series for the wave form would lead to?

(c) What is the velocity of the source as a function of time?

(d) What is the acceleration of the source as a function of time?

20. Repeat Problem 19 for a source whose motion is of the form

$$y = \frac{4}{\pi} A(\sin \omega t + \frac{1}{3} \sin 3\omega t + \frac{1}{5} \sin 5\omega t + \cdots).$$

(Note that $\frac{1}{1} - \frac{1}{3} + \frac{1}{5} - \cdots = \pi/4$.)

21. The velocity of typical simple harmonic waves in deep water is $v = \sqrt{g\lambda/2\pi}$, where g is the acceleration due to gravity. Find the group velocity in terms of the phase velocity.

22. The velocity of ripples on water is given by $v = \sqrt{2\pi T/(\rho\lambda)}$, where T is the surface tension constant and ρ is the mass density. Find the group velocity of the ripples in terms of phase velocity.

23. Two waves, plane-polarized in perpendicular planes, travel in the OX-direction at the same velocity. Find the resultant wave motion

(a) if $A_1 = 2A_2$ and the phases are the same,

(b) if $A_1 = 2A_2$ and the phases differ by $\pi/2$,

(c) if $A_1 = A_2$ and the phases differ by $\pi/2$.

(d) Write equations for the wave in (c) in cartesian coordinates and again in polar coordinates.

24. A note of wavelength 10 cm is sounded in air. The sound wave then enters water. What are the frequency and wavelength of the note under water? The velocity of sound in air = 340 m/sec, in water 1500 m/sec.

25. A heavy string is connected to a lighter string. The tension is 2 n and the masses are 16 gm/m and 4 gm/m. If a pulse of height 2 cm is sent out along the heavy string, what will be the height of the reflected and transmitted pulses?

26. If the end of the heavy string in Problem 25 is set in simple harmonic motion with frequency 5 cps and amplitude 2 cm,

(a) how much energy per second is delivered to the heavy string before the first reflected wave returns to the source?

(b) How large is the energy flow in each of the two strings?

(c) Is energy flow conserved?

27. Repeat Problem 25 for the case in which the source is at the end of the lighter string.

28. Plane light waves moving directly downward are incident on a plane surface of water. The speed of light in water is about three-fourths the speed in air.

(a) What are the amplitudes of the transmitted and of the reflected waves in terms of the incident amplitude?

(b) What is the relative intensity of the reflected light?

27

Electromagnetic Waves (Light)

27–1 INTRODUCTION

One-dimensional wave motion has been analyzed in Chapter 26. The particular example of waves on a string was treated in detail, starting from the mechanical properties of a continuous medium that possesses restoring forces. Upon applying Newton's second law, we obtained a differential equation (wave equation) that has wave-motion solutions. The velocity of the waves was correctly predicted in terms of the density and the strength of the restoring forces. The original source of the transverse waves on a string was found to be an external agent that exerted *lateral* forces on the string.

The importance of the simple harmonic wave solution was found to arise from (a) the fact that many sources can be approximately described by simple harmonic motion and (b) that nonharmonic waves are conveniently described by the superposition of harmonic waves of different frequencies. The effects of superposition of harmonic waves was discussed in detail. The importance of wave motion as a method for transmission of energy was stressed.

Finally, as far as wave motion itself is concerned, the results of the previous chapter are presumed to apply for any type of wave motion that satisfies the same general conditions (small amplitude, linear restoring force, etc.). It is to be emphasized, however, that we must be able to derive a wave equation in order to be able to *predict* wave motion in any particular type of physical system.

In the case of light, the situation is completely different in several respects from that of mechanical waves. With mechanical waves we can see the waves directly in many cases. With light, we cannot see the wave motion directly under any circumstances, that is, not in the sense of seeing directly either the wave form at a particular instant or the undulation with time at a particular point. With mechanical waves there is an obvious medium for the wave motion, even in the case of sound. With light, the waves can travel through vacuum. There is also a striking difference in the velocities, a difference of a factor of nearly a million. Finally, the origin of light waves (and also their interaction with matter) is slightly similar to that of mechanical waves *only* in the region of wavelengths far greater than those of visible light. In the visible region and the region of shorter wavelengths, we shall find (in later chapters) that interactions of light and matter do not follow the predictions of classical wave theory at all.

In view of the above complications, we shall introduce the subject of light by showing that equations of electricity and magnetism (Maxwell's equations) lead to wave equations for the electric and magnetic fields. Thus, the mathematical possibility of the existence of electromagnetic waves will be established. The question of the origin of the waves and their interaction with matter will then be briefly discussed in terms of the predictions of classical electromagnetic theory. We shall then turn to a detailed description of the propagation of light with particular application to the optics of visible light.

27–2 ELECTROMAGNETIC RADIATION: CLASSICAL THEORY AND EXPERIMENTS

It was shown in the first part of this book that classical mechanics, based on Newton's laws and

Galilean transformations, agrees with observation in the realm of velocities that are small compared with the velocity of light. It is only in the realm of high velocities that the relativistic modifications of Einstein need be introduced.

Similarly, classical electromagnetic theory is found to be satisfactory in a certain broad realm, the realm of macroscopic wavelengths. Therefore, it is useful to go a little further in our treatment of the classical theory, as background for understanding the significance of the modifications required in a theory applicable in the submicroscopic realm.

Before Maxwell's work, it was already known that (a) the force between charges at rest can be described by the electrostatic field, and (b) the force between charges in motion can be described by the magnetic field, where the velocities as well as the quantities of charge appear in the latter. Maxwell predicted an additional interaction, an interaction due to a transverse electric and magnetic field ensemble originating from a charge whose velocity was changing. The effect spreads outward from the accelerated charge in a wave-like manner. The effect on a second charge is a transverse force and a weak longitudinal force (radiation pressure in the direction of propagation).

Propagation. Before considering the origin and absorption of radiation, we will discuss Maxwell's theory of the propagation of radiation in more detail. A quantitative treatment for a simple case will now be given. It is first necessary to transform the Maxwell equations to differential form. This transformation can be performed readily by methods that you will learn in intermediate mathematics. However, we can make the transformation in a simple manner for the special case in which the electric and magnetic fields are unidirectional and vary with only one space coordinate, chosen as x in Fig. 27–1. The axes are chosen so that E is in the y-direction, and it will be assumed that B is in the z-direction. Both fields are assumed to vary with x and with the time t.

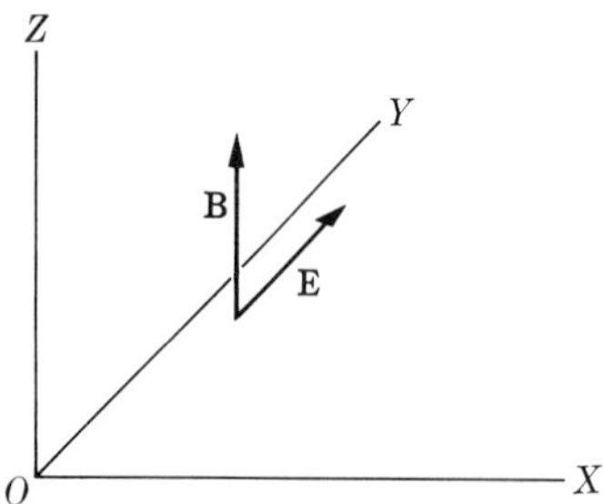

FIG. 27–1. Configuration of electric and magnetic fields assumed for the derivation of Maxwell's equations in differential form. The fields are assumed to vary only with x and with time.

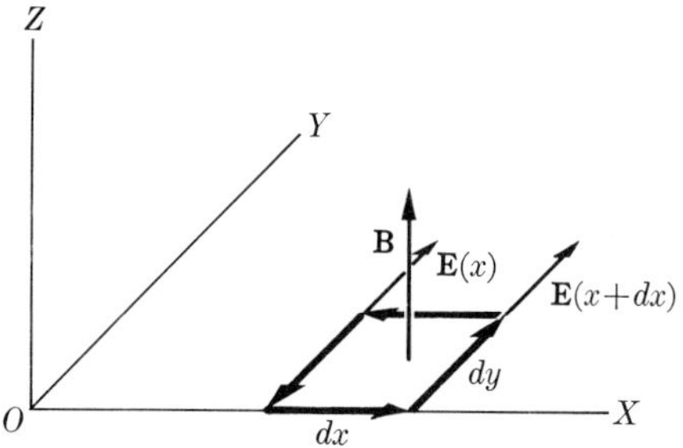

FIG. 27–2. Path of integration for the line integral of **E**. The path lies in the OXY-plane and is bounded by elements of length dx and dy.

The differential relationship between E and B required by Maxwell's equations (Section 25–9) will now be found. The particular equations that we are concerned with are

$$\oint \mathbf{E} \cdot d\mathbf{s} = -\frac{d}{dt}\int \mathbf{B} \cdot d\mathbf{S} \qquad (27\text{–}1)$$

$$\oint \mathbf{B} \cdot d\mathbf{s} = \epsilon_0\mu_0 \frac{d}{dt}\int \mathbf{E} \cdot d\mathbf{S}. \qquad (27\text{–}2)$$

If we consider a small square loop of sides dx and dy, as in Fig. 27–2, and perform the integrations of Eq. (27–1), the line integral on the left consists of four terms, one for each side. Since the terms for the sides dx are zero ($\mathbf{E} \cdot d\mathbf{x} = E\,dx \cos 90° = 0$), the line integral is just

$$E(x + dx)\,dy - E(x)\,dy, \qquad (27\text{–}3)$$

where the minus sign comes from the fact that $\cos 180° = -1$. The expression (27–3) can be simplified by noting that

$$E(x + dx) = E(x) + dE,$$

giving simply

$$dE\, dy \tag{27–4}$$

for the line integral. The surface integral in Eq. (27–1) becomes $B\, dy\, dx$. Therefore the right side of Eq. (27–1) is

$$-\frac{d}{dt}(B\, dy\, dx), = -\frac{dB}{dt}\, dy\, dx \tag{27–5}$$

since $dy\, dx$ is not a function of time.

Thus the integral equation (27–1) can be written

$$dE\, dy = -\frac{dB}{dt}\, dy\, dx. \tag{27–6}$$

Two comments are now necessary. Since E and B are functions of time as well as of position, it is customary to use the notation of partial derivatives. Second, since dy and dx are vanishingly small, it is valid to neglect the variation of B over the area $dy\, dx$. Upon making the above change in notation and dividing by $dy\, dx$, Eq. (27–6) becomes

$$\frac{\partial E}{\partial x} = -\frac{\partial B}{\partial t}. \tag{27–7}$$

A similar procedure can be followed for Eq. (27–2) (see Fig. 27–3), with the result

$$\frac{\partial B}{\partial x} = -\epsilon_0\mu_0\frac{\partial E}{\partial t}. \tag{27–8}$$

Note that the line integral path seems to have been followed clockwise in Fig. 27–3. Actually, the path was counterclockwise, as usual, when viewed from the positive side of the surface.

Equations (27–7) and (27–8) are special cases of Maxwell's equations in differential form. The particular field configuration that has been assumed is possible if it satisfies these equations. In order to solve the above differential equations,

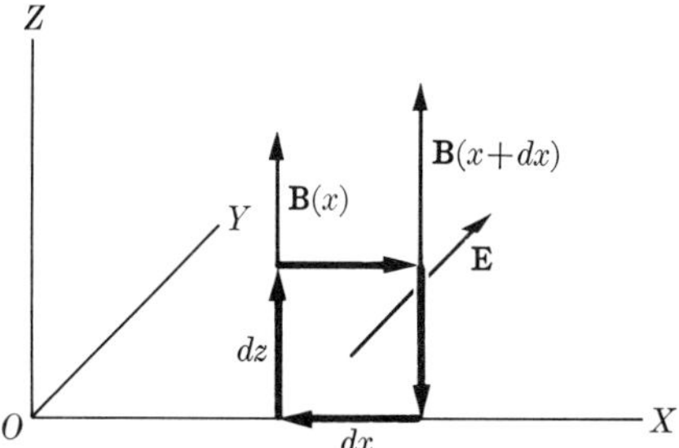

FIG. 27–3. Path of integration for the line integral of **B**. The path lies in the OXZ-plane and is bounded by the elements of length dx and dz.

it is convenient to transform them into second-order equations. If Eq. (27–7) is differentiated with respect to x and Eq. (27–8) is differentiated with respect to t, the resulting equations can be combined to give

$$\frac{\partial^2 E}{\partial x^2} = \epsilon_0\mu_0\frac{\partial^2 E}{\partial t^2}. \tag{27–9}$$

When the differentiations are done in the other order, we can obtain

$$\frac{\partial^2 B}{\partial x^2} = \epsilon_0\mu_0\frac{\partial^2 B}{\partial t^2}. \tag{27–10}$$

The above second-order equations are recognized as wave equations. The solutions have been studied in detail in Chapter 26. The solution is a wave of any form (for example, a pulse) that travels at velocity

$$c = \sqrt{1/\epsilon_0\mu_0} = 3.00 \times 10^8 \text{ m/sec.} \tag{27–11}$$

It has already been noted that this is the speed of light and therefore it seems likely that light waves are electromagnetic waves. The wave form must be the same for E and for B in order to satisfy Eqs. (27–9) and (27–10).

It was shown in Chapter 27 that the special wave form of sinusoidal motion was a particularly useful solution, since (a) it is easy to manipulate mathematically, and (b) any other wave form can be compounded of sinusoidal waves by means of

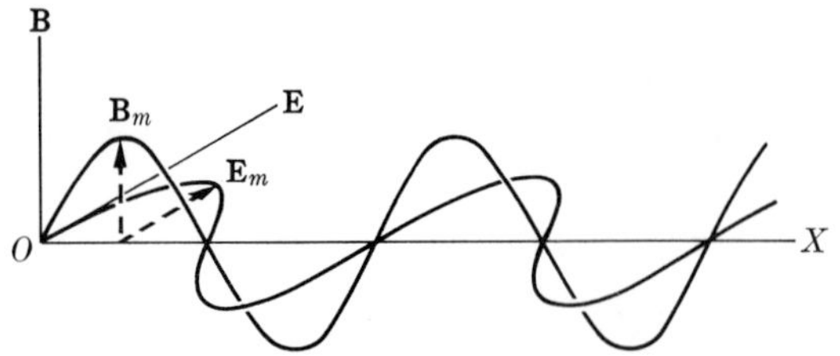

FIG. 27-4. Graphs showing the spatial variation of E and B along coordinate x at a fixed instant of time.

Fourier series or Fourier integrals. Therefore, we shall now take up the sinusoidal wave solution. The type of field configuration that was chosen for analysis can be displayed graphically at a particular instant of time, as in Fig. 27-4. Note that Fig. 27-4 is not a space representation of the E and B fields, since only one space coordinate, x, is displayed; E vs x and B vs x are simply two graphs drawn in perpendicular planes at a given instant of time. Actually, these graphs give a complete representation of the fields in this special case, because we chose the case in which E and B are independent of y and z. Such a wave is called a plane wave and this particular plane wave is also monochromatic.

In the notation that was used in Chapter 26, we have

$$E = E_m \sin (Kx - \omega t),$$
$$B = B_m \sin (Kx - \omega t), \qquad (27\text{-}12)$$

where

$$K \equiv \frac{2\pi}{\lambda}, \qquad \omega \equiv 2\pi f, \qquad c = \frac{\omega}{K}.$$

We see from Eqs. (27-12) that the ratio of E to B is constant. The ratio of E to B can be found from (27-7) or (27-8) by substituting Eq. (27-12). The result is

$$\frac{E_m}{B_m} = c \qquad \text{or} \qquad \frac{E}{B} = c \qquad (27\text{-}13)$$

for the relative magnitudes of E and B at any point in the wave.

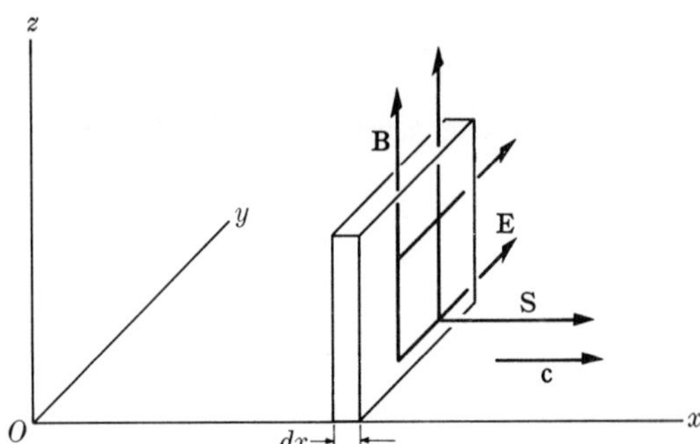

FIG. 27-5. Choice of a volume element with faces of unit area in the yz-plane and thickness dx in the x-direction.

The energy density in the wave can be found from the expressions for energy density in electric fields

$$\frac{\Delta W}{\Delta V} = \tfrac{1}{2}\epsilon_0 E^2 \qquad (27\text{-}14)$$

(Eq. 21-41) and in magnetic fields

$$\frac{\Delta W}{\Delta V} = \frac{1}{2}\,\frac{1}{\mu_0}\,B^2 \qquad (27\text{-}15)$$

(Eq. 25-49) that were derived in earlier chapters. For an element of volume of unit area normal to the wave velocity and thickness dx, as in Fig. 27-5, the total energy content is

$$dW = \tfrac{1}{2}\left(\epsilon_0 E^2 + \frac{1}{\mu_0}\,B^2\right) dx, \qquad (27\text{-}16)$$

which, by use of Eq. (27-13) and $c^2 = 1/\epsilon_0\mu_0$, reduces to any of the forms

$$dW = \epsilon_0 E^2\,dx = \frac{1}{\mu_0}\,B^2\,dx = \frac{1}{\mu_0}\,EB\,\frac{dx}{c}. \qquad (27\text{-}17)$$

Choosing the last form of (27-17) and noting that dx/c is the time dt for the wave to travel the distance dx, we have

$$\frac{dW}{dt} = \frac{1}{\mu_0}\,EB \qquad (27\text{-}18)$$

for the rate of energy flow. The *direction* of energy flow can be specified in a formal manner if we define an energy flow vector **S** (called the Poynting vector) as

$$\mathbf{S} = \mathbf{c}\,\frac{dW}{dx} = \frac{1}{\mu_0}\,\mathbf{E} \times \mathbf{B}. \qquad (27\text{–}19)$$

The average rate of energy flow or intensity I can be found by integrating the instantaneous flow **S** over a complete cycle. The result is one-half the maximum rate, or

$$I = \frac{1}{2}\,\frac{1}{\mu_0}\,E_m B_m = \tfrac{1}{2} c\epsilon_0 E_m^2. \qquad (27\text{–}20)$$

Origin. The origin of electromagnetic waves was also predicted by Maxwell. It has already been stated that the source of the radiation is accelerated charges, or, expressed in different terminology, changing currents. A qualitative argument will be given, followed by a statement of the quantitative results.

If the fields due to a charge propagate outward at the finite rate c, the effect of uniform motion of the charge is simply a change in direction of the lines of force of the electric field. But, if the charge is accelerated, most of the lines of force will be distorted from straight lines. For example, if a charge oscillated back and forth, a line of force that would otherwise extend outward perpendicular to the path is distorted, as shown in Fig. 27–6. The form of the line is the same as that of a stream of water sent out by a nozzle that oscillates perpendicularly to the axis of the nozzle. At large distances from the source, the field becomes essentially transverse and oscillates with the frequency of the oscillating charge. In the direction y of the axis of oscillation, there will be no effect of distortion; that is, there will be no wave.

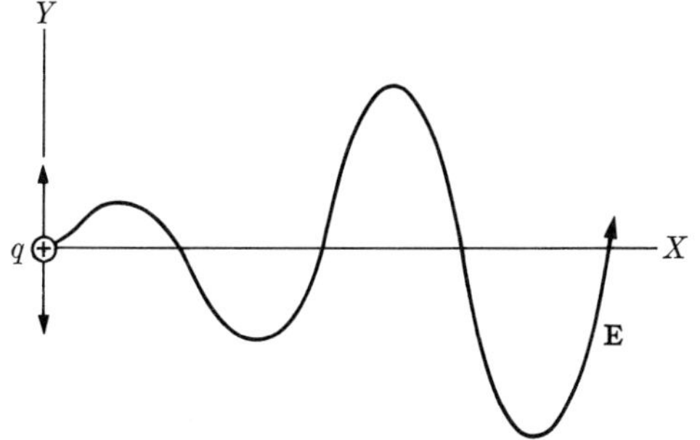

FIG. 27–6. Appearance of a line of the electric field of a charge q that is executing oscillatory motion along the OY-axis. We see that the field becomes more and more nearly transverse with increasing distance from the charge.

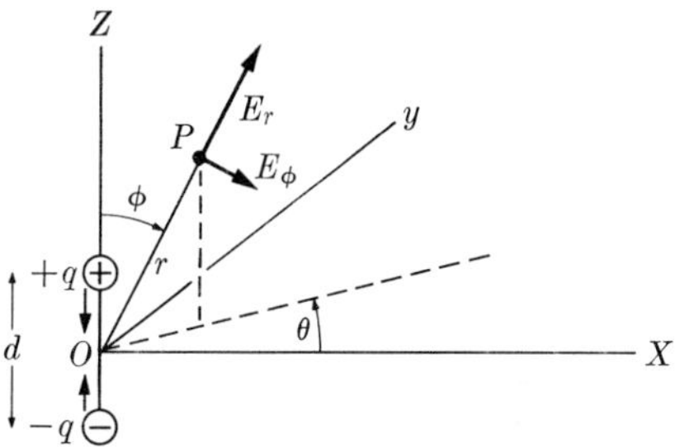

FIG. 27–7. Method of specifying the electric field at point P in terms of components, as shown. A dipole with its axis along OZ is the source of the field.

When the problem is treated analytically, the procedure is to find an expression for the fields E and B that (a) satisfies the three-dimensional wave equations (which are more general than the ones that we have given above), (b) satisfies Gauss' law, and (c) reduces to the expression for the "static" fields at points near the charge. The case of greatest interest is that of an oscillating electric dipole, positive and negative charges that oscillate 180° out of phase, as in Fig. 27–7. The *static* fields were found in a problem in Chapter 20 for points on OZ and points on OX. If the motion of the charges is given by

$$z = \frac{d}{2}\cos 2\pi f t, \qquad (27\text{–}21)$$

the fields at point D at large distances ($r \gg d$) are given by

$$E_r = 0$$
$$E_\phi = \frac{\pi q d}{\epsilon_0 c^2}\,\frac{f^2 \sin\phi}{r}\,\cos\left[2\pi f\left(\frac{r}{c} - t\right)\right], \qquad (27\text{–}22)$$

with corresponding expressions for B. The fields

are transverse and propagate outward as transverse waves.

The intensity can be obtained from Eq. (27–20) and (27–22),

$$I = \frac{\pi^2 q^2 d^2}{2\epsilon_0 c^3} \frac{f^4 \sin^2\phi}{r^2}, \tag{27–23}$$

where the inverse-square dependence on distance appears as expected. The increase in intensity with frequency (f^4) is seen to be extremely rapid. The dependence on direction is shown in a polar plot in Fig. 27–8.

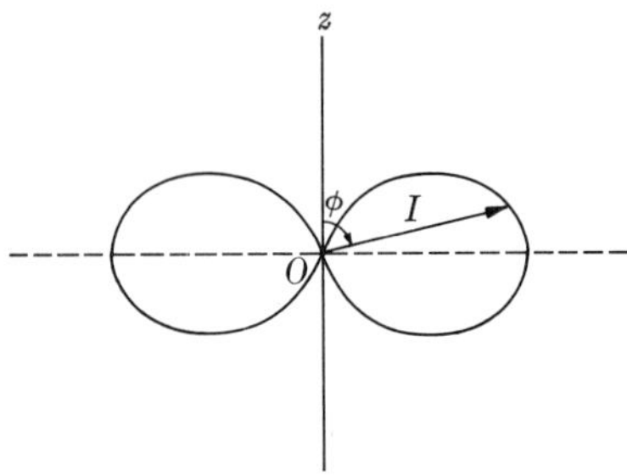

FIG. 27–8. The intensity I of radiation as a function of the angle ϕ plotted as a polar graph, with the angle measured from the dipole axis.

A second case of interest is the more general one of a single accelerated charge. If the acceleration of the charge is a, the electric field at point P (Fig. 27–9) due to radiation is given by

$$E_t = \frac{q}{4\pi\epsilon_0 c^2} \frac{1}{r} (a \sin\theta)_{t-r/c}, \tag{27–24}$$

where the field at time t is determined by the acceleration at an earlier time $t - r/c$, since r/c is the time of propagation from the charge to point P. The direction of E is that of the projection of a onto the plane at P that is normal to r. One interesting consequence is that a charge in circular motion will give rise to circularly polarized light for the waves propagated in the direction of the axis of the circle, linearly polarized light in the equatorial belt, and elliptically polarized light in other directions.

As in all wave motion, energy is transmitted by the waves. This energy must come from the accelerated charge. By way of contrast, no energy is required in principle to simply *maintain* electrostatic or magnetic fields.

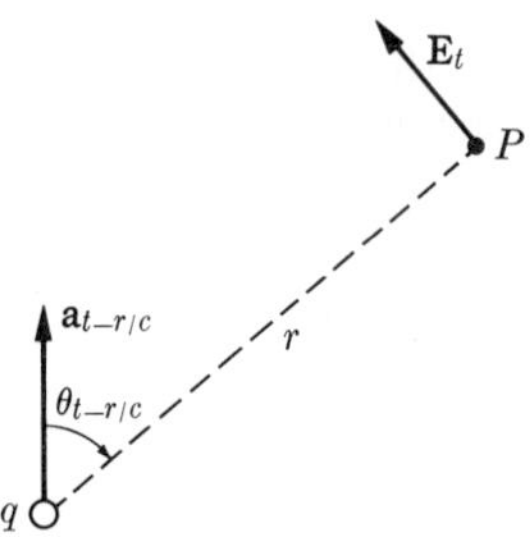

FIG. 27–9. The field E due to radiation by the charge q with acceleration $\mathbf{a}_{t-r/c}$. The field is in the plane of the acceleration and r. The field at time t is determined by the acceleration at a time earlier by r/c.

Maxwell's prediction was verified experimentally by Hertz in 1888. The acceleration of charge was produced by oscillations in a circuit that contained capacitance and inductance in series, as shown schematically in Fig. 27–10. The actual physical arrangement was more like Fig. 27–10(b) namely, a conductor broken by a spark gap. The capacitance and self-inductance are thereby made small with a consequent high natural frequency $1/(2\pi\sqrt{LC})$. The acceleration and consequently the radiation are thus increased (Eq. 27–23). A high voltage is applied across the spark gap S, thus charging the capacitor C. But when the potential reaches the sparking point, the air in the gap becomes conducting and

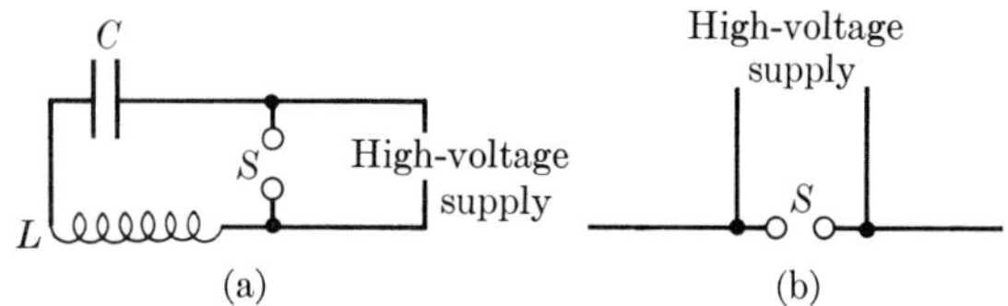

FIG. 27–10. A simple circuit for producing oscillatory currents. When the voltage across the gap S reaches the breakdown value, the gap becomes conducting and an oscillatory discharge of the capacitor C takes place. An arrangement that gives rise to high-frequency oscillations (because L and C are small) and that is an effective radiator for electromagnetic waves is shown in (b).

an oscillating current flows. The current diminishes, due to energy loss, and the spark dies out. During the oscillation, the charge is accelerated nearly sinusoidally with the natural frequency of the circuit, which can be made quite large. The emission of electromagnetic radiation was observed as predicted. The detection of the waves is discussed in the next paragraphs.

Detection, reflection, refraction, and absorption. The evidence for the existence of electromagnetic waves depends on some kind of interaction with charged particles. Classically, the detection of the waves must require the detection of an electric or a magnetic field. The definition of electric field involves a force on an electric charge. Therefore, the exploration of the properties of an electric field depends on the observation of the effects of the field on charges. For example, when a length of conductor is placed in a constant electric field, there is a displacement of the electrons (called electrostatic induction). When the electrons have become redistributed so that there are no resultant forces, motion of the charges ceases. But if the field is changing, the force on the charges changes and the electrons will continue to move. The result is a continuing electric current within the conductor. Finally, if electromagnetic waves are incident on the conductor, we expect a varying transverse force and therefore a varying current in conductors that may be at considerable distances from the source of the waves (astronomical distances).

Hertz detected the emission of radiation from his oscillator by observing the currents set up in a wire "antenna" (Fig. 27–11). When the natural frequency of the detecting antenna was adjusted to a certain frequency (presumably that of the waves), a spark was observed in the narrow gap in the detecting antenna.

Today's transmission of information by radio, TV, and radar is made possible by the emission, propagation, and detection of electromagnetic waves following the basic principles discussed above. Rapidly varying current is set up in an

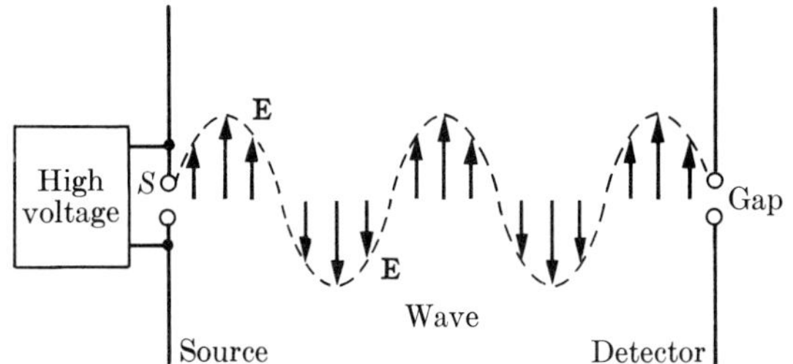

Fig. 27–11. Schematic diagram of a Hertzian oscillator as a source of electromagnetic waves, a wave itself, and a detector of the radiation.

emitting antenna by some electrical means. Electromagnetic waves are emitted. These waves are detected by the force qE on the electrons in a receiving antenna. The resulting current in the receiving antenna is amplified in circuits tuned for resonance at the frequency of the incoming wave.

Detailed calculations can be made for the effects on the waves when they are incident on extended conductors or nonconductors. Reflection and refraction effects similar to those for light are predicted by the theory. Direct confirmation of the theory came when Hertz and others made detailed observations of the reflection and refraction of the waves produced by electrical oscillations in emitting antennas.

Classical theory for the emission and absorption of light. Since it is found from experiment that light waves exhibit the same properties as electromagnetic waves during their propagation (such as velocity, reflection, interference, refraction, and polarization), it is natural to assume that light waves might also exhibit similar properties in their origin and absorption. That is, it would be predicted that they originate from accelerated charges and that the waves exert forces on charges given by $F = qE$ (where E is the wave displacement predicted by the wave properties). Any differences would be attributable to the differences in wavelength and frequency of the waves.

The measured wavelength of visible light waves is of the order of 5000 A ($=5 \times 10^{-7}$ m) with a corresponding frequency of the order 10^{15} cps. Therefore, if the source of visible light waves is in oscillating charges, their frequency of oscillation is several magnitudes higher than any oscillating circuit can produce. However, estimates of possible frequencies of oscillation of electrons within the atom are in this range, as we shall see when discussing models of the atom.

If the source of light is oscillating charge, it would be expected that a magnetic field might affect the frequencies of the oscillating charges and hence the frequencies of the emitted light. The method for studying such an effect is to choose an emitter of isolated frequencies such as hot sodium vapor. A shift in frequency due to a magnetic field can then be observed by noting a shift in the frequency. For example, there will be a change in the deviation of the light by a prism or in the diffraction angle of the light by a grating (discussed later in this chapter). Shifts were in fact observed by Zeeman in 1896. How do the observations agree with the theory of oscillating charges as the source of light?

The classical theory of the Zeeman effect starts with the assumption that light is emitted by charges oscillating at the frequency of the light. When an external magnetic field is applied, there is the usual force on the moving charge given by

$$\mathbf{F} = q\mathbf{v} \times \mathbf{B}. \tag{27-25}$$

The effect of **B** on the vibratory motion is most easily analyzed by first resolving the vibratory motion A into linear components, $A_{\parallel}$ and $A_{\perp}$, parallel and perpendicular to B, followed by a further resolution of $A_{\perp}$ into two circular components, A_c and $A_{c'}$ (Fig. 27-12). These components rotate in opposite directions and have half the amplitude of $A_{\perp}$. The effect of the application of the magnetic field will be a change in the velocity of the circular components to compensate for the change in the central force. Before the magnetic field is applied, there must

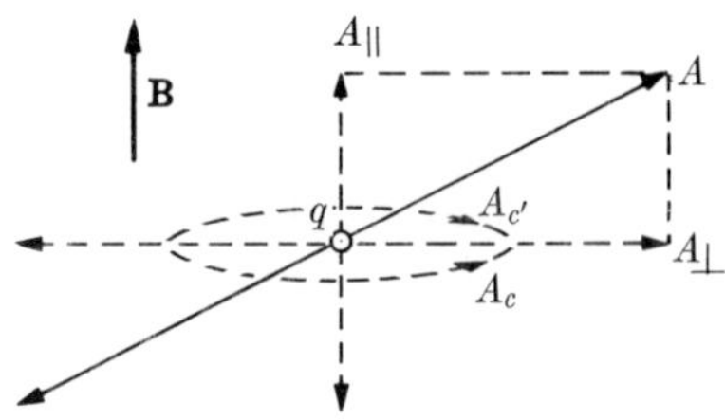

Fig. 27-12. A charge q is oscillating linearly with amplitude A. The motion is resolved into components $A_{\parallel}$ and $A_{\perp}$, with further resolution of the linear component $A_{\perp}$ into two uniform circular motions A_c and $A_{c'}$ whose sum is $A_{\perp}$.

be a central force exerted by other parts of the atom given by

$$F_0 = m\omega_0^2 r. \tag{27-26}$$

After the field is applied, the force equation becomes

$$F_0 \pm qvB = m\omega^2 r. \tag{27-27}$$

When F_0 is eliminated between (27-26) and (27-27), v is replaced by ωr, and some rearranging is done; there results

$$\omega^2 - \omega_0^2 = \pm \frac{q}{m}\,\omega B. \tag{27-28}$$

The left side of Eq. (27-28) can be factored, and the factor $\omega + \omega_0 = 2\omega - (\omega - \omega_0)$ can be replaced by 2ω, since $\omega - \omega_0$ can be shown to be much less than 2ω in most cases. The result is

$$\omega \simeq \omega_0 \pm \tfrac{1}{2}(q/m)B \tag{27-29}$$

or

$$f = f_0 \pm \frac{1}{4\pi}\left(\frac{q}{m}\right) B. \tag{27-30}$$

Thus the prediction is a shift in the frequency of the circular components. The component parallel with B is, of course, unaffected. The circular components should give rise to circularly polarized light when viewed along the direction of B. In a direction perpendicular to B the circular motion will be seen edge-on and therefore should emit linearly polarized light with the plane of polarization perpendicular to B, but the component of motion parallel with B results in a component of radiation of unchanged frequency and polarization parallel with B.

Since observations of the Zeeman effect of light from some sources agree with the above predictions and give q/m equal to e/m of the electron, it was natural to suppose that light is emitted by electrons oscillating within atoms. It should be noted, however, that some light has more complicated Zeeman patterns than the above, patterns that *cannot* be explained by the classical theory.

The phenomena of reflection and refraction (discussed later in the chapter) are due to the interaction of the waves with the charged constituents of the reflecting or refracting material. When the waves are incident on matter, the classical theory states that there is an additional force $F = qE$ (where E is the field due to the wave) on any charge q. In the case of metals, the conduction electrons play a dominant role. In the case of nonconductors, the electrons are all bound by restoring forces that tend to return them to an equilibrium position. In either case, the classical theory predicts that the charges are set into vibration and emit radiation themselves. The results of superposition of these secondary waves with the original waves are the reflected and refracted waves. The classical theory of these effects agrees with observation for radio and radar wavelengths and has some success even for light.

Radiation pressure and momentum. In addition to the transverse force qE experienced by a charge that is being irradiated by an electromagnetic wave, there is a longitudinal force due to the transverse motion (caused by the force qE above) in the magnetic field component of the wave. For example, if a free charge is located in the region of a plane wave, with E and B given by Eq. (27–12), we have

$$F_E = qE = qE_m \sin(Kx - \omega t).$$

Choosing the origin so that $x = 0$ at the charge and utilizing Newton's second law,

$$-qE_m \sin \omega t = m \frac{d^2y}{dt^2}, \tag{27–31}$$

where the y-axis has been chosen in the direction of E. A solution of Eq. (27–31) is

$$y = A \sin \omega t + v_0 t + y_0, \tag{27–32}$$

which yields

$$A = \frac{qE_m}{m\omega^2} \tag{27–33}$$

upon substitution of (27–32) into (27–31). The velocity can now be obtained by differentiating (27–32), giving

$$v_y = \omega A \cos \omega t + v_0. \tag{27–34}$$

The magnetic force on the charge $\mathbf{F}_B = q\mathbf{v} \times \mathbf{B}$ will be in the x-direction and is given by

$$F_x = -q\omega A(\cos \omega t + v_0)B_m \sin \omega t, \tag{27–35}$$

or

$$F_x = -\frac{q^2}{m\omega} E_m B_m(\tfrac{1}{2} \sin 2\omega t + v_0 \sin \omega t). \tag{27–36}$$

Since this force is seen to be alternately negative and positive in a symmetrical manner, the average value is zero.

However, if the charge in question loses energy due to collisions, as in the case of electrons in metals, the phase of the $\cos \omega t$ term in (27–34) will be altered, with the result that the average force will no longer be zero. The average force will be in the x-direction and is called *radiation pressure*. The result of collisions of the conduction electrons in a metal was described macroscopically as resistance in earlier chapters. When Ohm's law is applicable, the current is directly proportional to the applied voltage or, in different terms, the average velocity of the charge is directly proportional to the field strength or force on the charge. The average retarding force due to collisions must therefore be directly proportional to v. Consequently, in the case of metals, Eq. (27–31) becomes

$$-qE_m \sin \omega t - k \frac{dy}{dt} = m \frac{d^2y}{dt^2}. \quad (27\text{–}37)$$

The solution of this equation will be of the form

$$y = A \sin (\omega t + \phi), \quad (27\text{–}38)$$

where the y_0t and y_0 terms have been omitted since we have seen that they contribute nothing to the average force F_x. In the limiting case of $k \gg m$,

$$y = A \cos \omega t = \frac{qE_m}{k} \cos \omega t, \quad (27\text{–}39)$$

which can be seen directly by neglecting the last term in (27–37). In place of Eq. (27–35), which was for a free charge in space, we now have

$$F_x = qvB = \frac{q^2}{k} E_m B_m \sin^2 \omega t. \quad (27\text{–}40)$$

The average value is

$$F_x = \frac{q^2}{k} E_m B_m \frac{1}{2\pi\omega} \int_0^{2\pi} (\sin^2 \omega t)\, d(\omega t) = \frac{q^2 E_m B_m}{2k\omega}. \quad (27\text{–}41)$$

We now turn to the question of the effect of the charge on the incident wave. Since the above force on the charge q is exerted by the wave, there must be a corresponding change in the momentum of the wave given by

$$\frac{dp_x}{dt} = F_x = qvB. \quad (27\text{–}42)$$

In addition, there is a flow of energy to the charge given by

$$\frac{dW}{dt} = vF_E = cvqE. \quad (27\text{–}43)$$

From the two preceding equations, it is seen that

$$\frac{dW}{dp} = \frac{E}{B} = c, \quad (27\text{–}44)$$

since it has been shown that $E/B = c$ (Eq. 27–13). Since the velocity c is a constant,

$$\frac{W}{p} = c. \quad (27\text{–}45)$$

It is seen that the electromagnetic wave carries momentum given by

$$p = \frac{W}{c}, \quad (27\text{–}46)$$

where W is the energy carried by the wave.

The above relationship between momentum and energy is quite different from that of a material particle, which is, classically,

$$p = \sqrt{2mT}, \quad (27\text{–}47)$$

where T is the kinetic energy. But it is quite similar to the relativistic relationship (Chapter 13)

$$p^2c^2 = W^2 - m_0^2c^4, \quad (27\text{–}48)$$

where W is the total energy. In fact, we see that a "particle" of zero rest mass m_0 has the same relationship between energy and momentum as a light wave.

The predicted pressure of a light beam is extraordinarily small. Nevertheless, it has been verified experimentally by measuring the force exerted on a target when irradiated by light. The pressure is to be pictured as uniformly distributed over the cross section of the light beam, according to classical theory.

The effect of the energy flow in light waves is easily observed. The radiation is allowed to impinge on a target that absorbs the waves, and the temperature rise is measured. The observations agree with the theory.

Mention has been made of the emission of light of isolated frequencies by gases (such as sodium vapor). When light of all frequencies (white light) is sent through cool sodium vapor, absorption of light occurs at the frequency of the light that is emitted from hot sodium vapor. In another example, the light from the sun has many frequencies missing from its "white" light. The missing frequencies are called Fraunhofer absorption lines. The frequencies of the absorption lines in the sun's spectrum coincide with some of the emission frequencies from the vapor of sodium, calcium, iron, and other elements as observed in the laboratory. They are attributable to absorption in the "atmosphere" of the sun. It might seem evident that the electron oscillators that emit light can also absorb light of the same frequency, as expected from classical theory. However, closer examination reveals that many of the frequencies that are emitted do not occur in absorption. Again, the classical theory has only partial success in developing an understanding of light.

Summary. The classical theory of electromagnetic radiation is based on Maxwell's equations of electromagnetism. Maxwell's predictions of the properties of electromagnetic waves were confirmed by experiments of Hertz and others, who showed that oscillating currents do indeed give rise to electromagnetic waves and that the waves have the predicted properties.

The theory also accounts for many of the properties of light. It is completely successful in describing the propagation phenomena of velocity, interference, diffraction, and polarization (as we shall soon see). It is only slightly successful in explaining the origin of light and the interaction of waves with matter upon which they are incident.

Even in the case of propagation, there is one property of light that does not conform with classical theory, namely, the effect of motion on the observed velocity of light. We have already seen in Chapter 13 that it was necessary to make the complete break (represented by relativity) from classical ideas before the observations of the velocity of light from moving systems could be understood.

27–3 PROPAGATION OF WAVES IN THREE DIMENSIONS

In Chapter 26, one-dimensional waves were analyzed in detail. In the preceding section, it has been found that similar equations describe infinite plane waves in special cases. The essential limitation is that the wave displacement and velocity must be independent of all but one cartesian coordinate, in particular the coordinate in the direction of wave propagation. In addition to infinite plane waves, infinite line waves also fall into the above category if the displacement and velocity depend only on the coordinate in the direction of propagation. An example of the latter type of wave motion is water waves due to the wind, in which the waves are long, straight lines when they are in open water or when they are advancing directly toward a beach that presents the same bottom profile at all points along a wave front.

We shall now extend the treatment of wave motion to include effects that depend on two or three coordinates. For example, plane waves will still be considered on occasion, but effects due to boundaries that are *not* parallel to the wave fronts will be studied, namely, effects of boundaries at an angle and effects of curved boundaries (including mirrors and lenses). In addition, so-called diffraction effects due to the limiting of plane waves to finite areas will be studied.

We shall also analyze some of the propagation phenomena of three-dimensional waves that are not plane waves, the principal example being waves that are portions of spherical waves, at least to a first approximation. A two-dimensional example that resembles the spherical wave case is the set of circular waves sent out when a disturbance acts at a point on the surface of water. The waves spread out in concentric circles, as in Fig. 27–13. The dashed line in the figure is a graph of displacement versus distance. It is superimposed on the diagram of wave crests. If the wave is due to a dipole source, the amplitude will diminish toward the direction of the dipole axis.

When a point source sends out waves in three dimensions, the wave crests (or other loci of points of constant phase) form surfaces enclosing the source. If the medium is isotropic and at rest, on the average relative to the source, the

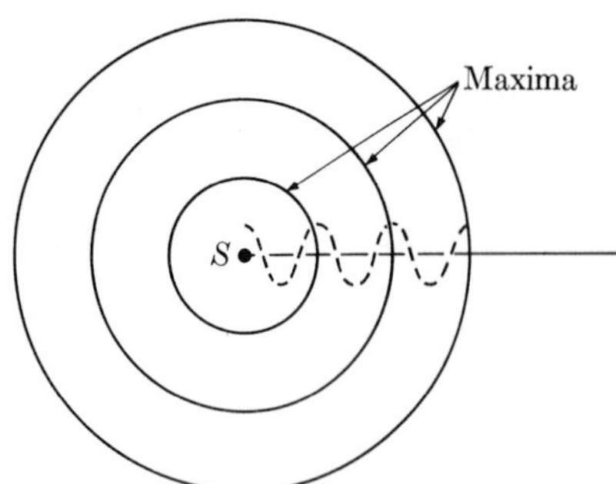

Fig. 27–13. Waves emanating from a point source S. A graph of displacement versus distance is shown by the dashed line.

wave surfaces are spheres centered on the source. A spherical surface representing the maximum in a wave emanating from a point source is shown in Fig. 27–14. The dashed lines represent graphs of displacement versus radial distance from the source in selected directions. This could be a representation of a sound wave sent out from a small source.

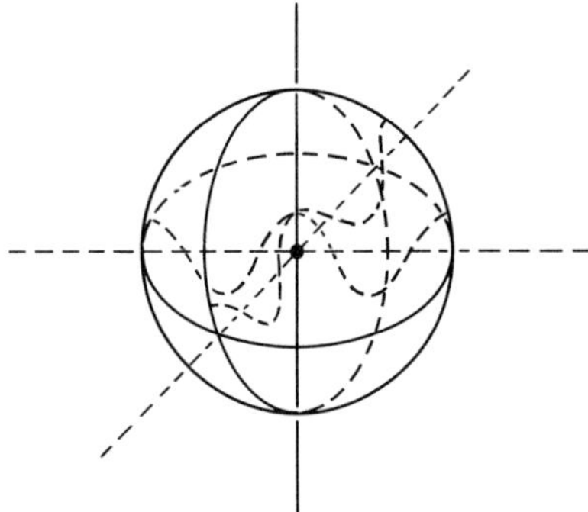

Fig. 27–14. A spherical wave crest from a point source at the center. Dashed lines indicate the wave form in the plane perpendicular to the acceleration of a charge in the case of electromagnetic radiation. The amplitude would be zero along the direction of the acceleration.

In many cases it is convenient to describe the waves in terms of *rays*, which are defined as lines in the direction of propagation of the wave. In many cases the direction of propagation is perpendicular to the wave fronts. We shall assume

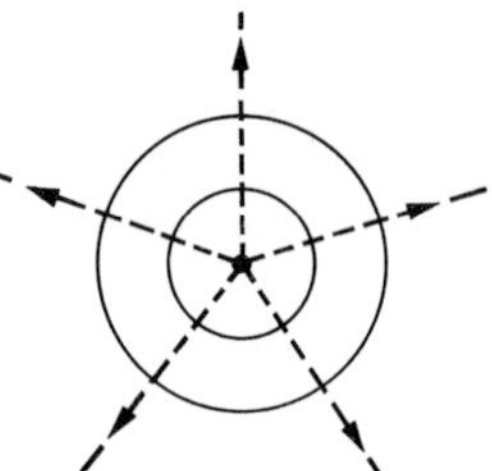

Fig. 27–15. Wave fronts (solid lines) and rays (dashed lines) from a point source.

this type of wave unless otherwise specified. Rays of a spherical wave are thus radial lines extending outward from the sources, as in Fig. 27–15.

Plane waves are waves in which the surfaces of equal phase are planes. In order to be strictly plane without nonplanar edge effects, the planes must extend to infinity (as we shall see in the section on diffraction). However, for many purposes a plane of finite extension is a good approximation. Figure 27–16 is a schematic representation of plane waves and shows planes at the maxima superimposed on graphs of displacement versus position. The rays corresponding to plane waves are parallel straight lines.

Small portions of spherical waves observed at large distances from point sources are plane waves to a good degree of approximation. Sound waves from distant sources and light from the sun or stars (or less distant sources) are common examples.

In the case of sound, plane waves can be generated by an oscillating plane that acts as the

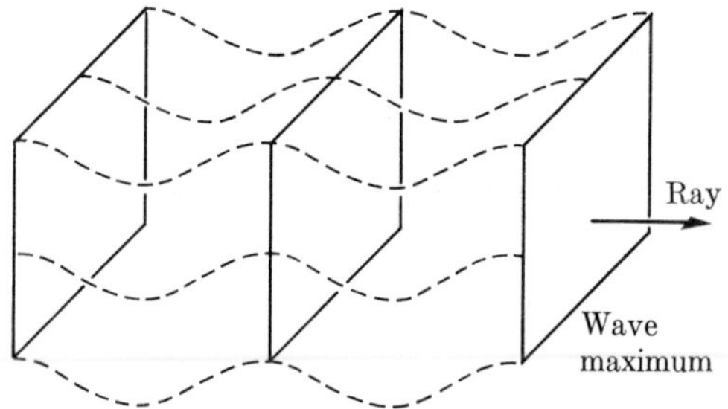

Fig. 27–16. Plane wave fronts (solid lines) and graphs of the wave form (dashed lines) for plane waves.

source, or by a closely spaced planar array of sources oscillating in phase (coherent sources). Plane electromagnetic waves can be produced in a similar manner by a planar array of antennas. The limitation in the latter case is in our inability to produce oscillating currents in the antennas when the wavelength is less than about one millimeter. Plane light waves of small area can be produced by arrays of atoms that are stimulated to emit waves in the same phase, as in optical masers. However, the most frequently employed method of producing plane light waves is to transform spherical waves (from point sources) into plane waves by means of lenses or mirrors. This method will be treated in sections to follow. Uniformity of phase is guaranteed, since all parts of the wave have the same source.

Intensity of spherical waves. Suppose that radiant energy is emitted by a point source at the rate of P watts. In the case of electromagnetic radiation, the source might be an accelerated charge or two oscillating charges constituting an oscillating dipole (Section 27–2). In any type of wave, the intensity, and hence the amplitude, may depend on the direction of emission from the source. However, if we select a particular direction, (Fig. 27–17) and consider the portion dP of the radiation power emitted in a narrow cone of solid angle $d\Omega$, we have

$$dP = I\,dA, \tag{27–49}$$

where dA is the element of area intercepted by

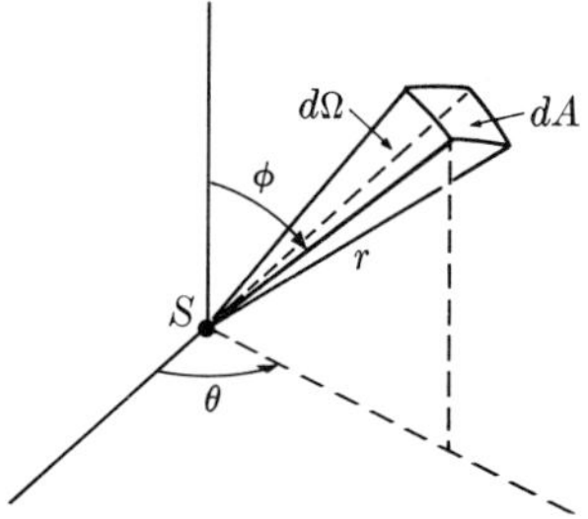

FIG. 27–17. A source S emits radiation. An element of solid angle $d\Omega$ is chosen for the analysis of the radiation emitted in the direction indicated.

$d\Omega$ at distance r from the source (Fig. 27–17). But since

$$d\Omega \equiv \frac{dA}{r^2}, \tag{27–50}$$

there results

$$I = \frac{dP}{d\Omega}(\theta, \phi)\,\frac{1}{r^2}\cdot \tag{27–51}$$

It is seen that the intensity follows an inverse-square law in its dependence on r, independent of direction. In Section 27–2 we found that the intensity of an electromagnetic wave is related with the amplitude E_m by (Eq. 27–20)

$$I = \tfrac{1}{2}c\epsilon_0 E_m^2. \tag{27–52}$$

It follows that the amplitude decreases as $1/r$, and hence the wave can be expressed as

$$\psi = \frac{A(\theta, \phi)}{r}\sin(Kr - \omega t), \tag{27–53}$$

where ψ is the displacement and $A(\theta, \phi)$ is a function of direction only. The displacement ψ is periodic in space and time with wave number K and angular frequency ω. The amplitude of motion at any point is A/r. It can be seen that A is the amplitude of the wave at unit distance from the source.

In a plane wave, there is no change in intensity from point to point in the wave. For a plane wave in space traveling in the x-direction, the wave equation is

$$\psi(x, t) = A\sin(Kx - \omega t), \tag{27–54}$$

which is identical with the solution of the one-dimensional wave equation. It must be observed, however, that the wave is not confined to a line.

27–4 HUYGENS' PRINCIPLE

Huygens' principle for wave motion was developed, historically, as a set of assumptions, or a *model*, which can be used to predict the motion of a wave in space. The model accurately predicts the progress of a wave in space. Today

Huygens' principle is reduced to a theorem since it can be derived on the basis of wave theory. Because of the complexity of the proof of the theorem, we follow here the historical method in which the model is used as a first principle. A statement of the principle follows:

Every point on a wave front is to be considered a new point source of wave disturbance. This new source emits what are called secondary waves, or wavelets, which are spherical waves traveling at the wave velocity characteristic of the medium. The new wave front at some later stage is the result of superposition of the wavelets. The new front is the envelope of the wavelets.

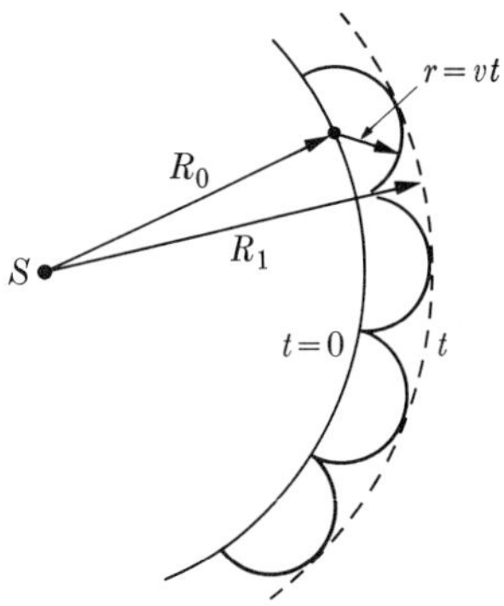

Fig. 27–18. Illustration of the use of Huygens' principle to find a new wave front (dashed line) from an earlier wave front (circle of radius R_0) by means of the construction of wavelets of radius r.

Let the application of this theorem be illustrated by some elementary examples. Assume that at some instant of time we have a spherical wave front corresponding to, say, a crest in the wave. Then a series of points is chosen on the front as centers of disturbances. The centers emit wavelets of radius $r = vt$, as in Fig. 27–18. Then at time t we draw the envelope, or common tangent surface to all the wavelets. This envelope is a spherical surface of radius $R_1 = R_0 + r$ or $R_1 = R_0 + vt$. Thus the wave front is perpetuated in spherical form, the radius expanding at the wave velocity. In the same way, it can be shown that a plane wave propagates as an advancing plane (Fig. 27–19). These elementary examples show the method of construction but do not expose the power of the model.

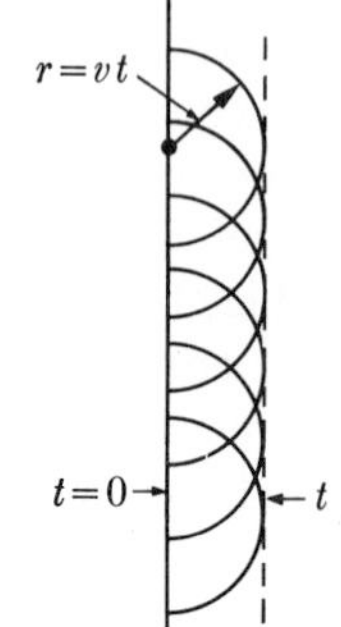

Fig. 27–19. Huygens' construction for plane waves.

The above examples also leave some basic questions unanswered, questions that can be answered rigorously only in terms of rather advanced analysis. However, moderately satisfying answers to these questions can be given in simple terms. First there is the question of why we ignored the wavelet in the backward direction. This question can be answered in general terms by considering the fact that the wave carries momentum and energy in the direction of propagation. If a backward wave started from a particular wave front at a particular time, backwardly directed waves must originate from *all* wave fronts at all times, since there can be no special property of a particular position or time in a homogeneous medium. If backwardly directed waves are continuously generated as the wave front advances, its energy would become depleted and it would die out. Furthermore, for conservation of momentum the forward wave would have to gain momentum if a backward wave were emitted. But this would require a source of additional energy available locally at the wave front.

The second question is one of edge effects when the wave surface is not a closed surface (such as a spherical surface) or an infinite plane. This question will be considered in some detail later under the names of diffraction and interference. For the present, we simply assert that it seems plausible to neglect edge effects when the dimensions of a finite wave front are very large compared with the wavelength. This assumption is, in fact, the basis of *geometrical optics,* which we consider in a moment.

27–5 REFLECTION

The experimental law of reflection states that a ray incident upon a plane-reflecting surface departs from the surface at an angle equal to the angle of incidence. The angle of incidence i is measured between the incident ray I and a line N normal to the surface. The angle of reflection r is measured between the reflected ray R and a line normal to the surface (Fig. 27–20).

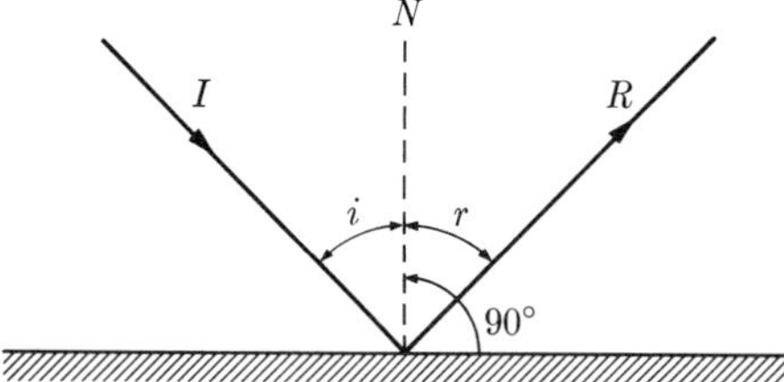

FIG. 27–20. The experimental result for the reflection of light from a plane surface, $i = r$.

We now ask whether the theory agrees with this experimental observation. Let the wave that is incident upon the surface be represented by a series of plane wave fronts impinging obliquely upon a plane-reflecting surface (Fig. 27–21). The rays (normal to the wave fronts) are parallel lines in the direction of propagation, as shown. Until the surface is encountered, the waves re-

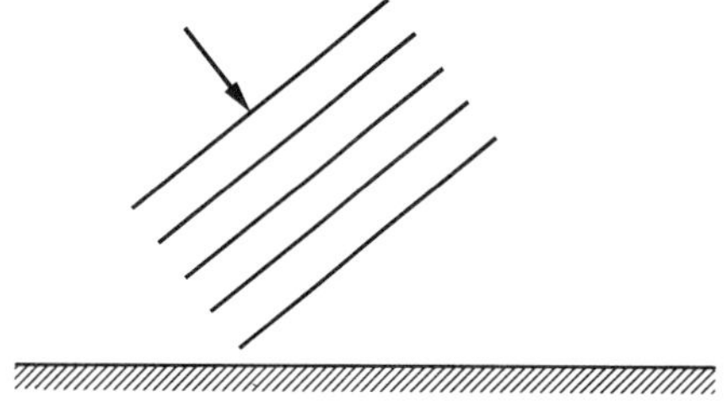

FIG. 27–21. Plane waves incident on a plane-reflecting surface.

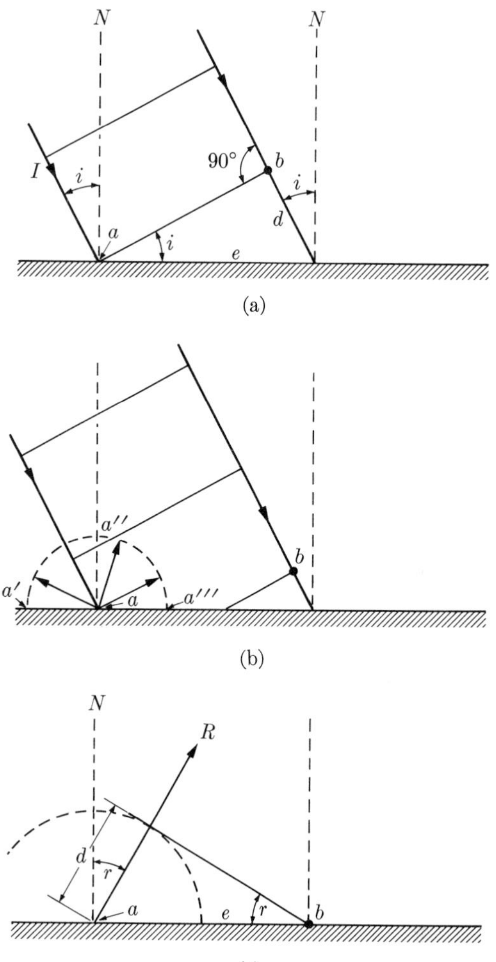

FIG. 27–22. Plane wave front, a–b is just striking the reflecting plane at a in (a). While it advances, a Huygens' wavelet a'–a''–a''' moves back from point a in (b). As the end of the wave front reaches b, the wavelet from a has advanced an equal distance d in (c), with the result that $i = r$.

main plane, as we have seen above in Fig. 27–19. We consider an instant when point a on a wave front is intercepted by the reflecting surface (Fig. 27–22a). Point a is represented as a source of a Huygens' wavelet which grows back into the wave medium as the remainder of the wave front advances toward the surface. Until the construction is completed, we have no knowledge of the direction of the rays in the wavelets a'–a''–a''', except that they are contained in a hemisphere in the wave medium (Fig. 27–22b).

We now choose a point b on the original wave front, which is at a distance d from the surface when point a on the same front touches the reflecting surface (Fig. 27–22a). Since all this wave motion is propagated at the same velocity, the wavelet from a has grown to a radius equal to d while b was traveling to the surface. At this stage we have minimum but sufficient information for the construction of a reflected wave front. Point b is on the new wave front: Its wavelet is of zero size. The new wave front must also be tangent to the wavelet from a. When the new front is drawn, the ray from a is defined: It is drawn to the point of contact of the tangent with the wavelet (Fig. 27–22c). Since the wavelet is circular, the ray is normal to the tangent. Looking back to Fig. 27–22(a), we see that the angle of incidence i is one angle of a right triangle of hypotenuse equal to e. In Fig. 27–22(c) the angle of reflection r is the corresponding angle of a right triangle of the same hypotenuse. Since the sides b are equal, the triangles are congruent and the angles are equal. Therefore the theory agrees with experiment; the reflected rays are parallel and describe a new plane wave emerging from the reflecting surface (Fig. 27–23) at an angle equal to the angle of incidence.

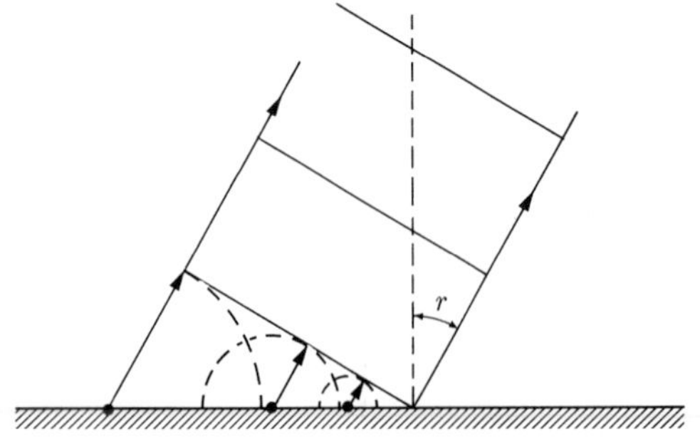

FIG. 27–23. A more complete diagram of the reflected plane waves of Fig. 27–22.

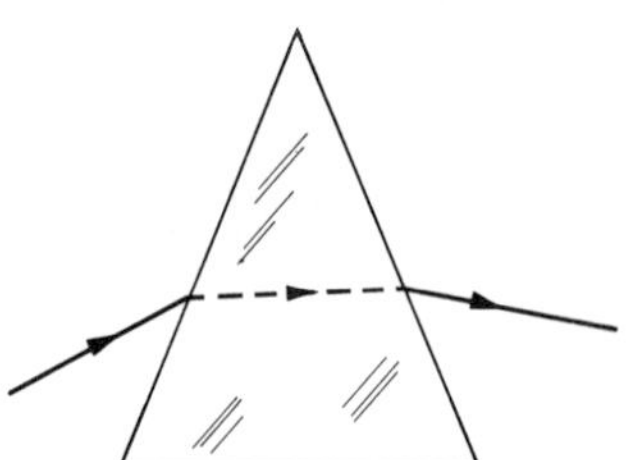

FIG. 27–24. The path of a ray through a prism.

27-6 REFRACTION

When light rays pass from one transparent medium to another with an angle of incidence different from zero, it is observed that the rays are deviated by an amount that depends on the angle of incidence, the nature of the media, and the color of the light. The phenomenon is called refraction. A common example is the deviation of light by a prism, as in Fig. 27–24. If the incident beam is white light, a band of colors called a spectrum is observed, as in Fig. 27–25. Newton studied the latter effect in detail and concluded that white light is compounded of many colors, each of which is refracted by a different amount.

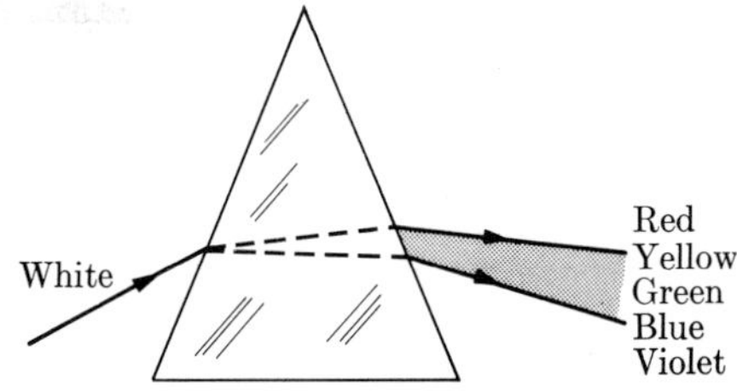

FIG. 27–25. The variation of path with color of light when it passes through a prism.

Willebrord Snell is credited with the experimental discovery that there is a simple relationship between the angle of incidence and the angle of refraction (for a given color) at a boundary between given media, as in Fig. 27–26. This relationship,

$$\frac{\sin i}{\sin r} = n, \qquad (27\text{–}55)$$

is known as Snell's law. The angles of incidence

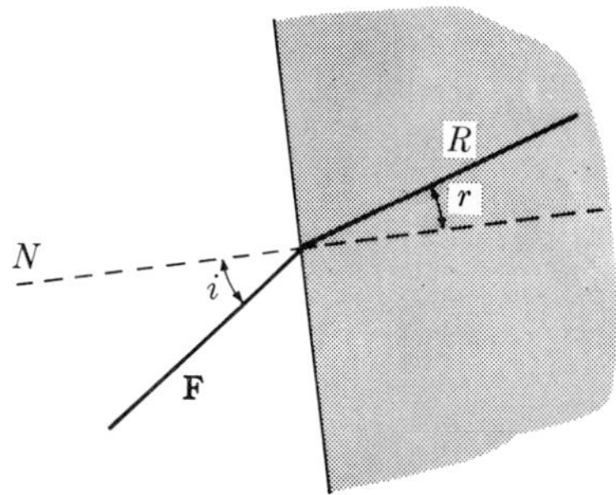

FIG. 27–26. Method of measuring the angle of incidence i and the angle of refraction r (from the normal N) when a ray passes into a refracting medium.

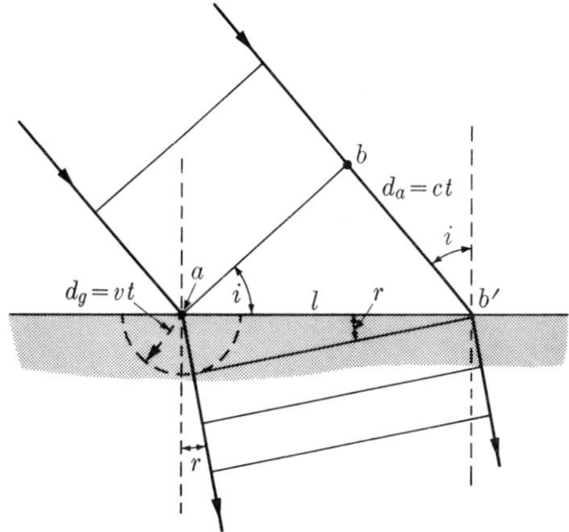

FIG. 27–27. Diagram illustrating the refraction of plane wave fronts incident on the plane surface of a refracting medium. A Huygens' wavelet is shown advancing from a.

and refraction are i and r, respectively, and n is a constant that depends on the color and on the medium.

Newton's analysis of refraction and other phenomena was based on a corpuscular model of light, in which the particles, or corpuscles, of light were not unlike mechanical particles. It can be remarked that the law of reflection is easily understood on the basis of the corpuscular model, since it requires only the assumption that the light particles bounce elastically from the surface. This elastic bouncing would be one property with which the corpuscles must be endowed. In the case of refraction, still another assumption is made. This is that there exists a power of attraction of the glass for the light particles. The consequent increase in the velocity component normal to the surface for obliquely incident particles would then cause an inward bending of the trajectory toward the surface normal, as observed. It will be shown in this section that a *wave* construction for the refraction effect requires the exact opposite to Newton's assumption; i.e., the light velocity in the glass must be *less* than the velocity in air if light is refracted toward the normal in air-to-glass refraction. The experiments on *direct* measurement of the velocity of light, which show directly that the wave theory is correct and the Newtonian form of corpuscular theory is wrong, will be discussed later.

We now use Huygens' method in order to apply wave theory to refraction of plane waves. Let a plane wave be incident, from air, upon a plane glass surface. A point a on a wave front coincides with the glass surface (Fig. 27–27). A wavelet is propagated in the transparent medium from a, and this wavelet grows while point b, on the same wave front, advances to the surface. The point b advances a distance d_a to the surface, given by

$$d_a = ct,$$

with c the velocity of light in air. However, in the glass we have

$$d_g = vt, \tag{27–56}$$

where v is the velocity of light in glass. When b arrives at the surface, a new wave front is drawn. It passes through b and is tangent to the wavelet that originated at a. The ray from a must go toward the point of tangency. Thus the direction of the refracted ray is perpendicular to the new wave fronts. (In doubly refracting materials, there is also an ellipsoidal wavelet. The rays are not necessarily perpendicular to the wave front in that case.) From the construction it can be seen that the sine of the angle of incidence is

$$\sin i = \frac{d_a}{l} = \frac{ct}{l}. \tag{27–57}$$

The sine of the angle of refraction is

$$\sin r = \frac{d_g}{l} = \frac{vt}{l}, \tag{27–58}$$

and the ratio of sines is

$$\frac{\sin i}{\sin r} = \frac{c}{v}. \tag{27–59}$$

Since the above analysis is done with wave fronts, the velocities c and v are *wave velocities*, not group velocities.

It is customary to define the velocity ratio in Eq. (27–59) as the *index of refraction* of the medium n (strictly, the *relative* index of refraction):

$$n \equiv \frac{c}{v}. \tag{27–60}$$

The absolute index of refraction, or simply, *the* index of refraction requires that c be the velocity in vacuum. Using the definition of Eq. (27–60), we have

$$\frac{\sin i}{\sin r} = n, \tag{27–61}$$

where n is the relative index. This result agrees with experiment (Snell's law).

From the above derivation, we see that the wave theory requires that the wave velocity be less in the second medium, if the rays are bent toward the normal.

We can measure the index of refraction experimentally by simply observing the angles of incidence and refraction. In the case of light, it is found that n depends on the wavelength (a phenomenon called *dispersion*, which we discussed in the previous chapter in the topic of group velocity). Dispersion is responsible for the effect of prisms on light shown in Fig. 27–26. In the case of most mechanical waves, including sound, there is no dispersion. The concept of absolute index of refraction is, of course, inapplicable to mechanical waves. We have already seen that water waves *do* exhibit dispersion.

TABLE 27–1

Substance	Index of refraction
Glass	1.4 to 2
Water	1.333
CS_2	1.629
Air	1.00029

Values of n for light in a few substances are given in Table 27–1 for a wavelength near the middle of the visible spectrum, 5.893×10^{-7} m.

The dependence of n on wavelength for a few substances is shown in Fig. 27–28. We shall see later how the wavelength of light can be measured. At the present it must suffice to label the different parts of the light spectrum according to the color sensations which they cause. The measurement of the refraction of light beams measures velocity alone. In vacuum, there is no variation of the velocity with wavelength, as evidenced by the simple observation that the color of certain stars whose intensity varies with time remains unchanged. The time variation can be caused by actual variation in intensity, by occultation (eclipse by a planet or the sun), or by eclipse of a bright member of a double star by a dark companion.

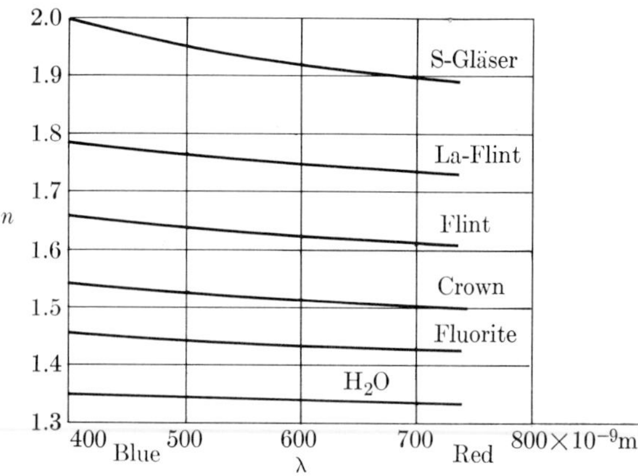

FIG. 27–28. The index of refraction n versus wavelength λ in several materials.

Both *reflection and transmission* (refraction) occur at a boundary between media, as we have seen for the special case of normal incidence in Chapter 26. Huygens' method should include not only wavelets in the new medium but also wavelets back into the original medium. If the incident rays are not normal to the boundary, the intensities of reflected and transmitted light depend on the plane of polarization in case of transverse waves. The analysis is slightly more complex than the analysis given in Chapter 26 for normal incidence. We give here (Fig. 27–29) simply the results. The graphs are for unpolarized light (light made up of an ensemble of waves of random phase and polarization). The relative index of refraction of the media is 1.5 in Fig. 27–29.

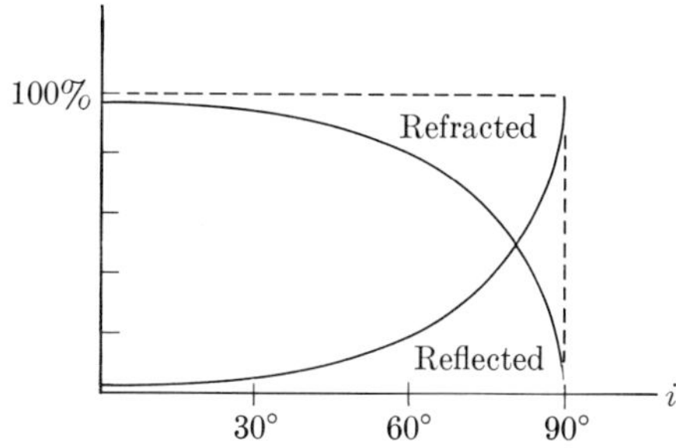

Fig. 27–29. The variation of the intensity of refracted and reflected light as a function of angle of incidence for a medium with $n = 1.5$.

If the second medium is less dense than the first (i.e., the wave velocity is greater), the relative index of refraction in Eq. (27–61) is less than one. In consequence, there is a limiting value of i corresponding to $r = 90°$, given by

$$\sin i_0 = n, \qquad (27\text{–}62)$$

where n is the index of the second medium relative to the first, as usual, and therefore is the reciprocal of the index of the first relative to the second. Since no wave can be refracted at angles greater than 90°, the waves must be totally reflected. The phenomenon is called total internal reflection, and i_0 is called the critical angle. The curves for reflected and refracted intensities are similar to those in Fig. 27–29, except for compression toward the left so that 100° reflection appears at i_0 as given by Eq. (27–62).

27–7 VELOCITY OF LIGHT

The history of optics is filled with interesting attempts, successful and otherwise, at the precise determination of the velocity of light. The description begun in Chapter 13 on relativity will now be continued. Galileo was one of the first of the experimental school of physicists to set up such a measurement. He wished to establish as great paths of travel as feasible, so as to enhance the time of flight of a beam of light. The choice was a path between two hilltops. The experiment was described in Chapter 13, but we repeat the basic idea here. In the experiment observers were stationed on each of two hilltops, and both observers were equipped with hooded lanterns. Observer 1 lifted his hood, initiating a light signal. Observer 2 was instructed to lift his hood when he saw the first signal. Observer 1 measured the time interval between his initiation of the first signal and his receipt of the second. The results were inconclusive. Subsequent measurements, operationally the same as this but more highly refined, give the value of light velocity as $c \simeq 3 \times 10^8$ m/sec. Therefore, even if the observers in Galileo's experiment had been stationed a diameter of the earth apart (1.3×10^7 m), the net transmission time would have been only 0.1 sec, about equal to the least reaction time of the observers.

A mechanization of the Galileo experiment was contrived by the physicist Fizeau. Light is sent through a slot in a many-toothed wheel. It advances to a mirror, is reflected, and then returns through another slot in the wheel. This arrangement is shown in Fig. 27–30. When the wheel is stationary, the mirror is adjusted so that the condition described above is obtained. Then the wheel is set into rotation. As it speeds up, the situation is finally reached in which the tooth

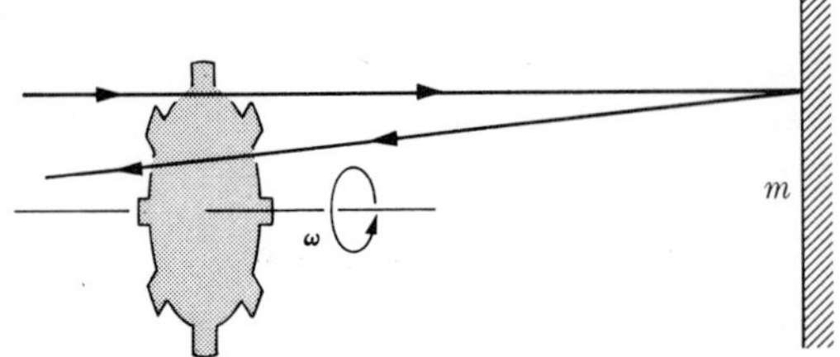

Fig. 27–30. A beam of light passes through one space of a toothed wheel. The mirror m is adjusted so that the light returns through an adjoining space when the wheel is at rest, as shown.

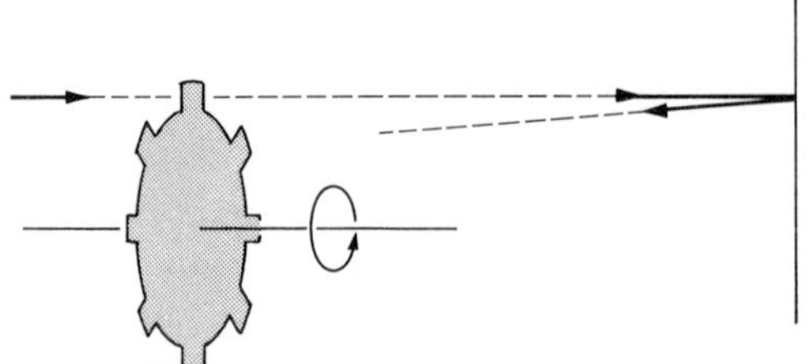

Fig. 27–31. A pulse of light shown en route from the wheel to the mirror and back. The light has been chopped off into a pulse by the rotation of the wheel.

separating the slot through which the beam first passes and the adjacent slot through which it returns moves appreciably during the transit time for the light to advance to the mirror and return. At just the right rotational speed, the tooth moves exactly into the position of the return slot and the light is blanked out. From a knowledge of the rotational period of the wheel and the distance the light must travel to the mirror and return, the velocity of light can be computed. If, for blanking, the rotational period is T and the number of teeth in the wheel is N, the transit time of light is $T/2N$. If the distance between the wheel and mirror is L, and the path of light travel is $2L$, the velocity of light is

$$c = \frac{d}{t} = \frac{2L}{(T/2N)} = \frac{4LN}{T}. \qquad (27\text{–}63)$$

The action of the rotating wheel is to chop the incident light into bundles, or packets, of light. It is apparent that we are not dealing with an infinite wave train, for which we define a phase velocity. Rather, the wave is chopped into groups (Fig. 27–31), and the group velocity is measured. However, since vacuum is not dispersive, phase and group velocity are identical, and this is not a vital point in an experiment if the light path is in vacuum.

Such methods of determination of light velocity make possible the measurement of light velocity in any medium, since any transparent material, such as water or glass, can be interposed in the light path between the wheel and mirror. By direct measurement, it is found that (a) light travels more slowly in transparent material media than in vacuum, and (b) light of different colors travels at different speeds in transparent media, blue light traveling more slowly than red. In consequence of (a) above, the wave theory of the refraction of light is supported, and Newton's theory of corpuscular refraction is ruled out.

27–8 GEOMETRICAL OPTICS

Geometrical optics is an important *approximation* which can be used for a satisfactory solution of many optical problems by the wave theory of light. The approximation comes in neglecting the effect of the finite area of the wave fronts. The method itself is simple. We can use the laws of reflection and refraction developed above to predict the course which a light ray will follow. Alternatively, the method of Huygens can be used directly. We shall follow this latter method in the treatment of a problem of both practical and theoretical importance in optics; it is the solution of the thin lens problem. Later, when the phenomena of diffraction and interference are introduced, it will be shown that the structure of the image is more complex than indicated by geometrical optics, which neglects effects due to the finite size of the wave fronts.

We first discuss the concept of *images*. When an object emits or reflects light, it appears as a source of light to an observer. If light from a

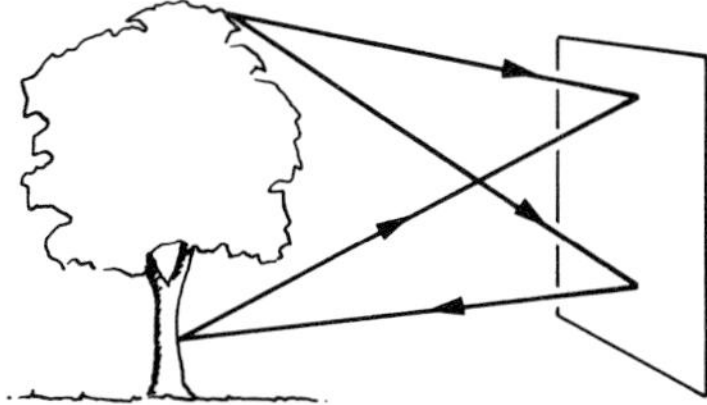

Fig. 27–32. Light from all parts of a tree reach all parts of a screen.

source can be cast on a screen in such a way that the illumination of a point on the screen is derived from a definite point on the source, then we say that a real image of the source is formed. The image need not be a good one; it may be warped and distorted. The requirement is basically that there should be a one-to-one correspondence between points on the source and on the screen.

If we hold a screen in the vicinity of a tree (Fig. 27–32), an image of the tree is not formed because light from all parts of the tree falls on all parts of the screen. However, an image is formed if a baffle is placed between the tree and the screen (Fig. 27–33) such that all light which reaches the screen must pass through a small hole in the baffle. Point P' on the screen can be reached only by a ray from point P on the tree. Excellent images can be obtained if the baffle and screen form part of an enclosure which excludes light from other sources. The device is called a pinhole camera.

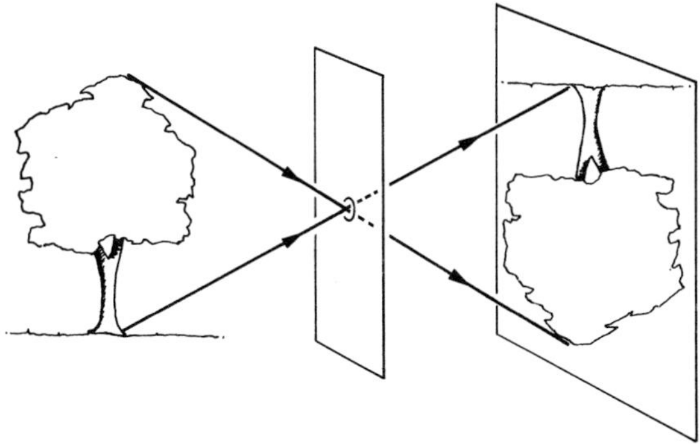

Fig. 27–33. Image of a tree formed as a result of interposing a baffle with a small hole in it between the tree and a screen.

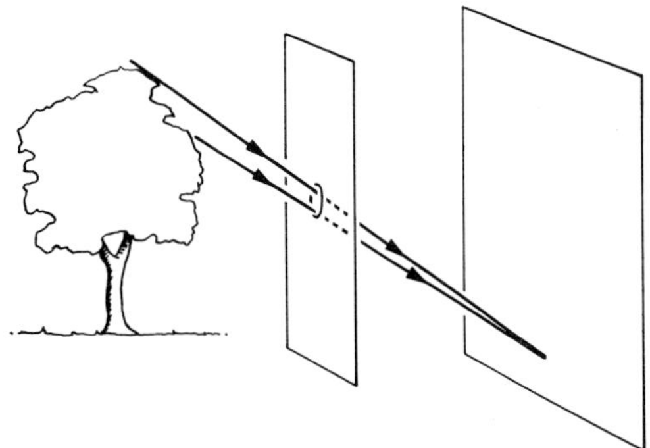

Fig. 27–34. When the hole in the baffle is enlarged to increase the brightness of the image, the image becomes blurred by the superposition of light rays from different parts of the tree.

The pinhole camera has a natural limitation. If the hole is of finite size, then the one-to-one correspondence between source and image is somewhat lost (Fig. 27–34). If the hole is made smaller and becomes a point, then no light passes through the hole. Therefore, a compromise must be made between illumination and sharpness of image. Even if illumination were not a problem, there exists another limitation, as we shall see later; namely, rays do not pass straight through a hole. As the size of the hole approaches zero, the rays emerge from the hole in all directions. This is an effect which is neglected in geometrical optics.

Since the pinhole method of image formation has the inherent limitations described above, we turn to devices that form images even with large openings in the screen. Clearly, we need a device that bends rays of light by varying amounts, depending on where the light passes through the opening. One such device is the *lens*.

The *lens* is a prism of variable angle. The amount of bending of a ray is made to depend on the point of entry in such a way that rays entering at larger angles from the axis (a line through the center, Fig. 27–35) are bent by correspondingly greater amounts. If this schedule of bending is just right, rays derived from a common point O on one side of the lens will intersect at a common

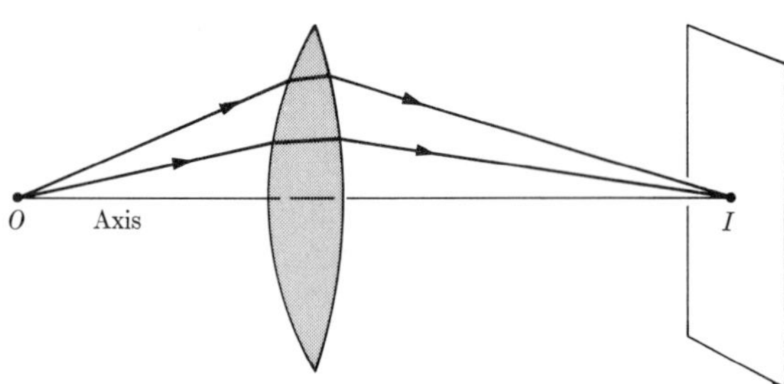

FIG. 27–35. The focusing effect of a lens; rays at all angles from O converge at I.

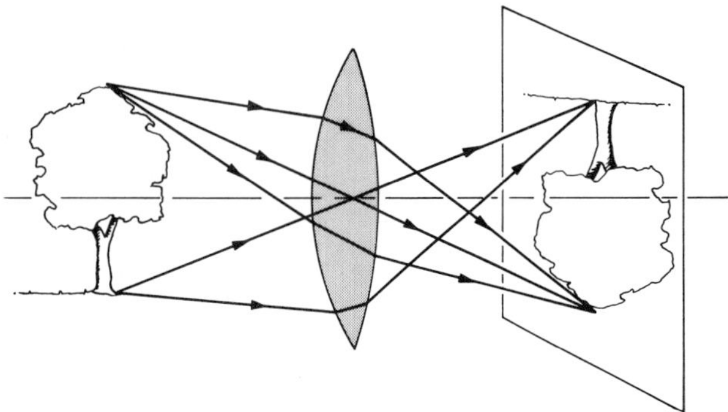

FIG. 27–36. The formation of an image of a tree by a lens.

point I on the other side of the lens. A lens is thus an instrument for image formation (Fig. 27–36). It is a large aperture device which permits far greater image intensity than the pinhole, although it performs the same basic function.

A straightforward approach to the lens problem would be to ask what geometric form of the lens surface will satisfy the requirements we have set for the lens. However, only spherical surfaces are easy to make and therefore we investigate their image-forming properties. We shall find that spherical surfaces are moderately satisfactory. This assertion is checked by an application of Huygens' principle to the solution of the "thin" spherical lens.

We first establish an approximate geometrical rule for spherical surfaces. Let a–a' be a portion of a spherical surface of radius r (Fig. 27–37). A half-chord is l and the sagittal distance is s.

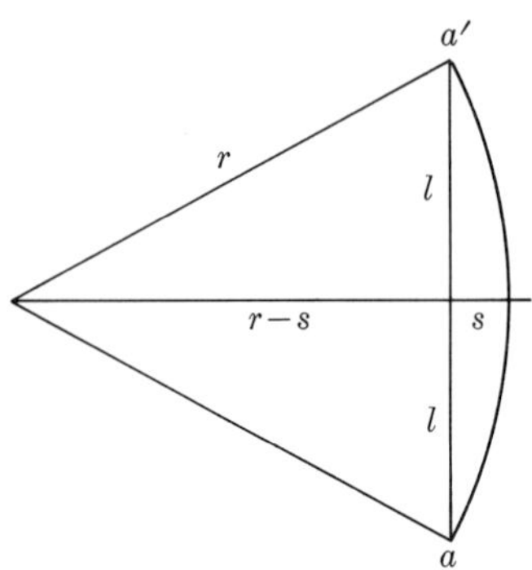

FIG. 27–37. Illustration of the quantities used in the sagittal theorem of Eq. (27–64).

From the theorem of Pythagoras, we have the relationship among r, l, and s,

$$r^2 = l^2 + (r - s)^2. \qquad (27\text{–}64)$$

If we consider such shallow surfaces that s is much smaller than r or l, the term s^2 in Eq. (27–64) can be neglected in comparison with the other terms, and we have the approximate expression

$$s = \frac{l^2}{2r}\cdot \qquad (27\text{–}65)$$

This expression is to be used in the thin-lens calculation, where the conditions are stipulated such that Eq. (27–65) is a good approximation.

A spherical lens is characterized by the radii of curvature of its two surfaces, r_1 and r_2 (Fig. 27–38). For each surface we have a sagittal distance, s_1 and s_2, and the thickness of the lens is the sum $s = s_1 + s_2$. Under the restriction

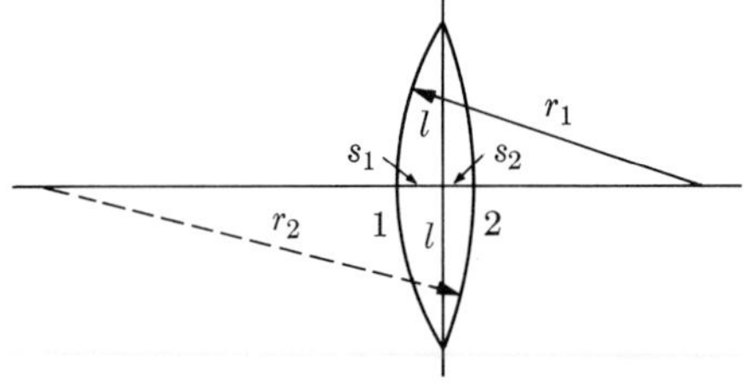

FIG. 27–38. The quantities used in specifying the geometry of a spherical-surfaced lens.

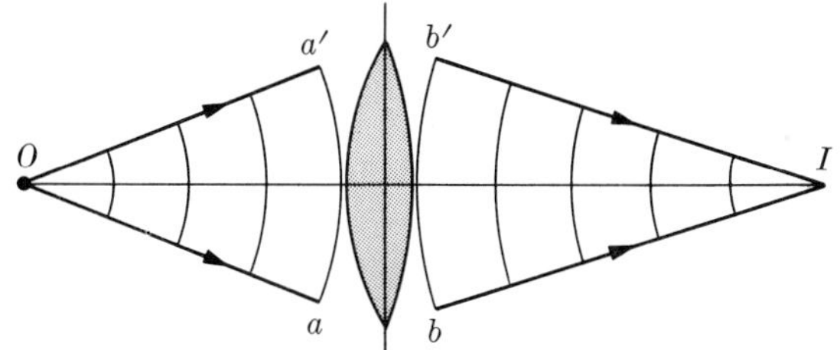

FIG. 27–39. Spherical wave fronts diverging from O and converted to converging wave fronts by a lens.

that this be a thin lens, we have [from Eq. (27–65)]

$$s = \frac{l^2}{2r_1} + \frac{l^2}{2r_2}, \tag{27–66}$$

where l is the radius of the lens. We let a point source of light O on the lens axis send a spherical wave of light toward the lens (Fig. 27–39). If all rays are bent toward a common point, the incident convex spherical wave a–a' must be transformed by the lens into a concave spherical wave b–b', converging toward a new center of curvature I. Qualitatively, this action of the lens can be understood. Light travels more slowly through the glass of the lens than in air, and the lens is thickest at its center. The central portion of the wave is retarded the most. The outer portion of the wave travels principally in air and is therefore the least retarded. The qualitative action of retardation is shown in Fig. 27–40.

Analytically, we solve for the relationship between the wave radius, p, when the incident

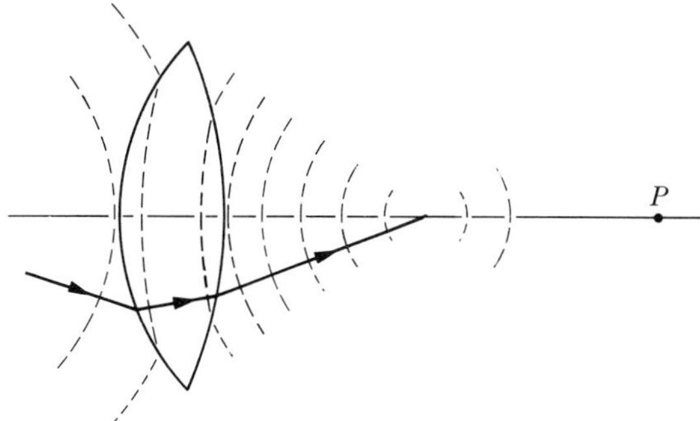

FIG. 27–40. Illustration of the wave fronts within a lens.

wave front just touches the lens at a' and the wave radius q, when the exiting wave front last touches the lens at b' (Fig. 27–41). We select for consideration two sections of light paths, one through the central part of the lens, of length s and one at the periphery of the lens, of length d. In order to have b–b' a new wave front, there must be *equal times* for any portion of the wave front a–a' to advance to the position b–b', that is, the wave must travel the distance s in the same time that it travels the distance d. The larger distance, d, from a to b is to be compensated for by the smaller velocity (in glass) from a' to b'. The distance s is given by Eq. (27–66). The distance d is given by

$$d = \frac{e + s_1}{\cos\theta_1} + \frac{g + s_2}{\cos\theta_2},$$

but for *small angles* $\cos\theta_1$ and $\cos\theta_2$ are about

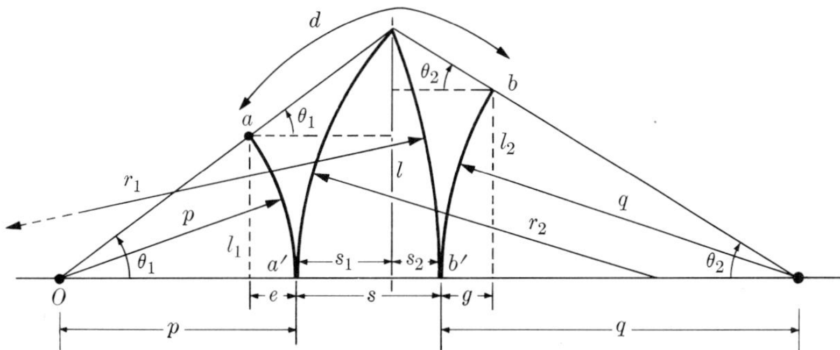

FIG. 27–41. The quantities involved in the calculation of the effect of a lens on spherical waves diverging from O.

one, and we have simply

$$d = e + s_1 + g + s_2 = s + e + g.$$

The approximation that $\cos\theta = 1$ means that we are neglecting small quantities of second order. On the other hand, the difference in the resulting approximate path length in air $(e + s + g)$ and the path length in the lens s is *first* order and can only be compensated for by a first-order effect, namely, the reduction in velocity within the lens. Let the distance of the source from the lens be p and the distance of the image from the lens be q. Both p and q are to be much greater than e, s, or g. Then $e \simeq l^2/2p$ and $g \simeq l^2/2q$ (since $l_1 \simeq l$ and $l_2 \simeq l$) and using Eq. (27–66), we have the expression for d,

$$d = \left(\frac{l^2}{2r_1} + \frac{l^2}{2r_2}\right) + \left(\frac{l^2}{2p} + \frac{l^2}{2q}\right). \qquad (27\text{–}67)$$

The time required for the wave to travel the distance d is $t_d = d/c$ (c = velocity of light in air) and to travel the distance s is $t_s = s/(c/n)$, where n is the index of refraction of the lens. Since the original condition was that $t_d = t_s$, we have $d = ns$. Using the formulas (27–66) and (27–67) for d and s, we have

$$\left(\frac{l^2}{2r_1} + \frac{l^2}{2r_2}\right) + \left(\frac{l^2}{2p} + \frac{l^2}{2q}\right) = n\left(\frac{l^2}{2r_1} + \frac{l^2}{2r_2}\right),$$

and by algebraic reduction this becomes

$$\frac{1}{p} + \frac{1}{q} = (n - 1)\left(\frac{1}{r_1} + \frac{1}{r_2}\right). \qquad (27\text{–}68)$$

The right-hand side of Eq. (27–68) can be given a special physical interpretation. If the object distance p is infinity, the image distance is specially designated by the letter f, that is, for $p = \infty$, we let $q = f$. Using this notation, Eq. (27–68) becomes

$$\frac{1}{f} = (n - 1)\left(\frac{1}{r_1} + \frac{1}{r_2}\right), \qquad (27\text{–}69)$$

where f is called the "focal length" of the lens. Points on the axis at a distance f from the lens are called principal focal points or simply focal points. Equation (27–69) is called the "lens-maker's equation." The choice of refractive index and the surface curvatures determine the focal length of the lens (Eq. 27–69). From the above, we might conclude that any combination of n, r_1, and r_2 that gives the desired f might be satisfactory. In the limit of small angles and thin lenses, this is true. But for large angles, for points off axis, or for short focal lengths, our approximations are poor. Special combinations of lenses must then be used. Finally, in terms of the definition of f, Eq. (27–68) is written

$$\frac{1}{p} + \frac{1}{q} = \frac{1}{f}. \qquad (27\text{–}70)$$

The choice of sign convention should be emphasized. It is customary to consider all signs positive for the example we have chosen, namely, object on the left of the lens, image on the right of the lens, first surface convex, and second surface convex. Any departure from the above, then, involves a negative sign.

Within the validity of the approximations that have been used, it has been shown that a lens has the property of perfect image formation. All rays emanating from one point on a source are returned to a single point (Fig. 27–42a) after passing through the lens. Now that the action of the lens upon the wave front has been found, the effect of the lens upon the rays can be described. The paths of individual rays can be constructed by using Snell's law to find the effect of refraction at each surface (Fig. 27–42b). For small enough angles, where $\sin\theta \simeq \theta$, we could derive Eq. (27–69) by the ray method. We chose to emphasize the wave method in order to keep clear the fact that a wave theory (not a corpuscular theory) is being used. Rays are not corpuscles; they are simply lines that show the local direction of wave propagation.

For a typical case of finite object and image distances, a convex spherical wave emerging from a point source is made concave by the lens

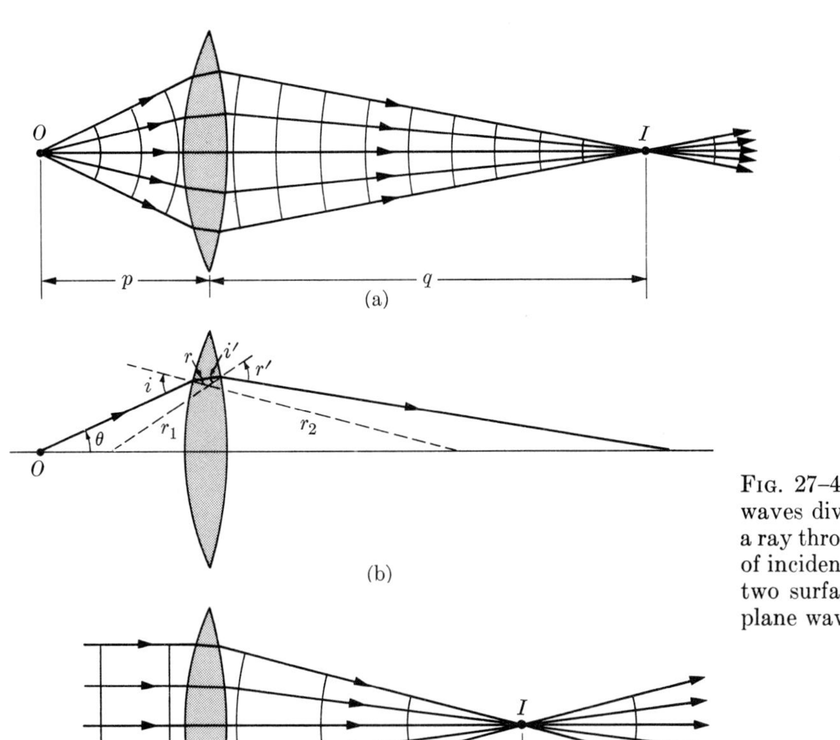

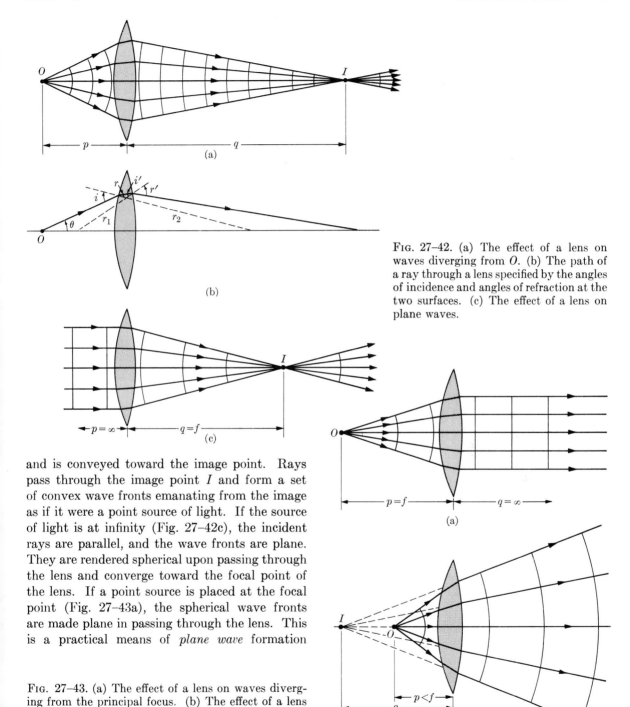

FIG. 27–42. (a) The effect of a lens on waves diverging from O. (b) The path of a ray through a lens specified by the angles of incidence and angles of refraction at the two surfaces. (c) The effect of a lens on plane waves.

and is conveyed toward the image point. Rays pass through the image point I and form a set of convex wave fronts emanating from the image as if it were a point source of light. If the source of light is at infinity (Fig. 27–42c), the incident rays are parallel, and the wave fronts are plane. They are rendered spherical upon passing through the lens and converge toward the focal point of the lens. If a point source is placed at the focal point (Fig. 27–43a), the spherical wave fronts are made plane in passing through the lens. This is a practical means of *plane wave* formation

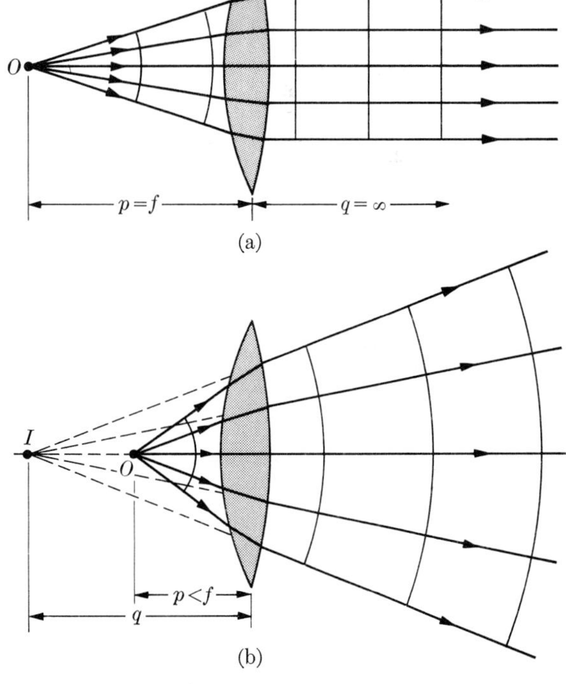

FIG. 27–43. (a) The effect of a lens on waves diverging from the principal focus. (b) The effect of a lens on waves diverging from a point inside the principal focus.

when a point source is used. If a source of light is placed closer than f to the lens (Fig. 27-43b), then the curvature of the incident spherical wave is reduced, but it continues as an outward-going spherical wave. From the lens equation,

$$\frac{1}{q} = \frac{1}{f} - \frac{1}{p}, \tag{27-70'}$$

if $p < f$, then q is negative. The point at distance q from the lens is no longer the position of a real optical image. Instead, the point at q is the "virtual source" of the spherical wave which emerges from the lens. We say that a *virtual image* occurs at q in this case.

The same type of argument that was used for a source on the axis can be used for a source that is off the axis by a distance O (Fig. 27-44). If O is small compared with q, it is found that Eqs. (27-69) and (27-70) again result. Therefore, an extended object O in a plane perpendicular to the

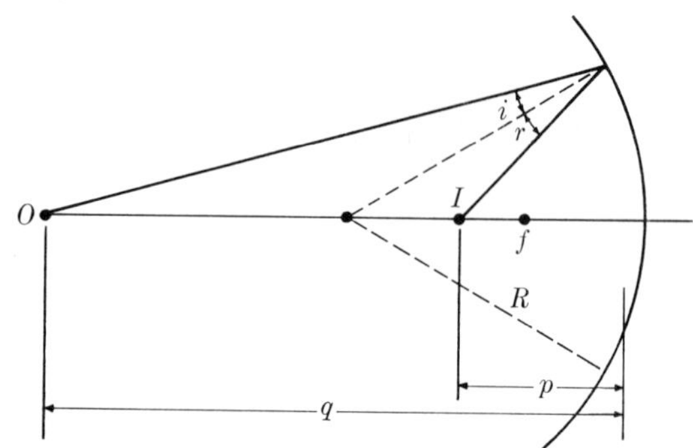

FIG. 27-46. Reflection of rays by a spherical mirror.

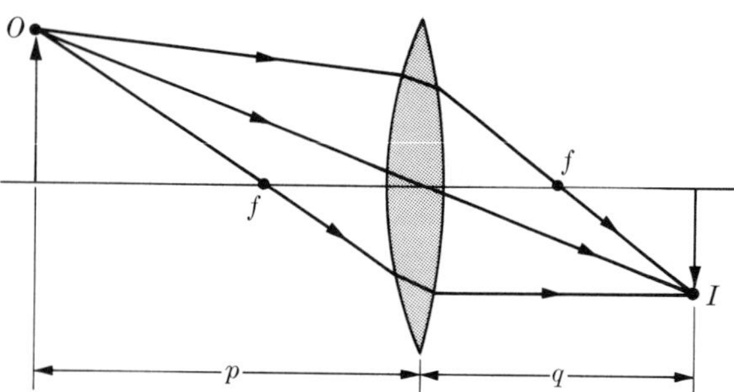

FIG. 27-44. The formation of an off-axis image by a lens.

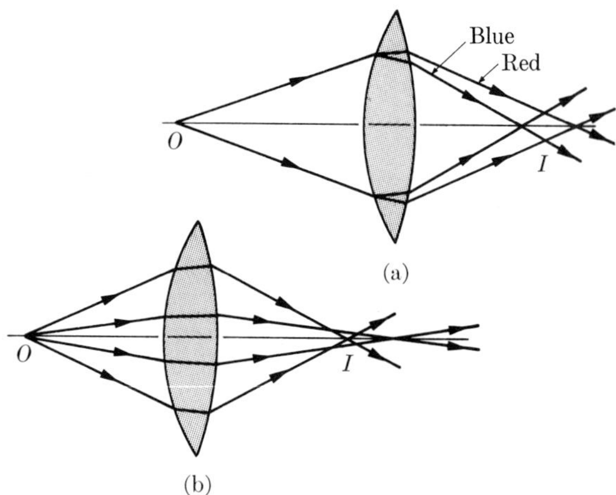

FIG. 27-47. Illustration of (a) chromatic aberration and (b) spherical aberration. In both cases there is no point image of a point source. A circular disk image, a circle of least confusion, occurs at a region between the places where the two sets of rays converge on the axis.

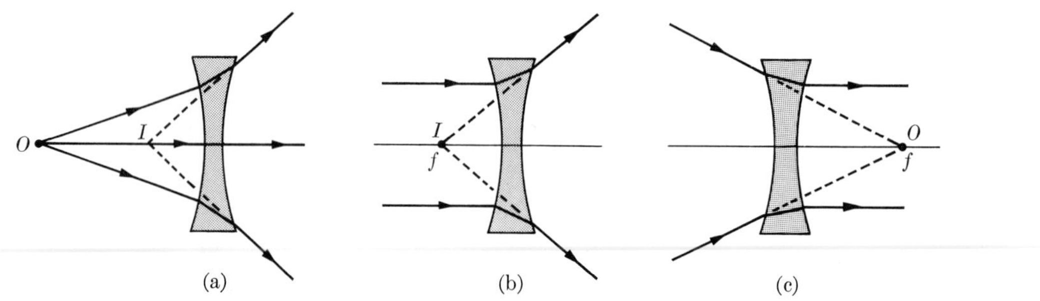

FIG. 27-45. Effects of a diverging lens (a) on waves diverging from O, (b) on plane waves, and (c) on waves that were converging on the principal focus f.

axis forms an image in a plane perpendicular to the axis. Details are left for the section on optical instruments.

The lens type used in the above examples is called a converging or positive lens. All rays have their angles *changed* toward the central ray (they are not necessarily convergent on the central ray). On the other hand, if the conbination of lens radii is such that f is negative, the change in angle of noncentral rays is away from the central ray. The lens is then called a diverging or negative lens. Examples of the effects of diverging lenses are shown in Figs. 27–45. In Figs. 27–45 (a) and (b), it is seen that no image is formed. However, the light appears to come from the points labeled I when an observer looks through the lens. The result is called a *virtual* image. The lens equation gives a negative number for the image distance in such cases. In Fig. 27–45(c), we speak of O as a virtual object. The object distance is negative in this case.

Mirrors with spherical surfaces can also be used to form point images of point sources to within the same degree of approximation as spherically surfaced lenses. The derivation of the equation relating p and q is similar to that for lenses and results in

$$\frac{1}{p} + \frac{1}{q} = \frac{2}{R}, \tag{27–71}$$

where R is the radius of the surface (Fig. 27–46). All quantities are positive in the case shown in the figure. Again, we define the right side of the equation as the focal length, and write

$$\frac{1}{p} + \frac{1}{q} = \frac{1}{f}. \tag{27–72}$$

Aberrations. The focal length of a lens depends on the index of refraction (Eq. 27–69), which is a function of the wavelength. Therefore, the focal length is a function of wavelength, and no point image can be formed if more than one wavelength is present (Fig. 27–47a). This effect is called chromatic aberration.

It has been emphasized that the lens equation is an approximation. In reality images of point objects are not points. For example, if a point object is on the lens axis, rays that leave the object at appreciable angles with the axis converge at points closer to the lens than rays at small angles (Fig. 27–47b). This effect is called spherical aberration.

When an object does not lie on the axis, additional image "defects" occur, such as coma, astigmatism, etc.

27–9 INTERFERENCE

In the discussion of reflection and refraction, we have not been particularly concerned with phase differences, primarily because we have been considering single wave trains, and no questions of superposition of wave trains arose explicitly. Of course our simple model of Huygens' principle utilized an idea of superposition of a sort, but not in the same sense that we use the term rigorously. In the next section, a quantitative application of Huygens' principle utilizing true superposition will be demonstrated in connection with diffraction. For the present, the treatment of interference will be confined to the effect of superposition of two different wave trains.

We have previously seen that standing waves occur due to the interference of waves traveling in opposite directions on a string if the wavelengths are the same. The simplest way of producing the second wave is by reflection. Is there an equivalent phenomenon in optics? As expected, the answer is yes. Experiments have been performed in which plane waves of monochromatic light are reflected at normal incidence from a very flat mirror. The existence of standing waves due to interference between the incident and the reflected waves was demonstrated by exposing a photographic emulsion that lay on the face of the mirror. The developed emulsion showed alternating light and dark layers corresponding to nodal and antinodal planes, respectively, with the expected separations of $\lambda/2$ between the planes.

The problem of seeing standing light waves directly with the eye is quite different from observing other types of standing waves, since the mechanism of observation is intimately connected with the phenomenon itself. It is necessary, first of all, to have both interfering waves traveling in the same direction, that is, toward the eye of the observer. Another difficulty is that, unlike mechanical waves or long wavelength "light" waves, it is not easy (except in a laser) to excite separate sources of light so that their phases are synchronized. The above difficulties can be avoided in a number of ways, all of which have in common the splitting of a single wave train into two or more wave trains traveling in the same direction and overlapping in space.

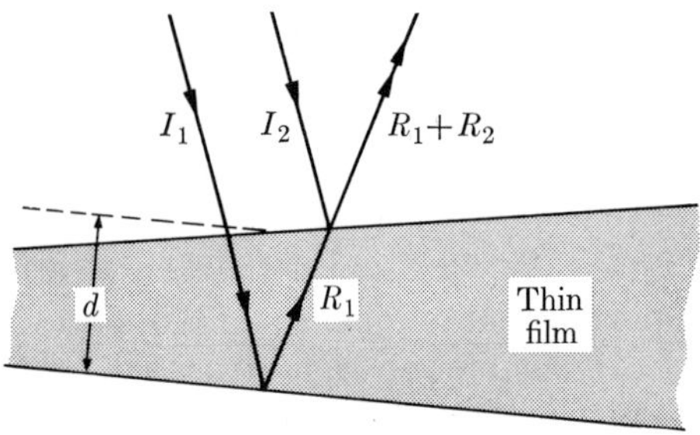

FIG. 27–48. Illustration of the superposition of rays reflected from the first and from the second face of a transparent film.

A frequently observed example of the above is the effect of reflection from thin films of non-uniform thickness, as in Fig. 27–48. A plane wave containing, among others, the rays I_1 and I_2 is incident on the thin film. A portion of each part of the wave is reflected at the top and at the bottom surfaces of the film. For the sake of clarity, the angle of incidence is not zero in the diagram. In this case, the portion of the first ray reflected from the bottom surface is superimposed on the portion of the second ray reflected from the top surface. The resulting amplitude $(R_1 + R_2)$ depends primarily on the relative phase of the two waves. For small angles of incidence, there is, first of all, a phase difference of $2d/\lambda$ wavelengths deriving from the extra distance, $2d$, traveled by the first ray. But, in addition, we recall from Section 26–12 that the phase of a reflected wave is unchanged upon reflection at a boundary where the velocity increases, and it is shifted by a half wavelength if the velocity decreases at the boundary.

When the phase difference between superimposed waves is $n - (\frac{1}{2})$ wavelengths, where n is an integer, the result is a minimum of intensity. At adjacent regions, where d is different in the above example, the phase difference will be $n - 1$ or n wavelengths, and the intensity will be a maximum. Thus, there will be alternating regions of maximum and minimum light. If white light is used, the regions will be colored because of removal of particular wavelengths by destructive interference given by $n\lambda = 2d$ or $(n - \frac{1}{2})\lambda = 2d$ depending on the nature of the film and its bounding media. The colored films observed when oil or gasoline films form on water in the street are due to interference in the manner analyzed above. Note that λ is the wavelength of the light while in the film.

Example 1. A lens of large radius r is placed on a flat glass plate, as in Fig. 27–49. When the system is illuminated from above by light of wavelength λ, what is the nature of the interference pattern due to the air film between the lens and the plate?

Solution: Since the first reflection is at a glass-to-air surface and the second reflection is at an air-to-

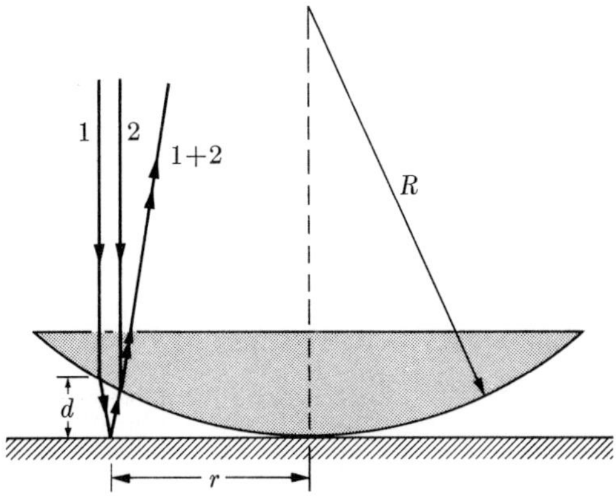

FIG. 27–49. A lens is placed on a flat glass plate. Rays 1 and 2 are superimposed upon reflection at two different surfaces, as shown. The resulting pattern is called Newton's rings.

glass surface, there will be a dark region at the center. Additional *dark* bands will occur when $2d/\lambda$ is an integer n, since the total phase difference will then be $n + (\frac{1}{2})$. A particular dark band will be in a region of constant d and will therefore be a circle of radius r that can be found from R and d. This pattern of alternating dark and bright circles is called Newton's rings.

The Michelson interferometer, which was discussed in the chapter on relativity, utilizes the interference between two "halves" of a beam of light that has been divided by means of a half-reflecting mirror. The student is referred to Chapter 13 for a description of the apparatus and its use in the Michelson-Morley experiment. The interferometer is also used for measuring distances and for comparing wavelengths.

Another method for demonstrating interference is to divide a train of light waves laterally, as in Fig. 27–50, and then to deflect the two trains so that they overlap as shown. In the figure, prisms are used for this purpose. Plane mirrors could have been used instead. In the diagram, dashed lines represent wave valleys, and solid lines wave crests at a particular instant of time. The bands represent regions in which overlapping waves will always be in phase and the intensity will therefore be a maximum. In the region between bands, valleys coincide with crests and the intensity will be a minimum.

In principle, the interference experiments described in this section can be done with waves of very large lateral extension. In consequence, it has not been necessary to include the effect of finite size of wave fronts. In the next section, interference experiments that require the restriction of wave fronts to small dimensions will be discussed.

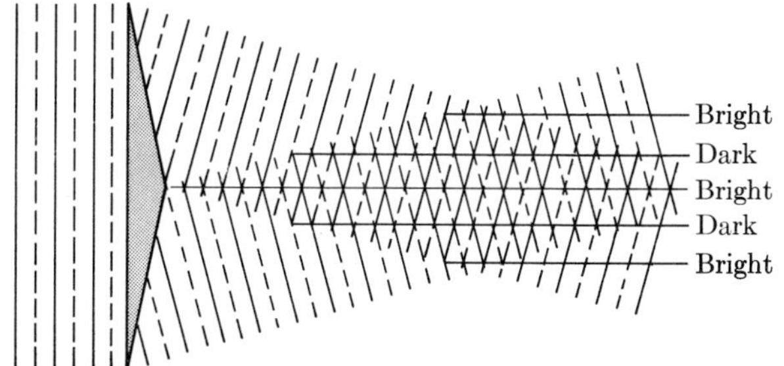

Fig. 27–50. The interference effect produced when a double prism is placed in the path of plane waves.

27–10 DIFFRACTION

In the preceding discussions of reflection and refraction, wave fronts with lateral dimensions very large compared with λ were used because prisms, lenses, and mirrors are large compared with the wavelength of light. The analysis of the propagation of wave fronts of smaller dimensions constitutes a portion of the subject called physical optics, which deals, in general, with the phenomena resulting specifically from the wave properties of light.

In the introductory discussion of Section 27–4, it was stated that the result of the application of the Huygens' method to an infinite plane wave was the prediction of another plane wave. The basis for the statement was an intuitive feeling that symmetry arguments could be invoked. The symmetry argument can, in fact, be detailed as follows: The resultant effect at P due to wavelets from two symmetrically located elements of area dS_1 and dS_2 is a transverse wave displacement parallel to the original plane wave front (Fig. 27–51). (The phase and magnitude of the two contributions are the same, since the distance from "source" to P is the same for both.) Thus the total contribution to the displacement by all elements of the wave front (taken in pairs, as above) is parallel to the originating wave front.

If the originating wave front is limited in area, the above argument no longer holds except for

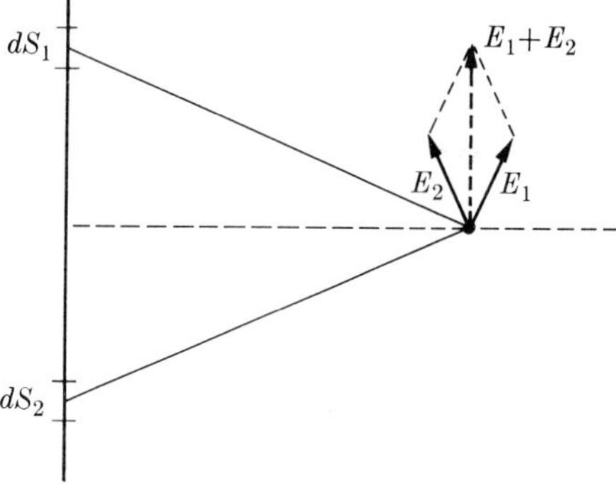

Fig. 27–51. The effect of superposition of wavelets from two symmetrically located points on a plane wave front.

special points and special symmetry. It becomes necessary, in general, to integrate or sum over the contributions by all parts of the originating wave front, taking into account the amplitude and phase of each contribution. The problem is complex in the general case. Therefore, only special cases will be analyzed here.

The discussion will be devoted primarily to cases of limitation of the wave in one dimension; for example, limitation to band-shaped areas of infinite length as obtained by placing a screen with long slit-like openings in the path of a wave. This limitation introduces a symmetry that reduces the problem to two dimensions instead of three.

The effects that limitation of area have on the further propagation of a wave are called *diffraction.* The area may be limited by placing screens with openings in the path of the waves, or by placing obstacles that remove the central part of the beam in the path, or by simply screening off half the wave front, etc. When a screen with two or more openings is placed in the path of the light, it is customary to call the effects attributable to superposition of waves from different openings interference and the effects due to superposition of contributions from a single opening diffraction.

We first consider diffraction qualitatively. Suppose that half an infinite plane wave is blocked off by a black screen, as shown in Fig. 27–52. As the wave approaches the screen, the successive application of Huygens' model leads to the prediction of continuing plane waves, as usual. But now consider the case of the wave front that is just in line with the screen, and predict a future wave front by Huygens' model. The envelope of wavelets drawn at points remote from the edge of the screen is another plane wave. Near the edge, however, the situation is quite different. The symmetry argument made in Section 27–4 (that only the component of vibration parallel to the source plane persists when contributions by symmetrically located source elements are added) can no longer be made. For

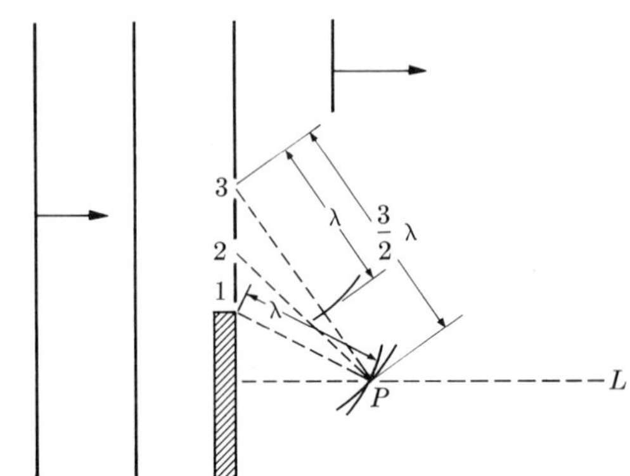

FIG. 27–52. Qualitative illustration of the production of an edge effect by Huygens' wavelets when a plane wave front is partly obstructed. The symmetry effect of Fig. 27–51 is destroyed.

example, at point P along the line L, it is difficult to believe that the effect of superposition of the Huygens' wavelets will be zero. The wavelets from 1 and 2 partially reinforce each other and it is not until the wavelet from 3 is considered that the phase shift is about $\lambda/2$ and cancellation occurs. In addition, the contribution from 3 is smaller because of its distance and also because of the inclination of the source area to the direction of propagation from 3 to P. Thus it is seen that there will be an edge effect in the "plane" waves beyond the screen. The "shadow" of the screen will not be infinitely sharp.

It must be admitted, though, that "good" shadows can be formed. How is the phenomenon of good shadows, that is, the nearly rectilinear propagation of light, to be reconciled with the prediction of diffraction effects? The portion of a wave front affected by diffraction is only a few wavelengths in size. Since the wavelength of visible light is about 5×10^{-5} cm, only a very small portion of a wave front, say a small fraction of a millimeter in width, is affected by diffraction at the edges. By contrast, audible sound waves may be several feet in wavelength, and rectilinear propagation for sound, in the presence of walls, doors, and tables, does not hold at all. Before the more quantitative aspects of diffraction are

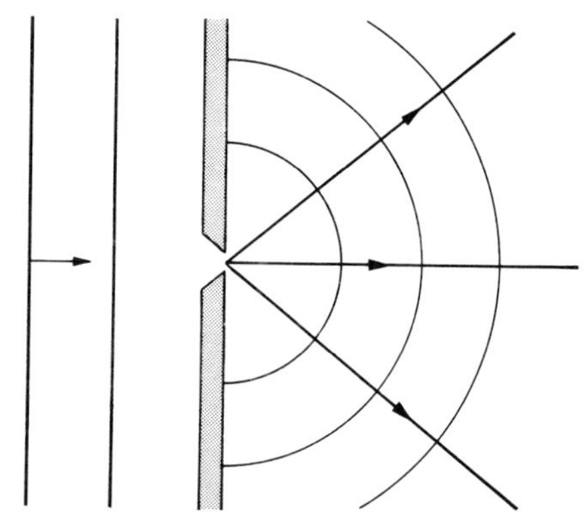

FIG. 27–53. When a plane wave front is completely obstructed, except for a small opening, the aspect of the wave is completely changed.

considered, some further descriptive qualities of diffraction will be explored.

Diffraction effects are most easily observed when waves impinge on a hole or slit in an opaque screen, as in Fig. 27–53. As the hole is made extremely small, Huygens' construction is made strikingly evident, for, as the unobstructed portion of the wave front approaches zero size, we may expect it to become a point source of a single spherical wavelet. In this manner, a small portion of a plane wave is transformed by diffraction into a nearly spherical wave. Thus, if the validity of Huygens' construction had been questioned at the outset, this direct experimental test could have been made: the observation of the action of an "element" of a wave front. There are complications when this is attempted experimentally with light waves, but the effect is readily demonstrated with mechanical waves.

These remarks on diffraction explain qualitatively some of the phenomena occurring when obstacles are placed in the path of a light beam. For example, a correction to lens theory is made immediately evident: A lens is by its nature a finite aperture, and therefore the effects of diffraction may be important to a lens system, as we shall see later. There are, however, further detailed processes inherent in the diffraction process. When the diffraction of light is observed, we observe not a diffuse smearing of a light beam but rather an intricate pattern of illumination. This is due to details of the interference effects among the Huygens' wavelets, as we shall see later.

The combined effects of diffraction and interference are shown in the most elementary fashion through the double-slit demonstration. A source of light is placed behind a barrier that contains a thin vertical slit, or opening. In Fig. 27–54 we view the system from the top and therefore see the width of the opening. A narrow ribbon of light emerges from the slit and illuminates two vertical, parallel slits. If the twin slits are sufficiently narrow, then the nearly plane wave incident upon them is broken, by diffraction, into two cylindrical wave systems. For the moment, we ignore the directional variations in the intensity and assume that the rays of light from each slit travel in nearly all directions. The illumination of a field point P is due to rays going from both slits to P. The analysis of the pattern of light which falls upon a screen containing P is the problem to be solved.

The wave fronts in the two slits are portions of the same wave front in the incident beam of light. Thus the waves which leave the slits are initially in phase. The slits may, for the moment,

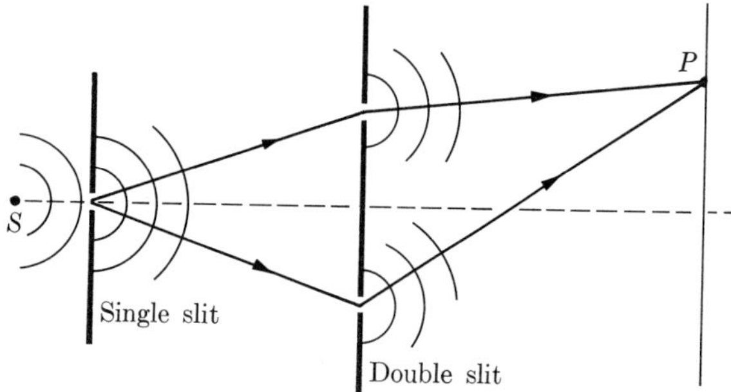

FIG. 27–54. Waves start from a source S. They emerge from the single slit as cylindrical waves that are in phase upon arrival at the two double slits. Cylindrical waves emerge from the double slits and produce superposition effects that can be seen on the screen. Point P on the screen is chosen for illustration.

be considered as line sources of light in equal phase. However, light which arrives at a given point P must generally travel different distances from the two slits (Fig. 27–54).

Let a line a–a' be drawn (Fig. 27–55) such that a–a'–P is an isoceles triangle. Then the distance δ is the "path difference" of the two rays. Let the slit separation d be very small compared with the distance D to the screen. Then the triangle a–a'–b is nearly a right triangle, and we write

$$\delta \simeq d \sin \theta. \qquad (27\text{–}73)$$

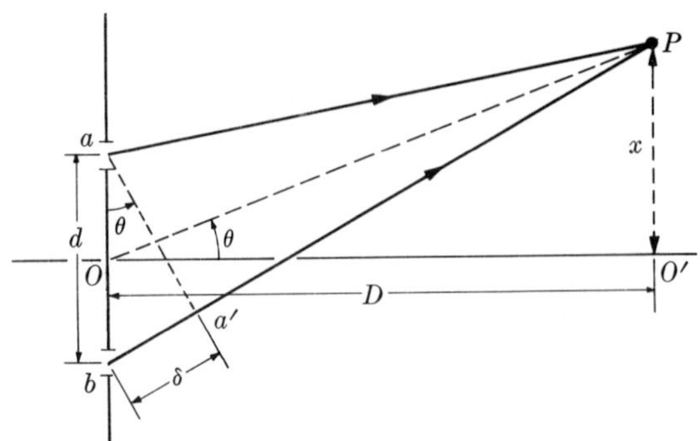

FIG. 27–55. The path difference between rays traveling to P is δ.

This is an expression for the path difference in terms of the angle θ, shown in the diagram, where θ is the angle between OP and OO' (Fig. 27–55). Whether there will be reinforcement between the two rays, or cancellation, at P depends on the value of δ. If the path difference is

$$\delta = n\lambda, \qquad (27\text{–}74)$$

where $n = 0, 1, 2, 3, \cdots$, δ is equal to an integral number of wavelengths, and there is *constructive* interference between the rays. The light intensity is a maximum when δ has these prescribed values, and the series of angles corresponding to constructive interference is given by the equation

$$n\lambda = d \sin \theta \qquad (n = 0, 1, 2, 3 \cdots). \qquad (27\text{–}75)$$

When the path difference δ has the values

$$\delta = \frac{\lambda}{2}, \frac{3\lambda}{2}, \frac{5\lambda}{2}$$

or

$$\delta = \frac{(2n+1)}{2}\lambda \qquad (n = 0, 1, 2, 3 \cdots), \qquad (27\text{–}76)$$

there is cancellation, and the light intensity is minimum. Since the fractional difference between light paths is very small ($\delta \lll D$) the amplitudes of the waves arriving at P are nearly equal, so that the minimum intensity is nearly zero, i.e. darkness.

The illumination of the screen beyond the two slits is then a pattern of alternating light and dark strips. These are called "fringes" or a "fringe pattern." The spacing of the light or dark fringes on the screen can be easily computed. Let x be the distance measured along the screen from the center of the screen O' to point P, as in Fig. 27–55. In terms of the angle θ,

$$x = D \tan \theta. \qquad (27\text{–}77)$$

For small angles, we may replace $\tan \theta$ in Eq. (27–77) by θ, and $\sin \theta$ in Eq. (27–75) by θ. Then the coordinate of the bright fringes is

$$x = \frac{Dn\lambda}{d} \qquad (n = 0, 1, 2, 3 \cdots). \qquad (27\text{–}78)$$

The fringes are equally spaced, so long as θ is small compared with unity. The distance between adjacent bright fringes is

$$\Delta x = \frac{D\lambda}{d}. \qquad (27\text{–}79)$$

Therefore, the result of interference would be an intensity pattern, as shown in Fig. 27–56. It must be remembered that the heights of the maxima will be affected by the diffraction patterns of the individual slits.

The wavelength of the light can be determined from measurements of D, x, and d. If white light is used, there will be a pattern of fringes for each color, with spacing proportional to λ for each

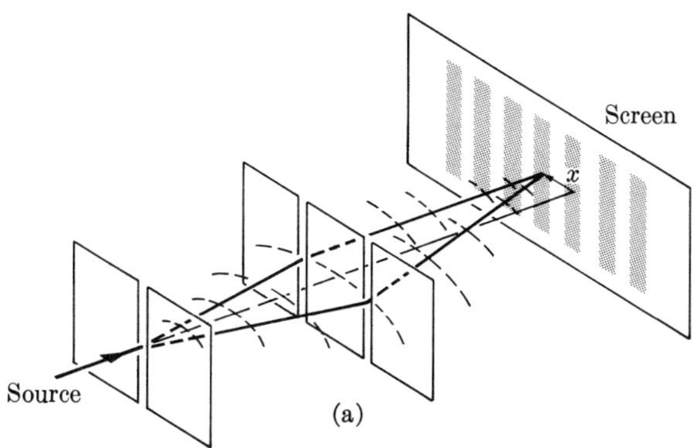

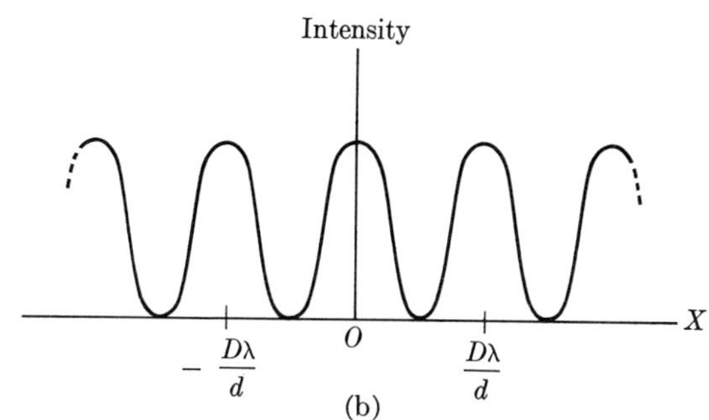

FIG. 27–56. (a) Double-slit interference pattern. (b) Graph of intensity versus x.

color. The overlapping fringe patterns will give rise to bands of various colors.

We now consider a *single* slit diffraction pattern quantitatively. The results will show how the interference pattern of Fig. 27–56 is to be modified in order to give a quantitative account of the heights of the intensity maxima. More importantly, the results will give an indication of the modifications to be made in our ideas of image formation by lenses and mirrors. *Every* portion of the wave front at a single slit opening sends its ray to a point P, as in Fig. 27–57. There is a gradual change in path difference from point to point on the wave front. The total illumination at P is found by summing the contributions from all portions of the wave front. For the purpose of this calculation, we require a quantitative formulation of Huygens' principle. This formulation can serve to illustrate the formal connection between the Huygens' construction and the wave theory which was advanced in the preceding chapter.

In our analysis of the double slit, the source and the image screen were both at finite distances from the double slits. As a result, the geometry was complicated and approximations were made that could have been avoided with a slightly different arrangement, namely, with the source and image screen at infinity. In practice, the same result can be obtained with the aid of lenses, as in Fig. 27–58. If the source is placed at the principal focus of lens 1, the light striking the slit will be a series of nearly plane parallel fronts, just as if the source had been at infinity and no lens were present. Similarly, the lens at 2 focuses plane waves into the plane of its principal focus, thereby giving the same effect as if there were no lens and the screen were at infinity,

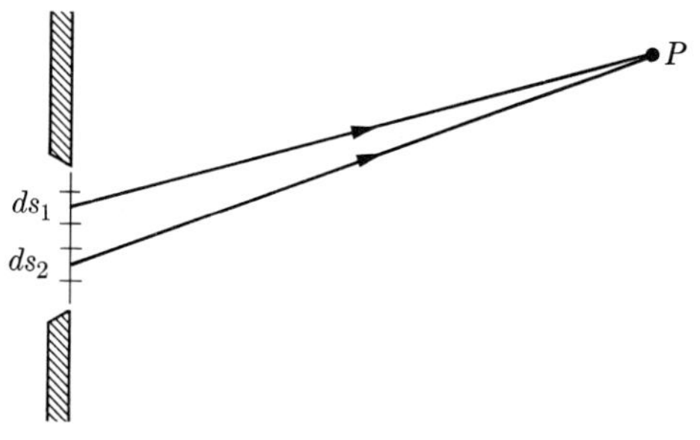

FIG. 27–57. Rays from elements of area ds_1 and ds_2 are superimposed at point P.

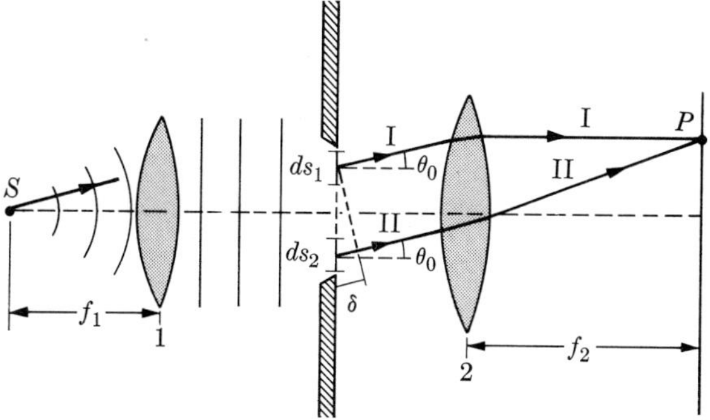

FIG. 27–58. Plane waves are incident on a single slit. The optical path difference between rays I and II is δ.

insofar as the interference effects are concerned. Since the rays that are superimposed at P left the single slit opening in the same direction, the geometry of the analysis is simplified. Diffraction effects for parallel plane waves are called Fraunhofer diffraction, while those for diverging and converging waves are called Fresnel diffraction.

In our treatment of diffraction, we shall take up only Fraunhofer diffraction because of the relative simplicity of the analysis. First of all, it should be remembered that there is no difference in phase between parts of a wave during its passage from an object point to an image point, as defined in geometrical optics. For example, in Fig. 27-59 the portions of the wave designated I, II, and III contain the same number of wavelengths between S and P_0, although the geometrical path lengths are quite different. The explanation of the equivalence, as measured in wavelengths, is that the wavelength in glass is less than in air and therefore the shorter geometrical path of II is compensated for by the relatively longer path of II in the glass. We say that the total *optical* paths are the same for all parts of the wave in its passage from S to P_0.

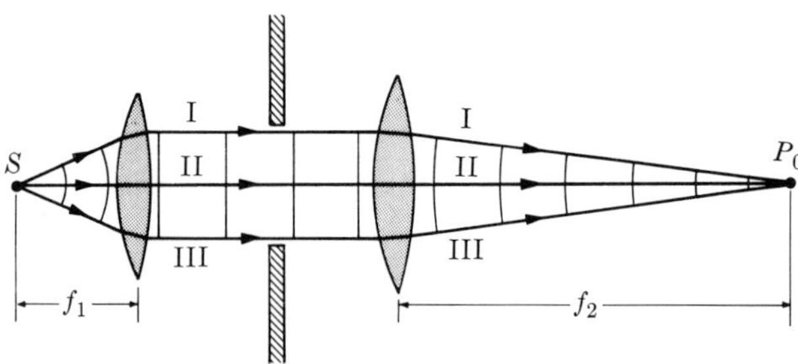

FIG. 27-59. The formation of an image by ideal lenses results in additive interference by the rays converging on the axis at P_0.

If we now consider a point P, as in Fig. 27-58, that is *not* a geometrical image of S, we see that the portions of the wave labeled I, II, and III cannot have the same optical path length from S to P. However, the departures from equality of optical path occur in the wedge-shaped region of base δ near the slit (Fig. 27-58). For example, the difference in the total optical paths from S to P for the two portions of waves I and II is just δ. Consequently, in Fraunhofer diffraction, it is necessary only to examine the region near the diffracting aperture or slit when evaluating path differences.

Finally, we have come to the question of the intensity distribution on the screen as we shift our attention from point P_0 (where all portions of the wave arrive in the same phase) to point P (where they cannot arrive in phase under any circumstances). The general method for finding the intensity as a function of the position of P, or better, as a function of the angle θ_0 to the point P (Fig. 27-58) is to integrate over the contributions from each element of area of the wave front at the slit (Huygens' principle).

A special formulation of the integral will first be used in order to obtain the positions of the minima of intensity. For this purpose, two elements of area, ds_1 and ds_2, are chosen with a separation $w/2$, where w is the slit width (Fig. 27-60). The angle θ is now chosen so that the path difference between rays I and II is $\lambda/2$, as shown. The result of superposition of these two contributions will be cancellation. The process

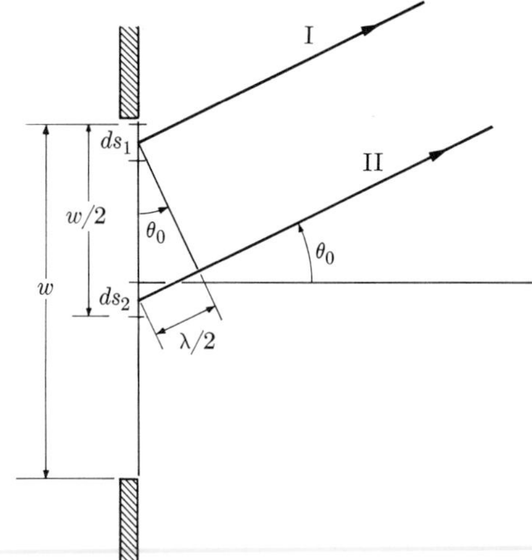

FIG. 27-60. Superposition of rays from elements of area in a single slit that are separated by half the slit width. At an angle θ_0 the path difference is $\lambda/2$, and the wavelets cancel.

of integration over the entire slit width now amounts to considering paired areas, ds_1 and ds_2, always separated by $w/2$, as the integration is carried down the width of the slit. The result of the integration is, of course, zero intensity at P. Thus the angle for the first minimum of intensity is given by

$$\sin \theta_0 = \frac{\lambda}{w} \cdot \tag{27–80}$$

It is easy to see that a similar argument can be carried out for any angle given by

$$\sin \theta_0 = n \frac{\lambda}{w}, \tag{27–81}$$

where n is an integer. Thus, Eq. (27–81) gives the angles for minimum intensity. It is interesting to note that width of the central maximum is twice that of the other maxima.

Approximate positions of the maxima can be obtained in a similar manner, as follows. If angle θ_m is chosen, as in Fig. 27–61, the contributions by ds_1 and ds_2 will again cancel, because their phase difference is $\lambda/2$. But as the integration is carried over the slit, only the upper two-thirds of the slit are covered by paired-off elements of area. The bottom third consists of area elements that have a *maximum* path difference of $\lambda/2$, or an average of $\lambda/4$. Therefore, the angle given by

$$\sin \theta = \frac{3}{2} \frac{\lambda}{w}, \tag{27–82}$$

or more generally,

$$\sin \theta = \frac{2n+1}{2} \frac{\lambda}{w}, \tag{27–83}$$

might be expected to correspond to maxima. The above is only an approximation, since we have failed to take into account the variation of intensity with angle θ_0 resulting from the variation in the area of the slit, as seen from the angle θ_0. This effect will be taken into account in the more accurate analysis of the next section. The heights of the secondary maxima relative to the central maximum can be estimated from the size of the noncanceling areas of Huygens' construction and the average phase difference of 45° among the contributions from the noncanceling region. The latter factor will be about 0.8 if we simply add two amplitude vectors at 45° and square the result to obtain relative intensity. The former factor is $\frac{1}{3}$, $\frac{1}{5}$, etc., for succeeding maxima. As a result, we estimate 0.28, 0.16, etc., for the intensities of the auxiliary maxima compared with the central maximum. A graph is given in Fig. 27–62.

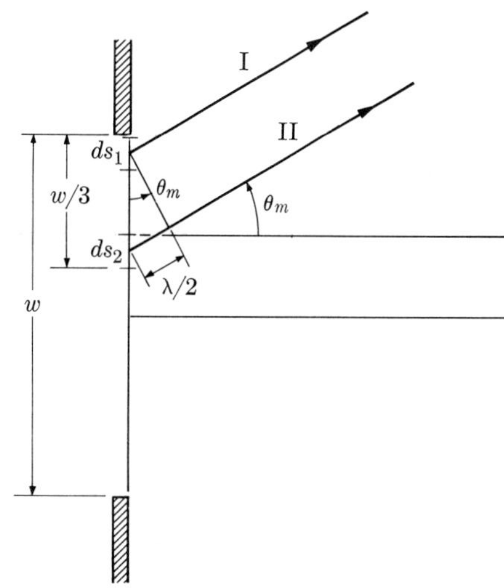

Fig. 27–61. Similar to Fig. 27–60 except that the elements of area are chosen with a separation of one-third the slit width. The angle θ_m for path difference $\lambda/2$ is now greater than θ_0.

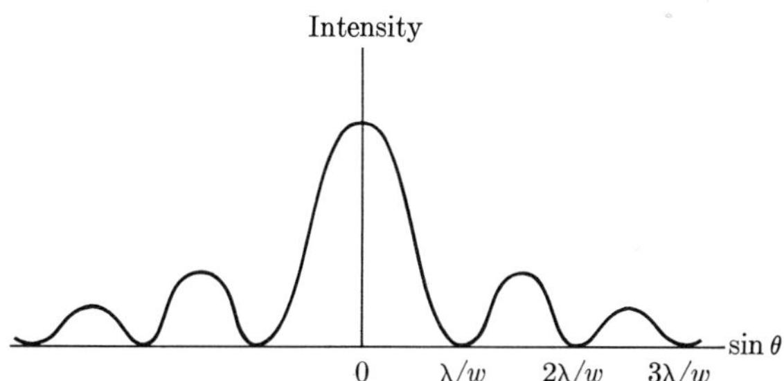

Fig. 27–62. Graph of intensity versus $\sin \theta$ for a single-slit diffraction pattern.

It should *not* be presumed that the wave elements add or cancel in just the order given above. The result of superposition is independent of the order in which the summations are made, and hence we were justified in the arbitrary and artificial choice of the above order of summation.

27–11 DETAILED ANALYSIS OF SINGLE-SLIT DIFFRACTION

The complete intensity distribution will now be found by integration over the single slit for *any* angle θ_0. A ray r_0 emerges from the center of the wave front at O and at an angle θ_0, as in Fig. 27–63. It strikes the screen at a point P. The ray from some element ds on the wave front, at a distance s measured along the front from O to the element, is to be considered. The particular ray that will arrive at P is the ray r, parallel to the central ray. Therefore, its angle relative to the normal to the wave front is also θ_0. It must, however, travel an extra path distance, shown as δ in the diagram. The path difference is given by the relationship,

$$\delta = s \sin \theta_0. \tag{27–84}$$

By Huygens' construction, each point on a wave front is to be considered a source of secondary waves. We write the displacement of the wave emitted by a portion of the wave front ds in the form

$$dy(r, t) = A\, ds \sin\left[2\pi\left(\frac{t}{T} - \frac{r}{\lambda}\right)\right], \tag{27–85}$$

where $A\,ds$ is the amplitude factor, that is, A is a measure of the amplitude of vibration contributed by a unit width of the wave front. The factor ds denotes that the amplitude of vibration is proportional to the width of the element of the wave front being considered. In the formulation of this amplitude expression, there are two factors which have been ignored. Generally, for a line source the amplitude of vibration diminishes as $1/\sqrt{r}$ where r is the distance from the point source. Since r varies so little, in terms of percentage, from point to point on the wave front, we assume it to be constant. For example, r may

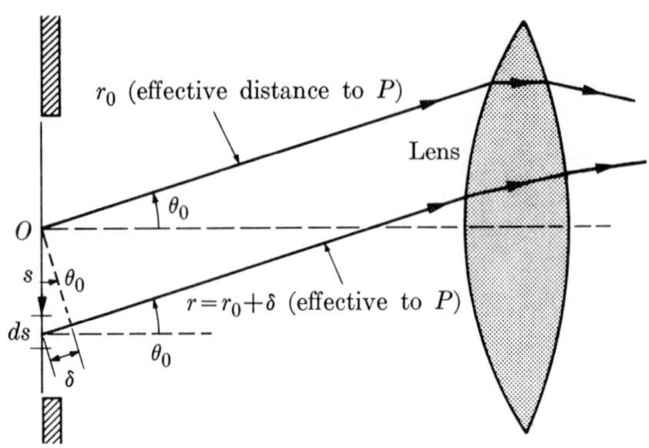

Fig. 27–63. Quantities to be used in the detailed analysis of single-slit diffraction.

be 10 cm while δ is equal to, at most, a few wavelengths of visible light. However—and this is vital to all such calculations as these—the whole interference effect which we are considering depends on such tiny variations in the term r that appears in the *argument of the sine function.* A *change* in r by one wavelength in the sine argument causes the function to oscillate through the whole range from plus 1 to minus 1. But a change of r by one wavelength affects the amplitude of the contribution by ds hardly at all and is therefore neglected. Another factor that is neglected, since it is usually small, is the "inclination factor." It can be shown that the amount of light emitted by a portion of a wave front depends on the angle of emission θ_0. This factor is proportional to the width of the wave front projected on the plane normal to the ray. Thus the amplitude of vibration is proportional to $\cos\theta$. (This factor can easily be included but is ignored here since we consider the case where θ is small compared with unity, so that $\cos\theta$ is nearly constant and unity.)

Returning, then, to the approximate wave expression in Eq. (27–85), we assume that the entire wave front is divided into strips of width ds. The expression for the central portion of the wave front is

$$dy(r_0, t) = A\, ds \sin\left[2\pi\left(\frac{t}{T} - \frac{r_0}{\lambda}\right)\right], \tag{27–86}$$

and for any portion

$$dy(r, t) = A\,ds \sin\left[2\pi\left(\frac{t}{T} - \frac{r}{\lambda}\right)\right], \tag{27–87}$$

where

$$r = r_0 + \delta = r_0 + s \sin\theta_0. \tag{27–88}$$

Therefore Eq. (27–87) can be written

$$dy(r, t) = A\,ds \sin 2\pi\left(\frac{t}{T} - \frac{r_0}{\lambda} - \frac{s\sin\theta_0}{\lambda}\right). \tag{27–89}$$

In the process of summation, a variation occurs only in the last term in parentheses, all other parts of the expression being the same for all portions of the wave front. We make a substitution, then, which emphasizes this point. Let the angle α be chosen so that

$$\alpha = 2\pi\left(\frac{t}{T} - \frac{r_0}{\lambda}\right), \tag{27–90}$$

where, in the integration, α is a constant. Let the angle β be chosen so that

$$\beta = \frac{2\pi s \sin\theta_0}{\lambda}, \tag{27–91}$$

where β will be variable in the integration. Equation (27–89) is written, using these substitutions, and becomes

$$dy = A\,ds \sin(\alpha - \beta). \tag{27–92}$$

The total amplitude at P is found by integration of dy over the width of the slit:

$$y = A\int_{-w/2}^{w/2} ds \sin(\alpha - \beta). \tag{27–93}$$

The integrand can be rewritten by trigonometric identity, giving

$$y = A\int_{-w/2}^{w/2} ds(\sin\alpha\cos\beta - \cos\alpha\sin\beta) \tag{27–94}$$

or

$$y = A\sin\alpha\int_{-w/2}^{w/2} ds\cos\beta - A\cos\alpha\int_{-w/2}^{w/2} ds\sin\beta. \tag{27–95}$$

From the definition of β, it can be seen that s is directly proportional to β, and hence

$$ds = K\,d\beta, \tag{27–96}$$

where K is a constant given by

$$K = \frac{s}{\beta} = \frac{\lambda}{2\pi\sin\theta_0}. \tag{27–97}$$

Thus we have

$$y = KA\sin\alpha\int_{-\pi w\sin\theta_0/\lambda}^{+\pi w\sin\theta_0/\lambda} \cos\beta\,d\beta - KA\cos\alpha\int_{-\pi w\sin\theta_0/\lambda}^{+\pi w\sin\theta_0/\lambda} \sin\beta\,d\beta. \tag{27–98}$$

The limits of integration have been expressed in terms of the variable β, according to

$$s = +\frac{w}{2}, \qquad \beta = +\frac{\pi w\sin\theta_0}{\lambda},$$
$$s = -\frac{w}{2}, \qquad \beta = -\frac{\pi w\sin\theta_0}{\lambda}. \tag{27–99}$$

Upon integration and substitution of limits, we have the following expression [noting that there is no contribution from the second integral in Eq. (27–98)]:

$$y = \frac{Aw\sin\alpha\sin\dfrac{\pi w\sin\theta_0}{\lambda}}{\dfrac{\pi w\sin\theta_0}{\lambda}}$$

or we have

$$y = \frac{Aw\sin\left(\dfrac{\pi w\sin\theta_0}{\lambda}\right)}{\dfrac{w\sin\theta_0}{\lambda}}\sin 2\pi\left(\frac{t}{T} - \frac{r_0}{\lambda}\right). \tag{27–100}$$

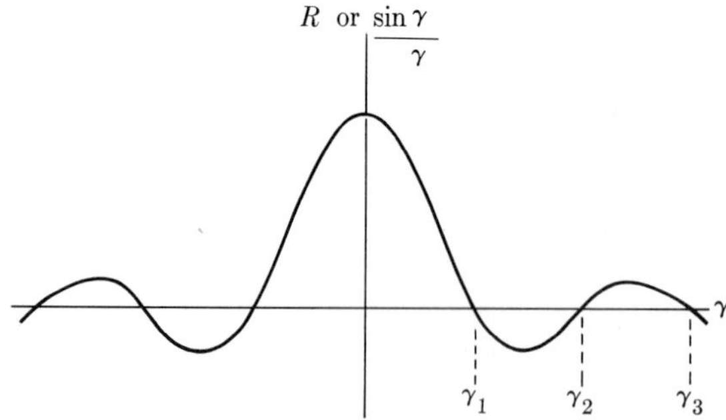

Fig. 27-64. The function $\sin\gamma/\gamma$ that occurs in the single-slit diffraction analysis.

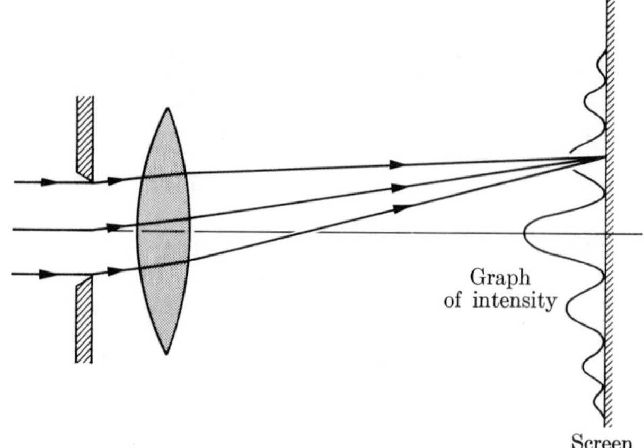

Fig. 27-65. Illustration of single-slit diffraction.

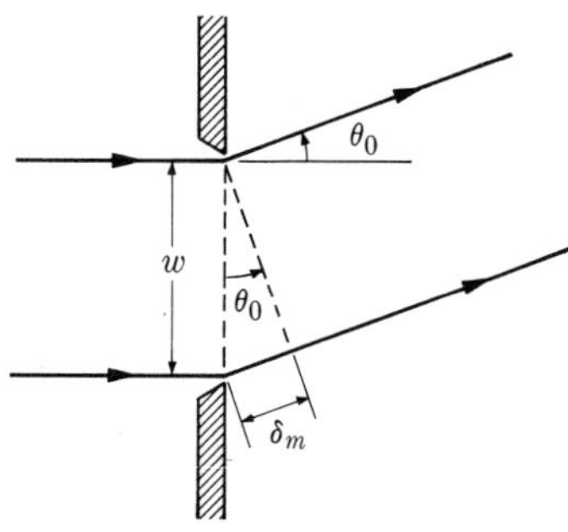

Fig. 27-66. The path difference δ_m for minimum intensity.

This is the form of a periodic wave arriving at the screen, and it is similar to the wave at the slit but of modified amplitude. The amplitude depends on the angle θ_0 of emission toward the screen. We can write the amplitude as R such that at the screen

$$y = R \sin 2\pi\left(\frac{t}{T} - \frac{r_0}{\lambda}\right), \quad (27\text{-}101)$$

where R is of the form

$$R = \frac{wA \sin \gamma}{\gamma}. \quad (27\text{-}102)$$

The function $\sin\gamma/\gamma$ is shown in the graph of Fig. 27-64. It is an oscillating function of diminishing amplitude for increasing value of γ. It is zero at the successive points $\gamma_1, \gamma_2, \gamma_3$, etc., and such points represent darkness in the diffraction pattern. The fact that R reverses sign is of no significance to the pattern. The sign reversal denotes a reversal in the phase of vibration, but the illumination depends on the amplitude squared:

$$I \sim R^2 = w^2A^2\left(\frac{\sin\gamma}{\gamma}\right)^2, \quad (27\text{-}103)$$

which is always positive. A graph is shown in Fig. 27-65. We now wish to relate the maxima and minima (zero) of the light intensity in the diffraction pattern to the path differences in the diffracted beam of light. For this purpose we denote as δ_m the path difference between the *extreme* rays passing through the slit shown in Fig. 27-66. Of course, δ for all rays varies between 0 and δ_m.

Generally, for dark fringes we have the condition $\sin\gamma = 0$ (except for $\gamma = 0$) where

$$\gamma = \pi, 2\pi, 3\pi, \cdots$$

or

$$\gamma = n\pi (n = 1, 2, 3, 4, \cdots)(n \neq 0). \quad (27\text{-}104)$$

Note that in the general series there is an important exception. When $\gamma = 0$, then $\sin\gamma/\gamma$ is an indeterminant form. The ratio approaches the limiting value of unity:

$$\lim_{\gamma\to 0} \frac{\sin\gamma}{\gamma} = 1.$$

Far from being zero, this is the maximum value of the function for any γ and corresponds to the central *bright* fringe in the pattern. With this exception, however, the remainder of the series, when n has integral values, accounts for all the *dark* fringes in the pattern. Since

$$\gamma = \frac{\pi w \sin \theta_0}{\lambda}, \qquad (27\text{–}105)$$

the condition for darkness is that

$$\sin \theta_0 = \frac{n\lambda}{w}, \qquad (27\text{–}106)$$

the same as the result obtained by the simplified argument in Section 27–9. Also, since

$$\delta_m = w \sin \theta_0, \qquad (27\text{–}107)$$

we have, for minimum intensity,

$$\delta_m = n\lambda, \qquad (27\text{–}108)$$

the condition that the extreme path difference is equal to an integral number of wavelengths. (In the double slit experiment, this was the condition for *maximum* intensity.)

The positions of the intensity maxima are found by obtaining the values of γ in Eq. (27–102) that maximize the value of the amplitude R. This is left as one of the exercises in the Problems.

The single slit diffraction effect which has been explored in this section demonstrates, quantitatively, an important principle of wave motion. This is that there is a definite limit to the fineness to which we can restrict a beam of light (or any wave motion) by means of slits. When a parallel beam is restricted by a "wide" slit, a shadow is formed and the beam which arrives at the screen is of the shape and about the same size as the slit. For large values of w, the diffraction "broadening" of the beam in Fig. 27–67 may be neglected. When w is halved, the size of the beam is approximately halved. However, as $w \to 0$, the diffraction broadening becomes very important, so that beyond a certain point a further narrowing of the slit effects an *increase* in the size of the emergent beam, as in Fig. 27–68. The "width" of the emergent beam is measured as the distance from the center to the first minimum, then

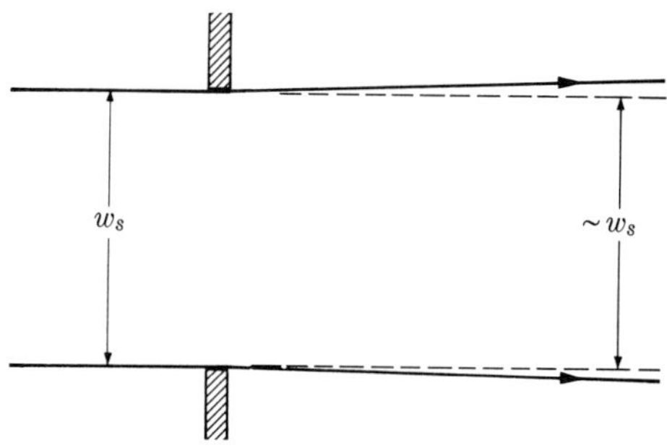

Fig. 27–67. The width of a beam of light after passing through an opening of width $w \gg \lambda$.

$$w_b = D \tan\left(\sin^{-1} \frac{\lambda}{w_s}\right); \qquad (27\text{–}109)$$

that is, w_b increases as w_s decreases.

Note that lenses have been omitted from Figs. 27–67 and 27–68, but that we still assume Fraunhofer diffraction. This is possible if we assume that the screen and the source are at infinite distances from the slit, i.e., at distances that are very much greater than w_s.

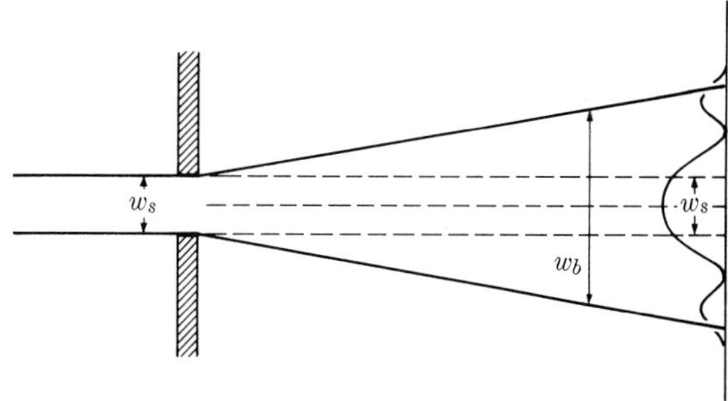

Fig. 27–68. The "width" of a beam of light after passing through an opening of width comparable with the wavelength of light.

27–12 DOUBLE-SLIT DIFFRACTION

In the early part of Section 27–10, double-slit interferences were treated independently of diffraction by simply ignoring the quantitative

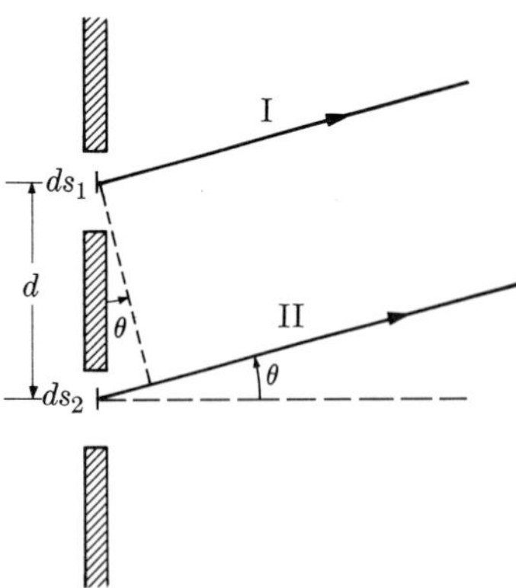

FIG. 27-69. Pairing of light from elements of area in different slits.

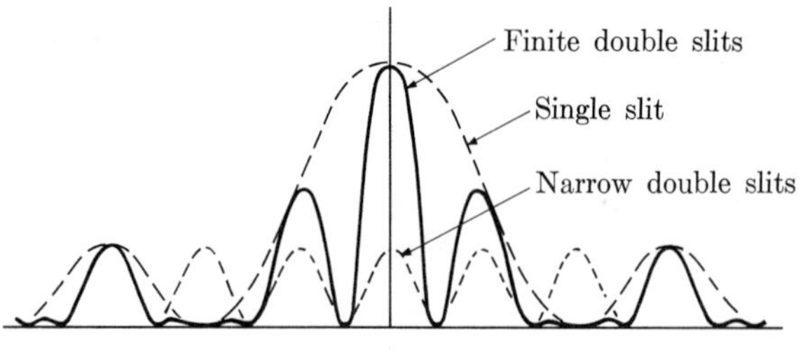

FIG. 27-70. Graphs showing the combined effect of single-slit and double-slit diffraction. The intensity must be zero where either effect goes to zero.

effects of the finite slit widths. In general, it is necessary to integrate the contributions of Huygens' wavelets (as in the preceding section), carrying out the integration over both slits. However, in the case of Fraunhofer diffraction, the following argument can be made: If rays I and II from corresponding parts of the two slits (Fig. 27-69) are superimposed, the resulting interference between these two rays is the same as in our earlier treatment of double-slit interference; that is, there will be minima at angles given by

$$\sin \theta = \frac{n+1}{2} \left(\frac{\lambda}{d}\right) \cdot \qquad (27\text{-}110)$$

All elements from similarly corresponding areas in the two slits can be paired off with this same result. On the other hand, for $\sin \theta = n\lambda/d$, there will be maxima, so far as superposition of the paired-off elements is concerned.

Now the question of the effect of the single slit diffraction can be taken into account by saying that the amplitude from the element ds_1(or ds_2), taken individually, is just the fraction ds_1/w (or ds_2/w) of the total amplitude from a single slit at angle θ, and is therefore determined by the single-slit diffraction. Consequently, the resultant amplitude in direction θ is the single-slit amplitude at angle θ times the double-slit amplitude at angle θ. The result can be described by saying that the double-slit interference pattern of Fig. 27-56 is modulated by the single-slit diffraction pattern of Fig. 27-62. The result is depicted in Fig. 27-70, where the dashed lines are the two separate patterns and the solid line is the resultant.

27-13 DIFFRACTION BY CIRCULAR APERTURES: IMAGES

Slit-shaped openings have been chosen above because of the simplicity of the analysis. When circular openings are considered, the integration of the contributions by the elements of area within the circle is more difficult than for a slit. Only the results will be given. The diffraction pattern has circular symmetry with a central maximum, as expected from the symmetry. The interference gives zero intensity at an angle given by

$$\sin \theta_m = 1.22 \frac{\lambda}{D}, \qquad (27\text{-}111)$$

where D is the diameter of the circular aperture. The width of the central maximum is seen to be greater than for a slit of width D. The above result is for Fraunhofer diffraction, but it is a good approximation for Fresnel diffraction as well.

Even if no screen with an aperture limits the lateral dimensions of a light wave, there is always a limitation imposed when an optical device, such as a lens or mirror, is used. For example, if a long cylindrical lens is used to form an image of a distant line source, the "image" is the diffraction pattern of a single slit whose width equals the lens width.

When an ordinary spherical lens (with circular outline) forms an image of a point object, the image is the diffraction pattern of a circular aperture of diameter equal to that of the lens. The diameter of the central disk of the diffraction pattern is given implicitly by Eq. (27–111). For example, if a lens forms an image of a distant point object, the image will be formed at the principal focal plane, and the radius of the central disk of the diffraction pattern (Fig. 27–71) will be approximately

$$r \simeq \theta_m f \simeq 1.22\,\frac{\lambda f}{D}, \qquad (27\text{–}112)$$

where θ_m has been obtained from Eq. (27–111).

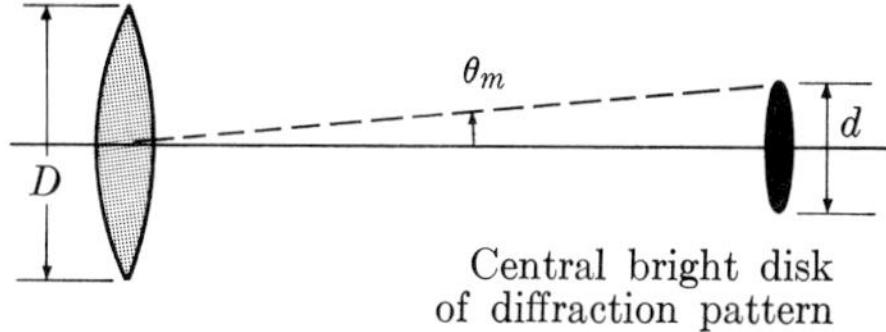

Fig. 27–71. Illustration of the central disk of the diffraction pattern due to limitation of a wave front to a circular portion selected by a lens.

From the above, we see that even a perfect lens cannot form a point image (unless the lens is infinitely large). In practice, most lenses are "imperfect," even though carefully made. Their surfaces are spherical and we have seen early in the chapter that such a lens forms approximately a point image only for small angles (neglecting diffraction). This lens limitation is called *spherical aberration*. Thus, two factors contribute to the finite size of the image of a point. For large lens diameter (large angles), spherical aberration is the predominant factor, but when the diameter of the lens is sufficiently reduced by a screen, diffraction predominates.

Astronomical telescope lenses are custom-shaped to parabolic surfaces, a form that eliminates the spherical aberration. Such a lens can form an exceedingly small image of a star, since the diffraction can be made very small by making the diameter of the lens sufficiently large. The principal reason for concern about the size of optical images is that the ability of optical instruments to bring out detail is limited by the smallest image that can be formed of a single *point* object. We will return to this question after studying the geometrical optics of typical instruments in the next chapter.

27–14 SUMMARY

Maxwell's equations in the integral form, developed in Chapter 25, are transformed into differential form for a special case of electric and magnetic fields that vary with only the x-coordinate. The resulting equations are

$$\frac{\partial E}{\partial x} = -\frac{\partial B}{\partial t} \qquad \frac{\partial B}{\partial x} = -\epsilon_0\mu_0\,\frac{\partial E}{\partial t}.$$

By differentiating and combining the two equations, we obtain

$$\frac{\partial^2 E}{\partial x^2} = \epsilon_0\mu_0\,\frac{\partial^2 E}{\partial t^2} \qquad \frac{\partial^2 B}{\partial x^2} = \epsilon_0\mu_0\,\frac{\partial^2 B}{\partial t^2},$$

which have the form of wave equations in E and in B. The velocity of the waves is

$$c = \frac{1}{\sqrt{\epsilon_0\mu_0}} = 3.00 \times 10^8\ \text{m/sec},$$

which is the speed of light found in experimental measurements. The sinusoidal wave solutions,

$$E = E_m \sin(Kx - \omega t) \qquad B = B_m \sin(Kx - \omega t),$$

are the most important, just as with other wave motions.

The ratio of the fields is

$$\frac{E}{B} = c$$

at any point in space. The rate of energy flow

is described by the Poynting vector

$$\mathbf{S} = \frac{1}{\mu_0} \mathbf{E} \times \mathbf{B}.$$

The origin of electromagnetic waves is accelerated charge. Equations are given for the electric field component of the wave originating from an electric oscillating dipole,

$$E_\phi = \frac{\pi q d}{\epsilon_0 c^2} \frac{f^2 \sin\phi}{r} \cos\left[2\pi f\left(\frac{r}{c} - t\right)\right],$$

and from a single accelerated charge

$$E = \frac{q}{4\pi\epsilon_0 c^2} \frac{1}{r} (a \sin\theta)_{t-r/c}.$$

The intensity of the radiation from the dipole is

$$I = \frac{\pi^2 q^2 d^2}{2\epsilon_0 c^3} \frac{f^4 \sin^2\phi}{r^2}.$$

The experimental verification of the above predictions of Maxwell was made by Hertz with a high-frequency oscillating current.

Since the propagation phenomena of light waves are explained by their electromagnetic wave nature, evidence was sought for the origin of light in accelerated charges. The experimental results on the effect of magnetic fields on light sources (Zeeman effect) are found to give some support to the idea of oscillating electrons as the source of light, i.e., some of the features of the frequency shifts and polarization lend support to the idea.

The pressure of electromagnetic waves on charges in a metal is analyzed and leads to the expression for the momentum,

$$p = \frac{W}{c},$$

in terms of the energy W and velocity c.

An appraisal is given of the success and failure of the classical theory of electromagnetic radiation in accounting for the observations of the behavior of light.

Three-dimensional wave propagation is introduced with a qualitative description of wave fronts and rays. The intensity of waves from a point source is found to be

$$I = \frac{dP}{d\Omega}(\theta, \phi) \frac{1}{r^2}.$$

Huygens' principle is invoked as an empirical rule for predicting the propagation of waves. It permits the construction of a new wave front by considering each point on an existing wave front as a point source of a new wave. The new wave front is then the envelope of the waves. The principle is derivable from electromagnetic theory.

The law of reflection, $i = r$, and the law of refraction (Snell's law),

$$\frac{\sin i}{\sin r} = n,$$

are derived for plane waves. The index of refraction n for a variety of transparent materials is given. It is found to depend on the wavelength of the light as well as on the refracting material. Curves for the relative intensity of the refracted and the reflected light as a function of angle of incidence are given for $n = 1.5$.

A description is given of the toothed wheel method for measurement of the velocity of light. The result agrees with the prediction of Maxwell's electromagnetic theory; that is, $c = 3.00 \times 10^8$ m/sec.

The idea of formation of an image is introduced by the example of a baffle with a small hole, the pinhole camera effect. A larger aperture image-forming device is a lens. The effect of a lens with spherical surfaces on an incident spherical wave is analyzed. For small angles and thin lenses, it is found that the outgoing wave is spherical and converges at a point I that is a distance q from the lens, given by

$$\frac{1}{q} + \frac{1}{p} = (n - 1)\left(\frac{1}{r_1} + \frac{1}{r_2}\right),$$

where r_1 and r_2 are the radii of the lens surfaces, n is the index of refraction, and p is the distance of the point source from the lens. The combination of constants on the right is characteristic of the lens alone and is called the focal length f of the lens. We then have

$$\frac{1}{q} + \frac{1}{p} = \frac{1}{f}.$$

A discussion is given of the formation of images for various ranges of values of p and for both converging and diverging lenses. The idea of virtual images and virtual objects occurs and is explained. The formation of off-axis images of off-axis objects follows the same equation if the angles are small.

The effects of the dependence of f on the angle of the rays and on the wavelength of the light are called aberrations of the lens.

The interference effect from the superposition of waves results in standing wave patterns if the superimposed waves have a constant relative phase. In the case of light, the waves of constant relative phase can be obtained by the division of a wave from a single source or by stimulated emission from different sources. Waves from reflections at two nearly parallel surfaces give rise to interference bands that are colored for incident white light and are alternatingly dark and bright for incident monochromatic light. In addition to the phase difference due to difference in the path length traveled by the two waves, it is necessary to include possible phase changes upon reflection.

The interference of two waves originating from the same wave front and selected by two narrow slits results in alternating dark and bright bands if the light is monochromatic. The spacing of the bands is uniform and given by

$$\Delta x = D\,\frac{\lambda}{d},$$

where D is the screen distance and d is the double-slit separation.

The interference pattern resulting when a wave front is limited by a transmitting slit of width w that is not extremely many wavelengths in width consists of a central band flanked by side bands that are half the width of the central band. The angular half-width of the central band is given by

$$\sin\theta = \frac{\lambda}{w}.$$

The analysis is simplest for the case in which the wave fronts are plane before and after passing through the slit. The incident waves are made plane by placing a lens with the source at its focus in front of the slit. Emerging plane waves are effective if a lens is placed behind the slit and the pattern is viewed on a screen at the focal plane of the lens. A moderately accurate evaluation of the amplitude of the resulting wave motion as a function of angle is made. The intensity of the side bands decreases rapidly as we consider bands more and more distant from the central band.

The total effect of including the interference between two slits and the interference among elements of the waves from one slit is represented graphically.

The diffraction pattern produced when a circular disk (rather than a band) is selected from a wave front consists of a central disk of radius

$$r = 1.22\,\frac{\lambda f}{D}$$

for a lens of diameter D and focal length f, when the object is a distant point source. It is pointed out that the resolution of even an ideal lens is limited by the diffraction effect.

Problems

1. An electron is vibrating with SHM of amplitude A and frequency f (Fig. 27–72).

(a) At what point P is the maximum transverse electric field, due to radiation, of the same magnitude as the Coulomb field? Assume that $A \ll r$.

(b) What is the acceleration of the electron at the instant E is a maximum at P?

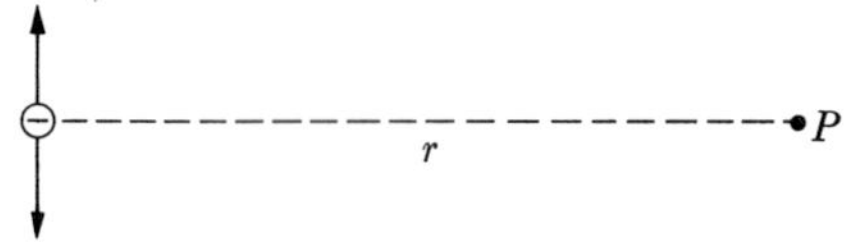

FIGURE 27–72

2. For radiation of wavelength 1/2 m, what should be the magnitude of LC in a circuit containing an inductance L and a capacitance C connected in parallel?

3. The yellow light from sodium has a wavelength of 5893 A. In a classical model the light might be due to an electron rotating or vibrating with the corresponding frequency.

(a) Assuming an electron rotating in a circle of radius r, find the *change* in frequency (if r is constant) for each direction of rotation when a magnetic field B is applied perpendicular to the plane of the circle.

(b) What would be the classical prediction for the effect on this light emitted by sodium atoms? (The observation agrees quite well with this prediction.)

4. A certain loudspeaker gives off 2 w of power in sound waves.

(a) Assuming that the intensity of 100 cps waves is uniform and concentrated in the forward hemisphere, find the intensity of the waves at a distance of 5 m.

(b) Assuming that the intensity of 5000 cps waves varies as $\cos\theta$ in the forward hemisphere, find the intensity of these waves as a function of θ at a distance of 5 m. The angle θ is the angle between the polar axis in the forward hemisphere and the direction in question.

5. (a) Use Huygens' method to show the reflection of a spherical wave from a plane boundary.

(b) Use the law of reflection to show the paths of several rays that emanate from a point source and strike a plane mirror. Where do the reflected rays appear to emanate from after striking the mirror?

6. How tall must a plane mirror be in order for a person to see his full length in the mirror? Make a diagram showing the paths of the pertinent light rays.

7. Use Huygens' method to show the refraction of a spherical wave emanating from a point source and striking the plane surface of water ($n = 1.33$). Repeat for the case in which the source is under water.

8. Make a diagram showing the path of a ray passing through a plane plate of refracting material. Prove that the ray has the same direction upon emergence that it had before entering. Find the amount of displacement of the ray as a function of angle of incidence, thickness of the slab, and its index of refraction.

9. Make a diagram of a vertical ray and one slanting ray from a point source under water. Find an expression for the apparent depth of the point below the surface. Repeat for an observer under water and a source above water.

10. Make a diagram showing the refraction of a slanting ray of light according to the Newtonian corpuscular theory and show that it requires an *increase* in velocity in the refracting medium if the tangential component of velocity remains constant.

11. A wave in a string of density 10 gm/m is incident on the boundary with a string of density 40 gm/m. Find the relative "index of refraction" of the strings.

12. A plane sound wave in air is incident on water. The speed in air is about 300 m/sec and in water about 1000 m/sec. Find the critical angle for the sound wave.

13. The index of refraction of air is proportional to its density. Show qualitatively what happens to plane waves moving initially in the direction shown in Fig. 27–73.

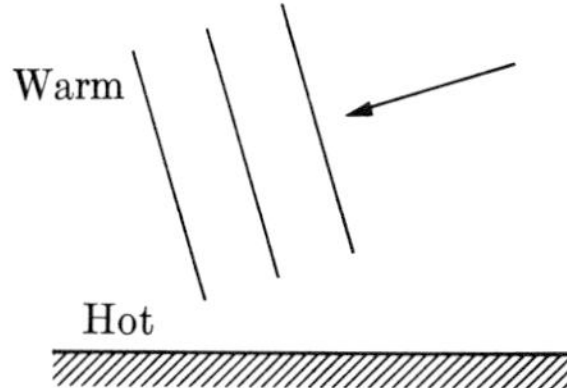

FIGURE 27–73

14. Show that the group velocity (Section 26–10) is given by (c = velocity in vacuum)

$$v_{gr} = c\frac{1}{n}\left(1 + \frac{\lambda}{n}\frac{dn}{d\lambda}\right),$$

where n is the refractive index. Find the group velocity in flint glass and in water for $\lambda = 5 \times 10^{-7}$ m (see Fig. 27–28 for n and n versus λ).

15. What percent of the light at normal incidence is reflected from glass of $n = 1.5$?

16. If a wheel of 20 teeth is to be used in the Fizeau method for measuring the velocity of light, and the mirror distance is 10 km, what must be the speed of the wheel for the first total extinction of the beam? What is the length of the light pulse?

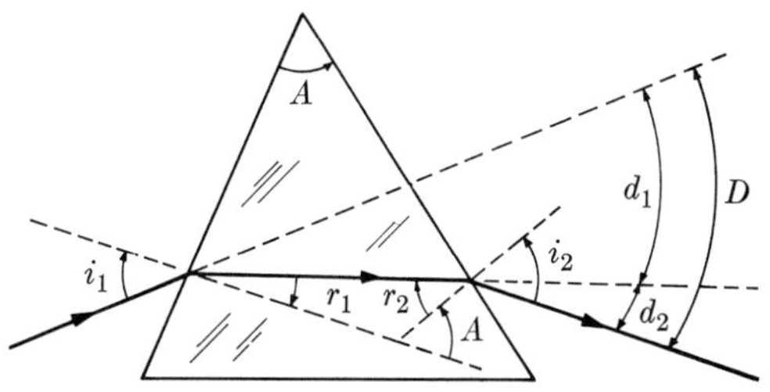

FIGURE 27–74

17. A ray of light is incident upon a prism (Fig. 27–74). The prism angle is A. The angle of incidence to the first surface is i_1 and the first angle of refraction is r_1. The ray of light is deviated at both surfaces —at the first by $d_1 = i_1 - r_1$, at the second by $d_2 = i_2 - r_2$. The total angle of deviation is $D = d_1 + d_2$.

(a) By application of Snell's law at the two surfaces, and by suitable algebraic reduction, prove that D can be expressed as

$$D = i_1 + i_2 - A,$$

or in terms of r_1 and A, as

$$D = \sin^{-1}(n \sin r_1) + \sin^{-1}[n \sin (A - r_1)] - A.$$

(b) Prove by the method of calculus that D has a minimum value, and that this value occurs for the symmetric case where $r_1 = r_2$ or $i_1 = i_2$ and therefore $D_m = 2i_1 - A$.

(c) Prove from the equation above that the small angle approximation expression (A, i, r are all small compared with unity) for D is

$$D = A(n - 1). \qquad (27\text{–}113)$$

18. White light is incident on a 30° flint glass prism at the angle of minimum deviation. Find the approximate angular separation of red and blue ($\lambda = 7 \times 10^{-7}$ and 5×10^{-7} m).

19. The radii of a double convex lens are 30 cm and 50 cm. If the lens is made of flint glass (see Fig. 27–28), find the focal points for light of wavelength 5×10^{-7} m and wavelength 7×10^{-7} m.

20. A lens of focal length 20 cm is placed 50 cm from an object.

(a) Find the image position.

(b) Repeat for an object distance of 15 cm.

(c) Repeat (a) and (b) for a lens of focal length —20 cm. Make ray diagrams for all cases.

21. An object and a screen are separated by 2 m. Find the positions of a lens of focal length 10 cm for the formation of an image of the object on the screen.

22. Prove analytically that the minimum distance between an object and its *real* image ($p + q$) occurs when $p = q = 2f$. What is the maximum distance? What is the minimum separation of an object and its virtual image?

23. The separation of two slits is 1 mm. They are illuminated by a point source 2 m away.

(a) What is the angular separation of the interference maxima for blue light of wavelength 5000 A (1 A = 10^{-10} m)?

(b) The double slit is held directly in front of an observer's eye. What is the apparent separation of the observed bands, if they are judged by the observer to be 2 m from his eye?

24. Make a graph of the amplitude versus angle for the Fraunhofer interference pattern of three equally spaced slits. Repeat for four slits.

25. Plane waves of wavelength 5000 A are incident on a single "slit" of width 10 cm.

(a) Make a graph of the amplitude pattern at the focal plane of a lens of focal length 50 cm that is placed just behind the slit.

(b) An observer holds the slit close to his eye and looks at a distant point source. What does he see?

26. Repeat Problem 25 for a slit of width 1 mm.

27. Light is diffracted in a double-slit diffraction experiment. The spacing of the slits is d and the width of each slit is w. It is found that the third ($n = 3$) bright fringe expected in the interference pattern is missing. There is darkness at that angle and it is suspected that this is due to the fact that this angle corresponds to the condition for zero intensity due to diffraction of either slit singly. What is the ratio of d to w that would make this so?

28. In the single-slit diffraction study, we obtained an equation for the illumination of the screen which gives the intensity as a function of the variable, γ:

$$R^2 = A^2\left(\frac{\sin\gamma}{\gamma}\right)^2.$$

The minima, and therefore the condition for dark fringes, were found to correspond to the zeros of $\sin\gamma$. For the maxima, it is *approximately* correct to say that $(\sin\gamma/\gamma)^2$ is maximum when $(\sin\gamma)^2$ itself is maximum; i.e., $\sin\gamma = \pm 1$. However, this condition, which is quite accurate for large γ, becomes quite inaccurate for small γ.

(a) Find the true positions of the maxima by differentiating $(\sin\gamma/\gamma)^2$. The result is a transcendental equation that you can solve graphically or numerically.

(b) Relate the values of $\gamma_{\max}$ to the values of δ_m for bright fringes.

29. There is a principle in optics that states that the course that a light ray will follow in going from point A to point B represents the *extreme* (*that is, greatest or least*) *optical path* between the two points. Optical path is, by definition, index of refraction n times distance. If n is variable, the element of optical path in terms of the local value of n is $n\,ds$. Then the full optical path is the line integral,

$$\int_A^B n\,ds.$$

The path for which this integral is a minimum is the geometric path of the ray. We address two simple problems.

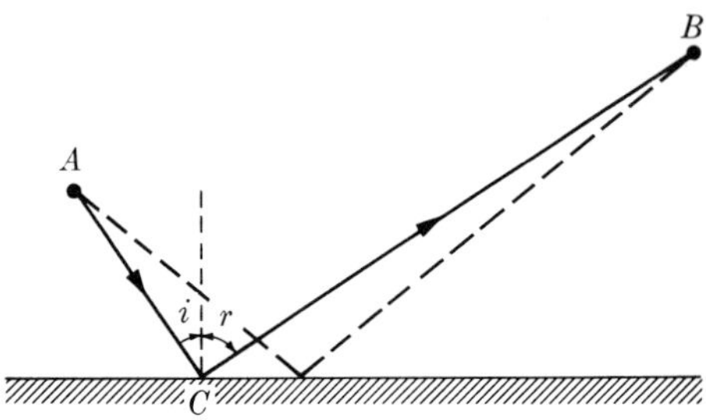

FIGURE 27–75

(a) In reflection by a plane surface, we join points A and B by broken straight rays which intersect at the reflecting surface (Fig. 27–75). Prove that the path ACB is minimum when $i = r$, the reflection law. (In this case n = constant, unity.)

(b) In refraction we join points A and B by broken straight rays which intersect at a point on the surface (Fig. 27–76). The optical path in the glass is $n(CB)$. The optical path in air is AC. Prove that $l = n(CB) + AC$ is a minimum when $\sin i/\sin r = n$.

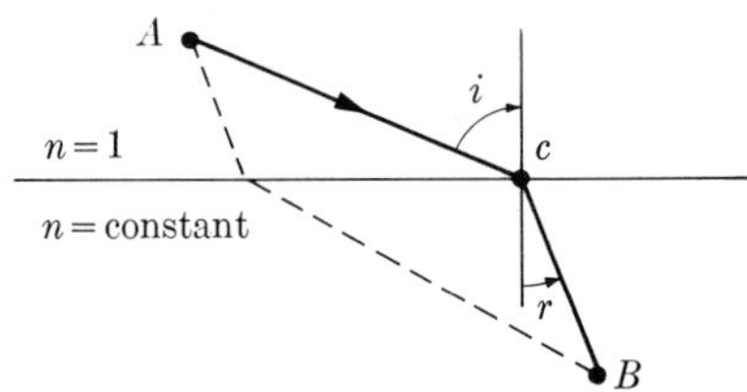

FIGURE 27–76

30. Consider a direction such that δ_m for a single slit is 2λ, as shown in Fig. 27–77. We know that this is a direction of minimum amplitude from the general equations. But suppose we divide the wave into halves and pair off rays such as a and b, which differ in path by one wavelength and therefore add constructively. We should therefore have a maximum. Find the fallacy in the argument.

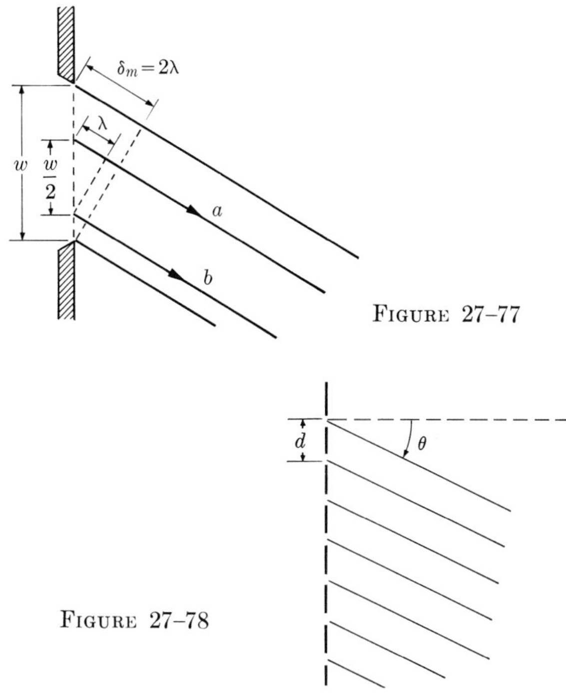

FIGURE 27–77

FIGURE 27–78

31. A diffraction grating consists of a large number of slits with uniform spacing d (Fig. 27–78).

(a) Show that interference maxima occur for

$$\sin\theta = n\,\frac{\lambda}{d}, \qquad (27\text{–}114)$$

where n is called the order of the spectrum.

(b) Find the angular separation of red and blue light (λ = 7000 A and 5000 A) in the second order for a grating with 4000 lines per cm.

32. Show that light of wavelength λ, which gives a maximum at an angle θ [given by Eq. (27–114) above] when passing through a grating, falls to its first minimum at angles differing from θ by

$$\pm\,\Delta\theta = \frac{\lambda}{Nd},$$

where N is the total number of slits. [*Hint:* Pair off rays coming from slits separated by $Nd/2$.]

33. Two synchronized sources of sound waves send out waves of equal intensity at a frequency of 680/sec. The sources are 0.75 m apart. The velocity of sound is 340 m/sec. Find positions of minimum intensity

(a) on a line that passes through the sources,

(b) in a plane that is the perpendicular bisector of the line between the sources,

(c) in a plane that contains the two sources.

(d) Is the intensity zero at any of the minima?

34. A thin soap film in air, with its plane vertical, appears red at its upper edge, indicating that blue light of wavelength about 5000 A suffers destructive interference. Find the minimum thickness of the top of the film, assuming that the index of refraction of the film is 1.33.

35. A film of oil of index of refraction 1.2 rests on water. Find the minimum thickness of a patch of oil that appears red, indicating that blue light of wavelength about 5000 A suffers destructive interference in that region of the film.

36. A certain Michelson interferometer (Chapter 13) has mirrors that are 4-cm squares. Ten light and ten dark bands are seen in the field of view when sodium light of wavelength 5890 A is used. Assuming that one mirror is perpendicular to the light axis, by how much is the other mirror tilted from perpendicular?

28

Optical Instruments

28–1 INTRODUCTION

The content of the chapters on wave motion and physical optics form the basis, as do all branches of physics, for a great structure of practical applications. The treatment of the questions of the *utility* of physical principles is somewhat foreign to the study of physics as a basic science. Practice and application are avoided wherever needless details, not vital to the structure of the science, must be brought in. This is not to say that details are trivial; they are the backbone of experimental technique. Technology is a science in itself. We depart here from the standard approach of this text by frankly addressing some topics in the application of optical principles. Optics lends itself particularly well to this departure for the following basic reasons: (a) In pressing the question of the ultimate precision of optical instruments, we uncover, in fact, a new principle of physics—that there exists an intrinsic limitation in the observation of very small objects. (b) Physics is based on observation and measurement, and an exploration of our "seeing power" is relevant to the means of perceiving natural events.

In this chapter we concentrate most of our attention on two instruments of basic importance to optical measurement, the telescope and the microscope. The analysis of these instruments illustrates the application of the lens laws to simple lens combinations. At the same time, the laws of diffraction will be used in particular reference to a problem of importance to both wave theory and to practical optics: the ultimate precision (or resolving power) of these instruments. The results demonstrate a case in which natural laws themselves, rather than human competence, limit the accuracy of measurement.

28–2 THE SINGLE LENS; REAL IMAGE

There are convenient devices for the geometrical construction of an image formed by a lens. These devices do not supplant the lens equations but, rather, they graphically illustrate the operation of the equations. We define the optic axis of the lens to be the line piercing the center of the lens normal to the lens surface. On the optic axis we place the points F at a distance from the lens equal to the focal length of the lens. Rays entering the lens parallel to the optic axis intersect at the point F on the opposite side of the lens. This is in accord with the lens equation. We erect an arrow at some point beyond F, away from the lens. The arrow acts as a convenient object whose image we wish to find by construction. We consider rays from the tip of the arrow (Fig. 28–1). Ray a, emitted parallel to the optic

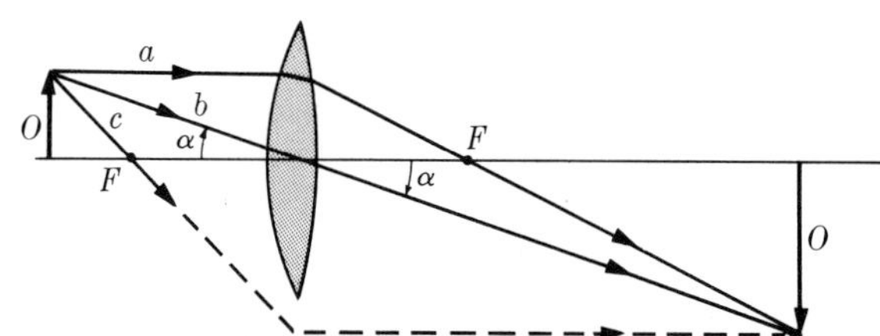

Fig. 28–1. Graphical construction of the image of an off-axis point.

axis, passes through F on the opposite side of the lens. Ray b, which passes through the center of the lens, is undeviated by the lens. Ray c passes through the point F on the same side of the lens. It is rendered parallel to the optic axis after passing through the lens. Two rays are sufficient for the construction of an image point, since all rays from a point on an object intersect at a common point after passing through the lens (according to our first-order theory). A third ray can be used as a check. In the final construction we show all three rays. We note a qualitative feature of the image which is formed. It is inverted relative to the object, just as in the case of the pinhole device.

Whether the image is larger or smaller than the object is a question of practical importance. Optical magnification is one of the major devices for extending the range of human perception. Magnification M is defined here as the ratio of image size I to object size O, or

$$M \equiv \frac{I}{O}. \tag{28–1}$$

From the construction in Fig. 28–1, which shows the straight ray passing through the center of the lens, we see that O and I are the sides of right similar triangles of angle α. From the similar triangles, we have the rule that the image and object sizes are in proportion to the image and object distances, namely,

$$M = \frac{I}{O} = \frac{q}{p}. \tag{28–2}$$

In principle, infinite magnification can be obtained: When $p = f$, $q = \infty$. However, an image cast on a screen an infinite distance away would be of little use to an observer. A finite image and object distance, whose sum equals the size of a laboratory room, imposes a limitation on the magnification to be obtained from a given single lens. More importantly, there are upper limits to useful magnification, as we shall see later.

A few examples of real images formed by "single" lenses are the camera (Fig. 28–2), the projector (Fig. 28–3), and the eye (Fig. 28–4). In the camera and the projector, the system must be refocused by changing the distances q or p, respectively, when photographing or projecting at different distances. With the eye, on the other hand, q is fixed and the eye "accommodates" for different object distances by adjusting the radii of the lens surfaces, which, as we have seen, affect the focal length.

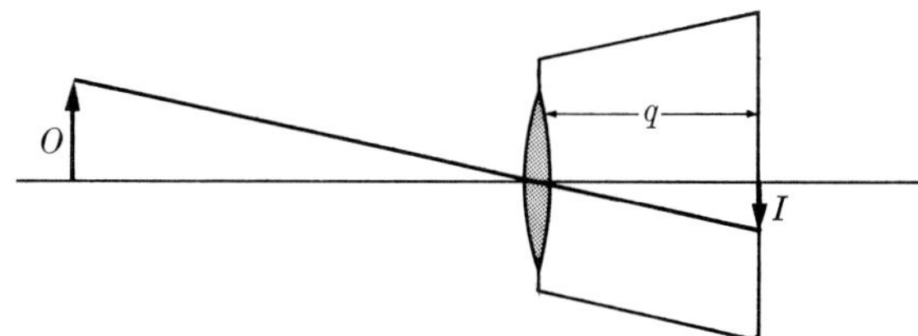

Fig. 28–2. Schematic diagram of a camera.

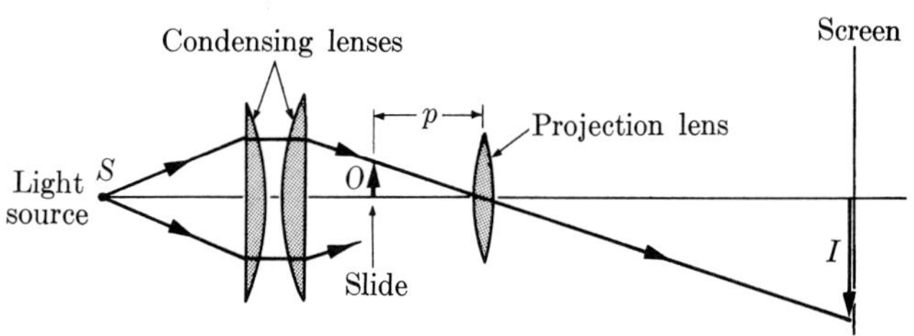

Fig. 28–3. Schematic diagram of a slide projector. The condensing lenses increase the amount of light that passes through the slide to the projection lens. The projection lens forms the image on the screen.

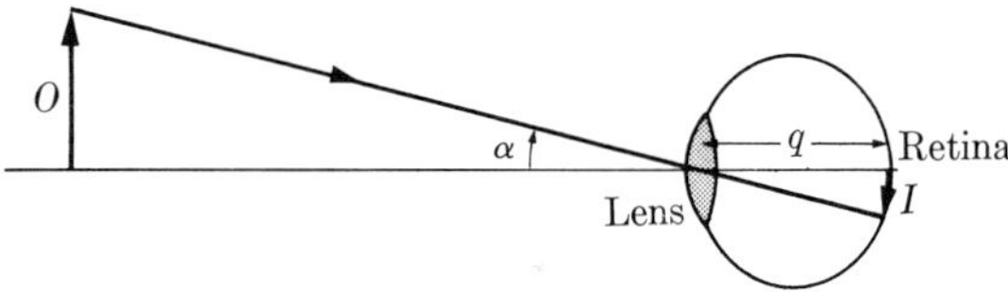

Fig. 28–4. Schematic diagram of the formation of an image by the eye.

28–3 THE SINGLE LENS; VIRTUAL IMAGES

The geometric constructions in the section above apply to the case in which the object is placed outside the focal point of the lens. When p is less than f, a qualitative change in the image occurs. Drawing rays a and b as before (Fig. 28–5), we find that they do *not* intersect after passing through the lens; they diverge and cannot form an image on a screen. To an observer looking through the lens, however, they appear

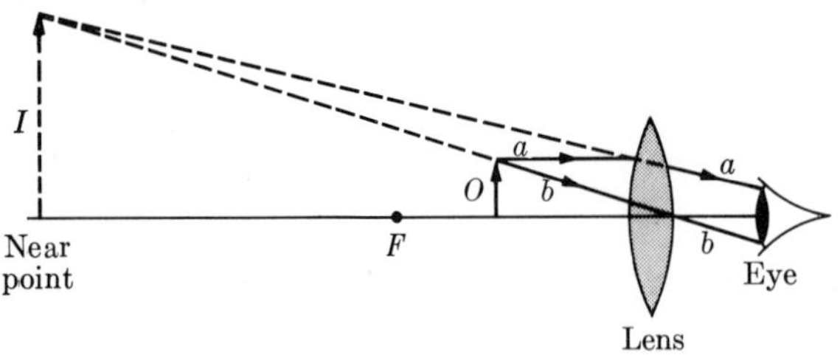

Fig. 28–5. The use of a single lens as a simple magnifier. The lens permits the eye to form an image on the retina of an object O that is closer than the near point of the eye.

to emerge from a common point of intersection on the same side of the lens as the object. We no longer place a screen behind the lens, but rather an eye which must be used in the matter of interpretation. The eye knows only the direction with which rays enter the eye; that is, prior bending of the rays is unknown to the eye. We interpret the past history of a ray as always having been a straight line. Therefore, an image of the source is carried back to the point of virtual intersection of rays, and what we see is called a virtual image. The rays from the head of the arrow appear to come from I.

We could still define magnification as the ratio of image to object size, and find M by construction. Such a definition would be to little purpose, however, since the image is usually observed visually and the *apparent* image size is a more useful concept than actual image size.

In the absence of information on the distance or size of objects, a series of objects of different sizes all appear to be the same size, provided that the ratio of actual size to distance from the eye is the same (Fig. 28–6). All such objects have the same "apparent size," and it is apparent size that counts in vision. Thus a penny placed about 7 feet from the eye has the same apparent size as the moon. If the moon were actually a scaled-up penny, with all the features of the penny held in correct proportion, we could make out the features with as much ease on the great moon-penny as on an ordinary penny placed 7 feet from the eye.

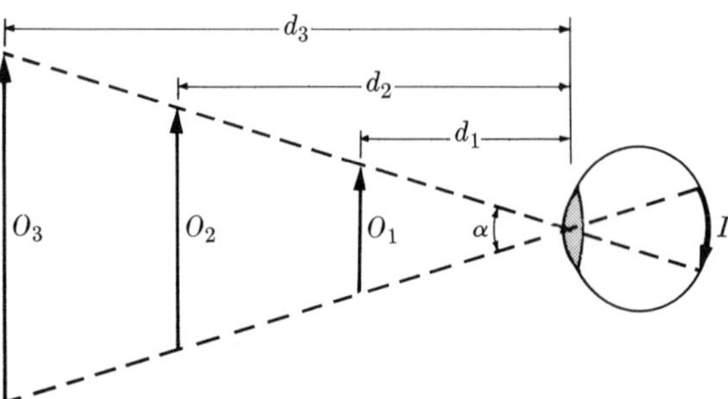

Fig. 28–6. Illustration of objects in a variety of sizes, all of which have the same apparent size, since the retinal images are the same size.

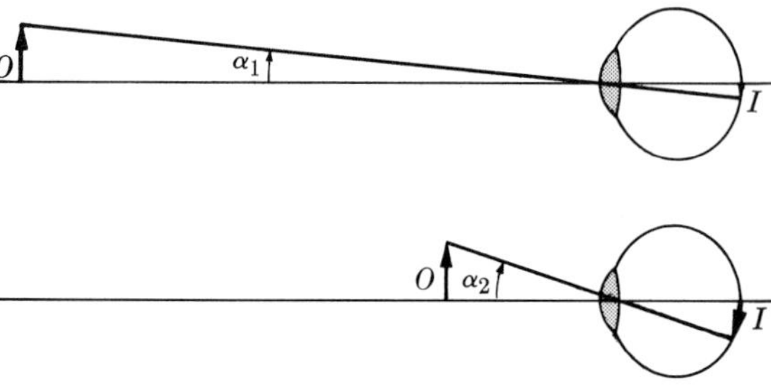

Fig. 28–7. The increase in apparent size of an object when it is brought closer to the eye.

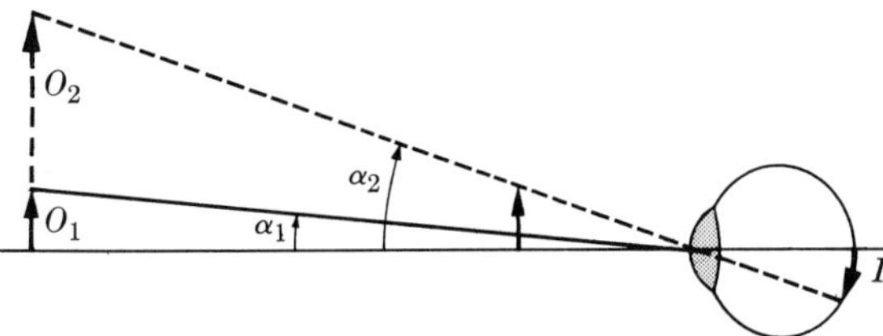

Fig. 28–8. The apparent magnification produced by bringing O closer to the eye.

A means of increasing apparent size is to bring an object closer to the eye, as in Fig. 28–7. In so doing we increase the subtended angle α and the image size on the retina. The effect is the same as if we had left the object at the original point and had literally increased its size until it subtended the angle α_2, as in Fig. 28–8.

When we wish to observe more detail in an object, we either bring the object closer to our eye or go closer to the object, if either of these possibilities is feasible. These procedures correspond to Fig. 28–8. But there are limits to the above methods for increasing the apparent size of objects. The normal eye cannot accommodate, that is focus, for objects closer than 25 cm in the one case, and the observer cannot or does not wish to move closer to objects in the other case. In both of these cases, the apparent size of an object can be increased by optical means.

The *apparent magnification* produced by an optical device is defined as the ratio of the apparent size of an object viewed through the optical device to the apparent size of the object viewed without the device. As we have seen above, the apparent size is given by the angle subtended at the eye.

By bringing objects closer to the eye, the process of magnification is limited by the eye itself, as mentioned earlier. (Try making out the lines in the skin of your finger when holding the finger 2 cm from the eye.) If an object is brought too close, the eye cannot form a clear image. The optimum distance is roughly 15 cm for your age group, but 25 cm is chosen as a sort of standard near distance. When the object is brought closer than the near point of the eye, a disk "image" of a point object is formed on the retina. The result is a loss of definition or resolution. Objects look bigger but the blurring is proportionately even greater, and hence even less detail can be seen. However, a simple lens can now be used to preserve the larger magnification characteristic of the nearness of the object while bringing the light to a focus on the retina (Fig. 28–9). Now if a lens is used to aid the eye, the image can be 25 cm from the eye. The object is placed within the focal length of the lens and, therefore, can be closer than 25 cm if f is less than 25 cm. Rays enter the eye with the angle α_2 approximately equal to O/f (see Fig. 28–9). The apparent size of the object is therefore O/f. With the *unaided* eye, the object must be placed at 25 cm from the eye and, therefore, its apparent size $\alpha_1 = O/25$. The magnifying power of the lens is therefore

$$M = \frac{\alpha_2}{\alpha_1} \simeq \frac{25}{f}, \tag{28–3}$$

when f is measured in centimeters. A lens used in this way is called a magnifying glass or simple magnifier. It is an instrument that permits objects to be seen clearly when closer than 25 cm from the eye, retaining the eye's ability to resolve detail. The limit of useful magnification by means of simple magnifiers is about ten because of inherent limitations, called aberrations, that the approximate lens formula does not reveal.

If the image is formed at 25 cm, the object cannot be placed at the point f and the magnifying power becomes (see Problems)

$$M = 1 + \frac{25}{f}. \tag{28–4}$$

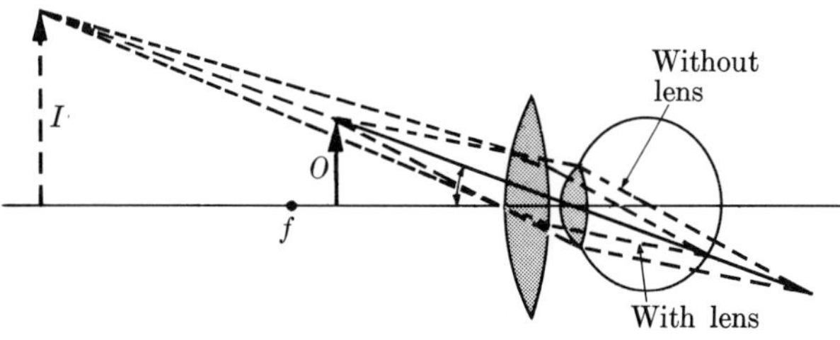

Fig. 28–9. Effect of the simple magnifier in enabling the eye to form an image of an object that is closer than the near point of the eye. The light after leaving the magnifier appears to be diverging from I in place of O. Since I is at the near point of the eye, the light can be focused by the eye onto the retina.

28–4 THE TELESCOPE

Telescopes are used not only because of their magnifying power but also because of their "light-gathering" power. The former property will be analyzed first.

A single lens cannot be a useful aid to visual observation of distant objects by a normal eye. A virtual image can be formed only if the object is *inside* the focal point. Thus a *very* long focal length lens would be required. However, the magnifying power could be no greater than one. When the single lens is used to form a real image,

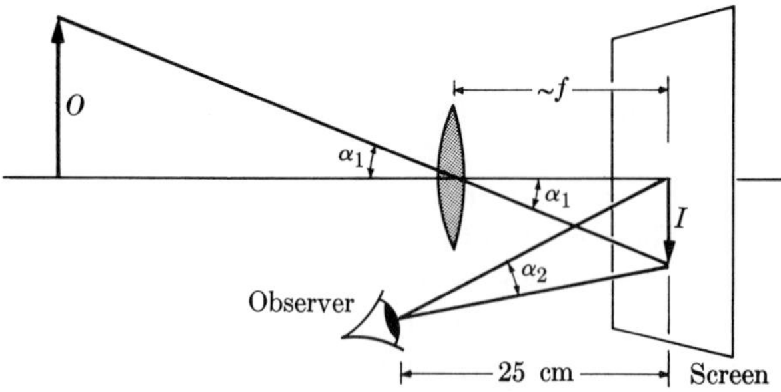

FIG. 28–10. An image I of a distant object O formed on a screen and viewed by an observer's eye.

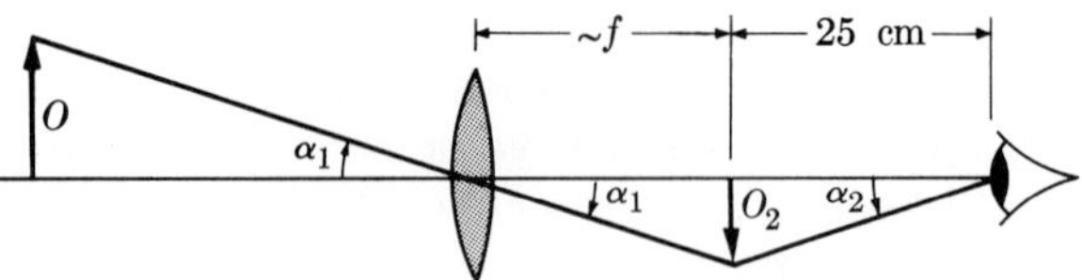

FIG. 28–11. Attempt to use a single lens as a telescope. The focal length of the lens must be greater than 25 cm and, more important, the field of view is limited to such an extent that the instrument has little use. In the figure, $f \simeq 25$ and $M \simeq 1$ for a distant object.

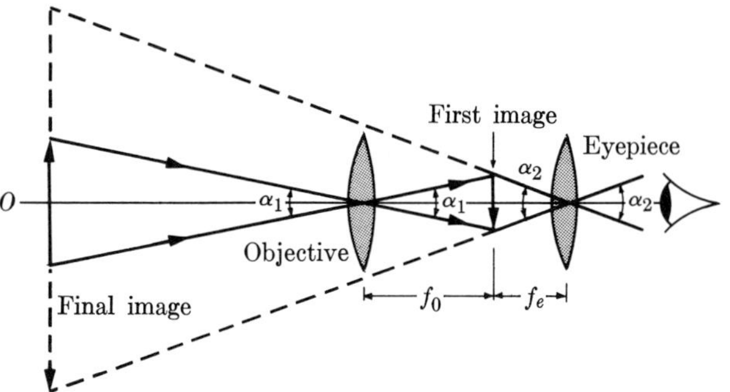

FIG. 28–12. The standard telescope consisting of a long focal-length objective and a short focal-length eyepiece. The diagram illustrates the calculation of the apparent magnification. The object O and the final image are actually far to the left.

the magnifying power can be greater than one if the focal length is greater than 25 cm. This can be seen from Fig. 28–10. The image of a distant object is formed in a plane that is very nearly at the focal distance. The image is shown on a screen which is viewed by the observer from the distance 25 cm. The apparent magnification is

$$M = \frac{\alpha_2}{\alpha_1} = \frac{f}{25}, \tag{28–5}$$

since O would subtend an angle α_1 when observed directly with the eye. The above system is not very useful, since it is awkward and since only the sun is bright enough to give a bright image on a screen. However, a photographic plate can be substituted for the screen, with a gain in sensitivity by means of long exposure. The photograph can be enlarged or it can be examined with a microscope, thus increasing the effective magnification still further. The photographic method for obtaining magnification is used in astronomy for observing extended objects such as the sun, nearby nebulas, etc.

The image formed by the single lens can be observed directly with the eye, provided that the eye is within the cone of light from the lens. The apparent magnification is again $\alpha_2/\alpha_1 = f/25$, as seen from Fig. 28–11. However, the field of view is so limited that the above system is not useful. (In Fig. 28–11, in which the size of the eye is tremendously exaggerated, the eye cannot see the head of the arrow; the light ray drawn to the eye is completely fictitious.)

The telescope is made useful for visual observation by a simple magnifier or eyepiece for viewing the image. If the final image is at infinity, the magnifying power of the eyepiece is $25/f_e$ (Eq. 28–3). The overall magnifying power, which is obviously the product of the separate magnifying powers, becomes

$$M(\text{telescope}) = \frac{f_0}{f_e}, \tag{28–6}$$

where f_0 and f_e are the focal lengths of the objective (the first lens) and the eyepiece, respectively. This result could be obtained directly (see Fig. 28–12). The objective lens forms an image at its focal plane, as before. This image, called O_2, is the object of a second lens which forms a virtual image of O_2. For the magnification, we divide the angle with which the final rays enter the eye, α_2, by the angle with which the rays from the original object enter the unaided eye, α_1. For small angles, $O_2 \simeq \alpha_1 f_0$ and $O_2 \simeq \alpha_2 f_e$, which leads to Eq. (28–6).

The second usefulness of the telescope, its light-gathering ability, depends on the area of the objective lens. In astronomy, it is important to have high light-gathering power in order to observe faint objects.

28–5 THE MICROSCOPE

In its general arrangement, the microscope is similar to the telescope. A first lens forms a real image of an object and, in turn, a magnifying glass is used to view the real image (Fig. 28–13). The great difference is that a microscope is for viewing close objects, and we have actual as well as apparent magnification. Since the object to be viewed is at hand, and not unavoidably remote, we bring it as close to the first lens as possible (Fig. 28–13). It must, however, remain outside the focal point of the first lens if a real image is to be formed. Therefore f_0, the focal length of the first lens, places a lower limit to the first-object distance. The upper limit to the first-image distance is dictated by the length L of the microscope tube, which, for our convenience of manipulation of specimens while we look in the microscope, is limited to about 25 cm. The magnification by the objective lens is therefore

$$M_0 = \frac{q_1}{p_1} \simeq \frac{L}{f_0}. \tag{28–7}$$

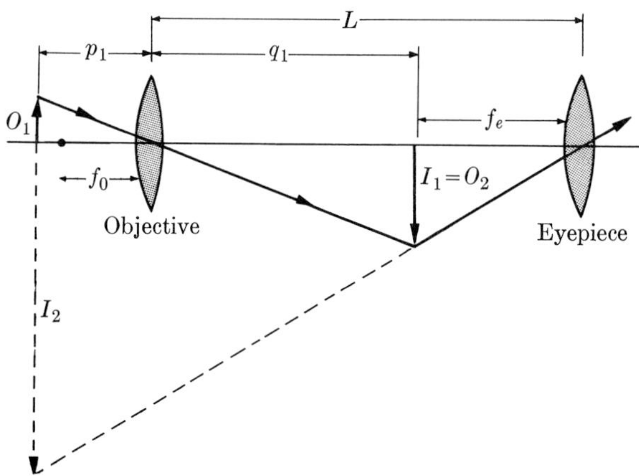

Fig. 28–13. Schematic diagram of a microscope. The enlarged image formed by the short focal-length objective becomes the object for the eyepiece. Since L is about 25 cm, in practice, the final image is usually about the same distance away as the original object.

The problems of observing this image are the same as with the telescope. A magnifier or eyepiece is almost a necessity. The final image formed by the eyepiece is usually at the near point of the eye. Therefore, its magnification is strictly given by Eq. (28–4). However, to a good degree of approximation, we can use Eq. (28–3), thus obtaining an overall magnification of

$$M \simeq \frac{L}{f_0}\frac{25}{f_e}. \tag{28–8}$$

It looks as if the magnification can be made as large as we wish by making the f's sufficiently small, but again our approximate lens theory conceals the failure of lenses to form good images when the focal lengths are made too small. Furthermore, we shall see in a later section that there is no advantage in magnifications beyond the point where the basic limit to the resolving power attributable to diffraction becomes evident.

28–6 RESOLVING POWER OF A TELESCOPE

The usual purpose of magnification is to increase the fineness of detail that can be observed. We have already said that lens aberrations can be a practical limit, but that diffraction is an intrinsic limit. Thus, there is a limit to useful magnification. We have studied in detail in the preceding chapter the diffraction produced by limiting a wave to a band from a slit. A lens selects a circular segment of a wave front but the results are not greatly different from a slit. Therefore, we shall use the simpler theory of the

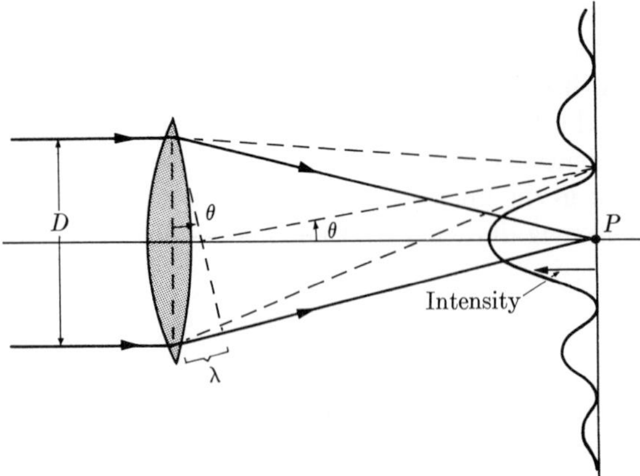

Fig. 28-14. The diffraction pattern that constitutes the "image" formed by an ideal lens of a distant point object. The pattern is indicated by a graph of intensity versus position.

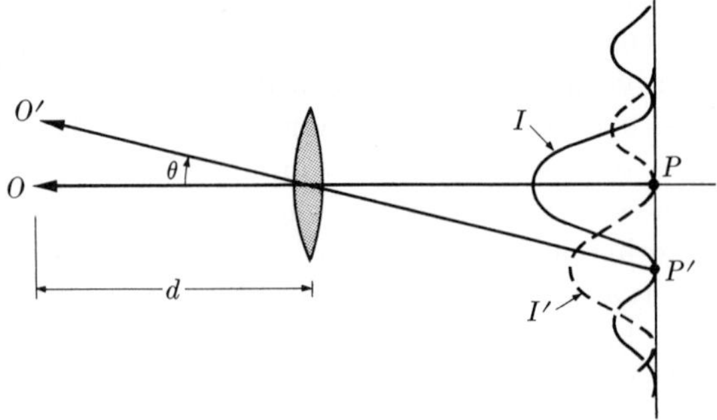

Fig. 28-15. Diffraction patterns (indicated by graphs of the intensities) for the images of two distant point objects separated by an angle θ.

single slit as a guide. Because of the lens, Fraunhofer diffraction theory is applicable; the lens focuses the rays as well as acts as an effective aperture. Plane waves from a distant point source are not focused to a point P (Fig. 28-14) but are distributed into a diffraction pattern of size determined by the wavelength of light and the size of the lens. We define the radius of the "spot" as approximately the distance from the center of the pattern to the first zero in intensity. The angle of diffraction θ for a slit of width D and light wavelength λ to the first minimum has been found to be given by

$$\sin \theta = \frac{\lambda}{D}. \tag{28-9}$$

The theory for a circular aperture of diameter D gives a result differing by a factor 1.22,

$$\sin \theta = 1.22 \frac{\lambda}{D}, \tag{28-10}$$

for the position of the first minimum.

A second distant point source will produce plane waves from a different direction and therefore a diffraction pattern centered at a different point p' (Fig. 28-15). Each object O and O', when viewed by a telescope, will form its own diffraction pattern in the image plane of the first lens. The central maxima of each pattern represent the objects being viewed. If these are far apart, the objects are resolved (Fig. 28-16). If the patterns overlap so much that they nearly coincide, they will not be resolved because the two patterns combine to give a maximum which appears as a single spot. The criterion for resolution customarily is that a dip in intensity must occur between the two maxima (Fig. 28-16). This is achieved when the maximum of one pattern lies on the first minimum of the other.

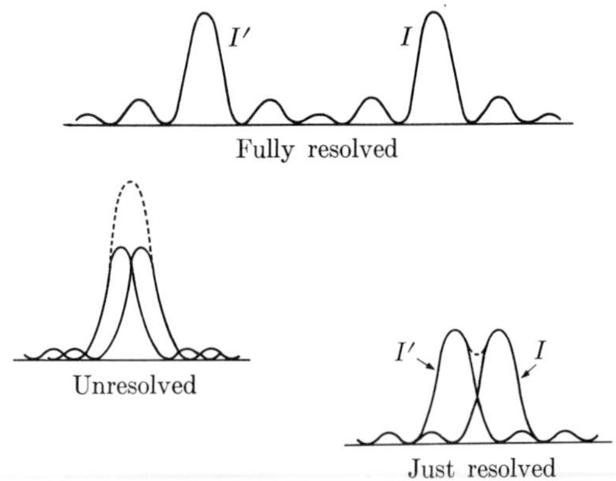

Fig. 28-16. Illustration of the diffraction patterns for the images of two point sources with three different separations.

The distinctness of the patterns is then barely detectable. Using this criterion, we can place a lower limit on the separation OO' of objects at a distance d such that they can be distinguished. The angular separation between the two centers, $\theta = OO'/d$, cannot be less than the angle of the first minimum, given by Eq. (28–10). Thus the minimum angle for resolution is

$$\theta_m = 1.22\,\lambda/D, \qquad (28\text{–}11)$$

and the minimum spatial separation for resolution is

$$OO'_m = 1.22\,\lambda d/D. \qquad (28\text{–}12)$$

Since d and λ are essentially fixed, the resolution can be improved only by increasing the lens diameter. Thus, finite resolving power, imposed by the wave nature of light, is an inescapable limitation on the precision of a telescope. In order to obtain this resolution, it is necessary that the lens itself be custom-made, with nonspherical surfaces, so that the emergent wave front will be truly spherical. An ordinary spherically surfaced lens displays the above resolving power only at rather small apertures, say a few millimeters for a telescope of ten times magnification. Ordinary camera and telescope lenses are made much larger than their resolution would justify. This is done in order to increase their light-gathering power. The criteria for a reflecting telescope are the same as above.

In the next section, the resolving power of a microscope lens will be derived. Finally, the effect of the eyepiece will be discussed.

28–7 RESOLVING POWER OF A MICROSCOPE

The clarity of an object viewed by a microscope is ultimately limited by the same diffraction process that takes place with the telescope. Needless to say, practical limitations on resolution can occur due to the fact that lenses form ideal images only to a first approximation. However, combinations of lenses have been designed that correct so well for the limitations of a single lens

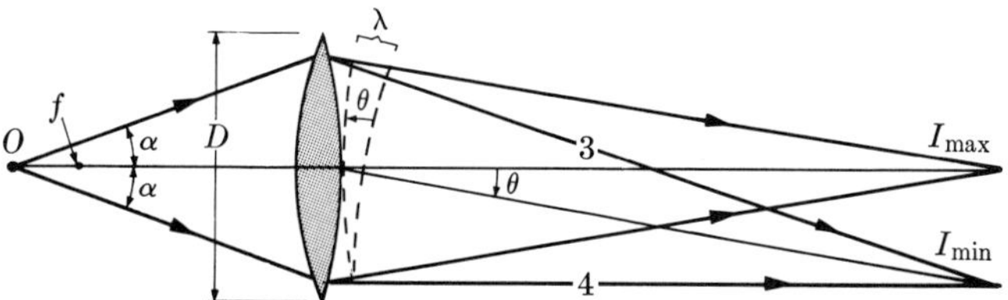

Fig. 28–17. Illustration of the path differences for rays that are chosen to demonstrate the theory for the position of the first minimum in the diffraction pattern of the image of a point source.

that diffraction does in fact provide the limit to the quality of the image in the case of a good microscope. The analysis for resolving power proceeds somewhat differently in the case of a microscope because we have an object that is placed extremely close to the first lens. This is a condition imposed by the desire for high magnification, as we have seen in Section 28–4. The rays from a single point P therefore enter the lens within a large range of angles 2α in Fig. 28–17. Since the rays from O are not parallel, the analysis is a little different from that of the telescope.

Consider a point object O on the axis, as in Fig. 28–17. The rays all have the same path

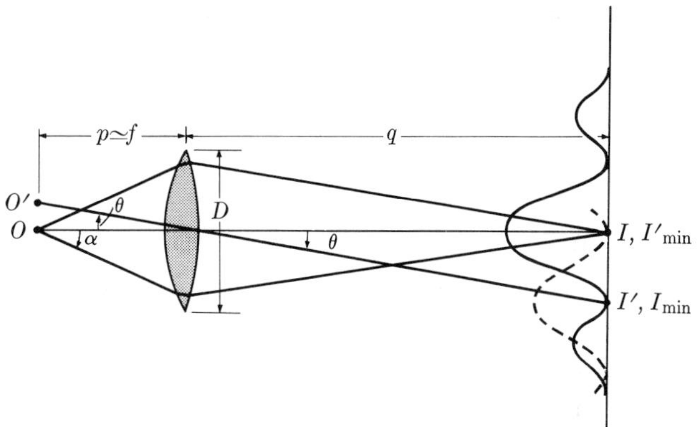

Fig. 28–18. Two points, O and O', form diffraction pattern images that are barely resolved. The illustration is for an objective lens of a microscope, which has a short focal length.

length (measured in wavelengths) to the point I, and therefore constructive interference occurs. Now consider rays starting from O, as before, but going to point I_{min}, as shown in Fig. 28–17. The distance of I_{min} from I is chosen so that the path difference of the extreme rays 3 and 4 is λ. For a slit the effect due to *all* rays would be destructive interference, as we have seen earlier. The result is approximately the same for a circular aperture. Thus the image of O has a central maximum with the first minimum at angle $\theta \simeq 1.22\lambda/D$, where D is the lens diameter.

Thus if another point object O' is located so that its central maximum is at I_{min}, the objects O and O' can just be resolved (Fig. 28–18). The angle θ can also be expressed as $\theta \simeq OO'/f$, which, combined with the expression in the preceding paragraph, leads to

$$OO' \simeq 1.22 \frac{f\lambda}{D}. \tag{28–13}$$

In actual practice, microscope objectives that give high-quality images can be made with $f \simeq D$. Thus, we see that objects whose separation is approximately equal to the wavelength of light can be resolved.

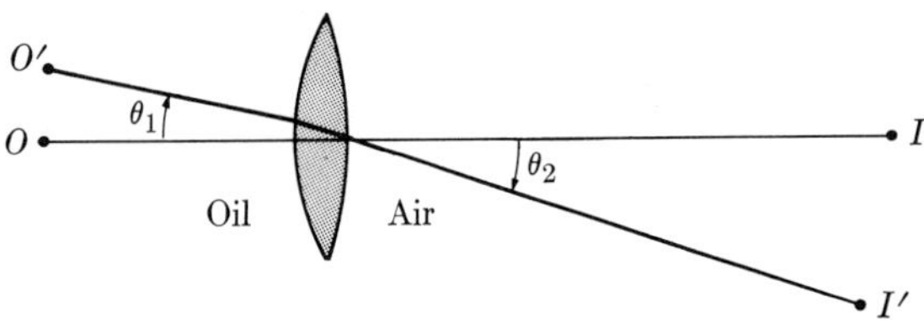

FIG. 28–19. Illustration of the effect of oil immersion of the objects O and O' on the apparent angular separation of the objects.

It is possible to improve the limit of resolution by putting oil between the object and the lens. In such a case the angles θ_1 and θ_2 (Fig. 28–19) are no longer equal. In fact, we have, from Snell's law, $\sin\theta_2/\sin\theta_1 = n$, or, for small angles, $\theta_2/\theta_1 \simeq n$. Thus Eq. (28–13) becomes more generally

$$OO' = 1.22 \frac{f\lambda}{nD}. \tag{28–14}$$

28–8 USEFUL MAGNIFICATION

A striking demonstration of the uselessness of producing magnification without providing a concurrent improvement in resolving power is the following: When a printed page is held within 2 or 3 cm of a normal eye, the print cannot be read. But if a tiny hole is made in a piece of paper and the hole is held very close to the eye, well-illuminated print can easily be read through the hole even when the print is a centimeter or two from the eye. The magnifying power of this simple device can be 10 or 20 times. *But* if you carefully look for improvement in seeing the detail of the magnified print, you will find that there is actually a loss rather than an improvement. Thus the magnification has no advantage in this case because the pinhole, which is required to improve the geometrical optics definition to the level of legibility, produces diffraction that limits the definition. At the optimum size of a pinhole, there is a net loss in definition compared with the unaided eye used at normal distance.

With microscopes and telescopes, the images formed by the objectives have a certain limit to the fineness of detail (resolution). In the best instruments, the limit approaches that of a perfect lens, namely, the limit of diffraction set by the finite size of the lens. The eyepiece magnifies the image formed by the objective but it cannot improve the definition; at best, it can only preserve the definition while increasing the size. If a certain eyepiece provides enough magnification to enable the eye to detect all the detail that exists in the image formed by the objective, a stronger eyepiece can increase the size (and convenience of observation) but it cannot increase the resolution (Fig. 28–20).

FIG. 28–20. Illustration of the magnification of unresolved images.

28-9 SUMMARY

The technique of graphical construction used to find the image formed by a lens is described. A single lens, in principle, is used in the camera and in the projector. It is also used as a simple magnifier. The concept of apparent magnification or magnifying power of an optical device that is used as an aid to observation with the eye is developed. The magnifying power of a simple magnifier is

$$M = \frac{25}{f} \quad \text{or} \quad 1 + \frac{25}{f},$$

depending on whether the final image is formed at infinity or at 25 cm.

The simplest telescope with high magnification consists of two converging lenses. The objective lens, of long focal length, forms a real image that is viewed by a short focal-length lens used as a simple magnifier to view the image. The magnifying power is the ratio of the focal lengths; that is, $M = f_0/f_e$, when the final image is at infinity.

The microscope utilizes a short focal-length lens to form an enlarged real image of a nearby small object. This image is then viewed with an eyepiece used as a simple magnifier. The magnifying power is

$$M \simeq \frac{L}{f_0}\frac{25}{f_e},$$

where L is the separation of the lenses.

The diffraction patterns produced by the restriction of the wave fronts to the size of the objective lens limit the fineness of detail that can be observed with an ideal lens system. The minimum angular separation of two point sources that can just be resolved by a telescope with an objective lens of diameter D is $\theta \simeq 1.22\,\lambda/D$. The minimum separation OO' of objects that can just be resolved with a microscope with an ideal lens is given by

$$OO' \simeq 1.22\,\frac{f\lambda}{D}.$$

If the object space is filled with oil of index n, the resolution is improved by a factor $1/n$.

Problems

1. If a 24 mm × 36 mm slide is to be projected to a size 1 m × $1\frac{1}{2}$ m on a screen, what should be the distance of the screen from the projector? The focal length of the lens is 20 cm.

2. Prove that the focal length f of a combination of two lenses placed very close together is given by

$$\frac{1}{f} = \frac{1}{f_1} + \frac{1}{f_2}.$$

3. Mountains rising to a height of 10,000 ft above a plain are observed from a distance of 50 miles. If the observer thinks the mountains are only 2000 ft high, how far away does he think they are?

4. A lens of focal length 5 cm is used as a simple magnifier. Find the magnifying power when the final image is (a) at 25 cm (b) at infinity (c) at 50 cm (d) at 10 cm (a near-sighted observer).

5. How much finer print can an observer read at 50 cm than at 5 m? Why?

6. A telescope lens of focal length 2 m is used to photograph the moon. What is the size of the image of the moon on the photograph? The moon's diameter is 3200 km and its distance is 400,000 km.

7. An eyepiece of focal length 5 cm is used in conjunction with the telescope lens of Problem 6. What is the actual size of the image of the moon

(a) if the final image is at the same distance away as the moon?

(b) if the final image (virtual) is at 25 cm?

(c) What is the angle subtended by the image in each case above?

(d) What is the apparent magnification in each case?

8. How can the lens combination of Problem 7 be used to form a real image? What is its size?

9. A microscope with an objective of focal length 5 mm is used with an eyepiece labeled 10 times magnification.

(a) What is the focal length of the eyepiece, assuming that the final image is at 25 cm for 10 times magnification?

(b) What is the overall magnifying power if the first image is at 25 cm from the objective?

(c) What is the distance between the two lenses?

10. At what distance can a person distinguish an oncoming motorcycle from a car at night if the headlights of the car are separated by 2 m? Assume that the pupils of the observer's eyes have a diameter of 4 mm.

11. A good microscope objective may have a radius equal to the focal length of the lens. Find the minimum spacing Δx of points that can be resolved by a good microscope

(a) with light of wavelength 5000 A

(b) if oil of $n = 1.5$ is used between the objective and the object.

12. The telescope lens of Problem 6 has a diameter of 10 cm. What is the spacing of the images formed by the lens of two stars that can just be resolved?

13. Discuss the effect on resolution if a telescope is designed to be filled with water between the objective lens and a photographic plate placed at the focus.

29

Constituents of the Atom

29–1 INTRODUCTION

Atomic physics and modern physics are often used as synonomous terms. To the classical or premodern era belong, largely, the subjects pertaining to the visible world about us, the world we perceive directly with our senses and experience in daily life. Certain physical instruments have been devised to measure classical phenomena. These instruments are designed as aids to our senses, but not as total replacements for the senses. Indeed, instruments not only sharpen the senses by being more quantitative, but they also extend the range of sense perception. It is in the latter range that we encounter the beginnings of modern physics. When we proceed to the postclassical domain, we enter into the study of the totally invisible world of atoms and quanta. The method of direct observation is abandoned altogether. Consequently, we abandon the store of experience which we have acquired in daily existence, a store which supplements directly the study of classical physics. A child must assimilate an immense fund of knowledge of the visible, or classical, world if he is to stay alive. Such a fund of experience, when systematized, amounts to the "intuition" to which we often refer. Only after maturity is reached and the instruments of atomic physics are understood can an intuition about atoms be gained.

Atoms are small, and by this we mean they are extraordinarily small compared with the size of objects of the visible world. The atomic size (as we shall see later) is of the order of an angstrom unit (A) of length measure. It will be recalled that the smallest length resolvable by a microscope is equal roughly to the wavelength of the light used for viewing. This wavelength, if it is to be visible, is of the order of 5000 A long. Thus the smallest volume which can be "seen" is about 1000 atoms on a side. If atoms are spaced 1 A units apart, such a volume contains one hundred billion atoms. The above numbers demonstrate the scale factor that separates the atomic domain from the world of direct observation. The remarkable point of discovery is that we find on the atomic scale a set of natural laws which depart very far from those which apply to classical systems. Not only are many of the rigorous classical laws abandoned, but even the general sense of classical life is abandoned. It must be understood that the measurements we have made on classical systems amount to sweeping averages over atomic detail, and that much of the atomic detail is lost in such averaging. Of course, the classical and modern systems must, at some point, merge smoothly. At least, this is a sensible expectation. The expectation is formulated in what is called the "correspondence principle," which describes the transition region between large and small objects.

29–2 THE STRUCTURE OF MATTER

In classical physics, the attributes of matter, such as inertial mass or electric charge, are regarded as continuous variables. Mass and charge can have any value. However, a basic conclusion that can be drawn from the experiments of modern physics is that matter is not divisible into arbitrarily small elements. Rather, we find "smallest" units of matter that apparently cannot be further divided. In addition to the discovery of smallest units is the discovery that, so far as precise measurement can tell, the smallest units are arranged into families whose members are *identical.* Thus, one of the smallest units of matter is the electron. There is no variation in electronic mass or electronic charge from one electron to another. Another element of matter is the proton, and again, all protons have the same mass and the same charge. There is still another unit called the neutron, which has no electric charge, but again, has a definite and invariable mass. With this listing of the classifications of electrons, protons, and neutrons, we have exhausted, in the present view, the components of ordinary matter which we see around us. This matter is not to be thought of, then, as having any arbitrary value of mass. The mass of an object must be some integral multiple of elementary particle masses. The particles of matter are countable and discrete. However, this discreteness is never apparent for gross objects. The mass of the particle components is so small that the addition of an atom or two to a gram of matter would not cause a detectable change in the mass. The experimental foundations upon which the particle theory of matter is built are to be described in this section.

The direct evidence for the elementary particle of matter, used by the chemist and physicist in the description of natural phenomena, is only about 60 years old. It first came with the discovery of the electron and the measurement of electronic properties. Even prior to the discovery of the electron, the concept of the particle construction of matter had proved useful and, in fact, almost inescapable in the understanding of the gas laws and the laws of chemical reactions. Going back still further, scientists of the Greek period in history advanced the idea of particles or atoms of matter on the basis of arguments which still prove to be interesting reading today. We have, today, an elaborate and strikingly successful theory of the detailed atomic structure of matter. We also have, at the frontier of scientific investigation, a host of new unstable particles—approaching 100 varieties at this writing—whose position in the theoretical structure of physics is not at all clear to the physicist.

In mechanics we have used the term particle or point mass to denote a mathematical simplification. It is a portion of matter whose position and motion can be described by point coordinates. It could, of course, have any mass and any electric charge with which we choose to endow it. There is a danger in thinking of *elementary particles* as simply tiny versions of particles which we can hold in our hands. The use of the term particle is therefore rather unfortunate, since it calls into mind a mechanistic concept that does not stand the tests of experiment and observation. Thus if we speak later of the *conflict* between the particle picture of matter and what we shall call the wave picture, we refer more to a conflict in preconceived notions than to a basic conflict in experimental evidence. It is far better to abandon, at the outset, the conception of the electron as a small poppy seed, which it is not, and instead simply try to understand the experimental evidence concerning electrons. To this end, we present the experiments which demonstrate the identity of the electron in a way which shows that a considerable amount of *interpretation*, along with the basic evidence, attends the development of the model of the particle nature of matter.

The first evidence for the particulate structure of matter is based on indirect observation. But since these first observations can be interpreted in terms of classical laws for point masses, it is natural to construct the first model in terms of a classical picture of tiny particles. As mentioned above, we must be careful *not* to consider this *model* as constituting physical reality.

29–3 THE ELECTRON

The first identification of the electron came from the observations of *cathode rays*, so-called because of the method of production. When electrodes at a high potential difference ($\sim$1000 v) are placed in a sealed chamber (Fig. 29–1) the gaseous conduction of electricity is initiated at suitably reduced gas pressure. Conduction can be affirmed by the use of meters, but also a color-

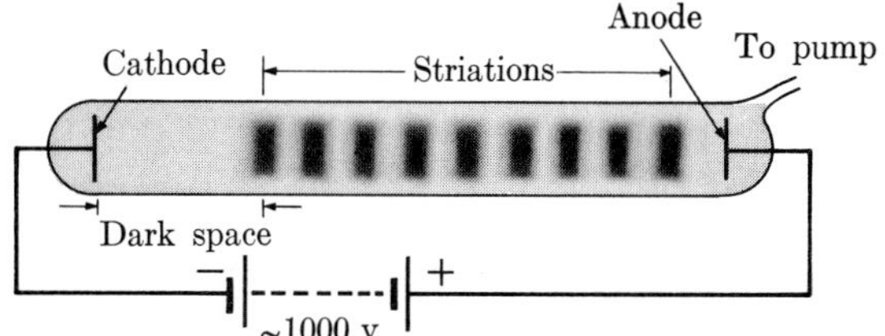

Fig. 29–1. Schematic diagram of the glow discharge in a gas at low pressure.

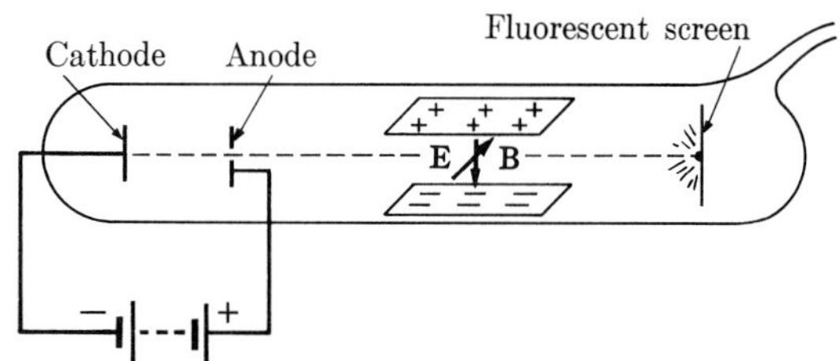

Fig. 29–2. Schematic diagram of a tube for studying cathode rays. The cathode rays are accelerated toward the anode. The particular rays that are traveling toward the hole in the cathode pass through the hole and form a collimated beam. The beam can then be subjected to lateral forces due to electric and magnetic fields and the resulting deflections on the screen can then be measured.

ful display of light is emitted by the gas at the onset of conduction. It is not our purpose here to describe the reproducible, definite, and beautiful striated patterns of light which are formed. These should be observed in the laboratory. As the gas pressure is reduced, toward what we call a better vacuum, a gross change is seen in the growth of a dark space which first surrounds the cathode, or negative electrode. Finally, the dark space can grow until it extends from cathode to anode, and, although the electrical current remains, it produces no visible effect in the gas in the chamber. In a darkened room, a visible evidence of conduction is seen at the anode end, in a fluorescent effect of the glass. Whatever has caused the glass to glow has come from the cathode end. The invisible "emanation" from the cathode end is called *cathode rays.*

The discovery of the electron is attributed to J. J. Thomson in 1897 when he measured electromagnetic deflections of cathode rays. Either electrostatic or magnetic fields, impressed in the region between anode and cathode, can deflect the rays or, more literally, shift the fluorescent region that appears on the glass. Thus, it was shown that the rays are charged, and therefore they cannot be invisible light waves. The measurement of the electromagnetic qualities of the beam is made in an apparatus more deliberately contrived to produce a collimated beam in what today would be called an electron gun. A hole is placed in the anode so that the rays pass as a beam into a region where deflections can be measured (Fig. 29–2). The beam is stopped by a fluorescent screen upon which a glowing spot is caused by the rays.

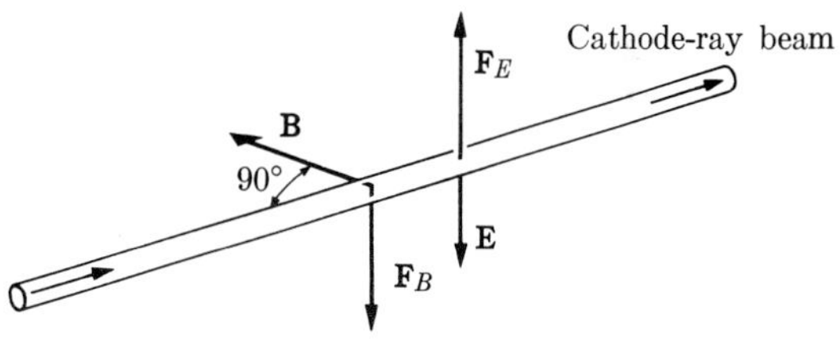

Fig. 29–3. Direction of the lateral forces on cathode rays that are passing through transverse fields **E** and **B**, as shown.

Neither the electric nor the magnetic deflection can be used to find the properties of the rays unless the velocity of the beam is known. The velocity can be measured by impressing crossed electric and magnetic fields upon the beam in the same region of space (Fig. 29–3). The strengths of the two fields are adjusted so that, their forces, acting in opposition, produce no deflection of the beam. For zero deflection, the sum of the forces is zero, and we have $E_1q = B_1qv$ or

$$v = \frac{E_1}{B_1}. \tag{29–1}$$

That zero deflection can be achieved is taken as proof that the beam is homogeneous in velocity.

However, the crossed-field method gives neither the mass of the beam nor its charge.

Having established a velocity for the beam, then either an electric field or a magnetic field can be used separately to cause a deflection of the beam. Consider the case of magnetic deflection. The motion of electric charge in a uniform magnetic field perpendicular to the velocity is circular, given by the condition

$$Bqv = \frac{mv^2}{r},$$

or

$$\frac{q}{m} = \frac{v}{Br}. \tag{29–2}$$

But since the velocity is known from the prior measurement in the crossed fields, B_1 and E_1, Eq. (29–2) becomes

$$\frac{q}{m} = \frac{1}{Br}\left(\frac{E_1}{B_1}\right). \tag{29–3}$$

The radius of motion r in the magnetic field can be related to the deflection of the spot x on the screen (Fig. 29–4). It is a brief exercise in geometry to show the relationship between the deflection x and the radius of curvature r.

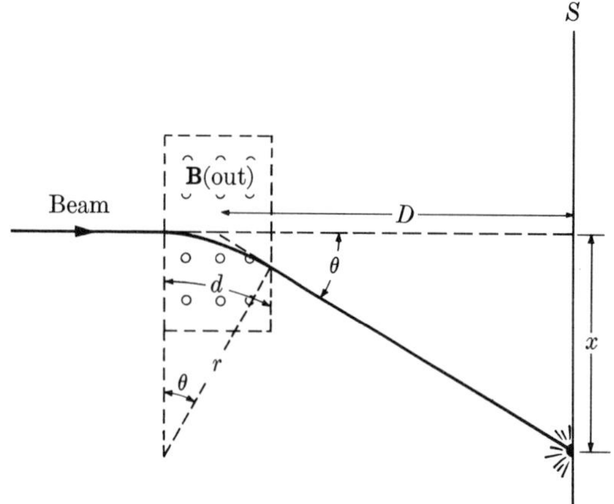

Fig. 29–4. Geometry for determining the radius of curvature of cathode rays while passing through a magnetic field that is confined to a restricted region of width d. The measured quantities are the distance D to the screen, the deflection on the screen x, and the strength and extent of the field.

What is found, then, is an electromagnetic property of the beam called the charge-to-mass ratio. Whatever arrangement is used, this is the *only* property of the beam which can be found by electric or magnetic deflection. The charge-to-mass ratio found for the cathode rays has the value,

$$\frac{q}{m} = 1.7 \times 10^{11}\,\frac{\text{coul}}{\text{kg}}, \tag{29–4}$$

independent of the gas that is used in the discharge tube.

The rays have a definite velocity, found by electromagnetic means. They also have a definite charge-to-mass ratio. There is no need, in the matter of interpretation, for invoking a particle structure for the beam. It could be a continuum with such properties that the mass and charge density must always be in fixed proportion. Also, even if the particle picture were used, there is no need for a definite mass or charge. Rather, such quantities could have any value provided that they are in fixed ratio. Another experiment, of a different kind, is required if either mass or charge is to be specified separately and if the particle nature of electrons is to be established.

29–4 THE IONIC CHARGE

The study of electrolysis, chemical reactions, gas laws, and Brownian motion had already, at the time of the cathode ray demonstrations, led to the idea and the measurement of the ionic charge. This idea received what appeared to be conclusive support in the result of the Millikan oil-drop experiment, which will now be described. Droplets of oil produced by atomizing frequently acquire slight amounts of electric charge in the process. The droplets so charged, and drifting down in air, can be moved by electric forces. Through a set of combined observations, the droplet charge can be determined as follows: A uniform, vertical electric field can be used to cancel the force of the gravitational field upon the droplet (Fig. 29–5). In the absence of an electric field, the droplet falls, and upon the application of just the right value of electric field, the droplet can be held in suspension. When the charge is at rest, the electric and gravitational forces are equal and $Eq = mg$ or

$$q = \frac{mg}{E}. \tag{29–5}$$

The determination of the droplet mass must be made in an auxiliary experiment. This is done by observing the terminal velocity of the droplet falling in the gravitational field alone. At equilibrium (that is, at constant velocity), the gravitational force equals the frictional drag of the air, $mg = 6\pi\eta rv$. Therefore, the droplet radius and hence its mass can be found.

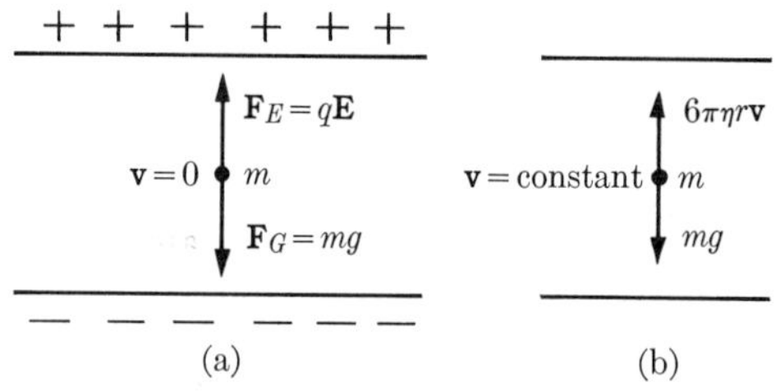

FIG. 29–5. The forces on an oil drop of mass m, radius r, and charge q. (a) The charged drop at rest under the influence of an electric field. (b) The drop falling at constant velocity under the influence of viscous drag and gravitational attraction.

The outcome of the experiment is the following: The droplets do not all carry the same amount of charge. The amount of charge is a fortuitous effect of the droplet formation. Still, whatever charge is found is always a multiple of a smallest unit, e; that is,

$$q = ne, \tag{29–6}$$

where n is an integer and

$$e = 1.6 \times 10^{-19} \text{ coul.} \tag{29–7}$$

Never do we find such values as $q = 1.5e$ or $q = 7.7e$. Also no charge q is ever found that is less than the value e.

We are to conclude, then, that electric charges always occur in definite parcels. Since the result is the same for positively charged drops, we are led to the same conclusion for positive charges. The charge on a drop may be e, $3e$, $4e$, etc. It is still another step to say that the basic ionic charge found in this experiment should be attributed to a *particle* in the cathode rays. Outwardly, and in concept, there is no connection except a mental one between the cathode ray experiment and the oil-drop experiment.

If we assume that (a) the beam of cathode rays is made of particles whose charge-to-mass ratio is 1.7×10^{11} and (b) each particles carries the elementary ionic charge, then the cathode ray particles have a definite mass

$$m = \frac{e}{1.7 \times 10^{11}} = \frac{1.6 \times 10^{-19}}{1.7 \times 10^{11}}$$
$$= 9.1 \times 10^{-31} \text{ kg}. \tag{29–8}$$

The electron of matter is the embodiment of the experimental data and interpretation of the cathode ray experiment and the oil-drop experiment. Just how the electron is incorporated into the structure of matter is a question to be answered by further test and speculation, which we take up later.

29–5 ATOMIC MASS

At the time of the measurement of the ionic charge, there was at hand the great body of systematic evidence about the properties of the chemical elements. The addition of the ionic charge into these data results in a determination of the atomic mass of the elements. The amount of a chemical substance in gaseous form, which at standard pressure and temperature occupies a volume of 22.4 liters, is called a mole of the substance (Chapter 15). It is found that a fixed amount of charge is required for the electrolytic deposition of one mole of a substance. This charge is $Q = 96{,}500$ coul, or $Q = 2 \times 96{,}500$ coul, or $Q = 3 \times 96{,}500$ coul, and so on.

The basic unit, $Q = 96{,}500$ coul, is called the faraday of electric charge. It is assumed that the ions which require one faraday for deposition of a mole carry a single ionic charge, ions which require two faradays carry twice the ionic charge, and so on. If we ask for the number of ions in a mole, then we have simply to divide the faraday of charge by the charge on a single ion. The number is called A (the Avogadro number), which is found from

$$A = \frac{Q}{e} = \frac{96{,}500}{1.6 \times 10^{-19}} = 6 \times 10^{23} \text{ ions/mole.} \tag{29-9}$$

(It should be mentioned parenthetically that A had previously been determined, but with less accuracy, by studies of Brownian motion. If the substance were in neutral form, this should be the number of "atoms" of the substance.)

Proceeding through the periodic chart of the elements, we find the mass of an atom of any element by dividing the mass of a mole of that element by the number of atoms in a mole. The results for the first five elements are shown in Table 29-1.

TABLE 29-1

DETERMINATION OF THE AVERAGE MASS OF AN ATOM FOR THE FIRST FIVE ELEMENTS

M (molar mass)/ (atoms in a molecule)	M/A (mass of an atom of the element)
H 1.00×10^{-3} kg	1.66×10^{-27} kg
He 4.0×10^{-3} kg	6.7×10^{-27} kg
Li 6.9×10^{-3} kg	11.5×10^{-27} kg
Be 9.0×10^{-3} kg	15×10^{-27} kg
B 10.8×10^{-3} kg	18×10^{-27} kg

Again, from chemical studies alone, it had been noted that the molar masses of most substances are nearly integral multiples of half the molar mass of hydrogen. In the present discussion, this same evidence is simply being displayed in terms of average masses of individual atoms. If the atomic masses of Table 29-1 are divided by the value for hydrogen, the figures of Table 29-2 result. It is attractive, but hardly justified by the detailed evidence, to think that the atomic masses are made up of whole-number multiples of the hydrogen mass. In fact, the series of multiples is not integral (Table 29-2) and even the qualitative idea of integral multiples has to be ruled out altogether when an element such as Cl is considered, where $M/M_{\rm H} = 35.5$.

TABLE 29-2

DEMONSTRATION THAT THE AVERAGE ATOMIC MASS OF AN ELEMENT IS NOT AN INTEGRAL MULTIPLE OF THE AVERAGE MASS OF HYDROGEN ATOMS

Element	Atomic number	$M/M_{\rm H}$	Nearest integer
H	1	1	(1)
He	2	4	(4)
Li	3	6.9	(7)
Be	4	9.0	(9)
B	5	10.8	(?)

29-6 ISOTOPES

The discussion of the preceding section concerns the *average* mass of atoms of a given element, since the experiments detected only averages. We now return to observations of the electrical discharge in gases and consider the first method used to measure directly the charge-to-mass ratio of atoms.

If the polarity is reversed in the tube of Fig. 29-2, it is found, under suitable conditions of gas pressure and applied voltage that rays of some sort travel through the hole in the cathode and form a beam in the field-free region to the right of the cathode. These rays are called *canal rays* because the hole in the cathode that produces the collimation into a beam is *canal* in the German language. Canal rays require transverse fields more than a thousand times stronger than in the case of cathode rays in order to produce comparable deflections. The beams are not homogeneous in velocity. The early method for finding Q/M was to use transverse E and B fields that are parallel. The result was that the beam spread out into a parabolic trace (Section 23–5), which was recorded on a photographic plate.

Two additional contrasts with the results of cathode ray studies were found: (a) the value of Q/M was different for each different gas used in the tube; (b) even for a single monatomic gas, such as neon, there were different but discrete values of Q/M. The interpretation of the experiments was that many chemical elements consist of mixtures of atoms of different masses called *isotopes*. Since the masses of isotopes prove to be nearly integral multiples of the mass of hydrogen, and hydrogen itself seemed to have only one isotope, the positively charged portion of the hydrogen atom (called the proton) was considered to be the fundamental unit for the positively charged portion of any atom. Later experiments showed (a) that neutral counterparts of the proton, called *neutrons*, are the constituents that account for the different isotopic masses of a given element, and (b) that the relativistic equivalence of mass and energy accounts for the small departures of atomic masses from integral multiples of the masses of the constituents as free particles.

Further discussion of isotopes is left for the subject of nuclear physics. It is sufficient here to note the properties of the hydrogen atom. The mass is $M_{\mathrm{H}} = 1.66 \times 10^{-27}$ kg. The ratio of this mass to that of the electron is

$$\frac{M_{\mathrm{H}}}{m_e} = \frac{1.66 \times 10^{-27}\ \mathrm{kg}}{0.91 \times 10^{-30}\ \mathrm{kg}} = 1840.$$

Thus if an atom of hydrogen should contain an electron, the influence of the electronic mass upon the atomic mass is less than 0.1%. The electron must be identified as an extraordinarily "light" component of matter. The "massive" component must be something else.

Hydrogen ions carry positive electric charge but hydrogen atoms are neutral. Therefore we identify the positive "component" of the hydrogen atom with a "particle" whose mass is about 1840 times the electronic mass and whose charge is equal and opposite to the electronic charge. This particle is called the proton, an elementary particle of matter. An electron and a proton together form a neutral hydrogen atom. The ionized hydrogen atom is a proton of matter. Again, the discovery of the unique ionic charge is not violated. The electron possesses a single ionic charge of negative sign, the proton possesses a single ionic charge of positive sign. The electric neutrality of the atom as a whole supports the idea of the ionic charge.

29–7 THE WAVE NATURE OF CATHODE RAYS

In an earlier section we described the measurement of one specific property that can be attributed to the cathode rays, the charge-to-mass ratio. The measurement of the ionic charge may be regarded as an auxiliary experiment, inescapably connected with the cathode ray but not performed directly upon the cathode rays. The experiment to be described in this section is to be placed in a class with the e/m measurement. It is a *direct* observation of the nature of cathode rays. It has to do with the wave nature of the rays. It is interesting to note that the wave-like nature of matter was predicted by de Broglie in 1924. Indirect confirmation of de Broglie's hypothesis came within a year or two, due to the success of wave mechanics in describing the observed spectra of atoms and molecules. Another year or two later, the direct demonstration of the wave nature of the cathode rays, through a diffraction-interference measurement, stands as one of the landmarks in the history of modern physics.

A method for producing interference at short wavelengths will first be given. Crystalline matter is used extensively as a fine diffraction grating for x-rays whose wavelengths are much shorter than those of visible light. Atoms are predominantly uniformly spaced in a crystal. Thus a crystal is a type of grating on an atomic scale. Typical atomic spacings are of the order of 2 A units

(2×10^{-10} m) of length. (Visible light wavelengths, by comparison, are several thousand Angstrom units long.) Waves incident on a crystal face are scattered by the atoms in the crystal. When the wavelength is comparable with the atomic spacing, interference patterns are observed in the scattered waves, corresponding to interference between rays scattered by different atomic centers.

If a crystal sheet of thickness one atom deep could be prepared, the interference pattern would have maxima for the same angles as the ordinary diffraction grating. In Fig. 29–6 this condition is illustrated for waves incident normally on a sheet of atoms. If the atom spacing is d, the scattered waves interfere constructively at angles θ given (at large distances) by $\eta\lambda = d \sin \theta$, just

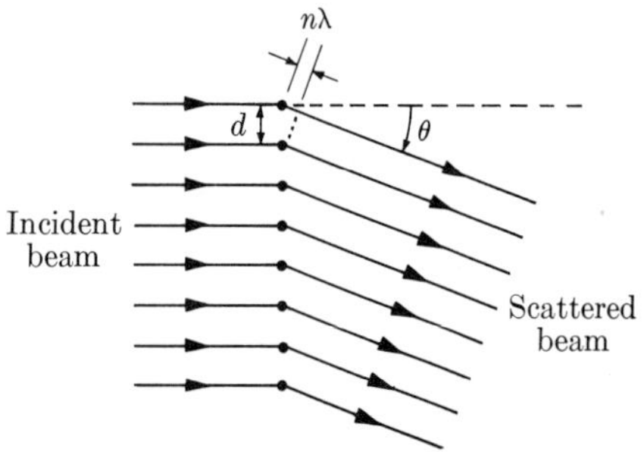

Fig. 29–6. Constructive interference of waves scattered by a one-dimensional array of scattering centers.

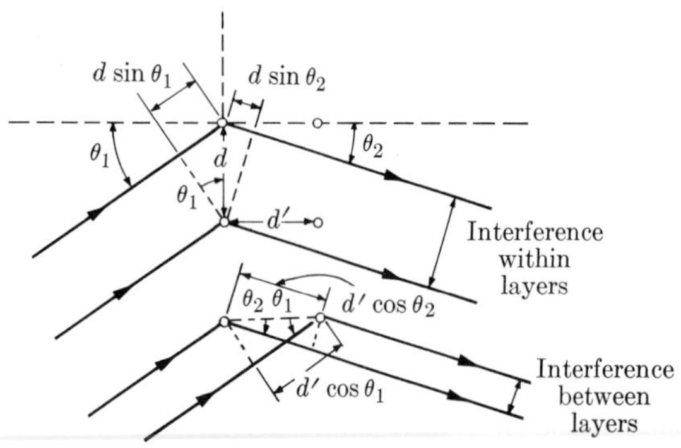

Fig. 29–7. Path differences for waves scattered by a two-dimensional array of centers.

as with a diffraction grating. (There is a slight difference because of the two-dimensional regularity of atom spacing. We are here considering only a plane, that of the incident beam.)

It is, of course, difficult to make a sheet of crystal one atom thick. Thus, we are forced to consider also the effect of interference between waves scattered by atoms in different layers, as in Fig. 29–7. In this figure, we have also chosen the more general case of angle of incidence θ_1 and angle of scattering θ_2, as shown. We then have, as the condition for constructive interference within a layer,

$$d \sin \theta_1 + d \sin \theta_2 = n\lambda, \qquad (29\text{–}10)$$

and between layers (of separation d'),

$$d' \cos \theta_1 - d' \cos \theta_2 = n'\lambda. \qquad (29\text{–}11)$$

In general, the two conditions of (29–10) and (29–11) cannot be met simultaneously, and the directions lying outside the plane of the incident rays must be considered. The problem is then a little more complex and we shall simply state here that in space there are directions that satisfy the conditions for constructive interference for certain wavelengths. Resulting on a screen is a two-dimensional pattern of spots.

We now turn to a special case, one in which $\theta_1 = \theta_2$. Then n' is zero and there simply remains

$$2d \sin \theta = n\lambda, \qquad (29\text{–}12)$$

which is known as the Bragg law. (Customarily the angle θ is measured between the crystal face and the incident ray and the sine then appears in place of the cosine.) If the scattering angle is greater than 90°, we speak of reflection, but the results are the same.

The standard method for measuring x-ray wavelengths or for determining the structure of a crystal is by diffraction of the above sort.

We now consider a standard experiment in which x-rays of predominantly one wavelength

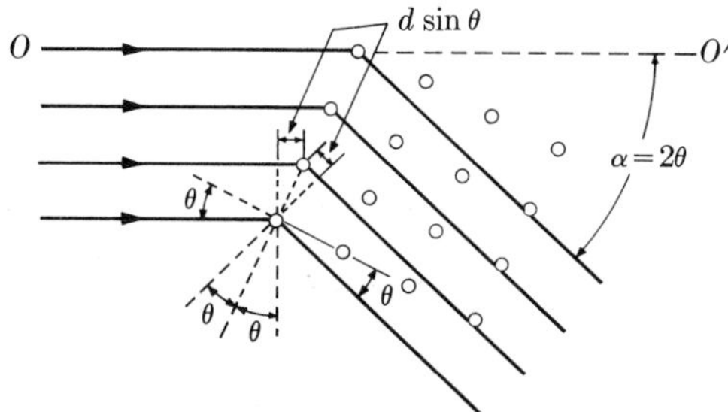

FIG. 29–8. Scattering by a two-dimensional array for the special case of zero path difference for the effect of the array in one dimension and path difference of $2d \sin \theta$ for the array in the second dimension (Bragg scattering).

are diffracted by a polycrystalline sample that has its crystals randomly oriented in direction. The result for a crystal that happens to have the right orientation θ with the direction of the incident beam OO', so that $n\lambda = 2d \sin \theta$, is shown in Fig. 29–8. All crystals with similar orientation θ with respect to OO', but with any azimuthal angle in a plane perpendicular to OO', will also satisfy Bragg's law and produce constructive interference. The result is a cone of constructive interference with angle $\alpha = 2\theta$ relative to OO', as in Fig. 29–9. When the cone is intercepted by a screen or photographic film, a circle is produced, as shown in Fig. 29–9. But there are also diagonal planes within a crystal which will have spacings

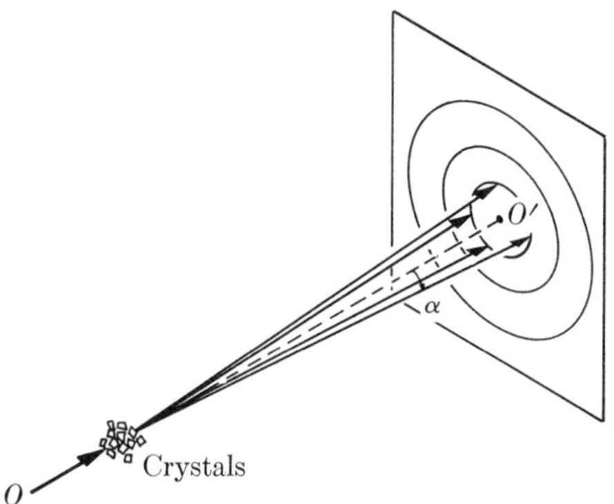

FIG. 29–9. Ring patterns resulting from Bragg scattering from many small crystals with random orientations (powder pattern).

between layers smaller than d. The result is a variety of angles θ for which constructive interference occurs. Remember that we have assumed crystals of all possible orientations in the target and, therefore, there are always some crystals at any required angle with the beam. The result is a family of circles on the screen. The relative values of the radii of the circles (or angles θ) will be characteristic of the particular kind of crystal. In general, the smallest circle corresponds to the largest d and, therefore, to the dimension d of Fig. 29–8 in a simple cubic crystal.

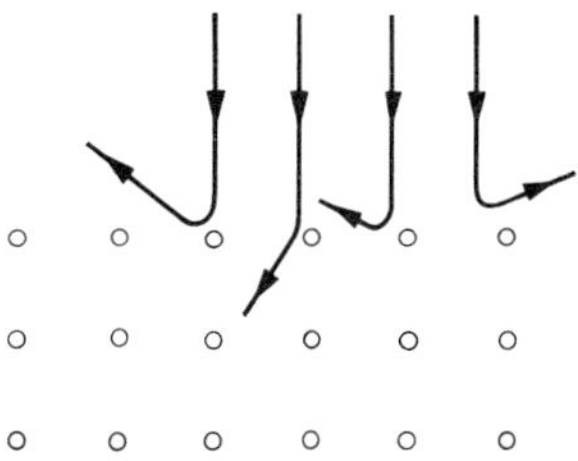

FIG. 29–10. Expected random scattering of electrons from even a perfect crystal face.

We now turn to an unexpected similarity between the diffraction of x-rays, as described above, and the scattering of electrons from the surface of a crystal. Since the surface of even a carefully polished crystal or metal must be rough on the atomic scale (Fig. 29–10), it is to be expected that incident particles will be scattered randomly in all directions. But in 1927, Davisson and Germer discovered preferential directions of "scattering" for electrons of particular energies. One such case is illustrated in Fig. 29–11. The

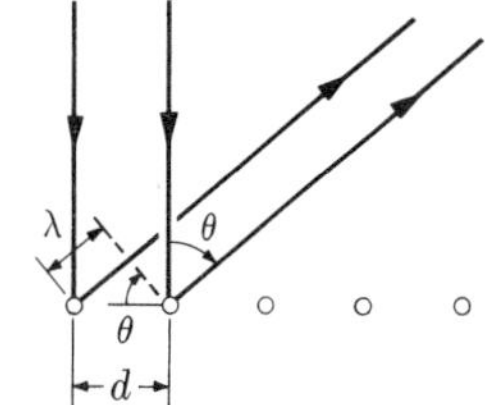

FIG. 29–11. Condition for constructive interference of waves scattered from the surface layer of atoms in a crystal.

beam is incident at 90° on a face of a nickel crystal. It was found that there is a strong peak in the scattering at 50° in the plane, with atom spacing $d = 2.15$ A for electrons that had been accelerated through 54 v potential difference. For the moment, we consider only the effects of scattering from the single (surface) layer. If we assume wave properties, constructive interference will occur when

$$\lambda = d \sin \theta = 2.15 \sin 50° = 1.65 \text{ A}. \quad (29\text{–}13)$$

The prediction of de Broglie, which will be discussed in more detail later, is that a *particle* of momentum p will exhibit the properties of a *wave* of wavelength

$$\lambda = \frac{h}{p}. \quad (29\text{–}14)$$

The constant $h = 6.6 \times 10^{-34}$ joule · second is called *Planck's constant.* It is a fundamental atomic constant that was first discovered in experimental and theoretical studies of the emission of radiation from hot solids. We shall come across this constant again and again in the study of atomic physics.

When the value of p corresponding to an electron of energy 54 ev is substituted in Eq. (29–14), the resulting wavelength agrees with the directly measured value $\lambda = 1.65$ A! Additional measurements at various angles and energies confirmed the correspondence between theory and experiment.

The effect included in Eq. (29–11) and shown in Fig. 29–7, the effect of interference *between* layers at different depths, was ignored. The added restriction imposed by interference between layers results in the limiting of the occurrence of maxima to particular energies and angles, such as 54 ev in the above example. Otherwise, it would be expected that any combination of energy and angle satisfying Eqs. (29–11) and (29–14), namely, $d \sin \theta = h/p$, would give a maximum. In addition, it was discovered that the result of interference between layers could only be understood if a shortened wavelength is used for the electrons that penetrate the crystal. The shortened wavelength results from the fact that the energy of the electrons is increased by a few electron volts upon entering the crystal.

Soon after the experiments by Davisson and Germer were made, the diffraction of high-energy electrons during their traversal of thin sheets of mica or thin metal foils was observed. Since the diffraction phenomenon is the same as for x-rays, our earlier analysis for x-rays is directly applicable (Figs. 29–11 and 29–12 and the accompanying analysis). Since the electron energies are typically many thousand electron volts (in order to traverse the sample), the effect of refraction is usually negligible; that is, the wavelength is not altered by more than a fraction of a percent upon entry into the material.

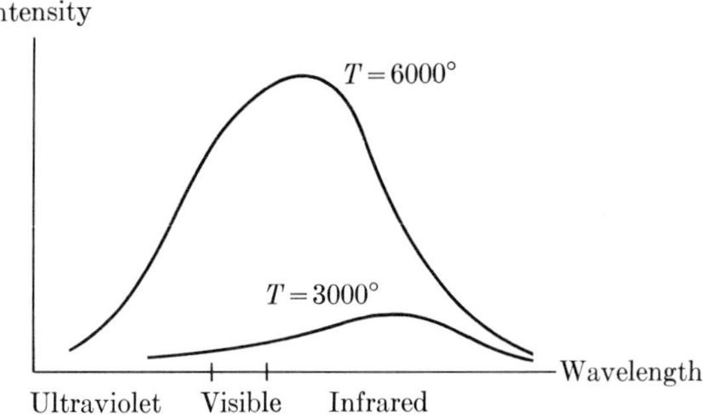

Fig. 29–12. Intensity of radiation from a cavity as a function of wavelength at two different temperatures.

Thus it is seen that cathode rays seem to lead a double life, since it is possible to measure directly a velocity and a charge-to-mass ratio of cathode rays on the one hand and a wavelength on the other hand. By less direct methods (or by direct methods, in principle) the charge can be inferred and hence the momentum. Thus the cathode rays (which we interpret as free electrons) exhibit particle and wave properties, as we know these properties on a macroscopic scale. The relationship predicted by de Broglie between the two types of properties is verified by experiment.

On the basis of direct experiment, we ascribe a wavelength to the cathode rays. Interpreting the rays as a beam of electrons, the wave property is attributed to the electron itself in the form of Eq. (29–13). We shall have cause in a later section to refer again to the particle-wave description of the cathode rays. It is sufficient to say, at present, that the wave nature exposed in this experiment must find its place in a general theory of atomic structure. The complementarity of the wave and particle properties will be treated later. We now turn to the question of electromagnetic waves and their interactions with matter.

29–8 BIRTH OF THE QUANTUM THEORY: ELECTROMAGNETIC RADIATION FROM HOT SOLIDS OR LIQUIDS

In the case of radio and radar waves, the source of radiation is directly energized by oscillators of known frequency. Thus charges are deliberately set into oscillation with known and predictable frequencies and the radiation has the same frequencies as the oscillators, just as predicted by theory. There are technical limitations that at present restrict this direct approach in the production of radiation to the spectral region from radio waves through radar waves to long infrared waves (wavelengths from kilometers to about a millimeter).

The methods for generating shorter wavelengths, including light, are indirect. Energy is added to atoms, molecules, or arrays of atoms or molecules (i.e., solids or liquids) by thermal agitation or by bombardment with beams of particles or radiation. In consequence of the indirect nature of the methods of excitation of the sources of radiation, we cannot say that we have set charges into oscillation. We can try to discover only indirectly the mechanisms for emission of radiation, for example, by studying the radiation itself and by observing the effect on the radiation of the conditions of excitation of the sources.

The source of light that might be expected to be simplest to understand is a cavity in a hot solid. The *spectrum* of radiation (intensity versus frequency or wavelength) is continuous. The distribution and magnitude of the intensity depend only on the temperature (Fig. 29–12) and not at all on the material. Classical theory predicts that oscillations of charges are set up due to thermal agitation. The intensity distribution of the resulting radiation can be calculated classically, but *the results do not agree with observation.* One feature of the classical theory should be noted particularly: The oscillators that emit and absorb radiation can gain or lose energy continuously, i.e., the increases or decreases in energy can be as small as we wish.

In 1900, Planck showed that a radical departure from classical theory made possible an accurate prediction of the spectrum of radiation from cavities in hot solids. The departure was in the form of the hypothesis that an oscillator could take on only discrete values of energy, in integral multiples of hf, where h is a universal constant and f is the frequency of oscillation: that is,

$$E = nhf, \tag{29–15}$$

where n is an integer. The constant h has since been called *Planck's constant* and is found to have the value 6.6×10^{-34} joule · second. The intensity distribution, as derived by Planck, is

$$I\,d\nu = \frac{2h\nu^3}{c^2}\,\frac{1}{e^{h\nu/kT} - 1}\,d\nu \text{ watts/cm}^2, \tag{29–16}$$

where ν is the frequency of the radiation and k is the Boltzmann constant (see the chapter on kinetic theory). (We shall use the notation ν for frequency of light and f for frequency of vibration or rotation of charged particles.) Equation (29–16) gives the power per unit area of emitter in a frequency interval $d\nu$ and at temperature T.

Thus a new basic concept, completely alien to classical theory, was introduced into physics. The quantization effect is not observed in radio and radar because the predicted minimum change in energy of an oscillator hf is so small that variations in energy would appear continuous. On the other hand, when we go to the other extreme of wavelengths, gamma-rays, we find that the emitter's quantum jumps in energy can be millions of electron volts.

It is interesting to note that quantization of the emitted *radiation* itself is implicit in Planck's theory, although he is reputed to have been reluctant to accept this implication.

In the next section additional evidence for the usefulness of the quantum hypothesis will be presented.

29–9 THE PHOTOELECTRIC EFFECT

In the preceding section, it has been seen that the success of the Planck theory gave a strong indication of a noncontinuous, that is, a quantized interaction between radiation and matter. We now turn to a direct experimental verification of the noncontinuous character of the interaction. Beginning with observations by Hertz in 1887, a series of experiments was performed on the conductivity produced in the space near a metal when the metal is illuminated by ultraviolet light. The phenomenon is called the *photoelectric effect.* The most definitive experiments were carried out in vacuum with apparatus somewhat as shown in Fig. 29–13. It is only when the cathode is irradiated with light that the photoconductivity effect appears. Thus it was surmised that a negative carrier of current is involved.

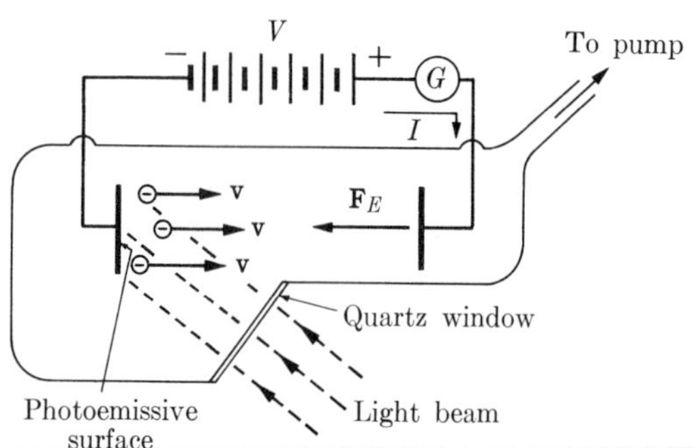

Fig. 29–13. Schematic diagram of apparatus for measuring the kinetic energy of electrons ejected from a metal by the photoelectric effect.

The discovery of the electron by Thomson was soon followed by the positive identification of the carrier of the photoelectric current as the electron. It was shown that the electric carrier has the same e/m ratio as the cathode ray beam. Electrons, then, are liberated from a metallic surface by an impinging light beam. They are called photoelectrons. What is the explanation of the photoelectric effect?

Electrons can also be emitted freely by a metallic surface when the metal is heated to temperatures above 2000°C. In this process, the electrons at high temperature acquire kinetic energies such that they can escape the metallic surface. At lower energies, the electrons are prevented from escaping by the force binding them to the metal. However, it is certain in the photoelectric experiments that the heating of the surfaces by the incident light is far from adequate to account for electron emission. Rather, photoemission appears to result from a direct interaction between the light and the electrons in the metal.

Energy is transmitted by a beam of light, and as a beam of light trained onto a metallic surface is made more intense, more energy is carried to the surface per unit of time. How should the intensification of a light beam affect the emission of photoelectrons? One of the possible answers is that, the photoelectrons should become more energetic. Another possibility is more photoelectrons per unit of time. The latter possibility is observed to be the sole intensity effect. As the light is made brighter, while retaining the same spectral distribution, the kinetic energy distribution of the emitted electrons remains the same. The only result is that more electrons are emitted per second. This raises a second and more specific question: what determines the kinetic energy distribution of the photoelectrons when emitted? This question is discussed in the next paragraph.

As the color, or frequency, of the incident light is varied, the kinetic energy of emission of the photoelectrons is found to be changed. The kinetic energy of emission from the cathode is measured by reversing the polarity of the externally applied emf in Fig. 29–13 and finding the current through the galvanometer G as a function of the retarding voltage V. As the retarding potential is increased, the photocurrent is reduced. Finally, a value is reached such that no electrons can penetrate the field. This maximum potential corresponding to zero current measures the maximum kinetic energy of the photoelectrons. Let U_m be the potential at which the current is reduced to zero and v_m the maximum photoelectron velocity. Then

$$\tfrac{1}{2}mv_m^2 = U_m e, \qquad (29\text{–}17)$$

where e and m are the charge and mass of the electron.

Photoelectrons are observed to have a range of velocities extending from zero to U_m. We assume that the electrons, after having absorbed light energy, may suffer varying energy losses before their escape from the metal. A relationship is sought, then, between the maximum energy of the ejected electrons and the property of the light which has induced emission of the electrons. The result is an extraordinarily simple relationship. The maximum electron energy is linearly proportional to the incoming light frequency. Red light produces lower energy electrons than

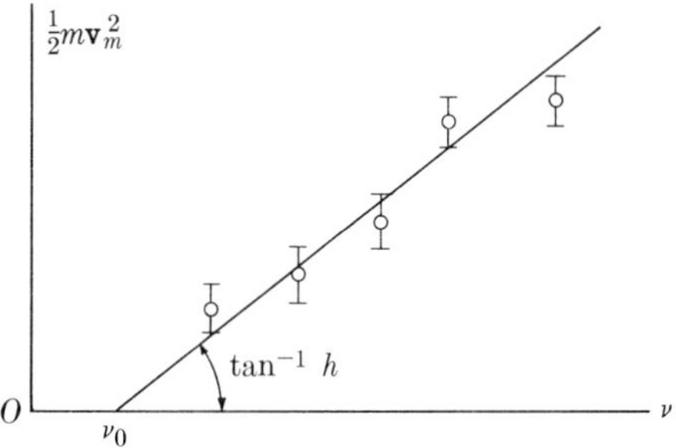

FIG. 29–14. Graph of the maximum kinetic energy of photoelectrons as a function of the frequency of the incident light. The extrapolated curve gives the threshold frequency as intercept on the axis of abscissas. The slope gives h (strictly, h/e, since the ordinate is actually Ue, where U is the measured retarding potential).

blue light. This linear relation is shown in Fig. 29–14. Remember that the light intensity affects only the number but not the energy of the photoelectrons.

At a certain minimum frequency ν_0, called the threshold frequency, the maximum electron energy is zero. Light below this frequency causes no emission at all. The relationship between maximum energy and frequency is therefore linear with a finite intercept ν_0 (Fig. 29–14). In algebraic form, the expression for the experimental results is

$$\tfrac{1}{2}mv_m^2 = h(\nu - \nu_0), \qquad (29\text{–}18)$$

where h is the *slope* of the curve and ν_0 is the intercept. The experimentally determined value of h is 6.6×10^{-34} j · sec, *the same constant* that was first introduced by Planck and that we have also seen used in the discussion of the wave properties of the electron.

The *classical theory* of interaction of light and matter predicts that the energy delivered by the wave to a charged particle (Section 29–2) depends on the *intensity* of the light. It is seen that this prediction disagrees directly with the experimental results of the photoelectric effect. For example, classical theory predicts a threshold intensity for emission of photoelectrons rather than a threshold frequency. Classical theory would also predict that U_m should be proportional to the intensity. Another striking contradiction is in the time required for the emission of a photoelectron. If the intensity of the light is sufficiently low, the time required for an electron to absorb sufficient energy to reach the threshold energy for emission is sufficient to give an easily detectable delay between the onset of irradiation and the emission of an electron. No such delay is ever observed.

The successful interpretation of the systematic effects found in the photoelectric experiment is due to Einstein and is known as the "quantum" hypothesis of light:

1. Whatever the wave nature of light may be, light has the further property of being divided

into definite "parcels" of energy. What we have regarded as plane waves of light can also be regarded as a stream of such parcels, called photons. Each photon has an energy which is proportional to the frequency of light, and the constant of proportionality is the Planck quantum of action, that is,

$$E_{\text{photon}} = h\nu. \tag{29–19}$$

2. There is a one-to-one interaction between photons and electrons in the metal. All the energy of a single photon is given over to a single electron. The energy equation (29–18) expresses the *conservation of energy* in this process. The energy $E_0 = h\nu_0$ is the minimum energy required to release an electron from the surface. It is called the binding energy or work function of the material. For metals, the work function E_0 is in the range 1 to 10 ev depending on the metal. The rest of the energy given to the electron appears in the form of kinetic energy. We thus have

$$h\nu = E_0 + \tfrac{1}{2}mv_m^2. \tag{29–20}$$

Electrons of kinetic energy less than the maximum occur because of energy losses suffered by some of the electrons before reaching the surface of the metal.

3. A more intense beam of light of given frequency gives rise to a *greater number* of photons arriving at the surface per second. Therefore an increase in intensity results in a greater yield of electrons, with, however, the same energy distribution of electrons.

The photon hypothesis for the structure of light is demanded again and again for the interpretation of other experiments in modern physics. The photoelectric process demonstrates the photon character of light in light absorption. It will be seen later that the photon character is required also in the interpretation of light creation by atoms and molecules.

Just as experiments on matter indicate the existence of smallest units of matter, the experiments on light indicate a smallest unit of light energy for any given frequency. The particle-construct applies to radiation as well as to matter.

29–10 THE COMPTON EFFECT

In the photoelectric effect the particle nature of light is evidenced by its absorption in discrete quanta of energy $h\nu$. The particle nature is even more strikingly demonstrated in the "scattering" of high-frequency radiation (x-rays). The scattered x-rays have two components, one in which the energy of the x-ray is essentially unchanged and the other in which the wavelength of the x-ray is increased. Classical theory predicts that the scattered radiation is the radiation emitted by charges that have been set in oscillation by the incident beam. Consequently, the wavelength of the scattered radiation could only be the same as that of the incident wave. Once again the quantum theory is successful where the classical theory fails. It was A. H. Compton who made the observations and gave the theory that explains the observations.

Compton assumed that the x-rays behave like particles in collision with matter. Just as in the photoelectric effect with light, an x-ray photon can be completely absorbed, giving all its energy to an electron. But there are other possibilities. Some x-ray photons collide elastically with an electron that remains bound to its atom, and the collision is effective with the atom as a whole. The atom is so heavy that the x-ray is deflected, with its energy essentially unchanged. Other x-rays collide with electrons that do not remain bound to the atom. The collision is essentially between an x-ray and a free electron in this case. The electron recoils with appreciable energy, which must be at the expense of the x-ray energy.

The quantitative analysis requires application of the conservation laws to the collision. We have already seen (Eq. 29–20) that the energy of a photon is $h\nu$. From classical theory of electromagnetic waves (Section 29–2), it has been shown that the momentum p of light is given by

$$p = \frac{E}{c}, \tag{29–21}$$

where E is its energy. Experimental observation of the pressure of a light beam confirms Eq.

(29–21). It was assumed by Compton that this result could be used when radiation displays particle properties, i.e., in general

$$p = \frac{h\nu}{c} \tag{29–22}$$

for photons.

We now turn to the relationship between energy and momentum for material particles. In classical mechanics, the energy of a particle is given by the equation,

$$E = \tfrac{1}{2}mv^2, \tag{29–23}$$

and the momentum is given by the equation,

$$p = mv. \tag{29–24}$$

Therefore, the connection between E and p is

$$E = \frac{p^2}{2m}, \tag{29–25}$$

or

$$p = \sqrt{2mE}. \tag{29–26}$$

In relativistic mechanics, the relationships and definitions are modified. Total energy is

$$W = mc^2 = \frac{m_0c^2}{\sqrt{1 - \beta^2}} = \gamma m_0c^2, \tag{29–27}$$

where $\beta \equiv v/c$ and momentum is

$$p \equiv mv = \frac{m_0v}{\sqrt{1 - \beta^2}} = \gamma m_0v. \tag{29–28}$$

From Eqs. (29–27) and (29–28), it can be shown that

$$W^2 = c^2p^2 + m_0^2c^4 \tag{29–29}$$

for particles.

In summary, we list and compare the mechanical attributes of material particles and of photons in Table 29–3. These relationships are tested in a complete way by examining a "collision" between a photon and a free electron, in which both energy and momentum must be conserved. The Compton effect pertains to such particles in free collisions.

TABLE 29–3

Comparison of the Expressions for Energy, Momentum, and the Relationship between Them for Particles and for Radiation

	Electron	Photon
Energy	$W = mc^2$	$E = h\nu$
Momentum	$p = mv$	$p = \frac{h\nu}{c}$
Relationship	$W = c\sqrt{p^2 + m_0^2c^2}$	$E = pc$

Some electrons are bound to atoms with energies of the order of only a few electron volts. The weakest binding energy is measured by the energy required to ionize an atom, which is found directly either by chemical or electric means to be at most about 20 ev. If photons of energy many times greater than the binding energy (x-rays) are used to bombard atoms, then the atomic electrons, to a good degree of approximation, may be considered to be free. The binding is of little consequence. Therefore, we picture the Compton process as a collision between a free electron at rest and an oncoming photon. This situation differs from the photoelectric reaction in one important respect: In that reaction we insisted that energy be conserved, but we placed no condition on momentum since the local material in the metal could absorb any amount of momentum. In that case, the total *photon* energy was absorbed. But in the case of the free electron, both momentum and energy must be conserved by the electron-photon system alone. It is a simple matter to prove that total absorption of the photon cannot take place under these circumstances (see Problems).

In Compton's study of photon-electron collisions, he observed photons of less than the incident energy emerging from the collision area. Photon theory was in its infancy at the time and the following hypothesis was not readily accepted. Nevertheless, it was finally verified in minute detail. It is this: In the event that a photon of light strikes an electron, a photon of lesser energy is formed. The new photon and recoil electron form the system after collision (Fig. 29–15).

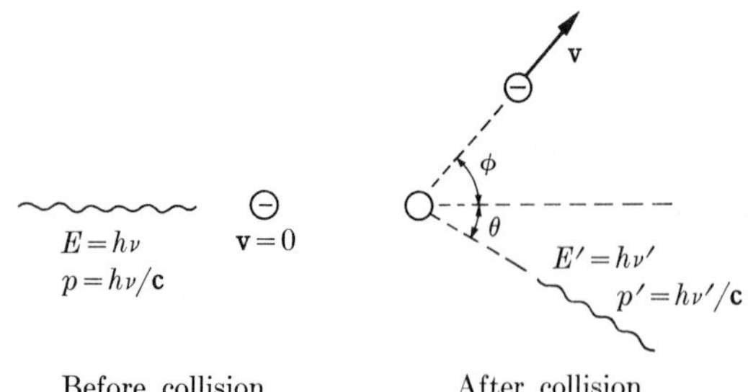

Fig. 29–15. Schematic diagram of the collision (interaction) between radiation (a photon) and a free electron.

For energy conservation, we equate the incident photon energy to the kinetic energy of the electron and the energy of the new photon after collision, thus

$$h\nu = h\nu' + \left(\frac{m_0c^2}{\sqrt{1-\beta^2}} - m_0c^2\right), \qquad (29\text{–}30)$$

where the term in parentheses is the kinetic energy of the electron, the total energy minus the rest energy. Momentum conservation gives us two equations. For the components of momentum along the direction of flight of the incident photon, we have

$$\frac{h\nu}{c} = \frac{h\nu'}{c}\cos\theta + \frac{m_0v}{\sqrt{1-\beta^2}}\cos\phi. \qquad (29\text{–}31)$$

In the perpendicular direction we have

$$0 = \frac{h\nu'}{c}\sin\theta + \frac{m_0v}{\sqrt{1-\beta^2}}\sin\phi. \qquad (29\text{–}32)$$

The general analysis of this set of three simultaneous equations is left to the Problems. Here we give the result for the change in wavelength ($\lambda - \lambda' = c/\nu - c/\nu'$) for the photon. The change in wavelength is

$$\lambda' - \lambda = \frac{h}{m_0c}(1 - \cos\theta). \qquad (29\text{–}33)$$

This prediction is accurately borne out by observation.

The expression h/m_0c is called the Compton wavelength. From Eq. (29–33), we see that the shift in wavelength of the scattered photon is never greater than twice the Compton wavelength of the struck particle. In the limit of very high energy for the incident photon, the wavelength λ approaches zero and the longest possible wavelength of the scattered photon is the Compton wavelength.

The fact that a photon of light can become involved in a mechanical collision with an electron, governed by the classical collision rules, is a striking demonstration of the particle nature of the photon.

Summary of electrons and photons. 1. Both matter and light are found to have a granular structure. The electron has a definite and invariable charge and mass. The photon of light for a given frequency has a definite energy and momentum.

2. Both matter and light have a wave quality. The wave and mechanical attributes are related by the de Broglie law, $p = h/\lambda$.

3. In addition to the material and electric constants found in nature, the electronic mass and charge, etc., we have found an irreducible unit of action in nature called the Planck constant.

29–11 ATOMIC CONSTITUTION AND DIMENSIONS

Earlier we discussed the evidence that leads to the conclusion that atoms of matter contain both positive and negative electric charge in equal amounts. We have also seen that charges occur in integral multiples of a unit of charge, the positive units being carried by the heavy components of matter, the protons, and the negative units of charge by the light components of matter, the electrons. More information is needed, however, before the laws of mechanics can be applied to the internal structure of the atom. It is necessary to know the relative positions and sizes of the interacting constituents. Since the constituents cannot be seen, a particular structure (called a model) is hypothesized.

The model is then tested by comparing calculated properties with observed properties, primarily the properties of emission of radiation.

In the absence of any direct knowledge of the atomic charge distribution, J. J. Thomson proposed a model which, although it was proved to be incorrect, served to place the speculation about atomic structure on a quantitative footing. In his model, positive atomic charge is spread uniformly within a sphere of radius equal to the atomic size itself. The diameter was known from the kinetic theory of collisions and the measured mean free path. The diameter was found to be roughly 10^{-10} m. The atomic electrons, assumed in this representation to be comparatively small, since they have only 1/1800 the mass of the lightest atom, are placed within the positive charge cloud (Fig. 29–16). For evident reasons, the model has been dubbed the raisin-pudding model. The electrons are the raisins and the positive charge is the matrix. If the model is valid, then we have the means of computing the electronic motion. The electric field within a uniformly charged sphere (assuming the electric laws are still valid at such distances), is

$$E_r = \frac{1}{4\pi\epsilon_0} \frac{Qr}{R^3}, \qquad (29\text{–}34)$$

where Q is the atomic positive charge and R is the atomic radius. In the case of an atom of hydrogen, the force on the electron is directed toward the center of the system, and has the value

$$F = Ee = -\frac{1}{4\pi\epsilon_0} \frac{Qer}{R^3}, \qquad (29\text{–}35)$$

where e is the electronic charge. This is a Hooke's law force on the electron, $F = -Kr$, since all other quantities are constants.

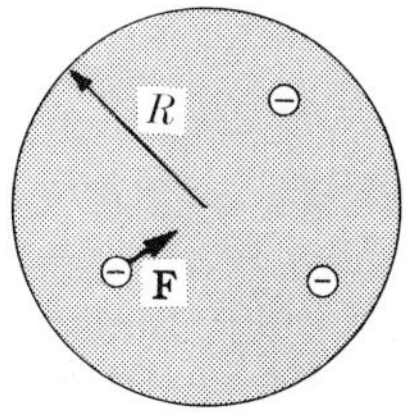

FIG. 29–16. Diagram of the raisin-pudding model of the atom of Thomson. The positive charge is distributed uniformly throughout the shaded region.

The motion of the electron would therefore be simple harmonic, with frequency given by

$$f = \frac{1}{2\pi} \sqrt{\frac{Qe}{4\pi\epsilon_0 m R^3}}. \qquad (29\text{–}36)$$

It will prove interesting to the reader to place the values of the atomic constants, Q, e, and R, into the frequency equation. The frequency is not far from the frequency of visible light, 10^{15} cps, given off by atoms. However, the model suffers when it is compared with the detailed results of atomic spectroscopy. The experimental evidence shows that atoms emit a complex *series* of frequencies, and not a single frequency. But the validity of the model was not tested on the basis of such indirect evidence. Instead, a direct experimental measurement of the size of the positive charge cloud ruled out the Thomson model altogether, as we shall now see.

Some of the heavy elements with atomic number above that of lead are found to emit particles with positive charge at high velocity. The charge-to-mass ratio of these particles shows them to be identical with twice-ionized helium, He^{++} (helium atoms stripped of both electrons). The name given these high-speed fragments is alpha-particle, or alpha-ray. The alpha-particle speed may be nearly unique for any particular atomic species, and it is generally in the range of about one-tenth the velocity of light. Therefore, alpha-particles constitute fast, massive, energetic projectiles appropriate for the exploration of the internal structure of atoms. If a narrow beam of such particles passes through matter, deflections will occur because of the Coulomb force between the alpha-particles and the charged constituents of the atoms. In order to study the deflections, Rutherford sent a beam through a thin gold foil. The particles emerge with sufficient energy to continue to a fluorescent screen where each particle registers as a visible momentary pinpoint of light (Fig. 29–17). If an observer watches the screen in the dark, with a low-power microscope, the scintillations are readily visible.

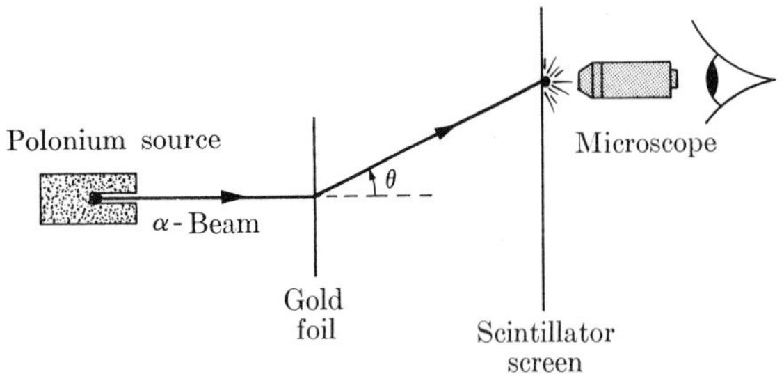

FIG. 29–17. Schematic diagram of the Rutherford alpha-particle scattering experiment.

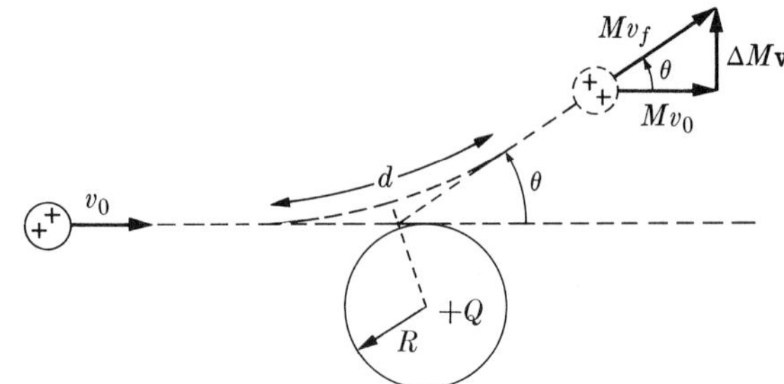

FIG. 29–18. Diagram of the path of an alpha-particle in its passage near an atom. Because of the rapid fall-off of an inverse-square force, it is assumed that the force is negligible beyond a few times the distance of closest approach (relative to the force at the point of closest approach).

What is expected in the way of deflections? The collision of alpha-particles with the electrons in atoms can result only in an extraordinarily small deflection. The electrons are too light to absorb a large amount of energy or momentum from the fast, heavy alpha-particles, since the alpha-particle mass is 4×1840 times the electron mass. For example, imagine a severe, head-on collision between a fast alpha-particle and a stationary electron. From the laws of elastic collisions, we have for the final velocities (u_1 for the alpha-particle and u_2 for the electron, after collision by an alpha-particle of velocity v_1):

$$u_1 = \frac{v(M - m)}{M + m} \simeq v_1,$$

$$u_2 = \frac{2Mv}{M + m} \simeq 2v_1. \qquad (29\text{–}37)$$

The alpha-particle recoil velocity is very nearly the original velocity. It continues with its velocity changed by less than 0.1%. Thus in a glancing collision, we should never expect the alpha-particle to be deflected from its path by as much as $\frac{1}{1000}$ radian. On the other hand, the electron will be ejected at high speed as a result of the encounter. It can be concluded, then, to a good degree of approximation, that an alpha-particle is affected only by the heavy (electrically positive) components of matter in a single encounter. Therefore, we can study the positive atomic charge without appreciable complicating effect by the electrons that are also present. This is a great convenience and it represents the principal strength of the method.

Assume, then, that an alpha-particle encounters a positive charge cloud of radius equal to 10^{-10} m. In the case of gold, the positive cloud is little affected since it is about 50 times as heavy as the alpha-particle. The biggest deflection of the alpha-particle will occur when, by chance, it grazes the surface of the charge cloud. At greater distance the force is reduced by the inverse-square law. For closer encounters, the charge cloud is penetrated and the force is again reduced (Eq. 29–35). We shall perform an order of magnitude calculation of the maximum deflection, since this is all that is needed for the present purpose. The path length d, throughout which there is a really strong interaction, is about equal to $2\,R$ (Fig. 29–18). At other points along the path, the force is reduced as the inverse square of the distance. When the particle sweeps by the atom, it experiences a sideways force given roughly by

$$F = \frac{1}{4\pi\epsilon_0} \frac{qQ}{R^2}. \qquad (29\text{–}38)$$

The force acts for a time $t \simeq d/v = 2\,R/v$. From the impulse formulation of Newton's second law, the product of force by the time is equal to the change in momentum of the particle, or $Ft = \Delta Mv$, which gives

$$\Delta Mv = \frac{2qQ}{4\pi\epsilon_0 Rv}. \quad (29\text{–}39)$$

The angle of deflection is about $\Delta Mv/Mv$ (see Fig. 29–18), giving

$$\theta \simeq \frac{2qQ}{4\pi\epsilon_0 MRv^2}. \quad (29\text{–}40)$$

Into this approximate expression we insert the values of the atomic constants,

$$q = 2 \times 1.6 \times 10^{-19} \text{ coul } (\alpha)$$
$$Q = 79 \times 1.6 \times 10^{-19} \text{ coul (gold)}$$
$$\frac{1}{4\pi\epsilon_0} = 9 \times 10^9$$
$$M = 4 \times 1.66 \times 10^{-27} \text{ kg } (\alpha)$$
$$v \simeq 10^{-1}c = 3 \times 10^7 \frac{m}{s} \ (\alpha).$$

The result is

$$\theta \simeq \frac{2 \times 10^{-14}}{R} \text{ rad.} \quad (29\text{–}41)$$

If $R = 10^{-10}$ m, as in the Thomson model,

$$\theta_{\text{max}} = 2 \times 10^{-4} \text{ rad}$$

for a single collision.

According to this model, we can expect only infrequent deflections as large as a degree even in case of successive additive collisions within the gold foil. For example, a typical foil is about 10^{-5} m, or about 10^4 atoms, in thickness. Even if each of 10^4 collisions resulted in maximum deflection in the same direction, the total deflection would be 2 rad. But it is extremely unlikely that all deflections will be in the same direction and it is impossible that they all will be a maximum. Try to construct a path through a regular cubic array of Thomson atoms such that all deflections would be maximum and in the same direction.

To Rutherford's amazement deflections up to 90° were not uncommon, and even backscattering occurred at times. Thus, the angle θ in Eq. (29–41) is of the order of one radian and therefore R must be of the order 10^{-14} m, a far cry from the Thomson model. The experimental results can only be explained if the massive part of the atom is 10^4 times smaller than the atom itself. Relative to atomic dimensions, the heavy, positively charged portion can be treated as a point charge.

The tiny but massive positively charged portion of the atom is called the nucleus. The atom is predominantly empty space occupying a region of radius about 10^{-10} m. Therefore, this distance must simply be the separation of nucleus and electron, both charges being considered points. The electron is in the inverse-square field of a massive, point, positive charge. It is upon this model that the Bohr postulates are to be built in the following sections.

The student is referred to any intermediate atomic physics text for the exact calculation for Rutherford scattering. For the purposes of calculation, the nucleus is assumed a point charge, and a $\csc^4 \theta/2$ angular distribution of scattering of alpha-particles is a direct and exact result. Since the experimental results agree with this distribution, we conclude not only that the nucleus is small but also that Coulomb's law holds for distances on the atomic scale or even on the nuclear scale.

29–12 THE NEUTRON

In order to account for isotopes it was believed for some time that the heavy constituents of the atom, i.e., of the nucleus, were all protons. Then, in order to account for the fact that isotopes of the same element must have the same number of electrons and hence the same net nuclear charge, it was assumed that the nucleus contained electrons in sufficient number to give the correct net charge. Thus the heavy stable isotope of hydrogen was supposed to have a nucleus composed of two protons and one electron. There seemed to be a certain amount of support for this model from the observation that high-energy electrons are ejected from the nuclei of some of the radioactive atoms. However, there are basic difficulties with this model that are particularly evident when the wave nature of electrons is taken into account. An example of the difficulty is left for the problems.

With the discovery of the neutron, the uncharged counterpart of the proton, it was no longer necessary to hypothesize electrons as stable nuclear constituents. The neutron was identified by the basic observations of the recoil energies and momenta of nuclei that were struck by fast neutrons. The mode of production of fast neutrons involves nuclear physics and need not concern us here.

Thus there are three stable constituents of atoms—protons and neutrons in the nucleus, and electrons at large distances from the nucleus. It is interesting to note that the neutron is unstable when removed from the nucleus and decays spontaneously into a proton, an electron, and a neutrino. Again this is a topic for nuclear physics.

Other particles originate from the nuclei of atoms even though they are not stable constituents of atoms. For example, plus and minus electrons are emitted from certain radioactive atoms, and nearly 100 different kinds of unstable particles have been produced by bombardment of nuclei. But if questions of what holds the nucleus together are avoided, we need only be concerned with the three stable constituents.

In the next chapter, we proceed to the question of the electronic structure of the atom.

29–13 SUMMARY

Electrons were identified and their charge-to-mass ratio determined from the transverse deflections of cathode rays by electric and magnetic fields. The result is

$$\frac{q}{m} = 1.76 \times 10^{11}\ \frac{\text{coul}}{\text{kg}}.$$

The charge on the electron was determined from the oil-drop experiment as

$$e = 1.60 \times 10^{-19}\ \text{coul}.$$

The number of atoms in a mole can be determined from the faraday, which is the total charge required to deposit a mole of monovalent ions in electrolysis, and the charge per ion, which is of the same magnitude as the electronic charge. The result is called Avogadro's number

$$A = 6.02 \times 10^{23} \text{ per mole.}$$

The average mass of atoms can be found by dividing the mass of a mole by Avogadro's number. The results seemed to suggest, since the masses of the atoms of most elements are nearly integral multiples of the hydrogen atom, that the hydrogen atom is the basic constituent of all atoms. The discovery of isotopes and the later discovery of the neutron clarified the problem. The basic constituents of matter are hydrogen (isotope 1) nuclei and neutrons, which constitute the nucleus, and electrons which make up the structure outside the nucleus. Thus the mixture of isotopes that constitutes a chemical element has an average mass that need not even approximate an integral multiple of the hydrogen mass. When the decrease in mass arising from the relativistic decrease in energy of particles assembled into a nucleus is taken into account, the small departures of isotopic masses from the sum of the masses of the constituent particles are accounted for.

Wave-like properties of particles were predicted by de Broglie and later confirmed directly by the experiments of Davisson and Germer. The wavelength predicted by de Broglie was

$$\lambda = \frac{h}{p},$$

where h is Planck's constant and p is the momentum of the particle. The wave properties were demonstrated by interference effects among the waves scattered by atoms in a regular crystalline array. The interference effect due to scattering from crystals is first discussed in its application to x-rays. The Bragg equation for constructive interference is

$$n\lambda = 2\,d \sin\theta$$

and the angle of incidence equals the angle of reflection. In the case of low-energy electrons, most of the scattering may occur from the surface layer of atoms in the crystal.

The study of the interactions of radiation (in the visible or near visible range of wavelengths) with matter is begun with the description of the radiation from a hot solid. Classical theory could not account for the spectral distribution. The quantum hypothesis of Planck, that the oscillator energy must be quantized

$$E = nhf,$$

led to a successful description of the spectrum.

The second example is the photoelectric effect, where, again, a quantum hypothesis is required for explanation of the observations. In this case, quantization of the energy of the radiation is the key to success,

$$E = h\nu,$$

leading to the Einstein equation for the photoelectric effect,

$$\tfrac{1}{2}mv^2 = h\nu - h\nu_0.$$

The threshold energy $h\nu_0$ is a constant characteristic of the surface of the metal.

The Compton effect, in which a light quantum interacts with a "free" electron, gives further evidence for the quantum nature of radiation. When energy $h\nu$ and momentum $h\nu/c$ are attributed to the incident photon, the conservation principles lead to a correct prediction for the wavelength (or frequency) of the scattered radiation

$$\lambda' = \lambda + \frac{h}{m_0 c}(1 - \cos\theta)\,.$$

The Thomson model of the atom and its contradiction by the alpha-particle scattering experiments of Rutherford are described. An approximate value for the deflection of a charged particle in an inverse-square-force field is calculated to be

$$\theta \simeq \frac{2qQ}{4\pi\epsilon_0 Mv^2 R},$$

where R is the distance of closest approach. The Rutherford experiment requires a value of R of the order of 10^{-14} m, a value that dictates the nuclear atom model with the heavy, positive portion of the atom confined to the above-sized region.

The discovery of the neutron eliminated the need to suppose that electrons were nuclear constituents.

Problems

$$\begin{aligned} h &= 6.6 \times 10^{-34} \text{ joule/sec} \\ e &= 1.6 \times 10^{-19} \text{ coul} \\ m_0 &= 9.11 \times 10^{-31} \text{ kg} \\ m_p &= 1.67 \times 10^{-27} \text{ kg} \end{aligned}$$

1. In Thomson's first method of determining e/m of cathode rays, he took data of the following kind:

(a) The beam was intercepted by a small target of mass M kg and specific heat S cal/gm·deg. The temperature of the target was measured with a thermocouple and was found to rise ΔT degrees in t seconds. Derive an expression for the total kinetic energy ($\frac{1}{2}Nmv^2$) of the N cathode rays that struck the target in time t, in terms of the measured quantities.

(b) With beam intensity the same as in (a), the beam charge was collected for a time t on the target and it was found that the target potential was raised by ΔV volts. The capacitance of the target was measured and found to be C microfarads. Find the total charge Ne collected in time t, in terms of the measured quantities.

(c) Finally, the beam was bent into a circular arc of radius R by application of a magnetic field of intensity B webers/m^2 in a direction perpendicular to the beam. Derive an explicit expression for e/m in terms of the measured quantities listed in (a), (b), and (c).

2. An oil drop of 0.5×10^{-4} cm radius has an excess charge of two electrons. It is located between plane-parallel horizontal conductors that are 2 cm apart. The density of the oil is 0.94 gm/cm^3.

(a) What potential difference between the plates is required to hold the drop stationary?

(b) If the friction *force* by air on a moving drop is $6\pi\eta rv$, where η is 1.8×10^{-4} gm·cm^{-1}·sec^{-1}, r is the radius, and v the velocity of the drop, what is the terminal velocity of free fall of the drop (no electric field)?

(c) Outline the actual measurements that would be made in order to find the charge on the drop, since the charge is usually the unknown.

3. Describe the steady-state motion of the oil drop of Problem 2, with and without the electric field, if the plates are in *vertical* planes.

4. A current of 10 amp flowing for one hour deposits 18.0 gm of material at the negative terminal in an electrolytic solution. What is the gross atomic weight, assuming that the material is an element with a valence of two?

5. A 1-mm steel sphere has a mass of about 3 mg.

(a) What is the de Broglie wavelength of the sphere when its velocity is 1 cm/sec?

(b) Discuss the feasibility of detecting the wave properties of a beam of 1-mm spheres.

6. Given a crystal with a simple cubic array of atoms spaced 1.5 A apart,

(a) what should be the velocity of electrons incident at 45° if an interference maximum is to be observed at 45° for the "scattered" beam?

(b) What is the energy of the electrons in electron volts?

7. Repeat Problem 6 for a beam of hydrogen atoms.

8. Derive an expression for the wavelength λ of electrons in terms of their kinetic energy expressed in electron volts

(a) in the *non*relativistic case and

(b) in the relativistic case.

9. Neutron diffraction is a method for studying the crystalline structure of solids. Find the wavelength of "thermal" neutrons at room temperature and comment on their usefulness for the above purpose. (Thermal energy at room temperature is about 1/40 ev.)

10. The energy of a carefully constructed pendulum can be measured accurately by measuring its amplitude of motion. With what accuracy would it be necessary to measure the amplitude of a pendulum of length 1 m and amplitude 2 cm in order to detect the quantization of its energy changes?

11. At 3000 degrees, the mean energy of thermal agitation is about $\frac{1}{4}$ ev. The radiation from an object at this temperature has considerable intensity at visible wavelengths, implying that there are oscillators excited at the frequency of visible light at this temperature (classical theory).

(a) What frequency corresponds to red light of wavelength 5000 A?

(b) What is the smallest quantum change of energy at this frequency?

(c) How does this compare in magnitude with an energy of $\frac{1}{4}$ ev that an oscillator might have at this temperature?

12. From the expression for the energy of a light quantum, $E = h\nu$, show that $E\lambda = 12{,}345$ (ev $\times$ A), where the last two figures are not correct but serve as an aid to the memory.

13. An intense light source can give rise to a sinusoidal electric field of amplitude $E_0 = 10^8$ v/m at short distances from the source, using the classical model of radiation. Consider an intense light source of wavelength 5000 A giving a field of amplitude 10^8 v/m at the surface of a metal of work function 2 ev.

(a) Show that a "free electron" in the metal experiences an acceleration $a = (e/m)E_0 \sin \omega t$.

(b) Show that the electron moves with SHM with displacement

$$X = -\frac{e}{m\omega^2} E_0 \sin \omega t.$$

(c) What is the frequency of the light and hence the value of ω?

(d) What is the maximum energy of the electron? Will it be ejected from the metal according to classical theory?

14. (a) Calculate the maximum kinetic energy of the photoelectrons ejected according to quantum theory in Problem 13.

(b) What is the maximum wavelength light that can eject electrons from the metal?

15. Derive Eq. (29–33) from the conservation equations.

16. (a) Show that the Compton shift h/m_0c is 0.0243 A.

(b) Find the modified (Compton) and unmodified wavelengths of x-rays of wavelength 0.1 A when the x-rays are scattered through an angle of 30°.

17. (a) What are the energies of the incident and the scattered photon in the case of Compton scattering in the preceding problem?

(b) What is the energy of the electron?

(c) What are the momenta?

(d) Draw a vector diagram illustrating the conservation of momentum in the "collision."

18. Repeat the preceding problem for the case of "unmodified" scattering, assuming that the atom is hydrogen.

19. Suppose an electron of energy 1 Mev passing through the dense radiation region close to the sun collides head-on with a photon of wavelength 3000 A.

(a) Write the conservation equations.

(b) Find the wavelength of the recoil photon.

20. Using Avogadro's number 6.02×10^{23} molecules/mole and the density of liquid hydrogen 0.07 gm/cm^3, calculate the size of the hydrogen atom, assuming that the atoms are in "contact" with their neighbors. (A *nonclose* packed cubical array of spheres may be the simplest geometry to assume for calculation.)

21. What is the maximum-energy alpha-particle that could be backscattered by a Thomson-model gold nucleus of radius 10^{-10} m (nuclear charge 79)? (Assume uniform charge density and consider a head-on collision, i.e., 180° scattering.)

22. Find the fundamental frequency of vibration of the electron in a hydrogen atom, according to the Thomson model, and compare with light frequencies.

23. Use the impulse method, $\int \mathbf{F}\,dt = \Delta M\mathbf{V}$, to find the deflection of a charged particle q that was traveling in a direction that would miss a point charge Q by distance d as shown in Fig. 29–19. The mass of Q is so large that it is assumed to remain essentially stationary. Assume that θ is small.

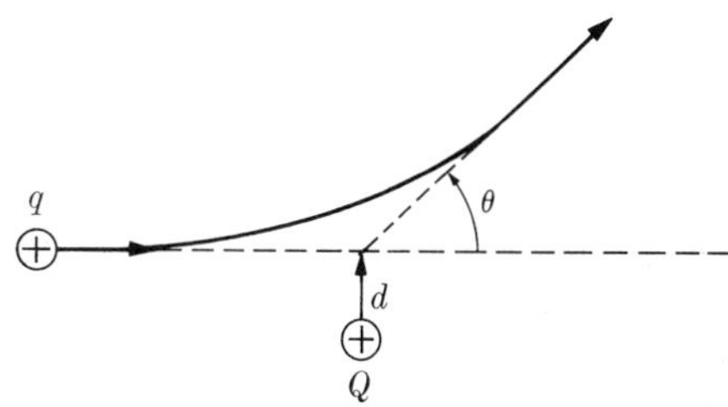

FIGURE 29–19

24. (a) Assuming a point charge, find the distance of closest approach of an alpha-particle of energy 6 Mev (nonrelativistic) to a gold nucleus (charge 79) in a head-on collision, neglecting the recoil of the gold nucleus.

(b) Since 180° scatterings are in fact observed, what can you conclude about the maximum size of the gold nucleus from the above result?

25. Part of the original evidence in the discovery of the neutron came from measurements of the recoil energy E_{H} of hydrogen nuclei and E_{N} of nitrogen nuclei when struck head-on by neutrons of unknown mass and energy. Derive the equation for the neutron mass in terms of the above energies and the known masses of H and N nuclei. The energies are nonrelativistic.

26. Calculate the de Broglie wavelength of an electron of 10 Mev (a typical possible binding energy of a particle in a nucleus). Compare this wavelength with nuclear dimensions 10^{-14} m and comment on the possibility of the electron as a stable nuclear constituent. (It would be required to have a standing wave pattern *within* the nuclear boundaries.) Note that $W^2 = p^2c^2 + m_0^2c^4$ becomes $W \simeq pc$ when $W \gg m_0c^2$.

27. List the nuclear constituents of

(a) the three isotopes of hydrogen, 1, 2, and 3;

(b) uranium 235 (atomic number 92).

30

Atomic Physics: The Structure of the Atom (Quantum Mechanics)

30–1 INTRODUCTION

In the preceding chapter, some of the evidence leading to our knowledge of the constituents of the atom was presented. It was found that classical laws could be used successfully in many cases, for example, in predicting the motion of free-particle atomic constituents in electric or magnetic fields. The conservation laws were found to be universally applicable. But when the scattering of free particles by matter was considered, it was found that a new concept, wave properties for particles, must be introduced.

Furthermore, some of the properties of electromagnetic radiation, classical and nonclassical, were treated. It was found that electromagnetic waves do not behave in the classical manner in their interactions with matter at the wavelengths of visible light, or shorter. The observations were made understandable only if particle properties are attributed to radiation.

Finally, it was found that the emission of short wavelength radiation by hot solids could be understood only if a *nonclassical* idea, the quantization of energy of oscillators, was introduced.

In this chapter, we continue the study of the interactions by means of which the "structure" of the atom can be inferred. We have already seen that the positive charge resides in a nucleus that behaves like a point charge down to distances at least 10^{-14} m. On the other hand, the size of the atom as a whole is about 10^{-10} m. Any attempts to define the geometrical structure of the atom more closely, by experiments that would define the position and velocities of the electrons, have proved unsuccessful. It is, in fact, believed that this is inherently impossible, as we shall see later when the uncertainty principle is discussed.

Instead, it is found that the internal energy of the atom, its angular momentum, and its interactions with radiation, particles, other atoms, or electromagnetic fields can be completely predicted. All these effects are due to so-called electromagnetic interactions, that is, forces due to electric charges. It is believed that this is a "closed" subject in the sense that the basic theory can, in principle, describe all observations. The detailed calculations may of course, involve mathematical difficulties, just as in the simple classical mechanical problem of the prediction of the motion of more than two interacting astronomical bodies where only Newton's laws are involved.

We first consider the absorption and emission of radiation by atoms, a subject entitled *spectroscopy*. In the last chapter we said something about the emission and absorption of energy by solids. We now turn to the case of emission and absorption by atoms that are sufficiently separated so that interatomic interactions are negligible.

30–2 ATOMIC SPECTRA

The order of presentation of basic experiments in modern physics given in this book does not

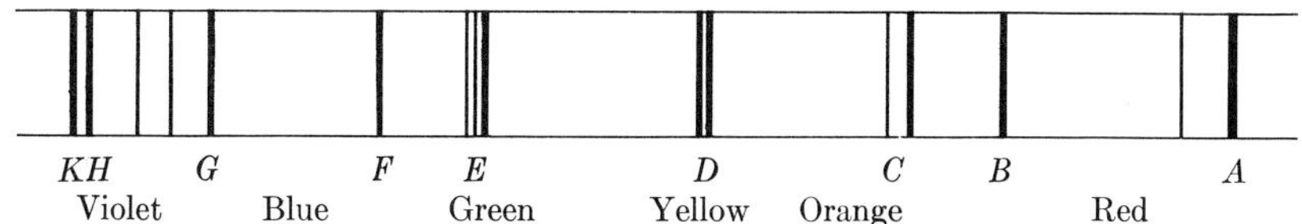

Fig. 30–1. Some of the Fraunhofer absorption lines observed in the solar spectrum. The majority of the lines are due to iron vapor. The D lines are from Na.

always follow the historical order. If it did there would have to be a considerable rearrangement of topics. Presented as a case study, there would also necessarily be included many of the mistakes and unfruitful ideas which, for lack of better evidence, often persisted for long periods. It is sufficient for our purpose here to remark that the subject of atomic spectra pervades the whole era of modern physics. Methods of obtaining spectroscopic data were refined to a high art and volumes of complex data were at hand before any theoretical sense was made of this evidence. The principal theoretical advances in modern physics arose through the analysis and unraveling of evidence from the complex spectra of atoms, rather than from the clear and demonstrative experiments which so well illustrate the physical properties of the individual constituents of atoms.

The analysis of spectral colors was begun by Newton, who demonstrated the refraction of white light by a prism into a continuum of colors. The source of white light was, of course, the sun, a hot, radiating object. The light generally emitted by dense, incandescent objects contains a continuous distribution of frequencies or colors, as we have seen. It is now known that the emission of radiation by such sources is a complex phenomenon involving interactions among atoms. Such light provides few clues to the properties of individual atoms. As might be expected, in retrospect, the independent atom is studied best in the gaseous state in which it is not bound to other atoms, but rather leads a quite independent existence in the periods between collisions. The first evidence about the spectral behavior of gaseous substances also was obtained from the study of sunlight. With the advent of excellently made diffraction gratings, the spectrum of sunlight could be more finely resolved. It was discovered by the physicist Fraunhofer, who used a good grating, that there exist many narrow *dark lines* in the sun's otherwise continuous spectrum (Fig. 30–1). These lines represent "missing colors" or frequencies, excluded by some mechanism, from the otherwise continuous spectrum. The explanation of the missing frequencies is that, while continuous light is emitted by the body of the sun, selective absorption of definite frequencies takes place in the sun's atmosphere. Thus the first hint of the action of gaseous substances is the absorption of definite frequencies of light. The same effect was reproduced on the earth by passing the white light of an arc through a gas-filled chamber. Again it could be observed that definite frequencies of light were missing after passage through the chamber. *A series of missing frequencies which are completely characteristic of the gaseous element always appears.* Even with mixtures of gases, where the characteristic series are superimposed, the spectra can be reduced to those characteristic of the components of the mixture. Thus a very powerful method for identification of the chemical elements was established. It provided a practical means of identifying the elements prevalent in the sun and remote stars, with a resulting revolution in the old subject of astronomy. In fact, the method led to the discovery of a new element, by the observations of characteristic frequencies that had not yet been identified on the earth. The discovery was that of helium gas, named after the sun, where it was first observed.

It was also found that gaseous incandescent substances emit definite and characteristic frequencies. The light from a sodium flame or a

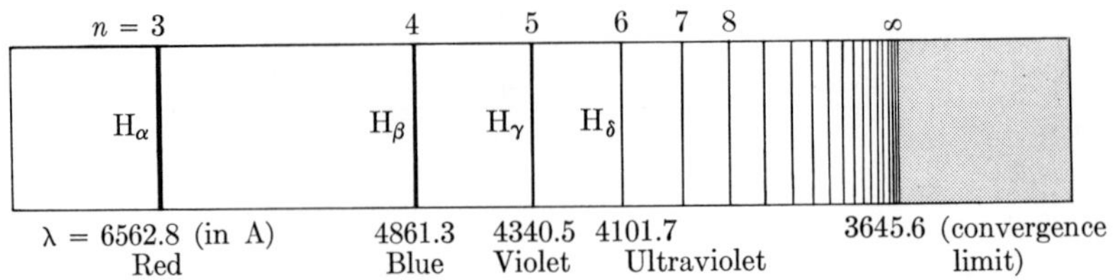

FIG. 30–2. The Balmer series of lines from atomic hydrogen.

mercury arc is not continuous but rather is all contained in thin "spectral lines" separated by darkness. Some of the frequencies that a gas will absorb are also observed in the emission spectrum.

For example, the well-known yellow lines emitted in a sodium flame mark the same frequencies which are missing from white light when it is passed through sodium vapor.

The physical content of these discoveries does not lie so much in the characteristic series of frequencies attached to each chemical element but in this more basic question: why should particular emission or absorption frequencies be preferred? In short, what is the physical basis for discrete line spectra? A short review of classical phenomena reveals some possible explanations, but none of them can explain the observed spectral series.

We first review the classical ideas. Atoms are known to contain electric charges in the form of electrons and protons. In the laboratory it can be shown that oscillating charges emit radiation of the same frequency as the frequency of oscillation of the charge. Thus we have a classical expectation that the emission of definite frequencies of light by an atom is connected with the existence of definite frequencies of vibration of the atomic system itself. It was seen in the last chapter that the Zeeman effect lends support to this idea. If it could be found that for some reason the atom can vibrate only at certain frequencies, we should have found why only certain frequencies of light are emitted. The Thomson model provided a specific model but we have seen that it provided only one frequency in the case of hydrogen. There are classical physical systems which exhibit characteristic *multiple* frequencies, which we might consider as analogs, e.g., a vibrating string. A string held at both ends exhibits a harmonic series of frequencies, given by

$$f = f_0, 2f_0, 3f_0 \cdots = nf_0,$$

where n is an integer. Standing waves in two dimensions (for example, in a drumhead), or in three dimensions (for example, sound in a room) have frequencies that are related to one another in slightly more complex ways. These classical analogies led to an analysis of characteristic spectra for rules of regularities in the spacing of the frequency lines. Not many regularities were found.

In the simplest spectrum of all, that of hydrogen, on which we shall concentrate our attention, the series was characterized by Balmer with an amazingly clever and fruitful formula. The formula was prepared for a family of lines in the hydrogen spectrum now known as the Balmer series. Figure 30–2 represents the observed spectrum. The Balmer formula for the wavelength series is:

$$\lambda = \lambda_0 \frac{n^2}{n^2 - 4}, \tag{30–2}$$

where $n = 3, 4, 5 \cdots \infty$ and $\lambda_0 = 3645$ A. The correspondence with the observed wavelengths is excellent. Other series of lines were discovered in the invisible ranges of infrared and ultraviolet spectra for hydrogen. These series could be described by the same sort of equation and, in fact, the one equation is easily generalized to include all the series of hydrogen, namely,

$$\lambda = b \frac{n_2^2}{n_2^2 - n_1^2}. \tag{30–3}$$

For later convenience we now depart from Balmer's formulation, in terms of wavelength, and rewrite Eq. (30–3) in terms of the reciprocal of wavelength $1/\lambda$ as

$$\frac{1}{\lambda} = R\left(\frac{1}{n_1^2} - \frac{1}{n_2^2}\right), \tag{30–4}$$

where n_2 is any integer greater than n_1, and n_1 is an integer with the values given below. The constant R can be found with great accuracy from the observed spectrum because wavelengths measured with a grating spectrometer can be determined to more than eight significant figures. The experimental value of R for hydrogen is

$$R = 109{,}677.5 \text{ cm}^{-1}. \tag{30–5}$$

The series are then classified in the following way, named according to their discoverers:

Lyman series

$$\frac{1}{\lambda} = R_0\left(\frac{1}{1^2} - \frac{1}{n_2^2}\right) \qquad n_1 = 1, \quad n_2 = 2, 3, 4, \cdots;$$

Balmer series

$$\frac{1}{\lambda} = R_0\left(\frac{1}{2^2} - \frac{1}{n_2^2}\right) \qquad n_1 = 2, \quad n_2 = 3, 4, 5, \cdots;$$

Paschen series

$$\frac{1}{\lambda} = R_0\left(\frac{1}{3^2} - \frac{1}{n_2^2}\right) \qquad n_1 = 3, \quad n_2 = 4, 5, 6, \cdots;$$

Brackett series

$$\frac{1}{\lambda} = R_0\left(\frac{1}{4^2} - \frac{1}{n_2^2}\right) \qquad n_1 = 4, \quad n_2 = 5, 6, 7, \cdots;$$

Pfund series

$$\frac{1}{\lambda} = R_0\left(\frac{1}{5^2} - \frac{1}{n_2^2}\right) \qquad n_1 = 5, \quad n_2 = 6, 7, 8, \cdots. \tag{30–6}$$

This is the elaborate complex of frequencies emitted by the hydrogen atom. No classical theory (radiation from oscillating charges) has been able to account for these frequencies (except for a correspondence in the limiting case of very large n's and $n_2 = 1 + n_1$ which we consider later). In the next section, the first success of quantum theory, the Bohr theory for hydrogen, will be discussed.

30–3 THE BOHR MODEL OF HYDROGEN

In 1910 Niels Bohr proposed a model for hydrogen that was revolutionary. Its particular importance stems from its economy of assumptions and its wealth of successful predictions. The model includes three basic assumptions which are stated at once, to be followed by a detailed exploration.

The Bohr postulates:

1. The atomic electron of hydrogen executes circular orbits about a point atomic nucleus, the proton. These orbits are governed by (a) the Coulomb law of force between electron and proton and (b) Newton's laws of motion.

2. The angular momentum of the electron (the momentum mv times the radius of motion) can assume only certain restricted values equal to n, an integer, times the Planck quantum of action divided by 2π, that is

$$mvr = n\left(\frac{h}{2\pi}\right),$$

where n is an integer. The electron does *not* radiate energy during its motion in any one of these orbits. We shall see later that the result is a restriction of the electron to orbits of certain radii only.

3. Denoting the energy of the system for one possible orbit as W_a and for another as W_b, the system may make *transitions* from one orbit to another. The energy change in the transition $W_a - W_b$ is equated to the energy of emitted

light determined by its photon character, i.e.,

$$W_a - W_b = h\nu.$$

These three assumptions are now investigated in detail.

Postulate 1. The electron executes circular orbits about the central nucleus (Fig. 30–3) and these orbits are governed by the classical laws of Coulomb and Newton. This postulate performs two functions: (a) It proposes a mechanical model of the atom, and (b) it tells which classical laws of physics are to be retained for atomic systems. The full model requires the use of all three postulates in concert, but, before the results of the combination are presented, we explore fully the classical expectations of the Bohr model. Assume that the nucleus is effectively stationary, since it is much more massive than the electron. Since the gravitational forces are negligible, the only significant force on the electron is the Coulomb force. Therefore, Newton's second law, $\sum \mathbf{F} = m\mathbf{a}$, gives

$$\frac{e^2}{4\pi\epsilon_0 r^2} = m\,\frac{v^2}{r}, \tag{30–7}$$

where e is the electronic charge and m is the mass of the electron.

From Eq. (30–7), we can derive the energy relationships for the classical system. Writing for the kinetic energy of the electron, $T = \frac{1}{2}mv^2$, we have [from Eq. (30–7)] the expression

$$T = \frac{1}{8\pi\epsilon_0}\,\frac{e^2}{r}. \tag{30–8}$$

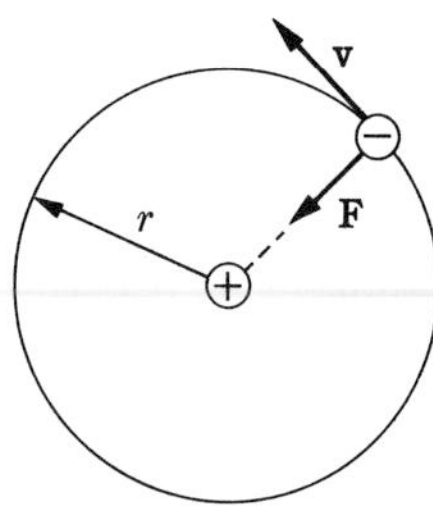

Fig. 30–3. The Bohr model of the hydrogen atom. The relative scales are distorted, since the radius of the particles should be less than a ten-thousandth the orbit radius r.

The potential energy V of the system is that of two point charges at a distance r apart. We use the convention that potential energy is zero when $r = \infty$, and obtain

$$V = -\frac{1}{4\pi\epsilon_0}\,\frac{e^2}{r}. \tag{30–9}$$

The potential energy is negative. In magnitude it is twice the kinetic energy, independent of the radius of the orbit.

The total energy W of the system is the sum of the potential and kinetic energy, giving

$$W = -\frac{1}{2}\,\frac{e^2}{4\pi\epsilon_0 r}, \tag{30–10}$$

which is negative for finite values of r. We note in passing that when $r = \infty$ and $v \neq 0$, we must go back to the original expression for T. We then have $W = \frac{1}{2}mv^2$ when $r = \infty$ and $v \neq 0$.

Plotting the total energy as a function of radius, we have the curve shown in Fig. 30–4. So long as the total energy is less than zero, the electron is said to be "bound" to the proton. If by some mechanism, say through a collision, the electron (i.e., the atom) can be given added energy equal to W, then the electron can escape the nucleus. In this case the atom is said to be ionized. We have evidence from collision experiments that a definite energy equal to 13.56 ev is required to ionize hydrogen, starting from its

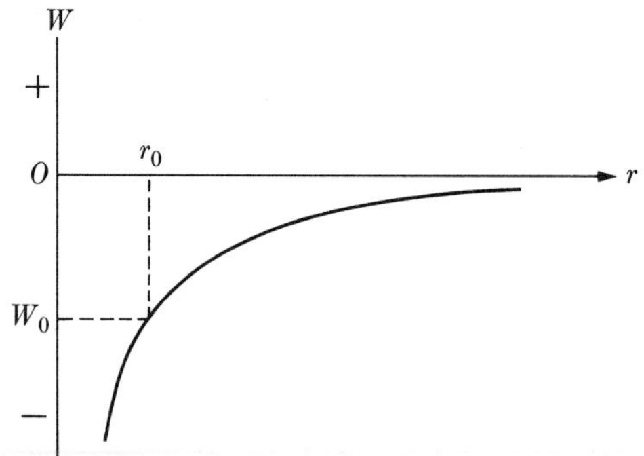

Fig. 30–4. Graph of the total energy of a particle in circular motion under the influence of an inverse-square force.

normal state. From this information we can deduce the radius of the electronic orbit in "normal" hydrogen, i.e.,

$$r_0 = \frac{-e^2}{8\pi\epsilon_0 W_0}. \qquad (30\text{–}11)$$

Expressing the physical values in mks units, $1/(4\pi\epsilon_0) \simeq 9 \times 10^9$, we have $W_0 = -13.56 \times 1.6 \times 10^{-19}$ joule and consequently,

$$r_0 = 0.53 \times 10^{-10}\ \text{m}. \qquad (30\text{–}12)$$

Since we have previously seen that the diameter of atoms obtained from mean free path or other observations is about 10^{-10} m, the Bohr model agrees with such observations.

It should be emphasized that the value (-13.56 ev) for total energy is obtained from empirical fact, and that we have no indication from classical theory why there should be this particular value of W_0 or of r_0 for the system. In fact, while we have found that the classical theory gives us the correct *relationship* between radius and energy for normal hydrogen, classical theory is in conflict with the idea of definite stationary values for either quantity. As we have seen, classical theory predicts that an electric charge under acceleration emits electromagnetic radiation, and that if the charge oscillates at a definite frequency, this is the frequency of radiation. Thus we have a classical mechanism for the emission of light by atoms. An electron in rotational motion has an acceleration, and the frequency of motion is the frequency of circulation in the orbit. Assuming the radius found above, does the atomic model predict a frequency of rotation corresponding, at least roughly, to the frequency of visible light, about 10^{15} cps? The answer is yes. If the above equations are used to find the frequency of rotation, it is in fact about 10^{15} cps.

Nevertheless, even the qualitative failure of the classical model is seen at once. Experimentally, hydrogen gas does not normally emit light. Light is emitted only if the gas is suitably heated or subjected to an electrical discharge. Left to itself, hydrogen reverts to the inactive state so far as light emission is concerned. But according to classical theory, there is no such stability so long as the electron is being accelerated. Thus the electron should radiate energy continuously, its energy should decrease accordingly, and it should therefore spiral in toward the nucleus. In the process the frequency of rotation would increase and a continuous spectrum of light would result. Finally, the atom would "collapse" as the electron spiraled into the nucleus. Obviously, these predictions disagree with observation. Therefore, Bohr postulated the breakdown of the classical law of radiation on the atomic scale.

Postulate 2. Bohr generalized the Planck hypothesis of quantization of an oscillator. He assumed that *any* periodic motion was restricted by the condition,

$$\oint p\, dq = nh, \qquad (30\text{–}13)$$

where n is an integer, p is the momentum, q is the corresponding coordinate, and the integral is to be taken over a complete cycle. The postulate is that a periodic system must satisy Eq. (30–13) and that this condition means that the system will not radiate energy in the classical manner. The states of the system as restricted by this quantum condition are called *stationary states.*

For the present periodic system (uniform circular motion) it is logical to use polar coordinates. Consequently, q is the angle coordinate θ, and p is the corresponding angular momentum mvr. Equation (30–13) thus leads to our earlier statement of Bohr's postulates, since

$$\oint pdq = \int_0^{2\pi} mvr\, d\theta = mvr2\pi = nh, \qquad (30\text{–}14)$$

which is equivalent to our earlier statement.

If the quantum condition is combined with the classical results of the first postulate (Eq. 30–7), the concept of "allowed orbits" appears, that is, if we use both conditions and solve for r and v, there results

$$r = \frac{(4\pi\epsilon_0)h^2}{4\pi^2 me^2}\, n^2, \tag{30–15}$$

$$v = \frac{2\pi e^2}{(4\pi\epsilon_0)h}\, \frac{1}{n}, \tag{30–16}$$

where n is an integer.

The radius of the orbit, called the atomic radius, is given in terms of the fundamental constants of atomic physics—the electronic charge, the electronic mass, and the constant of action. There is also a minimum radius given by $n = 1$. This is called the radius of the first Bohr orbit and is given the symbol r_0 where

$$r_0 = \frac{(4\pi\epsilon_0)h^2}{4\pi^2 me^2}. \tag{30–17}$$

In terms of r_0, the radius of any possible orbit is (Eq. 30–15),

$$r = r_0 n^2. \tag{30–18}$$

If we substitute values for the constants in Eq. (30–17), we have $r_0 = 0.53 \times 10^{-10}$ m. This is the first of a series of successes of the Bohr model: the prediction from first principles of a normal atomic radius that is in agreement with experiment. "Allowed" values for the atomic radii are then r_0, $4r_0$, $9r_0$, etc. This is the series of *possible values of the classical radius selected by the quantum condition.*

The velocity of the electron is also given in terms of the constants of nature. Using the same sort of terminology, we have for v_0, the electron velocity in the first Bohr orbit,

$$v_0 = \frac{2\pi e^2}{(4\pi\epsilon_0)h}. \tag{30–19}$$

The velocity for successively higher orbits is inversely proportional to n. That is, from Eq. (30–16), we have

$$v = \frac{v_0}{n}. \tag{30–20}$$

It is interesting to compare the value of this fundamental atomic velocity v_0 with another fundamental velocity in physics, the velocity of light. Usually in relativity we denote the ratio of particle velocity v to the light velocity c by the symbol beta, i.e., $\beta \equiv v/c$. It is customary to designate the special value of β corresponding to v_0/c by the alpha symbol, which is a dimensionless constant given by

$$\alpha = \frac{2\pi e^2}{(4\pi\epsilon_0)hc} = \frac{1}{137}. \tag{30–21}$$

This dimensionless number is called the "fine structure constant" of physics. For our purpose here, it is sufficient to note that the use of nonrelativistic mechanics is valid to a good degree of approximation in view of the smallness of this number. The velocities in higher orbits are even smaller (Eq. 30–20).

A diagram can be made representing the structure of the hydrogen atom with the properties derived by Bohr. The electron moves in one of the "allowed circular orbits," as in Fig. 30–5. Other possible orbits are shown by the dashed lines.

The *energy of the system* is also restricted by the quantum condition of the second postulate. If

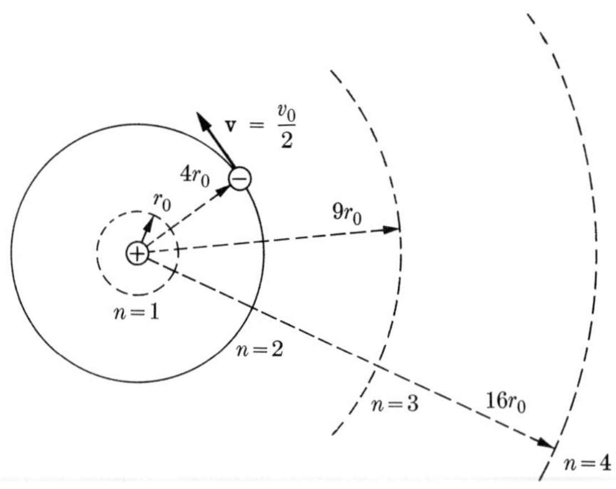

FIG. 30–5. The lowest four orbits of hydrogen, according to the Bohr theory. The electron is shown in the second orbit.

the "allowed" values of r, Eq. (30–15), are substituted into the classical expression for total energy, Eq. (30–10), there results

$$W = -\frac{2\pi^2 me^4}{(4\pi\epsilon_0)^2 h^2}\frac{1}{n^2}. \tag{30–22}$$

The values of W permitted by the quantum condition are given by Eq. (30–22). These are the energies of the so-called "stationary states" of hydrogen, states in which no radiation occurs according to Bohr's hypothesis.

It is convenient to express Eq. (30–22) in the form

$$W = -\frac{W_0}{n^2}, \tag{30–23}$$

where the numerical value of W_0, as evaluated from the atomic constants in Eq. (30–22), is

$$W_0 = 2.17 \times 10^{-18}\,\text{joule} = 13.56\,\text{ev}. \tag{30–24}$$

In experimental spectroscopy, where wavelengths are the measured quantities, it is customary to express W_0 in still different units (cm^{-1}), obtained by dividing W_0 by hc. This unit is called wave number, and W_0, expressed in wave numbers, is called the Rydberg constant. It is commonly designated by R and has the value

$$R = \frac{W_0}{hc} = 110{,}000\,\text{cm}^{-1}. \tag{30–25}$$

The restriction of such physical quantities as radius (amplitude) of motion, velocity of motion, or energy to a series of discrete values does not occur in classical systems. Classically, a mass suspended on a spring can have *any* energy or amplitude of motion. We are to think of an atomic spring-mass system as being restricted, for illustration only, to the possible amplitudes 10 cm, 20 cm, 30 cm, etc. An amplitude of 15 cm is not permitted. How, then, does the system execute a transition from one permitted form of motion to another? This is the topic which is treated by Postulate 3.

Postulate 3. The electron, or more properly the atom, can gain or lose energy by executing "quantum jumps" between permitted states. If there is a quantum jump, then the *principle of energy conservation* is applied. The radiated energy emitted or absorbed by the system is equal to the energy lost or gained by the atom. Using the Einstein interpretation of the photoelectric effect as a guide, Bohr set the radiated energy equal to the photon energy, Planck's constant of action times frequency, that is, $h\nu$. If the system executes a quantum jump from a state of energy W_2 to a state of energy W_1, the energy loss is $W_2 - W_1$. Therefore, the emission frequency is given by the conservation of energy as

$$h\nu = W_2 - W_1, \tag{30–26}$$

where ν is the frequency of light. Since Eq. (30–22) gives

$$W_2 = -\frac{e^4 m}{8\epsilon_0^2 h^2}\frac{1}{n_2^2}$$

or

$$\frac{-W_0}{n_2^2} \tag{30–27}$$

and

$$W_1 = -\frac{e^4 m}{8\epsilon_0^2 h^2}\frac{1}{n_1^2}$$

or

$$\frac{-W_0}{n_1^2}, \tag{30–28}$$

there results

$$h\nu = W_0\left(\frac{1}{n_1^2} - \frac{1}{n_2^2}\right), \tag{30–29}$$

or in terms of the constant $R = W_0/hc$,

$$\frac{\nu}{hc} = \frac{W_0}{hc}\left(\frac{1}{n_1^2} - \frac{1}{n_2^2}\right) \tag{30–30}$$

or

$$\frac{1}{\lambda} = R\left(\frac{1}{n_1^2} - \frac{1}{n_2^2}\right), \tag{30–31}$$

where $1/\lambda$ is called the *wave number*.

This result of the Bohr theory agrees in form with the experimental observations, as given in the Eq. (30-4) form of Balmer's empirical formula. This is already a remarkable achievement. But in addition, the numerical value of the constant W_0, calculated from the atomic constants in the form predicted by Bohr, agrees completely with the observed value of Eq. (30-5). The atomic constants are known only to about half as many significant figures as R, but the agreement is complete to within this accuracy.

30-4 ENERGY-LEVEL DIAGRAM

Later, the failures of the Bohr model will be stressed. But several important features of the Bohr model will always be retained. Among these is the concept of allowed energy levels, with emission or absorption of radiation occurring when the

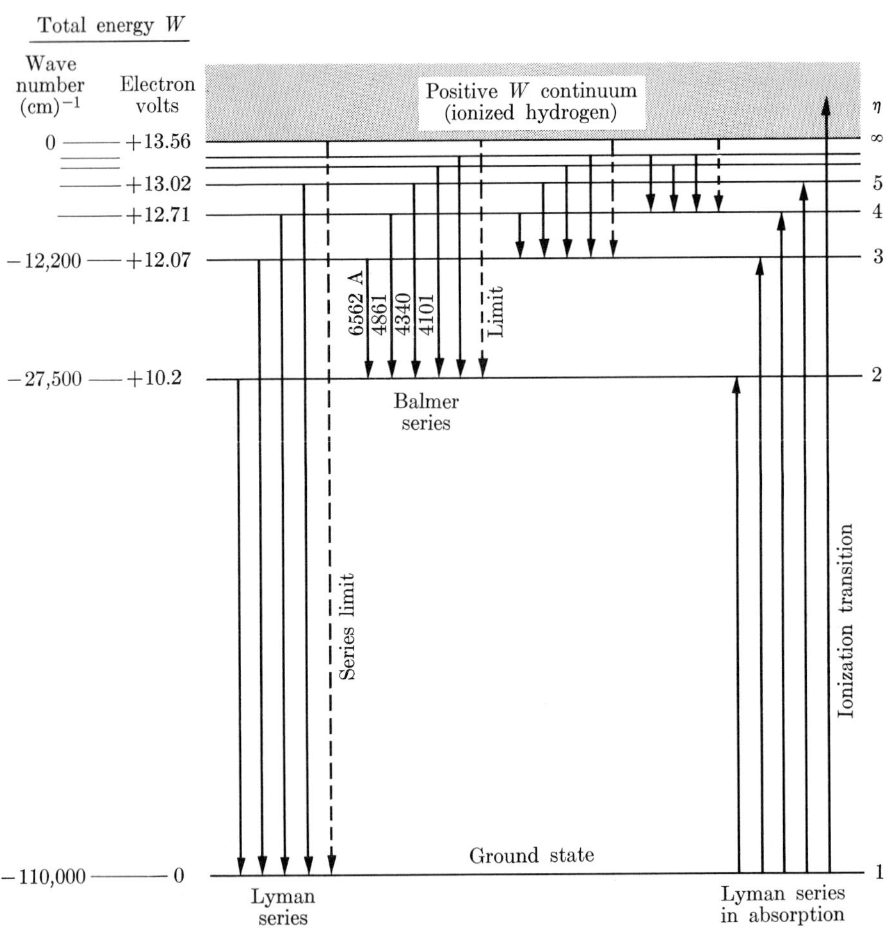

FIG. 30-6. Energy level diagram of hydrogen. The quantum numbers are given in the right-hand column. The two most frequently used energy scales are shown at the left. Note that the choice of the zero is different in the two cases. The wave number scale (cm^{-1}) is chiefly used in spectroscopy. The electron volt scale is chiefly used in discussing absorption experiments such as the Franck and Hertz experiment.

atom makes transitions between levels. This information is conveniently displayed graphically on an *energy-level diagram.* In Fig. 30–6, one of the common forms of energy-level diagram is given for the case of hydrogen. The energy scale on the left-hand side is given in the two forms that are commonly used. The left-hand scale (in cm^{-1}) is usually used when the absorption or emission of radiation is under consideration. The wave number is the reciprocal of λ in centimeters and it therefore depends *only* on the measured quantity λ, i.e., no other constants such as h or c come in to limit the accuracy. Thus since λ can be measured to very high accuracy, energy levels expressed in wave number can be given to equally high accuracy. The right-hand scale (electron volts) is convenient when absorption of energy by charged-particle collision is under consideration, as in the Franck and Hertz experiment, which is discussed later.

The diagram is a map of the allowed atomic states made by drawing a series of lines ("levels"), each corresponding to the total energy of the state. Each state is classified by a *quantum number n.* Normal hydrogen exists in the lowest, or ground, state $n = 1$. If by bombardment, collision, or any other means, the electron, i.e., the hydrogen atom is given added energy, the electron may be placed in a higher-energy level, say $n = 5$ (Fig. 30–7). Such action would correspond to energy absorption by the atom. It must be noted that the atom cannot freely absorb just any amount of energy. It must absorb an exact amount corresponding to the definite fixed-energy difference between the normal state and the final state ($W_5 - W_1$), in the example. The atom cannot absorb an amount of energy which would place it at a point of intermediate energy between allowed states. Thus we have before us the mechanism of the selective absorption of definite frequencies of light by the atom. Only those frequencies are absorbed such that $h\nu$ equals the energy difference between any higher state and the ground state. The absorption of a frequency not given by this condition would place the atom in a state in which it cannot exist. Moreover, under most conditions there will be just *one* absorption series, since in absorption, the electron will begin in the ground state and end in any of the higher ones.

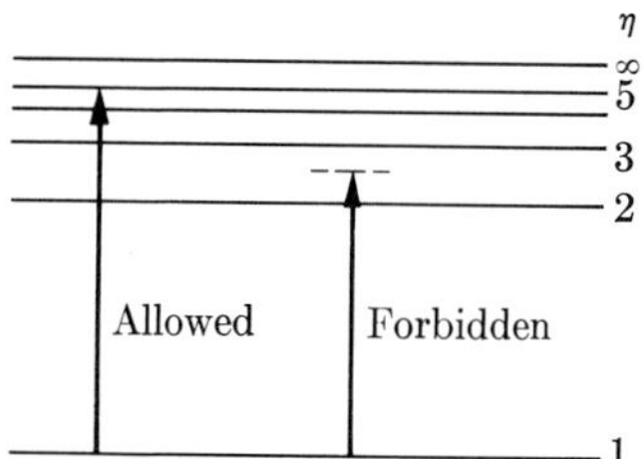

FIG. 30–7. Energy level diagram for illustrating the quantized absorption of energy by an atom.

What happens, then, when the electron is placed, by some process of absorption, in a higher state? It can fall to any of the lower energy states and emit radiation whose frequency (energy) equals the energy loss. However, in falling, it may fall to *any* of the lower states. Thus we obtain the various series of light emission, one corresponding to a fall from any of the higher states to the ground state, one corresponding to a fall from any of the higher states to the $n = 2$ level, and so on. These series correspond to the Lyman, Balmer, etc., series seen in experimental spectroscopy.

The ideas of this section are used in all studies of atomic and molecular structure and in nuclear structure. In solid state structure, it is found that some energy levels are in fact bands.

Some additional features of energy levels and transitions should be stated for the sake of completeness. No energy level is infinitely narrow. The inherent width will be discussed in the section on the uncertainty principle. For a more complete understanding and a more complete labeling of the levels, the angular momentum (as well as the energy) is specified. Finally, not all transitions from an excited level to lower levels are equally likely. So-called selection rules, expressed in terms of the labels for the levels, act as guides for predicting allowed transitions.

30–5 THE CORRESPONDENCE PRINCIPLE

Since it is found that classical predictions are correct for radiation at long wavelengths (low frequencies) but that quantum theory is necessary at short wavelengths, the quantum theory should *correspond* with classical theory at long wavelengths. This principle was used by Bohr in his development of the quantum theory for the hydrogen atom. An example will now be considered.

In the atomic transitions between any two of the lower-energy states, we are not dealing with a simple frequency relationship between the source and emitted radiation. Instead, three frequencies are involved. Consider the transition from the state $n = 2$ to the state $n = 1$. For each state the electron has a given frequency of rotation. These are called the orbital frequencies f. The electron does not radiate energy during its occupation of either state. It does emit light of a definite frequency ν, in a transition from one state to the other. Altogether, there are three frequencies involved: the frequency of rotation f_2 in the higher state, the frequency f_1 in the lower state, and the frequency of light ν emitted in a transition from the higher to the lower state. How are these frequencies related?

The orbital frequencies are given by the orbit radius and velocity, i.e.,

$$f = \frac{v}{2\pi r}. \qquad (30\text{–}32)$$

Substituting the general formulas for r and v of Eqs. (30–15) and (30–16), we obtain

$$f = \frac{4\pi^2 me^4}{(4\pi\epsilon_0)^2 h^3}\frac{1}{n^3} = \frac{2Rc}{n^3}. \qquad (30\text{–}33)$$

Referring to the Bohr formula, the frequency of radiation is

$$\nu = \frac{2\pi^2 me^4}{(4\pi\epsilon_0)^2 h^3}\left(\frac{1}{n_1^2} - \frac{1}{n_2^2}\right) = Rc\left(\frac{1}{n_1^2} - \frac{1}{n_2^2}\right). \qquad (30\text{–}34)$$

For the $n = 2$ to $n = 1$ transition, we then have

$$f_2 = \frac{1}{32}\frac{me^4}{\epsilon_0^2 h^3},$$

$$f_1 = \frac{1}{4}\frac{me^4}{\epsilon_0^2 h^3},$$

and

$$\nu_{2\to 1} = \frac{3}{32}\frac{me^4}{\epsilon_0^2 h^3}. \qquad (30\text{–}35)$$

It is seen that the frequency of radiation is intermediate between the two orbital frequencies.

As we proceed to transitions between much higher (but adjacent) states, where the energy levels become very closely spaced, the frequency of radiation is bracketed by the orbital frequencies of the states, but the three frequencies approach the same value (see Problems). Thus the classical rule is approached for very high quantum numbers, $n \to \infty$, and $\Delta n = 1$. Generally, when energy states become very closely spaced, we expect the classical laws to become more and more valid. In the classical world, where all energies are possible, we consider that the basic atomic states have become so close that we proceed smoothly from one energy to another. The phenomenon of discrete energy jumps has disappeared altogether. This remark justifies a very important question, raised by physicists upon the discovery of the quantum theory. We have two kinds of physical laws and experience quite different from each other. One is classical where amplitude and energies are continuous variables that may have any value. The other is atomic where physical "variables," such as amplitude and energy, have discrete values, and changes occur by discontinuous shifts from one value to another. We ask, "Is there a gradual transition from one kind of behavior to the other?" The answer is yes. The range of *very high* quantum numbers shows a smooth change from the granular quantum laws to the smooth classical laws.

Another, equivalent, point of view is that the quantum method is necessary only in the realm of small dimensions and wavelengths. As n becomes large, the size of the atom becomes large and classical theory must become a good approximation.

30–6 FRANCK AND HERTZ EXPERIMENT

Direct evidence for discrete energy levels in atoms was obtained by Franck and Hertz in 1914. They studied the effects of collisions between a beam of electrons of known energy and the atoms of a gas with an arrangement shown schematically in Fig. 30–8. Electrons emitted from a hot filament are accelerated in the electric field between F and A produced by the battery potential V. Since the tube contained a gas, the electrons collided with the atoms of the gas during their passage from F to A. The effect of the collisions on the energy of the electrons can be observed by the effect on the current through a galvanometer G.

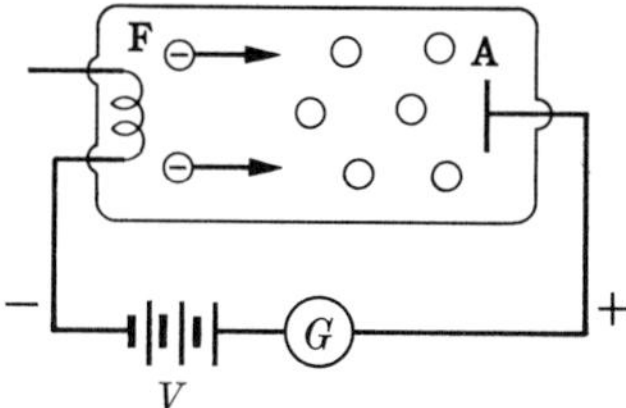

FIG. 30–8. Schematic diagram of the apparatus of the Franck and Hertz experiment. The electron current through a gas at low pressure is measured as a function of the accelerating voltage V.

The experimental results are shown in Fig. 30–9, where the galvanometer current i_G is plotted as a function of the accelerating voltage V. The interpretation of the results is that the collisions with the atoms are elastic until the electrons reach a critical energy V_i. At this energy the collisions suddenly become inelastic. Comparison with the energy levels of the atom, deduced from spectroscopic observation, show that V_i is just the difference in energy between the normal (lowest) state and the next higher state.

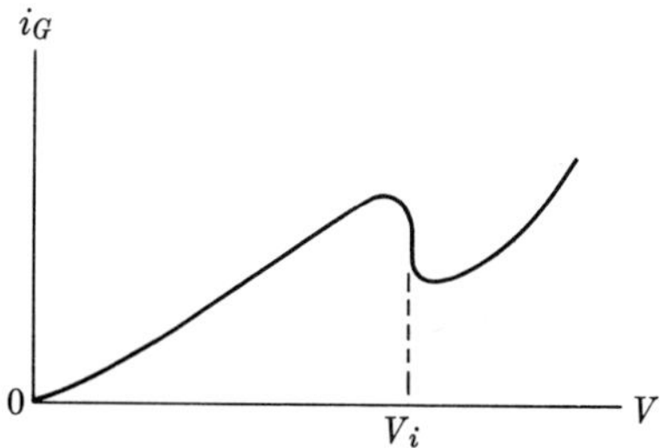

FIG. 30–9. Graph of the results of the experiment pictured in Fig. 30–8. As the accelerating voltage is increased from zero, the current increases until a critical voltage V_i is approached. The lack of sharpness in the break of the curve is due to variation in the energy of emission of electrons from the cathode, etc.

Thus the Franck and Hertz experiment directly confirms the fact that atoms can absorb energy only in discrete amounts. Confirmation of the above interpretation of the onset of inelastic collisions at energy V_i comes from the additional observation that a single spectrum line is emitted by the gas when the accelerating potential is equal to or slightly greater than V_i. The wavelength of the line is the value expected for a transition from the lowest excited state to the normal state. (The lifetime of atoms in most excited states is so short that it is unlikely a second collision will raise the atom to a still higher level.)

When V is raised still farther, evidence is found for the higher excitation levels. Furthermore, the onset of ionization can be detected at a potential V_0 that agrees with spectroscopic information.

30–7 FAILURE OF THE BOHR MODEL

The Bohr model is also successful in predicting the spectra of other two-body systems, such as singly-ionized helium. Results of the generalization of the model to include elliptical orbits, finite nuclear mass, and relativistic effects also agree with experiment. We have already stated that the general concept of discrete energy levels and transitions between them due to emission or absorption of radiation or other forms of energy is found to be universally applicable on the atomic scale.

On the other hand, the model fails to predict the observed spectrum of *any other* atom, even normal helium. Furthermore, it predicts the wrong angular momentum, even for hydrogen. The observed "orbital" angular momentum of the electron in the lowest energy level of hydrogen is actually zero! The Bohr theory does not accurately predict the relative intensities of the spectrum lines of hydrogen. Finally, the Bohr postulates, that the atom must be treated classically in part but nonclassically in other parts of the analysis, seem very artificial.

Thus the Bohr model was revolutionary in making a successful and important exploratory advance into the quantum-mechanical world. We still use it as a sort of aid to the memory and as a language in discussing some aspects of atomic structure. In addition, the concepts of "allowed" energy levels, transitions between the levels, and the correspondence principle are part of the fabric of the wave mechanics of today.

30–8 MAGNETIC PROPERTIES OF ATOMS; ELECTRON SPIN

One of the chief facts which has emerged in the experimental study of atomic structure is that in some cases the atoms show the effect of a net circulation of electrons about the atomic nucleus. The evidence comes from the fact that a circulating electric charge forms a current loop. A current loop produces a magnetic field, and the loop itself experiences a torque or a force in a magnetic field. Thus the study of the magnetic properties of atoms can be expected to yield important data relevant to atomic structure. This has indeed been the case, as we shall see.

The Bohr model contains a detailed prediction with respect to the magnetic property of the hydrogen atom. In hydrogen, the electron is said to circulate at a radius given by Eq. (30–16) and at a frequency given by Eq. (30–33). The effective current due to a point charge traveling in a circular orbit is the charge divided by the period of circulation,

$$I = \frac{e}{\tau} = ef,$$

which becomes

$$I = \frac{me^5}{4\pi\epsilon_0^2 h^3 n^3} \text{ amp.} \tag{30–36}$$

The magnetic moment μ of this current loop is, by definition, the product of current and area, giving [using (30–15) for r]

$$\mu = IA = I \cdot \pi r^2 = \frac{e}{2m}\frac{nh}{2\pi}. \tag{30–37}$$

In the next chapter, it will be stated that the wave-mechanical results (which are correct) give a slightly different result, namely, n is replaced by $\sqrt{l(l+1)}$ where l is an integer or zero. Therefore, anticipating the next chapter, we write the orbital magnetic moment more correctly as

$$\mu = \sqrt{l(l+1)}\,\frac{e}{2m}\frac{h}{2\pi}. \tag{30–38}$$

If there are any skeptics who do not believe in the Bohr model, they would be privileged to place atoms in a magnetic field to discover whether the atoms exhibit this predicted magnetic moment. They would be rewarded for their skepticism, because the Bohr prediction in this case does *not* stand experimental test. The magnetic moment due to the orbital motion of the electron is found experimentally to be *zero* in the lowest energy state of hydrogen! This is one of the failures of the Bohr theory mentioned earlier. However, in some excited states of hydrogen, the magnetic moment due to "orbital" motion is not zero. Also, there are elements lying higher in the periodic table that *do* exhibit magnetic moments in the normal state due to circulation of electrons. The first of these is boron.

Before describing an experimental method for measuring μ directly, the other source of magnetic effects of the electron, the *spin of the electron*, will be briefly discussed. Before 1925, a tremendous body of experimental data had been accumulated from measurements of the wavelengths of spectrum lines of many elements. The results had been systematized by the construction of energy-level diagrams of many elements. It became evident that there was a systematic "*fine structure*" in the spectrum lines and hence in the energy levels. For example, the sodium D line is really a doublet with components of 5890 A and 5896 A. Furthermore, the D lines are a member of a series of double lines with a systematic decrease in separation. Other series in sodium show double and triple lines and, most strikingly, one series of double lines shows a *constant energy* separation for all doublets in the series.

Other elements (including hydrogen) show similar systematic fine-structure effects. In addition, it is observed that the fine structure is altered in a systematic but complicated way when the source is put in a magnetic field (Zeeman effect). We implied earlier that the classical theory gave an explanation of the Zeeman effect, but actually, it is only the order of magnitude that agrees with classical theory.

All the above puzzling data were systematized by calculations based on the hypothesis of Goudsmit and Uhlenbeck (in 1925) that the electron has an intrinsic magnetic moment. The term *spin* is used descriptively to indicate the origin of the intrinsic magnetic moment and of the intrinsic angular momentum.

The splitting of energy levels resulting in fine structure is then attributed to magnetic forces of interaction, which are in addition to the Coulomb electrostatic force. The magnetic effect is small compared with the electrostatic effect in the examples we described, but in some atoms the converse may be true.

The magnetic effect of electron spin corresponds to a spin magnetic moment of

$$\mu_s = 2\,\frac{e}{2m}\,\frac{h}{2\pi}\,\sqrt{s(s+1)}, \qquad (30\text{–}39)$$

where $s = \frac{1}{2}$. Because of this result, it is customary to speak of the spin of the electron as $\frac{1}{2}$.

The ratio of orbital magnetic moment to orbital angular momentum, called the gyromagnetic ratio, for the Bohr model is just

$$\frac{\mu_e}{p_e} = \frac{\mu_e}{(nh/2\pi)} = \frac{e}{2m}, \qquad (30\text{–}40)$$

as can readily be seen from Eq. (30–37). The wave-mechanical result is the same. On the other hand, the spin angular momentum of the electron is

$$\mu_s = \frac{h}{2\pi}\sqrt{s(s+1)}, \qquad (30\text{–}41)$$

and therefore the gyromagnetic ratio of the electron is

$$\frac{\mu_s}{p_s} = 2\,\frac{e}{2m}\cdot \qquad (30\text{–}42)$$

For negatively charged particles such as the electron, the vectors that represent the magnetic moment and the angular momentum are oppositely directed. Therefore, strictly speaking, the signs should be negative in Eqs. (30–40) and (30–42) when these equations are intended to represent more than the ratio of the magnitudes of the quantities.

It is seen from the above that the intrinsic magnetic moment of the electron due to spin is twice as large as we would predict from its spin angular momentum, *if* we use the orbital results as a guide (Eq. 30–40). We say that the gyromagnetic ratio of the electron (due to spin) is "anomalous," since it is twice the value for a charge in a circular path.

The spin magnetic moment of the proton is smaller that that of the electron by a factor 1800 because of its mass; that is, for given spin angular momentum, the angular velocity of the proton is much less than that of a spinning electron. The neutron also has a magnetic moment even though it is an uncharged particle! The magnetic moment of the neutron is also small and, consequently, the magnetic effects of the nucleus, due to the spin of its constituents, are very small compared with the magnetic effects of electrons.

In order to interpret the systematics of the observed atomic energy levels, it is necessary to introduce still another quantum idea, namely, *space quantization* (quantization of direction of the magnetic moment). An elaborate, semi-empirical method of systematizing energy levels was developed, using the ideas of quantization that we have discussed. The method was based on the so-called *vector model* of the atom, in which both orbital and spin angular momenta were represented by vectors. Rules were developed for the addition of the vectors in multielectron atoms subject to a restriction called the Pauli exclusion principle, which will be discussed later.

30–9 STERN-GERLACH EXPERIMENT

The first direct experimental demonstration of the magnetic moment of atoms was made in 1921 by Stern and Gerlach. In this experiment, a beam of neutral atoms was sent through a region of *nonuniform* magnetic field. In the chapters on magnetic fields, we saw that a current loop experiences no resultant force in a uniform magnetic field. It does, of course, experience a torque, if M is not aligned with B. If M is aligned with B the torque is also zero, and the only effect of the field on the loop is an attempt to stretch the loop outward (Fig. 30–10). The force is perpendicular to both the field and the local current directions.

But in a nonuniform field, such as that portrayed in Fig. 30–11, the force vectors remain normal to both current and the field, but due to the flaring-out of the field, there is a net downward component of force on the loop. If the current were reversed, there would be a net upward component, as in Fig. 30–12. Thus current loops in a nonuniform field will be forced in the high-field or low-field direction, according to whether the moment is aligned with or against

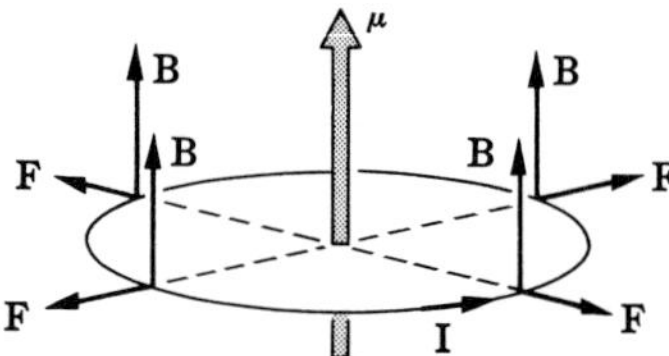

FIG. 30–10. Forces on selected elements of a circular current loop placed in a uniform magnetic field parallel to the magnetic moment μ of the loop.

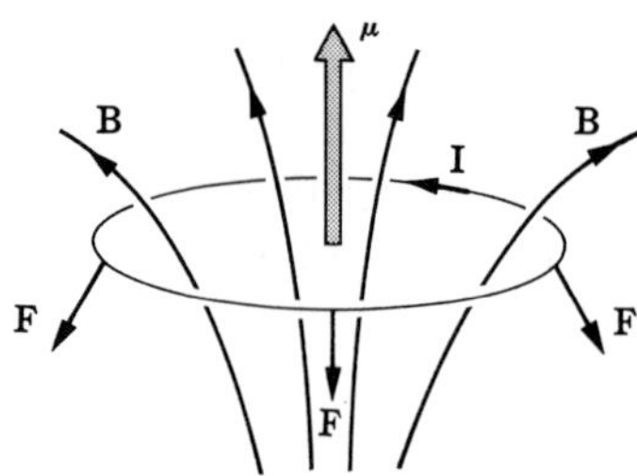

FIG. 30–11. Forces on elements of a circular current loop of magnetic moment μ placed in a divergent magnetic field.

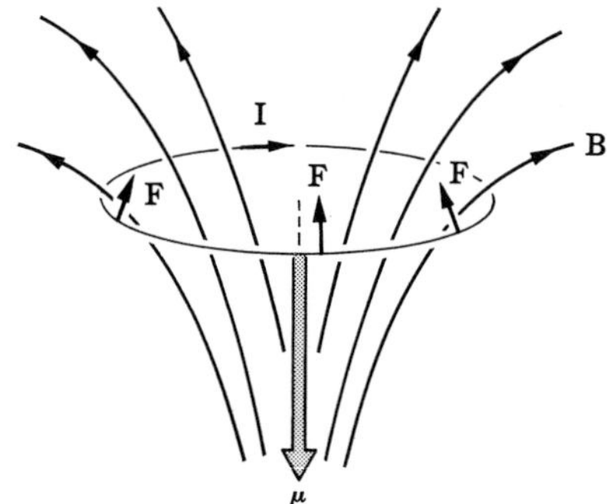

FIG. 30–12. Similar to Fig. 30–11 but with the field reversed relative to μ.

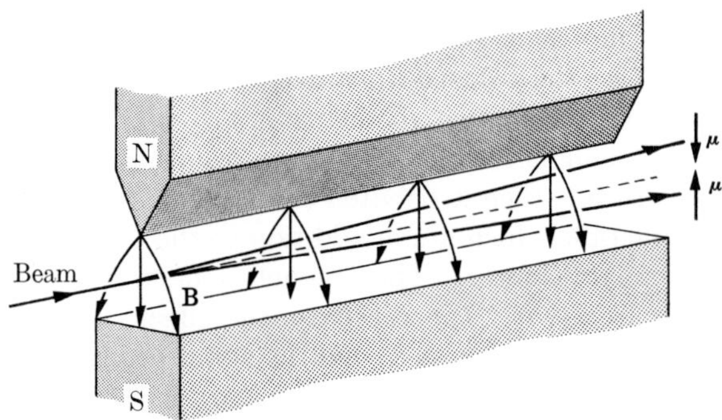

FIG. 30–13. Schematic diagram of the Stern-Gerlach experiment in which a beam of atoms is sent through a region of a strongly divergent magnetic field. The atoms acquire quantized orientations relative to the field if they have a magnetic moment and then experience transverse forces in the divergent field that depend on the direction of the moment.

the magnetic field direction. Smaller values of the resultant forces would obtain for intermediate angles of orientation of the loop.

In the Stern-Gerlach experiment, an atomic beam is projected through a region of nonuniform magnetic field, as in Fig. 30–13.

Atoms with orientations of magnetic moments with or against the field would be expected to be drawn up or down, respectively (Fig. 30–13). All intermediate orientations might be expected with consequent intermediate forces. The prediction is that the beam would be drawn out into a vertical ribbon by the action of the nonuniform magnetic field on the atomic currents. Actually, before the experiment was attempted, it was already anticipated that a new kind of behavior was to be expected for atomic systems, and such proved to be the case. In the simplest case, it is found that only the two extreme trajectories occur, with nothing in between. The interpretation is that an atomic current cannot have just any arbitrary orientation relative to a magnetic field. In the simplest case, the magnetic moment can only be aligned with or against the field. Other orientations are forbidden. Once again, the idea of discreteness in atomic systems is directly demonstrable, in this case a discreteness in space orientation. The alignment angle of an atom in a magnetic field can have only certain "allowed" values. We have previously discussed the evidence for discrete allowed values for such things as energy, amplitude, and angular momentum for atomic systems. In this section we have also found discrete values for space alignment, and this phenomenon is given the name "space quantization." A change in alignment cannot occur in a continuous manner; it must occur in quantum jumps in the angle.

If the idea of atomic alignment is granted, the analysis of the magnetic splitting of atomic beams proceeds in a standard way. From a knowledge of the magnetic field structure, the atomic beam velocity, etc., we can deduce the atomic magnetic moment from the measurements of the deflections, as follows.

As an illustrative example, we consider a current loop with the magnetic moment parallel with the average direction of the field, as in Fig. 30–14. Further, we choose the case in which the field diverges symmetrically relative to the OZ-axis, as shown. We let θ be the angle that the field makes, with the OZ-direction locally at the current. Then the z-component of force on an element of length dl of the current loop is

$$dF_z = dlIB \sin \theta,$$

and the total z-component is simply

$$F_z = -2\pi rIB \sin \theta. \tag{30–43}$$

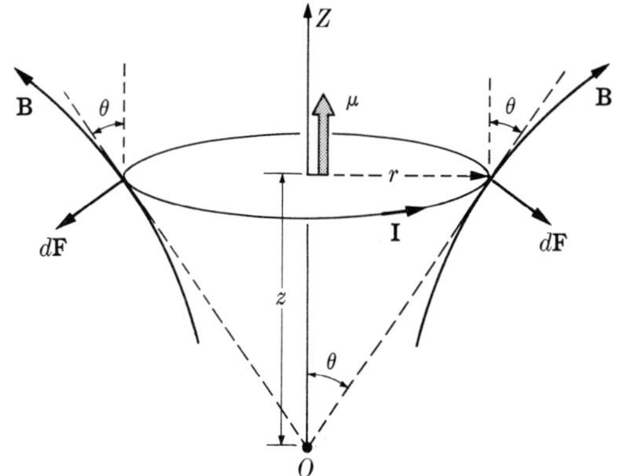

Fig. 30–14. Diagram of the quantities used in calculating the translational force on a current loop in a divergent magnetic field.

The above result can be put in a more general form as follows: The extensions of the directions of B at the current loop intersect the z-axis at O, which we then choose as the origin of coordinates. The plane of the loop is, therefore, at z. In practice, the length r is of atomic dimensions while z is of macroscopic dimensions for a magnetic field from a magnet of macroscopic size. Therefore, the angle θ is small, and we have

$$F_z = -2\pi rIB \frac{r}{z} = -2(\pi r^2 I) \frac{B}{z} = -2\mu \frac{B}{z}. \tag{30–44}$$

We note further that, near the plane of the loop, the field can be described by

$$B = \frac{K}{z^2}, \tag{30–45}$$

because the field appears to diverge radially from O at distance z when viewed from the position of the loop. Taking derivatives with respect to z, we have

$$\frac{dB}{dz} = -2\frac{K}{z^3} = -2\frac{B}{z}. \tag{30–46}$$

Therefore, the force on the loop can be written

$$F_z = \mu\frac{dB}{dz}. \tag{30–47}$$

This result can be shown to be quite general, even though we derived it for the special case of axial symmetry for the sake of simplicity.

Remember that the above result applies when μ is parallel or antiparallel to B. In the next chapter, it will be seen that the magnetic moment always makes a finite angle with B and therefore the above result gives an upper limit to the actual force.

30–10 SUMMARY

A brief description is given of the general character of the spectra of light emitted or absorbed by gases. Attempts to understand the frequencies in terms of a fundamental plus overtones or any system of characteristic frequencies based on a classical model were uniformly unsuccessful. A simple empirical expression for the frequencies or wavelengths of the lines in the visible region of the spectrum of atomic hydrogen was discovered by Balmer:

$$\frac{1}{\lambda} = R_0\left(\frac{1}{2^2} - \frac{1}{n_2^2}\right).$$

Bohr developed the analysis of the spectrum to be expected from hydrogen in terms of a nuclear model in which the electron traveled around the nucleus in circular orbits. He postulated that the electron is restricted to orbits in which the angular momentum has particular values given by the quantum condition

$$mvr = n(h/2\pi).$$

The result is that the energy of the electron, and hence of the atom, is restricted to the values

$$W = -\frac{2\pi^2 me^4}{(4\pi\epsilon_0)^2h^2}\frac{1}{n^2}.$$

He further postulated that radiation is emitted or absorbed when the energy of the atom changes from one of the quantum values of energy to another. The conservation of energy then gives

$$h\nu = \frac{hc}{\lambda} = \frac{2\pi^2 me^4}{(4\pi\epsilon_0)^2h^2}\left(\frac{1}{n_1^2} - \frac{1}{n_2^2}\right),$$

which is of the form of the empirical Balmer formula. When the constants are evaluated, it is found that there is detailed agreement with experiment! Furthermore, there is agreement with the other spectral series observed in hydrogen. In addition, the size of the hydrogen atom corresponding to the diameter of the first Bohr orbit is about 10^{-10} m, in agreement with observations of mean free paths observed in gases.

The above information is conveniently displayed on an energy-level diagram on which the allowed energy levels are spaced according to a selected energy scale and labeled with the quantum numbers n. Transitions corresponding to emission or absorption of radiation can also be displayed on the energy-level diagram. A commonly employed energy unit is the reciprocal of the wavelength, cm^{-1} or m^{-1}. Bohr also propounded the correspondence principle, which is the general statement that, in the limit of dimensions that approach the macroscopic domain, the quantum predictions should approach the classical predictions. As an example, the frequency of the radiation, when the Bohr atom has a transition between adjacent energy levels, approaches the frequency of motion of the electron in its orbit as the energy levels become very high, that is, as the size of the atom becomes very great.

The Franck and Hertz experiment demonstrated that atoms bombarded with electrons give rise to elastic scattering of the electrons when the kinetic energy of the electron is less than a certain critical value. When the electron energy is equal to or greater than the critical value, the collisions can be inelastic. These experiments thus gave direct evidence for discrete energy levels of atoms.

The limitations and failures of the Bohr model are enumerated—for example, the incorrect predictions for multielectron atoms, the approximate nature of the intensity predictions, etc.

The magnetic moment of a single electron atom due to the orbital motion of the electron, according to the Bohr model, is shown to be

$$\mu = n(e/2m)(h/2\pi).$$

The wave-mechanical theory, on the other hand, predicts

$$\mu = \sqrt{l(l+1)}\ (e/2m)(h/2\pi),$$

where $l = 0, 1, 2, \ldots$ The latter predicts the possibility of zero magnetic moment due to orbital motion, a result that agrees with experiment. In addition, it is necessary to attribute to the electron an intrinsic magnetic moment (spin magnetic moment) of

$$\mu_s = \sqrt{s(s+1)}\ \frac{h}{2\pi},$$

where $s = \frac{1}{2}$, in order to have agreement of magnetic properties with the result of experiment.

The Stern-Gerlach experiment demonstrated directly the existence of quantization of the orientation of the magnetic moment of atoms in the presence of a magnetic field. Furthermore, it permitted the measurement of the magnetic moment by means of the transverse force experienced by the atoms in a divergent magnetic field. The force is

$$F_z = \mu \frac{dB}{dz}$$

for an atom whose magnetic moment μ is oriented in the z-direction in a magnetic field that is nonuniform in the z-direction.

Problems

1. A certain violin string is tuned so that its fundamental frequency is 440 vibrations per second.

(a) List some of the frequencies in the "spectrum" of its emitted radiation, i.e., sound waves.

(b) Is there a series limit to the frequencies?

2. (a) Find the wavelength of the series limit in the Balmer series, depicted in Fig. 30–2, in A units.

(b) Find the series limit in terms of the wave number (cm^{-1}).

3. Do any of the first five series of hydrogen overlap?

4. How many series in hydrogen are possible? Explain.

5. (a) Which of Bohr's postulates would be altered if the gravitational force between electron and proton were taken into account?

(b) Calculate the error resulting from neglecting the gravitational force.

6. Describe the radiation to be expected from an electron in a circular orbit according to the classical theory of radiation. Would the orbit remain at constant radius?

7. Derive Eqs. (30–15) and (30–16).

8. How large is the relativistic correction to the mass of the electron in the first Bohr orbit?

9. Verify the numerical value of W_0 in Eq. (30–24).

10. Experiments show that negative μ-mesons are captured into Bohr orbits when the mesons are slowed down sufficiently by collisions. The μ-meson has one electronic charge and mass 215 times the electron mass. What is the radius of the first Bohr orbit for a hydrogen-meson atom? What is the energy in the first orbit? What is the wavelength of the first line of the Balmer series?

11. Make an energy-level diagram for a mesonic-hydrogen atom.

12. What is the radius of the first Bohr orbit of a μ-meson in lead? Compare with the radius of the nucleus itself. What would you expect to happen?

13. An "atom" called positronium is formed momentarily when a positive and negative electron approach each other with sufficiently low energy. Starting from *Bohr's postulates*, derive an expression for W of the stationary states.

14. Compare the frequency of a photon emitted by a transition $n = 21$ to $n = 20$ in hydrogen with the frequencies of rotation in the orbits $n = 20$ and 21. What does classical theory predict for the frequency? How large is the orbit?

15. What spectrum lines do you expect to observe from atomic hydrogen when it is bombarded with electrons of energy 13 ev?

16. What is the maximum wavelength for photoelectric emission of electrons from atomic hydrogen?

17. Demonstrate the correspondence principle by writing the term in parentheses in Eq. (30–34) as $(n_2^2 - n_1^2)/n_1^2 n_2^2$ and letting $\Delta n = 1$ and $n_2 \simeq n_1$ as the n's become large.

18. What is the size of a hydrogen atom for which a $\Delta n = 1$ radiative transition frequency is within 1% of the classical prediction?

19. In a Franck and Hertz experiment with atomic hydrogen, what is the accelerating voltage of the electron beam

(a) when the first line of the Balmer series would be observed?

(b) when positive ions would be detected?

20. (a) By assuming that the B field in a Stern-Gerlach experiment fans out in straight lines, as in Fig. 30–15, show that the resultant force on a current loop of radius r at a distance y from the effective center of divergence of the B lines is

$$\sum F = B 2\pi \frac{Ir^2}{\sqrt{y^2 + r^2}} = \frac{2B\mu}{\sqrt{y^2 + r^2}}.$$

(b) Find the transverse acceleration of a hydrogen atom, according to the Bohr model, in a B field of the above sort for $y = 1$ cm and $B = 1.5$ webers/m^2.

(c) How much deflection would be observed for atoms with 1 ev of energy over a longitudinal path length of 1 m?

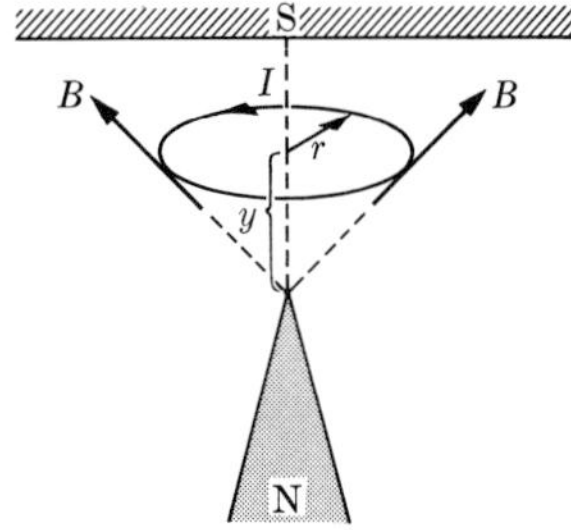

FIG. 30–15

21. Derive the gyromagnetic ratio (magnetic moment divided by angular momentum) for an electron in a Bohr orbit.

22. Derive the gyromagnetic ratio for a spinning particle that consists of

(a) a uniform solid spherical distribution of charge and mass,

(b) a uniform solid spherical distribution of mass and a uniform surface spherical distribution of charge.

(c) Which is a better model for the electron?

31

Wave Mechanics

31–1 INTRODUCTION

With all its ingenuity and success, the Bohr model depends on a set of *ad hoc* assumptions which require explanation in terms of fundamental principles. The accuracy of some of the predictions of the model makes it imperative, of course, that any new theory should agree with the successful predictions of the Bohr model. One ingredient, which was not used in the Bohr model, since it was not known at that time, is the wave property of the electron. Is the wave character of the electron important to the structure of the atom? The answer to this question is revealed in a dimensional check. We ask how the circumference of the Bohr orbit compares with the electronic wavelength. The wavelength is given by the de Broglie expression,

$$\lambda = \frac{h}{p} = \frac{h}{mv}\cdot \tag{31–1}$$

The second Bohr postulate leads to $mvr = nh(2\pi)$ which, combined with Eq. (31–1), yields

$$\lambda = 2\pi\,\frac{r}{n}\cdot \tag{31–2}$$

This indicates that the electron wavelength is of the same order of magnitude as the orbital dimensions. We therefore expect the wave properties to manifest themselves.

The second postulate of Bohr, the quantum condition for allowed orbits, can be made less arbitrary by utilizing wave properties. Since, as we have seen, free electrons can be regarded as traveling waves, it seems reasonable to assume that an electron confined in an atom might be required to form a standing wave. As a mechanical analogy, we can imagine traveling waves in opposite directions on a closed string in the form of a circle of radius r_0. The lateral displacement in the plane of the circle would be $r - r_0$. For standing waves to occur, the wavelength must be an integral submultiple of the circumference. If this idea is applied to an electron in an orbit, we have

$$n\lambda = 2\pi r_0, \tag{31–3}$$

or, substituting the de Broglie wavelength and rearranging, we have the same expression as the Bohr postulate gives, i.e.,

$$mvr = nh/(2\pi). \tag{31–4}$$

The above, with its reliance on a mechanical analogy, is far from an adequate portrayal of the proper wave model of the atom. It has nearly the same arbitrariness in its postulates as the Bohr model, it is a one-dimensional analysis, and, finally, it gives little more information than the Bohr model.

Before presenting the wave-mechanical description of the problem of atomic structure, we shall first elaborate on the description of photons and particles. The *probability interpretation* of wave amplitude, and the *uncertainty principle* are the important new ideas that will be introduced.

31–2 WAVE-PHOTON DUALITY; PROBABILITY

Considerable space in earlier chapters was devoted to the methods of predicting the effects of refraction, reflection, and interference (including diffraction) on the intensity patterns of waves. Light waves were used most frequently as an example. It was truthfully asserted that the predictions agreed with experimental observation. The above topics are categorized under the heading *wave propagation.*

In another chapter, the question of emission and absorption of waves was discussed. In this case, only electromagnetic waves were considered, since the emission and absorption of mechanical waves are completely understandable in terms of classical theory. (We can use the more general term, interactions with matter, to include emission and absorption and also scattering or any other question that does not have to do with mere wave propagation.) We saw that classical theory is successful in describing observations of the interactions of long wavelength radiation such as radio, radar, etc. But it was found that quantum theory is necessary for the understanding of the interactions at short wavelengths, for example, the photoelectric effect, the Compton effect, and the emission of light.

Thus we are forced to accept a corpuscular (i.e., photon) model of radiation for treating interactions, but we are forced to retain the wave model for treating propagation.

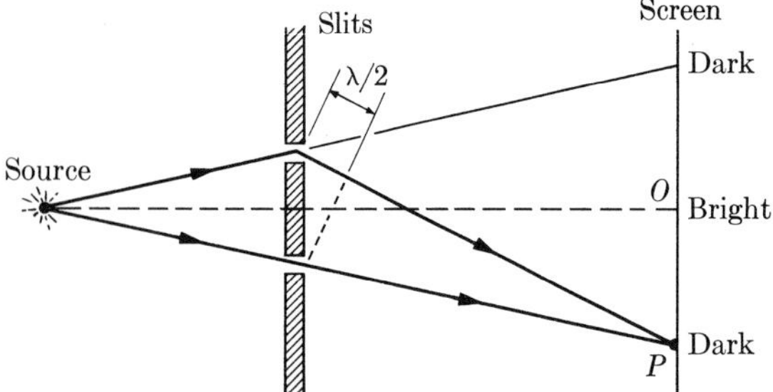

FIG. 31–1. An example of diffraction in which dark bands appear in regions where particles would be expected to be most abundant.

Can the photon theory also explain the propagation of light? The answer is no. The propagation of light through lenses, slits, etc. depends on the superposition of the effects of *all* parts of the previous wave front. How can a photon in one place influence a photon in another place? For example, consider a double-slit experiment such as in Fig. 31–1. The geometry has been deliberately chosen in such a way as to make the results very dramatic. Wave theory says that point P on the screen is dark because the path difference for the two rays is $\lambda/2$. We know from experiment that this is correct. But a photon from the source can pass directly through the lower slit and, by traveling in a straight line, strike the screen at P. How does this photon know that it cannot go to P? The answer must be that the mere presence of the other slit prevents the photon from going to P! This conclusion can be verified by blocking off the upper slit. The result is that P becomes bright, photons now go to P. But even the single-slit result is not understandable in terms of photons because the photons are not restricted to P; due to diffraction there is light, i.e., photons in the shadow. The photon theory makes no sense in the analysis of the *propagation* of light. We *must* use the wave theory to predict where the light (i.e. photons) will go. Ask yourself other questions. In the double-slit arrangement, how does a photon know that it can bend its path and go to O, or any other region of constructive interference? Which slit does the photon go through? In trying to find an answer to these questions, you will note that the photon picture seems completely absurd.

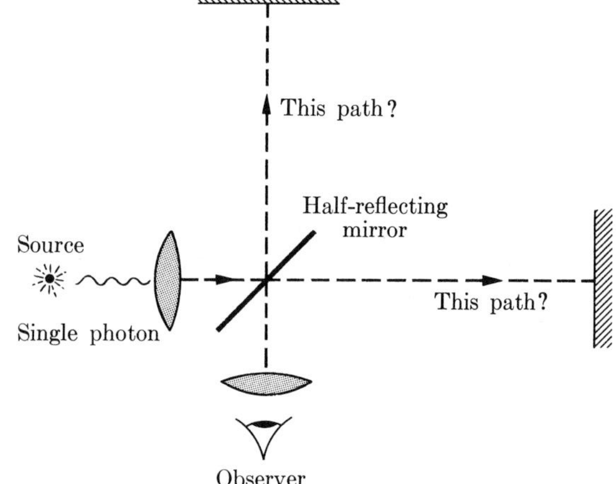

FIG. 31–2. The Michelson interferometer with a light source so weak that it is very improbable that there will be more than one photon in the apparatus at a given time.

The difficulties are removed by saying that the intensity at any point in space is obtained from the wave theory. The interpretation of intensity is no longer a continuous flow of energy through unit area in unit time. Intensity is the relative number of photons per unit area per unit time; or, if the intensity is very low so that there is only one photon passing through the apparatus at one time, the intensity at one point gives the relative *probability* that this one photon will pass through unit area at that point.

In Budapest, an experiment was performed in which a Michelson interferometer (Fig. 31–2) had a very weak light source. The light was so weak that, on the average, there was only one photon passing through the interferometer at a time. Which path did it take when it came to the half-silvered mirror? Could an interference effect be produced between light traveling in the two different paths? The experimental result was that the interference pattern was exactly as expected from classical wave theory, *even though* there was only a single photon in the apparatus at one time! Clearly, only the wave description makes sense in predicting intensities (i.e., probabilities).

Therefore, the wave theory predicts correctly the propagation of light wherever no detailed interaction with matter is involved. (We think of ordinary refraction and reflection as interactions with bulk matter which can then be described by wave theory.) The intensity, which is a function of position, is calculated from the wave theory as if the energy were smoothly distributed.

On the other hand, the emission and absorption of the radiation is understandable only with the quantum model. The probability model resolves the seeming paradox.

31–3 PARTICLE-WAVE DUALITY; PROBABILITY

In the case of particles, the situation, in principle, is the same as with light. The wave properties are not as evident as in the case of light simply because the wavelengths are usually so short that diffraction and other obvious wave phenomena are not usually evident. We tend to forget that so-called linear propagation is a wave phenomenon! If gamma-rays had been the visible light in our world, we would have first identified light as particles. The wave nature of this light would have been difficult to detect.

It has been shown that beams of electrons or other particles exhibit wave properties such as interference. In fact, wave theory must be used to predict the probability of finding a particle at a given place at a given time. Thus, the situation is exactly the same as with light.

31–4 THE UNCERTAINTY PRINCIPLE

In the discussion of relativity, it was found that great care must be exercised in defining methods of observation. For example, the operation of measuring the length of a moving object requires the equivalent of *two* observers stationed at points where each is adjacent to an end of the object at the same instant according to the observers. The need for unusual care in defining the method of observation in relativity stems from the high-velocity effects that our intuition has not prepared us for.

Similar problems occur in the realm of atomic structure, again because our intuition has not prepared us for the description of the submicroscopic world in terms different from those for the visible world. We have stated that the size of atoms can be inferred from kinetic theory and other methods. We have seen that the size of the nucleus can be found from alpha-particle scattering. Finally, you have learned that the energy states, the angular momentum states, and the magnetic moments of atoms can be deduced from their spectra, etc. The Bohr model postulates the details of structure (electron orbits), but this aspect of the model is not tested by experiment.

The question that we now ask is "How might we design an experiment to see where the electrons are in an atom?" It will be necessary to observe position to an accuracy greater than 10^{-10} m since this is the size of the atom. In Section 28–7, the microscope was found to have an ideal resolution of

$$\Delta x = \frac{\lambda}{n \sin \alpha}, \tag{31–5}$$

where λ is the wavelength of the radiation used for observation, n is the index of refraction of the medium in which the specimen is located, and α is the angle subtended by the lens (Fig. 31–3). Since n cannot be much greater than one, and $\sin \alpha$ cannot be at all greater than one, the smallest value of Δx is about the wavelength of the light used for observation. Since the wavelength of visible light is several thousand atomic diameters, it is hardly possible to see atoms, to say nothing of seeing their structure.

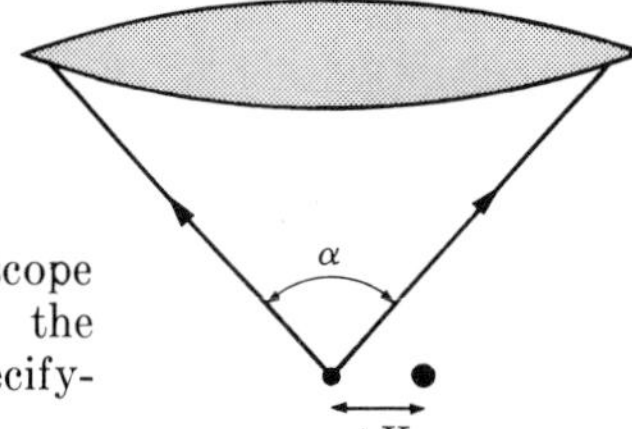

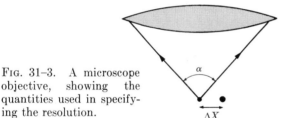

Fig. 31–3. A microscope objective, showing the quantities used in specifying the resolution.

The answer apparently lies in using shorter wavelength radiation for studying the atomic structure. This is exactly what is done in the electron microscope and in x-ray studies of matter. The effective wavelength of the electrons in an electron microscope can easily be 10^{-11} m or less. Basic problems in the "optics" of the electron microscope, however, limit its resolution to about 10^{-9} m. This resolution enables one to "see" large molecules. The regularities in the arrays of atoms in giant molecules, and in liquids and solids, can be "seen" by the diffraction effect on x-ray or electron (or neutron) beams of short wavelength. Even some features of the electron density distribution around the nucleus can be deduced when a regular array of atoms occurs as in a crystalline material. But this information concerning electron positions is statistical in nature, since the diffraction effects thus observed are averages over a tremendous number of atoms.

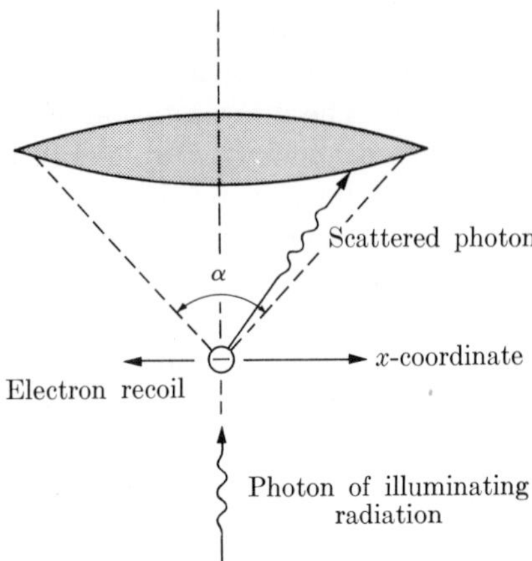

Fig. 31–4. Example of the way a particle can be "observed" with a microscope. The observed particle experiences an x-component of recoil due to the scattering of the photon used to observe the particle.

Can detail within a single atom be observed? Disregarding any possible technical difficulties, we might hope to observe an electron by viewing it through a super-microscope. The process requires that a photon strike the electron and then enter the instrument (Fig. 31–4). The collision is an example of the Compton effect, which will be appreciable since short wavelength radiation is required for intra-atomic resolution. We know from optical analysis that the resolving power of the instrument is given by Eq. (31–5). But it cannot be known where, within the angular opening α, the photon actually enters the lens. Thus the x-component of the momentum of the photon entering the lens can have any value from 0 to $(h\nu'/c) \sin \alpha$. Since momentum is conserved in the collision, the resulting x-component of momentum of the electron after the collision must also have a range of values from 0 to $(h\nu'/c) \sin \alpha$. The x-component of momentum of the electron is therefore uncertain by Δp_x, where

$$\Delta p_x = \frac{h\nu'}{c} \sin \alpha. \tag{31–6}$$

We form the product of the uncertainty of position in the x-direction Δx [from Eq. (31-5)] and the uncertainty in the x-component of momentum of the electron Δp_x [from Eq. (31-6)], obtaining

$$\Delta x \, \Delta p_x = \frac{\lambda' \nu'}{c} h$$

or

$$\Delta x \, \Delta p_x = h, \tag{31-7}$$

since $\nu'\lambda' = c$ for the light wave.

To our amazement we find that we cannot determine *both* the momentum *and* the position of the electron with unlimited accuracy. If we increase the accuracy in position by decreasing the wavelength or by increasing the aperture α of the lens, the uncertainty in momentum is increased by just the same factor that the uncertainty in position is decreased (Eq. 31-7). Planck's action constant appears as the limiting value of the product. When we inquire about the seriousness of this limitation, we need only to be reminded that the product of momentum itself and the radius is $mvr = nh/(2\pi)$, which is also of the order of magnitude of h. Hence, the uncertainties are comparable with the quantities themselves and therefore very little could be learned about the motion of the electron within an atom.

The next question might concern the possibility of a more ingenious way of observing the electron. The answer is that all methods lead to the same basic limiting values of the product $\Delta p \, \Delta q$, where p is the momentum corresponding to the coordinate q, given by Eq. (31-7) (within a factor of 2π). Examples will follow. It appears that nature has contrived to prevent us from answering the question of the detailed motion of electrons in atoms (or of any other particle anywhere else). One possible conclusion is that the question has no meaning.

Some examples of experiments designed to obtain detailed information for free particles will now be described. Suppose that we have a straight beam of electrons, as in the left-hand side of Fig. 31-5. If the electrons are supposed to travel exactly parallel to OX, their y-component of momentum must be exactly zero. The uncertainty principle says that Δy is then infinite; that is, we do not know the y-position of any particular electron. This agrees with the wave description, which requires that the waves must be infinite plane parallel waves if the rays (i.e., particle paths) are parallel. We now attempt to delineate the y-coordinate of a particular electron by interposing a barrier with a narrow slit Δy, as in Fig. 31-5. But diffraction now occurs, and we have seen that the angle α to the first minimum is given by

$$\sin \alpha = \frac{\lambda}{\Delta y} \tag{31-8}$$

from wave theory. But this means that a particular electron may now be traveling at any angle up to at least α, that is, its y-momentum is uncertain by $\Delta p_y = p \sin \alpha$ (Fig. 31-5). Using Eq. (31-8) and the de Broglie wavelength, we then have

$$\Delta y \, \Delta p_y \simeq h, \tag{31-9}$$

the usual uncertainty expression.

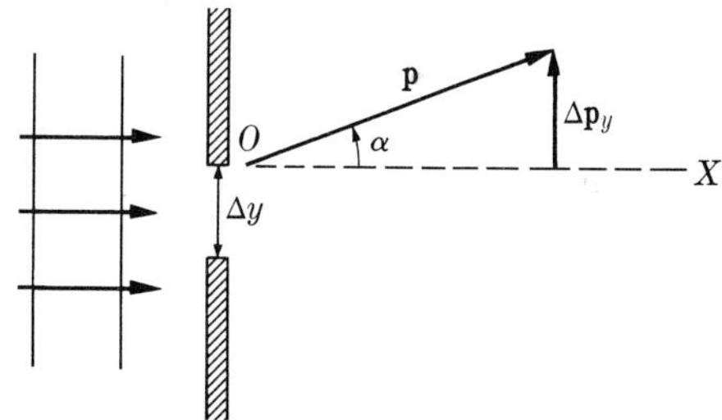

Fig. 31-5. The uncertainty in momentum $\Delta \mathbf{p}_y$ introduced by the single-slit diffraction of a wave.

Note that the wave particle duality always appears in the examples.

Suppose that an attempt is made to specify the x-component of position of an electron in the beam of the preceding example. If the beam on the left has an accurately known velocity, the uncertainty in momentum is small. *But* then, according to the uncertainty principle, the x-position of a particular electron is not known.

The wave description would be that, if p_x is accurately known, the de Broglie wavelength must be accurately known and hence the wave train must be very long. Thus the probability is about the same that the electron is anywhere in the x-direction. In order to delineate the x-position of the electron, the slit must be closed except for a short instant Δt, which then defines the position Δx to within $v\,\Delta t$. But the wave train is no longer very long, the wave is no longer a simple harmonic wave, and therefore a single wavelength no longer describes it. In the chapter on wave motion, it was stated that such a wave can be described by a band of simple harmonic waves with frequencies that extended over a region given by

$$\Delta f \simeq \frac{1}{\Delta t} = \frac{v}{\Delta x}, \qquad (31\text{-}10)$$

where Δx is the length of the train (Fig. 31-6). Using the de Broglie wavelength, we again have

$$\Delta x\,\Delta p_x \simeq h.$$

A more frequently used form of the uncertainty principle relates energy and time uncertainties. For example, the expression for Δp can be written

$$\Delta p = \Delta\left(\frac{h}{\lambda}\right) = \frac{h}{2\pi}\,\Delta\left(\frac{2\pi}{\lambda}\right) = \frac{h}{2\pi}\,\Delta K, \qquad (31\text{-}11)$$

where K is wave number. But we saw in the chapter on wave motion that $\Delta\omega/\Delta K = v_{\text{gr}}$, where $\omega = 2\pi\nu$ and v_{gr} is the group velocity. Thus, the uncertainty principle for a particle can be written

$$\Delta p\,\Delta x = \frac{h}{2\pi}\,\Delta K\,\Delta x = \frac{h}{2\pi}\,\Delta\omega\,\frac{\Delta x}{v_{\text{gr}}}. \qquad (31\text{-}12)$$

But $h\,\Delta\omega/2\pi = h\,\Delta\nu = \Delta E$, and $\Delta x/v_{\text{gr}} = \Delta t$, giving

$$\Delta p\,\Delta x = \Delta E\,\Delta t \simeq h. \qquad (31\text{-}13)$$

This equation indicates the connection between the uncertainties of energy and time. The same result is obtained for any other case. One of the most important applications is in the calculation of widths of energy levels of atoms or other systems. The lowest energy state of an atom can be very narrow, since it remains in the state for a long time, Δt. But atoms remain in typical excited states for times of the order of 10^{-8} sec. Since the lifetime of the excited state is only statistically predictable, the time uncertainty is about 10^{-8} sec and, therefore, ΔE is about 7×10^{-26} joule. Thus energy levels have finite widths (when the lifetime is finite) even when all other causes of widening are negligible.

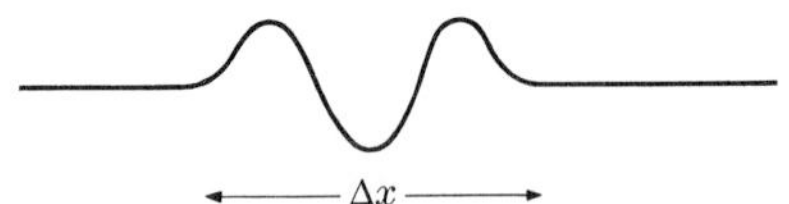

FIG. 31-6. A wave packet of about $1\frac{1}{2}$ wavelengths.

31-5 THE SCHRÖDINGER WAVE EQUATION

The subject of atomic structure can hardly be left without at least a qualitative account of the successful theory of atomic, molecular, and solid-state structure. The wave aspects of the electron led to a search for a *wave equation* whose solution might lead to a successful description of atoms.

Since beams of free particles display wave properties, it seems reasonable to postulate a wave amplitude that is to be associated with particles in the same way that the electric field of an electromagnetic wave is associated with photons. It has been seen that the relationship between photons and electromagnetic waves is obtained by interpreting the intensity of the electromagnetic wave as proportional to the probability of finding a photon at the point in question. Since the wave intensity is proportional to the square of the electric field strength, the probability is also proportional to the square of the field strength. In many cases, the time-averaged probability is the quantity of main interest. This probability would therefore be proportional to the square of the *amplitude* of the electromagnetic wave, that is

$$P \alpha A^2, \tag{31–14}$$

where P is the probability and A is the amplitude.

By analogy with electromagnetic waves, it might be expected that the probability of finding particles at a given point in space and time is proportional to the square of a wave displacement of some sort. This idea has already been used in the interpretation of the experiments on diffraction of electron beams by crystals. What procedure should be used in other cases of interactions among particles? Turning to electromagnetic radiation as a guide, the general procedure for finding the wave intensity is to solve Maxwell's wave equations, subject to the conditions imposed by the particular problem. Therefore, it might seem reasonable that the wave displacement for the wave properties of particles should be governed by a wave equation, and, furthermore, that the probability for the particle should be proportional to the square of the magnitude of the displacement given by a solution of the wave equation satisfying the conditions of the problem. This is the method of wave mechanics, which will be discussed in an introductory form in what follows.

In all types of wave motion treated in classical physics, the property described by the wave motion is a physical quantity that can be measured quite directly. Examples for mechanical wave motion are the lateral displacement of the elements of a string, the longitudinal displacement of particles in sound waves, etc. With electromagnetic waves, the physical quantity is electric (or magnetic) field strength, which can be measured by the lateral force exerted on charges. In nonclassical (i.e., quantum) physics of electromagnetic radiation, we have already seen that the wave amplitude has lost its direct physical meaning and must be reinterpreted in terms of probability. Thus, we are prepared for the discovery that the wave displacement for particle waves is not an observable physical quantity in the classical sense but is, instead, related to the probability of the presence of the particle at the point in question.

A still more difficult problem arises as a result of the fact that the particle wave is not a directly observable physical quantity. There is no way to derive a wave equation for particle waves from first principles, as in the case of mechanical waves or electromagnetic waves. Thus the wave equation for particle waves (the Schrödinger equation) is essentially a postulate. Its usefulness can only be ascertained by comparing with experiment the predictions derived from the wave equation. We state, in advance, that the predictions of the Schrödinger equation agree with the observed properties of individual atoms and molecules, and with their group properties as gases, liquids, and solids. Thus, the method of wave mechanics is highly successful in describing the world of atomic properties.

First, you are reminded of the form of the wave equation for mechanical waves or for electromagnetic waves. If we let P be the physical quantity in question and consider a one-dimensional or a plane wave, we have

$$v^2 \frac{\partial^2 P}{\partial x^2} = \frac{\partial^2 P}{\partial t^2}, \tag{31–15}$$

where v is the velocity. The symbol P represents a mechanical quantity such as displacement, density, etc. for mechanical waves, or electric or magnetic field strength for electromagnetic waves. Solutions to this equation represent traveling waves or standing waves, depending on the problem at hand. In order for any solution to be physically significant, the values of P must be everywhere finite, single-valued, and also (in some cases) continuous in the region of validity of the solution. The solutions must also meet the boundary conditions, for example, the conditions at the source or at a discontinuity in the medium. A frequently occurring example of boundary conditions is $P = 0$ for all values of t at boundaries where there can be no wave displacement, such as the displacement of the fixed ends of a string, or the electric field strength at a superconducting surface.

One additional feature of the possible solutions to Eq. (31–15) is worth noting at this time. The standing wave solutions must be of the form

$$P = \mathcal{P}(x, y, z) \cdot \pi(t), \tag{31–16}$$

where $\mathcal{P}(x, y, z)$ is the amplitude factor. The assumption that Eq. (31–16) is a possible solution of the wave equation can be justified by substitution into Eq. (31–15). The result of the substitution is

$$v^2 \frac{\partial^2 \mathcal{P}}{\partial x^2} \frac{1}{\mathcal{P}} = \frac{\partial^2 \pi}{\partial t^2} \frac{1}{\pi}, \tag{31–17}$$

which can only be true if both sides are constant. Consequently, the time-dependent wave equation (31–15) can be reduced to a time-independent equation

$$\frac{\partial^2 \mathcal{P}}{\partial x^2} = C\mathcal{P} \tag{31–18}$$

for the amplitude of a *standing wave*.

Solutions to Eq. (31–18) for which $\mathcal{P}$ is everywhere finite, single-valued, and continuous are possible for negative values of C, since sine or cosine functions are then possible solutions. Thus, a possible solution is

$$\mathcal{P} = A_0 \sin 2\pi \frac{x}{\lambda}, \tag{31–19}$$

where

$$\lambda = 2\pi/\sqrt{C}. \tag{31–20}$$

The boundary conditions further limit the solutions. The limitation is usually in the form of requiring that the wavelengths λ of the solutions be related to the dimensions of the system. For example, a vibrating rod of length L, with its center clamped and its ends free to move, would require

$$\lambda = 2L, \frac{2L}{3}, \frac{2L}{5}, \cdots 2L/(2n+1), \tag{31–21}$$

where n is an integer. Thus the phenomenon of quantization appears in the course of the solution of the problem as a result of the boundary conditions. Note that quantization was *not* introduced into the problem as a postulate.

The *energy* of the standing wave that consists of a wave with a single wavelength can be found by remembering that each element dx of the system is moving with simple harmonic motion with amplitude $\mathcal{P}$. Therefore, the energy due to the simple harmonic motion of the element dx is

$$dE = \frac{k}{2} \mathcal{P}^2 \, dx,$$

or, for the entire system,

$$E = \tfrac{1}{2} \int_0^L k\mathcal{P}^2 \, dx, \tag{31–22}$$

which (from Eq. (31–19)) leads to

$$E = \tfrac{1}{2} \int_0^L kA_0^2 \sin^2 \left(2\pi \frac{x}{\lambda}\right) dx. \tag{31–23}$$

The result of the integration is

$$E = \frac{k}{4} A_0^2 L. \tag{31–24}$$

The standing wave is a so-called stationary state, a state in which there is no energy flow (in contrast with a traveling wave).

Finally, we now turn to the problem of a wave equation for the waves associated with particles. This equation will play the basic role in wave mechanics, similar to the basic role played by Newton's second law, $\sum F = ma$, in classical mechanics. It has already been pointed out that this wave equation cannot be derived from first principles (in contrast with other types of wave motion). Thus this wave equation is essentially a postulate, as we said earlier.

The wave equation, which was presented by Schrödinger in 1926, can be written in one dimension for a free particle in a region of uniform potential as follows:

$$\frac{h^2}{8\pi^2 m} \frac{\partial^2 \Psi}{\partial x^2} = \frac{h}{i2\pi} \frac{\partial \Psi}{\partial t}. \tag{31–25}$$

Several features of the above equation require

special comment, some of which has already been made. The quantity Ψ is not an observable quantity. The square of its magnitude is observable in a statistical sort of way, since $|\Psi|^2\,dx\,dt$ is the probability that the particle be found between x and $x + dx$ in the time interval t to $t + dt$. The quantity Ψ is, in general, a function of the position coordinates and of the time, in a manner similar to the displacement in mechanical waves. Second, it is seen that $i(=\sqrt{-1})$ appears in the equation. As a result, Ψ may be a complex quantity. No difficulty results, since it is $|\Psi|^2$ or some other real numbers derived from Ψ that are finally used. Third, it is seen that Eq. (31–25) differs from the ordinary wave equation (31–15) in having a first derivative with respect to time.

In order that the probability $|\Psi|^2$ have physical significance, it should be finite, single-valued, and continuous in the regions of interest. The question of the difficulties that would arise if these conditions were not met is left for student discussion (Problems). In addition to the above general restrictions on Ψ, there are restrictions imposed by the boundary conditions of each particular problem. The effect of the boundary conditions in some cases is to place quantum restrictions on observable quantities such as energy and momentum. An advantage of the wave mechanics over the Bohr theory is immediately evident. Quantization is not introduced as an hypothesis. It appears as a necessity during the process of solving the wave equation subject to the conditions imposed by the nature of the problem. It may seem that one arbitrary hypothesis has simply been replaced by another, since the Schrödinger equation is an hypothesis. However, the Bohr theory required additional hypotheses, for example, that radiation is emitted only during transitions from one "allowed" energy to another. Furthermore, wave mechanics is not restricted in its success to the case of two-body systems.

An example of a solution to Eq. (31–25) will now be given. For a beam of free particles, the de Broglie equation indicates that the associated wavelength is given by $\lambda = h/p$. The success of the quantum theory of radiation suggests that the energy and "frequency" are related by $hf = W$. The wave number k then becomes

$$k \equiv \frac{2\pi}{\lambda} = \frac{2\pi}{h}\,p, \tag{31–26}$$

and the angular velocity

$$\omega \equiv 2\pi f = \frac{2\pi}{h}\,W. \tag{31–27}$$

The wave solution for a free particle then might be thought to be

$$\Psi = A\sin(kx - \omega t) = A\sin\frac{2\pi}{h}(px - Wt), \tag{31–28}$$

but when this trial solution is substituted in the above form of the Schrödinger equation (31–25), there is a sine term on the left side and a cosine term on the right side. Therefore, the trial solution (31–28) is unsatisfactory. It is now recalled that an exponential function with a complex exponent is related to trigonometric functions. As a result, the next trial solution is

$$\Psi = Ae^{(2\pi i/h)(px - Wt)}, \tag{31–29}$$

which is equivalent to

$$\Psi = A\cos\frac{2\pi}{h}(px - Wt) + iA\sin\frac{2\pi}{h}(px - Wt). \tag{31–30}$$

The exponential form suggests that this trial will satisfy the wave equation, while the dependence on $px - Wt$ indicates that the solution is wavelike. By substitution of either of the above expressions into the wave equation (31–25), it is found that they are indeed a solution, with the constants related by

$$W = \frac{p^2}{2m} \tag{31–31}$$

as expected for free particles in a region of uniform potential, if the potential is arbitrarily chosen as zero.

The above solution is a plane monochromatic wave, which means that the wave has a specific wavelength or the corresponding particle has a specific momentum. The uncertainty principle tells us that such a particle has infinite uncertainty in its position. The above wave-mechanical solution agrees with what has just been said, since

$$|\Psi|^2 = A^2, \tag{31-32}$$

which shows that the probability is constant, independent of position; that is, the particle may be anywhere with equal likelihood.

If the particle is to be localized, a wave packet must be constructed by using an ensemble of wavelengths, as we have seen in the chapter on wave motion. If the packet is to be a single, nonrepeating packet, an infinite number of component monochromatic waves are required; that is, a continuous distribution of contributing amplitude versus wavelength is required. As an example, the distribution in amplitudes for a single packet in the form of a single cycle of a sine curve of wavelength λ_0 is shown in Fig. 31-7. From the figure it is seen that when $x = \lambda_0$, the momentum $p = h/\lambda$ has a large probability of lying between $h/2\lambda_0$ and $2h/\lambda_0$. It is seen that $\Delta x \, \Delta p \simeq h$ as usual.

The most important consequence of the solution (31-29) is that there are no restrictions imposed on the magnitude of the energy of the particle; that is, there is no quantum restriction. This result agrees with the observations of free particles. An example of the use of the wave properties of free particles in the understanding of experimental observation has already been given in the discussion of the diffraction of a beam of electrons by a crystal lattice. The interpretation was based on the interference between plane waves.

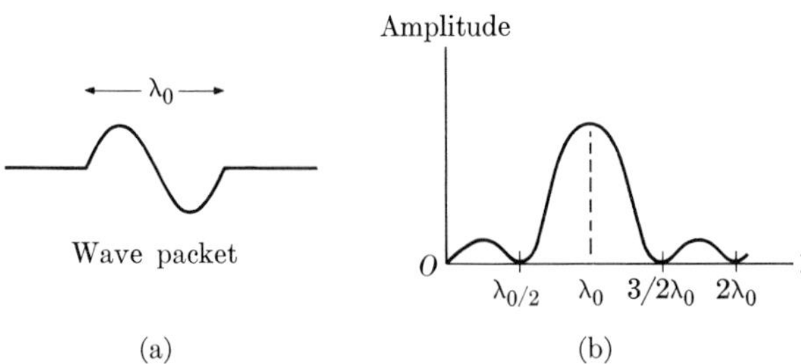

FIG. 31-7. (a) A wave packet of one wavelength and (b) the amplitude distribution in its Fourier integral representation. It is seen that the band of wavelengths required has a spread of the order of a factor of two in wavelength.

If the particle is in a region where its potential energy is a function of position, the Schrödinger equation is

$$\frac{h^2}{8\pi^2 m}\frac{\partial^2\Psi}{\partial x^2} - V\Psi = \frac{h}{2\pi i}\frac{\partial\Psi}{\partial t}. \tag{31-33}$$

When V is constant, it can be chosen equal to zero and the previous analysis applies. But if V is not constant, it is the total energy W given by (nonrelativistic)

$$W = \frac{p^2}{2m} + V \tag{31-34}$$

that remains constant. In consequence, the momentum p must change when V changes. The wave description is that the wavelength ($\lambda = h/p$) changes as V changes, with a decrease in V resulting in a decrease in λ.

31-6 STATIONARY ENERGY STATES; PARTICLE IN A BOX

The problem that we shall ultimately be concerned with is the hydrogen atom. The electron in the hydrogen atom is a bound particle, not a free particle. Our first interest will be in the possibility of stationary energy states of the atom. By analogy with waves in classical systems, we are led to the conjecture that standing wave solutions may correspond to stationary states. A standing wave solution to Eq. (31-33) can be expressed as the product of a position-dependent factor with a time-dependent factor. A simple harmonic time factor can be expressed in complex notation as

$$e^{-(2\pi i/h)Wt}. \tag{31-35}$$

The assumed standing wave solution is therefore of the form

$$\Psi = e^{-(2\pi i/h)Wt} \cdot \psi(x), \qquad (31\text{–}36)$$

where $\psi(x)$ is a function of position alone. When (31–36) is substituted into (31–33) the time-dependent factor drops out, leaving

$$\frac{\partial^2 \psi}{\partial x^2} + \frac{8\pi^2 m}{h^2}(W - V)\psi = 0. \qquad (31\text{–}37)$$

This equation cannot describe a hydrogen atom since the equation is one-dimensional. Therefore we shall first consider a one-dimensional bound system, a particle in a one-dimensional "box."

We now consider the example of a molecule of gas confined inside a box at low enough pressure so that the only collisions are with the walls. Furthermore, we consider the motion to be in the OX-direction only and we assume that the walls are completely impenetrable. These conditions are obtained by having V constant everywhere except at the walls where V goes discontinuously to infinity. Although the latter condition seems intuitively obvious, it will be discussed further in the next section. For simplicity, V is chosen to be zero inside the box. Since the molecule cannot penetrate the walls, ψ must go to zero at the walls (which are chosen to be at $x = 0$ and $x = L$). We are already acquainted with a problem of this sort—standing waves in a string that is fixed to immovable supports. Thus we try the solution

$$\psi = A \sin n\pi \frac{x}{L}, \qquad (31\text{–}38)$$

where n is an integer. When this trial solution is substituted into Eq. (31–37) (remembering that we chose $V = 0$), it is found that (31–38) is a solution if

$$W = \frac{h^2 n^2}{8L^2 m}. \qquad (31\text{–}39)$$

Thus the energy is quantized. Furthermore, the quantization has appeared during the solution of the problem in place of being introduced arbitrarily as a postulate. In this particular case of a macroscopic length L, the values of n are so large that the energy differences between quantum states are undetectably small.

What is the distance between the peaks in the probability distribution, that is, the peaks in the sine curve of Eq. (31–38)? At room temperature, the kinetic energy of a molecule is about 4×10^{-21} joule (from kinetic theory). For a box of side 1 cm, n would then be about 3×10^6. Consequently, the probability distribution $|\psi|^2$ would have a "granularity" so fine that the variations would be difficult to detect. In fact when the uncertainty principle is taken into account, the granularity is found to be undetectable.

31–7 PENETRATION OF BARRIERS

In the preceding section, one nonclassical result, the quantization of energy of a bound particle, was illustrated. A second result of wave mechanics that is in striking disagreement with classical theory is the penetration by particles into regions where their kinetic energy would be negative according to classical theory.

As an example, consider again a particle inside a box, but this time with walls where the potential rises only by a *finite* amount V_w. We can choose $V = 0$ inside the box, as before. For motion along one coordinate x, the potential energy will be as shown in Fig. 31–8. The origin has been chosen at the center of the box in order to introduce symmetry in the solutions to follow.

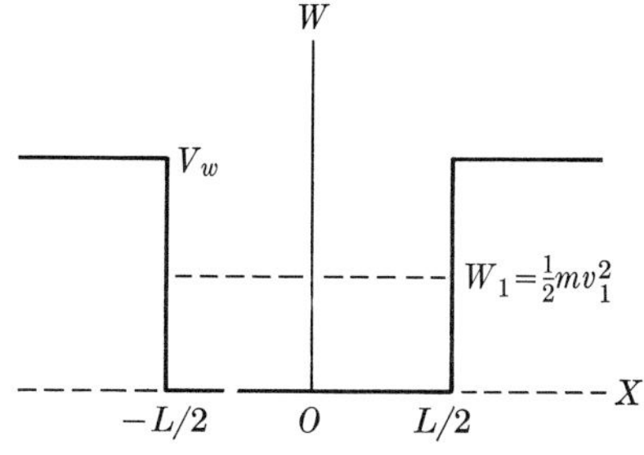

FIG. 31–8. A square potential well with walls of height V_w. The dashed line represents the energy level of a particle of kinetic energy $\frac{1}{2}mv_1^2$.

Classically, a particle moving along OX with velocity v_1 would have energy $W_1 = \frac{1}{2}mv_1^2$ inside the box, where v_1 and hence W_1 could take on any value. If $W_1 > V_w$, the classical result is that the particle will penetrate the "wall" and continue moving in the wall with kinetic energy $W_1 - V_w$, but if $W_1 < V_w$, the particle must be reflected by the wall.

What is the wave-mechanical result? Inside the box the particle will behave much the same as in the box that had an infinite rise in potential at the walls, except that we do not have even an intuitive reason to let $\psi = 0$ at the walls. That is to say, the solution to Eq. (31-37), with $V = 0$, is still sinusoidal, *but* the boundary conditions are not $\psi = 0$ at the walls.

The solution inside the box can be written

$$\psi = A \sin (kx + \phi), \qquad (31\text{-}40)$$

where k and ϕ are to be determined from the boundary conditions at the walls. The constant k can be related to the energy by substituting the trial solution (31-40) into the wave equation (31-37), (with $V = 0$), with the result that

$$k = \frac{2\pi}{h} \sqrt{2mW}. \qquad (31\text{-}41)$$

Consequently, the boundary conditions will also place limitations on the energy W.

In order to determine the conditions at the boundary walls, it is necessary to first find solutions to the wave equation for the region outside the walls. We consider the case in which the particle is confined to the box classically; that is, $W - V < 0$. Then the wave equation (31-37) has opposite signs for the two terms. The solution cannot be sinusoidal in form but is, instead, of exponential form with real exponents; that is,

$$\psi = Be^{\pm Cx}. \qquad (31\text{-}42)$$

Since ψ must remain finite, the negative exponent must be used for the $+x$ region and the positive exponent for the $-x$ region. The constant C can be found immediately by substitution of (31-42) into (31-37), with the result that

$$C = (2\pi/h)\sqrt{2m(V_w - W)}. \qquad (31\text{-}43)$$

The two solutions, one for inside the box and the other for outside the box, must join smoothly at the walls; that is, at $x = \pm L/2$. When this latter condition is applied to the two solutions, equations are found that relate the constants A, B, and ϕ. The calculations are left for the Problems. The results are shown graphically (Fig. 31-9) for two cases.

It is seen that the sinusoidal curves do not go to zero at the walls but that they alone would go to zero at points x_0 that are greater than $L/2$. The energy is quantized much as it is in the case of the impenetrable walls. The values of λ are restricted to

$$\lambda = 4\,\frac{x_0}{n}, \qquad (31\text{-}44)$$

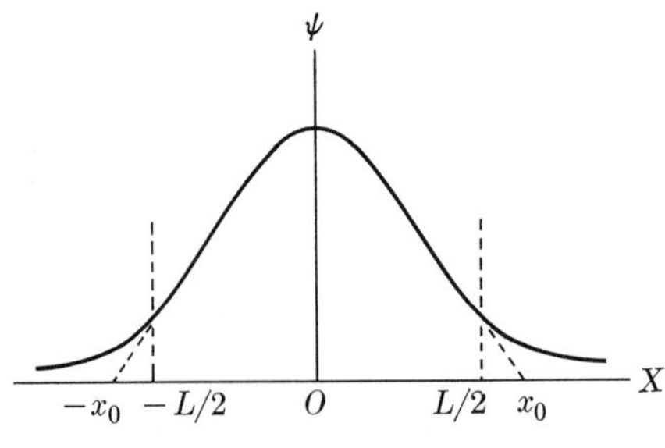

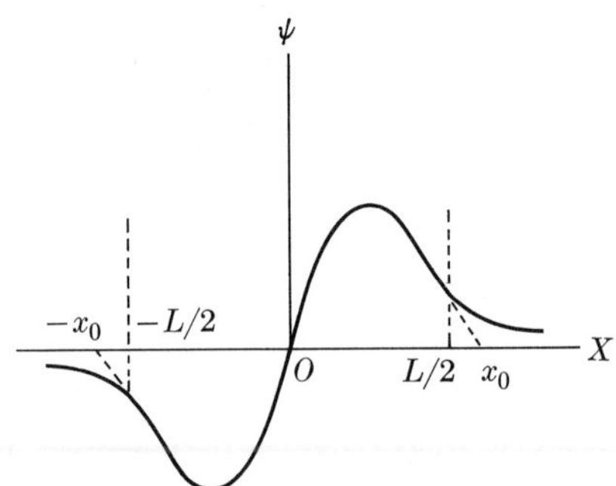

FIG. 31-9. Wave amplitude for the two lowest states of a particle in the square well of Fig. 31-8. The amplitude does not go to zero at the walls ($\pm L/2$).

where n is an integer and x_0 is a function of n, as will be seen in the Problems. The wave number $k(= 2\pi/\lambda)$ is thus quantized, with the result that the energy is quantized (Eq. 31–41).

As V_w goes to infinity, it will be found that the exponential tails outside the walls vanish and the assumption made in Section 31–6 is justified (that walls with infinite potential rises are completely impenetrable even in wave mechanics). The analysis is left for the Problems.

The most interesting result of the solutions for the box with finite walls is that the probability $|\psi|^2$ does *not* go to zero at the walls of the box but simply decreases exponentially with distance of penetration into the wall. A very important extension of the above conclusion is to the case in which the *thickness* of the wall is also finite.

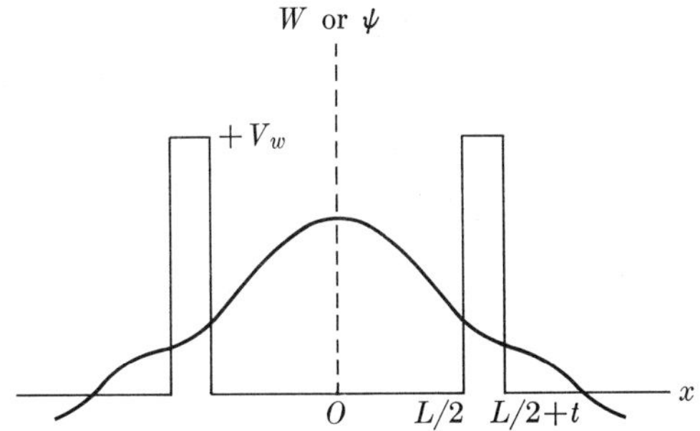

FIG. 31–10. A square potential well with potential walls of finite thickness. The wave amplitude for a case of a particle with energy less than V_w is plotted in a graph superimposed on the potential diagram.

If a box with walls of finite potential height and finite thickness—for example, with potential as shown in Fig. 31–10—is considered, the exponential tail of the preceding example will extend beyond the outer surface of the wall. As a result, a particle initially located inside the box will not be confined to the box indefinitely; that is, there is a finite probability of escape. In another sort of terminology, the lifetime of the state with the particle confined to the box is finite. The phenomenon that has been developed qualitatively in this paragraph is called the "tunnel" effect. It has no classical counterpart. It is strictly a wave-mechanical effect, which, for example, leads to an understanding of the field emission of electrons, the electron flow in tunnel diodes, and the alpha-particle emission by radioactive nuclei.

31–8 ONE-DIMENSIONAL HARMONIC OSCILLATOR

We now consider a problem that is related to the discovery of quantization by Planck in his successful theory of the emission of radiation from cavities (blackbody radiation). What does wave mechanics predict for the energies of simple harmonic oscillators?

In this case, the potential energy V is given by

$$V = \frac{k}{2}x^2, \tag{31–45}$$

as we learned in mechanics. The wave equation (31–37) then becomes

$$\frac{\partial^2\psi}{\partial x^2} + \frac{8\pi^2 m}{h^2}\left(W - \frac{kx^2}{2}\right)\psi = 0. \tag{31–46}$$

The solution of this equation can only be expressed in terms that are more complicated than we have used heretofore. Consequently, only the general ideas and the graph of the results will be given here.

It is expected that the solutions will be similar to the case of a particle inside a box since the potential rises rapidly with increasing x, as in Fig. 31–11, which is a graph of Eq. (31–45). In fact, classically, the particle is strictly confined

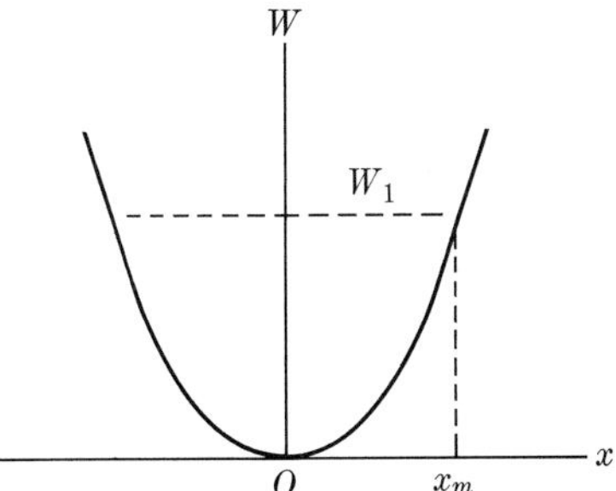

FIG. 31–11. A parabolic potential well. The classical amplitude x_m corresponding to a total particle energy W_1 is shown.

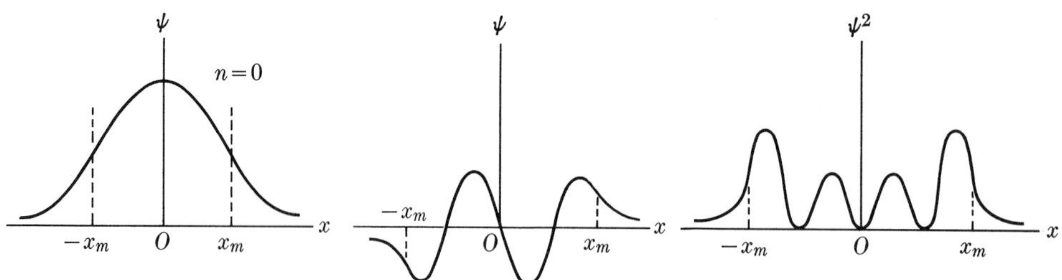

FIG. 31-12. Graphs of the wave-amplitude distribution for two low-energy levels. The third graph shows the probability distribution for the higher of the two levels.

to a region x_m determined by its total energy W (as in Fig. 31-11), but W can have any value. The wave-mechanical result, on the other hand, would be expected to have the two features found in Section 31-7, namely, discrete energy states corresponding to restrictions in the "wavelengths" of solutions that will fit into the potential well, and penetration of the particle beyond the classical limits.

The restrictions in energy are found to be given by

$$W = (n + \tfrac{1}{2})fh, \tag{31-47}$$

where n is an integer and f is the classical frequency of the oscillator. This result differs from Planck's hypothesis only in the additive constant $\frac{1}{2}$. Since the difference in energy between states is the same as in Planck's hypothesis, the agreement with experiment is equally good. One important advantage of the wave-mechanical method is that the quantization of energy appears during the solution instead of being introduced as an hypothesis.

The nature of the wave solutions for selected values of n are shown by the graphs of ψ in Fig. 31-12. Note the penetration beyond the classical amplitude x_m. The probability, which is proportional to $|\psi|^2$, is shown for $n = 3$ in the graph. Comparison with the classical probability is left for the Problems.

31-9 ATOMIC HYDROGEN

The wave-mechanical analysis of the two-particle system of atomic hydrogen is more complex than any of the above examples, since it is a three-dimensional problem with a potential that is position-dependent. However, certain aspects of the solution of the Schrödinger equation for hydrogen can be understood qualitatively in terms of the results for the simpler problems in the preceding sections.

To a good degree of approximation, the nucleus can be considered stationary, with the electron moving in the Coulomb field of the nucleus. The potential energy of the system can be written as the potential energy of the electron

$$V = -\frac{1}{4\pi\epsilon_0}\frac{e^2}{r}, \tag{31-48}$$

where V is chosen to be zero at $r = \infty$, as usual.

The potential well in this case (Fig. 31-13) bears a qualitative resemblance to the square well of Section 31-7 (Fig. 31-8). Hence, the solutions for ψ as a function of r are expected to be similar to Fig. 31-9; that is, they are expected (a) to result in quantization of the energy, and

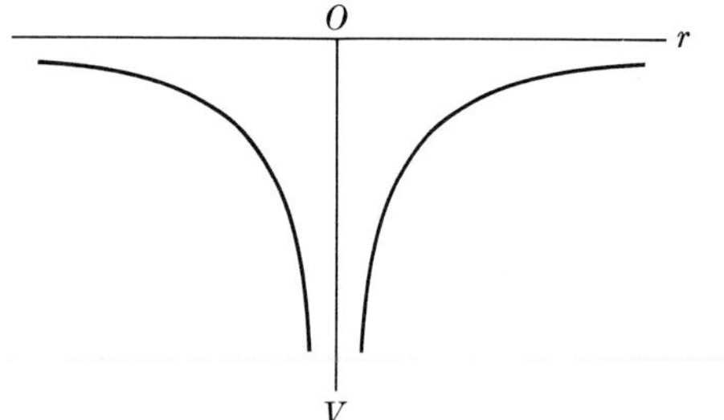

FIG. 31-13. The potential well for an inverse-square-law field of force.

(b) to have exponential tails that extend beyond the classical limits of excursion of an electron of given energy. The solutions will now be described in more detail.

The wave equation must be extended to three dimensions. The result, in cartesian coordinates, is simply the inclusion of terms in y and z, giving

$$\frac{\partial^2\psi}{\partial x^2} + \frac{\partial^2\psi}{\partial y^2} + \frac{\partial^2\psi}{\partial z^2} + \frac{8\pi^2 m}{h^2}\left(W - V\right)\psi = 0. \tag{31–49}$$

However, since V is expressed most simply in spherical polar coordinates (Eq. 31–48), it proves advantageous to express the entire equation in polar coordinates. The resulting equation is complicated in appearance, but the solution proceeds in a straightforward manner. Only the results will be given here.

Among possible solutions, only those that are everywhere finite, single-valued, and continuous are acceptable, as previously discussed. The coordinate system is shown in Fig. 31–14. The origin is at the nucleus. The point P is specified by r, θ, and ϕ, as shown. Integers appear in the solutions, as in some of the earlier examples, but in this case there are three, commonly designated as n, l, and m_l. The effect of the occurrence of these integers on observable physical quantities will be discussed in the following paragraphs.

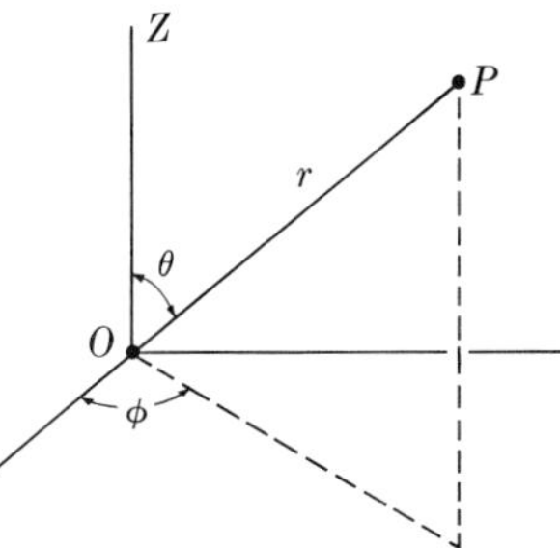

FIG. 31–14. The polar coordinate system used for the description of the position of an electron relative to the nucleus of a hydrogen atom.

An immediate consequence of the wave-mechanical solution is that the energy is quantized

$$W = -\frac{1}{4\pi\epsilon_0}\frac{2\pi^2 me^4}{h^2}\frac{1}{n^2}, \tag{31–50}$$

which is exactly the same as the Bohr result. But, as previously emphasized, quantization is *not* a postulate in the case of wave mechanics.

We now turn to the question of a model or a pictorial representation of the hydrogen atom. In the Bohr theory, the geometrical model of the hydrogen atom was included in the postulates. The electron moved in definite orbits around the nucleus. In wave mechanics, on the other hand, a method for calculating the probability distribution is postulated. The results of that calculation for hydrogen will now be described.

The solution for ψ is the product of three functions, $\Phi(\phi)$, $\Theta(\theta)$, and $R(r)$, each of which is a function of only one coordinate. However, the three integers mentioned previously enter into the solutions in a manner that introduces a certain type of interdependence, as we shall see shortly. The probability is given by

$$|\psi|^2 = |\Phi|^2 \cdot |\Theta|^2 \cdot |R|^2, \tag{31–51}$$

where Φ contains the integer (m_l), Θ contains the two integers (m_l and l), and R contains the two integers (l and n). The three integers are called quantum numbers, since they determine the quantized values of observable quantities.

The principal quantum number n specifies the energy, as we have seen from Eq. (31–50). The orbital quantum number l specifies the "orbital" angular momentum, as we shall note later. The magnetic quantum number m_l specifies the directional quantization of l, the effect of which was described in Section 30–9 (the Stern-Gerlach experiment). The quantum numbers are interrelated by the restrictions

$$|m_l| \leq l < n. \tag{31–52}$$

In Table 31–1, the expressions for the three factors in the probability are given for a few values of the quantum numbers. The complete expression for the probability is simply the product (Eq. 31–51) of the three factors given in the table. The constant a_0 appearing in the expressions for R is the Bohr radius for $n = 1$ [see Eq. (30–17)]. The function R is plotted in Fig. 31–15.

TABLE 31-1

THE PROBABILITY FUNCTIONS FOR SOME OF THE LOWER ENERGY LEVELS OF A ONE-ELECTRON ATOM

n	l	m_l	$\lvert\Phi\rvert^2$	$\lvert\Theta\rvert^2$	$\lvert R\rvert^2$
1	0	0	$1/(2\pi)$	$\frac{1}{2}$	$4(1/a_0)^3 e^{-2r/a_0}$
2	0	0	$1/(2\pi)$	$\frac{1}{2}$	$(1/2)(1/a_0)^3 \left(1 - \frac{r}{2a_0}\right)^2 e^{-r/a_0}$
2	1	0	$1/(2\pi)$	$\frac{3}{2}\cos^2\theta$	$(1/24)(1/a_0)^3 (r/a_0)^2 e^{-r/a_0}$
2	1	± 1	$1/(2\pi)$	$\frac{3}{4}\sin^2\theta$	$(1/24)(1/a_0)^3 (r/a_0)^2 e^{-r/a_0}$
3	0	0	$1/(2\pi)$	$\frac{1}{2}$	$(4/27)(1/a_0)^3 \left[1 - \frac{2r}{3a_0} + \frac{2}{27}\frac{r^2}{a_0^2}\right]^2 e^{-(2r/3a_0)}$
3	1	0	$1/(2\pi)$	$\frac{3}{2}\cos^2\theta$	$(2/3)(4/27)^2(1/a_0)^3 \left[1 - \frac{1}{6}\frac{r}{a_0}\right]^2 \left(\frac{r}{a_0}\right)^2 e^{-(2r/3a_0)}$
3	1	± 1	$1/(2\pi)$	$\frac{3}{4}\sin^2\theta$	$(2/3)(4/27)^2(1/a_0)^3 \left[1 - \frac{1}{6}\frac{r}{a_0}\right]^2 \left(\frac{r}{a_0}\right)^2 e^{-(2r/3a_0)}$

In addition, the quantity $4\pi r^2|R^2|$ is plotted in Fig. 31-15, since this quantity (when multiplied by dr) is the probability that the electron will be found at distance r to $r + dr$ from the nucleus.

Some general features of $|\psi|^2$ are worth noting. The probability has axial symmetry since it does not depend on the angle ϕ. The symmetry becomes spherical for $l = 0$. The radial dependence $|R^2|$ goes to zero at infinity and has $n - l$ peaks, including the central peak. The expressions have been "normalized" so that the integral of $|\psi|^2$ over all space is one (the electron must be somewhere and there is only one electron).

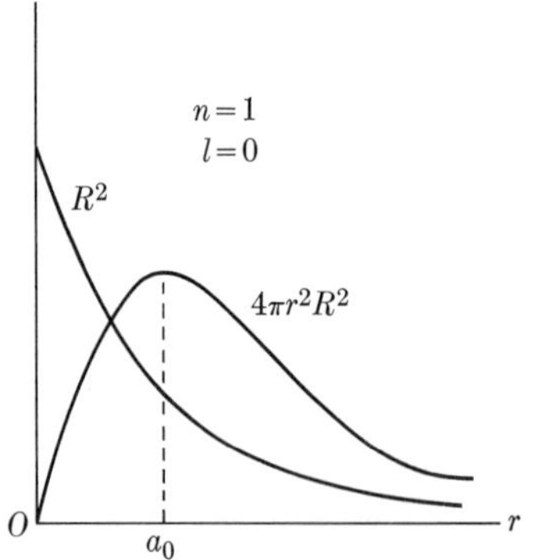

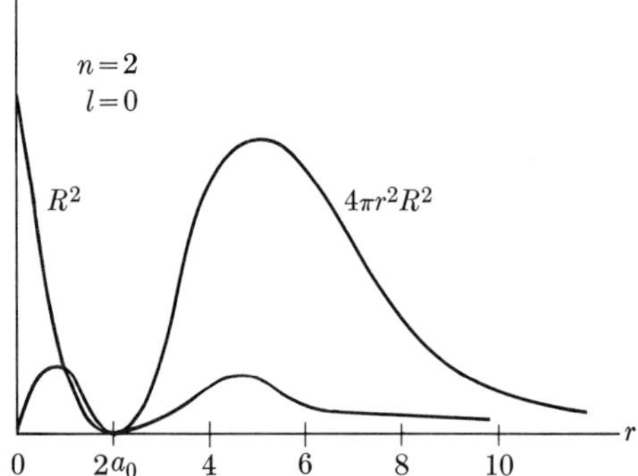

FIG. 31-15. The radial component of the probability distribution for the two lowest energy levels in hydrogen. The curve $4\pi r^2 R^2$ is the probability that the electron will be found at a distance r from the nucleus without regard for the direction from the nucleus.

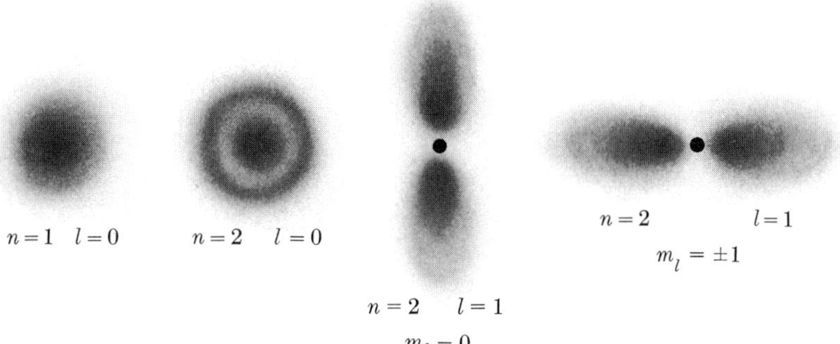

FIG. 31–16. The three-dimensional probability distribution for some of the lower energy states of a single-electron atom. The "clouds" are figures of revolution about a vertical axis. The density of the cloud is proportional to the probability.

The probability distribution can be simulated by a drawing in which the density in the drawing is proportional to probability. This is done in Fig. 31–16. The drawings would be figures of revolution about a vertical axis that lies in the plane of the paper. The angle θ is measured down from this axis. The most probable distance for $n = 1$ is actually a_0 and for $n = 2$ about $4\,a_0$, etc. (Fig. 31–15), as in the Bohr model. But we see that the probability is by no means zero elsewhere.

For some purposes, it is convenient to picture the time-average effect of the electron. In this case, the probability distribution is multiplied by the electron charge e and the resulting expression gives the equivalent *charge density* distribution in space. We then speak of the charge cloud or electron cloud around the nucleus. For example, the nearest experimental approach to an observation of the electron cloud distribution is the statistical average over many atoms obtained from observations of x-ray diffraction.

What results does the wave-mechanical method predict that can be confronted by experiment? The predicted energy levels are the same as from the Bohr theory and therefore agree with experiment. It should be pointed out that very fine details of the energy levels also depend on l and on electron spin and are explained by wave mechanics, but not by the Bohr theory.

The "orbital angular momentum" can be calculated by wave mechanics. It is found to be given by

$$p = \frac{lh}{2\pi} \tag{31–53}$$

and is therefore zero in the lowest energy level, in disagreement with the Bohr theory but in agreement with observation. (The root mean square value, which is $\sqrt{l(l+1)}\,h/2\pi$, is used in many calculations.)

If there is a magnetic field to define a preferred axis, the component of orbital angular momentum along that axis is given by

$$p_z = \frac{m_l h}{2\pi}, \tag{31–54}$$

which leads to the phenomenon that we have previously encountered and labeled space quantization (Section 30–9). Again, there is agreement with experiment.

Finally, and very importantly, the probabilities of transitions from one state to another, either spontaneous, as in the emission of radiation, or induced by outside influence, can be calculated. The results agree with experiment, which was not always the case with the Bohr theory.

The discussion above has ignored electron spin, which must be taken into account when greater accuracy is required. Dirac developed a relativistic wave-mechanical theory that predicts a spin property.

31-10 MULTIELECTRON ATOMS; THE PAULI EXCLUSION PRINCIPLE

A fourth quantum number must be listed before the present topic can be discussed definitively. The electron spin is found to result in an intrinsic (spin) angular momentum of $\frac{1}{2}h/(2\pi)$. Its direction is restricted to parallel or antiparallel with a preferred axis such as that of l or a magnetic field. This space quantization is specified by means of a quantum number $m_s = \pm\frac{1}{2}$, which specifies the orientation of the spin.

We thus have the four quantum numbers, n, l, m_l, and m_s, which describe the "state" of an electron that is bound to a nucleus. The energy is primarily determined by n in most cases, and secondarily by l, and still less by m_l and m_s. There are exceptions, however.

How are the electrons arranged around the nuclei of atoms of higher atomic number and what are the resulting energy levels, angular momenta, etc.? The Bohr theory gives the wrong answer even for the two electrons of helium. Wave mechanics gives the right answers, i.e., agreement with experiment.

Although it is difficult to calculate the energy levels of multielectron atoms, many general features can be discussed in terms of the quantum numbers. The normal state of any system is that of lowest energy. Each electron should, therefore, be at the lowest possible energy. Using the hydrogen results as a guide, this means that each electron should have the lowest possible value of n, namely, $n = 1$. This seems plausible since the probability distribution is nearest the attracting positive nucleus for $n = 1$.

The conclusion from the preceding paragraph would be that all electrons should have $n = 1$ in the normal state of any atom. This conclusion disagrees with experiment, since, for example, it predicts that all orbital angular momenta would be zero since all l's must be zero if $n = 1$. The result would be that all atoms in their normal state would have zero angular momentum, disagreeing with experiment. Therefore, an additional postulate must be made. It is the *Pauli exclusion principle*, which states that each electron must have a different set of quantum numbers. Within a particular atom this means that each electron must have a different set of values for n, l, m_l, and m_s.

In the lowest energy state of an atom each electron will then have the smallest value of n consistent with the exclusion principle, according to our general ideas of energy levels obtained from the hydrogen atom. We might also guess that the energy is less for the smaller of two possible l values, but more of this later.

31-11 THE PERIODIC TABLE

The ideas of the preceding section will now be applied qualitatively to some of the chemical elements.

(a) Helium. Both electrons can have $n = 1$, $l = 0$, since m_s can be $+\frac{1}{2}$ for one electron and $-\frac{1}{2}$ for the other. Wave mechanics predicts a chemically inert atom because the electrons have their spins paired off, and the electron cloud has spherical symmetry. We speak of the system as having a "closed shell" of electrons, the K-shell.

(b) Lithium. The third electron must have $n = 2$. Its probability distribution therefore extends out to regions such that the electron can interact with other atoms. Furthermore, because of its spin, it will tend to pair off with an unpaired spin of another atom, such as hydrogen, thereby forming compounds.

(c) Neon. There are 10 electrons. The first two have $n = 1$, the next two $n = 2$ and $l = 0$, while the last six have $n = 2$ and $l = 1$. The three allowed values of m_l for $l = 1$ make possible six different combinations of quantum numbers for $n = 2$. The combination of the six electron clouds for $n = 2$ leads to spherical symmetry, although four of the individual clouds are not symmetric. If we look back at the hydrogen case, we see that the distributions have $\sin^2\theta$ and

$\cos^2\theta$ factors, which add to give *no* variation with θ. Therefore, the chemical inactivity of neon is attributed to the completion of a second "closed" shell called the L-shells resulting in spherical symmetry and paired electron spins.

(d) Argon, krypton, xenon, and radon are the successive elements for which further closed shells occur.

(e) Properties recur periodically as the atomic number increases whenever the electrons outside closed shells have the same quantum numbers (except n) as an earlier atom.

(f) Certain irregularities occur when one "subshell" is skipped over momentarily and then filled later in the periodic table. The rare earths are an example. The rare earths differ only in number of electrons in the "skipped-over" subshell. Consequently, their chemical properties are nearly identical.

(g) An unusual occurrence of several unpaired spins in particular skipped-over subshells accounts for the unusual magnetic properties of iron, cobalt, nickel, and a few special alloys.

31–12 SUMMARY

In an overly simplified wave model of the hydrogen atom, the de Broglie wavelength of the electron can be required to fit into the circumference of a circle (centered on the nucleus) an integral number of times. The result is the Bohr quantum condition.

The wave-photon duality of radiation is interpreted in the following manner: The wave amplitude, which may be the result of interference, diffraction, etc., as well as simple propagation, is to be associated with the probability of finding a photon at the point in question. In particular, the intensity, which is proportional to the square of the amplitude, gives the relative probability of a photon being found at a given point. Examples show that only the wave aspect *or* the photon aspect of radiation can be manifested at any particular stage.

The particle-wave duality of particles is interpreted in exactly the same way as the wave-photon duality of radiation. The square of the wave amplitude is proportional to the probability of finding the particle at a given point.

The dualities expressed above lead to the uncertainty principle. Special cases are examined in which it is found that it is impossible to have arbitrary accuracy in determining both the position and the momentum of a particle (or of a photon) at the same instant. It is shown that

$$\Delta p\,\Delta q \simeq h,$$

where p is the momentum associated with a coordinate q.

It is found that an equivalent relationship occurs between energy and time; that is, the energy of a particle cannot be known with arbitrary accuracy within a given period of observation. The limitation is again $\Delta E\,\Delta t \simeq h$. The above ideas are part of the Heisenberg uncertainty principle.

The theory that has proved successful in describing the structure of atoms and molecules and that is believed to be capable of describing the structure of solids and liquids in detail is the theory of wave mechanics. The formulation of wave mechanics in terms of the Schrödinger wave equation is treated for some special cases. By way of review, the wave equation for one-dimensional mechanical waves, or electromagnetic waves, is discussed. It is shown that a standing wave solution can be found in a manner somewhat different from our earlier method of superimposing two traveling waves. The present method is to assume a general form for a standing wave solution,

$$P = \mathcal{P}(x, y, z)\pi(t),$$

from which a time-independent "wave equation" can be obtained:

$$\frac{\partial^2\mathcal{P}}{\partial x^2} = C\mathcal{P}.$$

Sinusoidal solutions are possible for negative values of C. When the boundary conditions are included (for example, zero amplitude at O and

L), the wavelength becomes quantized

$$\lambda = \frac{2L}{2n + 1}.$$

The energy has the value

$$E = \frac{k}{4} A_0^2 \frac{2n + l}{2} \lambda,$$

which is not quantized, since A_0 can have any value.

The Schrödinger equation is essentially an hypothesis (it cannot be derived from more basic principles),

$$\frac{h^2}{8\pi^2 m} \frac{\partial^2 \Psi}{\partial x^2} = \frac{h}{i2\pi} \frac{\partial \Psi}{\partial t}.$$

The test of the usefulness of this hypothesis is, as usual, whether it leads to predictions that are numerous and agree with observation. Wave mechanics meets the requirements of a successful hypothesis.

The Schrödinger equation is first applied to the case of a particle in a region of uniform potential. The solution leads to a wave amplitude that is independent of position, as expected, $|\Psi|^2 = A^2$ and constant energy, as expected, $W^2 = p^2/2m$. In the wave-mechanical description, the position of the above particle can be localized into a wave packet, if an ensemble of wavelengths is used in the description. The uncertainty principle then shows that the position is defined better and better as the range of wavelengths used in constructing the packet becomes broader and broader; that is, as the uncertainty in momentum $p = \lambda/h$ becomes greater and greater.

In the more general case, the Schrödinger equation (in one dimension) is

$$\frac{h^2}{8\pi^2 m} \frac{\partial^2 \Psi}{\partial x^2} - V\Psi = \frac{h}{2\pi i} \frac{\partial \Psi}{\partial t},$$

where V is the potential energy. A standing wave form of the equation is found by the same method used in the example of ordinary waves, with the result

$$\frac{\partial^2 \psi}{\partial x^2} + \frac{8\pi^2 m}{h^2} (W - V)\psi = 0.$$

It is assumed that solutions of this equation may represent stationary states.

The first example is a particle confined to a box. The boundary conditions are that ψ must go to zero at the walls of the box if the walls are defined by an infinitely sharp and infinitely high rise in the potential. In the one-dimensional case, the solution is the same as for standing waves on a string; that is,

$$\psi = A \sin n\pi \frac{x}{L}.$$

The total energy is limited to quantized values given by

$$W = \frac{h^2}{8L^2 m} n^2.$$

The second example is a particle in a square potential well; that is, a region bounded by an infinitely sharp rise in potential, where the height of the rise is finite. It is found that the wave amplitude does not go immediately to zero at the walls but dies exponentially to zero in the region outside the walls. The energy is still quantized, but at different values from the case of the infinite rise in potential.

If the potential barrier not only has finite height but also finite thickness, a particle initially confined inside the box has a finite probability of escape to the region outside the box. This wave-mechanical result leads to an understanding of alpha-particle emission from radioactive nuclei, electron tunneling in certain semiconductors, and other phenomena that cannot be understood in nonwave-mechanical theory.

The case of a particle in a parabolic potential well (the harmonic oscillator) is next discussed. Only the results are presented. The energy is quantized at the values

$$W = (n + \tfrac{1}{2})fh,$$

where f is the classical frequency of the oscillator. Graphs are shown for the wave amplitude for a number of values of n. This wave-mechanical result constitutes a derivation of the quantum condition for oscillators that Planck introduced as an hypothesis.

Finally, the results for a particle in a force field that fulfills the inverse-square law (the electron in hydrogen atom) are presented. Three integers appear during the solution of the Schrödinger equation for this three-dimensional case. The commonly chosen notation is n, l, and m_l. The quantum numbers are not independent, since

$$|m_l| \leq l < n.$$

The magnetic quantum number m_l can be positive or negative. The total energy is quantized at the value given by the Bohr theory,

$$W = -\frac{1}{4\pi\epsilon_0}\frac{2\pi^2 me^4}{h^2}\frac{1}{n^2}.$$

The probability distributions for the electron are given in terms of polar coordinates for sets of quantum numbers corresponding to the lowest energy levels. The angular momentum of the electron due to its "motion" around the nucleus is quantized in magnitude

$$p = l\frac{h}{2\pi}$$

and in direction. The direction quantization is described in terms of the component along the z-axis,

$$p_z = m_l\frac{h}{2\pi}.$$

The results of the latter two quantum conditions are evidenced by the magnetic properties displayed most directly in the Stern-Gerlach type of experiment. *However*, in order to obtain agreement with the observed results, it is necessary to include the effect of the intrinsic angular momentum (spin) of the electron. The spin angular momentum of the electron is

$$p_s = \frac{1}{2}\frac{h}{2\pi}.$$

Its space quantization is specified by the spin magnetic quantum number m_s, which can have the values

$$m_s = \pm\tfrac{1}{2}.$$

Atoms with more than one electron are discussed. The assignment of quantum numbers to the individual electrons is subject to the Pauli exclusion principle, which states that no two particles can have the same set of quantum numbers. In determining the quantum numbers for the lowest energy state of an atom, it is usually correct to assume that the lowest permitted values of n and l give rise to the lowest energy. However, the relative importance of n and l in determining the energy reverses from time to time as we consider atoms of larger and larger atomic number. In general, the importance of n is the greater of the two.

General properties of the various atoms are discussed in terms of the predicted electron configurations.

Problems

1. A certain weak light source emits 100 photons per second. The emission is spherically symmetric. Suppose a lens of focal length +5 cm and diameter 1 cm is placed 10 cm from the light source, with the light source on the lens axis.

(a) How many photons per second pass through the lens? (Neglect absorption.)

(b) How many photons per second pass through a point on the axis 10 cm beyond the lens, according to geometrical optics?

(c) Make a rough graph showing the relative number of photons per second striking a screen 10 cm from the lens as a function of transverse distance, r from the axis (include diffraction effects).

2. If the light in Problem 1 has a wavelength of 5000 A, find the power of the light source.

3. Suppose that the light source of Problem 1 emits only one photon. Repeat parts (a), (b), and (c) of Problem 1 in terms of probabilities for the one photon.

In Problem 1 what should be the area under the curve of part (c) if you plot probability times $2\pi r$ versus r?

4. A small bit of matter 10,000 A in size can be seen with visible light. Its mass would be about 10^{-12} gm. Find values for the uncertainty in its position and velocity when it is observed with a good microscope with light of wavelength 5000 A, assuming that the particle is very loosely "fastened" to its support.

5. Would an electron microscope be bètter than the gamma-ray microscope discussed in the text as a tool for observing the orbital motion of electrons in atoms? Analyze the problem quantitatively.

6. Find the wavelength spread in the first line of the Balmer series of hydrogen, assuming that the lifetime in each energy level is 10^{-8} sec.

7. Show that Eq. (31–29) is a solution of the Schrödinger equation (31–25).

8. Show that Eq. (31-36) is a solution of (31-33) and leads to (31–37).

9. Show that (31-38) is a solution of (31-37) and leads to (31-39).

10. Oxygen gas is contained at low pressure at room temperature in a vessel with dimensions of about 10 cm. As a molecule approaches the wall of the container, at what distance does the wave-mechanical probability start its final drop to zero? Can the molecule come close to the wall, macroscopically speaking?

11. The probability that an electron can be at distance r to $r + dr$ from the nucleus in hydrogen is $4\pi r^2|R|^2\,dr$.

(a) Explain the above statement.

(b) Plot $4\pi r^2|R|^2$ for the 1, 0, 0 and the 3, 1, 0 states of hydrogen versus r (with r in units of a_0).

(c) What is the most probable distance from the nucleus in each case? Compare with the Bohr model.

(d) Plot the probability that the electron can be at an angle θ versus θ for the 3, 1, 0 state.

(e) Sketch a three-dimensional probability cloud for the electron in the 3, 1, 0 state.

12. Estimate the areas under the curves that you drew in Problem 11(b). What should the areas be?

13. The "density" of nuclear matter is nearly constant. Consequently, the nuclear radius is approximately given by $1.4 \times 10^{-13}\,(A)^{1/3}$ cm, with (A) the mass number.

(a) Explain why the $(A)^{1/3}$ dependence follows from the uniform density statement.

(b) Show that the radius of the first Bohr orbit for a μ-meson (mass 215 m_e) is $2.3 \times 10^{-11}/Z$ cm where Z is the atomic number of the atom in question.

(c) Why is the force on the meson due to the electrons ignored?

(d) For what element would the radius of the mesonic Bohr orbit lie just within the edge of the nucleus? (The mass number of light elements is about $2\,Z$.)

14. List the quantum numbers for each electron in neutral sodium, atomic number 11. When sodium is excited, the last electron is raised to higher levels. Explain why you would expect highly excited levels of sodium to have about the same energy as the highly excited levels of hydrogen.

15. How is it possible for a μ-meson to occupy an $n = 1$ level in an atom such as He or a heavier atom, when the $n = 1$ levels are already filled?

32

The Nucleus

32–1 INTRODUCTION

At the beginning of atomic research, nuclear physics and atomic physics were not readily separable as different areas of investigation. Because a definitive model of the atom was lacking, the emission of visible light, x-rays, or alpha-particles could all be regarded as emissions from a complex atomic structure. The pioneering work of Becquerel and Curie on radioactivity was performed before a model of the atom had been correctly formulated. The Rutherford postulate of the nuclear atom (consisting of a point, massive positive charge at the center, surrounded by light satellite electrons) suggested a wide separation between what are known as specifically atomic processes and nuclear processes. The success of the Bohr hypotheses in relating the Rutherford model of the atom to the spectroscopic data for hydrogen firmly established the nucleus-satellite model of atomic structure. At that time, the principal research emphasis was placed on the intricate energy-level structure determined by the satellite electrons. It was through this effort that the new science of wave mechanics was evolved. To the purposes of that research, it was sufficient to consider the nucleus of the atom as an inert center of mass, charge, and magnetic moment for the atomic system.

The assumption of nuclear inertness was well founded by the observation that in the optical, electrical, and chemical reactions in which the satellite electrons were involved and in which the electronic structure was considerably perturbed, the atomic nuclei passed unmodified in any way from one reaction to the next. The false law of mass conservation—mass being concentrated largely in the nucleus—was based on this presumed inertness. The reason for the apparent resistance to change in the nucleus is now completely evident. Energy changes affecting atomic structure involve a few electron volts, but energy changes affecting nuclear structure involve about 100,000 or more electron volts. It is therefore not surprising that the nucleus remains passive in the most violent of chemical processes. Later, when the means of injecting millions of electron volts, and even much higher energies, into the atom were developed, the idea of a passive nucleus had to be abandoned. The artificial transmutation of the elements passed from an impossibility to a routine operation.

While pioneers in atomic physics could afford to regard the nucleus as a point, massive charge, research into the nucleus began to show that the nucleus had a finite size, an observable structure, and could undergo reactions. The Rutherford and Bohr models of the atom clearly placed the source of the radiations discovered by Becquerel in the nucleus. Rutherford's scattering experiments, which showed the nucleus to be very small compared to atomic dimensions, were extended to show not only the finite extent of the nucleus but also the relationship between nuclear size and atomic number. Mass spectroscopic data were gathered in great abundance and with very high precision. Since the mass of the atom lies chiefly in the nucleus, atomic mass data are relevant more to the nucleus than to the atom as a whole. But all these data were gathered under circumstances quite different from those that surrounded research in atomic physics.

As atomic physics progressed, the constitution of the atom was revealed and to a certain extent the configuration of the constituents. It was known that the problem of the interaction of the electrons with the nucleus and the interactions of the electrons among themselves had to be solved. One ingredient to the solution, the force laws operating among the atomic components, was on an extremely sound footing. The laws of electromagnetism apparently were the only force laws involved, and these had been developed to a high degree of theoretical perfection. The missing ingredient was the equation of motion. It was the failure of the classical laws of motion in the atomic scale that gave the atomic problem its great philosophical and practical interest. The evolution of the wave-mechanical equation of motion reduced the atomic problem to that of solving a problem with known ingredients with known techniques.

The success of wave mechanics in atomic physics has encouraged its use in nuclear physics. There has been a certain measure of success in the use of the ideas and methods of wave mechanics in nuclear physics, but at the present writing it is not clear that wave mechanics is adequate. The complicating factor is the lack of knowledge of an adequate force law. Consequently, it is difficult to localize the source of difficulty.

Nuclear physics grew to an advanced stage before the components of the nucleus were known. For this reason, a large fraction of nuclear research was performed on a puzzle rather than on a well-identified system. The proton was an undoubted component of the nucleus because of the rough agreement between the charge-to-mass ratio of the proton and of the nucleus. The most elementary of nuclei, that of the hydrogen atom, was known to be the proton. However, the charge-to-mass ratio of other nuclei is not precisely that of the proton, differing systematically by about a factor of two and erratically by somewhat smaller factors. Efforts were made to put the charge-to-mass ratio to rights by utilizing the electron as a nuclear component. By adding the comparatively massless electrons to a system of nuclear protons, the charge-to-mass ratio of the nuclei could be adjusted to agree roughly with observations. But the electron-proton nuclear model developed flaws and paradoxes from the beginning. Few of the observed phenomena could be explained.

The subsequent discovery of the neutron placed nuclear physics on a completely new footing. The neutron-proton model of the nucleus eliminated much of the mystery of nuclear structure, and put in its place some new and extremely difficult problems. Foremost among the new unknowns was the law of force between the neutron and the proton. The discovery of the basic composition of the nucleus was a great stride, but the most elementary knowledge about the force law governing the nuclear constituents was lacking, since the details of nuclear forces, unlike electrical and gravitational forces, are not revealed in macroscopic phenomena.

The nature of the gravitational force was discovered in an effort to explain the motion of the planets and moons in the solar system. While gravitational effects are felt by us on the earth, Newton's law of gravitation was verified by observations on the astronomical scale. In our present civilization, the main forces which we harness are electromagnetic. This same electromagnetic force which was studied in the laboratory experiments on electric and magnetic systems proved to be the precise set of forces governing the atomic and molecular systems. The force governing the nuclear system lacked any such precedents in scientific observations. Both the gravitational and the electromagnetic forces are characterized by an inverse-square law of force. Depending on the strength of the sources, gravitational and electromagnetic influences can be significant through billions of kilometers in the solar system. Even static electric and magnetic influences can be significant meters from their sources. In contrast, the nuclear force falls off with such extreme rapidity in distance from the source that the influence of the force is not markedly felt at distances from the nucleus equal to the radius of the nucleus itself. Since the nuclear radius is about 10^{-14} meter, the effects of nuclear forces are confined to an extremely small volume within the atom itself. Therefore, no macroscopic laboratory experiment can be contrived to investigate the details of the nuclear force. The only direct experiments must involve extremely close encounters with the nucleus itself. The encounters are in the nature of collisions or penetrations of the nucleus by other nuclear particles.

The performance of experiments on structure within the radius of the atomic nucleus is not easily contrived. A typical experiment includes a beam of atomic projectiles which are caused to strike a nuclear target. The projectile may be any of the atomic or nuclear fragments: electrons, protons, alpha-particles, photons, etc. Preferably, the projectiles are confined within a collimated beam so that direction is well defined. In early research, the projectiles were the emanations of radioactive nuclei, that is, high-energy electrons, α-particles, and photons ejected by naturally unstable nuclei. The nuclear emanations had energies in the million-ev range and thus were able to penetrate and perturb other nuclei. Later, such sources were supplemented and then replaced by high-energy particle accelerators, the Cockcroft-Walton generator, the Van de Graaff generator, the cyclotron, and the synchrotron. These had the advantages of producing highly directional, intense, and energetic beams of particles far beyond the capabilities of the radioactive sources. Energies of the early accelerators were in the submillion-ev range. The cyclotron produced 10 million-ev particles, an energy comparable with the binding energies of nuclear particles. Energies of contemporary machines transcend the nuclear-energy range and extend from 100 million-ev to multibillion ev. Such energies can also disintegrate nuclei, but they are most useful in inducing elementary particle reactions.

The target for the projectiles is, of course, not simply nuclear material but is a sample of ordinary matter, usually in the form of a foil. Thus, the impinging projectiles encounter an array of electrons and nuclei. However, a massive high-energy particle, to a considerable degree, is unaffected by the lightweight, loosely bound electrons of the atoms. The analogy might be a cannon ball passing through a thin cloud of buckshot. The buckshot is driven forward or aside by the heavy projectile which in turn is not greatly affected unless it penetrates an extremely thick cloud. An encounter with a nucleus is similar to an encounter with another cannon ball, and this encounter can strongly affect the momentum of the struck ball as well as that of the projectile. The general results of the collision can be successfully understood from conservation of energy and momentum. To a degree, then, a target of solid matter gives the appearance to a high-energy atomic projectile of a great amount of empty space interspersed with nearly point-like massive scattering centers, the nuclei of the target atoms.

An encounter between any projectiles and nuclei is entirely a matter of chance, and the likelihood is very small even for a single encounter. The nuclear radius is about 10^{-14} meter and, therefore, the cross-sectional area presented by one nucleus to an oncoming projectile is about $10^{-28}\ \text{m}^2$. Atomic spacings in most solid matter are about $2\ \text{Å}$ or 2×10^{-10} m. A target one monatomic layer deep exposes a nuclear area of $10^{-28}\ \text{m}^2$ per atom, but the area parceled to each target atom is 4×10^{-20} m. Therefore, the ratio of solid nuclear target area to empty space is about 10^{-9}. The chance of a direct encounter versus a clean miss is therefore about 10^{-9}. A source of projectiles sending in one particle per second would yield an encounter about every billion seconds, or every hundred years. Two ways are possible to increase the chance of collision, preferably up to one per second for a favorable experiment. The first way is to thicken the target and increase the intensity of the beam. Targets as thick as 10^5 atomic layers (about 10^{-3} cm) are usable, although energy losses due to collisions with electrons begin to be considerable at such thicknesses and to affect the accuracy of the experiment. Thus, a factor of 10^5 can be gained over the hypothetical monolayer target.

Beam intensity is the second means of enhancing the chance of collision. The early accelerators were capable of producing million-volt particles at a current of about one microampere, the net production of power being one watt. A microampere beam of particles, each having one electronic charge, conveys about 10^{13} particles per second. Such beams render entirely feasible a high rate for collisions, in spite of the small cross section of the nuclear target.

Cosmic rays have provided an important supplement to the radioactive isotopes and particle accelerators as the means of probing nuclear structure. Cosmic debris, almost certainly from our galaxy and possibly from others, impinges continuously on the earth's atmosphere. The discovery of this fact occurred through efforts to escape the "background" radioactivity known to exist in the earth's surface and in the walls and floors of the laboratory. An obvious way to reduce that background seemed to be to elevate the nuclear experiment in a balloon. Early experiments designed to detect the background radioactivity as a function of elevation above the earth's surface showed that the background increased with altitude. With this discovery, a completely new scientific field was born, even though the hopes of escaping radiation background were dashed. Later it was found that a more suitable route to the reduction of radiation background is in the opposite direction. Very low counting-rate experiments can be performed underground in mines in order to escape cosmic radiation.

Cosmic radiation falls quite uniformly over the earth's surface, and while the total flux of radiation is very high, the amount of radiation falling on a laboratory counter or cloud chamber is far below that to be obtained from an accelerator or a radioactive source. The advantage of cosmic rays to the study of the nucleus and elementary particles is the very wide range of energies of the cosmic-ray particles. Useful particle-intensities are to be found in the multibillion-volt range. The peak in the intensity at the earth's surface is at a few hundred million ev. This source of radiation was being actively harnessed in nuclear and particle studies before energies of one million ev were available from accelerators. Thus, the field of cosmic radiation has been rich in discoveries, while the accelerators have often been applied to the less dramatic task of obtaining more precise data.

The mu-meson, the pi-meson, the positron, and most of the heavier particles have all been discovered in observations of the cosmic rays and their secondaries. It was not known at first which part of the cosmic radiation observable at the earth's surface had arrived directly from outer space and which was a result of interactions between the arriving, or primary, radiation with the earth's atmosphere, producing what is called secondary radiation. It was found that almost all of what we observe at the earth's surface is secondary radiation, and that the primary radiation is mostly very high-energy protons and heavier nuclei arriving from outer space. Thus, cosmic radiation provides a nuclear laboratory on an astronomical scale. The incoming beam is composed of high-energy protons and heavier nuclei. The targets are the nuclei of the earth's atmospheric gas, and therefore the target nuclei are predominantly those of oxygen and nitrogen. The radiation seen at the earth's surface is the outcome of a collision by a high-energy proton with an oxygen or nitrogen nucleus. This recognition was not soon in coming, but the implications are now well recognized.

The mu-mesons, pi-mesons, K-mesons, and so on are produced either directly or through a chain reaction in an oxygen or nitrogen nucleus during the impact of a very high-energy proton. Consequently, there is much more to be known about nuclear structure than simply the relative positions, the wave functions, of the neutrons and protons in the nucleus. Nuclear physics is evidently richer than atomic physics where questions that can be asked about atomic structure are answered by the use of wave mechanics. Nuclear structure contains within it an ingredient of elementary particle "mechanics," involving mesons and hyperons, which has yet to be satisfactorily connected with the facts of nuclear structure as they are presently known.

32-2 GENERAL PROPERTIES OF THE NUCLEUS

From 1919 to 1930 a very considerable amount of information about the nucleus was gathered, with no theory available that was consistent with even the most elementary observations. The nucleus was considered to be made of electrons and protons, the only particles known in that period. The sequence of isotopes could be accurately assigned an atomic number Z, an integer representing the net number of protonic charges in the nucleus or the number of electrons in the neutral atom. Also a mass number A could be assigned, even though the mass increment among isotopes was not integral. Even so, the mass increment from isotope to isotope was sufficiently close to the protonic mass to allow the assignment of an integral number A to each isotope. The conventional representation of the above information for a nucleus of chemical element X is

$$X_Z^A, \tag{32-1}$$

where X represents the chemical element, specifically the chemical symbol for the element, A is the mass number, and Z is the atomic number.

TABLE 32-1

Chemical name	Isotope	Charge Z	Mass number A	Mass
Hydrogen	H_1^1	1	1	1.00814
Deuterium	H_1^2	1	2	2.01474
Tritium	H_1^3	1	3	3.01700
Helium (3)	He_2^3	2	3	3.01699
Helium	He_2^4	2	4	4.00387
Lithium (6)	Li_3^6	3	6	6.01703
Lithium (7)	Li_3^7	3	7	7.01823

The first seven isotopes in the periodic chart are given in Table 32-1, along with the chemical name, the nuclear isotopic representation, and the measured charge and mass. Charge is given in units of the protonic charge. Mass is given in units of $\frac{1}{16}$th the mass of oxygen isotope 16, called atomic mass units. The unit is 1.66×10^{-27}kg.

While the assignment of a mass number is evidently satisfactory for the identification of an isotope, the atomic mass is clearly not an integral multiple of the protonic mass. Moreover, the mass number and charge number bear no simple relationship. Generally, the mass number is roughly twice the atomic number for the first 20 elements:

$$A \simeq 2Z, \qquad (Z < 20). \tag{32-2}$$

Beyond $Z = 20$, the mass number tends to be somewhat greater than twice the atomic number, until for uranium the proportionality constant has reached about 2.6:

$$A \simeq 2.6Z, \qquad (Z = 92). \tag{32-3}$$

With the electron-proton model, the nucleus contains, by hypothesis, a number of protons N_p equal to the mass number A. The net nuclear charge is then reduced to Z by supposing that the nucleus also contains A-Z electrons.

$$\left.\begin{aligned} Z &= N_p - N_e \\ A &= N_p \end{aligned}\right\} \text{electron-proton nucleus.} \tag{32-4}$$

Thus the hydrogen atom contained one proton in the nucleus; deuterium, two protons and one electron; helium, four protons and two electrons; and so on. The nuclear charge is correct with this model. However, the sum of the masses of the constituents substantially exceeds the mass of the resulting nucleus. Other difficulties are encountered in explaining the nuclear facts through this model. The general facts and the conflicts are instructive in showing how far the experimental data had outstripped the capabilities of this simple model to explain the data.

32–3 SPIN

The spins of many nuclei were obtained from the analysis of molecular spectra and later from experiments on atomic beams, with results that were in general conflict with quantum theory as applied to the above model. The spins of the electron and the proton were both known to be one-half times $h/2\pi$. From quantum theory, the spin of an even number of particles should be an integer times $h/2\pi$; of an odd number of particles, a half-integer times $h/2\pi$, as follows:

$$\text{Even: } 0, \frac{h}{2\pi}, 2\frac{h}{2\pi}, 3\frac{h}{2\pi}, \ldots \tag{32–5}$$

$$\text{Odd: } \frac{1}{2}\frac{h}{2\pi}, \frac{3}{2}\frac{h}{2\pi}, \frac{5}{2}\frac{h}{2\pi}, \ldots \tag{32–6}$$

The experimentally observed nuclear spins were in conflict with this basic rule. For example, deuterium, with three particles, two protons, and one electron, had a spin of $1 \times (h/2\pi)$. Nitrogen 14, with 14 protons and 7 electrons, 21 particles altogether, had a spin of $1 \times (h/2\pi)$. Thus, the data were in conflict with the successful laws of spin alignment of quantum theory.

32–4 MAGNETIC MOMENT

According to Dirac theory, there is a relationship between the spin of a particle and its magnetic moment. This relationship gives for the magnetic moment μ of a particle of spin $\frac{1}{2}$

$$\mu = \frac{eh}{8\pi mc}. \tag{32–7}$$

This equation agrees with the measured electronic magnetic moment to a high degree of accuracy. According to the same theory, the protonic magnetic moment should be less than that of the electron by a factor of 1/1870 because of the higher mass of the proton. While the measured magnetic moment of the proton differs from this predicted value by about a factor of 2, the protonic moment is nevertheless less than the electronic moment by about a factor of 1000. The question posed for the electron-proton model of the nucleus was a sharp one: is the large, electronic moment ever observed in nuclei? The answer is no. The measured nuclear magnetic moments are of the order of the protonic moment, casting severe doubt on the idea of the presence of electrons in the nucleus.

32–5 ELECTRON-BINDING ENERGY

The radius of an average nucleus is about 10^{-14} meter. With this information an estimate can be made of the energy required to contain the electron in the nuclear volume. The estimate is obtained from the uncertainty principle for position and momentum,

$$\Delta x\, \Delta p \cong \frac{h}{2\pi} \text{ joule sec.} \tag{32–8}$$

We set Δx, the uncertainty in the position of the electron, equal to the nuclear radius,

$$\Delta x = R = 10^{-14} \text{ meter.}$$

This is a statement that the electron may be found anywhere within the nuclear volume but not outside. Then the momentum p of the electron must be at least of the order of its uncertainty Δp. The magnitude of p is therefore

$$p \cong \frac{h/2\pi}{\Delta x} \cong \frac{10^{-34}}{10^{-14}} = 10^{-20} \frac{\text{kg} - \text{m}}{\text{sec}}.$$

The kinetic energy corresponding to this momentum is

$$\text{KE} = \frac{p^2}{2m} \cong \frac{10^{-40}}{2 \times 10^{-30}} = \frac{10^{-10}}{2} \text{ joule,}$$

$$\text{KE} \cong 2 \times 10^8 \text{ ev.}$$

While internal energies of several million volts are observed in nuclei, energies of several hundred million volts are not observed. Moreover, if the kinetic energy were this high, the energy required to bind the electron in the nucleus would be still greater. Using the mass-energy equivalence, one hundred million ev in binding energy would be equivalent to about one-tenth the mass of the proton. This amount of mass could be readily observed in mass spectra and such mass losses, corresponding to electron binding, are an order of magnitude greater than what is observed. Thus the original notion that the light-weight electron would have only a secondary effect on nuclear mass proved to be in conflict with relativity and quantum theory.

The variances between fact and prediction rendered the electron-proton model virtually useless. Perhaps today, with such a proliferation of elementary particles at hand, physicists confronted with so many paradoxes would immediately invent a new particle to eliminate the paradoxes, as, indeed, later a neutrino and still other particles have had to be invented. Viewing the subject in retrospect, we realize that the need for a neutron, a particle of zero charge and protonic mass, was very great in 1930. With Chadwick's discovery of the neutron in 1932, all the paradoxes were removed, allowing studies to be directed toward the difficult problem of the proton-neutron interaction.

The neutron, a particle without electric charge, has nearly the mass and exactly the spin of the proton. It is given the isotopic designation n_1^0. The neutron-proton model of the nucleus contains Z protons and N neutrons. Since the proton and neutron masses are about equal, the mass number is equal to the number of protons plus the number of neutrons:

$$Z = P, \qquad A = P + N. \tag{32–9}$$

Isotopes of an element are explained as having a fixed number of protons and a varying number of neutrons. Since the mass number is about twice the atomic number for the light elements,

$$A \simeq 2Z,$$

there must be a tendency in nuclear structure for the number of neutrons to equal the number of protons,

$$N \cong P.$$

We now list some of the general successes of this model. As an example, both nitrogen 14 and deuterium have an even number of particles and so should have integer spin, as they do. In fact, the observed spins of nuclei always agree with theory. The magnitudes of the magnetic moments of the proton and neutron and the nuclei composed of these particles are in agreement. No excessive amount of binding attends the containment of the neutron (or the proton) in the nucleus. The relationships,

$$\text{KE} \cong \frac{(\Delta p)^2}{2m}, \qquad \Delta p \cong \frac{h}{2\pi R}, \tag{32–10}$$

for the heavier particles yield an energy of about 10^6 ev, which is in agreement with observed binding energies. Thus the old paradoxes vanish, but new questions arise. What force, clearly nonelectromagnetic, binds the neutron to the proton? What force binds the proton to the proton, even against the Coulomb repulsion of like charges? Why does the neutron have a magnetic moment, since the neutron charge is identically zero and, therefore, the particle should have no magnetic moment at all? But by measurement the neutron has a magnetic moment of the same order of magnitude as that of the proton.

Banishing the electron from the nucleus leaves another question unanswered. One of the more compelling reasons for hypothesizing an electron-proton model of the nucleus was that electrons are emitted from some radioactive nuclei. How is the electron emitted from a structure of which it is not a component? This question has a faint ring of nonsense about it, for one might ask how is a photon emitted from an atom when it is not a resident of the atom? Nevertheless, there is a difference because a photon has no rest mass and is known to be created by accelerating electric charge. The emission of the electron is different in that the creation of a particle of finite rest mass is involved. Elimination of the electron as a nuclear constituent required the hypothesis that the nucleus must create an electron in the process of emission.

The discovery of the neutron erased a number of paradoxes, but the new questions that were raised were much deeper. They were less in the nature of direct conflicts and paradoxes and more in the nature of penetration into an entirely new realm of physics. In that realm, at least one completely new force had to be discovered and described, and the subject of the creation and annihilation of elementary particles had to be considered.

32–6 DISCOVERY OF THE NEUTRON

The discovery of the neutron is tied in closely with the first systematic studies of the artificial transmutations of nuclei. Extensive observations of the disintegrations of elements in the *naturally* radioactive series had demonstrated that alpha-particles (helium nuclei), beta-rays (electrons), and gamma-rays (electromagnetic radiation) are emitted from some nuclei, but this sheds little light on the actual constitution of nuclei. However, the emissions from the naturally radioactive series of elements, once the components were identified, proved to be weapons of a new form. That is, the alpha-particles emitted by the heavy nuclei could be used as projectiles which could penetrate and transmute the lighter nuclei. Alpha-particles, possessing a double electric charge, are injected into nuclei only with difficulty because of the Coulomb repulsion between the positively charged nucleus and the alpha-particles. However, injection of high-energy alpha-particles (several million ev) is possible for the low Z elements.

Alpha-particle bombardment of nuclei yielded first a readily identified reaction of alpha-particle-in, proton-out, a reaction which increased the atomic number of the bombarded nucleus by one and the mass number by three. An example is the alpha-particle penetration of nitrogen 14:

$$\alpha_2^4 + \mathrm{N}_7^{14} \rightarrow \mathrm{O}_8^{17} + \mathrm{p}_1^1 + \mathrm{KE}. \qquad (32\text{–}11)$$

The reaction products are an isotope of oxygen and a proton. The observation of the proton energy, for example, by magnetic deflection in the cloud chamber, gave excellent evidence, along with the mass spectroscopy of the isotopes, of the binding energies of the nuclei.

More important to our immediate subject was the observation of the emanation of a new radiation produced in similar reactions. The bombardment of beryllium by alpha-particles gave rise to a new radiation which was non-ionizing and, therefore, presumed to be neutral. Even though the new particle was incapable of ionizing matter, it displayed the property of exchanging a considerable momentum with nuclei when it, presumably, underwent a direct collision with a nucleus. The general facts did not at first exclude that the new emission was a high-energy gamma-ray, since a gamma-ray is relatively non-ionizing and carries momentum.

The laws of motion, however, ascribe to the photon a very low momentum in comparison with that of a massive particle such as a proton, that has the same kinetic energy. Hence, to explain the recoil momenta observed when matter was bombarded with this neutral radiation, the photons would have to be assigned very high energies, of the order of 50 Mev, which is beyond the range of normal binding energies in nuclei. With so little information available about nuclear systems, this fact did not in itself exclude the photon as the radiation. The exclusion came about through Chadwick's research, which showed an inconsistency in the recoils of different target particles if the rays were photons. A principal target for detection of the new radiation was a hydrogenous material, such as paraffin, in which most of the target nuclei are hydrogen nuclei or essentially free protons at these energies. The observed recoil protons were highly energetic and readily detected. When the less energetic recoils of heavier nuclei, such as nitrogen, were observed, it was found that each target element gave recoils that required a different value of the momentum and energy for the incoming radiation, if that radiation were a photon. However, the incoming radiation was always the same.

On the other hand, if the incoming radiation were assumed to be a neutral particle, having a rest mass nearly equal to that of the proton, the calculated momentum and energy of the incident radiation were the same for all types of collisions. This is a case where the most elementary rules of classical mechanics, the rules of momentum and energy conservation in particle collisions, settled a matter of the greatest importance to subatomic physics. The collision of the neutron with a target proton is an example of the case of elementary collision theory (treated in the chapter on momentum conservation). Here an incident particle of mass M and velocity V strikes a stationary particle of the same mass M. In a head-on collision, the impinging particle becomes stationary, and the target particle continues on at velocity V, carrying with it all the momentum and energy of the incident particle. The maximum possible transfer of momentum and energy occurs in the above kind of collision. In this way, the high energy of recoil of protons out of paraffin, resulting from exposure to the neutral radiation, was explained. Having identified the neutral radiation as composed of high-energy neutrons, the physicist could write the alpha-beryllium reaction. The neutron is assigned the symbol n_0^1, an isotope of one atomic mass unit and zero atomic number. The reaction is then written,

$$\mathrm{He}_2^4 + \mathrm{Be}_4^9 \rightarrow \mathrm{C}_6^{12} + \mathrm{n}_0^1 + \mathrm{KE}. \qquad (32\text{–}12)$$

The reaction products are a carbon isotope and a neutron. In turn, the identification of the neutron suggested its use as a particle to induce transmutations in other elements. The neutron is especially effective in the transmutation of the heavy elements since, because the neutron has no electric charge, no Coulomb repulsion impedes the entrance of the neutron into the nucleus, as in the case of proton and alpha-particle projectiles. The primary effect of absorption of a neutron by a nucleus is the increase of the atomic mass number by one, leaving a heavier isotope of the same target element. Such isotopes are frequently unstable, and subsequent disintegrations are observed. The discovery of the neutron closed a long period in which nuclear research was conducted without a knowledge of the constitution of the nucleus itself. The study of the nucleus then became a study of the interaction of the protons and neutrons contained within the nucleus.

32–7 THE NUCLEAR RADIUS

An important landmark in the initiation of modern nuclear studies is the research of Rutherford on the nuclear size. The results of Rutherford's investigations of atomic structure by alpha-particle scattering introduced a striking clarity to atomic structure. The electrically positive and massive component of the atom was found to be very small compared with atomic and molecular dimensions. The electronic motion and structure became identified with the spectral and chemical behavior of the atom. From the point of view of such investigations, the nucleus remained as a massive, central, positive point in the atomic structure. The true study of the nucleus looks into the dimensions and structure of this "point."

The alpha-scattering experiments, which showed the nucleus to be very small compared with atomic dimensions, also gave the first evidence of the finite nuclear size. For very large angular deflections of alpha-particles, corresponding to very close encounters between the alpha-particle and the nucleus, the distribution of scattered alpha-particles departed considerably from the predictions of the Coulomb law, and this distribution was called anomalous scattering. The transition from Coulomb scattering to anomalous scattering could be readily interpreted in terms of a finite nuclear size. It is known from electrostatic theory that any spherically symmetric charge distribution produces an electric field beyond its boundaries which is identical with the electric field of a point charge. Therefore, the nuclear scattering of alpha-particles, consistent with the Coulomb law, could be explained either by a point nucleus or by a finite nucleus that had not been penetrated. Departure from the form of Coulomb scattering could be associated with penetration of the nuclear boundary by the alpha-particle. When a charge cloud is penetrated, the departure from the Coulomb law is typically abrupt and considerable. It will be recalled that the field of a spherical uniform-charge distribution changes discontinuously at the surface from a first-power law to an inverse-square law. Even when the form of the nuclear charge distribution within the nuclear boundary is not known, or when new forces are present within the nucleus, the electrostatic theorem by itself is sufficient to establish with accuracy the location of the nuclear surface. If the nucleus were a uniform, spherical distribution of electric charge, then as alpha-particles come closer to the nuclear surface, they would be scattered through larger angles by the increased force. But when the nuclear surface is reached and penetrated, an increase in scattering angle due to closer impact would not be observed. Instead, the scattering force would become weaker. The experimental scattering distribution confirms the effect expected of a nuclear surface.

The analysis of anomalous alpha-scattering experiments gave a nuclear radius of approximately 10^{-14} meter. Compared with the atomic dimensions of 10^{-10} meter, the nucleus is indeed very small, and hence the assumption of a point-nucleus in atomic structure is usually a good one. Scattering experiments performed on a series of atomic specimens gave a simple relationship between the nuclear size and the mass number of the element. The nuclear radius deduced from alpha-particle scattering is found to be proportional to the cube root of the mass number, with a proportionality constant of 1.4×10^{-15} meter.

$$R = 1.4 \times 10^{-15} A^{1/3} \text{ meter.} \tag{32–13}$$

This radius law yields an excellent first approximation to the distribution of charge within the nucleus (or mass, provided it is assumed that mass is distributed in the same way as charge). With this assumption, the radius law shows that all nuclei have the same charge density and mass density. Since the cube of the nuclear radius is proportional to the atomic number, the nuclear volume is proportional to the atomic number:

$$V \sim R^3 \sim A. \tag{32–14}$$

Therefore, it is concluded that each particle in the nucleus occupies the same volume. Ample precedent for this kind of density rule is to be found in liquid and solid matter, where again the volume of the matter is directly proportional to the number of particles contained in the matter.

32–8 NUCLEAR RADIATION

There are three modes of transition from one energy level to a lower level in nuclear systems. One is by emission of electromagnetic radiation (gamma-ray); another is by emission of electrons or positrons (beta-rays); and the third is by emission of alpha-particles (a stable grouping of two protons and two neutrons). The emissions of gamma-rays (photons) and beta-rays (electrons) are similar in that the "ray" did not exist in the nucleus previous to its emission. An emitted photon carries away an energy $h\nu$. An emitted electron removes an amount of energy mc^2, where m is the total mass of the electron (we shall see later that energy $m_\nu c^2$ is carried away by a neutrino). In executing the transition, the form in which the liberated energy is embodied is created: the photon or the electron (and neutrino) is born in the emission process; neither is a component of the emitting structure.

Each radiation process is characterized by a lifetime τ. The expectation P that a transition will occur *after* time t is exponential in time:

$$P \propto e^{-t/\tau},$$

and is independent of how long the system has already existed in its state of excitation. Beyond these points, the two processes of radiation differ considerably.

Gamma-radiation is neutral. The nuclear system before and after emission contains the same electric charge and remains, therefore, the same chemical element. The photon has no rest energy. Therefore, there is no least energy that the photon may carry away. Any transition is possible, provided the energy of the original state is higher than the final state, however slight the difference may be. The basic constituents of the parent and daughter are the same: the atomic number Z and the mass number A are unchanged in the transition. The principal detectable changes in the nucleus resulting from the transition are the nuclear spin and mass. Thus, the parent and daughter nuclei can be distinguished by experimental means. The distinction between the excited and deexcited forms of the nucleus has led to the term "nuclear isomers." Two nuclear isomers are different manifestations of the same nuclear system, that is, the same Z and A values. One isomer is in an excited state and the other is in a lower-energy state, usually the ground state of the system. Because of the exceedingly long lifetimes of some isomeric states, the parent nuclei are often readily available for study prior to transition. Gamma-ray transitions in nuclear systems occur, as in the atomic system, between discrete energy states. Therefore, the gamma-ray energies are also discrete. Mixtures of several discrete gamma-rays emitted by a radioactive sample are attributable to the presence of a number of transitions among different discrete states. No continuous spectra of gamma-rays are emitted by nuclear systems.

There are marked differences between the results of emissions of photons and of electrons. The electron possesses a unit charge, plus or minus, and therefore in beta-decay the charge of the emitting nucleus is altered. If the emitted particle is an electron of negative charge, the atomic number of the daughter nucleus is one unit charge greater than the parent nucleus:

$$Z_2 = Z_1 + 1, \qquad \text{electron emission.}$$

If the emitted particle is a positron then the atomic number of the daughter nucleus is one unit charge less than the parent nucleus:

$$Z_2 = Z_1 - 1, \qquad \text{positron emission.}$$

Beta-decay results in a transmutation of the elements, changing one chemical substance to another, leaving the mass number unchanged. An important distinction of the electron as a radiation is its finite rest mass. In the process of emission, the electron is created. Therefore, the least total energy that can be radiated is the rest energy of the electron.

$$\Delta E_{\text{min}} = m_0c^2 = 511{,}000 \text{ ev.}$$

Any amount of energy in excess of this minimum can be given over into the kinetic energy of the radiation. Therefore, nuclear systems have a greater stability against beta-radiation than against gamma-radiation, since the smallness of the transition is limited by the rest energy of the electron. Even so, beta-radiation is extremely common among nuclear isotopes and is one of the chief modes for the transition of an unstable isotope into a stable form. Observations of beta-decay disclosed several remarkable features of the process. First, beta-rays universally exhibit a continuous spectrum. This point deserved to be doubted at first, since the accurate measurement of beta-ray energies was difficult. Considerable energy losses can be sustained by electrons in escaping extremely small thicknesses of matter. Thus, even if the radioactive sample is only a few thousandths of an inch thick, allowances must be made for the energy loss of an electron while escaping from the sample. Eventually, the technique of preparing very thin samples was developed, and then the continuity of the electron spectrum was confirmed. Within the scope of the classical conservation laws, the emission of a continuous spectrum of energies was consistent only with the notion of a continuous mass spectrum of end products. This was impossible, since, although the number and variety of nuclear isotopes were large, they are also finite. In several cases careful observation of the parent and daughter nuclei that were associated with particular beta-ray transitions left no doubt that the transitions took place between well-defined, discrete energy states. Therefore, whatever amount of energy was given to the electron, the parent nucleus lost an unvarying amount of energy. The conflict with the principle of energy conservation was direct and challenging.

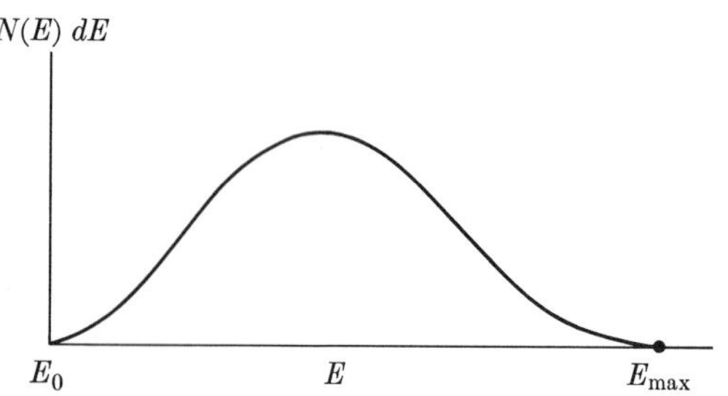

FIG. 32-1. The general form of the distribution for the number of beta-rays in the energy interval E to $E + dE$ as a function of E.

A typical spectrum of beta-ray energies is shown in Fig. 32-1. The usual means of obtaining such spectra is by deflecting the beta-rays from a radioactive source in a magnetic field. The deflection occurs within an evacuated chamber, to avoid scattering of the electrons by atmospheric gas. The deflected electron is detected by a Geiger counter. The magnet, chamber, source, and detection system are known as a beta-ray spectrograph. The maximum beta-ray energy is difficult to identify, since the number of detected electrons approaches zero at that point. The best evidence agreed with the rule that the maximum beta-ray energy equals the amount of energy lost in the nuclear transition $E = E_2 - E_1$, where E_2 and E_1 represent the energies of the parent and daughter nuclei, respectively. From the evidence, it appeared that the rules of beta-decay were in conflict with the rule of energy conservation. A conflict with the momentum conservation law was also found. With the energy (in fact, the momentum) of the emitted electron observable, the momentum of recoil of the emitting nucleus was readily calculable. Because of the rather low value of momentum taken up by the emitting nucleus, the measurements of the nucleus recoil momenta were not of high accuracy, but they showed that the recoil momentum did not balance the electron momentum.

Much sharper conflicts arose from the observations of the spin changes in the transition. The electron, because of its spin value, must carry off one-half a unit of angular momentum. A great emphasis was, therefore, placed on the measurements of the spins of the parent and daughter nuclei. The results were in conflict with the law of angular momentum conservation. The spin change in the nuclear transition was integral. The list of paradoxes in beta-decay was, therefore, lengthened to include all the conservation axioms of classical physics, which had also become an essential part of the newer quantum mechanics. It could not have been excluded that in the nuclear system physicists had found a regime in which the conservation rules no longer held. The more attractive alternative to this notion was the assumption that in beta-decay there was an as yet undetected particle emitted by the nucleus. Calorimetric measurements of the total decay energy were made by housing a beta-emitter in lead containers of large wall thickness to trap the hypothesized missing radiation. However, such measurements gave only the average energy of the beta-spectrum. As it turned out, the question was not to be resolved by experimental detection, which was achieved decades after the main questions were resolved, but instead the resolution came about through theoretical speculation.

Fermi postulated a companion particle in electron emission which, by hypothesis, possessed all the properties needed to satisfy all the conservation laws. This particle was called the neutrino. The hypothetical particle possessed no charge, since electric charge conservation was already followed in the simple beta-transition. The chargeless nature of the particle was consistent with the failure to detect the particle.

The shape of the beta-ray spectrum was argued from the rules of statistics, since if two particles sharing a total amount of momentum and energy were to be emitted, this sharing had to be constrained according to the mechanical laws. Beyond that point, the likelihood of sharing momentum and energy in any particular way was given by probability theory. It had to be assumed that on occasion the electron could carry away most of the energy and momentum, and the neutrino little, and vice versa. Also, angular correlation played a role: the electron and neutrino could be emitted in coincident directions, opposite directions, or at any arbitrary included angle between the two trajectories. So that the probability theory could be worked out, one property of the neutrino was made parametric—its rest mass—because the mass was completely unknown. Agreement with the measured beta-ray spectra was found to be best when the neutrino rest mass was assumed to be zero, or at least extremely small, compared with that of the electron. The neutrino is, therefore, without electric charge and without rest mass. With such attributes removed, it becomes fair to ask what is left. What is left is a spin of one-half times $h/2\pi$, since a spin equal to that of the electron is needed to explain the spin change in the emitting nucleus. While the particle is chargeless, a very small magnetic moment may be associated with the spin, although it is so small as to escape ordinary detection. Finally, a force field must be assumed that is associated with the process of creating the electron-neutrino pair.

The weakness of the neutrino interaction with matter gives it a unique role in nuclear processes. In nuclear disintegrations, the energy lost to the neutrino is essentially lost for good. A neutrino may readily penetrate the earth along a diameter and then continue on its travels to infinity. Several percent of the energy produced in a nuclear reactor is in the form of neutrinos and is, therefore, lost permanently. A substantial part of the sun's energy is produced in the useless form of neutrino radiation. While in a way the principle of energy conservation is made good again by the neutrino hypothesis, in another way something is permanently lost. The idea of energy conservation is predicated on the convertibility of energy forms into all other forms. The neutrino energy very nearly defies convertibility back into the other forms. Nevertheless, the bookkeeping of energy conservation is preserved by the neutrino postulate.

The neutrino postulate permits the writing of the elementary reactions of beta-decay in complete form. While the complete nuclear system may be involved in the decay, the net effect of decay is, in the electron emission process, to transform a neutron into a proton; in the case of positron emission, a proton is transformed into a neutron.

Thus:

$$\mathrm{n}_0^1 \rightarrow \mathrm{p}_1^1 + \mathrm{e}^- + \nu, \tag{32–15}$$

and

$$\mathrm{p}_1^1 \rightarrow \mathrm{n}_0^1 + \mathrm{e}^+ + \nu. \tag{32–16}$$

The free neutron possesses more total energy than the proton—enough, that is, to produce the rest mass of an electron and to have an energy remainder. The rest mass of the neutron is

$$M_{\mathrm{n}} = 1.008982 \text{ amu},$$

and the rest mass of the proton is

$$M_{\mathrm{p}} = 1.007593 \text{ amu}.$$

The difference in masses is:

$$\Delta m = 0.001389 \text{ amu},$$
$$\Delta mc^2 = 1.29 \text{ Mev}.$$

Therefore, in neutron decay by electron creation (rest mass 0.511 Mev) about 1780 kiloelectron volts are available to the kinetic energy of the electron and neutrino. The decay of the free neutron has been experimentally observed. The lifetime of the neutron at rest for this reaction is about 12 minutes. Since a free neutron will transform into a proton, the stable forms of free particles are evidently the proton, the electron, and the neutrino. Because of the energy of binding, the neutron in the nucleus is stabilized against decay—strongly, in the case of stable nuclei, only partly in the case of beta-active nuclei. But in the free state, the beta-decay of the neutron eliminates it as a stable free particle.

32-9 NUCLEAR BINDING ENERGY

One of the most direct sources of information on the energy of the nuclear systems is the vast amount of data gained through the systematic measurements of atomic masses by the technique of mass spectroscopy. The method of mass spectroscopy (in which an ionized atom is accelerated and then while traveling at known velocity, is deflected in a curved trajectory in a magnetic field) yields directly the charge-to-mass ratio of the ion. Since the ionic charge is an integral number times the electronic charge, a knowledge of the charge-to-mass ratio yields the atomic mass. Moreover, since the nucleus is the massive component of the atom, the data gained have a primary relevance to the mass of the atomic nucleus. The mass of the atomic electron is slight compared to the mass of the atom, and since the number of electrons (Z) and the mass of the electrons are accurately known, the nuclear mass itself may be readily obtained from the atomic mass. (Often the atomic rather than the nuclear mass is quoted in a table. The nuclear mass is obtained by subtracting the electronic mass.) Mass spectrographic techniques are capable of considerable accuracy, and most atomic masses can be quoted to six significant figures or better. As in the case of atomic spectroscopy, much of the precise data in mass spectroscopy were obtained before any good reason for having such high precision was known. However, part of the scientific process has to do with accuracy and orderliness. Many investigators worked exhaustively to measure with high accuracy the mass of every atom and of every isotope thereof.

In classical mechanics, mass measures inertia and strength of gravitational interaction. In relativistic mechanics, mass also measures the energy of the system through the relationship,

$$E = mc^2. \tag{32-17}$$

From this relationship, any change in a system affecting its energy will also affect the mass of the system. Of course, the mass-energy relationship is valid to the very lowest energies (compared to rest energy) and the very lowest velocities (compared with the velocity of light). However, in the classical region of energy measurements, energy changes, either kinetic or rest, are usually so slight compared with the rest energy as to imperceptibly change the energy or mass of the total system. Thus, when hydrogen reacts with oxygen, energy is liberated, and the water molecule weighs less than the sum of the weights of its free constituents. But this energy loss is a few electron volts, whereas the rest energy of the system is billions of electron volts. While there is no doubt that the relativistic laws are being followed in the chemical case, the observation of mass changes of the order of one part in one billion is beyond the reach of present measurement techniques. Were the percentage changes not so small, one of the most direct approaches to the energy change in chemical reaction would be to measure the masses of the constituents, before and after reaction.

In nuclear reactions we have an example in which the energy changes observably alter the mass of the total system. For example, a typical nuclear transition may alter the system energy by one million ev, while the system mass may be, for a light element, ten billion ev. The change in the total energy of the system is therefore one part in 10^4. Since mass spectroscopic precision extends to one part in 10^6 or better, the energy changes in nuclear reactions are readily observed by a mass measurement. Mass spectroscopy therefore does far more than tell of the inertia of nuclear systems; it charts the total energy and energy changes of the nuclear isotopes.

With the rules of relativity and with the information that the constituents of the nucleus are neutrons and protons, the binding energies of the nuclei can be readily deduced from the mass spectrographic data. When the masses, or total energies, of the atomic isotopes are examined, it is found that the increment in mass from isotope to isotope is not the same, but varies in an irregular fashion. Thus, although mass spectroscopy results yield the numbers of protons and neutrons in each isotope, the differences in the masses of the isotopes do not correspond to the masses of the protons and neutrons needed to form one isotope from another. The discrepancy between the masses of the isotopes and their free constituents is referred to in the literature as the mass defect. The name implies a failure of masses to add; whereas, on the basis of relativistic mechanics, the nonadditivity of masses is to be expected. The data of Table 32–1 are extended here in Table 32–2 to deduce the binding energies of the nuclear systems.

Listed in the first column of Table 32–2 are the isotope symbols which contain the atomic and mass numbers of the isotope. In the second column are the isotopic masses, which are the masses M_0 of the neutral atoms in a system of units in which the mass of one neutral oxygen atom (isotope 16) is chosen to be 16.000000 amu. In the third column are listed the total mass $Z \times m_e$ of the atomic electrons for the isotope, given in amu. The mass of the electrons is the atomic number Z times the rest mass of an electron m_e. The fourth column lists the nuclear mass M_{nuc}, the atomic mass minus the electronic mass. It can be seen that failure to account for the electronic mass (equivalent to about 0.5 Mev) would introduce a considerable error into nuclear calculations. In the next columns are listed the summed free-proton masses (ZM_p) and the summed free-neutron masses $(A–Z)M_n$ corresponding to the isotope. The sum of these two, the mass of the free protons and the mass of the free neutrons, gives the mass of the isotopic constituents before binding into the nucleus. In every case, except in the obvious ones for n_0^1 and H_1^1, the masses of the free constituents are significantly greater than the measured mass of the isotope, indicating that a considerable amount of energy is given up when the neutrons and protons are bound into the nucleus. The next column lists the differences in mass ΔM of the free constituents and of the bound constituents:

$$\Delta M = \sum M_p + \sum M_n - M_{nuc}. \quad (32\text{–}18)$$

TABLE 32–2

Isotope X_Z^A	M_0	$Z \times m_e$	M_{nuc}
n_0^1	1.008986	0	1.008986
H_1^1	1.008145	0.000549	1.007596
H_1^2	2.014740	0.000549	2.014191
H_1^3	3.017005	0.000549	3.016456
He_2^3	3.016986	0.001098	3.015888
He_2^4	4.003874	0.001098	4.002776
Li_3^6	6.017034	0.001547	6.015487
Li_3^7	7.018232	0.001547	7.016685

Isotope X_Z^A	ZM_p	$(A–Z)M_n$	Total M
n_0^1	0	1.008986	1.008986
H_1^1	1.007596	0	1.007596
H_1^2	1.007596	1.008986	2.016582
H_1^3	1.007596	2.017972	3.025568
He_2^3	2.015192	1.008986	3.024178
He_2^4	2.015192	2.017972	4.033154
Li_3^6	3.022788	3.026958	6.049746
Li_3^7	3.022788	4.035940	7.058728

Isotope X_Z^A	ΔM, amu	ΔE, Mev	$\Delta E/A$, Mev
n_0^1	0	0	0
H_1^1	0	0	0
H_1^2	0.002391	2.24	1.12
H_1^3	0.009112	8.55	2.85
He_2^3	0.008290	7.78	2.59
He_2^4	0.030378	28.52	7.13
Li_3^6	0.034259	32.17	5.36
Li_3^7	0.042043	39.40	5.63

Since the objective is to illustrate the energy of binding, the next column displays ΔE in units of Mev, utilizing the conversion ratio of 1 amu = 938.211 Mev. Of relevance to nuclear structure is the binding energy per particle, neutron or proton, in the nuclear system. This figure, $\Delta E/A$, is given in the final column.

Were the list extended, it would be seen that the very rapid rise in binding energy per particle ceases at He_2^4 and thereafter is quite constant at values of about 7 to 8 Mev per particle. This approximate constancy of binding energy per particle is a general characteristic of nuclear structure. Of further interest is the set of nuclei from hydrogen to helium. Deuterium H_1^2 is of special interest since it contains direct information about the interaction of a single proton and a single neutron. Evidently the energies of binding among neutrons and protons are enhanced by interaction in larger groups, since the binding energy of deuterium is lower than that of any other isotope. Strikingly evident in the table is the most stable grouping of neutrons and protons, the He_2^4 isotope. It has two neutrons and two protons, also known as the alpha-particle. The binding energy per particle is saturated at this point. The very high stability of this isotope suggests the reason why this particular grouping of nuclear particles, forming the alpha-particle, is emitted in the decay sequences in the naturally radioactive series. A high stabilizing energy is required to explain why an alpha-particle should be emitted in those cases rather than neutrons or protons separately.

Examined in detail, the binding energies of the isotopes show variations which for many years escaped explanation. A discovery of an extremely complex periodicity in the variations led to the formulation of the shell model of the nucleus. By analogy to atomic structure, neutrons and protons are grouped into shells, corresponding to orbital and spin quantum numbers. However, this periodicity is neither so simple nor so evident as in the periodic table of the chemical elements.

32–10 STABILITY OF THE ISOTOPES

The most general tendency in isotopic constitution is toward the equality of the number of neutrons and the number of protons. This tendency is attributed to a basic property of nuclear forces which produces in the nucleus a strong coupling between neutron-proton pairs, a weaker coupling between pairs of protons or

TABLE 32–3

Stable isotopes	Abundance, %	N_p	N_n	Characteristic
H_1^1	99.985		0	
H_1^2	0.015	1	1	Odd-odd
He_2^4	100.	2	2	Even-even
Li_3^6	7.52		3	Odd-odd
Li_3^7	92.48	3	4	Odd-even
Be_4^9	100.	4	5	Even-odd
B_5^{10}	19.		5	Odd-odd
B_5^{11}	81.	5	6	Odd-even
C_6^{12}	98.9		6	Even-even
C_6^{13}	1.1	6	7	Even-odd
N_7^{14}	99.64		7	Odd-odd
N_7^{15}	0.36	7	8	Odd-even
O_8^{16}	99.76		8	Even-even
O_8^{17}	0.04	8	9	Even-odd
O_8^{18}	0.20		10	Even-even
F_9^{19}	100.	9	10	Odd-even
Ne_{10}^{20}	90.92		10	Even-even
Ne_{10}^{21}	0.26	10	11	Even-odd
Ne_{10}^{22}	8.82		12	Even-even
Na_{11}^{23}	100.	11	12	Odd-even
Mg_{12}^{24}	78.60	12	12	Even-even
Mg_{12}^{25}	10.11	12	13	Even-odd
Mg_{12}^{26}	11.29	12	14	Even-even
Al_{13}^{27}	100.	13	14	Odd-even
Si_{14}^{28}	92.27	14	14	Even-even
Si_{14}^{29}	4.68	14	15	Even-odd
Si_{14}^{30}	3.05	14	16	Even-even
P_{15}^{31}	100.	15	16	Odd-even

pairs of neutrons. A periodicity to be noted in the isotope chart is attributed to this fact. This is the predominant stability of the even-even nuclei; that is, nuclei that have an even number of protons and an even number of neutrons. Next in stability are the even-odd combinations, and last is the odd-odd, which is rare in nuclear structure except in the very lightweight nuclei. A reference to the list of stable isotopes of the light nuclei in Table 32–3 illustrates the point. The tendency toward pairing is observed above the oxygen isotopes; O_8^{16} is a system made up of four alpha-particles. Up to that point, the small number of particles in the nucleus requires the treatment of each as a separate case. Beyond that point, it can be seen that the odd Z elements, F_9^{19}, Na_{11}^{23}, Al_{13}^{27}, and P_{15}^{31} are all 100% abundant, and each has an even number of neutrons. Isotopes adjacent to any of these would be odd-odd isotopes, and these are not stable. The even Z isotopes are often three in number, since this combination permits two even-even combinations and one even-odd. An inspection of the neutron numbers shows a like tendency. There are three chemical elements, each having the neutron numbers 10, 12, and 14. There is only one isotope each having the neutron numbers 11, 13, 15. These general features illustrate the pairing of neutrons and protons in the nucleus. However, the generalization cannot be pressed too far, since there are other structural qualities of the nucleus which can also affect isotopic stability. One of the dominant effects is Coulomb repulsion among the protons.

Among the lighter elements, the tendency toward the equality of neutron and proton number is striking. The most abundant of a sequence of isotopes is Ca_{20}^{40}. As the atomic number increases, the number of isotopes, especially for Z even, increases: Ca_{20} has six isotopes, Sn_{50} has ten. This is to be expected, since in the heavier elements a large number of isotopes does not proportionately upset the percentage balance between neutrons and protons as severely as in the lighter elements. Another tendency is just as striking; namely, among the isotopic sequences, the number of neutrons tends to exceed the number of protons, and as the atomic number increases, the tendency becomes more pronounced. Thus, the calcium isotopes are Ca_{20}^{40}, Ca_{20}^{42}, Ca_{20}^{43}, Ca_{20}^{44}, Ca_{20}^{46}, Ca_{20}^{48}. The number of neutrons either equals or exceeds the number of protons. Turning again to tin, we see that the stable isotopes are Sn_{50}^{112}, Sn_{50}^{114}, Sn_{50}^{115}, Sn_{50}^{116}, Sn_{50}^{117}, Sn_{50}^{118}, Sn_{50}^{119}, Sn_{50}^{120}, Sn_{50}^{122}. Here the least number of neutrons exceeds the atomic number by 12. The greatest number of neutrons exceeds the atomic number by 22. The tendency for pairing persists, but a displacement has been caused by some other factor. This factor is the electrostatic repulsion among the protons, the apparent effect of the excess neutrons being to dilute the proton density and therefore to reduce the repulsion.

Because of the large relative magnitude of the nuclear forces, the Coulomb repulsion in the lighter nuclei has little effect. However, there is a difference in character between the nuclear forces and the electrical forces that portends a catastrophy at some point as the atomic number is increased. The catastrophy occurs, in fact, at $Z = 92$, uranium, which is the last stable element, and, therefore, forms a bound to the periodic table. The nature of nuclear structure and nuclear binding energy points to a saturation characteristic of nuclear forces. That is, each particle does not interact with equal strength with all the rest. Rather, the particles appear to interact predominantly with nearest neighbors. Thus, the binding energy per particle in the nucleus is about constant, and the total binding energy of the system as a whole has a very nearly linear dependence on the number of constituent particles. This property is quite different from that of an electrical system. In the electrical system of point charges, each particle interacts with all the rest, leading to a system energy which depends on the square of the number of particles, the constant of proportionality depending on the detailed distribution. Therefore, even though the electrical force per particle-pair is weaker than the nuclear force, the square law of electrical system energy must eventually cause the disruptive force of electrical repulsion to nullify the attraction of the specific nuclear forces.

The detailed distribution of the electrostatic charge in the nucleus cannot be given with certainty. A spherical distribution is preferred, and the tendency toward neutron-proton pairing suggests a homogeneity rather than a segregation of neutrons and protons. The constant binding energy per particle suggests a high degree of homogeneity of the whole. Therefore, it will be assumed that the protons are uniformly distributed within a sphere. With these assumptions, it will be recalled that the electrical potential energy of a uniform sphere of total charge q and radius R is given by the relation

$$W = \frac{3}{5}\frac{1}{4\pi\epsilon_0}\frac{q^2}{R}. \qquad (32\text{–}19)$$

The nuclear charge is $q = Ze$ where e is the protonic charge. The nuclear radius is $R = 1.45 \times 10^{-15} A^{1/3}$ meters. The Coulomb energy of the nucleus is therefore

$$W = \frac{3}{5}\frac{1}{4\pi\epsilon_0}\frac{Z^2e^2}{1.45 \times 10^{-15}A^{1/3}}. \qquad (32\text{–}20)$$

Sample calculations show the effect of Coulomb repulsion in Table 32–4. The nuclear binding energy is taken to be 8 Mev per particle.

TABLE 32–4

Element	Z	A	R, meters	W_{elect}, Mev	W_{nuc}, Mev
Ne	10	20	3.9×10^{-15}	22	160
Zn	30	64	5.8×10^{-15}	135	510
Sn	50	120	7.2×10^{-15}	300	960
Yb	70	174	8.1×10^{-15}	520	1390
Th	90	232	8.9×10^{-15}	785	1850

At $Z = 30$, the electrical energy is 26% of the nuclear energy, sufficient to cause a slight imbalance in the number of protons and neutrons. At $Z = 70$, the electrical energy is 37% of the nuclear, making the paired neutron-proton system unstable. At $Z = 90$, the electrical energy is 42% of the nuclear energy, approaching the point where the nuclear system is disrupted.

The chemical elements become unstable in a gradual manner before the periodic table is terminated. The elements in the range between $Z = 82$ and 92 are generally those which are part of the naturally radioactive series. The endpoints of these series are lead and bismuth. From this point, it is interesting to note the abundance of the stable isotopes.

TABLE 32–5

Stable isotope	Abundance, %	Lifetime
Pb_{82}^{204}	1.48	
Pb_{82}^{206}	23.6	
Pb_{82}^{207}	22.6	
Pb_{82}^{208}	52.3	
Bi_{83}^{209}	100.	
Po_{84}	None	
At_{85}	None	
Rn_{86}	None	
Fr_{87}	None	
Ra_{88}	None	
Ac_{89}	None	
*Th_{90}^{232}	100.	1.39×10^{10} years
Pa_{91}	None	
*U_{92}^{234}	0.0058	2.48×10^5 years
*U_{92}^{235}	0.715	7.15×10^8 years
*U_{92}^{238}	99.28	4.51×10^9 years

*Or long-lived.

The elements above lead and bismuth in the periodic table evidently form a special category, since none of their isotopes is stable and yet they are present as appreciable components of the earth's crust. Some of the elements are present because they are continually replenished: they are the products of nuclear decay processes. But the highest elements in the periodic table are the sources of those lower unstable elements and remain on the earth for another reason. These are the extremely long-lived unstable elements whose lifetimes are given in Table 32-5. By chance, their lifetimes are roughly comparable to the age of the earth. Thus, although they are in a state of continual decay, a substantial fraction of the amount of that material formed in the creation of the earth remains today in the earth's crust along with the completely stable elements.

32-11 STRUCTURE OF THE DEUTERON

Since the deuteron consists of only two particles, its structure is determined by the simplest possible interaction, that of two bodies. On the laboratory or larger scale, two-body interactions can be analyzed exactly, using Newtonian mechanics and known force laws. On the atomic scale, the two-body problem can also be analyzed exactly by using wave mechanics and known force laws. *But* on the nuclear scale, the validity of wave mechanics is not certain and the force law is not known. The following is an illustration of what can be accomplished under the latter circumstances.

It has been noted that the nucleus is a saturated structure. By this we mean that as neutrons and protons are added to the nucleus, the spacing between adjacent particles tends to be constant. From this, it can be concluded that the forces between the neutron and proton are short-range. That is, the force between particles falls off much more rapidly than, for example, the inverse-square law that pertains to electromagnetism and gravitation. In fact, it may be said that the force, while still very strong at the interparticle distance (about 2×10^{-15} m in the nucleus), will have practically vanished at twice that distance. In this way, nearest neighbor particles in the nucleus would interact strongly, but particles once removed from nearest neighbors would hardly interact at all. The short-range type of force would agree with the nearly constant spacing of particles in the nucleus. It would also agree with the nearly linear dependence of total nuclear binding energy on the number of particles in the nucleus.

One analytical form proposed to express the nature of the short-range force, given in terms of a potential, is

$$V = -\frac{1}{r} e^{-r/r_0}. \tag{32-21}$$

In this expression, a characteristic length r_0 appears which, in a satisfactory theory, should be derivable from first principles. In the absence of such a theory, the value of r_0 is used as an arbitrary parameter. A qualitative comparison of the forms of the exponential and inverse-square laws of force is shown in Fig. 32-2. Beyond arguing the short-range nature of the force, it must be recognized that it is not known whether the potential indeed goes to minus infinity at the origin or whether it breaks off and becomes finite at $r = 0$. Possibly there is a repulsion between particles as they approach zero separation. The potentials corresponding to these different cases are shown in Fig. 32-3. The intermediate case, with potential finite at the origin, can be

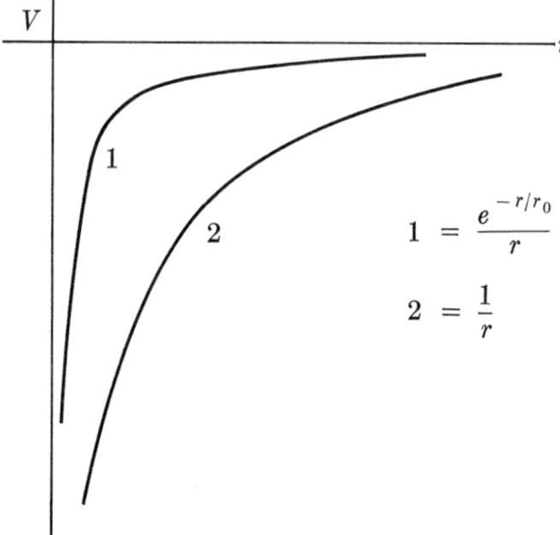

FIG. 32-2. The form of the potential energy for central forces of attraction: (1) Yukawa exponential form, (2) Coulomb law.

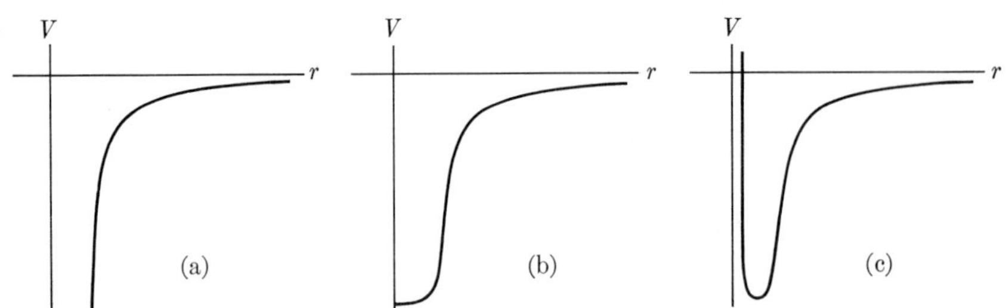

FIG. 32–3. (a) Potential infinite in magnitude at the origin. (b) Potential finite at the origin. (c) Repulsion near the origin.

approximated by a "square-well" potential, as shown in Fig. 32–4. The square-well potential, offering one of the simplest exercises in quantum mechanics, is characterized by two parameters, the depth V_0 and the range r_0. It is to be interpreted as corresponding to zero force everywhere except at the distance r_0 where the force is infinite and attractive. This is an extreme simplification of a short-range force.

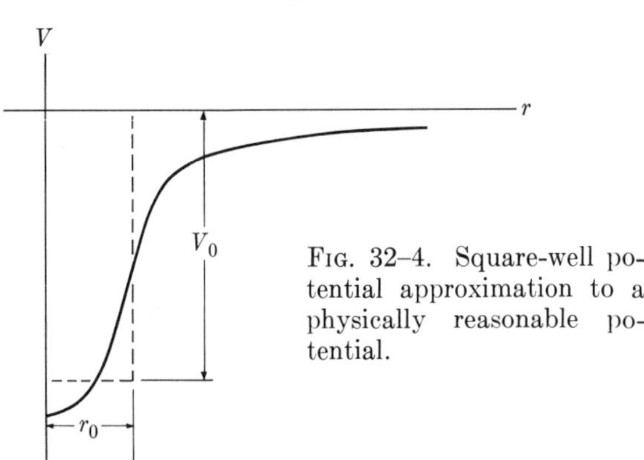

FIG. 32–4. Square-well potential approximation to a physically reasonable potential.

In the absence of finer details about the nuclear force, the square-well potential is a satisfactory and interesting point of departure for investigating the interaction of the neutron and proton. Of the two parameters available, V_0 should represent the strength of interaction between nuclear particles, and r_0 the range of interaction.

Assume, then, that the force of interaction between a neutron and a proton is characterized by a square-well potential. This potential will be used in an exercise in quantum mechanics to obtain a relationship between the binding energy and the radius of the deuteron. A square-well, representing a central force-field, permits not only radial motion of particles within the force-field but also angular motion. For simplicity in the exercise, the angular motion will be excluded, although no essential difficulty attends its inclusion.

The Schrödinger equation for motion in three dimensions is

$$\frac{\partial^2\psi}{\partial x^2} + \frac{\partial^2\psi}{\partial y^2} + \frac{\partial^2\psi}{\partial z^2} + \frac{8\pi^2 m}{h^2}(E - V)\psi = 0. \tag{32–22}$$

For a central-force potential, that is, a potential which is a function of r alone, a considerable simplification in obtaining a solution results from the introduction of polar coordinates. Direct transformation of coordinates in Eq. (32–22) to the polar coordinates r, θ, and ϕ yields the polar form

$$\frac{1}{r^2}\frac{\partial}{\partial r}\left(r^2\frac{\partial\psi}{\partial r}\right) + \frac{1}{r^2 \sin\theta}\frac{\partial}{\partial\theta}\left(\sin\theta\,\frac{\partial\psi}{\partial\theta}\right) + \frac{1}{r^2\sin^2\theta}\frac{\partial^2\psi}{\partial\phi^2} + \frac{8\pi^2 m}{h^2}[E - V(r)]\psi = 0. \tag{32–23}$$

The variables in this equation can be separated readily by expressing the solution in the product form,

$$\psi = R(r)\Theta(\theta)\Phi(\phi), \tag{32–24}$$

where the functions R, Θ, and Φ are functions of r, θ, and ϕ alone, respectively. Insertion of this function into Eq. (32–23) will show that separation of variables is achievable. At this point, however, the original assumption that there is no angular motion will be used. Assume that $\Theta = 0$ and $\Phi = 0$. The radial equation for $R(r)$ becomes

$$\frac{1}{r^2}\frac{d}{dr}\left(r^2\frac{dR}{dr}\right) + \frac{8\pi^2 m}{h^2}[E - V(r)]\psi = 0. \tag{32–25}$$

A further simplification is obtained by using the function

$$u(r) = rR(r). \tag{32–26}$$

The wave equation for radial motion then becomes

$$\frac{d^2u}{dr^2} + \frac{8\pi^2 m}{h^2}[E - V(r)]u = 0. \tag{32–27}$$

Two separate regions exist in which Eq. (32–27) is to be solved. In region I the particle is within the well; in region II the particle is outside. Since a stable solution is being sought (the deuteron being known to be stable), it is assumed that the total energy E of the system is less than the potential energy V_0.

An essential difference between the hydrogen atom and the deuterium nucleus as examples of two-particle systems stems from the relative masses of the particles. In the hydrogen atom, the heavy central proton may, to a good approximation, be considered infinitely massive compared to the electron. Therefore, the proton is usually considered to be the centroid of the hydrogen atom, with only a slight error arising from this assumption. In the deuterium nucleus, the two particles, the neutron and the proton, are of very nearly equal masses, and for simplicity it is assumed that the masses are precisely equal. Under this assumption, the two-particle problem is readily simplified, as in classical mechanics, to be a single particle in motion about the center of mass of the system. In the case where the original particles are of equal mass, the mass of the equivalent single particle moving about an infinitely massive particle is half the particle masses:

$$m = \frac{M}{2}, \tag{32–28}$$

where M represents the proton or the neutron mass.

In region I, the differential equation is

$$\frac{d^2u}{dr^2} + \frac{4\pi^2 m}{h^2}Eu = 0. \tag{32–29}$$

It is convenient to represent the product of constants simply as

$$K^2 = \frac{4\pi^2 m}{h^2}E. \tag{32–30}$$

Then the Eq. (32–29) becomes

$$\frac{d^2u}{dr^2} + K^2u = 0, \tag{32–31}$$

for which the general solution is

$$u = A \sin Kr. \tag{32–32}$$

In region II, outside the well, the differential equation of motion is

$$\frac{d^2u}{dr^2} - \frac{4\pi^2 m}{h^2}(V_0 - E)u = 0, \tag{32–33}$$

and the constant term is represented as

$$K_1^2 = \frac{4\pi^2 m}{h^2}(V_0 - E). \tag{32–34}$$

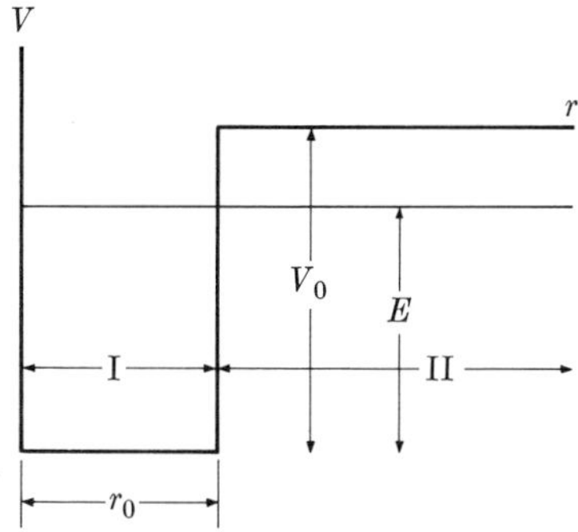

FIG. 32–5. Square-well representation of the potential energy of a neutron-proton system (deuteron).

Equation (32-33) then becomes

$$\frac{d^2u}{dr^2} - K_1^2 u = 0, \tag{32-35}$$

for which the general solution is

$$u = Be^{-K_1 r}. \tag{32-36}$$

At this point, the problem is solved from the standpoint of having analytical solutions for the wave functions at all points in space. However, the physical problem is not solved until the boundary conditions are imposed. These boundary conditions exist at the division between regions I and II. To be a physical solution, the wave function must at all points be continuous in magnitude and in the first derivative. The impression of these conditions at the boundary will yield a relationship between the as yet arbitrary constants K and K_1. Since these constants contain the system energy, the relationship yields the desired information about the system energy.

For continuity in value between regions I and II, we have the condition

$$A \sin Kr_0 = Be^{-K_1 r_0}. \tag{32-37}$$

For continuity in first derivative between regions I and II, we have the condition

$$KA \cos Kr_0 = -K_1 Be^{-K_1 r_0}. \tag{32-38}$$

Dividing Eq. (32-37) by Eq. (32-38), we obtain a relationship between K_1 and K:

$$\tan Kr_0 = -\frac{K}{K_1}. \tag{32-39}$$

Substituting the expressions for K and K_1, we obtain a relationship between the energy of the system and the range of the force:

$$\tan \sqrt{4\pi^2 mE/(h^2\, r_0)} = -\sqrt{E/(V_0 - E)}. \tag{32-40}$$

This is a transcendental equation which may be solved to any desired precision by successive approximations. The solution is left as an exercise. To obtain a solution, assume that the range of the nuclear force is

$$r_0 = 2.8 \times 10^{-15} \text{ meter}.$$

Under this assumption, it can be shown that the deuteron is stable with the following values of total energy and potential energy:

$$E = 20 \text{ Mev}, \qquad V_0 = 22 \text{ Mev}.$$

This exercise yields a predicted depth of the interaction potential of the neutron and the proton of 22 Mev and a binding energy of 2 Mev. The latter figure is directly verifiable by experiment, which gives the binding energy of the deuteron to be 2.19 Mev. However, it will be noted that the arbitrary assumptions made in calculating the binding energy were numerous, including an assumed range for nuclear forces. Thus, the close agreement between calculation and experiment was planned, rather than derived from first principles. What has been shown is that a square-well model of the nuclear potential yields a stable deuteron of correct binding energy when the range of the nuclear force is taken to be about 2.8×10^{-15} meter.

32-12 ELEMENTARY PARTICLES

If the discovery of the neutron marked the beginning of contemporary nuclear science, the discovery of the transcendental particles, starting with the mesons, has opened a completely new field. Elementary particles were long considered to be, as their name implies, the immutable basic stuff of which matter, atoms, and nuclei are composed. There were good reasons for the notion of immutability, for as one proceeds from the study of atomic reactions to nuclear reactions, and then to elementary particle reactions, more and more energy is required to induce the reaction. The atom is disrupted by energies of a few electron volts. A million volts is required to excite the nucleus, and several million volts are required to remove one particle from the nucleus.

But 150 Mev is required to produce a meson, and billions of electron volts are required to produce the heavier particles. Thus, man's attitude toward the properties of matter has been gradually altered, in large part by the availability of high-energy particles. The emergence of the cyclotron in the 1930's and the synchrotron and its modifications in the 1940's has led to the discovery not only of many new particles but of many reactions through which one particle is transformed into another.

The elementary particles are not immutable. Instead, there is now what can be called a chemistry of the elementary particles, a science of systematizing all the interactions among the particles. Many of these newly discovered particles have a direct bearing upon the nature of nuclear forces. Thus, the earlier work on the nuclear force laws was done in the absence of the most vital information. The studies of the nucleus and the studies of the basic properties of the elementary particles are strongly interconnected.

Prior to the discovery of the intermediate particles, the known particles were the proton, neutron, electron, positron, and the neutrino, the latter being known through inference rather than direct detection. The interaction of the electron and the positron, leading to the total annihilation of both particles, was already known. The total rest energy of the two particles is given over to the energy of two photons which are produced in the annihilation process. The net charge of the electron-positron pair is zero, so charge conservation is maintained:

$$\mathrm{e}^+ + \mathrm{e}^- \rightarrow 2h\nu. \qquad (32\text{–}41)$$

This was the first observation of the complete transformation of rest mass or rest energy into another form, the mass transformation in nuclear reactions being only a small fraction of the total rest mass of the system. Paired particles of detailed opposite properties are known as antiparticles to one another. Because of the constitution of the world around us, we designate the elcetron as matter and the positron as antimatter, but this is obviously an arbitrary designation. All particles of spin $\frac{1}{2}$, including the neutron, proton, and neutrinos, are observed to have antiparticles. Therefore, the original family of particles, the proton, neutron, electron, and neutrino, is doubled to include the antiparticle of each. In a way, these can be identified as the durable particles, if not immutable. Each can be completely annihilated by its antiparticle. However, antiparticles are not present in abundance, and the balance of ordinary particles in our part of the world appears to be quite stable. It has been noted that the free neutron is unstable through spontaneous beta-decay:

$$\mathrm{n}_0^1 \rightarrow \mathrm{p}_1^1 + \mathrm{e}^- + \nu. \qquad (32\text{–}42)$$

The neutron by itself is therefore not durable. However, the neutron bound in the nucleus is safe against decay. Such are the stability arguments about ordinary matter: ordinary matter is not absolutely stable. The more recently observed particles are, by comparison, extremely unstable and are, therefore, referred to as transient matter.

The discovery of the mesons is of fundamental importance to nuclear structure. On theoretical grounds, Yukawa predicted the existence of a particle of mass intermediate (hence the name meson, or, earlier, mesotron) between the electron and the proton. His reasoning applied to the short-range character of the nuclear force. Just as there is associated with the inverse-square law of electromagnetism a particle, the photon, of zero rest mass, there must be associated with the short-range nuclear force a particle of finite rest mass. From the observed strength and range of nuclear forces, as well as they could be identified, the mass of the meson was placed at about 250 electron masses. There was considerable excitement when this novel prediction was apparently confirmed by the discovery of a particle of mass 208 electron masses in cosmic rays. This particle, designated the mu-meson, or μ-meson, was the first of the intermediate particles to be identified.

It was observed to have a lifetime at rest of 2×10^{-6} second. Subsequent research proved disappointing since the μ-meson, supposedly accountable for the nuclear interaction, appeared scarcely to interact with nuclei at all. Its decay scheme identified it closely with the electron and neutrino,

$$\mu^+ \rightarrow e^+ + \nu + \tilde{\nu},$$
$$\mu^- \rightarrow e^- + \nu + \tilde{\nu}, \qquad (32\text{–}43)$$

where $\tilde{\nu}$ denotes an antineutrino.*

The speculation that the μ-meson might be involved in nuclear beta-decay did not throw any light on that process. It was therefore gratifying when, again in cosmic radiation, a slightly heavier meson, the π-meson, was finally observed, a meson that interacted strongly with nuclei. This meson, even more unstable, with a lifetime of about 2×10^{-8} sec, had a rest mass of about 273 electron masses, and interacted very strongly with nuclei. One of the means of detection is through the induction of a nuclear "star." When a π-meson is absorbed by the nucleus, the nucleus is so disrupted that several of its components fly out radially, giving a star appearance in a nuclear emulsion. Since the π-meson is not incorporated as a particle in the nuclear structure, its entire rest energy is necessarily absorbed by the nucleus as kinetic energy, about 137 Mev. When we consider that the binding energy per particle in the nucleus is 8 Mev, the disruption caused by absorption of a π-meson is very considerable.

The π-meson exists in a triplet of states (as contrasted with the electron, proton, neutron, and neutrino doublets). It exists in three charge states designated π^+, π^0, and π^-, having a unit plus charge, no charge, and unit minus charge, respectively. This triplet of states is in turn connected with the fact that there is a stronger interaction between a proton and a neutron than between neutron and neutron or proton and proton. The interaction of protons and neutrons is associated with the exchange of a π-meson. Two exchange reactions hold between the neutron and proton:

$$n_0^1 \rightleftarrows p_1^1 + \pi^-, \qquad p_1^1 \rightleftarrows n_0^1 + \pi^+. \qquad (32\text{–}44)$$

Only one reaction connects the proton to proton or neutron to neutron:

$$n_0^1 \rightleftarrows n_0^1 + \pi^0, \qquad p_1^1 \rightleftarrows p_1^1 + \pi^0. \qquad (32\text{–}45)$$

The decay modes and short lifetimes of the π-mesons explain why these mesons escaped detection for so long. The three decay schemes are:

$$\pi^+ \rightarrow \mu^+ + \nu',$$
$$\quad \hookrightarrow e^+ + \nu + \tilde{\nu}$$
$$\pi^- \rightarrow \mu^- + \nu',$$
$$\quad \hookrightarrow e^- + \nu + \tilde{\nu}$$
$$\pi^0 \rightarrow 2h\nu. \qquad (32\text{–}46)$$

Therefore, the μ-mesons observed as copious components of cosmic radiation are in reality the debris of π-meson decays. The π-mesons, produced by encounters in the upper atmosphere, have primarily decayed into μ-mesons, electrons, and photons by the time the radiation reaches the earth's surface. Thus, it was not until high-altitude research was undertaken that the connection (the Yukawa force) between mesons and the nucleus was made. It is an interesting commentary on the routes that research must follow that the penetration into the subatomic realm involved mountain climbing and the use of high-altitude balloons. Later, as the technology of high-energy accelerators advanced, all the intermediate particles of cosmic radiation were produced in the laboratory.

Some of the unstable particles of higher mass undoubtedly have a bearing on nuclear forces, but the relationships are more remote than the ones just traced. Particles heavier than the π-mesons, yet lighter than the proton, have been identified; for example, the tau-meson, which

---

*It has been shown conclusively that the neutrinos in (32–43) are different from the neutrinos of beta-decay.

decays into three π-mesons:

$$\tau^0 \rightarrow \pi^+ + \pi^- + \pi^0. \qquad (32\text{–}47)$$

There are many others. The detailed reactions, reaction rates, and the reasons why some reactions among the particles are allowed and some forbidden are beyond the scope of this review.

In closing it is interesting to note a general effect of the discovery of a sequence of hyperons which are heavier than the proton and neutrons. Thus, protons and neutrons are decay products of hyperons. Until hyperons were discovered, it was speculated that perhaps all the transient particles in nature were mesons, that is, intermediate in mass between the durable protons and neutrons at the high end of the mass spectrum and the electron and neutrino at the low end. If this had been the case, it would have been attractive to postulate that the number of elementary particles is finite, since the mass spectrum is probably discrete, and the placing of bounds at either end would impose another restriction. The discovery of the heavy transient particles ends such speculation.

The speculation is now turned to the nature of the hyperon and the notion that the hyperons may be excited states of the neutron and proton. If this were the case, we would have in the proton a new type of atom in which the discrete energy states lie so far apart that a single excitation enhances the system mass by hundreds of electron masses. In addition, bound states in which groups of π-mesons form short-lived systems have been discovered. A considerable amount of study will be required before these systems are known with the fineness of detail and self-consistency as, for example, the structure and spectrum of the hydrogen atom, which in itself was a frontier subject not so long ago.

32–13 SUMMARY

In the introduction, it was pointed out that the energies involved in nuclear structure are sufficiently large to bring into prominence the Einstein mass-energy equivalence. A second consequence of the large energies is the need for high-energy probes (particles or radiation) as tools for the study of nuclear structure. The method of wave mechanics, which is successful for atomic structure, is presumed to be useful for analysis of nuclear structure. However, since a basic force law has not yet been formulated for nuclear structure, the theory of nuclear structure cannot be developed systematically. The roles of accelerators and of cosmic radiation in providing particles of energy sufficiently high to be useful as probes in the study of nuclear structure is described.

The standard notation for specifying the atomic number Z and the mass number A of isotopes is

$$X_Z^A.$$

The model of the nucleus, with protons and electrons as the stable nuclear constituents, is discussed. This model predicts spin values and magnetic moments that are in conflict with experimental observation. The value of the measured magnetic moments is much smaller than the moment of the electron. Furthermore, according to the uncertainty principle, the energy of an electron confined to the small dimensions of the nucleus is much greater than the binding energy available to keep a particle in the nucleus.

The neutron-proton model is shown to eliminate the above difficulties, but new questions are raised, questions that are still not completely answered. The discovery of the neutron was based on an application of the simple laws of momentum and energy conservation during elastic collisions. The mass of the colliding particle (neutron) was thus found to be about the same as the mass of the proton. The lack of charge was evidenced by its penetrating power; that is, the particle produced very little excitation and ionization of the atoms through which it passed. The origin of the high-speed neutron that was thus identified by Chadwick is described by the nuclear reaction equation,

$$\mathrm{He}_2^4 + \mathrm{Be}_4^9 \rightarrow \mathrm{C}_6^{12} + \mathrm{n}_0^1,$$

which illustrates the method for writing nuclear reactions.

From the observed scattering of alpha-particles, the radius of nuclei was found to be small and to increase very slowly with the mass of the nucleus,

$$R = 1.4 \times 10^{-15} A^{1/3} \text{ meters.}$$

The radius of the nucleus is defined as the distance at which the force law begins to depart markedly from the electrostatic force law. The above shows the uniform density of nuclear matter and the saturation nature of nuclear forces.

Certain species of nuclei are naturally unstable. Some emit gamma-rays (radiation), others beta-rays (electrons), and others alpha-particles (helium nuclei). The emission is statistical, with a characteristic lifetime before emission that depends on the species. In the case of nuclei made artificially unstable by induced transformations, positive electrons are emitted in some cases. In the case of beta-decay, the energy of the decay electron from a given radioactive isotope varies from zero to a maximum value, but the change in energy of the nucleus is always the same! Energy conservation is maintained by the emission of a neutrino with energy that also varies from decay to decay. Both the electron and the neutrino are created at the time of emission according to

$$\mathrm{n}_0^1 \rightarrow \mathrm{p}_1^1 + \mathrm{e}^- + \nu.$$

The above process also takes place with a free neutron with a lifetime of 12 minutes.

Since the mass equivalent of nuclear binding energies is not a negligible fraction of the masses themselves, measurements of the mass give data that are pertinent to the question of stability. The results of precision measurements of masses are given in tabular form. From these figures, the binding energy per nucleon is derived. It is noted that the binding energy is a maximum for helium.

Another measure of the relative stability of isotopes is the relative abundance of isotopes of the same element. Is is found that the observed relative stabilities are consistent with the idea that the nuclear force of attraction is strongest between neutron and proton, less strong between proton pairs or neutron pairs. The well-known electrostatic force of repulsion between like charges results in a positive energy term that competes with the negative energy of binding attributable to the nuclear force of attraction between nucleons. The result is decreasing stability with increasing nuclear charge culminating with natural radioactivity at the higher end of the periodic table and a termination of the periodic table at Z of 92.

Several forms for the short-range nuclear force between two nucleons are given, with the simplifying assumption that the force depends only on the separation of the nucleons. The wave-mechanical solution for the case of a force that is zero except at the distance r_0 (a square-well potential) is presented. It is found that a well of depth 22 Mev of radius 2.8×10^{-15} meter results in a normal state for the two-particle system of energy 20 Mev. Thus, the assumed form of nuclear force gives a result that agrees with the observed binding energy of the deuteron of 2.19 Mev. It is noted, however, that other similar forms of short-range force would give the same result.

Some of the unstable particles that can be created when energies of hundreds and of thousands of Mev are used are discussed. There are the mesons with masses between the mass of the electron and the proton. The mesons are definitely associated with nuclear forces. They are the quanta of the nuclear force field in the same way that the photon is the quantum of the electromagnetic force field. One of the "mesons," the mu-meson, is really a heavy electron in the sense that it exerts only electric forces and not nuclear forces. It is a decay product of the pi-meson. Equations are given for the exchange of pi-mesons between nucleons. These exchanges are responsible for the force of attraction between nucleons.

Particles heavier than nucleons, called hyperons, can be formed in conjunction with the creation of the heavier mesons. The hyperons decay into nucleons and therefore can be considered to be excited states of nucleons.

Problems

1. The observed magnetic moment μ of the proton is about twice the value predicted by Eq. (32–7). What does this suggest concerning the internal structure of the proton, that is, the charge distribution relative to the mass distribution?

2. By way of contrast with the impossibility of containing an electron in a nucleus, show that it *is* possible for the electron to be a constituent of the atom without violating the uncertainty principle.

3. How many protons and how many neutrons does the nucleus U_{92}^{238} contain?

4. (a) Show that the kinetic energy of the neutron in Eq. (32–12) is about 15 Mev for an incident alpha-particle with kinetic energy 5 Mev.

(b) Use the conservation of momentum to justify neglecting the kinetic energy of the carbon nucleus.

(c) Find the velocity of the neutron and thus justify your use of nonrelativistic expressions for momentum and kinetic energy.

5. Show that the emission of a Compton proton with kinetic energy 6 Mev from paraffin requires an incident gamma-ray of at least 60-Mev energy.

6. In his discovery of the neutron, Chadwick compared the maximum recoil energy of a proton ejected when paraffin is bombarded by neutrons with the maximum recoil energy of a nitrogen nucleus when nitrogen gas is bombarded by neutrons of the same energy. Find the expected energy of the recoil proton relative to that of the recoil nitrogen nucleus.

7. Assuming a head-on collision, what is the minimum energy of an incident alpha-particle that will just reach the surface of (a) a lithium nucleus? (b) a uranium nucleus? (Neglect the attractive nuclear force.)

8. When H^3 decays by beta-emission, the maximum energy of the beta-ray (electron) is about 15,000 ev.

(a) What is the energy of the neutrino when a beta-ray of maximum energy is emitted? What is the energy of the recoil nucleus?

(b) Find the energy of the beta-ray electron emitted when the nucleus has no recoil.

9. The free neutron decays into a proton, electron, and neutrino. Find the maximum energy of the electron emitted by the decay of a neutron at rest.

10. (a) Calculate the energy released in the fusion of H^2 to form He^4.

(b) Estimate the minimum kinetic energy (in electron volts) of the deuterons required for fusion to take place. (Assume that fusion occurs when the deuterons come within a nuclear radius of one another.)

11. (a) Write the equation of beta-decay of H^3.

(b) Calculate the maximum kinetic energy of the beta-ray.

12. Show that the electrostatic energy of a nucleus of He_2^4 is about +30 Mev compared with the nuclear binding energy of about −30 Mev. How large is the binding energy due to the attractive nuclear force?

13. Explain qualitatively the relative abundances of the uranium isotopes.

14. (a) Why must at least two photons result from the annihilation of a free electron-positron pair?

(b) Calculate the energy of the resulting photons if the annihilating pair was at rest.

(c) By how much is the annihilation photon energy changed, if it is recognized that the annihilation occurs from the ground state of positronium, an "atom" consisting of the positron and electron? [*Hint:* the Bohr theory can be used.]

15. In the process of exchanging π-mesons [Eqs. (32–39) and (32–40)], a π-meson must be created ($\Delta E = m_\pi c^2$) and destroyed periodically. The time for the π-meson to be exchanged is at least $\Delta t = R/c$, where R is the separation of the interacting nucleons. The uncertainty principle permits uncertainty in energy ΔE (and thus the existence of the π-meson) for a time Δt. Show that the predicted mass of the π-meson is therefore about 250 m_e if R is about 10^{-14} meter.

16. Find the kinetic energy of a μ-meson (mass = 208 m_e) resulting from the decay at rest of a π-meson (mass = 273 m_e).

17. Find the energy of the gamma-rays resulting from the decay of a π^0-meson of low kinetic energy (mass = 264 m_e).

18. Prove that the velocity vectors of three π-mesons resulting from the decay of a tau-meson at rest must lie in the same plane.

Appendix

Trigonometry

1. *Definitions and fundamental identities.*

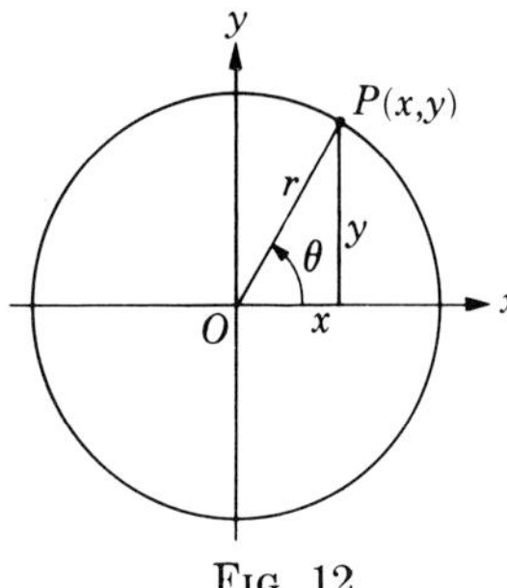

Fig. 12

$$\sin\theta = \frac{y}{r} = \frac{1}{\csc\theta}.$$

$$\cos\theta = \frac{x}{r} = \frac{1}{\sec\theta}.$$

$$\tan\theta = \frac{y}{x} = \frac{1}{\cot\theta}.$$

$$\sin(-\theta) = -\sin\theta, \quad \cos(-\theta) = \cos\theta.$$

$$\sin^2\theta + \cos^2\theta = 1.$$

$$\sin 2\theta = 2\sin\theta\cos\theta, \quad \cos 2\theta = \cos^2\theta - \sin^2\theta.$$

$$\sin(\alpha+\beta) = \sin\alpha\cos\beta + \cos\alpha\sin\beta.$$

$$\cos(\alpha+\beta) = \cos\alpha\cos\beta - \sin\alpha\sin\beta.$$

2. *Angles and sides of triangle.*

Law of cosines: $a^2 = b^2 + c^2 - 2bc\cos A$.

Law of sines: $\dfrac{\sin A}{a} = \dfrac{\sin B}{b} = \dfrac{\sin C}{c}$.

Area $= \frac{1}{2}bc\sin A = \frac{1}{2}ac\sin B = \frac{1}{2}ab\sin C$.

Greek Alphabet

Α	α	Alpha	Ν	ν	Nu
Β	β	Beta	Ξ	ξ	Xi
Γ	γ	Gamma	Ο	o	Omicron
Δ	δ	Delta	Π	π	Pi
Ε	ϵ	Epsilon	Ρ	ρ	Rho
Ζ	ζ	Zeta	Σ	σ	Sigma
Η	η	Eta	Τ	τ	Tau
Θ	θ	Theta	Υ	υ	Upsilon
Ι	ι	Iota	Φ	ϕ	Phi
Κ	κ	Kappa	Χ	χ	Chi
Λ	λ	Lambda	Ψ	ψ	Psi
Μ	μ	Mu	Ω	ω	Omega

PERIODIC TABLE OF THE ELEMENTS

Atomic weights are based on the most recent values adopted by the International Union of Chemistry. (For artificially produced elements, the approximate atomic weight of the most stable isotope is given in brackets.)

Period	Series	I	II	III	IV	V	VI	VII	VIII			O
1	1	1 H 1.0080										2 He 4.003
2	2	3 Li 6.940	4 Be 9.013	5 B 10.82	6 C 12.011	7 N 14.008	8 O 16.0000	9 F 19.00				10 Ne 20.183
3	3	11 Na 22.991	12 Mg 24.32	13 Al 26.98	14 Si 28.09	15 P 30.975	16 S 32.066	17 Cl 35.457				18 A 39.944
4	4	19 K 39.100	20 Ca 40.08	21 Sc 44.96	22 Ti 47.90	23 V 50.95	24 Cr 52.01	25 Mn 54.94	26 Fe 55.85	27 Co 58.94	28 Ni 58.71	
4	5	29 Cu 63.54	30 Zn 65.38	31 Ga 69.72	32 Ge 72.60	33 As 74.91	34 Se 78.96	35 Br 79.916				36 Kr 83.80
5	6	37 Rb 85.48	38 Sr 87.63	39 Y 88.92	40 Zr 91.22	41 Nb 92.91	42 Mo 95.95	43 Tc [99]	44 Ru 101.1	45 Rh 102.91	46 Pd 106.4	
5	7	47 Ag 107.880	48 Cd 112.41	49 In 114.82	50 Sn 118.70	51 Sb 121.76	52 Te 127.61	53 I 126.91				54 Xe 131.30
6	8	55 Cs 132.91	56 Ba 137.36	57–71 Lanthanide series*	72 Hf 178.50	73 Ta 180.95	74 W 183.86	75 Re 186.22	76 Os 190.2	77 Ir 192.2	78 Pt 195.09	
6	9	79 Au 197.0	80 Hg 200.61	81 Tl 204.39	82 Pb 207.21	83 Bi 209.00	84 Po 210	85 At [210]				86 Rn 222
7	10	87 Fr [223]	88 Ra 226.05	89– Actinide series**								

*Lanthanide series:	57 La 138.92	58 Ce 140.13	59 Pr 140.92	60 Nd 144.27	61 Pm [147]	62 Sm 150.35	63 Eu 152.0	64 Gd 157.26	65 Tb 158.93	66 Dy 162.51	67 Ho 164.94	68 Er 167.27	69 Tm 168.94	70 Yb 173.04	71 Lu 174.99
**Actinide series:	89 Ac 227	90 Th 232.05	91 Pa 231	92 U 238.07	93 Np [237]	94 Pu [242]	95 Am [243]	96 Cm [245]	97 Bk [249]	98 Cf [249]	99 E [253]	100 Fm [255]	101 Md [256]	102 No	103

NATURAL TRIGONOMETRIC FUNCTIONS

Angle					Angle				
Degree	Radian	Sine	Cosine	Tangent	Degree	Radian	Sine	Cosine	Tangent
0°	.000	0.000	1.000	0.000					
1°	.017	.018	1.000	.018	46°	0.803	0.719	0.695	1.036
2°	.035	.035	0.999	.035	47°	.820	.731	.682	1.072
3°	.052	.052	.999	.052	48°	.838	.743	.669	1.111
4°	.070	.070	.998	.070	49°	.855	.755	.656	1.150
5°	.087	.087	.996	.088	50°	.873	.766	.643	1.192
6°	.105	.105	.995	.105	51°	.890	.777	.629	1.235
7°	.122	.122	.993	.123	52°	.908	.788	.616	1.280
8°	.140	.139	.990	.141	53°	.925	.799	.602	1.327
9°	.157	.156	.988	.158	54°	.942	.809	.588	1.376
10°	.175	.174	.985	.176	55°	.960	.819	.574	1.428
11°	.192	.191	.982	.194	56°	.977	.829	.559	1.483
12°	.209	.208	.978	.213	57°	.995	.839	.545	1.540
13°	.227	.225	.974	.231	58°	1.012	.848	.530	1.600
14°	.244	.242	.970	.249	59°	1.030	.857	.515	1.664
15°	.262	.259	.966	.268	60°	1.047	.866	.500	1.732
16°	.279	.276	.961	.287	61°	1.065	.875	.485	1.804
17°	.297	.292	.956	.306	62°	1.082	.883	.470	1.881
18°	.314	.309	.951	.325	63°	1.100	.891	.454	1.963
19°	.332	.326	.946	.344	64°	1.117	.899	.438	2.050
20°	.349	.342	.940	.364	65°	1.134	.906	.423	2.145
21°	.367	.358	.934	.384	66°	1.152	.914	.407	2.246
22°	.384	.375	.927	.404	67°	1.169	.921	.391	2.356
23°	.401	.391	.921	.425	68°	1.187	.927	.375	2.475
24°	.419	.407	.914	.445	69°	1.204	.934	.358	2.605
25°	.436	.423	.906	.466	70°	1.222	.940	.342	2.747
26°	.454	.438	.899	.488	71°	1.239	.946	.326	2.904
27°	.471	.454	.891	.510	72°	1.257	.951	.309	3.078
28°	.489	.470	.883	.532	73°	1.274	.956	.292	3.271
29°	.506	.485	.875	.554	74°	1.292	.961	.276	3.487
30°	.524	.500	.866	.577	75°	1.309	.966	.259	3.732
31°	.541	.515	.857	.601	76°	1.326	.970	.242	4.011
32°	.559	.530	.848	.625	77°	1.344	.974	.225	4.331
33°	.576	.545	.839	.649	78°	1.361	.978	.208	4.705
34°	.593	.559	.829	.675	79°	1.379	.982	.191	5.145
35°	.611	.574	.819	.700	80°	1.396	.985	.174	5.671
36°	.628	.588	.809	.727	81°	1.414	.988	.156	6.314
37°	.646	.602	.799	.754	82°	1.431	.990	.139	7.115
38°	.663	.616	.788	.781	83°	1.449	.993	.122	8.144
39°	.681	.629	.777	.810	84°	1.466	.995	.105	9.514
40°	.698	.643	.766	.839	85°	1.484	.996	.087	11.43
41°	.716	.658	.755	.869	86°	1.501	.998	.070	14.30
42°	.733	.669	.743	.900	87°	1.518	.999	.052	19.08
43°	.751	.682	.731	.933	88°	1.536	.999	.035	28.64
44°	.768	.695	.719	.966	89°	1.553	1.000	.018	57.29
45°	.785	.707	.707	1.000	90°	1.571	1.000	.000	∞

CONVERSION FACTORS

(See Chapter 1, page 5, for method of conversion)

LENGTH:

1 m = 100 cm = 1000 mm
1 km = 1000 m = 0.6214 mile
1 m = 39.37 in.; 1 cm = 0.3937 in.
1 ft = 30.48 cm; 1 in. = 2.540 cm
1 mi = 5,280 ft = 1.609 km
1 A = 10^{-8} cm; 1μ (micron) = 10^{-4} cm

AREA:

1 cm^2 = 0.155 $in.^2$; 1 m^2 = 10^4 cm^2 = 10.76 ft^2
1 $in.^2$ = 6.452 cm^2; 1 ft^2 = 144 $in.^2$ = 0.0929 m^2

VOLUME:

1 liter = 1000 cm^2 = 10^{-3} m^3 = 0.0351 ft^3 = 61 $in.^3$
1 ft^3 = 0.0283 m^3 = 28.32 liters; 1 $in.^3$ = 16.39 cm^3 = 7.5 gal

VELOCITY:

1 cm/sec = 0.03281 ft/sec; 1 ft/sec = 30.48 cm/sec
1 mile/min = 60 mi/hr = 88 ft/sec

ACCELERATION:

1 cm/sec^2 = 0.03281 ft/sec^2 = 0.01 m/sec^2
30.48 cm/sec^2 = 1 ft/sec^2 = 0.3048 m/sec^2
100 cm/sec^2 = 3.281 ft/sec^2 = 1 m/sec^2

FORCE:

1 dyne = 2.247×10^{-6} lb = 10^{-5} newton
1.383×10^4 dynes = 0.0311 lb = 0.1383 newton
4.45×10^5 dynes = 1 lb = 4.45 newtons
10^5 dynes = 0.2247 lb = 1 newton

MASS:

1 gm = 6.85×10^{-5} slug = 10^{-3} kgm
453.6 gm = 0.0311 slug = 0.4536 kgm
1.459×10^4 gm = 1 slug = 14.59 kgm
10^3 gm = 0.0685 slug = 1 kgm

PRESSURE:

1 atm = 14.7 $lb/in.^2$ = 1.013×10^6 $dynes/cm^2$

ENERGY:

1 joule = 10^7 ergs = 0.239 cal; 1 cal = 4.18 joule
1 ev = 10^{-6} Mev = 1.60×10^{-12} erg = 1.07×10^{-9} amu
1 amu = 1.66×10^{-24} gm = 1.49×10^{-3} erg = 931 Mev

FUNDAMENTAL CONSTANTS

Largely based on values in the *American Institute of Physics Handbook* (1957). The probable error for each value has been omitted here; it should properly be considered part of the datum.

Name of Quantity	Symbol	Value
Velocity of light in vacuum	c	2.9979×10^8 m/sec
Charge of electron	q_e	-1.602×10^{-19} coul = -4.803×10^{-10} statcoul
Rest mass of electron	m_e	9.108×10^{-31} kgm
Ratio of charge to mass of electron	q_e/m_e	1.759×10^{11} coul/kgm = 5.273×10^7 statcoul/gm
Planck's constant	h	6.625×10^{-34} j·sec
Boltzmann's constant	k	1.380×10^{-23} j/°K
Avogadro's number (chemical scale)	N_0	6.023×10^{23} molecules/mole
Universal gas constant (chemical scale)	R	8.314 j/mole·°K
Mechanical equivalent of heat	J	4.185×10^3 j/kcal
Standard atmospheric pressure	1 atm	1.013×10^5 new/m^2
Volume of ideal gas at 0°C and 1 atm (chemical scale)		22.415 liter/mole
Absolute zero of temperature	0°K	−273.16°C
Acceleration due to gravity (sea level, at equator)		9.78049 m/sec^2
Universal gravitational constant	G	6.673×10^{-11} new·m^2/kgm^2
Mass of earth	m_E	5.975×10^{24} kgm
Mean radius of earth		6.371×10^6 m = 3959 mi
Equatorial radius of earth		6.378×10^6 m = 3963 mi
Mean distance from earth to sun	1 AU	1.49×10^{11} m = 9.29×10^7 mi
Eccentricity of earth's orbit		0.0167
Mean distance from earth to moon		3.84×10^8 m $\doteq$ 60 earth radii
Diameter of sun		1.39×10^9 m = 8.64×10^5 mi
Mass of sun	m_S	1.99×10^{30} kgm = 333,000 × mass of earth
Coulomb's law constant	C	8.98×10^9 new·m^2/coul^2
Faraday's constant (1 faraday)	F	96,500 coul/mole
Mass of neutral hydrogen atom	m_{H^1}	1.008142 amu
Mass of proton	m_p	1.007593 amu
Mass of neutron	m_n	1.008982 amu
Mass of electron	m_e	5.488×10^{-4} amu
Ratio of mass of proton to mass of electron	m_p/m_e	1836.12
Rydberg constant for nucleus of infinite mass	R_∞	109,737 cm^{-1}
Rydberg constant for hydrogen	R_H	109,678 cm^{-1}
Wien displacement law constant		0.2898 cm·°K

Numerical constants: $\pi = 3.142$; $e = 2.718$; $\sqrt{2} = 1.414$; $\sqrt{3} = 1.732$

COMMON LOGARITHMS

N	0	1	2	3	4	5	6	7	8	9
0	....	0000	3010	4771	6021	6990	7782	8451	9031	9542
1	0000	0414	0792	1139	1461	1761	2041	2304	2553	2788
2	3010	3222	3424	3617	3802	3979	4150	4314	4472	4624
3	4771	4914	5051	5185	5315	5441	5563	5682	5798	5911
4	6021	6128	6232	6335	6435	6532	6628	6721	6812	6902
5	6990	7076	7160	7243	7324	7404	7482	7559	7634	7709
6	7782	7853	7924	7993	8062	8129	8195	8261	8325	8388
7	8451	8513	8573	8633	8692	8751	8808	8865	8921	8976
8	9031	9085	9138	9191	9243	9294	9345	9395	9445	9494
9	9542	9590	9638	9685	9731	9777	9823	9868	9912	9956
10	0000	0043	0086	0128	0170	0212	0253	0294	0334	0374
11	0414	0453	0492	0531	0569	0607	0645	0682	0719	0755
12	0792	0828	0864	0899	0934	0969	1004	1038	1072	1106
13	1139	1173	1206	1239	1271	1303	1335	1367	1399	1430
14	1461	1492	1523	1553	1584	1614	1644	1673	1703	1732
15	1761	1790	1818	1847	1875	1903	1931	1959	1987	2014
16	2041	2068	2095	2122	2148	2175	2201	2227	2253	2279
17	2304	2330	2355	2380	2405	2430	2455	2480	2504	2529
18	2553	2577	2601	2625	2648	2672	2695	2718	2742	2765
19	2788	2810	2833	2856	2878	2900	2923	2945	2967	2989
20	3010	3032	3054	3075	3096	3118	3139	3160	3181	3201
21	3222	3243	3263	3284	3304	3324	3345	3365	3385	3404
22	3424	3444	3464	3483	3502	3522	3541	3560	3579	3598
23	3617	3636	3655	3674	3692	3711	3729	3747	3766	3784
24	3802	3820	3838	3856	3874	3892	3909	3927	3945	3962
25	3979	3997	4014	4031	4048	4065	4082	4099	4116	4133
26	4150	4166	4183	4200	4216	4232	4249	4265	4281	4298
27	4314	4330	4346	4362	4378	4393	4409	4425	4440	4456
28	4472	4487	4502	4518	4533	4548	4564	4579	4594	4609
29	4624	4639	4654	4669	4683	4698	4713	4728	4742	4757
30	4771	4786	4800	4814	4829	4843	4857	4871	4886	4900
31	4914	4928	4942	4955	4969	4983	4997	5011	5024	5038
32	5051	5065	5079	5092	5105	5119	5132	5145	5159	5172
33	5185	5198	5211	5224	5237	5250	5263	5276	5289	5302
34	5315	5328	5340	5353	5366	5378	5391	5403	5416	5428
35	5441	5453	5465	5478	5490	5502	5514	5527	5539	5551
36	5563	5575	5587	5599	5611	5623	5635	5647	5658	5670
37	5682	5694	5705	5717	5729	5740	5752	5763	5775	5786
38	5798	5809	5821	5832	5843	5855	5866	5877	5888	5899
39	5911	5922	5933	5944	5955	5966	5977	5988	5999	6010
40	6021	6031	6042	6053	6064	6075	6085	6096	6107	6117
41	6128	6138	6149	6160	6170	6180	6191	6201	6212	6222
42	6232	6243	6253	6263	6274	6284	6294	6304	6314	6325
43	6335	6345	6355	6365	6375	6385	6395	6405	6415	6425
44	6435	6444	6454	6464	6474	6484	6493	6503	6513	6522
45	6532	6542	6551	6561	6571	6580	6590	6599	6609	6618
46	6628	6637	6646	6656	6665	6675	6684	6693	6702	6712
47	6721	6730	6739	6749	6758	6767	6776	6785	6794	6803
48	6812	6821	6830	6839	6848	6857	6866	6875	6884	6893
49	6902	6911	6920	6928	6937	6946	6955	6964	6972	6981
50	6990	6998	7007	7016	7024	7033	7042	7050	7059	7067
N	0	1	2	3	4	5	6	7	8	9

COMMON LOGARITHMS

N	0	1	2	3	4	5	6	7	8	9
50	6990	6998	7007	7016	7024	7033	7042	7050	7059	7067
51	7076	7084	7093	7101	7110	7118	7126	7135	7143	7152
52	7160	7168	7177	7185	7193	7202	7210	7218	7226	7235
53	7243	7251	7259	7267	7275	7284	7292	7300	7308	7316
54	7324	7332	7340	7348	7356	7364	7372	7380	7388	7396
55	7404	7412	7419	7427	7435	7443	7451	7459	7466	7474
56	7482	7490	7497	7505	7513	7520	7528	7536	7543	7551
57	7559	7566	7574	7582	7589	7597	7604	7612	7619	7627
58	7634	7642	7649	7657	7664	7672	7679	7686	7694	7701
59	7709	7716	7723	7731	7738	7745	7752	7760	7767	7774
60	7782	7789	7796	7803	7810	7818	7825	7832	7839	7846
61	7853	7860	7868	7875	7882	7889	7896	7903	7910	7917
62	7924	7931	7938	7945	7952	7959	7966	7973	7980	7987
63	7993	8000	8007	8014	8021	8028	8035	8041	8048	8055
64	8062	8069	8075	8082	8089	8096	8102	8109	8116	8122
65	8129	8136	8142	8149	8156	8162	8169	8176	8182	8189
66	8195	8202	8209	8215	8222	8228	8235	8241	8248	8254
67	8261	8267	8274	8280	8287	8293	8299	8306	8312	8319
68	8325	8331	8338	8344	8351	8357	8363	8370	8376	8382
69	8388	8395	8401	8407	8414	8420	8426	8432	8439	8445
70	8451	8457	8463	8470	8476	8482	8488	8494	8500	8506
71	8513	8519	8525	8531	8537	8543	8549	8555	8561	8567
72	8573	8579	8585	8591	8597	8603	8609	8615	8621	8627
73	8633	8639	8645	8651	8657	8663	8669	8675	8681	8686
74	8692	8698	8704	8710	8716	8722	8727	8733	8739	8745
75	8751	8756	8762	8768	8774	8779	8785	8791	8797	8802
76	8808	8814	8820	8825	8831	8837	8842	8848	8854	8859
77	8865	8871	8876	8882	8887	8893	8899	8904	8910	8915
78	8921	8927	8932	8938	8943	8949	8954	8960	8965	8971
79	8976	8982	8987	8993	8998	9004	9009	9015	9020	9025
80	9031	9036	9042	9047	9053	9058	9063	9069	9074	9079
81	9085	9090	9096	9101	9106	9112	9117	9122	9128	9133
82	9138	9143	9149	9154	9159	9165	9170	9175	9180	9186
83	9191	9196	9201	9206	9212	9217	9222	9227	9232	9238
84	9243	9248	9253	9258	9263	9269	9274	9279	9284	9289
85	9294	9299	9304	9309	9315	9320	9325	9330	9335	9340
86	9345	9350	9355	9360	9365	9370	9375	9380	9385	9390
87	9395	9400	9405	9410	9415	9420	9425	9430	9435	9440
88	9445	9450	9455	9460	9465	9469	9474	9479	9484	9489
89	9494	9499	9504	9509	9513	9518	9523	9528	9533	9538
90	9542	9547	9552	9557	9562	9566	9571	9576	9581	9586
91	9590	9595	9600	9605	9609	9614	9619	9624	9628	9633
92	9638	9643	9647	9652	9657	9661	9666	9671	9675	9680
93	9685	8689	9694	9699	9703	9708	9713	9717	9722	9727
94	9731	9736	9741	9745	9750	9754	9759	9763	9768	9773
95	9777	9782	9786	9791	9795	9800	9805	9809	9814	9818
96	9823	9827	9832	9836	9841	9845	9850	9854	9859	9863
97	9868	9872	9877	9881	9886	9890	9894	9899	9903	9908
98	9912	9917	9921	9926	9930	9934	9939	9943	9948	9952
99	9956	9961	9965	9969	9974	9978	9983	9987	9991	9996
100	0000	0004	0009	0013	0017	0022	0026	0030	0035	0039
N	0	1	2	3	4	5	6	7	8	9

ISOTOPES

Isotopes which are naturally radioactive are indicated by (NR). Only those most commonly found are listed.

The data for this table were obtained from the *Trilinear Chart of Nuclides* by William H. Sullivan. (Courtesy of Oak Ridge National Laboratory.)

At. no. Z	Element	Symbol	Mass no., A	Isotopic mass, amu (phys. scale)	Relative abundance, %	No. of isotopes	
						Stable	Radio-active
0	Neutron	n	1	1.008986			1
1	Hydrogen					2	1
		H	1	1.008145	99.985		
		D	2	2.014740	0.015		
		T	3 (NR)	3.017005	...		
2	Helium	He				2	2
			3	3.016986	1.3×10^{-4}		
			4	4.003874	99.9999		
3	Lithium	Li				2	4
			6	6.017034	7.5		
			7	7.018232	92.5		
4	Beryllium	Be				1	5
			9	9.015046	100		
5	Boron	B				2	4
			10	10.016119	18.7		
			11	11.012795	81.3		
6	Carbon	C				2	4
			12	12.003803	98.89		
			13	13.007478	1.11		
7	Nitrogen	N				2	4
			14	14.007520	99.635		
			15	15.004862	0.365		
8	Oxygen	O				3	3
			16	16.000000	99.759		
			17	17.004534	0.037		
			18	18.004855	0.204		
9	Fluorine	F				1	4
			19	19.004448	100		

At. no. Z	Element	Symbol	Mass no., A	Isotopic mass, amu (phys. scale)	Relative abundance, %	No. of isotopes	
						Stable	Radio-active
10	Neon	Ne				3	4
			20	19.998769	90.92		
			21	21.000499	0.257		
			22	21.998354	8.82		
11	Sodium	Na				1	6
			23	22.997053	100		
12	Magnesium	Mg				3	3
			24	23.992640	78.60		
			25	24.993752	10.11		
			26	25.990854	11.29		
13	Aluminum	Al				1	6
			27	26.990081	100		
14	Silicon	Si				3	4
			28	27.985775	92.18		
			29	28.98566	4.71		
			30	29.983252	3.12		
15	Phosphorus	P				1	6
			31	30.98356	100		
16	Sulfur	S				4	4
			32	31.98220	95.018		
			33	32.98189	0.750		
			34	33.97864	4.215		
			36	35.97844	0.017		
17	Chlorine	Cl				2	7
			35	34.97990	75.53		
			37	36.97754	24.47		
18	Argon	Ar				3	5
			36	35.97892	0.34		
			38	37.97479	0.06		
			40	39.97505	99.60		
19	Potassium	K				2	7
			39	38.97604	93.08		
			40 (NR)	39.97665	0.0119		
			41	40.97476	6.91		
20	Calcium	Ca				5	7
			40	39.97523	96.96		
			42	41.97189	0.64		
			43	42.97235	0.145		
			44	43.96934	2.07		
			46	. . .	0.0033		
			48 (NR)	47.9677	0.185		

Answers to Odd-Numbered Exercises

Chapter 1

1–9. (a) $0.0112\ \text{m}^3 \pm 0.0002\ \text{m}^3$
(b) $0.66\ \text{m}^2 \pm 0.01\ \text{m}^2$

Chapter 2

2–3. 1/1.6 rad; 36°
2–11. 5, 83° above OX; 5, 23° below OX
2–17. $6\sqrt{2(1 \pm \sqrt{2})}$ at $22\frac{1}{2}°$ from $-OX$

Chapter 3

3–7. $50\sqrt{5}$ m, 27° E of S
$50\sqrt{5}$ m, 27° W of N; Unchanged
3–11. 0.4 hr; 0.5 hr; with stream; ∞
3–13. (a) 27 km/hr (b) 33 km/hr
3–15. 10^{-4} rad
3–17. (a) Direction (b) No (c) No
(d) Not necessarily

Chapter 4

4–3. $m_A = \frac{8}{7}$ kg; $m_B = \frac{40}{21}$ kg
4–7. (a) 0.3 kg-m/sec (b) 0.45 kg-m/sec
4–9. 1.25 km/hr
4–11. (a) $\frac{0.5}{3}\frac{\text{m}}{\text{sec}}$ (b) $\frac{0.5}{3}\frac{\text{m}}{\text{sec}}$
(c) 0.5 m/sec
(d) If $v \cos\theta$ relative to earth is zero.
4–13. $v_C = v_0$, $v_B = \sqrt{2}v_0$
4–17. $\frac{20}{7}$ n
4–19. 6×10^4 n, 37° S of E
4–25. (a) $-\mathbf{A}$ (b) $\mathbf{A} \sin 37°$, $\mathbf{A} \cos 37°$
4–29. (a) 2.1 m (kg-m)/sec
(b) $-2.1\ m$(kg-m)/sec (c) No
(d) $\frac{1}{80}\Delta v$ (e) 5000 km

Chapter 5

5–7. 150 n/m
5–9. (a) $2\ \text{m/sec}^2$ (b) 6 n
5–13. (a) gR^2/G (b) $g^2R^2/4G$
(c) Gravitational
5–15. $\sqrt{3}\,\dfrac{Gm^2}{l^2}$
5–21. $W \tan\theta$; $W/\sqrt{3}$; $\sqrt{3}W$; ∞
5–25. (a) mg (b) mg
5–29. (a) $mg\,\dfrac{\sin\theta + \mu\cos\theta}{\cos\theta - \mu\sin\theta}$
(b) $mg\,\dfrac{\sin\theta - \mu\cos\theta}{\cos\theta + \mu\sin\theta}$
(c) Negative if $\mu\cos\theta > \sin\theta$
5–31. (a) 120 n in vertical rope, 320 n in 30° rope, 400 n on strut
(b) 120 n on ground by rope plus strut
5–35. 16 kg/m

Chapter 6

6–3. (a) 11.2, 6, 3, 1.5, 0.7, 0.4 m/sec
(b) 0.15, 0.075, 0.037, etc., m/sec^2
6–11. 14 m/sec
6–13. 20 m
6–19. $v_r = 24$ m/sec, $v_\theta = 20.9$ m/sec, $\theta = 26\frac{1}{2}°$
6–21. (a) at 120,000 m
(b) $v_x = 900$ m/sec, $v_y = 0$
6–23. $v_x = 2(1 - t)$, $v_y = t\left(1 - \dfrac{t}{2}\right)$
6–25. 200 sec, 350 km
6–29. (a) $2\sqrt{5}$ rad/sec (b) $10\sqrt{5}$ m/sec

6–31. 80 min

6–33. 7×10^{-5} rad/sec due to diurnal rotation toward north

Chapter 7

7–1. (a) bt (b) $bt - p_0$

7–3. $\sqrt{5}/3$ m/sec^2, $\tan^{-1} 0.5$; $(\sqrt{5}/3)t$ m/sec, $\tan^{-1} 0.5$

7–5. (a) (b) (c) $\frac{50}{3}$ n (d) No

7–7. 100 m to right and 12.5 m up

7–9. 16 n, 2 m/sec^2, 1 m/sec^2

7–11. 11.1 n, 27.8 n. Because $v \neq$ constant

7–15. (a) 10 tan 30° m/sec^2, 20 cos 30° n (b) 27°, 22 n (c) Either way

7–17. $\frac{2}{3}g$, down, moving either way

7–19. No; resultant

7–21. Mass of string negligible

7–23. (a) g (b) $g/100$ m (c) $g - 100x$ (d) Not by direct integration (e) g, $(2g/k)^{1/3}$, $g - (k/2)x^3$

7–25. (a) $0 < t < 2, a_A = 0, a_B = 0$
$2 < t < 2\sqrt{3}, a_A = \frac{5}{2}t^2 - g, a_B = 0$
$t > 2\sqrt{3}, a_A = \frac{5}{2}t^2 - g,$
$a_B = \frac{5}{6}t^2 - g$
(b) $\frac{5}{4}t^2 - g$

7–27. (a) $k = 4$ kg/m (b) 707 m/sec

7–31. (a) $v_x =$ constant

7–37. $\sqrt{10}/2\pi$ sec^{-1}, 60°

7–43. 15 n, 12 n

7–45. (a) $2\pi\sqrt{r/g}$ (b) $2\,mg$ (c) $\sqrt{2}\,mg$ (d) 10 n by earth, 40 n by water, 100 n by man

7–47. 5000 km

7–49. $\tau^2 = \dfrac{4\sqrt{3}\,\pi^2}{mG}\,r^3$

7–51. 6.6 R_e; no

7–55. (a) 56.5 m/sec^2 (b) 4500π (c) 30 m/sec

7–59. (a) 1625 n (b) 1410 n

Chapter 8

8–7. $D = A\cos\theta_0$, $E = A\sin\theta_0$

8–9. (a) $1/(20\pi)$ sec^{-1}, 20π sec, 14 m
(b) $x = 12.3$ m at $t = 0$
(c) 1.4 m/sec, 0.14 m/sec^2
(d) 7.6 m, —11.8 m/sec, —0.076 m/sec^2

8–11. $\dfrac{1}{2\pi}\sqrt{g/0.3}$

8–13. $2\pi\sqrt{ml/(4T)}$

8–15. $v = \dfrac{m}{M+m}\,v_b\cos\left(\sqrt{\dfrac{k}{M+m}}\,t\right)$

8–19. $\dfrac{\tau_1}{\tau_2} = \dfrac{R_1}{R_2}$;

$$\frac{\Delta\tau}{\tau} = \frac{\Delta R}{R} = \frac{1}{6.4 \times 10^6} = 1.56 \times 10^{-5}\%$$

8–21. (a) 0.55 sec (b) 0.97 sec

8–23.

(c) $v_x = \dfrac{8D}{\pi^2}\,2\pi f\,(\cos 2\pi ft - \frac{1}{3}\cos 6\pi ft + \cdots)$

(d) $a_x = \dfrac{8D}{\pi^2}\,(4\pi f)^2(-\sin 2\pi ft + \sin 6\pi ft - \cdots)$

8–25. (a) $v_0 = \dfrac{1}{2\pi}\sqrt{g/0.3} = 0.91$ m/sec

(b) $\frac{5}{3}$ cm, $\frac{20}{3}$ cm (c) $\frac{1}{3}v_0$, $\frac{1}{5}v_0$, ...

8–27. $F = -mg\sin\gamma \simeq -mg\,\dfrac{dy}{dx'}$,

$$-\frac{dy}{dx'} \simeq \frac{-k}{mg}\,x'$$

8–29. (a) 0.37 sec (b) 0.54 sec

Chapter 9

9–1. (a) 10^5 n-sec (b) 170 n

9–3. (a) 6.9×10^7 n-sec (b) 6.9×10^4 m/sec

9–5. (a) $50\sqrt{3}\mathbf{j}$ (b) $\sqrt{3}/11$ (c) $\sqrt{3}/21$

9–7. None

9–9. (a) $-6\,\mathbf{j}$ (b) $1.5\,\mathbf{j}$ (c) $-4.5\,\mathbf{j}$ (d) $-4.5\,\mathbf{j}$

9–11. $-\dfrac{k}{2}(x_2^2 - x_1^2) + kx_0(x_2 - x_1)$

9–15. $\dfrac{k}{4}(x_2^4 - x_1^4)$

9–17. (a) $mgr_0^2\left(\dfrac{1}{r_0} - \dfrac{1}{r}\right)$

9–21. (a) 87 j (b) 107 j (c) 72 j
9–23. 0.14 m/sec
9–25. (a) 1.7 m/sec, $\sqrt{gl}$

(b) 1.8 m/sec, $\frac{\pi}{3}\sqrt{gl}$

9–27. (a) mgd by gravity, $-mgd/4$ by spring
(b) $(4\ mg/k)^{1/3}$ or $4^{1/3}d$
9–33. 2.5 m (with $g = 9.8$ m/sec^2); 1.3 mg j
9–35. $\frac{5}{2}R$
9–37. $3g^2$ joules to heat and turbulence
9–39. $\sqrt{2gR_e} = 11{,}000$ m/sec

9–41. $W = Gmm_e \int_{R_e}^{R_0} \frac{1}{r^2}\,dr - \frac{Gmm_e}{80}\int_{R_e}^{R_0} \frac{dr}{(d-r)^2}$,

where $d = 3.6 \times 10^8$ m, and

$R_0 = d\Big/\left(1 + \frac{1}{\sqrt{80}}\right)$ is the point of change

9–43. $0.984\sqrt{2gR_e}$; yes
9–45. $6.6R_e$
9–47. (a) 0.47, 0.16 m/sec (b) 0.55, 0.18 m/sec
9–49. (a) $x_{\max}^2 - 2\,d\,\frac{m}{M}\,x_{\max} - 2\,dh\,\frac{m^2}{M(m+M)} = 0,$

$A = x_{\max} - \frac{m+M}{M}\,d,$

$\tau = 2\pi\sqrt{\frac{m+M}{Mg}\,d}$

(b) $x_{\max} = 2m\sqrt{2hd}\,/(m+M),$

$A = x_{\max},\ \tau = 2\pi\sqrt{d/g}$

9–57. (b) $\sqrt{3.2} \times 10^{10}$ cm/sec
9–59. 0, all
9–61. $4\,\frac{M}{m}\sqrt{gl}$
9–65. (a) 0 (b) +24 j (c) +144 j
(d) force in (a)
9–67. (a) $x = 0.5 \sin 2t,\ v = \cos 2t$
(b) (i) $x = 1/\sqrt{6}\,\sin 2\sqrt{\tfrac{2}{3}}\,t,$
$v = \tfrac{2}{3}\cos 2\sqrt{\tfrac{2}{3}}\,t$
(ii) $x = 0.5 \sin 2\sqrt{\tfrac{2}{3}}\,t,$
$v = \sqrt{\tfrac{2}{3}}\cos 2\sqrt{\tfrac{2}{3}}\,t$

Chapter 10

10–3. $3\frac{1}{2}$ days
10–5. $2\pi\sqrt{R/g}$
10–7. (b) at ∞
10–11. (a) $-GmM/R$
(b) $v^2 = GM\left(\frac{1}{R} - \frac{1}{\sqrt{R^2 + z^2}}\right)$
10–13. (a) $\frac{\pi}{9}$ rad/sec, 0.1π m/sec (b) $0.02\pi^2$ j
10–15. 22 cm, 53 cm
10–17. (a) No (b) Yes
10–19. (a) $mv_0\,d$; $\frac{1}{2}mv_0^2$
(b) $r_{\min}^2 - \frac{2Kqq'}{mv_0^2}\,r_{\min} - d^2 = 0$
10–21. $v_1 = \sqrt{G/(m_1R)} \times (m_1 + m + m\sqrt{2R_m/(R+R_m)})$
10–25. $4\frac{2}{3}$ days (neglecting motion of earth)
10–27. No; $\sum F$ is not a central force.

Chapter 11

11–1. $x = 1.2$ m, $y = 1$ m; no
11–3. The moon-earth system rotates about the center of mass of the sun-earth-moon system, located 455 km from the center of the sun.
The moon executes oscillatory motion about the moon-earth path of amplitude ~400,000 km.
The same for the earth but with amplitude 4880 km.
11–5. 1.43 m from original position of 2 kg
At point of original impact
11–7. Directly below his original position
$\frac{5}{3}$ m from above point
11–9. Initial velocity of system: $v_x = -3$ m/sec, $v_y = -3$ m/sec
Rotation with angular momentum 1540 kg-m^2/sec
11–11. $ma_L = ma,\ v = v_0 + a_Lt,$
$x = x_0 + v_0t + \frac{1}{2}a_Lt^2$

Chapter 13

13–1. (a) $x = \frac{v_0}{\sqrt{2}} t,\ y = \frac{v_0}{\sqrt{2}} t - \frac{1}{2}gt^2$

(if $x = y = 0$ at $t = 0$)

(b) $x = \left(\frac{v_0}{\sqrt{2}} - v\right) t,\ y = \frac{v_0}{\sqrt{2}} t - \frac{1}{2}gt^2$

(c) $y = x - \frac{g}{v_0^2} x^2$,

$$y = \frac{v_0}{v_0 - \sqrt{2}\,v} x - \frac{1}{2}g \frac{x^2}{[(v_0/\sqrt{2}) - v]^2}$$

13–3. 16.5 m/sec

13–5. (a) 1.67 sec (b) 2.4×10^5 m
(c) 1 sec

13–7. 1.15×10^{11} m

13–11. $\Delta t' = \gamma\, \Delta t$

13–13. 82.5 cm, 49°

13–15. (a) Noon + $\frac{2}{3} \times 10^{-8}$ sec
(b) Noon + 0.002 sec

13–21. $-0.105c$

13–23. $R = \frac{5}{3}R_0$, i.e., 1.74 m compared with 1.04 m

13–25. $\frac{v}{c} = 1 - 4.5 \times 10^{-10}$

13–29. Always c

13–31. (a, b) Dilation: 1.2×10^{-14} sec
Synchronization: 2.3×10^{-14} sec
(c) No

Chapter 14

14–5. $x = 2R/\pi,\ y = 0$

14–7. $x = a/3,\ y = b/3$ measured along legs from 90° vertex

14–9. (a) $y = \frac{\sqrt{3}}{4} L$ (b) $y = \frac{\sqrt{3}}{6} L$

14–13. $(\frac{2}{5})mR^2$

14–17. $a = \frac{(m_2 - m_1)g}{m_1 + m_2 + m_3/2}$

$$T_1 = \frac{2m_1m_2g + \frac{1}{2}m_1m_3g}{m_1 + m_2 + \frac{1}{2}m_3}$$

$$T_2 = \frac{2m_1m_2g + \frac{1}{2}m_2m_3g}{m_1 + m_2 + \frac{1}{2}m_3}$$

14–19. (a) $(\frac{9}{5})F/(mL)$
(b) $(9/5)F/(mL),\ a = F/(2m)$

14–21. $v = \sqrt{\frac{5}{3}gR}$

14–23. (a) $\sqrt{6gL}$ (b) $\frac{3}{4}g$ (c) No

14–25. (a) $\frac{4}{\pi} \frac{g \sin\theta}{R}$ (b) $\sqrt{\frac{8}{\pi} \frac{g}{R}}$

14–27. $\frac{2\,mg \sin\theta}{\pi\mu}$

14–29. $\omega_1 = \omega_0 \frac{m_1 R_1^2}{m_2 R_1 R_2 + m_1 R_1^2}$

$$\omega_2 = \omega_0 \frac{m_1 R_1^2}{m_1 R_1 R_2 + m_2 R_2^2}$$

14–31. (a) 2 kg-m^2/sec (b) If $\frac{6}{m^2 g} > 1$

14–33. 9.6×10^4 j, if object starts from rest

14–35. (a) $v_{CM} = v \frac{m}{m + M},\ \omega = \frac{v}{R} \frac{m}{(M + 3m)}$

(b) $v_{CM} = v \frac{m}{m + M}$,

$$\omega = \frac{v}{R} \frac{2m}{(2M + 3m)}$$

(c) E conservation:

$$\frac{1}{2}mv^2 = \frac{1}{2}mv_f^2 + \frac{1}{2}MV^2 + \frac{1}{2} \frac{MR^2}{2} \omega^2$$

Momentum conservation:

$$m\sqrt{v^2 + v_f^2} = MV$$

Angular momentum conservation:

$$mv \frac{R}{2} = mv_f \frac{\sqrt{3}}{2} R - \frac{MR^2}{2} \omega,$$

from which the final velocity v_f of the bullet, the final velocity V of the disk and its angular velocity ω can be found.

Chapter 15

15–1. 4.5×10^5 n/m^2

15–3. $\frac{1}{2}p_0$ at 6.15 km, $10^{-9}p_0$ at 182 km, $0.403p_0$ at 8 km, where p_0 corresponds to ~10-m depth of H_2O

15–5. $0.1 \dfrac{\text{kcal}}{\text{sec}}$, $2.32 \times 10^{-5} \dfrac{\text{kcal}}{\text{sec}}$, 2900°K

15–7. For $\epsilon = 0.25$, $A = 1.84$ cm^2

15–9. p_0V, decrease in temperature of gas

Chapter 16

16–1. 1.85 hr 16–3. 1720 j 16–5. 6400°C

16–7. 70.5 j, 36 j, 208°K; 53.5 j, 36 j, 17 j

16–9. 90%

16–11. Ratio is $-T_2/T_1$, therefore $-dT_2$ is more effective.

16–13. (a) $N = \dfrac{p_1V_1}{RT_1}$

(b) $T_B = T_1$, $T_C = \dfrac{V_1}{V_2} T_1$

(c) $T_a = T_1$; $T_b = \dfrac{T_1}{V_2} V$; $T_c = \dfrac{T_1}{p_1} p$

(d) $W_a = p_1V_1 \ln (V_2/V_1)$
$W_b = -p_1V_1(1 - V_1/V_2)$
$W_c = 0$

(e) $\Delta Q_a = p_1V_1 \ln (V_2/V_1)$ absorbed
$\Delta Q_c = \frac{3}{2}p_1V_1(1 - V_1/V_2)$ absorbed

(f) $\Delta Q_b = \frac{5}{2}p_1V_1(1 - V_1/V_2)$ emitted

(g) $\Delta U_a = 0$
$\Delta U_b = -\frac{3}{2}p_1V_1(1 - V_1/V_2)$
$\Delta U_c = \frac{3}{2}p_1V_1(1 - V_1/V_2)$

(h) $E = \dfrac{\ln (V_2/V_1) + (V_1/V_2) - 1}{\ln (V_2/V_1) - \frac{3}{2}(V_1/V_2) + \frac{3}{2}}$

Chapter 17

17–1. 430 m 17–3. 33,400 j

Chapter 18

18–1. 3.35×10^{22}; 30×10^{-24} cm^3; 3.1×10^{-8} cm

18–3. 2×10^{-5} cm

18–11. $f(v)$ has the units of $1/v$

18–13. 1/9000

18–15. 14,500°K

18–19. $\Delta\text{KE} \simeq 2v_p\sqrt{mkT}$, where v_p is the piston velocity and m is the mass of the gas atom. $f = Mg/(2\sqrt{mkT})$, where M is the piston mass.

18–21. $\dfrac{1}{2^3 \times 10^{-19}} = 10^{-9 \times 10^{-18}}$; 20 molecules

Chapter 19

19–3. 2.85×10^{26} n; 6.67×10^{-17} n

19–5. 1.56 n

19–9. $\dfrac{18x}{(x - 0.5)^2(x + 0.5)^2}$ n; $\dfrac{18}{x^3}$ n

Chapter 20

20–1. (a) 190×10^3 n/coul at 85° from a line through the charges
(b) 2.5 m from 5 μcoul charge on line through the charges

20–5. (a) $E_x = \dfrac{\lambda}{\pi\epsilon_0} \dfrac{d}{x^2 - d^2}$, $E_y = E_z = 0$

(b) $E_x = -\dfrac{\lambda}{\pi\epsilon_0} \dfrac{d}{y^2 + d^2}$, $E_y = E_z = 0$

(c) $E_x \simeq \dfrac{\lambda d}{\pi\epsilon_0} \dfrac{1}{x^2}$, $E_x \simeq -\dfrac{\lambda d}{\pi\epsilon_0}$

(e) $F = \dfrac{\lambda^2}{4\pi\epsilon_0 d}$

20–7. $\dfrac{1}{4\pi\epsilon_0}\left(\dfrac{q}{x^2} - \dfrac{2\lambda}{d - x}\right)$

20–9. $\dfrac{q^2}{2\pi\epsilon_0 V_0 d}$

20–17. $E_A = \dfrac{2}{\epsilon_0}$; $E_B = \dfrac{4}{\epsilon_0}$; $E_C = -\dfrac{2}{\epsilon_0}$

20–19. Inside $E = \dfrac{\rho_0 t}{\pi\epsilon_0} \cos \dfrac{\pi x}{t}$,

outside $E = \pm \dfrac{\rho_0 t}{\pi\epsilon_0}$

20–21. (a) $\pm \dfrac{\sigma}{2}$ (b) $\dfrac{\sigma}{2\epsilon_0}$ (c) $\dfrac{\sigma}{2\epsilon_0}$, $\pm \dfrac{\sigma}{2}$

20–23. $\dfrac{R_B^2\sigma}{\epsilon_0 r^2}$

20–25. $q_0\alpha e^{-\alpha r}$; q_0

20–27. (a) $\pm 4\epsilon_0$
(b) $E_1 = +2$; $E_2 = -4$; $E_3 = 0$, $E_4 = +4$, $E_5 = -2$

Chapter 21

21–1. 0

21–3. (a) $\dfrac{2q}{4\pi\epsilon_0 d}\left(\sqrt{2} - \dfrac{2}{\sqrt{5}}\right)$

(b) $\dfrac{4q}{4\pi\epsilon_0 d}\left(1 + \dfrac{1}{\sqrt{5}}\right)$

(c) $\dfrac{2\sqrt{2}\,q}{4\pi\epsilon_0 d}$; 0

21–5. (a) 0; $\dfrac{\lambda}{2\epsilon_0}$ (b) 0; $\dfrac{q}{4\pi\epsilon_0 R}$

21–7. Circle of $R = \dfrac{0.2}{3}$ m, center at $x = -\frac{1}{3}$ m from +5 charge

21–9. (a) 5.9×10^5 m/sec, 1.3×10^7 m/sec, $0.272c$
(b) Last case, if few percent accuracy required.

21–11. 9.6×10^{-12} j

21–15. (a) $\dfrac{-\sigma x}{\epsilon_0}$ (b) $\dfrac{-\sigma(a + x)}{\epsilon_0}$

21–21. $2\pi\epsilon_0/\ln(R_2/R_1)$

21–27. 2.6×10^3 j

21–29. (a) 0.77×10^{-9} coul; 0.23×10^{-9} coul
(b) 4.5×10^{-9} j; 3.5×10^{-9} j

21–31. (b) $\frac{1}{3}W_0$; $\frac{2}{3}W_0$

21–33. (a) $\dfrac{\rho}{3\epsilon_0}\left(\dfrac{R_2^3 - R_1^3}{r}\right)$ for $r > R_2$

$\dfrac{\rho}{3\epsilon_0}\left(\dfrac{3}{2}R_2^2 - \dfrac{r^2}{2} - \dfrac{R_1^3}{r}\right)$ for $R_1 < r < R_2$

$\dfrac{\rho}{2\epsilon_0}(R_2^2 - R_1^2)$ for $r < R_1$

(b) $W = \dfrac{2\pi\rho^2}{3\epsilon_0}\{\frac{2}{5}(R_1^5 + R_2^5) - R_1^3R_2^2\}$

21–37. (a) $\dfrac{\lambda^2}{4\pi\epsilon_0}\ln(R_2/R_1)$ (b) ∞
(c) Same

21–39. $v^2 = e^2/(4\pi\epsilon_0 mR)$

Chapter 22

22–1. 10^{-6} amp

22–3. 1.6×10^{-4} amp

22–5. $\Delta U = d\sqrt{2F/(\epsilon_0 A)}$

22–7. (b) $\dfrac{q}{q_0} = \dfrac{C}{C_2} + \left(1 - \dfrac{C}{C_2}\right)e^{-t/RC}$

$I = \dfrac{q_0}{RC_1}e^{-t/RC}$,

where $\dfrac{1}{C} = \dfrac{1}{C_1} + \dfrac{1}{C_2}$

22–9. (a) 5000 amp

(b) $q = \dfrac{1}{36\pi 10^7}e^{-18\pi 10^{11}t}$

$I = 5000e^{-18\pi 10^{11}t}$

22–11. (a) $J_0 = 55.5\dfrac{1}{r^2}$ (b) 222π amp
(c) $0.45/\pi$ ohm

22–13. 3 ohms

22–15. $I_{\text{bat}} = 12.3$ amp, $I_{\text{light}} = 18.9$ amp, $I_{\text{gen}} = 6.6$ amp, $V = 5.69$ volts for each

22–21. (a) $R = \dfrac{V}{I}\dfrac{1}{[1 - (V/IR_V)]}$

(b) $R = \dfrac{V}{I} - R_A$ (c) Fig. 34; Fig. 35

22–23. (a) 1.92 watts (b) 18 watts
(c) Generator 37.5 watts, battery 70 watts, light 107.5 watts

22–25. (a) 7 volts, 30 watts, 21 watts, 9 watts
(b) 13 volts, 30 j, 9 watts

22–27. (a) $\sim 7 \times 10^7$ m/sec (b) 9×10^{12} m^{-3}
(c) 1.4×10^{-6} coul/m^3

22–29. (a) $J = Ne/A$; $\rho = \dfrac{N}{A}\sqrt{\dfrac{md}{2e\,\Delta Ux}}$

(b) $\dfrac{Nd}{2}\sqrt{\dfrac{m}{2e\,\Delta U}}$ (c) $Ne\,\Delta U$

Chapter 23

23–1. (1) $F_z = vB$, (2) $F = 0$, (3) $F_z = vB/\sqrt{2}$, (4) $F_x = -vB/\sqrt{2}$, (5) $F_x = -vB$, (6) $F = vB\sqrt{2/5}$ at 45° in $XO(-Z)$ quadrant

23–3. 0.8 m; $\pi 10^{-8}$ sec

23–5. (a) 3.4 cm (b) 37 cm (c) $2.3 \times 10^5\ \text{sec}^{-1}$

23–7. 0.103 m

23–9. $1.4 \times 10^6\ \text{amp/m}^2$ if set E–W

23–11. 1.18 webers

23–13. $\mathcal{E} = \dfrac{d^2B^2I}{m}t$

23–15. Side: $x = 0$ $x = 0.1$ $y = 0, 0.1$
Force: 0 0.01 n 0.005 n
$\sum F = F_x = 0.01$ n

23–17. (a) $0.001D$ joule (b) 0 (c) $0.01D$ joule

23–19. 0.0005 n-m

23–21. $-90°$; for small $\Delta\beta$; $0.005 \sin\beta$

23–23. $\sqrt{3}\pi RBI$

23–25. (a) 3.73 j (b) 0.0005 j

23–27. (a) $E = \dfrac{IB}{\sigma w}$ (b) $n = \dfrac{1}{e}\sqrt{\dfrac{IB\epsilon_0}{w}}$

Chapter 24

24–1. (b) $\dfrac{\mu_0}{2}\dfrac{IR^2}{(x^2 + R^2)^{3/2}}$

24–3. (a) $\sum F = 32 \times 10^{-6}$ n (b) $1.2 \times 10^{-5} \ln 3$ j (c) 0, 0 (d) 0 (e) $6 \times 10^{-7} \ln 3$ weber

24–5. 0.04π n

24–7. (a) $\dfrac{\mu_0 i}{\pi}\tan^{-1}\dfrac{w}{2d}$ (b) $\dfrac{\mu_0 i}{2\pi d}$

24–9.

B:	0	$\dfrac{\mu_0 I}{2\pi r}\dfrac{R_3^2 - r^2}{R_3^2 - R_2^2}$	$\dfrac{\mu_0 I}{2\pi r}$	$\dfrac{\mu_0 Ir}{2\pi R_1^2}$
r:	$r > R_3$	$R_3 > r > R_2$	$R_2 > r > R_1$	$R_1 > r$

24–19. (a) $F_E = \dfrac{1}{4\pi\epsilon_0}\dfrac{e^2}{r^2} = 2.3 \times 10^{-20}$ n

$F_B = \dfrac{v^2}{C^2}F_E = -2.56 \times 10^{-23}$ n

(b) $F = F_E = 2.3 \times 10^{-20}$ n

(c) $F_E = 3.8 \times 10^{-20}$ n
$F_B = -2.4 \times 10^{-20}$ n,
$F = (F_0)_E = 2.3 \times 10^{-20}$ n

Chapter 25

25–1. (a) $0.27\sqrt{3}$ volt (b) No

25–3. (a) $19.6Bt$ (b) $2\sqrt{19.6}B\sqrt{y_0 - y}$

25–5. (a) 0.2 volt (b) $0.2t$ volt (c) 0 (d) 0.1 amp; $0.1t$ amp; 0

25–7. (a) $\dfrac{0.04}{3}$ watt; $\dfrac{0.04}{3}t^2$ watt (b) 0.04 j

25–9. $-0.27\pi \cos 300t$

25–11. $\dfrac{2\pi\mu_0 INA}{\omega L}$

25–13. (a) 10^{-3} coul (b) 0.0025 amp (c) 5×10^{-7}j (d) $5 \times 10^7 + \Delta$KE (e) 1.25×10^{-6} watt (f) Only if velocity is known.

25–15. (a) $\mathcal{E}_2 = 0.2\dfrac{N_2L_1}{N_1}\dfrac{I_0}{t}$

(b) $\mathcal{E}_2 = 0.2\dfrac{N_2L_1}{N_1}I_0 \sin\omega t$ (c) 0

(d) $\mathcal{E}_2$ same as (a); $I_2 = \dfrac{\mathcal{E}_2}{R + R_2}$

(e) $\mathcal{E}_2$ same as (b); $I_2 = \dfrac{\mathcal{E}_2}{R + R_2}$

(f) $\mathcal{E}_2 I_2$

25–19. (b) $q = Q\cos(t/\sqrt{LC})$

(c) $I = -\dfrac{Q}{\sqrt{LC}}\sin\dfrac{t}{\sqrt{LC}}$

25–21. $\dfrac{\mu_0}{2\pi}\ln\dfrac{R_2}{R_1}$

Chapter 26

26–1. $\sqrt{10^3 g} \simeq 100$ m/sec

26–3. $y = -vt$

26–7. (a) 0; 0.009; 0.017; 0.019 (b) 0.009; 0.003; -0.003 (c) $v_y = 0.06\cos(2t - 3x)$; 0.06 m/sec (d) 0.67 m/sec (e) 0.67 m/sec

26–11. $y_1 = A \sin 2\pi 1000 \left(\frac{x}{10} - t\right)$

$y_2 = A \sin 2\pi 1010 \left(\frac{x}{10} - t\right)$

$y = 2A \sin 2\pi(100.5x - 1005t)$
$\times \cos 2\pi(0.5x - 5t)$

26–13. (b) $v\ (\sin) = \dfrac{\omega_1 - \omega_2}{\omega_1 + \omega_2} v;$

$v\ (\cos) = \dfrac{\omega_1 + \omega_2}{\omega_1 - \omega_2} v$

if wave (1) moves to right and (2) to left

(c) $\omega_1 > \omega_2,\ \omega_1 < \omega_2$

26–19. (b) Triangular wave form

(c) $v = \pm \dfrac{2\omega A}{\pi}$

(d) $a = -\infty$ at $t = (n + \frac{1}{4})\tau$,
$a = +\infty$ at $t = (n + \frac{3}{4})\tau$,
$a = 0$ all other t,
where n is an integer and τ is the period, i.e., $\tau = (2\pi/\omega)$

26–21. $v_{gr} = v/2$

26–23. (a) Plane polarized, $A = \sqrt{5}A$
(b) Elliptically polarized
(c) Circularly polarized
(d) $y = A \sin (kx - \omega t)$
$x = A \cos (kx - \omega t)$
$r = A,\ \theta = kx - \omega t$

26–25. $A_R = \frac{2}{3}$ cm, $A_T = \frac{8}{3}$ cm

26–27. $A_R = -\frac{2}{3}$ cm, $A_T = \frac{4}{3}$ cm

Chapter 27

27–1. (a) $r = \dfrac{c^2}{(2\pi f)^2 A}$ (b) $\omega^2 A \cos 2\pi f \dfrac{r}{c}$

27–3. (a) $\Delta f \simeq \pm \dfrac{1}{4\pi} \dfrac{e}{m} B$

(b) $\Delta\lambda \simeq \pm \dfrac{\lambda^2}{4\pi c} \dfrac{e}{m} B$

27–9. $d' = d \dfrac{\tan i}{\tan r} \simeq \dfrac{d}{n},\ d' \simeq nd$

27–11. $n = 2$

27–15. 4%

27–19. 29.4 cm, 30.2 cm

27–21. $1 \pm \sqrt{0.85}$ m

27–23. (a) 5×10^{-4} rad (b) 1 mm

27–27. 3

27–31. 4.5°

27–33. (a) Between sources at 0.25 m from either source; everywhere outside the sources
(b) None (c) Hyperbolic cones
(d) No

27–35. 1500 A

Chapter 28

28–1. 8.3 m

28–3. 10 mi

28–5. $\frac{1}{10}$ as large

28–7. (a) 40 times moon (b) 9.6 cm
(c) 0.32 rad, 0.38 rad (d) 40, 47.5

28–9. (a) $\frac{25}{9}$ cm (b) 500 (c) 27.5 cm

28–11. (a) 2.5×10^{-7} m (b) 1.7×10^{-7} m

Chapter 29

29–1. (a) $MS\,\Delta TJ$ (b) $C\,\Delta V$

(c) $\dfrac{e}{m} = \dfrac{1}{BR}\left(\dfrac{2MS\,\Delta TJ}{C\,\Delta V}\right)^{1/2}$

29–5. (a) 2×10^{-26} m

29–7. (a) 1.85×10^3 m/sec (b) 18 ev

29–9. 2×10^{-10} m = 2 A

29–11. (a) 0.6×10^{15} sec^{-1}
(b) 4×10^{-19} j (c) 0.4×10^{-19} j

29–13. (c) $\omega = 3.8 \times 10^{15}$ sec^{-1}
(d) 0.6×10^{-4} ev, no

29–17. (a) 123 Kev, 119 Kev (b) 4000 ev
(c) 6.6×10^{-23}, 6.4×10^{-23}, 3.5×10^{-23} kg-m/sec

29–19. (a) $h\nu + E = h\nu' + E'$,

$\dfrac{h\nu}{c} - p = -\dfrac{h\nu'}{c} + p'$ (b) 150 A

29–21. 36,000 ev

29–23. $\theta = \dfrac{1}{4\pi\epsilon_0} \dfrac{qQ}{d\frac{1}{2}MV^2}$

29–25.

$$m_n \simeq M_N \frac{E_N}{2E_H - E_N - 2\sqrt{E_H(E_H - E_N)}},$$

where it has been assumed that $m_p \simeq m_n$

29–27. (a) $1p$; $1p, 1n$; $1p, 2n$ (b) $92p, 143n$

Chapter 30

30–1. (a) 440, 880, etc. (b) None in principle

30–3. Paschen and Brackett, Brackett and Pfund

30–5. (a) First (b) $4/10^{40}$

30–13. $\frac{1}{2}W$ of hydrogen

30–15. 3 Lyman lines, 2 Balmer lines, 1 Paschen line

30–19. (a) 12.07 volts (b) 13.56 volts

Chapter 31

31–1. (a) $\pi/4\ \text{sec}^{-1}$ (b) $\pi/4\ \text{sec}^{-1}$

31–3. (a) $\pi/400$, (b) $\pi/400$; $\pi/4$

31–11. (c) a_0, $12a_0$

31–13. (a) Because $r = \left(\frac{3}{4\pi}\right)^{1/3} V^{1/3}$

(d) $Z \simeq 40$

Chapter 32

32–3. (c) $v = 5.5 \times 10^6$ m/sec

32–7. (a) 2.3 Mev (b) 30 Mev

32–9. 780,000 ev

32–11. (a) $H^3 \rightarrow He^3 + e + \nu$
(b) KE $\simeq$ 18,000 ev

32–17. 67.5 Mev

Index

ABCDE698765